Best
Restaurants
1999

YOU HAVE EATEN AND DRUNK ENOUGH

Produced by:
AA Publishing

Maps prepared by:
the Cartographic Department of
The Automobile Association
Maps © The Automobile Association 1998

Restaurant assessments and rosette awards are based on reports of visits carried out anonymously by the AA's Hotel and Restaurant Inspectors. Although our Inspectors are a highly trained and very experienced team of professional men and women, it must be stressed that the opinions expressed are only opinions, based on the experience of one or more particular occasions, and assessments are therefore to some extent necessarily subjective and may not reflect or dictate a reader's own opinion on another occasion. See page 5 for a clear explanation of how, based on our Inspectors' inspection experiences, establishments are graded. If the meal or meals experienced by an Inspector or Inspectors during an inspection or inspections fall between award levels the restaurant concerned may be awarded the lower of any award levels considered applicable.

Editor: Elizabeth Carter

Restaurant descriptions have been contributed by the following team of writers: William Boden, David Hancock, Phil Harriss, Clarissa Hyman, Julia Hynard, Roger Mordan, Hugh Morgan, Jenni Muir, Simon Wright

Cover illustration by:
Sue Climpson, Whitchurch, England

Typeset by:
Anton Graphics, Andover, England

Printed and bound in Spain by:
Gráficas Estella, SA, Navarra

Published by:
AA Publishing, which is a trading name of Automobile Association Developments Limited whose registered office is Norfolk House, Priestley Road, Basingstoke, Hampshire RG24 9NY
Registered number 1878835.

AA Ref 10186

ISBN 0 7495 19347

Contents

LUCKNAM PARK

How to use this guide

1. The Guide's entries are divided into sections. London restaurants are listed alphabetically by name (but see also the hotels featured on page 153). There is also a London postcode index on page 844. In the rest of Britain, establishments are listed in country and county order, by town, and then alphabetically within that town. There is also an index by establishment name.

2. ![NEW] indicates an entry new to the Guide this year

3. ![teddy bear] indicates an establishment which genuinely welcomes families with children of all ages.

4. ![rosette] is the Guide's rosette award for cooking quality. Every restaurant included has been awarded one or more rosettes, up to a maximum of five. See below for a clear explanation of how they are graded.

5. Directions are given wherever they have been supplied by the proprietor.

6. The establishment's address and postcode.

7. The map number. In the London section, each restaurant has a map reference number to help locate its approximate position on the Central or Greater London maps on pages 824. In the remainder of the Guide, the map references refer to the 16 pages of maps of Britain starting on page 848. First is the map page number, followed by the National Grid Reference. To find the location, read the first figure across and the second figure vertically within the lettered square.

8. The establishment's telephone number, including its STD code.

9. The names of the chef(s) and owner(s). These are as up-to-date as we could make them at the time of going to press, but changes in personnel often occur, and may affect both the style and the quality of the restaurant.

10. Alc is the cost of a meal for one person, including coffee and service but not wine. Fixed-price lunch and dinner menus come

SAMPLE ENTRY (fictitious)

	2.	3.	4.
1. BRISTOL, The Restaurant	NEW	![bear]	![rosettes]

5. DIRECTIONS: City centre
6. The Street XY21 1AB
7. MAP 3: ST57
8. TEL: 0111 2345678   FAX: 0111 3456789
9. CHEF: John Brown   OWNER: John & Mary Brown
10. COST: Alc £26.50, fixed-price L £11.50 (2 courses)/D £22 H/wine £9.75. ☺
11. TIMES: Noon-last L 2pm/7pm-last D 10pm. Closed L Sat, Sun, Mon, 1 wk Easter, 1 wk summer, 10 days Xmas, Bhs
12. ADDITIONAL: Bar meals; Sunday L; Children welcome; ![v] dishes
13. SEATS: 40. Private dining room 26. Jacket & tie
14. SMOKING: No smoking in dining room
15. ACCOMMODATION: 3 en suite
16. CREDIT CARDS: ![card symbols]

next. If these meals have more or less than three courses we have indicated this. The cost of the house wine or one of the cheaper wines on the list follows. Prices quoted are a guide only, and are subject to change without notice. ☺ indicates where restaurants have told us they offer dinner for under £25 a head (excluding wine).

11. The times of the first and last orders for meals, and the days of the week the restaurant is closed, together with seasonal closures. Note that opening times are liable to change without notice. It is always a good idea to telephone any establishment which you are intending to visit to avoid disappointment.

12. In addition to meals in the restaurant, bar meals are served at lunch and/or dinner; Sunday lunch is served; Children are welcome, any age limitations are specified; ![v] indicates where a vegetarian choice is always offered on a menu. Almost all restaurants featured will prepare a vegetarian dish or accommodate a special diet if given prior notice, but even where a symbol appears by an entry it is wise to check with the restaurant first.

13. The number of seats in the restaurant. Not all restaurants will take private parties, the number given is for the maximum number of people in a party. Jacket and tie are compulsory in a few restaurants, and this is specified.

14. Establishments that do not allow smoking in the dining room may allow it elsewhere, in a lounge of bar, for instance. If you are a smoker, it is worth checking beforehand.

15. Accommodation is also available.

16. The credit cards accepted by the establishment.

![] Mastercard	
![] American Express	
![] Delta	![] Visa
![] Diners	![] Connect
![] Switch	JCB JCB

TELEPHONE FOR DIRECTIONS appears where an establishment has not supplied us with current details.

SIGNATURE DISHES appear at the end of the main entry and are supplied by chefs from establishments who have three or more Rosettes. Some entries do not show signature dishes either because the chef has chosen not to give them, or the establishment was a late appointment.

4

How the AA assesses restaurants for rosette awards

The AA's rosette award scheme is the only home-grown, nation-wide scheme for assessing the quality of food served by restaurants and hotels.

The rosette scheme is an award scheme, not a classification scheme and although there is necessarily an element of subjectivity when it comes to assessing taste, we aim for a consistent approach to our awards throughout the UK. It is important, however, to remember that many places serve enjoyable food but do not qualify for an AA award.

Our awards are made solely on the basis of a meal visit or visits by one or more of our hotel and restaurant inspectors who have an unrivalled breadth and depth of experience in assessing quality. They award rosettes annually on a rising scale of one to five.

Recommendations from users of the guides are always welcome and will be passed on to the inspectors on merit for their consideration, but we do not guarantee a meal visit or an entry in the guide. Rosette awards are made or withdrawn only on the basis of our own inspectors' meal visits.

So what makes a restaurant worthy of a Rosette award?

For our inspectors, frequently eating alone, the top and bottom line is the food. They are not swayed by a fashionable or luxurious setting, by the friendliness or immaculate uniforms of the staff, by fussy, over-elaborate presentation, or even by the size of the bill.

The taste of the food is what counts for them, and whether the dish successfully delivers to the diner what the menu promises. A restaurant is only as good as its worst meal.

Although presentation and competent service should be appropriate to the style of the restaurant and the quality of the food, they cannot affect the rosette assessment as such, either up or down.

The following summaries attempt to explain what our inspectors look for, but are intended only as guidelines. The AA is constantly reviewing its award criteria and competition usually results in an all-round improvement in standards, so it becomes increasingly difficult for restaurants to reach award level.

At the simplest level, one rosette, the chef should display a mastery of basic techniques and be able to produce dishes of sound quality and clarity of flavours, using good, fresh ingredients:

Summary

- Fresh ingredients
- Sound quality
- Basic technical skills - e.g. pastry, sauce-making
- Home-made desserts, stocks, sauces
- Clarity of flavours
- Simple, uncomplicated dishes
- Food served at correct temperature

To gain two rosettes, the chef must show greater technical skill, more consistency and judgement in combining and balancing ingredients and a clear ambition to achieve high standards. Inspectors will look for evidence of innovation to test the dedication of the kitchen brigade, and the use of seasonal ingredients sourced from quality suppliers.

Summary

- Dedicated approach
- Sound technical skills, both classical and modern
- Seasonal, high quality ingredients
- Clear, well defined flavours
- Consistency throughout all courses
- Side dishes matched to main ingredients
- Some innovative dishes
- Balanced, harmonious combinations
- More sophisticated and appropriate garnishes

This award takes a restaurant into the big league, and, in a typical year, fewer than 10 per cent of restaurants in our scheme achieve this distinction. Expectations of the kitchen are high, and inspectors find little room for inconsistencies. Exact technique, flair and imagination will come through in every dish, and balance and depth of flavour are all-important.

Summary

- No inconsistencies
- Extra quality checks made
- Ancillaries (e.g. appetisers, bread, garnishes, petits fours), if provided, should contribute to the meal, not merely be padding
- The diner's high expectations should be fully met
- Higher technical skills successfully executed
- Vegetables, as a general rule, an integral part of main dish
- Depth of flavour in stocks and sauces
- Flair and imaginative combinations of ingredients
- Specialist, high quality suppliers

This is an exciting award because, at this level, not only should all technical skills be exemplary, but there should also be daring ideas, and they must work. There is no room for disappointment. Flavours should be accurate and vibrant.

Summary

- No disappointments & few faults
- Ingredients from suppliers of international repute
- All items made in-house
- Thorough grounding in classical techniques
- Repertoire equally at home in traditional and modern dishes
- Evolving ideas and concepts, with an element of excitement and daring

This award is the ultimate, awarded only when the cooking is at the pinnacle of achievement. Technique should be of such perfection that flavours, combinations and textures show a faultless sense of balance, giving each dish an extra dimension. The sort of cooking that never falters and always strives to give diners a truly memorable taste experience.

Summary

- Faultless presentation
- Perfection in every element at every inspection visit
- Attention to detail throughout
- Intense, exciting flavours
- Harmonious marriage of ingredients
- Skilful use of luxury ingredients
- Secret ingredients giving an extra dimension to a dish
- All culinary skills come to fruition together

AA

Villeroy & Boch©

Villeroy & Boch have sponsored the superb plates which are presented annually to all restaurants who have been awarded rosettes for their high standards of cuisine.

THE TOP TEN PERCENT

EDEN's pale yellow floral motifs conjure up visions of spring where in your own private paradise, beautiful china does not have to be forbidden fruit!

Rosettes, ranging from one up to five, are awarded by the AA for culinary excellence, and an explanation of the levels is given on page 5. Tableware designers and manufacturers Villeroy & Boch provide specially designed award plates to all the restaurants in this guide, but the index below lists only the highest rated restaurants. It is illustrated with photographs of designs which you may see either when dining out or on sale in the china departments of many of Britain's best stores. Full details of all the restaurants listed will be found in the directory, with the exception of those in the Republic of Ireland which appear in list form.

❀❀❀❀❀

LONDON

Chez Nico,
At Ninety Park Lane, W1
☎ 0171 409 1290

Le Gavroche,
43 Upper Brook Street, W1
☎ 0171 408 0881

Le Meridien Piccadilly, The Oak Room, Marco Pierre White
21 Piccadilly, W1
☎ 0171 734 8000

ENGLAND
BERKSHIRE

L'Ortolan,
Church Lane, Shinfield
☎ 0118 9883783

DEVON

Gidleigh Park,
Chagford
☎ 0164 7432367

OXFORDSHIRE

Le Manoir Aux Quat' Saisons,
Great Milton
☎ 0184 4278881

SCOTLAND
HIGHLAND

Altnaharrie Inn,
Ullapool
☎ 01854 633230

❀❀❀❀

LONDON

The Capital,
Basil Street, Knightsbridge, SW3
☎ 0171 589 5171

Pied a Terre,
34 Charlotte Street, W1
☎ 0171 636 1178

Mandarin Oriental Hyde Park
66 Knightsbridge, SW1
☎ 0171 235 2000

The Square,
6, Bruton Street
☎ 0171 495 7100

ENGLAND
BERKSHIRE

Waterside Inn,
Ferry Road, Bray
☎ 01628 620691

BUCKINGHAMSHIRE

Cliveden,
Taplow
☎ 01628 668561

CUMBRIA

Michael's Nook,
Grasmere,
☎ 015394 35496

GLOUCESTERSHIRE

Le Champignon Sauvage,
24, Suffolk Road ,Cheltenham
☎ 01242 573449

HAMPSHIRE

Gordleton Mill,
Silver Street, Hordle, Lymington
☎ 01590 682219

LINCOLNSHIRE

Winteringham Fields,
Winteringham
☎ 01724 733096

RUTLAND

Hambleton Hall,
Oakham
☎ 01572 756991

SOMERSET

Restaurant Lettonie,
35, Kelston Road, Bath
☎ 01225 446676

Castle Hotel,
Castle Green, Taunton
☎ 01823 272671

❀❀❀

LONDON
EC1

Maison Novelli,
29, Clerkenwell Green
☎ 0171 251 6606

Tatsuso
32, Broadgate Circle
☎ 0171 638 5863

EC2

Searcy's Brasserie,
Library Floor, Barbican Centre,
Silk Street
☎ 0171 588 3008

EC4

City Rhodes,1,
New Street Square
☎ 0171 583 1313

NW1

Landmark Hotel,
222 Marylebone Road
☎ 0171 631 8000

SW1

Auberge de Provence,
41, Buckingham Gate
☎ 0171821 1899

Le Caprice,
Arlington House, Arlington Street
☎ 0171629 2239

The Halkin Hotel,
Halkin Street
☎ 0171 333 1000

The Lanesborough,
Hyde Park Corner
☎ 0171 259 5599

Sheraton Park Tower,
101 Knightsbridge
☎ 0171 235 8050

Zafferano,
15, Lowndes Street
☎ 0171 235 5800

SW3

Bibendum,
Michelin House, SW3
☎ 0171 581 5817

Chavot,
257-259 Fulham Road
☎ 0171 351 7823

Turners,
87-89 Walton Street
☎ 0171 584 6711

SW7

Hilaire,
68, Old Brompton Road
☎ 0171 584 8993

SW10

The Canteen,
Harbour Yard, Chelsea Harbour
☎ 0171 351 7330

SW13

Riva Restaurant,
169, Church Road, Barnes
☎ 0181 748 0434

SW17

Chez Bruce,
2, Bellevue Road
☎ 0181 672 0114

W1

Alastair Little Restaurant,
49 Frith Street
☎ 0171 734 5183

Cafe Royal, Marco Pierre White at the Grill Room,
68 Regent Street
☎ 0171 437 9090

The Connaught,
Carlos Place
☎ 0171 499 7070

The Criterion,
224, Piccadilly
☎ 0171 930 0488

The Dorchester, The Oriental,
Park Lane,
☎ 0171 629 8888

L'Escargot,
48 Greek Street,
☎ 0171 437 6828

The London Hilton on Park Lane,
22 Park Lane
☎ 0171 493 8000

Hotel Inter-Continental,
1, Hamilton Place, Hyde Park
☎ 0171 409 3131

Lindsay House,
21 Romilly Street
☎ 0171 439 0450

Mirabelle,
56 Curzon Street
☎ 0171 499 4636

L'Odeon,
65, Regent Street
☎ 0171 287 1400

The Orrery,
55-57 Marylebone High Street
☎ 0171 616 8000

Quo Vadis,
26-29 Dean Street
☎ 0171 437 9585

Les Saveurs de Jean-Christophe Novelli,
37a Curzon Street
☎ 0171 491 8919

W6

River Cafe,
Thames Wharf Studios, Hammersmith
☎ 0171 381 8824

W8

Royal Garden Hotel,
2-24 Kensington High Street
☎ 0171 937 8000

W11

Halcyon Hotel,
81, Holland Park
☎ 0171 727 7288

Leith's,
92, Kensington Park Road
☎ 0171 229 4481

W14

Chinon,
23, Richmond Way
☎ 0171 602 5968

WC2

The Ivy,
1, West Street, Covent Garden
☎ 0171 836 4751

The Savoy, River Restaurant
The Strand
☎ 0171 836 4343

ENGLAND
BEDFORDSHIRE

Flitwick Manor,
Church Road, Flitwick
☎ 01525 712242

BERKSHIRE

The Fat Duck,
High Street, Bray
☎ 01628 580333

Fredrick's Hotel,
Shoppenhangers Road, Maidenhead
☎ 01628 635934

Royal Oak Hotel,
The Square, Yattendon
☎ 01635 201325

BRISTOL

Harveys Restaurant,
12, Denmark Street, Bristol
☎ 0117 927 5034

BUCKINGHAMSHIRE

Hartwell House,
Oxford Road, Aylesbury
☎ 01296 747444

CAMBRIDGESHIRE

Midsummer House,
Midsummer Common, Cambridge
☎ 01223 369299

CHESHIRE

Crabwall Manor,
Parkgate Road, Mollington, Chester
☎ 01244 851666

The Chester Grosvenor,
Eastgate, Chester
☎ 01244 324024

Nunsmere Hall,
Tarporley Road, Oakmere, Sandiway
☎ 01606 889100

CORNWALL & ISLES OF SCILLY

Pennypots,
Maenporth Beach, Falmouth
☎ 01326 250251

VILLA MAGICA- the very finest quality bone china with a classical shape, complimented by delicate blue bands and fine gold filets.

Well House Hotel,
St Keyne, Liskeard
☎ 01579 342001

The Seafood Restaurant,
Riverside, Padstow
☎ 01841 532485

St Martin's On The Isle,
Lower Town, St Martin's
☎ 01720 422092

CUMBRIA

Sharrow Bay,
Howtown
☎ 017684 86301

Underscar Manor,
Applethwaite, Keswick
☎ 017687 75000

Rampsbeck Country House Hotel,
Watermillock
☎ 017684 86442

Gilpin Lodge,
Crook Road, Windermere
☎ 015394 88818

Holbeck Ghyll,
Holbeck Lane, Windermere
☎ 015394 32375

DERBYSHIRE

Fischer's Baslow Hall,
Calver Road, Baslow
☎ 01246 583259

The Old Vicarage,
Ridgeway Moor, Ridgeway
☎ 0114 2475814

DEVON

Holne Chase Hotel,
Two Bridges Road, Ashburton
☎ 01364 631471

Carved Angel,
2, South Embankment, Dartmouth
☎ 01803 832465

The Horn Of Plenty,
Gulworthy
☎ 01822 832528

Arundell Arms,
Lifton
☎ 01566 784666

Chez Nous,
13, Frankfurt Gate, Plymouth
☎ 01752 266793

Whitechapel Manor,
South Molton
☎ 01769 573377

Pophams,
Castle Street, Winkleigh
☎ 01837 83767

DORSET

Summer Lodge,
Evershot
☎ 01935 83424

Stock Hill Country House Hotel,
Stock Hill, Gillingham
☎ 01747 823626

GLOUCESTERSHIRE

Buckland Manor,
Buckland, Broadway
☎ 01386 852626

The Greenway,
Shurdington, Cheltenham
☎ 01242 862352

Lower Slaughter Manor,
Lower Slaughter
☎ 01451 820456

Thornbury Castle,
Castle Street, Thornbury
☎ 01454 281182

Lords Of The Manor,
Upper Slaughter
☎ 01451 820243

GREATER LONDON

Chapter One,
Farnborough Common,
Locksbottom, Bromley
☎ 01689 854848

GREATER MANCHESTER

Juniper,
21, The Downs, Altrincham
☎ 0161 929 4008

Normandie Hotel,
Elbut Lane, Bury
☎ 0161 764 3869

HAMPSHIRE

Le Poussin,
The Courtyard, Brockenhurst
☎ 01590 623063

36 On The Quay,
47 South Street, Emsworth
☎ 01243 375592

The Three Lions,
Stuckton, Fordingbridge
☎ 01425 652489

Hollington Country House,
Woolton Hill, Highclere
☎ 01635 255100

Gordleton Mill,
Silver Street, Hordle, Lymington
☎ 01590 682219

Chewton Glen Hotel,
Christchurch Road, New Milton
☎ 01425 275341

Old Manor House,
21, Palmerston Street, Romsey
☎ 01794 517353

HERTFORDSHIRE

Edgewarebury Hotel,
Barnet Lane, Elstree
☎ 0181 953 8227

Marriott Hanbury Manor,
Ware
☎ 01920 487722

KENT

Eastwell Manor,
Boughton Lees, Ashford
☎ 01233 219955

Wallett's Court,
St Margarets-At-Cliffe, Dover
☎ 01304 852424

Read's Restaurant,
Painters Forstal Faversham
☎ 01795 535344

Sandgate Hotel,
The Esplanade, Folkestone
☎ 01303 220444

LANCASHIRE

Northcote Manor,
Langho
☎ 01254 240555

Paul Heathcote's Restaurant,
104-106 Higher Road, Longridge
☎ 01772 784969

LINCOLNSHIRE

Harry's Place,
17, High Street, Great Gonerby,
Grantham
☎ 01476 561780

NORFOLK

Morston Hall,
Blakeney
☎ 01263 741041

Adlard's Restaurant,
79, Upper Giles Street, Norwich
☎ 01603 633522

NOTTINGHAMSHIRE

Harts Restaurant,
1 Standard Court, Nottingham
☎ 0115 9110666

SWITCH 3 - the ideal way to spice up your dining table with a mix and match collection. It's young and modern - perfect for informal eating and relaxed entertaining.

Villeroy & Boch

OXFORDSHIRE

Chavignol,
7, Horsefair, Chipping Norton
☎ 01608 644490

Beetle & Wedge,
Ferry Lane, Moulsford
☎ 01491 651381

The Feathers,
Market Street, Woodstock
☎ 01993 812291

SHROPSHIRE

Merchant House,
62, Lower Corve Street, Ludlow
☎ 01584 875438

Oaks Restaurant,
17 Corve Street, Ludlow
☎ 01584 872325

Overton Grange,
Hereford Road, Ludlow
☎ 01584 873500

Sol Restaurant,
82, Wyle Cop, Shrewsbury
☎ 01743 340560

Old Vicarage Hotel,
Worfield
☎ 01746 716497

SOMERSET

The Moody Goose,
7a Kingsmead Square, Bath
☎ 01225 466688

Royal Crescent,
16, Royal Crescent, Bath
☎ 01225 823333

Hunstrete House Hotel,
Hunstrete
☎ 01761 490490

Charlton House Hotel,
Charlton Road, Shepton Mallet
☎ 01749 342008

White House Hotel,
Long Street, Williton
☎ 01984 632306

SUFFOLK

Hintlesham Hall,
Hintlesham
☎ 01473 652334

SURREY

Pennyhill Park,
London Road, Bagshot
☎ 01276 471774

Michels',
13, High Street, Ripley
☎ 01483 224777

SUSSEX EAST

Röser's Restaurant,
64, Eversfield Place,
St Leonards-on-Sea
☎ 01424 712218

Horsted Place,
Little Horsted, Uckfield
☎ 01825 750581

SUSSEX WEST

Gravetye Manor,
East Grinstead
☎ 01342 810567

South Lodge Hotel,
Brighton Road, Lower Beeding
☎ 01403 891711

FRENCH GARDEN conjures up the warmth
of the French countryside and the spirit
of Summer with colourful ripe fruit
designs, fresh pale yellow and green
borders with fluted edging.

Villeroy & Boch

Manleys Restaurant,
Manleys Hill, Storrington
☎ 01903 742331

TYNE & WEAR

21 Queen Street,
Quayside, Newcastle Upon Tyne
☎ 0191 222 0755

Vermont Hotel,
Castle Garth, Newcastle Upon Tyne
☎ 0191 233 1010

WARWICKSHIRE

Mallory Court Hotel,
Harbury Lane, Bishop's Tachbrook,
Royal Leamington Spa
☎ 01926 330214

WEST MIDLANDS

Swallow Hotel,
12, Hagley Road, Five Ways,
Birmingham
☎ 0121 452 1144

Nuthurst Grange,
Hockley Heath
☎ 01564 783972

ISLE OF WIGHT

George Hotel,
Quay Street, Yarmouth
☎ 01983 760331

WILTSHIRE

Manor House Hotel,
Castle Combe
☎ 01249 782206

Lucknam Park,
Colerne
☎ 01225 742777

London House Restaurant,
Market place, Pewsey
☎ 01672 564775

Howard's House Hotel,
Teffont Evias, Salisbury
☎ 01722 716392

WORCESTERSHIRE

The Lygon Arms,
Broadway
☎ 01386 852255

Brockencote Hall,
Chaddesley Corbett
☎ 01562 777876

Croque-En-Bouche,
221, Wells Road, Malvern
☎ 01684 565612

YORKSHIRE, NORTH

Middlethorpe Hall,
Bishopthorpe Road, York
☎ 01904 641241

YORKSHIRE, SOUTH

Smith's Of Sheffield,
34, Sandygate Road, Sheffield
☎ 01142 666 096

YORKSHIRE, WEST

Restaurant Nineteen,
19, North Park Road, Bradford
☎ 01274 492559

Box Tree Restaurant,
35-37, Church Street, Ilkley
☎ 01943 608484

Pool Court At 42,
44, The Calls, Leeds
☎ 0113 244 4242

Rascasse,
Canal Wharf, Leeds
☎ 0113 244 6611

CHANNEL ISLANDS

JERSEY

Longueville Manor,
St Saviour
☎ 01534 25501

SCOTLAND

ABERDEENSHIRE

Darroch Learg,
Braemar Road, Ballater
☎ 013397 55443

ARGYLL & BUTE

Isle Of Eriska,
Eriska
☎ 01631 720371

Ardanaiseig Hotel,
Kilchrenan
☎ 01866 833333

Kilfinan Hotel,
Kilfinan
☎ 01700 821201

Airds Hotel,
Port Appin
☎ 01631 730236

AYRSHIRE, SOUTH

Lochgreen House,
Troon
☎ 01292 313343

DUMFRIES & GALLOWAY

Kirroughtree House,
Minnigaff, Newton Stewart
☎ 01671 402141

Knockinaam Lodge,
Portpatrick
☎ 01776 810471

DUNBARTONSHIRE, WEST

Cameron House Hotel,
Balloch
☎ 01389 755565

11

EDINBURGH, CITY OF

Atrium,
Cambridge Street, Edinburgh
☎ 0131 228 8882

Martins Restaurant,
70, Rose Street, Edinburgh
☎ 0131 225 3106

The Sheraton Grand Hotel,
1, Festival Square, Edinburgh
☎ 0131 229 9131

FIFE

Cellar Restaurant,
24, East Green, Anstruther
☎ 01333 310378

Ostlers Close,
Bonnygate, Cupar
☎ 01334 655574

The Peat Inn,
Peat Inn
☎ 01334 840206

GLASGOW, CITY OF

One Devonshire Gardens,
Glasgow
☎ 0141 339 2001

Stravaigin,
30, Gibson Street, Glasgow
☎ 0141 334 2665

HIGHLAND

Arisaig House,
Beasdale, Arisaig
☎ 01687 450622

Inverlochy Castle,
Torlundy, Fort William
☎ 01397 702177

Harlosh House,
Harlosh, Isle Of Skye
☎ 01470 521367

The Cross,
Tweed Mill Brae, Kingussie
☎ 01540 661166

LOTHIAN, EAST

La Potiniere,
Main Street, Gullane
☎ 01620 843214

PERTH & KINROSS

The Gleneagles Hotel,
Auchterarder
☎ 01764 662231

Kinloch House,
Blairgowrie
☎ 01250 884237

Kinnaird,
Dunkeld
☎ 01796 482440

STIRLING

Braeval,
Aberfoyle
☎ 01877 382711

WALES

CEREDIGION

Ynyshir Hall,
Eglwysfach
☎ 01654 781209

CONWY

Tan-Y-Foel,
Capel Garmon, Betws-Y-Coed
☎ 01690 710507

SWITCH PLANTATION reflects a tropical colonial atmosphere where tropical fruit motifs are complimented by bold terracotta borders and yellow rattan bands.

Villeroy & Boch

The Old Rectory,
Llansanffraid Glan Conwy, Conwy
☎ 01492 580611

Bodysgallen Hall,
Llandudno
☎ 01492 584466

St Tudno,
Promenade, Llandudno
☎ 01492 874411

DENBIGHSHIRE

Tyddyn Llan,
Llandrillo
☎ 01490 440264

GWYNEDD

Plas Bodegroes,
Nefyn Road, Pwllheli
☎ 01758 612363

Hotel Maes Y Neuadd,
Talsarnau
☎ 01766 780200

MONMOUTHSHIRE

Walnut Tree Inn,
Llanddewi Skyrrid
☎ 01873 852797

Crown At Whitebrook,
Whitebrook
☎ 01600 860254

POWYS

Carlton House,
Dolycoed Road, Llanwrtyd Wells
☎ 01591 610248

Llangoed Hall,
Llyswen
☎ 01874 754525

SWANSEA

Fairyhill,
Reynoldston
☎ 01792 390139

NORTHERN IRELAND

BELFAST

Deanes,
38-40, Howard Street, Belfast
☎ 01232 560000

DOWN

Shanks,
The Blackwood,
Crawfordsburn Road, Bangor
☎ 01247 853313

NORTHERN IRELAND

CORK

Longueville House Hotel,
Mallow
☎ 022 47156

DONEGAL

Harvey's Point Country Hotel,
Lough Eske, Donegal
☎ 073 22208

DUBLIN

The Clarence,
6-8 Wellington Quay, Dublin
☎ 01 6709000

Hibernian Hotel,
Eastmoreland Place, Ballsbridge,
Dublin
☎ 01 6687666

Thornton's Restaurant,
1 Portobello Road, Dublin
☎ 003531 454 9067

KERRY

Park Hotel Kenmare,
Kenmare
☎ 064 41200

Aghadoe Heights Hotel,
Killarney
☎ 064 31766

KILDARE

The Kildare Hotel,
Straffen
☎ 01 6017200

LIMERICK

Dunraven Arms Hotel,
Adare
☎ 061 396633

Hotel Booking Service

**The AA Hotel Booking Service - Now
AA Members have a free, simple way
to find a place to stay for a week,
weekend, or a one-night stopover.**

Are you looking for somewhere in
the Lake District that will take pets;
a city-centre hotel in Glasgow with
parking facilities, or do you need a
B & B near Dover which is handy
for the Eurotunnel?
The AA Booking Service can not
only take the hassle out of finding
the right place for you, but could
even get you a discount on a
leisure break or business booking.

And if you are touring round the
UK or Ireland, simply give the AA
Hotel Booking Service your list of
overnight stops, and from one
phone call all your accommodation
can be booked for you.

Telephone
0990 050505

to make a booking.
Office hours 8.30am - 7.30pm
Monday - Saturday.

**Full listings of the 8,136 hotels and B & Bs available through the
Hotel Booking Service can be found and booked at the
AA's Internet Site:**

http://www.theaa.co.uk/hotels

chefs' chef
of the year 1999

Who will be the AA Chefs' Chef for 1999? Now in its third year, this prestigious award, considered the ultimate compliment by previous winners Gordon Ramsay (1997) and Jean-Christophe Novelli (1998), has captured the imagination of our 1800 AA Rosetted chefs. Once again we asked them to vote for their choice and the votes poured in:

Our finalists for 1999 are as follows, listed alphabetically:

MARTIN BLUNOS

Lettonie, Bath 🏵 🏵 🏵 🏵

After a decade in a Bristol suburb, a move to new premises has given Martin Blunos a sense of freedom. Gone are the cramped conditions of the original Lettonie, instead there is the comfort of space provided by a fine Georgian house on the outskirts of Bath. He's happy, no longer has that feeling of being held back. Borsch terrine with beef piragi, and scrambled duck egg, Sevruga caviar, blinis pancakes and a glass of iced vodka, reveal eastern European roots (Martin was born in Bath of Latvian parents) but contemporary France (Lettonie is French for Latvia) provides the inspiration for dishes such as calves sweetbreads with ham and chicken mousse, toasted almonds and a lemon cream sauce.

MICHAEL CAINES

Gidleigh Park, Chagford 🏵 🏵 🏵 🏵 🏵

He was 25 years old when he took over the kitchens at Gidleigh Park, and a complete unknown. That was four years ago. Today, Michael Caines is regarded as one of Britain's most talented chefs. Confident from the start, when it came to training it was nothing but the best. Raymond Blanc's Le Manoir is where it all began, and Blanc's innovation and style remain with him. But it was the hard regime imposed in Joël Robuchon's kitchen in Paris that sharpened technical skills and discipline, and from Bernard Loiseau, at Saulieu in Burgundy, came a deep feel for flavour. However, his ideas are his own with modern French cuisine as a firm base, although ingredients are as local as possible. Caines believes the most memorable part of a meal is taste and flavour, for him each dish must live up to expectations.

PIERRE KOFFMANN

La Tante Claire, London 🏵️ 🏵️ 🏵️ 🏵️ 🏵️

He has seen it all. In his time chefs have risen to famous heights, and disappeared. But Pierre Koffmann remains, the supreme craftsman with the kitchen as his workshop, dedicated to the time-consuming business of cooking. He was born in Gascony, a region that provided the inspiration for his first book Memories of Gascony, and gives its spark to the Koffmann style. But it is the broader canvas of French regional cuisine that he explores more fully, in a precise, disciplined but spirited manner. His repertoire ranges from simple dishes such as warm langoustines with a gentle shallot dressing and impeccable large white beans from Tabe, to the more complex 'pied de cochon aux morilles et pommes mousseline', a signature dish that has been famously copied but never equalled.

RICK STEIN

The Seafood Restaurant, Padstow 🏵️ 🏵️ 🏵️

Rick Stein has done a lot for fish. A self-taught chef, Stein rose to prominence in the 80s, noted for cooking that was based on tiptop fresh fish and simplicity of technique; his guides the cookery books of Elizabeth David, Jane Grigson and Anton Mossiman. Neither an acclaimed TV series nor a celebrated restaurant, which can be booked up for months in advance, have eroded his basic tenets, and he remains faithfully on course. A dramatic looking platter of fruits de mer, based on the freshest selection of shellfish and served with nothing more than mayonnaise and shallot vinegar, remains one of the restaurant's most popular dishes. Like many chefs of his generation, he acknowledges the work of George Perry-Smith in making possible the food culture we have today.

KEVIN VINER

Pennypots, Falmouth 🏵️ 🏵️ 🏵️

It has been a busy year for Kevin Viner, what with being voted National Chef of the Year and appearances on TV, as well as opening a European-style bar and grill beneath his already popular restaurant. Not bad for a civilian chef from the Royal Military Academy at Sandhurst. He's been running his own show for some eleven years but cooking still gives him a tingle. Seafood features strongly in his repertoire, perhaps a single scallop, roasted and sliced into the thinnest of rings with an oriental sauce tweaked with garlic and herbs - fresh basil is a favourite - but some of his best dishes have been based on game. He admires Nico Ladenis (for whom he once worked), Pierre Koffmann, and the Roux Brothers for pushing the industry forward, and has a special regard for the father of modern British cooking, George Perry-Smith.

PREVIOUS WINNERS:
1997 - Gordon Ramsay, Aubergine, London 1998 - Jean-Christophe Novelli, Maison Novelli, London

THE AA
Wine Award

Sponsored by **T&W Wines**

An exciting new award is being launched in this year's guide, with the aim of promoting a serious interest in wine among staff working in the restaurant industry. The award has been sponsored by Wine Merchant Trevor Hughes, of T & W Wines in Thetford, Norfolk, three times winner of the Fine & Rare Wine Merchant of the Year Award at the International Wine Challenge, and Austrian Winemaker Willi Opitz, himself the winner of many accolades, especially for his Late Harvest dessert wines.

The Competition

Willi Opitz offers the winner of the Wine Award the prize of a week-long stay as his guest on his vineyard near Vienna on the Austria-Hungary border

We invited all restaurants which had featured in the 1998 Best Restaurants Guide to enter the competition and send in their wine lists for the first round of the award. The judges were not looking for the list with the highest prices for heirloom bottles, nor the longest, nor even the one with all the hidden bargains or famous names. The criterion was the intelligence and awareness that had gone into constructing a list.

Aperitif
Risotto with wild mushrooms

Seafood mousse with white fish and scallops, served with two sauces: meat jus and a champagne sauce

Roast rack of spring lamb

Cheese: Lanark Blue

Dessert: Tarte Tatin

Digestif

Round Two

This test consisted of six questions, ranging from a definition of the role of the sommelier or wine waiter, to a prediction of the next most fashionable wine-producing country, by way of the most difficult question of all, which was choosing two wine suggestions to match each of five courses on the carefully devised but deceptively simple menu shown here.

Entries for round two, not unexpectedly, proved even more difficult for the panel of judges than assessing the wine lists themselves. The challenge was not only to partner each dish appropriately, but also to consider the procession of courses and ensure that the wines chosen would follow on harmoniously one from the other. A shortlist of 50 entries emerged, with a further shortlist of 11 finalists, unanimously chosen by all three experts.

THE AA WINE AWARD

Picking the Winners

The difficult task of arbitration of these last eleven has fallen to Gerard Basset, the highly respected and knowledgeable former Sommelier at Chewton Glen, who is now part owner of the Hotels du Vin and Bistro at Winchester and Tunbridge Wells. The winner will be announced in October.

Fine & Rare. Wine Merchant Trevor Hughes, sponsor of the AA Wine Award, at his Thetford premises

The shortlist of 50, who each receive a certificate, are, in alphabetical order:

Angel Inn, *Hetton*

Ashdown Park, *Forest Row*

Atrium, *Edinburgh*

Ballathie, *Kinclaven*

Belfry, *Handforth*

Callow Hall, *Ashbourne*

Capital, *London*

Champany Inn, *Linlithgow*

Chewton Glen, *Chagford*

Corse Lawn, *Corse Lawn*

Cottage in the Wood, *Malvern*

Creggans Inn, *Strachur*

Crosby Lodge, *Carlisle*

The Cross, *Kingussie*

Fairy Hill, *Reynoldston*

Fischers, Baslow Hall, *Baslow*

French Partridge, *Horton*

Le Gavroche, *London*

Gidleigh Park, *Chagford*

Graveteye Manor, *East Grinstead*

Hambleton Hall, *Oakham*

Hartwell House, *Aylesbury*

Hintlesham Hall, *Hintlesham*

Hollington House, *Highclere*

Kinnaird House, *Dunkeld*

Langley House, *Wiveliscombe*

Leiths, *London*

Llangoed Hall, *Llyswen*

Lombard Room, *Birmingham*

Lucknam Park, *Colerne*

Meltons, *York*

Northcote Manor, *Blackburn*

Old Bridge, *Huntingdon*

Olive Tree (Queensberry Hotel), *Bath*

One Devonshire Gardens, *Glasgow*

L'Ortolan, *Shinfield*

Paul Heathcotes, *Longridge*

Pheasant, *Keyston*

Pied à Terre, *London*

Ransome's Dock, *London*

Savoy, *London*

Sharrow Bay, *Howtown*

Starr, *Dunmow*

Le Talbooth, *Dedham*

Taychreggan, *Kilchrenan*

36 On The Quay, *Emsworth*

Trengilly Wartha, *Falmouth*

White Hart, *Ford*

White House, *Williton*

Winteringham Fields, *Winteringham*

The eleven finalists are:

England

Ashdown Park Hotel, Forest Row, East Sussex

Hambleton Hall, Oakham, Rutland

Hintlesham Hall, Ipswich, Suffolk

Hollington House, Highclere, near Newbury, Berks

The Old Bridge, Huntingdon, Cambridgeshire

Ransome's Dock, London

36 on the Quay, Emsworth, Hants

Wales

Llangoed Hall, Llyswen, Powys

Scotland

The Atrium, Edinburgh

Champany Inn, Linlithgow, West Lothian

Kinnaird, Dunkeld, Perth and Kinross

AA Hotel Services, T & W Wines and Willi Opitz would like to thank all the restaurants who took part, and congratulate everyone on the high standard of entries for what has been a fascinating first year of the Award. We look forward to doing it all again next year, for the Millennium edition of the Guide. For more information about the spectacular wines of Willi Opitz, please contact Trevor Hughes at T&W Wines, 51 King Street, Thetford, Norfolk IP24 2AU Tel: 01842 76546

The Austrian Wine Marketing Board has generously offered the return flight for the winner from London to Vienna.

All in the Family

Do you genuinely welcome children? That was the question we posed to every establishment appearing in this edition of the Guide. And the replies streamed in:

'As I sit here in my office staring at my Dennis the Menace wallpaper, I wonder how I can communicate how we cater for children', wrote Mrs Jenkinson from the Evesham Hotel in Worcestershire. '...how else are children going to learn to eat out and fill the restaurants of the future', exclaimed Charles Whittaker from Country Friends in Dorrington, Shropshire. 'A child must surely benefit from an exposure to a wide range of foods and friendly adult company providing an example by eating the same food with them. Is this not what we admire in other cultures?' asked Michael and Lucy Hjort, from Melton's in York.

From a nation that once thought children should be seen and not heard, we are obviously beginning to get it right, becoming almost continental. But what about chefs themselves, wearing another hat as a parent, what do they think about taking their children to restaurants, about children's menus? We asked some of our top rosetted chefs to tell us.

Children's joke: Why are chefs cruel?

Because they beat eggs, whip cream, and batter fish.

PETER JUKES
The Cellar, Anstruther

'It has to be the right place', says Peter Jukes, father of Grace 6, Alice 4, and Rachel 15 months. His girls love going to restaurants. Tthey think it's posh and important, but as a family they only ever eat out in restaurants that genuinely cater for children. For the Jukes family that means Italian, simple pasta places like the Bella Pasta chain, and the restaurant that brought out some pasta dough for the kids to play with. 'We work so hard so its nice to have other people cook for us, and we like the children to come with us'. But he regards standard children's menus as 'horrendous'. In his own restaurant, if children can manage dishes on the menu, he will do small portions. 'We must educate children to eat'.

HESTON BLUMENTHAL
The Fat Duck, Bray

Heston Blumenthal is a self-taught chef, passionate about food, which he cooks with attitude. This means long hours in the restaurant and just one day off a week, which he naturally wants to spend with his family, Jack 5, Jessica 3, and Joy 6 months. He also enjoys eating out. For the Blumenthals, Chinese restaurants seem to strike the perfect balance, being 'very pleasurable for us and the kids, relaxed and sufficient food for them to eat'. Heston feels it is important for children to get used to eating in restaurants and the restaurant culture. However, he considers run-of-the-mill children's menus to be 'unimaginative and deep-fried'.

RICHARD CORRIGAN
Lindsay House, London

Richard Corrigan is a man who pours his heart and soul into his food, so when he has time off eating out is 'a way all the family can be together, to eat nice food and relax'. Children, Richard 9, and Jessica 3, enjoy eating out immensely, but the family's preference, however, is for children friendly restaurants which are fun and where the children can be themselves - the Corrigans often go to Charlie's in Crouch End. Richard thinks that overall children's menus are fine, but thinks some restaurants in the UK have a lot to learn 'vis à vis child diners; unlike the French, who welcome children with their parents in quite serious restaurants. Maybe one day the UK will be the same!'

GARY RHODES
City Rhodes, London

'Eating out is time out as a family', explains Gary Rhodes, 'and 'so I don't have to cook at home'. He is one chef who has really reached out to children through his zany children's BBC TV programme Roald Dahl's Revolting Recipes - basically, simple but imaginative cooking for kids. Both Gary's sons, Sam 9, and George 8, love eating in restaurants, which is just as well as 'I like my kids to try different foods'. Chinese food is their current favourite, especially Xian in Orpington, although Sam is developing a taste for Indian food. Fun places such as Planet Hollywood also get the thumbs up from the Rhodes family. Gary thinks children's menus can be a good idea 'although not always imaginative, they are useful'.

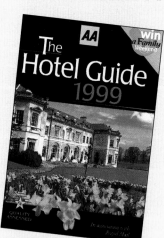

The *Master Chefs* of GREAT BRITAIN

The membership list of The Master Chefs of Great Britain reads as a who's-who of chefs who have all achieved one common goal - to produce the highest quality food using the best ingredients. They may not all be household names, for many are chef-patrons who have little time to spend on anything other than running the kitchen, but they do produce excellent food. Indeed, this is more than apparent when one leafs through AA Best Restaurants to see what the AA inspectors have said about these predominantly three and four rosetted chefs.

For the chef...

This quest for excellence is clearly reflected in the aims, activities and joining criteria of the association which was established in 1980 as a forum for the exchange of ideas between many of Britain's leading chefs.

Raising the profile of Britain's quality food producers, through events and demonstrations in this country and abroad, is important to all the member chefs.

Full membership is by invitation, although chefs may write to the Chairman, enclosing their curriculum vitae, and their application then goes before the 22 strong Executive Committee. Other membership categories include Pastry Chef, Sous Chef, and the Young Chefs Club.

The association works with other industry bodies to assist in the running of competitions and initiatives, and their Annual General Meeting and Luncheon in November attracts guests from the whole of the food industry, journalists and Gourmet Club members.

For the person who enjoys food...

The association's aims are reflected their full colour magazine, The Master's Table, which is traditionally published quarterly and brings together chefs, leading food and wine writers, and industry figures, to provide articles that are both informative and entertaining. Besides being available in the hotels and restaurants, this quality magazine can be obtained through subscription (£15 for four issues including P&P) and has a growing readership both in this country and abroad.

In addition, the association runs a Gourmet Club (joint annual membership £45 per annum), which holds events throughout the British Isles. These bring together the food interested public, chefs and suppliers, not just to experience great food and wine but, hopefully, to learn a little about what goes on behind the scenes.

Benefits of the Gourmet Club include:

- a free subscription to The Master's Table magazine, a full colour glossy magazine that contains articles from leading food and wine writers and a host of recipes from the Master Chefs themselves.

- complimentary access to the Fine Food Club which, with over 1000 small quality food producers on its data base, has the resources to source and send out speciality produce to both gourmets and the chef.

- details of cookery courses held both by member chefs at their hotels and restaurants and venues around the country, special tuition rates can apply.

- a cornucopia of benefits at selected member establishments, aimed at people who are interested in food and wine. It could be a discount, or you might find yourself on a tour of the wine cellar or kitchen, or eating a specially prepared dish.

- a bi-monthly Gourmet Club Newsletter giving details of events being held around the country.

- a selection of quality wine and product offers available to members, either through the Gourmet Club Newsletter or the magazine, as well as Reader Offers and Competitions for such things as wines, books, and even the odd weekend away.

For the future...

Under the Presidency of the Earl of Bradford, a growing membership ensures that the organisation remains pro-active working within the industry and consumer markets to ensure that British chefs and produce are recognised world-wide. Training initiatives remain high on the agenda, and it is recognised by the members through the MCGB Modern Apprenticeship Scheme that young chefs must be given a classical grounding from which to move on and create new and innovative dishes.

For further information about The Master Chefs of Great Britain, their Gourmet Club and magazine, The Master's Table, please call 01442 264777 or fax 01442 264778, or write to:

The Master Chefs of Great Britain,
c/o Aztec Marketing Solutions Ltd.,
North Wing, 51 Marlowes,
Hemel Hempstead, Herts HP1 1LD

or simply fill in the form below...

The Master Chefs of Great Britain

NAME

ADDRESS

Telephone number

Fax number

I would like to join The Master Chefs of Great Britain Gourmet Club. ❏
ANNUAL JOINT MEMBERSHIP £45 PER ANNUM.

I would like to subscribe to The Master's Table magazine at the subscription rate of £15 inc P&P. ❏
Please send me details of various levels of 'chef membership' of The Master Chefs of Great Britain. ❏
Please make all cheques payable to The Master's Table Ltd

Please return this form to:
The Master Chefs of Great Britain c/o Aztec Marketing Solutions Ltd., North Wing, 51 Marlowes,
Hemel Hempstead, Herts HP1 1LD

LONDON

Abingdon ❀❀

54 Abingdon Road W8
Map GtL: C3
Tel: 0171 9373339
Fax: 0171 7956388
Chef: Brian Baker
Owner: Capital Radio Restaurants
Cost: *Alc* £23, fixed-price L £9.95
(2 courses). ☺ H/wine £9.75
Times: Noon-last L 2.30pm/6.30-last
D 10.45pm. Closed 25, 26 Dec
Additional: Bar food L; Sunday L;
Children welcome; ♨ dishes
Seats: 60
Smoking: No pipes & cigars; Air
conditioning
Credit cards: ▆ ▆ ▆ ▆ ▆ ▆ ▆

Directions: Nearest Tube – High
Street Kensington.

Stylishly cool neighbourhood restaurant and bar decorated in
glossy, vibrant colours. The reasonably priced French rustic food
is a crowd pleaser; it's hard to go wrong with the likes of Bayonne
ham with marinated goats' cheese, and grilled breast of chicken
with confit of garlic and mushroom mash, but the standard of
cooking rarely falters. Popular trends are reflected in dishes such
as roasted fillet of salmon with buttered endive and saffron and
pan-fried lambs' kidneys with wild rice and mustard sauce. Lemon
tart and rich dark chocolate mousse, both with crème fraîche, are
among the good, but predictable, choice of desserts.

The Academy ❀❀

Nothing dingy about the basement restaurant at this
Bloomsbury hotel. Side-street windows, judicious use of
mirrors and modish decor give the place an upbeat feel which
extends to a menu with Southern European sympathies.
Roasted peppers come 'Piedmont style', whilst a range of
salads include avocado with feta cheese and piquant olives, or
a spicy chorizo variety with grilled artichokes and capsicums.
The geography stretches as far as the Lebanon for marinated
lamb steaks served with yogurt and tabouleh. Numbered
amongst a conservative range of desserts are panettone bread-
and-butter pudding, or lemon mousse brûlée.

17-21 Gower Street WC1E 6HG
Map: D4
Tel: 0171 6314115
Fax: 0171 6363442
Chef: John O'Riordan
Owner: Alan Rivers
Cost: *Alc* £19.70. ☺ H/wine £9.95
Times: Noon-last L 3pm/6-last
D 10.45pm. Closed Sat, Sun
Additional: Bar food; Children
welcome; ♨ dishes
Seats: 48. Private dining room 16-30
Smoking: No pipes & cigars; Air
conditioning
Accommodation: 48 en suite
Credit cards: ▆ ▆ ▆ ▆ ▆ ▆ ▆ JCB

Directions: Five minutes walk from Oxford St, Tottenham Court
Road Tube, Goodge St

L'Accento ❀

*Rustic, lively and cheerful Italian with stripped-wood floor,
terracotta walls and dark-stained wooden furnishings. Cooking is
fresh with bold flavours, the short carte listing fresh tagliolini with
crab, lamb shank with red wine and rosemary, grilled tuna with
borlotti and salsa verde, and orange crème caramel.*

Smoking: Air conditioning. **Credit cards:** ▆ ▆ ▆ ▆ ▆ ▆

Directions: Nearest Tube station Bayswater

16 Garway Road W2 4NH
Map GtL: C3
Tel/Fax: 0171 2432201
Chef: Enrico Sartor
Owner: Giovanni Tomaselli
Cost: *Alc* £25, fixed-price L & D
£11.50 (2 courses). ☺ H/wine £9.50
Times: Last L 2.15pm/last D 11.15pm.
Closed Bhs
Additional: Sunday L; Children
welcome; ♨ dishes

Adams Café

*Tunisian/Moorish-style restaurant with hand-painted tile borders,
ceramics and traditional artefacts. The cooking is North African
with Tunisian and Moroccan specialities, including a range of
couscous dishes, tagines and grills, and starters such as harira – a
vegetable, lentil and chickpea soup.*

Additional: Children welcome; 🌙 dishes
Credit cards: � ▭ ▭ ▭ 🅲

Directions: Nearest Tubes – Shepherd's Bush and
Hammersmith

77 Askew Road W12 9AH
Map GtL: C2
Tel/Fax: 0181 7430572
Chef: Abdel Boukraa
Owners: Abdel & Frances Boukraa
Cost: *Alc* £16. ☺ H/wine £8
Times: D only, last D 10.30pm

Alastair Little

Simple and modern are the by-words here. The lunch and
dinner menu change daily, and temptation springs off the page.
Note items taken from a mid-week March menu: seafood
bourride, nettle risotto, calves' liver with beetroot and
horseradish, and rhubarb and saffron custard tart. Italian
influences show in dishes such as lasagnette alla Genovese,
'maiale' tomato and grilled sea bass with purple sprouting
broccoli and anchovy dressing, but the cooking also looks
further East with Japanese-style duck salad, and grilled tuna
with soba noodles and coriander. And there's probably
nowhere else in London where you're likely to get goose egg
and sorrel omelette, chips and salad.

Directions: From Ladbroke Grove Tube station turn R, Lancaster
Road is 1st R

136a Lancaster Road
W11 1QU
Map: C2
Tel: 0171 2432220
Chef: Edwin Lewis
Owners: Alastair Little,
Kirsten T Pedersen,
Mercedes André-Vega
Cost: Fixed-price D £25. H/wine £12
Times: 12.30-last L 2.30pm/7-last
D 11pm. Closed Sun, Bhs
Additional: Children welcome;
🌙 dishes
Seats: 42
Credit cards: ▭ ▭ ▭ ▭ ▭ 🅲 JCB

Alastair Little Soho

'Simple, simple, quality, quality', is the mantra at Alastair
Little. The daily changing menu has the freshest, best quality
ingredients sourced from the market place. Some would argue
that this style of cuisine is easier to execute than the flowery,
over-garnished menus of some restaurants. Perhaps, but
discerning the quality of produce is an art few chefs are aware
of, let alone skilled in. The long, narrow restaurant – small
tables, wood floor, some extra tables downstairs – sees punters
queuing for a chance to dine most evenings. The tiny kitchen
can be seen at the back, chefs industriously labouring away,
headed by Jonathan Ricketts. Breads arrive as one is seated,
focaccia for instance, not an hour old, flecks of sea salt tingling
the tongue. Our winter dinner opened with antipasto that was
pronounced 'a plateful of heaven'. Eight different tasters that
included chicken liver crostini with fresh herbs stirred in,
brandade crostini, Parma ham, rocket, home-preserved
artichokes that had been marinated in mint-flavoured oil,
salted anchovies, home-dried tomatoes just bursting with
flavour, and olive salad. Sea bass came next, simply done, the
skin cooked to crisp, flesh white and meltingly tender, the
accompanying parsley salad had tomato, olives and lemon
through it. Chocolate torte was a classic flourless-style
chocolate cake with a little coffee added to intensify the
flavour – very powerful – and served with fresh-tasting vanilla
ice cream. Dinner is truly excellent value. Alastair Little's wine
list is treated in a similar style to his food, in other words
excellent quality wines, not the most expensive, written on a

49 Frith Street W1V 5TE
Map: D4
Tel: 0171 7345183
Chef: Jonathan Ricketts
Owners: Alastair Little,
Kirsten Tormod Pedersen
Cost: Fixed-price D £33. H/wine £13
Times: Noon-last L 3pm/6-last D
11pm. Closed L Sat, all Sun, Bhs
Additional: Children welcome;
🌙 dishes
Seats: 35. Private dining room 20
Smoking: Air conditioning
Credit cards: ▭ ▭ ▭ ▭ ▭ 🅲 JCB

piece of A4. Chassagne-Montrachet *premier cru* Lamy-Pillot at £48, is the priciest white; Château La Lagune Haut-Médoc 1989, £80, the most expensive red.

Directions: Nearest Tubes: Leicester Square, Tottenham Court Road.

Alba Restaurant

107 Whitecross Street EC1
Map: F4
Tel: 0171 5881798
Please telephone for further details

A spacious modern restaurant, close to the Barbican, that is a popular lunchtime haunt for the local businesses who come here to enjoy a range of regional Italian dishes. Leave room for desserts like almond nougat ice cream cake, pannacotta and the good lemon tart served with stewed fresh summer fruits that concluded our last test meal. There's strong espresso coffee to round things off and a large selection of grappas.

Directions: 100 yards from entrance to Barbican Arts Centre; 3 mins walk from Barbican Station.

Al Bustan

Motcomb Street SW1X 8JU
Map: B2
Tel: 0171 2358277
Fax: 0171 2351668
Chef: Inam Atalla
Owners: Mr & Mrs Atalla
Cost: Alc £22, fixed-price L £13/D £25. ☺ H/wine £11
Times: Open all day, last D 11pm. Closed 25-26, Dec, 1 Jan

Elegant Lebanese venue offering formal dining in smart surroundings. The authentic mezze include makanek (little spicy sausages), baby aubergines stuffed with pine nuts, and herbed Lebanese pizza. If you can manage a main course, try the ace grilled chicken with garlic sauce.

Additional: Sunday L; No children under 4; ⚫ dishes
Smoking: No-smoking area
Credit cards: █ ▨ ▧ ▢ ▤ ▐ ▨ JCB

Directions: Behind Carlton Tower Hotel, off Lowndes Street.

Alfred

245 Shaftesbury Avenue WC2 8EH
Map: D3
Tel: 0171 2402566
Fax: 0171 4970672
Chef: Andy Harman
Owner: Fred Taylor
Cost: Alc £23, fixed-price L & D £15.90. ☺ H/wine £11.95
Times: Noon-last L 3.30pm/6-last D 11.30pm. Closed Sun, Xmas, New Year
Additional: Children welcome; ⚫ dishes

A procession of chef's in recent months at this up-beat, sunny looking venue. Yellow Formica tables and glossy blue walls play host to some no-nonsense cooking with a modern Brit feel. Expect Glamorgan patties (leeks and cream cheese) with chive butter, roast guinea fowl with cabbage and bacon or fishcakes with butter sauce. Heavyweight desserts include gingerbread pud with lavender custard, and good old bread-and-butter pudding.

Seats: 56. Private dining room 16
Smoking: No pipes & cigars; Air conditioning
Credit cards: █ ▨ ▧ ▢ ▤ ▐ ▨ JCB

Directions: Close to Shaftesbury Theatre

L'Altro Restaurant

210 Kensington Park Road W11 1NR
Map: C3
Tel: 0171 7921066
Fax: 0171 7921077
Please telephone for further details

A super little Italian restaurant, now part of a successful London chain. Designed to look like a crumbling Italian street, the Notting Hill original has a real buzz about it – locals crowd in to enjoy quality cuisine in rustic surroundings complete with wrought-ironwork, wooden floor and random tables. There is a very good set menu, and the choice at dinner is equally tantalising. A late summer meal started with Italian sausage and wild mushroom salad with mixed leaves, which was followed by a main course of fresh tuna steak with a garlic and olive oil mash. Dessert was a very good vanilla pannacotta with fresh berry purée, but we could have tried panettone tiramisu with cinnamon spiced figs, or the cheeseboard, which provides a good choice of regional Italian cheeses.

Directions: Nearest tubes Ladbroke Grove/Notting Hill Gate, straight down Kensington Park Road to Westbourne Park Road end, opposite health centre

Al San Vincenzo ❀❀

They have their priorities straight at this tiny little restaurant just off the Edgware Road. The decor, though simple and attractive, is irrelevant to the food, and this view is endorsed by the difficulty of getting a table here. The atmosphere is pure Italian; Signora Borgonzolo presides, fussing over regulars and tutting loudly at mobile phones. Interesting, uncompromising dishes include the bits shunned by many timid Brits: sliced eels fried in olive oil and chilli, soup made with spicy pork offal, and tongue with Savoy cabbage. An awareness of the seasons is implicit in this sort of cooking. In January, there was escalope of goose breast served with a light jus flavoured with mandarin and pomegranates; in February, fillet of red mullet and its liver with blood orange sauce, served with an orange salad. There's singularly light panettone bread-and-butter pudding, or fresh pears with Gorgonzola before you hit the espresso and vin santo.

30 Connaught Street W2 2AF
Map: B3
Tel: 0171 2629623
Chef: Vincenzo Borgonzolo
Owners: Elaine & Vincenzo Borgonzolo
Cost: *Alc* £30. H/wine £13
Times: 12.30-last L 1.45pm/7-last D 9.45pm. Closed L Sat, Sun, Xmas
Seats: 24
Smoking: No pipes and cigars
Credit cards: ▬ ▬ ▬▬ ▬▬

Directions: 2nd left in Edgware Road, from Marble Arch

Anglesea Arms ❀

A busy, smoky traditional corner pub with real fire, dark wood and dim lighting. The nightly scramble for tables starts at 7pm: no bookings and ditherers may wait a long time for food, kindly staff are well versed in saying 'you'll have to wait'. Its the simple, robust dishes that work best here, calves' liver on mash with back bacon, red wine jus and charred cabbage worked well on a freezing winter night. Lemon tart was full of citrus zing. Inexpensive wine list.

35 Wingate Road W6 0UR
Map GtL: C3
Tel: 0181 7491291
Fax: 0181 7491254
Chef: Dan Evans
Owners: Dan & Fiona Evans
Cost: *Alc* £18. ☺ H/wine £8.95
Times: Last L 2.45pm/last D 10.45pm. Closed 1 wk summer, 1 wk Xmas

Additional: Children welcome; ❹ dishes
Credit cards: ▬ ▬ ▬▬ ▢ **[**

Directions: Off Goldhawk Road; nearest Tube: Goldhawk Road or Ravenscourt Park

Anna's Place ❀

The eponymous Anna has retired, her place taken by some of her staff. The popular Swedish specialities remain – gravad lax, ceviche and raw herrings, and cubed fillet of beef marinated in Swedish mustard – but more modern ideas are coming through with rabbit brioche and pan-fried fillets of cod in butter and dill with leek mash.

90 Mildmay Park
N1 4PR
Map GtL: D3
Tel: 0171 2499379
Chefs/Owners: Patrick Schyum, Magnus Falk
Cost: *Alc* £21. H/wine £9.95. ☺
Times: Last L 2.15pm/last D 11pm. Closed Sun, Mon, L Aug, 2 wks Xmas

Additional: Children welcome; ❹ dishes. **Credit cards:** None

Directions: Left off Balls Pond Road into Mildmay Park. On the corner of Newington Green, Bus 73, 171, 141 to Newington Green

Apprentice Restaurant

A great place to try out – tomorrow's star chefs could begin their careers here, training at Butler's Wharf restaurant school. Set in an old spice warehouse, the restaurant has a modest feel, bentwood chairs, simple blue tables and red brick walls. Expect modern British dishes such as pan-fried sea bream with tarragon tagliatelle, and bags of enthusiasm.

Additional: Children welcome; ❸ dishes
Smoking: No-smoking area
Credit cards: 💳 💳 💳 💳

Directions: On S side of river, two minutes from Tower Bridge; nearest Tubes – Tower Hill and London Bridge

31 Shad Thames
SE1 2YR
Map: G3
Tel: 0171 2340254
Fax: 0171 4032638
Chef: Gary Witchalls
Owners: Butler's Wharf Chef School
Cost: Alc £22, fixed-price L £12.50/D £17.50. ☺ H/wine £8.95
Times: Last L 1.30pm/last D 8.45pm. Closed Sat, Sun, Bhs, Xmas week

Arcadia ✿

Tucked away off Kensington High Street, near Kensington Palace and Gardens, Arcadia is a pleasing little local restaurant with considerable charm. The menu has a modern slant with dishes based on good fresh ingredients.

Directions: From High Street Kensington Tube turn R, take 3rd turning on L. Signed path leads to Kensington Court

Kensington Court
35 Kensington High Street
W8 5EB
Map GtL: C3
Tel: 0171 9374294
Please telephone for further details.

Assaggi ✿

NEW

Small, popular, fun and located above a pub, with an easy relaxed atmosphere. Italian-simple dishes work best: baked sea bass; veal with truffle essence; chanterelles, pancetta and red onion salad. Assaggi pasta loaf is a cross between a raviolo and lasagne. Fabulous focaccia.

Additional: Children welcome; ❸ dishes
Smoking: Air conditioning
Credit cards: 💳 💳 💳 💳 💳 💳 JCB

Directions: Nearest Tube – Westbourne Grove

39 Chepstow Place W2
Map GtL: C3
Tel: 0171 7925501
Chef: Nino Sassu
Owners: Nino Sassu, Gianpietro Fraccari
Cost: Alc £32
Times: Last L 2.30pm/last D 11pm. Closed Xmas

Les Associés ✿✿

A good place to brush up your French – it's the language of choice in Dominique Chéhère's small French outpost in Crouch End. The menu, hand-written in French with English translations, is short but

172 Park Road
N8 8JT
Map: B5
Tel: 0181 3488944
Chef: Marc Spindler

full of interest with some unusual combinations such as fillet of beef with lobster sauce, pan-fried cod with bacon and a chicken jus, and salmon cake with mussels and beetroot sauce. Desserts are more familiar: mousse au chocolat; crème brûlée; nougat glacé, tarte du jour. Very good espresso coffee and a short but well-chosen wine list. There's a front terrace for alfresco eating in summer.

Seats: 40
Smoking: No-smoking area
Credit cards:

Directions: Nearest Tube – Finsbury Park

Owners: Dominique Chéhère, Marc Spindler
Cost: Alc £21, fixed-price L £12.50. ☺ H/wine £10.40
Times: Noon-last L 2pm/7.30pm-last D 10pm. Closed L Sat, Mon, 2 wks Sept, 2 wks Jan
Additional: Sunday L; No children under 6; ✦ dishes

Athenaeum Hotel ❀❀

116 Piccadilly W1V 0BJ
Map: C3
Tel: 0171 4993464
Fax: 0171 4931860
Chef: David Marshall
Owners: Ralph Trustees Ltd
Cost: Alc £30. ☺ H/wine £13.95
Times: 12.30-last L 2.30pm/6-last D 11pm. Closed L Sat, Sun & Bhs
Additional: Children welcome; ✦ dishes
Seats: 60
Smoking: No-smoking area; Air conditioning
Accommodation: 157 en suite
Credit cards: ▰ ▰ ▰ ▰ ▰ ▰ ▰ JCB

Overlooking Green Park, this most elegant of London hotels offers high levels of service from staff who promote a relaxed and welcoming atmosphere. This extends to Bullocks restaurant where trompe l'oeil tapestry decoration and abstract art works create a stylish setting for a menu of good value modern classics. Start with the likes of seared scallops with roast tomatoes and pancetta, Caesar salad or tempura shrimps with rocket and spicy butter, before such mains as grilled swordfish with herb risotto and olives, veal sausages with mash, woodland mushrooms and shallot sauce, or steamed sea bass with stir-fried vegetables and lime. The highlight of our last meal was an excellent tarte Tatin with Calvados and apple sorbet, chosen from a dessert list that also included home-made date and toffee pudding and truffle ice cream bombe with caramelised bananas.

Directions: Hyde Park Corner/Green Park on Piccadilly

Atlantic ❀❀

Located in a grimy street off Piccadilly Circus, this is a young, brash place with a cosmopolitan following. On a jam-packed Saturday night, we were nodded past the bouncers and fought our way through the crowds clustering around the American-style bar. Once seated, we enjoyed a decent starter of warm chestnut, ricotta and Roquefort tart with onion marmalade and organic leaf salad. This was followed some time later by a main dish of roasted butternut squash and sage risotto, with crisp lotus root and Gorgonzola. Other choices include cracked peppercorn duckling with tangy citrus noodles, and grilled fillet

20 Glasshouse Street W1
Map: D3
Tel: 0171 7344888
Fax: 0171 7343609
Owner: Oliver Peyton
Times: Noon-last L 3pm/6pm-last D midnight. Closed L Sat, L Sun, Bhs D.
Additional: Bar food. Children welcome. ✦ dishes.
Seats: 180. Private dining room 60
Smoking: Air conditioning
Credit cards: ▰ ▰ ▰ ▰

of Aberdeen Angus with sauce choron and 'sumo' chips. Desserts are kept fairly simple – we opted for coconut tart infused with lemon and served with Belgian chocolate ice cream, which proved to be a fitting finale to the meal. Reservations are essential for dinner.

Directions: Just off Piccadilly Circus

Auberge de Provence, St James Court Hotel ❀❀❀

Hotel and apartment complex that is one of the jewels in the crown of the Taj Hotel Group. The Auberge de Provence is one of three restaurants in the hotel with the Inn of Happiness for Chinese, the more casual Le Mediterranée for Indian-style cooking. The Auberge has strong connections with L'Ousteau de Baumanière in Provence, and cuisine here is very provençale. Warm duck foie gras on an apple ring with five spices, a light scallop mousse, and game ravioli with wild mushrooms glazed with brandy, opened a late winter dinner. Main courses included a nicely thought out dish of flashed monkfish medallions and Dublin Bay prawns with tomato and spinach gratin plus a langoustine sauce, and a comforting, deeply flavoured risotto of wild mushrooms with morel essence. Desserts brought walnut pithiviers perfumed with orange and served with pistachio cream, Tia Maria cappuccino served in a chocolate cup, and iced anise mousse with Morello cherries on a nougat crust. The cheese board is worth exploring, all are in peak condition. Service is a highlight, professional and courteous and not at all stuffy. The wine list has a large selection of provençale wines, with good house wines by the glass and vintage ports too.

Directions: Off Victoria Street, close to St James's Park Tube station

41 Buckingham Gate SW1E 6AF
Map: D2
Tel: 0171 8211899
Fax: 0171 6307587
Chef: Bernard Brique
Owner: Taj International
Cost: *Alc* £30, fixed-price L & D £17 (2 courses). ☺ H/wine £13.50
Times: Noon-last L 2.30pm/7-last D 10.30pm. Closed L Sat, all Sun
Additional: Bar food
Seats: 60. Jacket & tie preferred
Smoking: No pipes & cigars; Air conditioning
Credit cards: 💳

Aubergine

As we went to press Gordon Ramsay left Aubergine and the restaurant was temporarily closed.

Aubergine eschews opulence or pretension, the atmosphere is understated, and the colourful chairs and tables reasonably spaced. Villeroy and Boch aubergine plates at each setting co-ordinate with the purple menus and wine list, and the

11 Park Walk SW10
Map: A1
Tel: 0171 3523449
Fax: 0171 3511770
Chef: Gordon Ramsay
Owners: Gordon Ramsay & A-Z Restaurants
Cost: *Alc* £50, fixed-price L £25/D £50. H/wine £15
Times: Noon-last L 2.30pm/7-last D 10.30pm. Closed L Sat, all Sun, 2 wks Aug, Bhs
Additional: Children welcome
Seats: 45
Smoking: No pipes & cigars; Air conditioning
Credit cards: 💳

Change of CHEF

mostly French staff are perfectly gracious. There are lots of luxury items but they are treated in a modern way, as in ravioli of lobster poached in a lobster bisque with fine basil purée and confit tomatoes. A stunning appetiser of tomato consommé, light, fresh and summery, with two juicy slices of langoustine, a single basil 'leafette' and a 'droplet' of olive oil launched a summer meal into orbit. But it was a new dish which really caught our eye, a panaché of roasted sea scallops, sliced, browned and beautifully sweet, on a bed of purée cauliflower with beignets made from the vegetable and a white raisin vinaigrette. A winter first course of risotto aux truffes blanches, ceps sautés was as good as our inspector had ever tasted 'with the exception of a small country restaurant in Umbria'; another starter, ham knuckle, calves' tongue, foie gras pressé with salad of green beans was equally outstanding, the foie gras at its peak, the ham juicy and robust. Main courses have been impeccable - brill with sea urchin sauce that burst with a deep but not heavy flavour, perfectly paired with sauté girolles; sauté baby red mullet on a bed of tomato couscous; succulent roast spring lamb with crushed new tomatoes, sautéed artichokes and thyme jus. Puddings hit the heights with a pyramid of white chocolate filled with lime parfait and a divine fromage blanc sorbet with black pepper stands out in the constellation.

Directions: Fulham Road. Heading west, 2nd road L after MGM cinema

Au Jardin des Gourmets

5 Greek Street
W1V 5LA
Map: D4
Tel: 0171 4371816
Fax: 0171 4370043
Chef: Vincent Hiss
Cost: Alc £32.75, fixed-price L £10/D £16.50 (both 2 courses).
☺ H/wine £9.95
Times: 12.15-last L 2.30pm/6-last D 11.15pm. Closed L Sat, all Sun, Xmas, last 2 wks Aug
Additional: Children welcome; 🍴 dishes
Seats: 80. Private dining room 80
Smoking: No-smoking area; No pipes; Air conditioning
Credit cards:

Soho lunches are not invariably long and lengthy, and this 'London's oldest French restaurant', offers an excellent 2-course, £10 lunchtime express menu with the likes of goats' cheese croustillant and beef rib eye steak with Pommery mustard. Going up a gear, the fixed price £16.50 menu includes chilled vichyssoise with caviar Chantilly and fish bourride Antiboise. The *carte*, however, really throws down the gauntlet with challenging dishes such as marinated brill, papaya and lime with green peppercorn, monkfish osso buco with vanilla and orange fumet, swede and saffron risotto, and minute of sea bass with fennel, candied tomato and basil mash with a balsamic emulsion. Three little crème brûlée with different flavours make an enchanting dessert.

Directions: Near Soho Square and Oxford Street; nearest Tube – Tottenham Court Road.

The Avenue ✿

A bright, modern restaurant in St James's. The brasserie-style menu is geared to a fast turnover – this is a great place for a quick lunch. Starters are well priced at around £5 and could include seared scallops with apple and Parmesan salad, or roast tomato, mozzarella and rocket salad; and crab and fennel pappardelle.

Directions: Green Park Tube, R past The Ritz, R into St. James's Street

7-9 St James's Street SW1
Map: C3
Tel: 0171 321 2111
Fax: 0171 321 2500
Please telephone for further details

Ayudhya Thai Restaurant ✿✿

14 Kingston Hill
Kingston-upon-Thames
KT2 7NH
Map GtL: B2
Tel: 0181 5495984/5465878
Chef/Owner: Somjai Thanpho
Cost: *Alc* £19. ☺ H/wine £8.75
Times: Noon-last L 2.30pm/6.30-last D 11pm. Closed L Mon, 25-26 Dec, Bhs
Additional: Children welcome; 🍴 dishes
Seats: 82. Private dining room 22
Smoking: No-smoking area
Credit cards: 🔲 🔲 🔲 🔲 🔲 🔲 🔲

A classic Thai meal centres on a dish of rice surrounded by a number of side dishes including soup, salad with a spicy sauce, curry and fried, steamed or grilled meat fish or poultry, thus including a diversity of flavours: hot, mild, salty, bitter, sweet, sour. While most westerners chose to construct a meal more conventionally, all the classic elements are on the menu here. We enjoyed a well-balanced tom yam gai (hot-and-sour chicken soup flavoured with the sweet ginger taste of galangal, plus lime leaves, chilli and aromatic herbs), yam ruam mit talay (spicy seafood salad with baby squid and prawns) and an excellent green chicken curry. From a choice of half-a-dozen, we chose fragrant jasmine rice. There's also a good selection of noodle and vegetarian dishes. Drink jasmine tea or Singha Thai beer.

Directions: 0.5 mile from Kingston town centre on A308, and 2.5 miles from Robin Hood Roundabout at the junction of A3

Babur Brasserie ❀❀

119 Brockley Rise
Forest Hill SE23 1JP
Map GtL: D2
Tel: 0181 2912400
Fax: 0181 2914881
Chef: Enam Rahman
Owner: Babur Ltd
Cost: *Alc* £15. ☺ H/wine £7.50
Times: Noon-last L 2pm/6pm-last
D 11pm. Closed L Fri, 25-26 Dec
Additional: Sunday L; Children
welcome; ❸ dishes
Seats: 56
Smoking: No-smoking area; Air
conditioning
Credit cards: ▨ ▨ ▨ ▨ ▨ ▨ ▨ JCB

Look out for the Bengal tiger – a life-size model – that leaps
out of the wall above the entrance in order to find this south
London Indian restaurant. Inside, the muted decor is less
remarkable than the refreshingly short menu. This offers a
distinctively modern interpretation of Indian regional cooking
based on the best available ingredients. There is a nod towards
the Raj and some western influences in the presentation. Start
with the likes of lightly fried pomfret fillet on a bed of crispy
spinach and pineapple chutney or gingery fresh squid with a
warm salad before mains such as Barracudan tuna steak in a
sweet-and-sour sauce (nicely balanced with aromatic spices),
strips of marinated chicken breast with a superb sauce of
puréed coriander, mint and tamarind, Bengali lamb-on-the-
bone curry, or monkfish cooked in coconut milk with jeera,
tamarind and coriander. Stick to the more traditional Indian
puds to finish.

Directions: 5 mins walk from Honor Oak BR Station, where
parking is available

Baileys Hotel ❀

See Where London Meets Section page 153

Bank Restaurant ❀❀

1 Kingsway WC2B 6XF
Map: E4
Tel: 0171 3799011
Fax: 0171 3799014
Chef: Christian Delteil
Owner: Tony Allan
Cost: *Alc* £30, fixed-price L & D
£16.50. ☺ H/wine £11.50
Times: Noon-last L 3pm/5.30-last
D 11.30pm. Closed Xmas, Bhs
Additional: Children welcome;
❸ dishes
Seats: 200
Smoking: Air conditioning
Credit cards: ▨ ▨ ▨ ▨ ▨ ▨ ▨ JCB

It's a bustling, buzzy place, with a popular front bar, glass-
screened open-to-view kitchen, and a huge, lively restaurant.
Staff wheel around, moving tables, delivering food; it's punchy
and pacy, not the place for quiet intimacies. We love the way
Bank describe their cooking as 'liberated French'. It's
absolutely apt for a free-wheeling style that takes in griddled
scallops, garlic pomme purée and red wine sauce, as well as
roast rabbit leg, couscous and spiced crab, and starters such as
seared rare spiced tuna with mango salad, and creamed salt
cod with sesame feuillantine. Bank specials include Caesar
salad and grilled kingfish with sauce vierge, spinach and wild
garlic. Saturday and Sunday brunch includes a Children's
Choice. Great breakfasts – liberate some extra cash for the
caviar breakfast with potato waffle and crème fraîche.

Directions: Nearest Tube – Holborn. On Aldwych opp Bush
House

Bardon Lodge Hotel

See Where London Meets Section page 153

Basil Street Hotel ❀

See Where London Meets Section page 153

Belair House ❀❀

NEW

The late 18th-century mansion was rescued from run-down municipal hell by Gary Cady. The revitalised building is magnificent, set in a little park in leafy Dulwich, with a striking period spiral staircase and bold colour schemes of brilliant yellow and stark navy blue. The larger dining room is filled with light from enormous windows, the bar has the best views of the park. A short menu keeps the emphasis on quality and the seasons. The cooking is up to date with the likes of gazpacho blanc and shaved truffle and breast of guinea fowl, sweet potato and bok choi indicating that this may well be the suburbs but the kitchen is well aware of what they are doing up town. Oysters in red wine jelly opened our May test meal, followed by sea bass fillet, lavender potatoes and baby vegetables with a few seasonal asparagus in amongst them. Pudding was an excellent peach Tatin with a very good black pepper ice cream. The set lunch menu is brilliant value for money. The short wine list is well annotated and informative with some good New World wines, and a good choice by the glass.

Gallery Road SE21 7AB
Map GtL: D2
Tel: 0181 2999788
Fax: 0171 2996793
Chef: Colin Barnett
Owner: Gary Cady
Cost: Àlc £30, fixed-price L £12.50/D £24.95. ☺ H/wine £13.50
Times: Noon-2.30pm/7pm-10.30pm
Additional: Sunday L; Children welcome; ❹ dishes
Seats: 55
Credit cards: JCB

Directions: From Brixton: Gallery Road is the first turning off the South Circular after passing West Dulwich train station. From Catford: 1st turning off South Circular after Dulwich College.

Belgo Centraal ❀

Waiters dress as Trappist monks at this vast (upwards of a 1000 seats) bustling establishment not far from Leicester Square. Choose between thebeer hall (first-come, first-served at communal tables) or the bookable restaurant for Belgian specialities such as mussels, in various guises, with frites and mayonnaise, and waterzooi.

50 Earlham Street WC2 9HP
Map: D4
Tel: 0171 8132233
Fax: 0171 2093212
Please telephone for further details

Directions: Nearest Tube – Covent Garden

Belgo Noord ❀❀

'Trappist monks serve moules and frites to hungry guests in Belgian eating hall.' No, it's not a scene from *The Name of the Rose*, it's the highly successful Belgo Noord, a Belgian-themed restaurant just minutes from Chalk Farm tube. The Belgian flag is painted across the full face of the building, while inside plain wooden tables and a long sunken bar serving schnapps set the scene. The menu features the best of Belgian cooking. Yes, moules and frites are there, but so too are the likes of roast cod with creamed leek mash, roast garlic and curry oil; fillet of grey mullet on a bed of ribbon courgettes; and filo parcel of grilled yellow peppers and aubergines with goats' cheese. 'Belgo Bargains' include lunch for a fiver (12-4pm), and 'Beat the Clock' – between 6 and 7.30pm pay the price at the time shown on your order for one of three special dishes.

72 Chalk Farm Road
NW1 8AN
Map GtL: C3
Tel: 0171 2670718
Fax: 0171 2844842
Chefs: Brian Sullivan, Richard Coates
Owners: Belgo Group plc
Cost: *Alc* £18.50, fixed-price L £14.95/D from £19.50. ☺ H/wine £9.75
Times: Noon-last L 3pm/6-last D 11.30pm. Closed 25 Dec
Additional: Bar food; Children welcome; ❹ dishes
Seats: 140. Private room 20
Smoking: No pipes & cigars; Air conditioning
Credit cards: JCB

Directions: Nearest Tube – Chalk Farm or Camden Town. Opposite the Roundhouse

La Belle Epoque,
La Brasserie ❀

NEW

Set in a former Harrods warehouse, this sleek all-day brasserie is a must for Brompton Cross habitués. The menu, which includes breakfast and afternoon teas, suits all figures. Recommended are chilli squid salad, lemon-pepper duck confit with creamed potatoes and steak hâchée with French fries. In summer, head for the pleasant outdoor tables.

Additional: Bar food; Sunday L; Children welcome; ❧ dishes
Smoking: No-smoking area; No pipes & cigars; Air conditioning
Credit cards: ▨ ▨ ▨ ▨ ▨ ▨ ▨ JCB

Directions: Nearest Tube – South Kensington

151 Draycott Avenue SW3 3AL
Map: B1
Tel: 0171 4605000
Fax: 0171 4605001
Chef: Winston Matthews
Owner: Le Palais du Jardin Ltd
Cost: *Alc* £40. ☺
Times: Open all day, last D midnight. Closed 25-26 Dec

Belvedere ❀❀

Modern and airy, the Belvedere was originally the summer ballroom of Holland House. The setting is more Kew Gardens than Kensington, and the restaurant itself is on two floors – yellow cloths, blue carpets, and windows showing the park setting, spotlights shining on tables which are set with candles and fresh flowers. Contemporary cooking gets a thorough airing here, as was noted in a summer inspection meal that opened with well thought out poached chicken and artichoke salad served with couscous lifted by cinnamon and coriander, went on to tender blackened tuna with salad niçoise, and finished with berry trifle. Modern classics include duck liver pâté with port and redcurrant jelly and toasted brioche, Caesar salad, fishcakes with warm tartare sauce, and steak and kidney pie with chive mash and a paysanne of vegetables.

Directions: On Kensington High Street side of Holland Park. Nearest Tube – Holland Park

Abbotsbury Road
Holland Park W8 6LU
Map GtL: C3
Tel: 0171 6021238
Fax: 0171 6104382
Chef: Duncan Wallace
Owner: Mr J Gold
Cost: *Alc* £25. H/wine £10.50
Times: Noon-last L 3pm/7-last D 10.30pm. Closed D Sun, 25 Dec, 1 Jan
Additional: Sunday L; Children welcome; ❧ dishes
Seats: 150
Smoking: Air conditioning
Credit cards: ▨ ▨ ▨ ▨ ▨ ▨ ▨ JCB

Bengal Clipper ❀

Butlers Wharf
SE1 2YE
Map GtL: D3
Tel: 0171 3579001
Fax: 0171 3579002
Chef: Azam Khan
Owner: Mukit Choudhury
Cost: *Alc* £30, fixed-price L £9.95 (2 courses)/D £28 (2 courses). ☺ H/wine £8.95
Times: Last L 3pm/last D 11.30pm
Additional: Sunday L; Children welcome; ❧ dishes
Credit cards: ▨ ▨ ▨ ▨ ▨ ▨ ▨ JCB

Set within an old cardamom warehouse at Butler's Wharf, this respected Indian restaurant offers a short menu of mainly Bengal and Goan specialities in its clean and spacious dining room. Typical dishes include Bengal tiger fish hara masala, butter murgh (chicken marinated in spices and yogurt), and lamb pasanda.

Directions: By Tower Bridge, nearest Tube – Tower Hill

Bentley's ❀❀

11-15 Swallow Street W1R 7HD
Map: C3
Tel: 0171 7344756
Fax: 0171 2872972
Chef: David Lem
Owner: Oscar Owide
Cost: *Alc* £40, fixed-price L & D
£19.75. ☺ H/wine £15.75
Times: Noon-last L 3pm/6-last D
11.30pm. Closed Sun, 25-26 Dec,
1 Jan
Additional: Bar food; Children
welcome; ❹ dishes
Seats: 120. Private dining room 16
Smoking: Air conditioning
Credit cards: ▆ ▆ ▆ ▆ ▆ ▆ ▆ JCB

One of London's most famous fish restaurants, established in 1916, Bentley's continues to offer a varied selection of traditional seafood dishes such as oysters, dressed crab, fresh cod and chips, and simply grilled Dover sole, alongside more modern dishes. Choose from the shorter, predominantly seafood menu in the less formal Oyster Bar, located on the ground floor, or from the more extensive *carte* in the club-like first-floor restaurant. Begin with a robust and full-flavoured lobster soup with rouille and croûtons, or plump seared scallops niçoise. For main course, either sample one of the classic traditional fish dishes or, perhaps, sea bass with Asian noodles, roast monkfish with sun-dried tomato pesto, pan-fried black bream with roast vegetable Tatin, or maybe a non-fish dish like beef with garlic mushroom and lime hollandaise. The separate dessert menu may list lemon tart with passion fruit sorbet, and bread-and-butter pudding.

Directions: Nearest Tube – Piccadilly Circus. Swallow Street links Regent St & Piccadilly and is opposite St James's Church on Piccadilly

The Berkeley

As we went to press it was announced that Pierre Koffmann, who runs the five AA Rosetted La Tante Claire, will move the restaurant into the 65-cover restaurant of the Berkeley hotel.

Directions: 200 yds from Hyde Park Corner. Nearest Tube – Hyde Park Corner

Wilton Place SW1X 7RL
Map: B2
Tel: 0171 2356000
Fax: 0171 2354330
Please telephone for further details

The Berkshire ❀

See Where London Meets Section page 153

Bibendum ❀❀❀

Well-established Conran restaurant in the landmark Michelin Building, where you can enjoy a light meal at the oyster bar, or head up the staircase to the airy, magnificent dining room for Matthew Harris's serious cooking. An early summer lunch opened with plump herbed olives and great sunflower bread.

Michelin House
81 Fulham Road
SW3 6RD
Map: A1
Tel: 0171 5815817
Fax: 0171 8237925
Chef: Matthew Harris

Bibendum

Owners: Sir Terence Conran, Lord Hamlyn, Simon Hopkinson, Graham Williams
Cost: *Alc* £35, fixed-price L £28. H/wine £10.95
Times: Noon-last L 2.30pm/7-last D 11.30pm. Closed 24-26 Dec
Additional: Sunday L; Children welcome; ❸ dishes
Seats: 72
Smoking: No pipes; Air conditioning
Credit cards:

These were followed by paupiettes of sole with a duxelle of mushroom farce, just-wilted spinach and a vibrant chive butter sauce. Then two whole-roasted quails accompanied by a rich poivrade sauce and pimento pepper accompanied by a thick potato pancake to mop everything up. Dessert was a fine pear and almond tart with creamy almond ice cream. Dinner brings a more extensive menu. Highlights of the dishes we tried were a daily special of duck confit cleverly put together as part of a deep potato cake; pea and mint risotto, well timed, creamy and soupy with big fat peas and enough mint to enhance them without overkilling; roast pigeon with sage; and a 'divine' chocolate tart, a huge wedge just slightly warmed through with excellent crisp pastry and deep filling, served with a sumptuous pistachio ice cream. Petits fours include gorgeous melt-in-your mouth dark chocolate rough-cast truffles. The exhaustive wine list is a real talking point. Extraordinary depth and great representation from around the globe ensure that all tastes are catered for. An impressive array of half-bottles and a number of wines by the glass are also offered.

Signature dishes: Asparagus with morels and poached egg; roast grouse with game chips and bread sauce; grilled halibut with sauce vierge; salted ox tongue with beetroot and horseradish purée

Directions: Nearest Tube – South Kensington

Bice ❀❀

13 Albemarle Street W1X 3HA
Map: C3
Tel: 0171 4091011
Fax: 0171 4930081
Chef: Antonello Tagliabue
Owners: Mr R Ruggeri & Mr S Fritella
Cost: *Alc* £27.50, fixed-price L £20 (2 courses). ☺ H/wine £14.
Times: Noon-last L 2.45pm/7-last D 10.45pm. Closed Sun, L Sat
Additional: Children welcome; ❸ dishes
Seats: 105. Private dining room 18
Smoking: No-smoking area; Air conditioning
Credit cards: JCB

The basement below DKNY is as stylish a location as they come these days. Enormous vases of exotic flowers, muted colours, banquettes and lots of polished wood make the all-important design statement; the food, however, speaks (in Italian) for itself with good, fresh flavours and dishes of a consistently high standard. The *carte* embraces most of the all-time, and timeless, Italian greats: marinated sword fish carpaccio with vegetable tagliatelle; linguine with fresh clams; risotto with fresh asparagus; veal cutlet milanese-style with fresh tomatoes and rocket salad; baked breast of duck with spinach and gorgonzola cream sauce. Pan-fried fillet of turbot topped with an olive crust with sautéed artichoke, tomato and onion typified the uncomplicated excellence of the cooking, as did the dessert of apple crostada. Staff are mostly Italian, and the knowledgeable sommelier is good at helping guests with their choices and matching the food.

Directions: Off Piccadilly, near Old Bond Street. Nearest tube – Green Park

Big Night Out ❀❀

148 Regents Park Road NW1 8XN
Map GtL: C3
Tel: 0171 5865768
Fax: 0171 5860943
Please telephone for further details

Expect friendly, attentive staff and an informal atmosphere at this restaurant just to the north of Regents Park. In contrast to a rather plain and simple setting the interesting menu is full of Mediterranean flare with flavoursome saucing to freshly prepared dishes such as seared scallops with tarragon butter sauce, and roast poussin with rosemary and balsamic vinegar. Look for a deliciously moist tiramisu among the desserts and finish with good, strong espresso coffee.

Directions: Near Primrose Hill, 750yds from Chalk Farm tube station, on L going N

The Birdcage of Fitzrovia ❀❀

110 Whitfield Street W1P 5RU
Map: C3
Tel: 0171 3833346
Chef: Michael Von Hruschka
Owners: Michael Von Hruschka, Caroline Faulkner
Cost: £26, fixed-price L £18/D £35. ☺ H/wine £15
Times: Noon-3pm/6-11.30pm. Closed L Sat, all Sun
Additional: Bar food; Children welcome; ❀ dishes
Seats: 24
Smoking: No smoking in dining room
Credit cards: ▆▆ ▆▆ ▆ ▆▆

Quirky and original new venue inspired by the Far East, and decorated with antiques from Burma, Cambodia and Thailand (although the 18th-century birdcages are from France). The menu is an exciting and well-judged selection of fusion dishes. Try the 'Toma Lin' plate – actually a wire basket – featuring a bowl of crisp Japanese salad, a delicious soup flavoured with coconut milk and lemon grass, and a sushi with spicy dip. Next up, chicken curry with lime risotto served with a choice of lime-peel-tied chopsticks or the restaurant's stunning cutlery. The Orient was also the reference point for a dessert of Japanese gold plum, ginger jelly and syrup and lemon grass ice cream. Afterwards, there could be a choice of flavoured coffees and porcelain boxes of chocolate-covered coffee beans. For something of a more medicinal nature, look in the doctor's bag brought to the table, filled with herb and spice-flavoured liqueurs.

Directions: Nearest Tube – Goodge Street

Bistro 190 ❀❀

190 Queen's Gate
SW7 5EU
Map: A1
Tel: 0171 5815666
Fax: 0171 5818172
Chef: Dean Whooley
Owner: Simpsons of Cornhill
Cost: *Alc* £21. ☺ H/wine £10.75
Times: Noon-last D 11.30pm.
Closed 25 Dec

There's a self-aware 'simplicity' to Bistro 190. The large, high-ceilinged room is painted a light mustard yellow, and the bench seating and wooden floors, cluttered selection of pictures and wine served in tumblers, all make a bit of a statement, which is somewhat lost in the loud soulful music emitting from every corner. The standard of bistro cooking, however, was excellent on our visit – especially a plate of 'Asian Flavours' – sushi, crab cakes and marinated prawns. Ribeye steak was cooked perfectly to order and was a quality piece of meat, served with rocket and large chargrilled field mushrooms. The chargrill features widely, used for salmon and cod fishcake with spinach and sorrel sauce, and veal escalope with crushed butternut squash and Jersey Royals. The cooking is fashionable but does not follow blindly – note crispy chilli squid with salsas and frites, and pan-fried duck breast with braised butter beans and chorizo.

Directions: Next to Gore Hotel on Queensgate; easy walking distance from South Kensington Tube station

Additional: Sunday L; Children welcome; ❸ dishes
Seats: 60
Credit cards: ▆ ▆ ▆ ▆ ▆ ▆ ▆ JCB

Bluebird ❀❀

Part of the Conran empire, Bluebird is much more than just another fashionable, high-volume eaterie; a flower shop, street café, kitchen shop, posh supermarket and outdoor market are all part of the experience. The last is overlooked by the windows of the main eating area with its cathedral nave-style roof boasting a skylight that runs the full length of the restaurant, flooding it with natural light. The menu is uncomplicated with the main ingredient of each dish being simply stated along with two or three of the additional flavours involved: seared foie gras + apples, cress; chicken Kiev + garlic, butter; duck breast + wood-roasted parsnips, onions. Also featured are dishes from the crustacea bar, rotisserie and large wood-fired brick oven, where a wide variety of meats, fish, poultry and vegetables are cooked over different types of wood – whole rabbits over olive wood, for example. Highlight of our last meal was seared bream with anchovy, caper and tomato dressing given a kick with a little chilli.

Directions: Nearest Tube – Sloane Square

350 Kings Road
SW3 5UU
Map: B1
Tel: 0171 5591000
Fax: 0171 5591111
Chef: John Torode
Owner: Sir Terence Conran
Cost: *Alc* £35, fixed-price L & D £15.75. H/wine £11.75. ☺
Times: Noon-3.30pm (4.30pm Sun)/6pm-11.30pm (Sun 11pm)
Additional: Sun brunch; Children welcome; ❸ dishes
Seats: 270. Private dining room 24
Smoking: Air conditioning
Credit cards: ▆ ▆ ▆ ▆ ▆ ▆ ▆ JCB

Blue Print Café ❀

The Design Museum
Shad Thames SE1 2YD
Map: G3
Tel: 0171 3787031
Fax: 0171 3578810
Chef: Jeremy Lee
Owner: Sir Terence Conran
Cost: *Alc* £30. ☺ H/wine £14.50
Times: Last L 3pm/last D 11pm. Closed D Sun, Good Fri, 25-26 Dec
Additional: Sunday L; Children welcome; ❸ dishes
Credit cards: ▆ ▆ ▆ ▆ ▆ ▆ ▆ JCB

Lively Conran-stable brasserie on the first floor of the Design Museum. Ideal for summer lunches/dinner when the Thames-side location and views of Tower Bridge (from the worth-fighting-for window seats) come into their own. Assured, rustic cooking, strong on flavours, takes in saffron risotto, tagliatelle with asparagus, broad beans, peas and Parmesan, and sea bass with a vibrant watercress purée. Pavlova with raspberries and vanilla-flecked cream is a great retro-classic. Charming service.

Directions: SE of Tower Bridge, on mezzanine of the Design Museum

Bombay Bicycle Club ❀

Stylish neighbourhood Indian with a discernible western feel, loyal clientele and pleasant staff. Standard menu ranging from meat samosas to monkfish cooked in the tandoor with mild green curry and coconut. Desserts are variations on an ice cream theme. Decent wine list.

Additional: Children welcome; 🍃 dishes
Seats: 80. Private dining room 24
Credit cards: 💳 💳 💳 💳 💳 💳 💳

Directions: Nearest Tube – Clapham South

95 Nightingale Lane
SW12 8NX
Map: G3
Tel: 0181 6736217
Fax: 0181 6739100
Chef: B J Gurung
Owners: D Sawuck, J Cahn
Cost: *Alc* £24. ☺ H/wine £9.90
Times: D only, 7-last D 11pm. Closed Sun, 25 Dec

Boyd's Atrium Restaurant ❀❀

A small intimate restaurant with polished wood floors, white-clothed tables and classic still-life paintings on the walls. The menu is modern Mediterranean, with some forays deeper into France with dishes such as pan-fried foie gras on toasted vermicelli with a light red wine and olive oil dressing. Facing up to stiff competition from nearby Kensington Place, the kitchen at Boyd's knows what's what, consistently producing first-class dishes along the lines of chargrilled monkfish and baby squid with roast tomato vinaigrette and olives, honey-roast breast of duck with bitter orange sauce, and home-made papardelle with duck in red wine and tomato sauce. Dessert could be chocolate and mascarpone mousse with Chantilly, or perhaps fresh strawberries with vanilla ice cream. The wine list offers a good balance of European and New World bottles, with some interesting pudding wines and a fair choice by the glass.

Directions: Nearest Tube – Notting Hill Gate. 2 blocks south

135 Kensington Church Street
W8 7LP
Map GtL: C3
Tel: 0171 7275952
Fax: 0171 2210615
Chefs: Maria Zarari, Lorenzo Spinozzi
Owner: Maria Zarari
Cost: *Alc* £28, fixed-price L £14.50. ☺ H/wine £11.75
Times: 12.30-last L 2.45pm/7-last D 10.45pm. Closed L Sat, all Sun, Xmas, Bhs
Additional: No children under 7; 🍃 dishes
Seats: 50. Private room 15
Smoking: Air conditioning
Credit cards: 💳 💳 💳 💳 💳 💳

The Brackenbury ❀❀

A pair of shops, joined at the back by a bar and small seating area, is the setting for this light and airy neighbourhood restaurant with an informal and friendly ambience inside and tables outside in summer. The daily-changing menus have much of interest as they move around the Mediterranean and back to Blighty with deep-fried cod and chips, or roast rib of beef. Mussel and saffron soup makes a fine starter, as do flavourful crab cakes with fennel and lime salad. Spicy Savoy cabbage is served with duck confit, pepperonata and rocket with roast turbot, and couscous and a tomato vinaigrette with pork tenderloin, while roast chicken breast, crispy skinned and moist, might appear with potatoes, bacon and an onion and sage gravy one day and with mash and a garlic and thyme jus on another. Steamed jam pudding with custard, or banana fritters with cinnamon ice cream are as likely to be among puddings as zesty-tasting orange and Mascarpone sorbet. Around a dozen wines are sold by the glass from a short, interesting list that runs up from Vin de Pays d'Oc to Puligny-Montrachet.

Directions: Off Goldhawk Road. Nearest tubes – Hammersmith & Goldhawk Road

129-131 Brackenbury Road
W6 0BQ
Map GtL: C3
Tel: 0181 7480107
Fax: 0181 7410905
Chef: Marcia Chang Hong
Owners: Nick Smallwood, Simon Slater
Cost: *Alc* £25, fixed-price L £10.50. ☺ H/wine £10.50
Times: 12.30-last L 2.45pm/7-last D 10.45pm. Closed L Sat, D Sun, Xmas, some Bhs
Additional: Sunday L; Children welcome; 🍃 dishes
Seats: 50
Smoking: No pipes & cigars
Credit cards: 💳 💳 💳 💳 💳 💳

Brown's, 1837 ♟♟

Albemarle Street
Mayfair W1X 4BP
Map: C3
Tel: 0171 4081837
Fax: 0171 4939381
Chef: Gregory Nicholson
Cost: *Alc* £50, fixed-price L £27/D
£55 (5 courses). H/wine £18
Times: 12.30-last L 2pm/7-last D
10.30pm. Closed L Sat, all Sun, Bhs
Additional: Children welcome;
☽ dishes
Seats: 88
Accommodation: 118 rooms
Credit cards: ■ ■ ■ ■ ■ ■

The interior of this Mayfair landmark has the decor,
furnishings and atmosphere of a grand country house. Dining
takes place in the refined surroundings of the new 1837
restaurant, which retains its original panelling, and an equally
new chef carries on flying Brown's flag. A complimentary
cappuccino of truffle and Jerusalem artichoke – 'delicious,'
noted an inspector – might arrive before a starter of well-
flavoured chicken consommé with truffles under a puff pastry
lid 'a mile high', to be followed by accurately cooked veal
sweetbreads heavily coated in parsley and tarragon in mustard
sauce served with crisp braised leeks and a potato galette.
Otherwise, crab ravioli with crayfish sauce, tournedos Rossini,
lobster Thermidor or steamed Bresse chicken with truffles are
what to expect. A hot soufflé of the day, chocolate perhaps, a
pear tarte Tatin, or a selection of seasonal fruit sorbets round
things off. Great vintages, a good spread of affordable bottles
and a huge number sold by the glass are plus-points of the
wine list.

Directions: Main entrance in Albemarle Street, off Piccadilly.
Nearest Tubes – Piccadilly Circus, Green Park

Buchan's ♟♟

62-64 Battersea Bridge Road
SW11 3AG
Map GtL: C2
Tel: 0171 2280888
Fax: 0171 9241718
Chef: Jan Melia
Owner: Anthony Brown

Close to Battersea Bridge, the spacious front-of-house wine bar
is a great after-work hang-out, and the bright, light restaurant is
at the back. A Scottish dimension to the menu – haggis, neeps
and tatties, Angus rump steak – has been largely eclipsed in

favour of a more international approach. Corn fritters with roasted tomato, bacon and rocket, and chargrilled squid with sauté new potatoes, chilli and coriander were both starters on an April menu. Main course dishes that have pleased include roasted quails with sherry vinegar, grilled brill with sauce antiboise, and brochette of king scallops and tiger prawns with Thai salad and glass noodles. The eclectic approach is also reflected in desserts such as espresso coffee chocolate tart and ricotta hot cake stack with banana and honeycomb butter.

Directions: 200 yards S of Battersea Bridge. Nearest Tubes – Sloane Square, South Kensington

Cost: *Alc* £27, fixed-price L £8.50 (2 courses). ☺ H/wine £9.95
Times: Noon-last L 2.45pm/7-last D 10.45pm. Closed 26 Dec, 1 Jan, Good Fri, Easter Mon
Additional: Bar food; Sunday L; Children welcome; ⚘ dishes
Seats: 70. Private dining room 50
Credit cards: JCB

Butlers Wharf Chop House ✾✾

Walk through the bar (quicker bites and particularly good-value set meals in here) to reach the restaurant proper, with its stripped-wood floor, oak banquettes and leather seating giving it the air of a boathouse – appropriately, with the Thames just the other side of the window; tables outside have even better views over the water and of Tower Bridge. Dickens would have been familiar with some of the British stalwarts on offer: pea and ham soup, steak and kidney pudding, with and without oysters, roast rib of beef with Yorkshire pudding, and fillet of pork with apples and chestnuts. Flavoursome duck terrine plated on brown lentils and Madeira sauce, moist and tender rack of pork stuffed with apricots, and burnt orange tart, disappointingly lacking flavour, are what an inspector ate. Old-school bread-and-butter pudding, or rhubarb and apple crumble jostle with red wine jelly with poached berries, or dark chocolate fondant with white chocolate sorbet among desserts. Plenty of wines are sold by the glass, and there's even Theakston's on draught.

Directions: On river front, on SE side of Tower Bridge

The Butlers Wharf Building
36e Shad Thames SE1 2YE
Map: D3
Tel: 0171 4033403
Fax: 0171 4033414
Chef: Andy Johns
Owner: Sir Terence Conran
Cost: *Alc* £27; fixed-price L £22.75. ☺ H/wine from £11.95
Times: Noon-last L 3pm/6-last D 11pm. Closed L Sat, D Sun, 1-3 Jan
Additional: Bar food; Sunday L; Children welcome; ⚘ dishes
Seats: 115
Credit cards: JCB

Byron's Restaurant ✾

Efficiently run by a youthful team, Byron's is a simple but elegant townhouse restaurant. A romantic candlelit dinner in the regency dining room might include spinach and tomato gnocchi with béchamel sauce, followed by grilled fillet of tuna with saffron mash. For an opulent dessert go for the double chocolate mousse with Kahlua sauce.

Additional: Sunday L; Children welcome; ⚘ dishes
Smoking: Air conditioning
Credit cards:

Directions: Nearest Tube stations – Hampstead, Belsize Park

3a Downshire Hill NW3
Map GtL: C4
Tel: 0171 4353544
Fax: 0171 4313544
Chef: Jonathan Coxon
Owner: Richard Horwood
Cost: *Alc* £25. ☺
Times: Last L 5pm/last D 11pm. Closed L Mon-Fri, 25-26 Dec

Cadogan Hotel ✾✾

The long dining room of the Cadogan has seen many a famous face in its time, and the sculptured ceilings and leaded windows hark back to the era of Lily Langtry and Oscar Wilde who frequented the place. Now a more modern touch is offered. Breads are made twice a day, small rolls of dill, white and brown 'which ate rather too well'. Warm salad of Parma ham with artichokes followed, notable for the sheer quality of

75 Sloane Street
SW1X 9SG
Map: B2
Tel: 0171 2357141
Fax: 0171 2450994
Chef: Graham Thompson
Owner: Historic House Hotels
Cost: *Alc* £38, fixed-price L £17.90/D £25.50. H/wine £13.50

the ingredients. Next came a particularly well-executed roast wild salmon with vegetable solferino and an accurate champagne cream Other choices that day were lambs' kidney and sweetbreads with peas and sherry vinegar, and a pot-au-feu of quail. Dessert was a good, classic apricot soufflé with apricot sorbet. Petits fours consisted of tiny lemon tarts with a caramel crust, fresh raspberry tarts and an assortment of professional looking chocolate truffles. Staff are quiet and courteous.

Directions: Nearest tubes – Sloane Square & Knightsbridge

Café des Arts ✿

Lively, relaxed place in the heart of Hampstead. The kitchen delivers a range of typical French brasserie dishes with a nod to modern trends: fish soup with rouille, goats' cheese tart, pan-fried grey mullet with black olive mash and provencale-style sauce, clafoutis with vanilla ice cream. Wine list keenly priced with specials on a blackboard.

Additional: Children welcome; ◖ dishes
Smoking: No-smoking area; No cigars & pipes
Credit cards: ▬ ▭ ◥ ◖ ▤ ◖ ▣

Directions: Middle of Hampstead High Street, next door to Post Office. Nearest tube – Hampstead

Café du Jardin ✿

A buzzing cosmopolitan brasserie in the midst of the theatre district. A well-reported early summer meal started with a creamed leek and smoked bacon tartlet with tomato cumin dressing, followed by sauté of giant prawns, chickpeas and peppers with a sweet chilli-butter sauce and lime-scented basmati rice.

Additional: Sunday L; Children welcome; ◖ dishes.
Smoking: Air conditioning
Credit cards: ▬ ▭ ◥ ◖ ▤ ◖ ▣

Directions: On the corner of Wellington Street and Tavistock Street. Nearest Tube – Covent Garden

Cadogan Hotel

Times: 12.30-last L 2pm/5.30-last D 9.45pm. Closed L Sat
Additional: Bar food; Sunday L; No children under 10; ◖ dishes
Seats: 36. Private dining room 32.
Smoking: No pipes & cigars; Air conditioning
Accommodation: 65 en suite
Credit cards: ▬ ▭ ◥ ◖ ▤ ◖

82 Hampstead High Street NW3
Map GtL: C4
Tel: 0171 4353608
Fax: 0171 3795035
Chef: Eric Bouilloux
Owner: Brian Stein
Cost: *Alc* £20, fixed-price L £5/D £7.95 (2 courses). ☺ H/wine £9.50.
Times: Last L 3.50pm/D 11.20pm (noon-11pm Sun).

28 Wellington Street WC2E 7BD
Map: D3
Tel: 0171 8368769/8368760
Fax: 0171 8364123
Chef: Tony Howorth
Owners: Robert Seigler, Tony Howorth
Cost: *Alc* £23.50, fixed-price L&D £13.50. ☺ H/wine £9.50
Times: Last L 3pm/last D midnight

Le Café du Marché ✿

*An air of rural France pervades this bustling restaurant that
continues to pull the business crowd with honest, rustic cooking
and live jazz. A popular starter is the salad of boudin blanc
with morels. Superb mains include veal liver with balsamic
reduction and freshest brill with olive, sun-dried tomato and
caper sauce.*

Times: Last L 2.30pm/last D 10pm. Closed L Sat, all Sun,
Xmas
Smoking: No pipes; Air conditioning
Credit cards: ▨ ▨ ▧ ▢

Directions: Nearest tube – Barbican

Charterhouse Mews
Charterhouse Square EC1M 6AH
Map: E5
Tel: 0171 6081609
Fax: 0171 3367055
Chef: Simon Cottard
Owner: C K Graham Wood
Cost: *Alc* £22.95, fixed-price L&D
£22.95 . ☺ H/wine £11

Café Fish ✿✿

As we went to press Café Fish moved 'just fifty paces around
the corner' to Rupert Street. It gives them more space, 210
seats to be exact. The 'busy, bustling seafood restaurant with a
lively atmosphere' remains the same; this is how we found
them on our last visit to the old premises. The meal kicked off
with a good thick fish soup, topped with crunchy croûtons.
Salmon and crab fish cakes followed; served with a spicy
home-made tomato sauce this dish had a 'well-balanced
flavour'. Other choices include pan-fried fillet of sea bass,
and baked monkfish with smoked bacon and spinach. For
dessert, a rich chocolate cake came with a pool of creamy
rum and orange sauce and fresh segments of orange.
Lovely fish-shaped chocolates accompanying coffee were a
fun touch. The short wine list covers bottles from around the
world, and are well chosen to complement the restaurant's
fish dishes.

Directions: Nearest tube Piccadilly Circus. Off the Haymarket

36-40 Rupert Street W1
Map: D3
Tel: 0171 930 3999
Fax: 0171 839 4880
Please telephone for further details

Café Royal,
MPW at The Grill Room ✿✿✿

68 Regent Street W1R 6EZ
Map: C3
Tel: 0171 4371177
Chef: Spencer Patrick
Owner: Marco Pierre White
Cost: *Alc* £48, fixed-price
L £24.50/pre-theatre D £27. H/wine
£26.50
Times: Noon-last L 2.30pm/6-last
D 11pm. Closed L Sat, all Sun, Bhs
Additional: Children welcome;
⚓ dishes
Smoking: Air conditioning
Credit cards: ▨ ▨ ▧ ▢ ▨ ▣

Such is life. When the rest of the world was taking advantage
of the first sniff of summer to take its sandwiches to Green
Park, we went to lunch at the Café Royal. The lavish,
extravagant dining room, where the combination of warm red

velvet, mirrors, cherubs and gilding galore dictate long, lazy lunches and intimate dinners, is not an obvious first choice of summer venue. However, the kitchen rose to the occasion, and a beautifully chilled, clear tomato consommé was just the ticket, a clear reminder of the sunshine outside. Marco Pierre White has now taken over the kitchen and placed Spencer Patrick at the head of the brigade. The style is less classically French than under Herbert Berger, but with all the MPW hallmarks of well-sourced ingredients, technique, and discipline. Our lunch continued with sea scallops with caramelised oranges and beurre orange on a bed of endives, went on to a wonderfully straightforward fillet of venison with crispy Ventreche and a rich, well-composed jus, and finished with an immaculate raspberry soufflé with the inner circle cut by the waiter at table and the freshest raspberry purée drizzled in to create 'as much marbling as you can bear to wait for before tucking in.' Perfect. Petits fours were almost an assiette in their own right, a testimony to Spencer Patrick's time at Hambleton Hall where the intricacy of petits fours is renowned. Other dishes worth noting are a signature galantine of duck and foie gras with peach and apple compote, and fillet of sea bass with scallops.

Directions: End of Regent Street, near Piccadilly Circus

Cambio de Tercio NEW

Bullfighting paraphernalia and modern photographs adorn walls of vibrant yellow, red and pink. Sopa de pescado included all varieties of fish in a rich bouillon, and tender deep-fried squid came with traditional squid-ink flavoured aïoli. The wine list is 100% Spanish and there is an impressive range of sherries.

163 Old Brompton Road
SW5 0LJ
Map: A1
Tel/Fax: 0171 244 8970
Chef: Manuel Alburquerque
Owners: Abel Lusa, David Rivero
Cost: *Alc* £26. ☺ H/wine £11.50

Times: Last L 2.30pm/last D 11.30pm. Closed 10 days Xmas
Additional: Children welcome; ❸ dishes
Credit cards: ▬ ▨ ▧ ▣ ▤

Directions: Close to junction with Drayton Gdns. Nearest Tube – Gloucester Rd

Canal Brasserie ❀

A lunch-only restaurant providing a trendy 'canteen' for the media companies in surrounding offices. The key word is 'fusion' with influences coming from everywhere for the short daily-changing menu. Moist Moroccan chicken with preserved lemons and Italian-style salsa, and lemon tart with cocoa-enriched pastry were our choice last time around. A dozen wines (half red, half white) and great espresso.

Canalot Studios
222 Kensal Road W10 5BN
Map GtL: C3
Tel: 0181 9602732
Fax: 0181 9645180
Chef: Zane Cooper
Owner: Antony G Harris
Cost: *Alc* £18

Times: L only, last L 3pm. Closed Sat, Sun, Bhs
Additional: Bar food L; Children welcome; ❸ dishes
Smoking: Air conditioning
Credit cards: ▬ ▨ ▧ ▣

Directions: Turn right at the top of Ladbroke Grove, just before bridge crossing canal, 300 yds on L inside Canalot Studio building

The Canteen ✿✿✿

Harbour Yard Chelsea Harbour
SW10 0XD
Map GtL: C2
Tel: 0171 3517330
Fax: 0171 3516189
Chef: Ray Brown
Owners: Michael Caine,
Claudio Pulze
Cost: Alc £28, fixed-price L £19.50.
H/wine £15
Times: Noon-last L 3pm/6.30-last
D 11.30pm. Closed L Sat, D Sun,
Xmas, New Year
Additional: Sunday brunch;
Children welcome; ✆ dishes
Seats: 140
Smoking: No pipes; Air conditioning
Credit cards: ▦ ▦ ▦ ▦ ▦ ▦

Though large, this is a bright and airy, smart restaurant right on
Chelsea Harbour, its theme of the four suits of playing-cards
stamped all over the place. The style of cooking is basically
French, pulling in ideas from other cuisines, a soup of chicken
and chilli with a coconut and spring onion wun-tun a more
extreme example of what the kitchen's about than, say,
ballotine of foie gras, a 'good, vibrant' plate of roasted
provençale vegetables with haloumi, or a tian of crab and
prawns with gazpacho sauce. Fish main courses are well-
reported: braised fillet of cod of excellent quality, well timed,
served with anchovy beignets, braised leeks and baby onions,
or steamed sea bream on tagliolini with mussels and clams.
Pea purée makes a fine summer accompaniment to braised
shank of lamb, roasted scallops join apples and cashew nuts in
a salad, and the marriage of flavours and ingredients is said to
be a happy one, even in a pineapple jus with peppered duck
breast. Puddings hit the button: a first-class soufflé with
griottes, or chocolate and banana crème brûlée so good that
'you should be able to get this on prescription'. The wine list
shows a bias towards France, although Italy, Spain and the
New World get a look in too. House wines are Vin de Pays
d'Oc.
  Signature dishes: Ravioli of oriental sole and crab; sautéed
medallions of monkfish with champ, peas and bacon; chump of
lamb casseroled with lentils and potatoes with rosemary
carrots.

Directions: Off Kings Road, Chelsea. Nearest Tubes – Earls
Court & Fulham Broadway

Cantina del Ponte ✿

*Informal, bustling Conran restaurant on the quayside by Tower
bridge. Enjoy a summer meal outside looking on to the River Walk,
or in the simple Italian-style restaurant. Dishes from the Med-
inspired menu could include roast loin of pork wrapped in
prosciutto with mozzarella, and salad of roast peppers and chicken
with black olives. Good service.*

Additional: Sunday L; Children welcome; ✆ dishes
Smoking: Air conditioning
Credit cards: ▦ ▦ ▦ ▦ ▦ ▦ ▦ JCB

Directions: SE side of Tower Bridge, by riverfront

The Butlers Wharf Building
36c Shad Thames SE1 2YE
Map GtL: G3
Tel: 0171 4035403
Fax: 0171 4030267
Chef: Jonathan Nicholson
Owners: Sir Terence Conran
Cost: Alc £30. ☺
Times: Last L 3pm/last D 11pm.
Closed Good Fri, 25 Dec

The Capital ❀❀❀❀

Basil Street Knightsbridge SW3 1AT
Map: B2
Tel: 0171 5895171
Fax: 0171 2250011
Chef: Philip Britten
Owner: David Levin
Cost: *Alc* £55, fixed-price L £28/D £55 (7 courses), H/wine £14.50
Times: 12.30-last L 2.30pm/7-last D 11.15pm. Closed D 25 Dec
Additional: Sunday L; Children welcome; ❧ dishes
Seats: 44. Private dining room 24
Smoking: No pipes & cigars; Air conditioning
Accommodation: 48 en suite
Credit cards: ▪▪ ▪▪ ▪ ▪▪ ▪ ▪

The exclusive hotel is in the very heart of Knightsbridge, and the small, discreet dining-room, styled by Nina Campbell and Lord Linley, reflects the scale of the hotel. Our inspector wrote that the restaurant deserves recommending for the espresso alone, but that would be to seriously under sell the place. Philip Britten and his team produce some of the most consistent cooking to be found in London. Two tasting menus, the seven-course 'Temptation' and nine-course 'Seduction', are a showcase for Britten's high-powered star dishes, served on Limoges china. We opted for the former menu, which began with perfectly cooked asparagus on a very light savoury tuile with a sabayon of lime scented with truffle to blend well with the asparagus. Next came delicately textured boudin of foie gras with freshly fried, crisp, thin chips ('a touch of genius'), followed by scalded lobster on distincly separate sage and vanilla pasta flavoured with just a hint of lemon and ginger. There was more clever use of spicing in an aubergine timbale with red onions, peppers and cumin. Tender, fresh-tasting langoustine couscous proved no exception, and the final savoury course of new season rack of lamb was cooked just pink, tasted beautifully tender, and was served on spinach with a light stew of white beans, bacon and really meaty chipolatas. A selection of desserts included a white chocolate pyramid filled with passion fruit, a rice pudding and a mix of individually sorbets. Details, such as petits fours, canapés of mini cheese scones and goujons of sole in Sauternes batter, and an *amuse-bouche* of roasted red onions and smooth pesto with tangy gazpacho keep the standard high at every point. Service is professional and knowledgeable, attentive and friendly but not falsely cloying. The wine list reflects David Levin's own interest – and examples from his Loire vineyard. There is a largely French construction with clarets and Burgundies taking top billing, but the New World is carefully chosen.

AA Shortlisted for Wine Award-see page 16

Directions: Between Harrods and Sloane Street. Nearest Tube – Knightsbridge

Le Caprice ❀❀❀

Arlington Street SW1A 1RT
Map: C3
Tel: 0171 6292239
Fax: 0171 4934008
Chef: Martin Dickenson
Owners: Jeremy King, Christopher Corbin

'It's a cool place', remarked an inspector on this London landmark tucked behind the Ritz. The stark modern decor of white walls, black and chrome, and large black and white photos of 'celebs' attracts a designer-clad crew but the atmosphere is far from intimidating, and the service, though slick and bustling, remains friendly at all times. There's a new chef at the stove, but reports are positive, indicating that the place is just as good as ever. The menu is a wonderful mix of great classic dishes: Caesar salad; eggs Benedict; salmon fishcake with sautéed spinach and sorrel; and pan-fried calves' liver with grilled bacon and bubble-and-squeak; balanced by some more lively up-to-date ideas: sashimi of tuna with pickled ginger; Mexican griddled chicken salad with guacamole and piquillo peppers; and Thai-baked sea bass with fragrant rice and soy dip. In between there are satisfying dishes of braised ham hock with broad beans, seared cauliflower and Cabernet Sauvignon jus, and chopped steak americaine with tomato relish and pommes allumettes. What makes this diverse mixture of dishes and styles stand out, is the sheer quality of the ingredients, and the quiet confidence of the kitchen. Puddings should not be missed, whether it is chocolate brownie ice cream or Bakewell tart with custard. There is a good, concise wine list that 'doesn't make the credit card squeal'. About ten wines are available by the glass and there are some good halves, as well as a few classic Burgundies and clarets.

Signature dishes: Seared yellow fin tuna, spiced lentil and wild rocket; plum tomato and basil galette; dressed Cornish crab remoulade.

Cost: *Alc* £40. H/wine £9.75
Times: Noon-last L 3pm (Sun 3.30pm)/5.30-last D midnight (Sun from 6pm)
Additional: Sunday brunch; ✪ dishes
Seats: 70
Smoking: Air conditioning
Credit cards: ▨ ▨ ▨ ▨ ▨ ▨ ▨

Directions: Nearest Tube – Green Park. Arlington St runs beside the Ritz, Le Caprice is at the end

Caraffini ✿✿

Bowls of huge black and green marinated olives, baskets of ciabatta and olive oil on the tables – Caraffini is a smart and popular Italian restaurant that starts as it means to go on. The menu mixes traditional Italian dishes with more modern ones, and the *carte* is supplemented by around half-a-dozen daily specials. Antipasti include beef carpaccio with spinach and mushroom, and sardines with balsamico and virgin olive oil. Amongst the pasta e riso dishes are tagliatelle with rocket mushrooms and sun-dried tomatoes, and linguine in clam sauce. Gratinéed scampi, and artichoke and monkfish chargrilled with fresh herbs, are lined up against calves' liver with sage, and breast of chicken with buffalo mozzarella, oregano and tomato in the meat corner. Given the lengthy choice, the cooking is remarkably consistent; risotto al porcini, followed by escalope of veal topped with asparagus and Bel Paese with tomato and herb sauce were both satisfyingly well cooked.

Directions: Nearest Tube – Sloane Square

61-63 Lower Sloane Street
SW1W 8DH
Map: B2
Tel: 0171 2590235
Fax: 0171 2590236
Chef: Marcelino Tome
Owners: Frank di Rienzo, Paolo Caraffini
Cost: *Alc* £21. ☺ H/wine £8.95
Times: Noon-last L 2.30pm/6.30-last D 11.30pm. Closed Sun, Bhs
Additional: Children welcome; ✪ dishes
Seats: 70
Smoking: No-smoking area; No pipes & cigars; Air conditioning
Credit cards: ▨ ▨ ▨ ▨ ▨ ▨

The Cavendish, 81 Restaurant ✿✿

There's a Spanish feel to the *carte* at the 81 Restaurant, part of a large, modern hotel popular with corporate guests. Galette of cornfed chicken on an olive oil and gazpacho sauce, a warm red pepper and picos brûlée with chive and black olive sabayon, and charred medallions of beef fillet on fondant potato with paprika rioja jus all have a flavour of the Iberian sun. Other dishes are more broadly Mediterranean – scallops are roasted with herb risotto and pepperonata, and turbot served on saffron mash with a broth of mussels and clams. A main course of wonderfully fresh sea bass on a bed of diced potato and tomato concasse with a rich vanilla jus showed the kitchen at its stylish best.

81 Jermyn Street
SW1Y 6JF
Map: D3
Tel: 0171 9302111
Fax: 0171 8392125
Chef: Ian Fellowes
Owner: Forte
Cost: *Alc* £30, fixed-price L £16.50 (2 courses)/D £21.50. ☺ H/wine £12.95
Times: Noon-last L 2.30pm/6-last D 10.30pm. Closed L Sat, L Sun
Additional: Bar food; Children welcome; ✪ dishes
Seats: 81. Private room 80

Caviar House

The decor almost upstages the food. Styled like an underwater cave with mosaic highlights, bubbling water sculptures and pierced ostrich egg shell chandeliers, the star turn has to be the designer loos with striped zebra toilet seats. Loads of caviar at prices you might expect at this address, served with blinis, sour cream and Jersey potatoes – or just get a taste with baked scallops with Sevruga caviar and chive butter sauce. There's also seared tuna with confit of tomato, ginger and coriander, as well as whole grilled lobster with parsley and garlic butter. Fillet of venison is stylishly served with celeriac purée, wild mushrooms and raspberry sauce.

Directions: Nearest tube – Green Park

161 Piccadilly W1V 9DF
Map: C3
Tel: 0171 4090445
Fax: 0171 4931667
Chef: Masayuki Hara
Cost: *Alc* £40, fixed-price L £21.50 (2 courses). ☺ H/wine £11.95
Times: Noon-last L 3pm/7-last D 10.30pm. Closed Sun, some Bhs
Additional: Bar food; Children welcome; 🕭 dishes
Seats: 35. **Smoking:** Air conditioning
Credit cards: 🖃 🖃 🖃 🖃 🖃 🖃 JCB

Chapter One

Locksbottom Farnborough Common BR6 8NF
Map GtL: E1
Tel: 01689 854848
Fax: 01689 858439
Chef: John Wood
Owner: Selective Restaurants Group
Cost: *Alc* £25, fixed-price L £19.50. ☺ H/wine £10
Times: Noon-last L 2.30pm/6.30-last D 11pm
Additional: Bar food L; Sunday L; Children welcome; 🕭 dishes
Seats: 120. Private dining room 60
Smoking: No pipes & cigars; Air conditioning
Credit cards: 🖃 🖃 🖃 🖃 🖃 🖃 JCB

The roadside gin-palace kind of place (the former Fantail of Bromley) with wrap-around car park is not the normal setting for cooking of the quality found here. Mercifully, there is a gentler Conranesque decor within: some stained glass, bare boards, blues and yellows in good balance, bar to one side, spacious restaurant to the other, with quite a cosmopolitan crowd for the location – not quite Bromley but a village a few miles away. John Wood offers a lively, ultra-modern menu. He is not afraid to experiment, has some good ideas and an assured hand with flavours. This was obvious in a starter of an unusual skate terrine with capers, French beans with some

chorizo and saffron potatoes – the taste combinations of salt
from the chorizo, sweet from the skate, and hint of acidity
from the capers, plus the textural combinations, was stunning.
Roast duck with orange and lime glaze and spiced potatoes
comes with strong Indian and Thai overtones – the delicate
duck breast sliced thin as bacon, the lime so intense yet subtle,
the delicately spiced potatoes a foil to the other tastes. On the
other hand, a superbly restrained fillet of baked cod on a base
of chunky cod brandade with spinach leaf through this, was a
picture of precise cooking and timing. Puddings are equally
brilliant, especially an individual apple crumble with clotted
cream fudge ice cream, and an excellent chocolate tart 'which
gave Gordon Ramsay's a run for its money'. Petits fours are
also excellent and bread is well made. Another branch,
Chapter Two, is at 43-45 Montpelier Vale, Blackheath Village
SE3. Tel: 0181 3332666

Directions: At junction of A21 and A232

Chapter One

Chavot ❀❀❀

Many dishes hark back to the not-so-distant days when Eric
Chavot was at L'Interlude, but his re-location to the Fulham
Road has been seamless. Polished wooden floor and muted
walls with some lively pictures and objets d'art make a discreet
background for what is essentially classic French cooking that
leans to the South, but borrows from here and there and
everywhere as appropriate. Confident and assured cooking has
resulted in brilliantly flavoured tian of crab with olive oil and
coriander dressing, and pin-point timing for barley roasted sea
scallops with a fine ceps risotto. Stuffed leg of rabbit with squid
and barely risotto was the highlight of our inspection meal, a
wonderful and surprising mix of powerful flavours and
lightness of texture combined with considerable delicacy.
Other main courses might include roasted pigeon with braised
lettuce and truffle jus, and pot-roast lobster with red onion and
sweet corn vinaigrette. Desserts tend to the architectural and
can be quite stunning in appearance; but Chavot has the
confidence to include a simple lemon tart with a dazzling depth
of flavour. The wine list is mostly French with a few New
World bottles and is generally good value; there is also an
admirable selection of over a dozen by the glass.
  Signature dishes: Saddle of rabbit stuffed with squid served
with a barley risotto; pan-fried sea bass with crab tortellini;
pan-fried foie gras with Tatin of endive; roast partridge with
trompettes de la mort mushrooms

Directions: Close to junction of Fulham Rd and Old Church St

257-259 Fulham Road SW3 6HY
Map: A1
Tel: 0171 3517823
Fax: 0171 3764971
Chef/Owner: Eric Crouillère-Chavot
Cost: *Alc* £40, fixed-price L £18.50.
H/wine £15
Times: Noon-last L 2.30pm/7-last
D 11pm. Closed L Sat, all Sun, Bhs
Additional: No children under 7;
❀ dishes
Seats: 60. Private dining room 12
Smoking: Air conditioning
Credit cards: ▨ ▨ ▨ ▨ ▨ ▨ ▨

The Chesterfield Hotel ❀❀

Privately owned, the hotel has a discreet and exclusive
atmosphere appropriate to its prestigious Mayfair address. The
feeling is maintained in a traditionally styled wood-panelled
restaurant where service is unhurried to a fault. By contrast,
the menu is a well-balanced blend of familiar and more modish
offerings. The former might include Caesar salad, best end of
lamb with spiced bubble-and-squeak, Guinness and steak pie,
and our perfectly cooked calves' liver on a scallion mash with
crispy bacon and caramelised sweet-and-sour onions; the latter
are represented by the likes of Thai crab cakes with sweet chilli

35 Charles Street Mayfair W1X 8LX
Map: C3
Tel: 0171 4912622
Fax: 0171 4914793
Chef: Stephen Henderson
Cost: *Alc* £30, fixed-price L £10.50/
D £15.50. H/wine £13.95
Times: Noon-last L 2.15pm/5.30pm-
last D 10.45pm. Closed L Sat
Additional: Bar food; Sun L; Children
welcome; ❀ dishes
Seats: 60-90. Private dining room 12

and cucumber sauce, Spanish tortilla (a starter), chicken piri piri, and seared salmon on sun-dried tomato linguine with olive butter sauce. Desserts range from warm pecan pie with chocolate chip, and Jack Daniels ice cream, via crème caramel, to sliced fruit with a crunchy Amaretto sabayon.

Directions: Nearest Tube – Green Park. Bottom of Berkeley Square, on corner of Charles Street & Queen Street

Smoking: No-smoking area; Air conditioning
Accommodation: 110 rooms
Credit cards: ▆ ▆ ▆ ▆ ▆ ▆ ▆

Chez Bruce ✿✿✿

Few restaurants fit the 'urban rustic' tag as well as the earthy delight that is Bruce Poole's Wandsworth creation. The textured ceiling may be distressed but in all other respects the ambience is determinedly easy-going. Spare decor, stripped wooden floors and laconic service all combine in a relaxed, unpretentious mix that stretches to the crafted simplicity of the cooking. A set-price lunch menu reappears in an extended selection at dinner, on a daily-changing *carte* shot through with the aromas of a French country kitchen. Soupes paysanne, terrines de campagne, and rillettes, all feature heavily amongst the starters, along with a duck and foie gras ballotine that was as 'meaty and succulent as one could hope'. Straightforward côte de boeuf frites with sauce béarnaise sounds like a dish to die for in the hands of Mr Poole, but our inspector was equally struck by a 'wonderful spring offering' of pan-fried halibut with asparagus and shrimp risotto that starred excellent fish and tarragon tinged rice. A faithful list of French desserts – crème brûlée, tarte Tatin aux poires, banana mousse delice with griottines – can include a mighty Saint Emillion au chocolat that took chocolate cake into 'previously unknown realms of flavour'. An appealing wine list offers heaps of character at fair prices and an enlightened selection of wines by the glass.

Signature dishes: Charcuterie; côte de boeuf, sauce béarnaise; hot chocolate pudding with praline parfait.

Directions: 2 mins walk from Wandsworth Common (BR), 5 mins from Balham Tube

2 Bellevue Road
Wandsworth Common SW17 7EG
Map GtL: C2
Tel: 0181 6720114
Fax: 0181 7676648
Chef/Owner: Bruce Poole
Cost: Fixed-price L £18/D £25. H/wine £10.95
Times: Noon-last L 2pm/7-last D 10.30pm. Closed D Sun, 1 wk Xmas, Bhs (except Good Fri)
Additional: Sunday L (12.30-3pm); No young children at D; ✦ dishes
Seats: 70. Private dining room 20
Smoking: No pipes & cigars; Air conditioning
Credit cards: ▆ ▆ ▆ ▆ ▆ ▆ ▆ JCB

Chez Max ✿✿

A discreet place in a quiet residential area (but immense fun). Country-style French dishes are lovingly prepared and served with little fuss by friendly staff. Unpretentious decor (green walls hung with menus from times past, wooden floor and tables) set the scene in the basement dining-room. The *menu du jour* is written, uncompromisingly, in French but, once translated, snails, mussels and baby clams in a watercress butter sauce arrived beautifully seasoned and flavoured. Cloves of slowly roasted garlic added to the interest of noisettes of lamb, cooked pink, with a crust of herbs, and perfectly matched with a white onion mousse. Our inspector claimed the tarte Tatin with crème fraîche was the best ever tried – made with fabulously flavoured pears cut thick enough to ensure the flavour still remained after cooking. The board of French cheeses, in superb condition, beckons irresistibly. At lunch, you can just have a cheese plate with bread – that's what a real local restaurant should be all about.

Directions: Turn off the Fulham Road into Ifield Road, restaurant is 500 yds on the L

168 Ifield Road
SW10 9AF
Map: C2
Tel: 0171 8350874
Fax: 0171 2440618
Chef: Zak el Hamdou
Owners: Graham Thomson, Steven Smith
Cost: Fixed-price L £10 (2 courses)/D £25. ☺ H/wine £11.50
Times: Noon-last L 2.30pm/6.30-last D 11pm. Closed L Sat, all Sun, Mon, Xmas, Aug
Additional: Children welcome; ✦ dishes
Seats: 50. Private room 14
Smoking: No pipes & cigars
Credit cards: ▆ ▆ ▆ ▆ ▆ ▆

Chez Moi ❀❀

At the tranquil end of Kensington, just off Holland Park
Avenue, this romantic little restaurant *du quartier* has been run
with unflagging enthusiasm by Richard Walton and Colin
Smith for over 30 years. Richard casts his net far and wide
when it comes to seeking inspiration for his menu, which might
include lamb tagine from Morocco, borsch from Poland,
Japanese-style scallops, and a spicy chicken dosa from India,
alongside more recognisably French offerings such as deep-
fried goujons of sole with tartare sauce, veal kidneys in
mustard sauce and tournedos beurre rouge. Oursins Chez Moi
(a lemon-scented, creamy concoction of tender shellfish in a
light batter wrapped in angel hair noodles) was a highlight of
one evening visit. Service is attentive and quiet. A
predominantly French wine list and good choice of digestifs.

Directions: N side of Holland Park Avenue, opposite
Kensington Hilton. Nearest Tube – Holland Park

1 Addison Avenue W11 4QS
Map GtL: C3
Tel: 0171 6038267
Fax: 0171 6033898
Chef: Richard Walton
Owners: Richard Walton, Colin Smith
Cost: *Alc* £29.50, fixed-price L £15.
H/wine £9.75
Times: Noon-last L 2pm/7pm-last
D 11pm. Closed L Sat, Sun, Bhs
Additional: Children welcome (no
small babies); ❧ dishes
Seats: 45
Smoking: No pipes & cigars; Air
conditioning
Credit cards: ▨ ▨ ▨ ▨ ▨ ▨ ▨ JCB

Chez Nico at Ninety Park Lane ❀❀❀❀❀

The restaurant has the feel of a gentleman's club: lots of wood
panelling, muted colours, crisp linen and throngs of classically
clad staff. The table flowers, by contrast, have a lovely feminine
appeal, as if they've been picked out of a cottage garden.
Combined with the luxury of space, the wide tables,
comfortable chairs, it all adds up to a wonderful, discreet
environment in which to enjoy some of the best cooking in
London. Dishes have a spareness to the descriptions,
emphasising the fact that the cooking is based as much on the
very best ingredients as on a high level of accomplishment.
Paul Rhodes interprets Nico Ladenis' ideas perfectly, but the
great man remains the driving force. Risotto with white truffle
purée, and grilled sea bass with basil purée and red wine sauce
have both been memorable, as much for the seeming simplicity
that belied the sheer technical skill in their composition, as for
powerful flavours. Another stunning idea has been ravioli of
boudin blanc with a rich, slightly sweet sauce. One report was
strewn with superlatives for an accurately executed meal that
opened with terrine of foie gras: three slices, each differently
flavoured, consisting of truffle, green peppercorns, and a
superb griottine balancing with bitter sweetness the richness of
the foie gras, and first-class grilled scallops with buttered leeks.
Next came a superb roasted Dover sole with truffled pasta and
hollandaise sauce, a classic fillet of Scotch beef with celeriac
and truffles, and a pithiviers of lambs' kidneys and sweetbreads
with some notably stunning saucing. Apple brûlée was studded
with dried fruit and caramelised apple, and chocolate Negus,
an old favourite, consisted of chocolate marquise with a lightly
minted crème anglaise and pistachio praline. Delicious breads
with Échiré butter, strong espresso, and petits fours of lovely
miniature lemon tarts, mini rum baba, truffles and fondant
physallis rounded off the meal. The wine list offers lots of
interest. Although there's a heavy weighting of French wines,
there are still some good New World and Euro listings, as well
as a reasonable choice under £30, and a good number of
halves. Some excellent vintages too.

Directions: Part of Grosvenor House Hotel

90 Park Lane W1A 3AA
Map: B3
Tel: 0171 4091290
Fax: 0171 3554877
Chefs: Paul Rhodes, Nico Ladenis
Owners: Nico & Dinah-Jane Ladenis
Cost: *Alc* £68.50, fixed-price L
£34.50/D £64. H/wine £18.50
Times: Noon-2pm/7-11pm. Closed L
Sat, all Sun, 10 days Xmas, Bhs
Additional: No children under 7;
❧ dishes
Seats: 65. Private dining room 20
Jacket & tie preferred
Smoking: No pipes; Air conditioning
Credit cards: ▨ ▨ ▨

Chinon Restaurant ❀❀❀

23 Richmond Way W14 0AS
Map GtL: C3
Tel: 0171 6025968
Chef: Jonathan Hayes
Owners: Barbara Deane,
Jonathan Hayes
Cost: *Alc* £30, fixed-price D £18.
☺ H/wine £11.50
Times: D only, 7pm-last D 10.30pm.
Closed Sun
Additional: No young children;
❧ dishes
Seats: 30
Smoking: No pipes & cigars;
Air conditioning
Credit cards: ▬ ▬ ▚ ▗

The setting may be a traditional-looking English parade of shops, but once inside the look is more of a French provincial restaurant. It's a long, narrow room, tiered towards the back and giving out on to peaceful gardens. There is no pigeon-holing Jonathan Hayes' cooking, however. It is ambitious and imaginative, based on respect for prime quality ingredients and prepared with a faultless but simple technique. The hand-written menu stays deliberately short to ensure freshness and seasonality. Tempura of prawns with lemon-raisin chutney and curry oil, and main courses of breast of corn-fed chicken and oyster mushrooms tagliatelle, or roast saddle of hare with root vegetables, salsify and baby parsnips, show the original style, the characteristics of which are an unwillingness to conform to fashions latest dictates, yet tempered with an ability to stay in touch. Thus 'wonderful, fresh tasting' combination of paper-thin ravioli encasing fresh crab and leeks with butter sauce was just 'gorgeous'. The main course, a simple dish of three big, fat collops of tender roast monkfish and four giant prawns was served with a poppyseed pastry box – in the centre of which was some mashed potato encased in a Savoy cabbage leaf – and accompanied by a rich shellfish cream. Dessert was a stunning, refreshing fruit soup, a thick, amber-laden liquid rich with cinnamon and containing a poached pear and brilliant strawberries, cherries, kumquat and scoops of mango sorbet. Bread is excellent. Service, overseen by Barbara Deane, is solicitous.

Directions: Off Blythe Road which is off Shepherd's Bush Road

The Chiswick ❀❀

131-133 Chiswick High Road W4
Map: B3
Tel: 0181 9946887
Fax: 0181 9945504
Chef: Mark Broadbent
Owners: Katie & Adam Robinson
Cost: *Alc* £24, fixed-price L & D
£9.50 (2 courses). ☺ H/wine £9.75
Times: 12.30-last L 2.45pm/7-last
D 11pm. Closed L Sat, D Sun, 4 days
Xmas, Bhs

In summer, the front windows open to allow for pavement seating; at other times, the minimal sea-green interior with beech tables is given a subtle look with uplighting. The menu changes daily and the choice is eclectic and colourful. If Szechuan aubergine with peanut sauce doesn't take your fancy, try the potato pancake with wood pigeon and truffle oil, followed by grilled sea bass with choi and black beans, or rump of lamb with tabouleh salad. Buttermilk pudding with apricot compote and white peach ice-cream are amongst the super-sounding desserts. The early evening menu, available until 8pm, is exceptional value for two courses plus coffee at £9.50.

Additional: Children welcome; ❧ dishes
Seats: 75. **Smoking:** No pipes & cigars; Air conditioning
Credit cards: ▬ ▬ ▚ ▗ ▬ ▐

Directions: On Chiswick High Road close to junction with Turnham Green Terrace. 3 mins walk from Tube station

Chor Bizarre ❀

16 Albemarle Street
W1X 3HA
Map: C2
Tel: 0171 6299802/6298542
Fax: 0171 4937756
Chef: Deepinder Sondhi
Owners: Mahinder Kaul,
Rohit Khattar

Chor Bizarre translates as 'thieves market', a pretty Mayfair restaurant with antique-shop decor and a well-researched exploration of Indian cooking. Tandooris, and samosas are familiar but it's better to use your sense of adventure here. Try one of the thalis for a decision-free introduction to the cooking. Wines are helpfully matched with the dishes.

Directions: Nearest Tube – Green Park

Chor Bizarre

Cost: Alc £25, fixed price L £12.95/D £22.50 (4 courses). ☺ H/wine £11.95
Times: Last L 2.45pm/last D 11.30pm. Closed 25, 26 Dec
Additional: Sunday L; Children welcome; ❹ dishes
Smoking: No-smoking area; Air conditioning
Credit cards: ▬ ▬ 🇳 🇨 ▬ 🇨 🇵 JCB

Christopher's ❀❀

Christopher Gilmour continues to draw the crowds to his all-American show. The bar-grill, on three floors, linked by a great stone staircase, offers unapologetically brash cooking, administered with precision – flavours are punchy, textures are crisp, and presentation is bold. Inspiration comes from America, whether classic reworkings of Caesar salad, and Maryland crab cake, or more upbeat dishes such as sauté of wild mushrooms with Texas toast and Texas steak sauce. Desserts take in the likes of baked New York cheesecake. Relaxed but slick and outgoing service. The wine list is of reasonable depth and is, unsurprisingly, strong on North America.

Directions: 100 yards from the Royal Opera House; nearest Tube – Covent Garden

18 Wellington Street WC2E 7DD
Map: E3
Tel: 0171 2404222
Fax: 0171 8363506
Chef: Adrian Searing
Owner: The Hon Christopher Gilmour
Cost: Alc £35. H/wine £11.50
Times: Noon-last L 3pm/6-last D 11.30pm. Closed D Sun, Xmas
Additional: Bar food; Sunday L; Children welcome
Seats: 150. Private dining room 50. Jacket & tie preferred
Smoking: Air conditioning
Credit cards: ▬ ▬ 🇳 🇨 ▬ 🇨 🇵 JCB

Churchill Inter-Continental ❀❀

30 Portman Square
W1A 4ZX
Map: B4
Tel: 0171 4865800
Fax: 0171 4861255
Chef: Idris Caldora
Owner: Inter-Continental Hotels
Cost: Alc £28, fixed-price L £23. ☺ H/wine £14.50.
Times: 12.30pm-last L 2.30pm/6pm-Last D 11pm. Closed L Sat

Wood-panelled walls and works by British artists make this a very English setting for a menu that kicks off in the Mediterranean, then sets off to rove the world. Spicy fillet of red snapper with lemon noodles, crisp farmed mandarin quail with grilled pineapple and plum wine glaze, and rack of lamb with couscous and smoked tomato confit, are all presented highly professionally, but the occasional off note has been sounded. At inspection a starter of red mullet with mango and cucumber looked good, but was dominated by pieces of raw, diced pepper. However, Caesar salad with duck confit brioche croûton, quails' eggs and Parmesan shavings was innovative, and seafood risotto, served in a large white china bowl, was generously stocked with lobster and other molluscs and had well-flavoured broth. A good white chocolate tarte finished the meal.

Directions: Close to Marble Arch, just off Oxford Street

Additional: Sunday L; Bar meals; Children welcome; dishes
Seats: 120
Smoking: No-smoking area; Air conditioning
Accommodation: 448 en suite
Credit cards: JCB

Chutney Mary Restaurant ❀

535 King's Road
Chelsea SW10
Map GtL: C2
Tel: 0171 3513113
Fax: 0171 3517694
Chef: Hardev Singh Bhatty
Owners: Ms Namita Panjabi, Mr Ranjit Mathrani
Cost: *Alc* £23, fixed-price L & D £12.50 (2 courses). ☺ H/wine £10.95
Times: Last L 2.30pm /last D 11.30pm. Closed D 25 Dec
Additional: Sunday L; Children welcome; dishes
Smoking: No-smoking area; No pipes & cigars; Air conditioning
Credit cards: JCB

Colonial-style restaurant specialising in the Anglo-Indian cooking of the British Raj, as well as regional specialities. Mildly spiced fresh salmon in filo pastry served with mint chutney, a fiery curry from Goa with fresh lemon sole, and hill station bread-and-butter pudding exemplify the dishes.

Directions: On corner of King's Road and Lots Road; 2 mins from Chelsea Harbour. Nearest Tube – Fulham Broadway

Cibo ❀❀

A small, bright, shop-fronted restaurant close to Olympia, with white-clothed tables. The bar is the focal point, although the eye may equally be drawn to the nudes adorning the walls. Waitresses in skirts like pelmets offer baskets of ciabatta and focaccia and bring appetiser dishes of huge black olives and thin slices of pizza. Fish and shellfish are the backbones of the menu, from baby squid filled with crabmeat in tomato sauce, and seafood risotto among starters, to main courses ranging from grilled swordfish to lobster, prawns and langoustines stewed with tomato, wine and herbs. For more variety, start with sautéed broad beans with prosciutto and goats' cheese, while those who need a fix of meat could opt for grilled beef fillet with rocket and garlic. Finish with silky smooth, rich chocolate cream, and cappuccino served with petits fours. As you'd expect, wines are exclusively Italian.

Directions: Russell Gardens is a residential area off Holland Road. Nearest tubes – Kensington (Olympia); Shepherd's Bush

3 Russell Gardens W14 8EZ
Map GtL: C3
Tel: 0171 3712085
Fax: 0171 6021371
Chef: Roberto Federici
Owner: Gino Taddei
Cost: *Alc* £25, fixed price L £12.50 (2 courses). ☺ H/wine £9.75
Times: Noon-3pm/7-11pm. Closed L Sat, D Sun, Xmas
Additional: Sunday L; Children welcome; dishes
Seats: 50. Private dining room 12, 16
Smoking: Air conditioning
Credit cards: JCB

The Circle Bar Restaurant

Opened in late 1997, The Circle is a relative newcomer to that collection of fashionable eateries to be found at Butlers Wharf on the south bank of the Thames by Tower Bridge. Modern in style, the main restaurant is on a balconied mezzanine overlooking a bar where informal snacks are available. Described as modern British, the compact *carte* reflects chef Michael Moore's globetrotting career with dishes such as deep-fried ravioli with soy and orange dressing, grilled scallops infused with lemongrass on a bed of barley saffron risotto, and grilled breast of guinea fowl with braised cabbage and Chinese spring roll. Our test meal included a pastry-topped wild mushroom and leek casserole that had a good balance of flavours, a beautifully cooked fillet of cod on sweet potato purée with pesto and spinach sauce, and a well-executed dark and white chocolate pyramid with a mango sorbet.

Directions: *Please telephone for directions*

The Circle
Queen Elizabeth Street
SE1 2JE
Map: G3
Tel: 0171 4071122
Fax: 0171 4070123
Chef: Michael Anderson Moore
Owners: Iain Hailday, Phil Murthy
Cost: Alc £30, fixed-price L & D £12.95. ☺ H/wine £9.95
Times: 11.30am-last L 2.30pm/6-last D 10.15pm. Closed L Sat, all Sun, Bhs
Additional: Bar food; Children welcome; ⓓ dishes
Seats: 65
Smoking: No-smoking area; No pipes & cigars; Air conditioning
Credit cards: ▬ ▬ ▬ ▬ ▬ ▬ ▬

City Miyama ❀

Sister restaurant to Miyama in Mayfair (see entry), this friendly little establishment, with its helpful staff and reasonable prices, would be a good place to try Japanese cuisine for the first time. Dining is on two levels with sushi and teppanyaki (griddled meats and fish) on the first floor and the main restaurant downstairs.

Smoking: Air conditioning
Credit cards: ▬ ▬ ▬ ▬ ▬ ▬ JCB

Directions: South side of St Paul's churchyard, behind city information centre

Godliman Street EC4V 5BD
Map: F3
Tel: 0171 4891937
Fax: 0171 2360325
Chef: Isao Ebina
Owner: K Furuya
Cost: Alc £20, fixed-price L & D £40 (7 courses). H/wine £10
Times: Last L 2.30pm/last D 9.30pm. Closed D Sat, all Sun, Bhs
Additional: Children welcome; ⓓ dishes

City Rhodes Restaurant ❀❀❀

Surrounded by offices, and looking rather like an office block itself, a sweeping modern staircase leads to the very 90s restaurant – lots of fluid curves, abstract flower arrangements, groovy cutlery, blue lighting and dog tooth check banquette seating. The name does bring in the punters, and although sightings of Gary Rhodes may be uncertain, there is no doubt that he is in control. He has ensured that an honest, simple approach defines the cooking, which is based on robust flavours and lack of fuss; this is admirably interpreted by head chef Wayne Tapsfield who has been with Gary since the Greenhouse days. A first course of grilled trout fillet with sauté lime pickle potatoes was a far cry from the curry house special that the description implied; instead, it was an appealing combination of beautifully moist fish with the thinnest slivers of lime and onion mixed through the potatoes and courgette, plus a crispy square of trout skin with a fiery chilli coating. Braised pigs trotter 'bourgignone' came with a rich, intense red wine reduction, so tender that it was easier to eat with a spoon than a knife and fork. A 'British pudding plate', reminding us that reworking of traditional English puddings are a speciality with Rhodes, was perfect fodder for any glutton – jaffa cakes will never be the same again.

Signature dishes: Scallops with roast chicory and foie gras butter sauce; pressed tomato cake with peppered goats' cheese; steamed halibut with gravad lax sauce; steak and oyster pie

1 New Street Square EC4A 3JB
Map: E4
Tel: 0171 5831313
Fax: 0171 3531662
Chef: Gary Rhodes
Owners: Gardner Merchant
Cost: Alc £50. H/wine £12.50
Times: Noon-last L 2.30pm/6-last D 8.45pm. Closed Sat, Sun, Bhs
Additional: Children welcome; ⓓ dishes
Seats: 96. Private dining room 14
Smoking: No pipes & cigars; Air conditioning
Credit cards: ▬ ▬ ▬ ▬ ▬ ▬ ▬

Directions: Off Shoe Lane, behind International Press Centre

Claridges ❀❀

In a hotel that engenders so much affection, the word change could spark a riot. No art is more delicate than restoring an old master, and the multi-million refurbishment at Claridges has been handled with the deftest of strokes. Whilst the rooms boast the subtle integration of the latest technology, the kitchen has absorbed modern influences yet still retains its special character. This is not a restaurant that seeks to intimidate, simply grilled Dover sole is only a request away, and service is rendered with a cheerful professionalism that is an example to others. Accuracy and understatement are welcome watchwords, with a trio of foie gras allowed to speak for itself in the restrained company of an elderflower sauce and aromatic spiced bread. Similarly, the sweetest of lamb fillets comes with a shortcrust basket of crunchy, spring vegetables and a passive mustard and thyme jus. Desserts, mainly classic French, are a strength with an iced apple soufflé with Calvados caramel striking a typically judicious balance between sharpness and sugar.

Directions: At the corner of Brook & Davies Street

Brook Street W1A 2JQ
Map: C3
Tel: 0171 6298860
Fax: 0171 8728092
Chef: John Williams
Owner: The Savoy Group
Cost: *Alc* £45, fixed-price L £29/D £38. H/wine £17.50
Times: 12.30pm-last L 3pm/7pm-last D 10.45pm
Additional: Sunday L; Children welcome; ❧ dishes
Seats: 110. Private dining room 14 Jacket & tie preferred
Smoking: No-smoking area; Air conditioning
Accommodation: 197 en suite
Credit cards: ▬▬ ▬▬ ▢ ▬▬ ▣ JCB

Clarke's ❀❀

Sally Clarke has a talent for almost magically enchanting dishes to give of their utmost and honest best – a little seasoning, a little heat, good use of herbs, dash of oil, a shaving of garlic. Flavours are dynamic, yet subtle, complementary yet individual. Her simple precept of prime quality produce treated with utter simplicity and offered on a daily-changing, no-choice menu, has stood the test of time. Several meals taken this year have highlighted dishes such as warm San Danielle ham with trevisse and parsley purée ' a lot of powerful flavours bouncing around here', grilled Cornish Brill with sun-dried tomato, chive and onion relish, and roast Cornish cod with lemon, gherkin, caper and onion relish, crisp potato pancake and leaf broccoli. Incidentals are good, excellent Clarke bread – if only they would leave a basket of it on the table! – good cheeses with home-made oat biscuits. Tables however, are far too close together, and staff , though professional, lack warmth. Wines can get pricy with a range starting at £9 and going through to £225, but there is a good selection and a thoughtful relationship between the menu and the wine list with a heavy emphasis on rustic country French wines and a wide variety of Californian whites.

Directions: Near Notting Hill Gate Tube station

124 Kensington Church Street W8 4BH
Map GtL: C3
Tel: 0171 2219225
Fax: 0171 2294564
Chefs: Sally Clarke, Elizabeth Payne
Owner: Sally Clarke
Times: 12.30-2pm/7-10pm. Closed Sat, Sun, 10 days Xmas, 3 wks Aug
Additional: Children welcome; ❧ dishes
Seats: 90
Smoking: No-smoking area; No pipes & cigars; Air conditioning
Credit cards: ▬▬ ▬▬ ▢ ▬▬

Coast Restaurant ❀❀

Always busy, this loud restaurant is a bright, airy affair set in a converted car showroom. Adam Gray's menu fizzes with freshness and originality, resulting in fantastic dishes such as borsch 'en gélée' (pigeon stock and beetroot) with crème fraîche and caviar. Our inspector arrived for dinner in late spring, and found the menu true to the season, with plenty of hints of warmer climes to come. The meal started with roasted langoustine on glass noodle salad with a tamarind bisque dressing. Grilled Devereux chicken followed – exquisitely

Albemarle Street W1
Map: C3
Tel: 0171 4955999
Fax: 0171 4952999
Chef: Adam Gray
Owner: Oliver Peyton
Cost: *Alc* £30. H/wine £12.50. ☺
Times: Noon-last L 3pm/6pm-last D 11.30pm. Closed Bhs
Additional: Sunday L; Children welcome; ❧ dishes

timed with a crisp skin and succulent flesh. Thin slices of the chicken were served on hearty, grill-finished potatoes accompanied by morels, baby broad beans and a frothy cream jus. The meal was polished off with a bloodied lemon tart with blood orange sorbet and 'Gaggia' espresso. The interesting wine list features over two hundred wines, with a strong showing from across the Channel.

Seats: 150
Smoking: Air conditioning
Credit cards: 🔳 🔳 🔳 🔳

Directions: Nearest Tube – Green Park

The Collection ❀❀

264 Brompton Road SW3
Map: B1
Tel: 0171 2251212
Fax: 0171 2251050
Chef: Cass Titcombe
Owner: Signature Restaurants
Cost: Alc £30, fixed-price L £12.95.
☺ H/wine £11.50
Times: Noon-last L 3pm/7-last
D 11.30pm. Closed L Mon & Tue,
all Sun, Bhs
Additional: Bar food; Children
welcome; ❹ dishes
Seats: 180
Smoking: Air conditioning
Credit cards: 🔳 🔳 🔳 🔳 🔳 🔳 🔳

The sushi menu gives a clue to the uninitiated – this is a super-fashionable spot serving smart Pacific Rim food. The huge New York loft-style interior boasts monstrous wooden pillars and incorporates a cocktail bar and two restaurants. The ground floor specialises in noodles, as well as dishes such as seared tuna sashimi with cucumber, shiitake and mooli salad. The mezzanine struts its stuff with grilled chicken skewers with tamarind, seared salt-cured salmon with porcini crust and celeriac, char siu loin of pork with sweet potato mash and chilli pickled cabbage, and cumin and lemon crusted lamb with baby aubergines and harissa.

Directions: Nearest Tubes – Brompton Cross, South Kensington

The Connaught ❀❀❀

The winds of change may continue to blow across British cooking but the Connaught stands stoic as an oak, defiantly unbent by fad or fashion. The menu (identical in both Restaurant and Grill Room) of untranslated French and esoteric descriptions broadcast an assumption of familiarity. Indeed, far from being a forgotten relic, these dining rooms remain amongst the best attended in the capital, a haven of stability and comfort for those who seek reassurance that although the times may be a changing, vestiges of the old worlds remain. Dishes will be offered for approval, withdrawn for carving, saucing and garnishing then deftly re-presented. Lobster, turbot, truffles and foie gras are liberally dispensed, less luxuriant produce well chosen: a sea fresh and chunky crab bisque of Cornish origin; new-season lamb sweetened on Welsh grass. Some dishes are encumbered by traditions – expect the lamb to be offered with a sugary mint sauce, and the generally admirable Connaught terrine (duck, wild

Carlos Place W1Y 6AL
Map: C3
Tel: 0171 4997070
Fax: 0171 4953262
Chef: Michel Bourdin
Cost: Alc £40, fixed-price L £27.50/D
£40. ☺
Times: 12.30-last L 2pm/6-last
D 10.45pm
Additional: Sunday L; Children
welcome; ❹ dishes
Seats: 65. Private dining room 22
Jacket & tie preferred at D
Smoking: Air conditioning
Accommodation: 90 en suite
Credit cards: 🔳 🔳 🔳 🔳 🔳 🔳 🔳 JCB

mushrooms, pistachios, foie gras) to keep the company
of a pub-like garnish of quartered tomatoes and radish slices.
On the other hand, near forgotten classics such as marvellous
soufflé potatoes make a strong case for their imminent revival,
although the Connaught is unlikely to be spearheading any
campaign.

    Signature dishes: All game in season (8-10 varieties); fillet
de boeuf en croûte, légère strasbourgeoise; summer pudding
Reform

Directions: On corner of Mount Street and Carlos Place,
between Bond Street and Hyde Park Corner Tube stations

Conrad International London ❀

See Where London Meets Section page 153

The Cook House ❀

*Tiny restaurant with minimalist decor – white walls, terracotta floors
– and a bring your own drinks policy (cover/corkage £2). Typical
dishes are skate wing with paprika aïoli, rocket salad and chips, and
roast rabbit with tomatoes, basil, olives and fettucine. Favourites to
finish are treacle tart and bread-and-butter pudding.*

Additional: Children welcome
Seats: 28
Smoking: No-smoking area; No pipes & cigars, Air
conditioning
Credit cards: ▇ ▇ ▇ ▇

Directions: Nearest Tube – Putney Bridge

56 Lower Richmond Road
Putney SW15 1JT
Map GtL: C2
Tel: 0181 7852300
Chef: Tim Jefferson
Owners: Tim Jefferson,
Amanda Griffiths
Cost: *Alc* £23.50. ☺
Times: D only, 7-11pm.
Closed Sun, Mon

Copthorne Tara ❀

See Where London Meets Section page 153

Coulsdon Manor ❀❀

The former home of Lord Byron, now noted for fine cooking.
Dishes such as lasagne of Sussex goats' cheese and plum
tomatoes and warm piperade vinaigrette, and pan-fried fillet of
wild sea bass with saffron risotto, fennel purée with sautéed
scallops, langoustine and crayfish have been well received but
the kitchen's style can be unnecessarily fussy. Inspector's
reports indicate it is best to stick with less fussy dishes such as
pan-fried noisette of English lamb cooked pink, served with a
selection of chargrilled vegetables and a balsamic jus, as simple
ideas are often the best here. Desserts take in the likes of
white chocolate mousse with vanilla ice cream.

Accommodation: 35 en suite
Credit cards: ▇ ▇ ▇ ▇ ▇ ▇ ▇ JCB

Directions: M23 N until road becomes A23. After 2.5 miles, R
after Coulsdon S Railway Station onto B2030 (Purley). Follow
uphill 1 mile, L past pond, 0.5 mile, and turn R into Coulsdon
Court Rd.

Coulsdon Court Road
Croydon CR5 2LL
Map GtL: D1
Tel: 0181 6680414
Fax: 0181 6680342
Chef: Robert Bird
Owner: Marston Hotels
Cost: *Alc* £33, fixed-price L £15.95/D
£24.95. ☺ H/wine £12
Times: 12.30-last L 2pm/7-last
D 9.30pm. Closed L Sat
Additional: Bar food; Sunday L;
Children welcome; ♦ dishes.
Seats: 100. Private dining room 120
Smoking: No smoking in dining room

The Cow Dining Room

Best to make a reservation before turning up at this bustling unpretentious restaurant above the Cow Saloon bar (which, incidentally, also serves good food, especially seafood). Turn right up the stairs immediately on entering the pub to reach the simply adorned dining room, where you will find a short daily-changing menu listing imaginative dishes that are freshly prepared to order. There's a relaxing atmosphere generated by efficient staff who manage to successfully combine friendliness and professionalism. Begin with lobster bisque, rock oysters or, as we did, with a well-made and very gamey pigeon, chicken liver and bacon terrine, then move on to duck with chargrilled pineapple and black bean sauce, spicy chickpea and tomato stew on minted couscous, or baked turbot with samphire, pickled cucumber and hollandaise. A delicious summer berry crème brûlée, dark and white chocolate torte, or French cheese with oatcakes and chutney may feature on the list of puddings.

89 Westbourne Park Road W2 5QH
Map GtL: C3
Tel: 0171 2210021
Chef: Caroline Perry
Owner: Tom Conran
Cost: *Alc* £36.50, fixed-price
D £18.50 (Sun-Tue only). H/wine
£12.50
Times: D only, 7.30-last D 11pm
Additional: Bar food; ✪ dishes
Seats: 32
Credit cards: ▆▆ ▆▆ ▆▆ ▆ ▆ JCB

Directions: Nearest Tubes – Royal
Oak, Westbourne Park, Queensway.
5 mins from Portobello Market

The Criterion ✿✿✿

224 Piccadilly W1V 9LB
Map: C3
Tel: 0171 9300488
Fax: 0171 9308380
Chef: Peter Reffell, Richard Phillips
Owners: Marco Pierre White &
Granada
Cost: *Alc* £28, fixed-price L £17.95.
☺ H/wine £13
Times: Noon-2.30pm (till 3pm Sat &
Sun)/6-midnight. Closed 25-26 Dec,
1 Jan
Additional: Sunday L; Children
welcome; ✪ dishes
Seats: 180
Smoking: No pipes & cigars
Credit cards: ▆▆ ▆▆ ▆▆ ▆ ▆ ▆

The ceiling of the Rococo, Grade II listed building glitters with gold mosaic along its entire 45 metres length. Marbled walls, studded with semi-precious stones, are pierced by arched, shallow alcoves hung with mirrors and oriental paintings. A rather menacing sketch of Marco Pierre White, unruly Medusa locks coiled like octopus tentacles, glares out from the back of the menu – the inscription reads 'To know how to eat well, one must first know how to...wait!' However, service is fast-paced, geared up for haute-cuisine fast food; in other words classic brasserie fare given a Marco spin by his chefs Peter Reffell and Richard Phillips: risotto of langoustine; cromesquis of oysters with deep-fried herbs and sauce grebiche; pot-roast pork with spices and ginger and étuvée of young vegetables – not forgetting the lemon tart which, once tasted, is never forgotten. Mediterranean influences thread through the menu – carpaccio of tuna with caviar and a salad of preserved lemon and fennel, or roast calamari with parsley – but the foundations are French bourgeois – poached egg with sauce béarnaise, for example, or escalope of veal Holstein, and pain perdu with caramelised apple. Dishes that crop up on menus throughout the MPW empire appear, those tried at inspection included a classic risotto nero, caramelised skate with winkles and capers, and a great crème brûlée Granny Smith.

Signature dishes: Grilled tuna with aubergine caviar, pomme boulangere, sauce antiboise; roast rump of lamb with herbs, provençale vegetables, jus roti; sea bass à la vapeur, croquant of fennel, sauce beurre noisette

Directions: Nearest Tube – Piccadilly

Crowne Plaza London – Heathrow ❀

See Where London Meets Section page 153

Crowthers Restaurant ❀

Popular little restaurant run by a husband-and-wife team. Typical dishes are seared scallops with spiced basmati rice and a light curry dressing, and noisettes of spring lamb with rosemary and redcurrant. To finish, perhaps rhubarb and walnut shortcake with vanilla sauce.

Additional: Children welcome; ❦ dishes
Smoking: Air conditioning
Credit cards: ▄▄ ▄▄ ▅▅ ▆ ▐

Directions: Train to Mortlake; train or tube to Richmond. Between junction of Sheen Lane & Clifford Ave

481 Upper Richmond Road West
East Sheen SW14 7PU
Map GtL: B2
Tel/Fax: 0181 8766372
Chef: Philip Crowther
Owners: Philip & Shirley Crowther
Cost: Fixed-price D £23.50. H/wine £9.50
Times: Last L 1.30pm/last D 10.30pm. Closed L Sat, all Sun, Mon, 2 wks Aug

Cucina ❀❀

45a South End Road NW3 2QB
Map GtL: C4
Tel/Fax: 0171 4357814
Chefs: A Poole, S Baker
Owners: V Mascarenhas, A Poole, S Baker
Cost: *Alc* £18.50, fixed-price L £10 (2 courses)/D £16.95. ☺ H/wine £10.95
Times: Noon-last L 2.30pm/7-last D 10.30pm. Closed D Sun, 25 Dec
Additional: Sunday L; Children welcome; ❦ dishes
Seats: 96
Smoking: No pipes & cigars; Air conditioning
Credit cards: ▄▄ ▄▄ ▅▅ ▆ ▄▄ ▐

Directions: Opposite Hampstead BR station. Nearest Tubes – Belsize Park or Hampstead

Loud paintings on vibrantly coloured walls, stripped pine floor and trendy modern chairs make the decor as distinctive as the cooking at this appealing restaurant in a parade of shops near Hampstead Heath underground station. Full of interest, there's a strong Pacific Rim influence to the sensible length menu. For starters we enjoyed crispy prawn wun-tuns nicely complemented by a chilli, lemon grass and coriander flavoured risotto, and meaty duck and sweet potato fritters with a mild piccalilli. Next came a beautifully tender rump of lamb on coarse parsnip mash with sage jus and grilled tuna on a niçoise of waxy new potatoes, baby tomatoes, black olives, anchovy fillets and raw French beans tossed in a balsamic dressing. Surprise hit of the meal was a warm chocolate and beetroot cake (the slight acidity of the beetroot cutting through the richness of the chocolate) with a well-balanced beetroot and ginger sauce.

Dan's Restaurant ❀

Any garden restaurant in the middle of London has a head start, but it's worth coming here for a good choice of modern British dishes. Try crab, ginger and onion tart, and chargrilled calves' liver with sautéed pancetta and curly kale whatever the weather.

Additional: No young children; dishes
Credit cards:

Directions: At Kings Road end of Sydney Street. Nearest Tube – South Kensington

119 Sydney Street SW3 6NR
Map: B1
Tel: 0171 3522718
Fax: 0171 3523265
Chef: Anthony Beaton
Owner: Dan Whitehead
Cost: *Alc* £25, fixed-price L £12.50 (2 courses). H/wine £12.50
Times: Last L 2.25pm/last D 10.25pm. Closed L Sat, all Sun, Xmas, New Year

Daphne's ❀❀

Under the guidance of Mogens Tholstrup, Daphne's attracted celebs, wannabe celebs, and the curious, who gathered to see and to be seen. It remains to be seen whether the new Belgo management have the same *Hello!* charm (although Tholstrup maintains an executive role). However, the decor is still very Med, with burnt umber walls, flagstone floors and terracotta pots. The straightforward breezy Italian menu offers a good range of salads, risottos, roasts and grills, and there is a special brunch menu for lazy Sundays with the likes of scrambled egg and smoked salmon bagel, baked truffled eggs with toasted ciabatta, and prosciutto San Danielle with dates and walnuts. We visited in early June for a meal that started with risotto primavera and finished with a 'wonderfully light' tiramisu. In between, there was grilled sea bass with fennel, and chargrilled tuna with baby tomatoes and basil. The hundred-strong wine list includes some reliable bottles from the New World.

Directions: Jnc of Draycott Avenue & Walton Street. Nearest Tube – South Kensington

110-112 Draycott Avenue SW3 3AE
Map: B1
Tel: 0171 5894257
Fax: 0171 5812232
Chefs: Chris Benians, Lee Purcell
Owner: Signature Restaurants
Cost: *Alc* £48. H/wine £11.50
Times: Noon-last L 3pm/7-last D 11.30pm. Closed 25 Dec-1 Jan
Additional: Sunday L; Children welcome; dishes
Seats: 110. Private dining room 50
Smoking: No pipes; Air conditioning
Credit cards:

The Depot Waterfront Brasserie ❀❀

NEW

Situated on the riverside between Barnes and Mortlake, The Depot Waterfront Brasserie has picture windows from which you can sit and watch the Thames go by. A simply decorated restaurant with parquet floors, white walls, and a bit of brick here and there, the menu and wine list offer good value for money. Gazpacho with basil cream is a pretty soup garnished

Tideway Yard
Mortlake High Street
SW14 8SN
Map GtL: C2
Tel: 0181 8789462
Fax: 0181 3921361
Chef: Paul Webster
Owner: Tideway Restaurants Ltd

with a cube of frozen olive oil, perfect on a hot day. Fish cakes are a speciality. Made from cod and crab or maybe salmon and sorrel, they are fresh, full of flavour and boast good crisp texture. The former come served with cucumber and lemon crème fraîche for a refreshing contrast. Can't decide on a dessert? Go for the chef's plate, temptingly presented. The passion fruit mousse, treacle tart, vanilla ice cream, poached pear and chocolate mousse are so delicious you may want to lick the dish clean.

Directions: Between Barnes Bridge and Mortlake train stations

Cost: £18, fixed-price L £12.50/D £14.50. ☺ H/wine £10.50
Times: Noon-3pm/6-11pm. Closed 24-26 Dec
Additional: Children welcome; ❸ dishes
Seats: 120
Smoking: No-smoking area
Credit cards: ▉ ▨ ▚ ▢ ▨ ▣ ▨ JCB

The Dorchester, Grill Room ❀❀

Park Lane W1A 2HJ
Map: C3
Tel: 0171 3176336
Fax: 0171 4090114
Chef: Willi Elsener
Owner: The Audley Group
Cost: Alc £40; fixed-price L £28/D £37 (4 courses). H/wine £21.50.
Times: 12.30pm-last L 2.30pm/6pm-last D 11pm
Additional: Sunday L; Children welcome; ❸ dishes
Seats: 81
Smoking: Air conditioning
Accommodation: 244 en suite
Credit cards: ▉ ▨ ▚ ▢ ▨ ▣ ▨ JCB

The trolley is alive and well and living in the Dorchester Grill Room; puddings (and cheeses) are rolled out for inspection, and although this has a degree of theatrical charm it can sometimes limit the selection available. Still, this is a fabled place in which to dine – the opulent decor, with beautiful tapestries and gold-leaf detail on the ceiling, is modelled on an old Spanish palace and remains much as it was when the hotel opened in 1931. Luncheon specialities have pride of place – if it's roast shoulder of pork then you know it's Thursday. Other favourites include classic shepherd's pie, and the mixed grill, but there are more contemporary dishes along the lines of oven-baked salmon with morels and Chinese greens. From the Dorchester's sister hotel, The Beverley Hills Hotel in California, come signature dishes such as ginger crab cakes and corn-crusted chicken breast with horseradish.

Directions: Two-thirds of the way down Park Lane, fronting a small island garden. Nearest Tube – Hyde Park

The Dorchester, The Oriental ❀❀❀

The room is lavishly decorated: Oriental furniture, luxurious carpets, rich silk robes, antique vases and Eastern object d'art. The main tilt of the cooking is Cantonese, and although it can lack the expression and boldness to be found in Chinatown, there is a delicacy and finesse to Kenneth Poon's food, and service is of course top-notch. The set menus are a far cry from the average Chinese banqueting menu; here they are

Park Lane W1A 2HJ
Map: C3
Tel: 0171 3176328
Fax: 0171 4090114
Chefs: Willi Elsener, Kenneth Poon
Cost: Alc £60, fixed-price L £28/D £37-£82 (5 courses). H/wine £21.50
Times: Noon-last L 2.30pm/7pm-last D 11pm. Closed L Sat, all Sun, Aug

The Dorchester, The Oriental

Additional: No children under 5;
dishes
Seats: 51. Private dining rooms 5-16
Smoking: Air conditioning
Accommodation: 244 en suite
Credit cards: ▪▪ ▪▪ ▪▪ ▪ ▪▪ ▪ ▪ JCB

carefully constructed for taste and balance, and particular wines are recommended to accompany the food. Thus, Fragrant Garden could bring you, amongst other things, Oriental combination of deep-fried prawn and mango wrapped in rice paper, scallop soup with conpoy and egg white, wok-fried medallions of beef Cantonese-style, wok-fried duck with fresh asparagus, and chilled fresh mango pudding. Abalone and shark's fin are imported directly from Hong Kong and feature in the likes of hot-pot of braised abalone and chicken with oyster sauce, and braised superior shark's fin with crab meat. Roasted Peking duck – the real thing – is served in two courses for six to eight people. Stir-fried fillet of Dover sole with broccoli, and deep-fried boneless pigeon with orange sauce, have both been praised, and lunchtime dim sum is recommended – no clattering trolleys here.

Signature dishes: Steamed slices of duck with preserved vegetables and Chinese mushrooms; pan-fried slices of goose liver flavoured with five spice; braised diced chicken with fresh bean curd and salted fish' wok-fried sliced monkfish with ginger and carrot.

Directions: See Dorchester Grill Room (previous entry)

Drones of Pont Street ❀❀

Apricot walls, Mediterranean-style decor, wrought-iron chairs, small fountains and even a live olive tree all add to the chic, cool ambience at this Knightsbridge haunt. 'I didn't even feel left out without a designer bag and mobile phone,' noted an inspector. A leaning towards Italy shows up in some dishes – bresaola with Parmesan and rocket, or strozzapretti (spinach gnocchi) with roasted walnuts – but Caesar salad, Devon crab with mango and prawns, or Moroccan-style sardines could equally be found among the starters. 'Wonderfully pink and tender' new season's lamb coated in mustard impressed an inspector; it came with courgette and basil confit and a ratatouille-type charlotte, all rounded off with thyme sauce. Elsewhere, classic saltimbocca may turn up with olive mash and red wine sauce, and grilled tuna steak with guacamole and beans. Delicately poached pears – hints of orange and honey – with honey ice cream made 'a lovely send off' for one. France outweighs Italy on the wine list, though the New World is well represented too.

1 Pont Street SW1X 9EJ
Map: B2
Tel: 0171 2596166
Fax: 0171 2596177
Chef: Ian McKensie
Owner: Simpsons of Cornhill
Cost: *Alc* £30. ☺ H/wine £12
Times: Noon-last L 3.15pm/7-last D 11.15pm. Closed 25 Dec
Additional: Sunday L; Children welcome; dishes
Seats: 80. Private dining room 50
Smoking: Air conditioning
Credit cards: ▪▪ ▪▪ ▪▪ ▪ ▪▪ ▪ ▪ JCB

Directions: Nearest Tubes – Knightsbridge and Sloane Square

The Eagle ❀

159 Farringdon Road EC1R 3AL
Map GtL: E5
Tel: 0171 8371353
Chef: Tom Norrington-Davies
Owner: Michael Belben

A popular media hang-out where tables are at a premium and the food is robust with strong Med overtones. Hand-scrawled blackboard with typical dishes including roast loin of pork 'al arista' (a white onion and parsley salsa), and marinated anchovies with slow-roasted tomatoes on toasted ciabatta. For dessert try 'Pastel de Nata' – a Portuguese custard tart.

Times: Last L 2.30pm (3.30 Sat/4pm Sun)/last D 10.30pm. Closed D Sun, Easter, 10 days Xmas, Bhs
Additional: Sunday L; Children welcome; ❹ dishes
Credit cards: None

Directions: N end of Farringdon Road close to Mount Pleasant. Nearest Tube – Farringdon

Elena's L'Etoile ❀❀

30 Charlotte Street W1P 1HJ
Map: C4
Tel: 0171 6367189
Fax: 0171 6370122
Chef: Kevin Hopgood
Owners: The Restaurant Partnership plc
Cost: *Alc* £27.50, fixed-price D £16.50 (2 courses). ☺ H/wine £13.75

The legendary Elena's star still shines brightly at the show-biz-friendly hang-out in the middle of media-land. The classical French menu keeps within its set terms of reference, and whilst it holds few surprises, does what it sets out to do extremely well. Ever-popular choices include ham, chicken and parsley terrine, salad of chicory and asparagus with poached egg and bacon, and warm potato and chive pancake with smoked salmon. For the main course there are shallow-fried skate wings with parsley mash and caperberries, fillet of beef 'Wellington' and roast corn-fed chicken supreme with petit pois, morels and herb jus.

Times: Noon-last L 2.30pm/6-last D 10.45pm. Closed L Sat, all Sun, Bhs
Additional: Children welcome; ❹ dishes
Seats: 65. Private dining room 28
Smoking: No-smoking area; Air conditioning
Credit cards: ■ ■ ■ ■ ■ ■ ■ JCB

Directions: Southside of Goodge Street, between Goodge Street and Oxford Street. Nearest Tube – Tottenham Court Road

Ellington's ❀

140 Station Road Chingford E4 6AN
Map GtL: E5
Tel: 0181 5245544
Fax: 0181 5594993
Chef: Ian Jones
Owner: Brian Hutchinson
Cost: *Alc* £22.50, fixed price L £7.95 (2 courses)/D £19.95. ☺ H/wine £10.50

Neighbourhood hang-out sporting a jazz theme and an enthusiastic modern menu that draws on global inspiration. Try gazpacho with charred chorizo and olive oil ice cube, sticky duck served with Chinese leaf, coriander, beansprout and alfalfa, roasted curried skate with tomato butter, or dartoise of pork fillet with prune, parsnip rösti and bourbon cream sauce.

Times: Last L 2pm/last D 10pm. Closed L Mon, D Sun
Additional: Sunday L; Children welcome; ❹ dishes
Smoking: Air conditioning
Credit cards: ■ ■ ■

Directions: Opposite Chingford railway station

English Garden Restaurant ❀❀

10 Lincoln Street SW3 2TS
Map: B1
Tel: 0171 5847272
Fax: 0171 5812848
Chef: Brian Turner
Owner: Roger Wren
Cost: *Alc* £28, fixed-price L £17.
☺ H/wine £11
Times: 12.30-last L 2.30pm/7.30-last
D 11.15pm. Closed 25-26 Dec
Additional: Sunday L; Children
welcome; ❹ dishes
Seats: 70. Private dining room 30
Smoking: Air conditioning
Credit cards: ▬ ▬ ▰ ▱ ▤ ▣ JCB

This long-established restaurant, in a terrace of residential houses off the King's Road, is made up of two connected dining-rooms, the one at the front with faux marble walls, the one at the back with white-painted brick walls, large mirrors and a domed skylight. The seasonally changing menus may have their heart in England, but they burst with good ideas that all seem to work. Plump, accurately timed grilled scallops come with slowly roasted shallots in saffron jus garnished with crisp sage leaves, duck confit with beetroot and pear compote, and seared tuna with pickled lettuce and red pepper oil. Successes among main courses range from a simple dish of roast ham on a mound of mustard mash, through Arbroath smokie fishcake with herb relish, to saddle of venison with wild boar sausage and celeriac gratin. Simplicity also marks out moist banana-flavoured sponge with hot fudge sauce, and a mousse of bitter chocolate and rum. Breads are of good quality, Yorkshire fudge is served with coffee, and Bordeaux dominates the almost exclusively French wine list.

Directions: Nearest tube – Sloane Square

The English House ❀❀

The glitzy Chelsea boutiques may be a stone's throw away, but this is still unknown territory for ladies-who-lunch. It is well worth venturing down the tranquil side street in order to lunch in elegant and (despite the name) chintz-free style. The seasonal English menu displays some suitably robust touches – crab cakes with crab and whisky sauce, and beef Wellington with pickled walnuts. Game terrine came with velvety, sweet-and-sour pickled vegetable relish, and calves' liver was cooked well. Hot puddings are the business here, a sticky toffee pudding with thick butterscotch sauce was the highlight of the meal, but calorie counters can choose fresh fruit water ices instead. Then, all one has to do is try and resist the Yorkshire fudge.

3 Milner Street SW3 2QA
Map: B1
Tel: 0171 5843002
Fax: 0171 5812848
Chef: Danny Leahy
Owner: Roger Wren
Cost: *Alc* £32, fixed-price L £15.75.
H/wine £11
Times: 12.30pm-last L 2.30pm (2pm
Sun)/7.30pm-last D 11.30pm (10pm
Sun). Closed 26 Dec

Additional: Sunday L; Children welcome; ❹ dishes
Seats: 26. Private dining rooms 14
Smoking: No pipes and cigars in dining room
Credit cards: ▬ ▬ ▰ ▱ ▤ ▣ JCB

Directions: Between South Kensington and Sloane Square
Tubes

L'Escargot ⚘⚘⚘

48 Greek Street W1V 5LQ
Map: D4
Tel: 0171 4376828/4372679
Fax: 0171 4370790
Chef: Billy Reid
Owner: Jimmy Lahoud
Cost: *Alc* £42, fixed-price L & pre-theatre D £17.95. ☺ H/wine £13
Times: 12.15-2.15pm/6-11.30pm.
Closed L Sat, all Sun, 25 Dec, 1 Jan,
Picasso Room closed Aug
Additional: Children welcome; ⚘
dishes
Seats: 120. Private dining room 10-60
Smoking: No pipes & cigars; Air conditioning
Credit cards: ■■ ■■ ■ ■ ■ ■ ■ JCB

A gentle face-lift has given this grand Soho landmark a new lease of life. It's almost a mini art gallery with the works of Miró lining the walls of the downstairs restaurant, Andy Warhol up the stairs, and the intimate first-floor dining room dedicated to Picasso with original prints, drawings and ceramics. However, the building retains a well-lived in feel, the stairs still creak, and there are splendid period L'Escargot lamps and doorstoppers. Billy Reid heads the team on the ground-floor, offering a cracking menu that marches in tune with the seasons and is bang up to date. A hot summer evening was matched by wonderfully light, plump scalded scallops with a little leek pomme purée, a Madeira butter of intense flavour, and crisp asparagus, plus a dessert of fresh fruits in a champagne jelly with splashes of raspberry and mango coulis. Otherwise there could be a classic L'Escargot starter of potato salad, smoked salmon, poached egg and chive vinaigrette, a splendid terrine of duck confit with white beans and foie gras, or calves' liver with sautéed lettuce and Alsace bacon. Staff are charming and genuinely helpful.

Directions: Nearest Tubes –
Tottenham Court Rd, Leicester Sq

Fats ⚘

Not quite what you expect to find in discreet Maida Vale, Fats is a small informal restaurant offering a selection of Cajun, Creole and Caribbean cooking in a jolly, fun atmosphere. The likes of chicken jumbalaya, spicy deep-fried salt fish rolls and seafood gumbo give an idea of what to expect.

Directions: Off Harrow Rd, via Chippenham Rd. Nearest Tubes –
Warwick Avenue, Queen's Pk, Kilburn Pk, Westbourne Pk

178 Shirland Road
Maida Vale W9 3JR
Map: B3
Tel: 0171 2893884
Please telephone for further details

Fifth Floor Restaurant ⚘

Great room with nothing much in the way of decor – the clientele provide the interest – but the buzz is terrific. Henry Harris's mod Med menu offers the likes of parsley, spinach and mozzarella risotto, pan-fried fillets of lemon sole with a wild mushroom cream sauce, and prune and Armagnac custard tart. Popularity means that service, and the cooking can come under pressure.

Credit cards: ■■ ■■ ■ ■ ■ ■ ■ JCB

Directions: Nearest Tube – Knightsbridge. Entrance via Sloane Street

Harvey Nichols
Knightsbridge SW1X 7RJ
Map: B2
Tel: 0171 2355250
Fax: 0171 8232207
Chef: Henry Harris
Owner: Harvey Nichols & Co Ltd
Cost: *Alc* £45. Fixed-price L £23.50.
Times: Last L 3pm/last D 11.30pm.
Closed D Sun, 25-26 Dec
Additional: Sunday L; Children welcome; ⚘ dishes.
Smoking: No pipes; Air conditioning

The Fish Restaurant at 190

The trouble with basement restaurants with comfortable seating and an agreeably clubby atmosphere is that you can be lulled into a sense of timelessness. Downstairs at 190 has gone from modern minimalism to mulberry-panelled walls and spotlit white-clothed tables. Fish and seafood obviously predominate, and although there are plenty of classics (Salcombe bay potted brown shrimps; langoustines with citrus mayonnaise; grilled Dover sole) there are also more stylish ideas such as spiced mussel and saffron soup, tea and cinnamon-smoked scallop salad, and oysters with lime and peppercorn sabayon. An interpretation of bouillabaisse is thicker than usual, with tuna, salmon, clams, mussels and bass, and the fish has good flavour. Desserts both look and taste good, especially the orange cake. The staff, mostly French, are efficient.

Directions: Next to Gore Hotel on Queensgate; easy walking distance from South Kensington Tube station

190 Queensgate SW7 5EU
Map: A1
Tel: 0171 5815666
Fax: 0171 5818172
Owners: Simpsons of Cornhill
Cost: Alc £30, fixed price L £22/D £22.50. H/wine £10.75
Times: Noon-last L 2.30pm/7-last D 10.30pm. Closed D Sun, L Mon-Fri, Bhs
Additional: Sunday L; No children under 6; 🅰 dishes
Seats: 70. Private room 30
Smoking: Air conditioning
Credit cards: ▆▆ ▆▆ ▆▆ ▆▆ ▆▆ ▆ ▆ JCB

Foundation

A basement is a basement by any other name except when it's a lower ground floor (in Harvey Nicks speak). Simply decorated in plain wood with comfortable, steel-frame chairs, visual impact comes from a glass water wall running the length of the 30 foot bar (where light snacks are served), lit in glacial blues, greens and silver. The menu suits both salad toyers, with the likes of rocket, fennel and orange salad with grilled, marinated leeks, and those requiring a bit more sustenance, perhaps wild mushroom risotto with Parmesan shavings, smoked haddock with spinach, deep-fried poached egg and hollandaise, or grilled rabbit with polenta, tomato sauce and pesto. Croustillant of pear with caramel sauce was superbly light, rich and sweet. Set lunches along the lines of lobster salad with porcini dressing, and medallions of monkfish are very good value given the location and general quality of the food.

Directions: Nearest Tube – Knightsbridge. Entrance off Seville Street opposite The Sheraton Hotel

Harvey Nichols Seville Street
Knightsbridge SW1X 7RJ
Map: C3
Tel: 0171 2018000
Fax: 0171 2018080
Chef: Simon Barnett
Owners: Harvey Nichols
Cost: Alc £24, fixed-price L £16.50/D £19.50. ☺ H/wine £12.50
Times: Noon-last L 3.30pm/6.30pm-last D 11pm. Closed D Sun
Additional: Bar food D; Children welcome; 🅰 dishes
Seats: 80
Smoking: No-smoking area; No pipes; Air conditioning
Credit cards: ▆▆ ▆▆ ▆▆ ▆▆ ▆▆ ▆ ▆ JCB

The Four Seasons Hotel

At the time of going to press the Four Seasons Restaurant was about to undergo an impressive sounding facelift. The current surroundings have been home to some legendary cooking, but the merging of the old Four Season restaurant with Lanes, the hotel's second dining room, will create a new, distinctive 90-seater restaurant. Menus are also being redesigned, but Four Seasons chef, Shaun Whatling, with executive chef, Eric Deblonde, remain in place. At our last inspection in the old Four Seasons, our inspector commented on top-notch raw materials used in dishes such as a fragrant spring vegetable minestrone with scallops, excellent medallions of venison, and a banana tarte Tatin. And, our inspector noted, given the opulent surroundings, the wine list offers some down-to-earth mark-ups, and there's plenty of quality to be found for under £25.

Directions: Nearest Tubes – Hyde Park Corner, Green Park. Set back from Park Lane in Hamilton Place

Park Lane W1A 1AZ
Map: C3
Tel: 0171 4990880
Fax: 0171 4936629
Chef: Eric Deblonde, Shaun Whatling
Owner: Four Seasons Hotels & Resorts
Additional: Bar food; Sunday L; Children welcome; 🅰 dishes
Accommodation: 220 en suite
Credit cards: ▆▆ ▆▆ ▆▆ ▆ JCB

The Fox Reformed

Saloon-style wine bar, relaxed and informal, with lots of regulars who come for the backgammon club, wine club and so on. Good, simple cooking summed up by home-made fennel seed rolls, duck liver pâté, pork and spinach sausages with homely thickened gravy, and Venetian rice pudding – a mass of fruit, risotto-style rice with pine nuts and sultanas in lemon scented cream, all topped with greengage jam.

Credit cards: ▆ ▆ ▆ ▆ ▆ ▆ ▆

Directions: Opposite the junction with Woodlea Road

176 Stoke Newington Church Street
N16 0JL
Map GtL: D4
Tel/Fax: 0171 254 5975
Chef: Paul Harper
Owners: Carol & Robbie Richards
Cost: Alc £17.50. H/wine £8.55
Times: Last L 2.30pm/last D 10.30pm.
Closed 25-26 Dec
Additional: Sunday L; Children welcome; ❹ dishes

Frederick's Restaurant

Hidden away amongst the antique shops of Camden passage, Frederick's is a real mixture of styles. The bar area is all modern, chrome, and pale wood, the first dining area high ceilinged with tapestries and the sort of grand paintings one gets in National Trust houses, the second dining area is conservatory-style with black tubular furniture and Mediterranean touches The menu is equally eclectic ranging from crispy duck with tabouleh and chilli jam to the more traditional beef Wellington. The kitchen also offers a great British lunch of two courses with the likes of eggs Benedict, shepherd's pie, and pork chop and apple sauce. Highlight of an inspection meal was brill baked with croûtons, ratatouille and basil mash, and tarte Tatin with vanilla ice cream. The wine list offers a good selection from France and the New World.

Directions: Nearest Tube – Angel, 2 mins walk to Camden Passage. Restaurant amongst the antique shops

Camden Passage N1 8EG
Map GtL: D3
Tel: 0171 3592888/3593902
Fax: 0171 3595173
Chef: Andrew Jeffs
Owner: Louis Segal
Cost: Alc £45, fixed-price L & D £12 (2 courses). ☺ H/wine £10.95
Times: Last L 2.30pm/last D 11.30pm.
Closed Sun, Xmas, New Year, Bhs
Additional: Bar food; Children welcome; ❹ dishes.
Smoking: No-smoking area;
Air conditioning
Credit cards: ▆ ▆ ▆ ▆ ▆ ▆

French House Dining Room ✵

Intimate first-floor venue above an historic pub. The decor, like the cooking, is imaginative yet unpretentious. Dishes include pan-fried duck livers with chickpeas, poached chicken with ox tongue sausage and green sauce, orange bavarois with a spicy fruit compote. Wine list features good French names. Grab a window table to watch passing Soho life.

Directions: Above the French House pub. Nearest Tubes: Leicester Square, Tottenham Court Rd & Piccadilly Circus

49 Dean Street W1V 5HL
Tel: 0171 4372477
Fax: 0171 2879109
Chef/Owner: Margot Henderson
Cost: Alc £25
Times: Last L 3pm/last D 11.15pm.
Closed Sun, Xmas, New year, Bhs
Additional: Children welcome;
❹ dishes
Credit cards: ▆ ▆ ▆ ▆ ▆ ▆ ▆

Frère Jacques ✵   NEW

Every table has a river view at this popular brasserie, and guests can eat on the canopied and heated riverside terrace all year round. Staff and menus are French, offering the likes of fish soup, medallions of lamb with rosemary, and tarte Tatin. The menu 'rapide' offers great value at lunchtime.

Additional: Sunday L; Children welcome; ❹ dishes
Smoking: No-smoking area; No pipes & cigars; Air conditioning
Credit cards: ▆ ▆ ▆ ▆ ▆ ▆

Directions: 50 mtrs south of Kingston side of Kingston Bridge by the river

10-12 Riverside Walk
off Bishops Hall KT1 1QN
Map GtL: B2
Tel: 0181 5461332
Fax: 0181 5461956
Chef: Yves Tatard
Owners: John & Clare Scott, Frank Trutet
Cost: Alc £18, fixed price L £6.95 (2 courses)/D £14.90. ☺ H/wine £10.90
Times: Open all day, last D 11pm.
Closed 25 Dec, 1 Jan

Friends Restaurant 🐾

Modern Anglo/French dishes continue to draw the crowds at this 400-year-old timbered restaurant. A late summer meal might start with sun-dried tomato and onion seed rolls followed swiftly by a starter of grilled goats' cheese salad. Main courses include paillard of salmon with sorrel, and pan-fried lamb steak with parsnip mash.

11 High Street Pinner
HA5 5PJ
Map GtL: A4
Tel/Fax: 0181 8660286
Chefs: Terry Farr, Ben Denny
Owner: Terry Farr
Cost: *Alc* £27, fixed-price L £15.95/D £19.95. ☺ H/wine £9.95
Times: Last L2pm/last D 10pm. Closed D Sun, Bhs
Additional: Sunday L; Children welcome; 🐾 dishes
Smoking: No-smoking area; No pipes & cigars
Credit cards: 🔳 🔳 🔳 🔳 🔳 🔳 🔳

Directions: Follow A404 from Harrow. In the centre of Pinner

Fung Shing 🐾🐾

Try and make the most of a visit here, as it is certainly one of the best, though not the cheapest, in London's Chinatown. It's a simple rule – the more people you go with, the more dishes you can sample. The menu offers a good mix of familiar dishes with more unusual ones such as stir-fried fresh milk with scrambled egg white, or pan-fried minced pork with salted fish. Our inspector lost her nerve, alas, and went for the easy option, which to be fair, is what most people would usually order. This proved a good bet – everything was fresh, carefully cooked and presented. Spring rolls filled with Chinese mushrooms were crisp and dry, soft shell crab, deep-fried in a light batter, came with slivers of deep-fried garlic and tiny rings of red-hot chilli. A sizzling dish of tender chicken with ginger and spring onion came out the kitchen so piping hot it necessitated the removal of the smoke alarm from above the table!

Directions: Nearest Tube – Leicester Square. Behind Empire Cinema

15 Lisle Street
WC2H 7BE
Map: D3
Tel: 0171 4371539
Fax: 0171 7340284
Chef: Mr XT Ly
Owner: Forum Restaurant Ltd
Cost: *Alc* £25, fixed-price L&D £16 (2 courses). ☺ H/wine £10.
Times: Noon-last D 11.15pm. Closed 3 days Xmas
Additional: Children welcome; 🐾 dishes
Seats: 120. Private dining room 24-40.
Smoking: Air conditioning
Credit cards: 🔳 🔳 🔳 🔳 🔳 🔳

The Gate 🐾🐾   NEW

'Quite a revelation' was our inspectors reaction to this vegetarian restaurant: 'no pulses, lentils, veggy Stroganoff or lasagne but dishes that stand entirely on their own merit with accurate flavours and every ingredient playing its part'. Equally impressive was the presentation of dishes like Jerusalem artichoke tart with porcini custard, and grilled pepper, herb and mascarpone risotto with sun-dried tomato pesto, and Parmesan, mushroom and spinach rösti with light Dijon mustard sauce, and red Thai curry served with wild rice and finished with a pineapple salsa. Desserts might include date pudding with butterscotch sauce, and roast quinces with maple syrup, cumin shortbread and vanilla ice cream. The otherwise plain, hall-like setting is broken by a series of large photographs around the walls; the atmosphere is informal and relaxed.

51 Queen Caroline Street
W6 9QL
Map GtL: C3
Tel: 0181 7486932
Fax: 0181 5631719
Owner: M & A Daniel
Cost: *Alc* £17. ☺
Times: Noon-last L 2.45pm/6-last D 10.45pm. Closed L Sat, all Sun, Bhs
Additional: Children welcome; 🐾 dishes
Seats: 50
Smoking: No pipes & cigars
Credit cards: 🔳 🔳 🔳 🔳 🔳 🔳

Directions: *Please telephone for directions*

Le Gavroche
Restaurant ❀❀❀❀❀❀

Michel Roux seems to have cut the umbilical cord, in menu terms anyway, at his Mecca for foodies. Gone are the former dishes of 'hommage à mon père', and the new man is running on his own two feet with new menus – the set-price one considered good value – and with his own ideas superimposed on the classic French repertoire and classic techniques. Thus, a starter of what the menu describes as a 'crispy pancake' of foie gras and duck flavoured with cinnamon turns out to be 'decadence at its most subtle, understated best', silky-soft, pink, tongue-melting foie gras a perfect contrast to the bite of shredded duck confit, in a crispy oriental-style triangular pancake of filo, in barely spiced cinnamon sauce. There may be nothing too clever in the dish, just first-class ingredients artfully brought together by a master of combinations and a brigade hugely confident in what it can do. The menu isn't confined to luxury ingredients, although truffles go into starters of pea soup and a vinaigrette for asparagus with Parmesan shavings, as well as into whole Bresse chicken with Madeira sauce. Quail fillets on Puy lentils and baby spinach, or pan-fried scallops with five-spice sauce extend the range of starters, and there's something homely about main courses of rissoles of veal sweetbreads with a sweet-and-sour sauce, saddle of rabbit with crispy potatoes, and roast rack of lamb with parsley sauce. A signature dish of omelette Rothschild (aka apricot and Cointreau soufflé), may be a hangover from Albert's days at the stoves, and l'assiette du chef shows what the kitchen can do with desserts: rum baba oozing pineapple syrup, raspberries sandwiched in sablé biscuits, a thimble of tiramisu. Petits fours feature more babas, properly chewy meringue discs, and vanilla sponge, but canapés are felt to be more inspired: langoustine beignets, quail's eggs in pastry, and humble- sounding small cheese biscuits with creamcheese and chives. Staff are solicitous and informed, with the manager visiting each table as often as three times and even Michel Roux making a round. The wine list is a run-through of the great and the good, centred on France. Careful perusal will uncover something at around £20 or even less.
   Signature dishes: Mousseline de homard au champagne; le bar en papillote farci au fenouil; all game in season.

Directions: From Park Lane, into Upper Brook Street (one way), restaurant is on R. Nearest Tube – Marble Arch

43 Upper Brook Street W1Y 1PF
Map: B3
Tel: 0171 4080881/4991826
Fax: 0171 4090939/4914387
Chef: Michel A Roux
Owner: Le Gavroche Ltd
Cost: *Alc* £100, fixed-price L £40/D £85 (7 courses) H/wine £20
Times: Noon-last L 2pm/7pm-last D 11pm. Closed Sat, Sun, Xmas, New Year, Bhs
Seats: 60. Private dining room 20. Jacket & tie preferred
Smoking: No pipes, cigars in lounge only; Air conditioning
Credit cards: 🔲 🔲 🔲 🔲 🔲 🔲 🔲 JCB

AA Shortlisted for Wine Award-see page 16

Gay Hussar ❀

Possibly the most famous Hungarian restaurant in London, established in 1953, serving authentic dishes in a friendly atmosphere. Frequented by politicians, it has a strong international following. Mixed hors d'oeuvre, fish dumplings, veal goulash, and wiener schnitzel are included on an extensive menu.

Additional: Children welcome; 🍴 dishes
Smoking: Air conditioning
Credit cards: 🔲 🔲 🔲 🔲 🔲 🔲 🔲

Directions: Off Soho Square. Nearest Tube – Tottenham Court Road

2 Greek Street W1V 6NB
Map: D4
Tel: 0171 4370973
Fax: 0171 4374631
Chef: Laszlo Holecz
Owners: Restaurant Partnership plc
Cost: *Alc* £25-£30, fixed-price L £17.50. ☺ H/wine £10.50
Times: Last L 2.30pm/last D 10.45pm. Closed Sun, Bhs

Gilbey's ✿✿

NEW

All change at this Ealing address (formerly Noughts and Crosses). Along with their name, the new owners have introduced fresh contemporary decor, a 'modern British' menu and fine French wines imported direct from the growers. The latter, remarkably, are rolled out at shop prices with, for instance a tasty range of white Burgundies available at around the £15 mark. Encouragingly, the value-for-money approach doesn't end at the wine list, with a sensibly short *carte* being modestly priced and offering many of the starters – moules marinière, Caesar salad or salmon and herb fishcakes – in main course proportions that are ideal for a snappy lunch. Whilst innovation is not a spur, the freshness and clarity of the approach has won praise for dishes such as stir-fried squid with a carpaccio of courgettes, Parmesan shavings and a chilli lemon dressing. No surprise to find chocolate marquise, tarte Tatin and lemon tart amongst the puds, but few complaints at a spring inspection that found the latter to be light, incisive and served with 'superb' in-house ice cream.

Directions: A 3 minute walk from Ealing Broadway tube

77 The Grove Ealing W5 5LL
Map GtL: B3
Tel: 0181 8407568
Fax: 0181 8401905
Chef: Stephen Spooner
Owners: The Gilbey Family
Cost: *Alc* £20, fixed-price L £8.95.
H/wine £5.55
Times: Noon-last L 3pm/7-last
D 10.30pm
Additional: Sunday L; Children welcome; ✦ dishes
Seats: 50. Private dining room 30
Smoking: No pipes & cigars
Credit cards:

Gladwins Restaurant ✿✿

Set in the heart of the City's insurance district, this contemporary basement restaurant, decorated with bright colours and light wood, bustles with business suits, all out to sample the cosmopolitan mix of dishes listed on the fixed-price lunch menu. Starters range from Lebanese cucumber and prawn soup to seafood tapas featuring queen scallops, squid and marinated sardines, served with chargrilled peppers, olives and garlic potatoes. With an even balance between fish and meat, main course options may include casserole of monkfish, fennel and potato, crispy chilli beef with egg fried rice, lime and coriander, and medallions of veal with asparagus and sage butter. Round off what may be a very speedily served lunch with plum and orange tart with cinnamon ice cream, summer pudding with blackcurrant jus, or a savoury such as smoked Cheddar rarebit, followed by good cafetière coffee.

Directions: Opposite Fenchurch Station, between Fenchurch Street & Eastcheap. Nearest Tubes – Bank or Monument

Minster Court Mark Lane EC3R 7AA
Tel: 0171 4440004
Fax: 0171 4440001
Chef/Owner: Peter Gladwin
Cost: Fixed-price L £33. H/wine
£12.50
Times: L only, noon-last L 2.30pm.
Closed Sat, Sun, Xmas, Bhs
Additional: ✦ dishes
Seats: 124
Smoking: Air conditioning
Credit cards:

Gloucester Hotel ✿

See Where London Meets Section page 153

Goring Hotel ✿✿

The Goring is a wonderful example of good old-fashioned hospitality in the true British tradition of hotel-keeping. Traditional is the word that best describes the decor too. The restaurant is a light and airy room, with plenty of space between tables, high-backed terracotta-coloured chairs adding a degree of intimacy to diners. Don't expect modish fireworks on the menus; tried-and-tested dishes of skate wing with capers, braised oxtail and steak and kidney pie are what the kitchen excels at. Staid-sounding crab Marie Rose turns out to be full-flavoured white crab flecked with herbs served on a

Beeston Place Grosvenor Gardens
SW1W 0JW
Map: C2
Tel: 0171 3969000
Fax: 0171 8344393
Chef: John Elliot
Owner: George Goring
Cost: Fixed-price L £27/D £36.
H/wine £19
Times: 12.30-2.30pm/6-10pm
Additional: Bar food; Sunday L;
No children under 5; ✦ dishes

Goring Hotel

Seats: 60. Private dining rooms 8-50
Smoking: No pipes & cigars; Air conditioning
Accommodation: 75 en suite
Credit cards:

salad of bitter leaves to provide contrast and with a boat of tasty, well-made sauce on the side. Calves' liver with bacon is a typical main course, chargrilled, nicely firm but tender, with onion gravy and mash. Pecan pie could figure among puddings, lifted by perhaps excellent maple syrup ice cream. Canapés precede dinner, petits fours come with coffee, and bottles of classy Bordeaux tumble off the long wine list.

Directions: In central London behind Buckingham Palace. Exit from Victoria tube station onto Victoria Street, turn L into Grosvenor Gdns, cross Buckingham Palace Road, 75 yds turn L into Beeston Place

Granita ❀❀

Unfussy and offering excellent value, its little surprise that this Islington restaurant was bustling at a spring lunchtime inspection. Bare wooden tables and unadorned walls add up to a strikingly spare interior with the long zinc bar being the only interruption. Weekly-changing menus are similarly matter-of-fact with the plainest of language used to describe dishes that are broadly European, but with influences from further east. Amongst half-a-dozen starters, queen scallops with coriander, black bean sauce and Thai noodles has been judged a well-balanced success, and a similar intelligence was apparent in roast duck in a herbed broth with black-eyed peas. Almond and apricot tart rounded off a 'very pleasing meal' for one inspector. Staff in black jackets are friendly and helpful but should you want to test their patience you could always ask to be shown to the table where Messrs Blair and Brown had that meeting in 1994.

Directions: Nearest Tubes – Highbury & Islington, and Angel. Opposite St Mary's Church.

127 Upper Street Islington N1
Map GtL: D3
Tel: 0171 2263222
Fax: 0171 2264833
Chef: Ahmed Kharshoum
Owners: Ahmed Kharshoum, Vikki Leffman
Cost: A/c £25, fixed-price L £13.95. ☺ H/wine £10.50
Times: 12.30-last L 2.30pm/6.30-last D 10.30pm(Sun 10pm). Closed Mon, L Tue, Xmas, Easter, summer
Additional: Sunday L; dishes
Seats: 70
Smoking: No pipes & cigars; Air conditioning
Credit cards:

Green Olive ❀❀

Located on the bottom floor of an historic walk-up, close to the canals of Little Venice, with exposed brick walls and hard-wood floors making a friendly setting for the modern Italian style of cooking. Home-made pasta includes tortelli filled with veal and herbs served in a potato cream, and there are risotto and fish dishes of the day. Start with carpaccio of tuna with shaved fennel, lime vinaigrette and coriander oil, then consider main courses such as roasted cod served with oven-dried

5 Warwick Place
W9 2PX
Map GtL: C3
Tel: 0171 2892469
Fax: 0171 2894178
Chef: Stefano Savio
Owner: Bijan Behzadi
Cost: A/c £23.50. ☺ H/wine £12.50
Times: 12.30-last L 2.30pm/7-last D 10.45pm. Closed Bhs

tomato and squid ink polenta in a saffron and mushroom sauce, or roast shank of lamb with caponata of roast aubergine, courgette and peppers in a thyme jus. Italian cheeses and Illy coffee are excellent.

Directions: Nearest Tube – Warwick Avenue

Additional: Sunday L; Children welcome; 🍴 dishes
Seats: 58. Private dining room 22
Smoking: No pipes & cigars; Air conditioning
Credit cards: ▬ ▬ ▬ ▬ ▬

The Greenhouse Restaurant ❀❀

The Greenhouse is fairly large, smart, and bright, with plants scattered around, prints of vegetables on the walls, and a terraced-style garden outside. Lunchtime specials appear on the same days of the week: boiled bacon with mustard sauce and braised cabbage on Wednesdays, roast cod with olive oil mash on Fridays, for instance. The menus may have an English feel about them, as witnessed by deep-fried cod with chips and mushy peas, but plenty of other good ideas bounce around. Pistachio nuts are added to well-textured, moist pork terrine, given bite with freshly made piccalilli, and celeriac rémoulade acts as a foil to lambs' sweetbreads and tongue. Chargrilled sea bass on a julienne of carrot and courgette has been singled out for the subtlety of its citrus fruit dressing, while hare braised in red wine with bacon and mustard dumplings makes a gutsier main course. Sticky toffee and banana pudding – 'beautifully moist, fresh banana flavour' – and bread-and-butter pudding remain comfort food of the best sort. Some quality producers are found on the short list of wines; those who want to push the boat out should ask for the fine wine list.

Directions: Behind Dorchester Hotel just off Hill St, nr Berkeley Sq.

27a Hay's Mews W1X 7RJ
Map: C3
Tel: 0171 4993331
Fax: 0171 4995368
Chef: Graham Grafton
Owner: David Levin
Cost: Alc £27. ☺ H/wine £12.50
Times: 12.30-2.30pm/6.30-11.15pm. Closed L Sat
Additional: Bar food L; Sunday L; Children welcome; 🍴 dishes
Seats: 95
Smoking: No pipes; Air conditioning
Credit cards: ▬ ▬ ▬ ▬ ▬

Green's Restaurant & Oyster Bar ❀❀

36 Duke Street SW1Y 6DF
Map: C3
Tel: 0171 9304566
Fax: 0171 4917463
Chef: Patrick Williams
Owner: Simon Parker-Bowles
Cost: Alc £35. ☺ H/wine £12
Times: 12.30-3pm/5.30-11pm
Additional: Bar food; Children welcome; 🍴 dishes
Seats: 70. Private dining room 36
Smoking: No-smoking area; Air conditioning
Credit cards: ▬ ▬ ▬ ▬ ▬ ▬ ▬ JCB

Sit on one of the well-padded stools at the bar and watch the staff prepare salads and open the oysters or eat in the adjoining restaurant, with cream walls, panelling and comfortable banquettes. As you'd expect, fish and shellfish are what it's all about, from crab bisque, through smoked eel fillets, to fish and chips with mushy peas or Dover sole meunière. Everything is unfussy and wholesome and portions are generous. Salmon fishcakes with a well-balanced sauce of roast pepper and tomato comes as a starter or a main course, and an inspector noted that 'they seemed to be selling an awful lot of Dorset crab' out of the shell with salad. Herby bangers with mash, bacon and onion gravy make a 'wonderful, succulent' meaty alternative, and grilled fillet of beef, or roast saddle of rabbit stuffed with a mixture of liver and apricots might show up on the monthly-changing menu. The bulk of the puddings are as traditional as the rest of the fare – apple pie, spotted Dick with custard sauce – with the occasional diversion to something like passion fruit crème brûlée.

Directions: Opposite the Cavendish Hotel

Grosvenor House, Café Nico

Massive picture windows show the hustle and bustle of Park Lane and the more relaxed environs of Hyde Park beyond. This Grosvenor House restaurant is overseen by Nico Ladenis (see entry, Chez Nico), who has lent a name, and a lot of expertise to the operation – he himself eats here regularly, a great commendation in itself. The style is up-market brasserie food and the service has a certain Gallic formality, professional and sure of what it is doing. An accurate, rich risotto with rocket and foie gras, sea bass with olive crust and tomato-based sauce accompanied by perfect snow peas, and a simple vanilla ice cream with chocolate sauce and some 'wonderful' long fingers of florentines, made a memorable impression at inspection. Other choices could have been leek and potato soup, cannelloni of lobster, crispy duck confit in the oriental style, and smoked haddock with spinach, poached egg and fish velouté. Puddings are traditional: crème caramel, treacle pudding and chocolate marquise.

Directions: In the Grosvenor House Hotel

Grosvenor House Hotel
Park Lane W1A 3AA
Map: B3
Tel: 0171 4952275
Fax: 0171 4933341
Chef: Ralph Porciani
Cost: Alc £32, fixed-price L & D £29.50
Times: Noon-last L 3pm/6-last D 10.30pm. Closed Mon, 2 wks Jan
Additional: Sunday L; Children welcome; ◔ dishes
Seats: 100
Smoking: No-smoking area; Air conditioning
Accommodation: 448 en suite + 136 apartments
Credit cards: ▨ ▨ ▨ ▨ ▨ ▨ ▨ JCB

Halcyon Hotel ✿✿✿

81 Holland Park W11 3RZ
Map GtL: C3
Tel: 0171 2215411
Fax: 0171 2298516
Chef: Martin Hadden
Cost: Alc £45.50, fixed-price L £18 (2 courses)/D £45.50. H/wine £14
Times: Noon-last L 2.30pm/7-last D 10.30pm. Closed Sat L, Bhs

The exquisite townhouse hotel occupies two superbly restored Belle Époque houses, and The Room at the Halcyon is just too discreet to use the word restaurant in its name. It is a perfect spot for intimate little dinners, especially in fine weather when tables are set under giant parasols in the adjoining patio. The cooking is both stylish, skilful and mostly delicious, from a little appetiser of leek and potato soup with white truffle oil, to sticky petits fours. Martin Hadden has favourite ingredients – foie gras, truffles and truffle oil, artichokes, and morels, all of which may feature more than once on the menu, but then that suits the executive nature of the prices. The repertoire of dishes is also geared towards a sophisticated audience: grilled boudin blanc with French beans and truffle oil; salad of calves' sweetbreads with tomato and basil mayonnaise; escalope of sea bass with confit red peppers and celeriac purée; roast breast of pigeon with Savoy cabbage and foie gras. A langoustine ravioli with lobster sauce sacrificed temperature for frothy, creamy sauce but had a beautifully flavoured and tender filling and delicate pasta. A nicely poached, juicy chicken had been cooked with slivers of truffle slipped under the skin and the foie gras in the sauce. A sharp and tangy caramelised lemon tart was an excellent choice from a list that might include pink grapefruit gratin with honey ice cream, or crème caramel with a compote of fruits. Service, under the supervision of restaurant manager Jason Phillips, is highly attentive.

Directions: 200 metres up Holland Park Ave from Shepherds Bush roundabout. 2 mins walk from Holland Park Tube

Additional: Bar food; Sunday L; Children welcome; 🍷 dishes
Seats: 45. Private dining room 12
Smoking: No pipes in dining room
Accommodation: 43 en suite
Credit cards: ▪▪ ▪▪ ▪▪ ▪▪ ▪▪ ▪▪ ▪▪

The Halkin Hotel, Stefano Cavallini at The Halkin 🌸🌸🌸

Halkin Street Belgravia SW1X 7DJ
Map GtL: C2
Tel: 0171 3331000
Fax: 0171 3331100
Chef: Stefano Cavallini
Owner: Como Holdings
Cost: Alc £45, fixed-price L £25/D £45 (5 courses). H/wine £17.50
Times: 12.30-last L 2.30pm/7.30-last D 11pm. Closed L Sat, L Sun
Additional: Bar food; Children welcome; 🍷 dishes
Seats: 45. Private dining room 30
Smoking: No pipes & cigars; Air conditioning
Accommodation: 41 en suite
Credit cards: ▪▪ ▪▪ ▪▪ ▪▪ ▪▪ ▪▪ ▪▪ JCB

A smart, contemporary Italian restaurant with trendy lighting, marble floors and mosaics. During the day, natural light floods the elegant restaurant through arched windows which overlook a private garden; by night, guests can enjoy dinner by candlelight. Stefano Cavallini has been rewarded for his commitment and style with the eponymous renaming of the restaurant, which continues to go from strength to strength. Stefano describes his philosophy of cooking as 'la cucina essenziale' – in other words, the reinterpretation of old Italian recipes to suit modern tastes and expectations. At a recent meal our inspector noted clear, robust flavours in dishes such as steamed foie gras with beetroot vinegar and baby broad beans, and casseroled monkfish in a light beurre blanc that was topped with three poached quails' eggs and shaved black truffle. Starters could include marinated tuna with balsamic vinegar and soy sauce, and pan-fried foie gras with Castelluccio lentils, while main dishes of note include roasted fillet of veal with Parma ham, courgettes and shiitake, stuffed gnocchi with artichokes and a white wine and ginger sauce, and saddle of venison with grilled white polenta, broccoli and blueberry sauce. With temptations like banana gratin with rum sabayon, and chocolate soufflé with orange and cardamom sorbet, dessert should not be skipped. Sommelier Bruno Besa has selected an extensive range of Italian wines, listed regionally, with a small number of bottles from the rest of the world. Take advice and try something unusual – there are plenty of classics to choose from.

Signature dishes: Monkfish casserole with autumn vegetables and poached quail's eggs; duck ravioli with foie gras and Savoy cabbage; salad of asparagus and langoustine

Directions: Between Belgrave Square & Grosvenor Place. Access via Chapel St into Headfort Place and L into Halkin St

The Hampshire

See Where London Meets Section page 153

Heather's ✿   NEW

74 Macmillan Street
SE8 3HA
Map GtL: D3
Tel: 0181 6916665
Fax: 0181 6923263
Chefs/Owners: Jo Lewis, Mike Harris
Cost: Fixed price L £7/D £12. ☺
H/wine £6.50
Times: Last L 2.15pm/last D 10.30pm. Closed L Sat, all Mon, 4 wks yearly
Additional: Sunday L; Children welcome; ✆ dishes
Smoking: No smoking in dining room
Credit cards: None

Laid-back restaurant serving good-value vegetarian and vegan home cooking. Spacious premises include a garden and roof terrace. An eat-as-much-as-you-like buffet operates evenings and Sunday lunchtime. Favourite dishes include spicy Thai rice soup, Cuban fruit curry and pumpkin pie. Great value.

Directions: 400 mtrs from Deptford railway station on the Thames Path Walk opposite St Nicholas' Church.

Hilaire ✿✿✿

'You don't need to be fashionable to succeed', exclaims an inspector, appreciative of the straightforward approach adopted by Bryan Webb, who over the years has stuck to his guns and not followed any trends. When asked to described his food, he replied 'I think I serve good food and I would like more people to come and enjoy it', which says it all. The shop-front restaurant with friendly, unpretentious staff, is intimate and welcoming. The short menu, just nine starters and seven main courses, puts the emphasis on prime quality ingredients, summed up by the Sally Clarke bread served here – Webb feels he could do no better. Presentation follows a less than minimalistic approach, it is the food that matters. Our late spring dinner opened with excellent Glamorgan sausages of deep-fried

68 Old Brompton Road
SW7 3LQ
Map: A1
Tel: 0171 5848993
Fax: 0171 5812949
Chef: Bryan Webb
Owners: Bryan Webb, Dick Pyle
Cost: Fixed-price L £18.50 (2 courses)/D £30 (2 courses). H/wine from £12.50
Times: 12.15pm-last L 2.30pm/6.30pm-last D 11.30pm. Closed L Sat, all Sun, Bhs
Additional: Children welcome; ✆ dishes

Hilaire

Seats: 70. Private dining room 30
Smoking: No pipes & cigars;
Air conditioning
Credit cards: ▬ ▬ ▬ ▬ ▬ JCB

Caerphilly with herbs, and went on to delicately flavoured foie gras and chicken liver parfait served with outstanding plum chutney. Turbot, grilled to perfection, came next, set on a vibrant basil pesto risotto with 'absolutely gorgeous' spring vegetables: simple peas, chopped fine beans, the odd tiny broad one, a few tomato diamonds for contrast, in a 'lovely creamy fish-based sauce'. Pudding was a prune and almond tart with first-class thin pastry – 'I'm amazed it was able to support the depth and weight of the filling,' and served with creamy mascarpone Armagnac ice cream. The wine list is separated generically, as in 'fragrant and fruity', and 'light(ish) reds'.

Directions: On N side of Old Brompton Rd about half way between South Kensington Tube and junction with Queensgate

The Hogarth ✿

See Where London Meets Section page 153

Holiday Inn Mayfair ✿

See Where London Meets Section page 153

Hotel Inter-Continental ✿✿✿

Le Soufflé is located within this deluxe hotel – stylish and elegant, it is decorated in pale, muted colours that engender a relaxed, sophisticated atmosphere. The comfortable seats add

1 Hamilton Place Hyde Park Corner
W1V 0QY
Map: C2
Tel: 0171 3188577
Fax: 0171 4910926
Chef: Peter Kromberg
Owner: Inter-Continental Hotels & Resorts
Cost: *Alc* £45, fixed-price L £29.50/D £35. H/wine £15
Times: 12.30pm-last L 3pm/7pm-last D 10.30pm (till 11.15pm Sat). Closed L Sat, D Sun, all Mon, Xmas, Bhs
Additional: Bar food; Sunday L; ❸ dishes.
Seats: 80
Smoking: No pipes; Air conditioning
Accommodation: 460 en suite
Credit cards: ▬ ▬ ▬ ▬ ▬ ▬ ▬ JCB

to the general sense of well-being. Peter Kromberg continues to cook in his quiet, highly skilled manner, dishes that are utterly refined imbued with masterly flair and brio. The celebrated signature soufflés 'du moment': new potatoes enhanced with Périgord truffles, served with wild mushroom sabayon; wild salmon and black caviar with smoked lobster butter sauce; mango with coconut sorbet, continue to re-define the genre. Typical of the rest of the repertoire are complex modern French dishes such as roasted tail of anglerfish with coriander seeds and soft polenta with a touch of mascarpone and Jura wine, or fricassée of duck, guinea fowl and squab pigeon with creamy morel mushroom sauce perfumed with vanilla. Many dishes carry a 'Healthy Heart' symbol, denoting those which are low in fat, calories and carbohydrates and high in fibre – it might sound boring, but that's before one considers the attractions of roasted giant prawns with mussels and clams and papardelle noodles in their own broth, maybe crispy crab pastry wafers with marinated lobster tail and cauliflower dressing, or canon of Welsh lamb wrapped and baked in oriental leaves, garnished with roasted winter fruits and vegetables and enhanced with spicy vinegar.

Signature dishes: Pot au feu of wild salmon; hot English berry soufflé with crème fraîche; chestnut and pheasant soufflé; cannon of venison with black truffle ravioli.

Directions: On Hyde Park Corner. Nearest Tube – Hyde Park Corner

The Hothouse ✿

78-80 Wapping Lane E1 9NF
Map GtL: D3
Tel: 0171 4884797
Fax: 0171 4889500
Chef: Marc Smith
Owner: Nigel Fenner-Fownes
Cost: *Alc* £20, fixed-price L & D
£13.95. ☺ H/wine £10.50
Times: Noon-last D 10.45pm. Closed
L Sat & Sun, Bhs

A converted spice warehouse on two levels with vibrant decor, some sofa seating, and live jazz and blues seven nights a week. There's a choice of fixed-price and carte menus, and dishes range from the Hothouse burger to milk-fed veal cutlet with girolles and asparagus.

Additional: Bar food; No children under 8; ❹ dishes
Smoking: No-smoking area; Air conditioning
Credit cards: ▬ ▬ ▼ ⌐ ▬ ▐

Directions: Nearest tube stations Tower Bridge and Wapping

Hyatt Carlton Tower Hotel, Grissini ✿✿

Cadogan Place SW1X 9PY
Map: B2
Tel: 0171 2351234
Fax: 0171 2359129
Chef: Fabio Trabocchi
Cost: *Alc* £24, fixed-price L 12/D
£28.50. ☺ H/wine £16
Times: 12.30-last L 2.45pm/6.30-last
D 10.45pm. Closed L Sat, all Sun
Additional: Bar food; Children
welcome; ❹ dishes
Seats: 88. Private dining room 50
Smoking: No-smoking area; Air
conditioning
Accommodation: 220 en suite
Credit cards: ▬ ▬ ▼ ⌐ ▬ ▐ ▣ JCB

Reflecting its status as a busy international hotel in the heart of Knightsbridge, the Hyatt Carlton Tower offers a choice of dining rooms to suit all moods. Newest is Grissini, a modern Italian restaurant, offering good value lunches. There's antipasti such as buffalo mozzarella and tomato terrine, or a selection of baby greens with basil-flavoured olive oil and balsamic vinegar. Mains may be a fresh herb risotto with roast quail and crisp leeks, or pappardelle with skate, chanterelles and rosemary. And, of course, there's tiramisu for dessert. More traditional dining can be found in the Rib Room, where simple roasts, grills and seafood are the specialities and starters tend to be old favourites such as French onion soup, asparagus with hollandaise and Scottish smoked salmon. The Chinoiserie lounge, at the heart of the hotel's ground floor, bustles for afternoon tea.

Directions: Nearest Tubes – Knightsbridge & Sloane Sq

Hyatt Carlton Tower Hotel, Grissini

The Rib Room Restaurant

Ikkyu ❀

Lively, simple basement restaurant popular with young Japanese visitors on a budget. Little translation is given on the menu, so it's preferable to be familiar with the repertoire before you go, or feel in an adventurous mood. Offal yakitori is particularly good. Very smoky, but fun.

Directions: Nearest Tube – Goodge Street

67a Tottenham Court Road
W1P 9PA
Map: C3
Tel: 0171 6369280/4366169
Fax: 0171 3235378
Chef: Mr M Kawaguchi
Owner: Ms Komori
Cost: *Alc* £15, fixed price L £7/D £15. ☺ H/wine £9.15
Times: Last L 2.30pm/last D 10.15pm. Closed Sat, L Sun (D Sun before Bhs), 10 days Xmas, 4 days Easter,
Additional: Children welcome; 🍴 dishes
Smoking: Air conditioning
Credit cards: ▆ ▆ ▆ 🔳

Indian Connoisseurs ❀

Small, unassuming Paddington curry house where staff are more than willing to advise customers. The menu includes some ten regional Bangladeshi specialities such as awshi gosht, lamb cooked with pumpkin. Starters include the more familiar prawn puri, and a creamy chicken tikka makhani.

Additional: Bar food; Sunday L; No children under 10; 🍴 dishes
Smoking: No-smoking area; No pipes & cigars; Air conditioning
Credit cards: ▆ ▆ ▆ ▆ ▆ ▆ 🔳

Directions: Off Praed Street close to BR Paddington. Nearest Tubes – Paddington & Edgware Road. Opp St Mary's Hospital

8 Norfolk Place W2 1QL
Map: A4
Tel: 0171 4023299
Chef: Mr Kabir Miah
Owner: Mr M Ahmed
Cost: *Alc* £25, fixed-price D £25. ☺ H/wine £6.95.
Times: Last L 2.30pm/last D midnight. Closed 25 Dec

Interlude ❀❀

After a period of unrest at the stoves, Paul Merrett has settled in well at this snug three-roomed restaurant styled in a mix of co-ordinating washes and colours. The focused, fine cooking has drawn considerable praise. Note a July dinner that opened with an amuse-bouche which set the tone of the entire meal – stunning little chicken quenelles set on an artichoke base and served with lightly dressed leaves. Then came an ambitious, successful cheese soufflé en croûte (set in a very fine filo cup), accompanied by an unusual salad of asparagus spears and skinned baby tomatoes. Seared scallops with little beignets of anchovy and coriander came with a risotto of ginger, coriander and white crabmeat, the whole lightly drizzled with olive oil and tomato dressing. A pre-dessert was a teaspoon of coconut sorbet with a tiny, very refreshing brunoise of pineapple and peach, followed by dessert proper – a stunning banana rösti with dried banana twirls, caramelised banana, and a nougatine base caramel ice cream. Watch this space.

Directions: Oxford Street end of Charlotte Street. Nearest Tubes – Tottenham Court Road, Goodge Street

5 Charlotte Street W1P 1HD
Map: C4
Tel: 0171 6370222
Fax: 0171 6370224
Chef: Paul Merrett
Owner: Charles Ullmann
Cost: Alc £32, fixed-price L £17.50.
☺ H/wine £14
Times: 12.15-last L 2.30pm/7.15-last D 11pm. Closed L Sat, all Sun, 1 wk Xmas, 2 wks Aug
Additional: No children under 12; ❹ dishes
Seats: 70. Private dining room 20
Smoking: No-smoking area; Air conditioning
Credit cards: 💳 🖃 📷 💳 🖃 💳 📱 JCB

The Ivy ❀❀❀

Yellow orchids in deep blue vases wave gracefully from each table, and the oak panelling, dark green leather banquettes and leaded windows create the impression of the urbane civility of an earlier age. Lighting is at a level which shows both food and guests to their best advantage – no wonder the place is so popular. As a result, booking needs to be planned with a certain amount of strategy; prime times need to be booked weeks ahead. First-timers are usually surprised by the breadth of the menu: Caesar salad; dressed Cornish crab; eggs Benedict; kedgeree; escalope of veal Holstein; bollito misto; even curried chicken masala. It's like a very grand supermarket selection. Perennials include The Ivy hamburger, roast poulet des Landes with truffle jus and dauphin potatoes (for two), and Scandinavian iced berries with white chocolate sauce. Seasonal dishes expand an already extensive choice with roasted brill with Jersey royals and hollandaise, and fines de Claire oysters with shallot relish leading in spring. A selection of mixed Eastern hors d'oeuvres were an excellent interplay of sweet, spicy, hot and tangy flavours, as smart, sassy and polished as the clientele, and included chicken with smooth peanut sauce, spring rolls the thickness of a pen, tuna upon a bed of pickled ginger and wasabi, and onion bhajis. Perfectly cooked cod came with a vivid green sauce and mash as smooth as the atmosphere. Braised chicory proved the right thing to order alongside, giving extra texture, sweetness and bite. A clever wheeze to add citrus flavour to the caramel on a tarte Tatin, removed some of the sweetness, the pastry was thin and crisp, and the crème fraîche ice cream perfectly delicious. The wine list is short but sweet, with champers in abundance. Fast and incredibly efficient service is by people who genuinely seem to enjoy their work.

Directions: Nearest Tube: Leicester Square or Covent Garden

1 West Street
Covent Garden
WC2H 9NE

Map: D3
Tel: 0171 8364751
Fax: 0171 2409333
Chef: Des McDonald
Owners: Jeremy King, Chris Corbin
Cost: Alc £40. H/wine £9.75
Times: Noon-last L 3pm/5.30-last D midnight. Closed 25-26 Dec, 1 Jan, Aug Bh
Additional: Sunday L; ❹ dishes
Seats: 100. Private dining room min 20
Smoking: Air conditioning
Credit cards: 💳 🖃 📷 💳 🖃 💳 📱

Jason's Restaurant ❀❀

Built on a wharf overlooking Regent's Park Canal, the seafood restaurant, flooded with light during the day, candlelit at night, has a nautical feel with wood-panelled walls, apexed ceiling and plain wooden tables – and open-plan galley. The food is Mauritian and that translates as French with a spicy oriental twist. Scallops in a chive sabayon, and lobster and spinach in puff pastry demonstrate classic saucing skills, while the more exotic fricassée des îles – three fish of the day cooked with chilli, ginger and herbs – works very well, although rice would have been a better accompaniment than sauté potatoes. Shellfish dishes include lobster with lime and spring onion sauce, and tiger prawns with black beans and chilli. Desserts, such as silky-smooth crème caramel, are standard French repertoire.

Opposite 60 Blomfield Road W9 2PD
Map GtL: C3
Tel: 0171 2866752
Fax: 0171 2664332
Chef: Sylvain Ho Wing Cheong
Owner: Anthony Hopkins
Cost: Alc £25, fixed-price L £14.95/D £19.95 (both 2 courses). ☺ H/wine £9.95
Times: Noon-last L 3pm/6.30-last D 10.30pm. Closed D Sun, 25, 26 Dec, 1 Jan
Additional: Sunday L; Children welcome; ♨ dishes
Seats: 40. (35 on terrace in summer)
Credit cards: ▰ ▰ ▰ ▱ ▰ ▰ ▰ JCB

Directions: Off Edgware Road. Nearest Tube – Warwick Avenue

Justin de Blanc ❀ NEW

Popular, lively, glass-fronted brasserie with zinc-topped tables, wooden floor, and a great buzz. Well-made asparagus and Parmesan tart, classics such as Wiener schnitzel with beurre noisette, capers and mash, and great British puds of rhubarb tart with bay custard are amongst favourites that re-appear on the weekly changing menu.

Directions: In the bend of Old Marylebone Lane after turning off Marylebone High Street. Nearest Tube – Bond Street

120-122 Marylebone Lane W1M 5FZ
Map: C3
Tel: 0171 4865250
Chef: Julie Anderson
Times: Noon-last L 3pm/5.30pm-last D 10pm
Seats: 40
Credit cards: ▰ ▰ ▱ JCB

Kai Mayfair ❀❀

65 South Audley Street W1Y 5FD
Map: C3
Tel: 0171 4938507
Fax: 0171 4931456
Chef: Vincent Looi
Owner: Bernard Yeoh
Cost: Alc £40, fixed-price L £25. H/wine £16.50
Times: Noon-last L 2.15pm/6.30-last D 11pm (Sun 10pm). Closed 25 Dec, 1 Jan
Additional: Children welcome; ♨ dishes
Seats: 110. Private dining rooms 6, 12
Smoking: Air conditioning
Credit cards: ▰ ▰ ▰ ▱ ▰ ▰ ▰ JCB

With dishes such as the 'The Symbols of Wealth and Prosperity' on the menu, this most opulent of Chinese restaurants can't be accused of hiding its light under a bushel. Fine china from Hong Kong, ceramics from Thailand and silverware decorated with Brazilian jasper are all part of the glitzy equation, but it is the all-encompassing sweep of the menu that really impresses. Specialist chefs are recruited from all regions and whether its Szechuan or Peking, the consistency of the cooking is a hallmark. Outlandish descriptions are sprinkled throughout the lengthy *carte*, with items such as 'The Enrichment of the Surprised Piglet' – tender minced pork with bamboo shoots – generally living up to their whimsical billing. Along with the more prosaic offerings, such as pan-fried chicken with ginger and Chinese mushrooms, there is an abundance of luxury items of the shark's fin and abalone variety. These latter two form part of an extravagant soup entitled 'Buddha Jumps Over the Wall', which at almost £100 for the dish, may well have been his reaction to the price.

Directions: Marble Arch onto Park Lane, situated behind Dorchester, or Oxford St into N Audley St, past American Embassy into S Audley St

Kai Mayfair

Kastoori ☞

Reliable, well-regarded vegetarian restaurant. Strong Gujerati and Indo-African influences – the Thanki family came to the UK from Uganda. Dahl puri, special tomato curry, chilli banana, stand out amongst the samosas, dosas and bhajias. Thanki europeene is the family's euroveg speciality, with rhubarb in amongst the spinach, aubergines and leeks. Various thalis are a good introduction to the style.

Additional: Children welcome; ◎ dishes. **Seats:** 82
Smoking: Air conditioning
Credit cards: ▬ ▬ ◖

Directions: Between Tooting Bec & Tooting Broadway tube stations

188 Upper Tooting Road SW17 7EJ
Map GtL: C2
Tel: 0181 7677027
Chef: Manos Thanki
Owner: Dinesu Thanki
Cost: H/wine £7.50
Times: 12.30-last L 2.30pm/6-last D 10.30pm. Closed L Mon & Tue, 1 wk mid Jan

Kensington Place ☘☘

201/205 Kensington Church Street W8 7LX
Map GtL: C3
Tel: 0171 7273184
Fax: 0171 2292025
Chef: Rowley Leigh
Owners: Nicholas Smallwood, Simon Slater
Cost: *Alc* £30, fixed-price L £14.50/D £24.50. ☺ H/wine £10.50
Times: Noon-last L 3pm/6.30-last D 11.45pm. Closed 25 Dec
Additional: Bar food; Sunday L; Children welcome; ◎ dishes
Seats: 140
Smoking: Air conditioning
Credit cards: ▬ ▬ ▬ ◢ ◻ ▩

It was the definitive hang-out of the 80s, and although there are those who feel that Kensington Place is living on the semi-spent fuel of its former fashionability, the atmosphere is still buzzing and demand to get a table is as high as ever. The menu manages to be extensive yet make every dish sound enticing. One Friday in April it included wild garlic soup, poached oysters with laverbread and bacon, John Dory with citrus fruits, sauté of veal with mushrooms and fennel, and breast of duck with chilli and pineapple. The dishes are always extremely well conceived. However, puddings are the Achilles heel. A yummy sounding dish of orange chocolate and nougat gâteau L'Opera belied its description, being little more than dry sponge, lacking the creaminess needed to bind the cake.

Directions: 150 yds before junction of Kensington Church St & Notting Hill Gate

Laicram Thai ❀❀

Long established and as popular as ever, this warm and friendly place is a treat, especially on a cold winter's night. Thai fishcakes have become somewhat ubiquitous, but here they are particularly well made with fresh cod minced with red curry paste, lightly fried with a clear sweet-and-sour dipping sauce with cucumber and chilli. Yum wun sen is another good dish, cold this time, made from vermicelli noodles with prawns, minced pork and dried shrimps with carrot and spring onion in a truly tart, spicy lime dressing. Gaeng phed ped yang is an unusual roast duck curry with coconut, basil, tiny aubergines, pineapple and chilli, particularly excellent when served with the perfectly cooked fragrant steamed rice. The groaning sweet trolley includes a calorie-laden Thai egg custard made with eggs, coconut and palm sugar. Staff in native costume are shy and unassuming, but helpful when called upon.

Directions: Off the main shopping street, in a side road near the Post Office. Opposite the station

1 Blackheath Grove Blackheath SE3
Map GtL: E2
Tel: 0181 8524710
Chef/Owner: Mrs S Dhirabutra
Cost: Alc £25. ☺ H/wine £8.50
Times: Noon-2.30pm/6-11pm. Closed Mon, Bhs
Additional: Children welcome; ❀ dishes
Seats: 50
Smoking: Air conditioning
Credit cards:

Landmark Hotel, The Dining Room ❀❀❀

222 Marylebone Road NW1 6JQ
Map: E4
Tel: 0171 6318000
Fax: 0171 6318011
Chef: Andrew McLeish
Cost: Alc £45, fixed-price L £24/D £34. H/wine £18

It's easy to see why the **Landmark** is a listed building: put up in Victorian times as the hotel for Marylebone Station, its central eight-storey-high, glass-roofed atrium must be unique. Light meals and drinks are served here under the palm trees to the sounds most nights of a harpist. The main restaurant, The

Dining Room, is notable for its high ceiling, chandeliers, fresh flowers and more palms and, of course, quality napery and silverware. The kitchen's grounding in the classic repertoire, overlaying some modern touches, and technical skill show up on the menus. Luxury ingredients there may be – foie gras crops up among the starters, as does lobster, both as consommé and plainly grilled plated with shallot and ginger butter – but what made an inspector sit up and pay attention was a 'rich, carefully devised and well-constructed' terrine of pig's trotter, mushrooms and quail with a red wine and port jelly. Simple and accurately cooked seared Scottish scallops followed; these came with a nicely balancing sauce vierge and deep-fried okra to give some crunch. Rich and sticky fig tart, pecan nuts added to the fruit, ended the meal, and if the pastry was a little 'hard-going' the custard was enjoyable. Elsewhere on the menus there may be traditional native oysters, fillet of Aberdeen Angus, updated with balsamic vinegar and pesto, and roast loin of lamb with caramelised sweetbreads and a chicory tarte Tatin. Breads have been praised, service is attentive without being overbearing, and an extensive wine list complements the food.

Directions: Directly opposite Marylebone BR & Tube stations

Times: 12.30-last L 2.30pm/7-last D 11pm. Closed L Sat, D Sun
Additional: Sunday L; Children welcome; ⓓ dishes
Seats: 80
Smoking: No-smoking area; Air conditioning
Accommodation: 305 en suite
Credit cards: ▄▄ ▄▄ ▜▌ ⌐ ▄▄ ▐ ▣

The Lanesborough ❀❀❀

Hyde Park Corner SW1X 7TA
Map: C3
Tel: 0171 2595599
Fax: 0171 2595606
Chef: Paul Gayler
Owner: Rosewood Hotels & Resorts
Cost: Alc £40, fixed-price L £24.50/D £29.50. H/wine £17.50
Times: Noon-2.30pm/6.30-midnight
Additional: Bar food; Sunday L; Children welcome; ⓓ dishes
Seats: 106. Private dining rooms 80. Jacket & tie preferred
Smoking: No-smoking area; Air conditioning
Accommodation: 95 en suite
Credit cards: ▄▄ ▄▄ ▄▄

Something of a pioneer of East-West cooking, Paul Gayler's approach to fusion is rather more sensitive than some. 'Its light and it feels healthy' decided a relieved sounding inspector after an early spring dinner. The Conservatory restaurant is itself a bright and airy venue with its curved glass ceiling and trickling fountains being home to a collection of chinoiserie well-matched to the menu. The oriental twist is far from all-encompassing though; Mediterranean, classic French, Greek and modern British notes are all to be found on an enterprising *carte* that varies little between lunch and dinner. The kitchen copes well with the mix of styles and a welcome lightness of touch is the defining characteristic of a skilful team. Lettuce spring rolls have offered classic crab and ginger flavours with a crunchy julienne of vegetables that benefited from a sprightly soy and sesame dressing. Equally punchy was a roast fillet of sea bream that came with squid, clams, garlic and judiciously handled chilli. Spiced barbecue salmon with coconut rice and fragrant Thai vegetables, or lobster with braised artichokes and wild mushrooms, are amongst the more innovative combinations. Little, though, could compete in the outlandish stakes against the frozen Brie parfait with blood orange and raspberries that provoked our initially sceptical inspector into rapturous praise.

Directions: On Hyde Park Corner

Langan's Brasserie ❀❀

For over 20 years this enormous, bustling brasserie, set on two floors just off Piccadilly, has been one of the capital's most popular eating places. Adorned from floor to ceiling with modern art, including paintings by Hockney and Proctor, it still retains that feel of being the place to see and be seen in, despite being firmly on the tourist map these days. Cooking standards are consistent, and the long list of well-loved British dishes and brasserie favourites has become reassuringly familiar over the years. A recent inspection meal yielded tender smoked duck with apple and a light mayonnaise for starters, followed by moist, correctly cooked sea bass served with a well flavoured garlic and butter sauce. Poire Belle Hélène with chocolate sauce and good filter coffee rounded off the meal nicely. Further main course choices include monkfish kebab with chilli and lime dressing, gammon with butter beans, and Langan's bangers and mash with white onion sauce.

Directions: Stratton Street is about half-way along Piccadilly. Nearest Tube – Green Park

Stratton Street W1X 5FD
Map: C3
Tel: 0171 4918822
Fax: 0171 4938309
Chef: Ken Whitehead
Owners: Richard Shepherd, Michael Caine
Cost: Alc £45. H/wine £11
Times: Open all day, 12.30pm-last D 11.45pm (Sat from 7pm).
Closed L Sat, all Sun, Bhs
Additional: Children welcome.
❀ dishes
Seats: 275
Smoking: Air conditioning
Credit cards: ▨ ▨ ▨ ▨ ▨ ▨ ▨ JCB

The Langham Hilton London ❀

See Where London Meets Section page 153

Launceston Place ❀❀

1a Launceston Place W8 5RL
Map: A2
Tel: 0171 9376912
Fax: 0171 9382412
Chefs: Philip Reed & Terence Eden
Owners: Nick Smallwood & Simon Slater
Cost: Alc £35, fixed-price L & D £17.50. ☺ H/wine £10.75
Times: 12.30-last L 2.30pm/7-last D 11.30pm. Closed L Sat, D Sun, Bhs
Additional: Sunday L (12.30-3pm); Children welcome; ❀ dishes
Seats: 85. Private dining room 12, 30
Smoking: No pipes & cigars; Air conditioning
Credit cards: ▨ ▨ ▨ ▨ ▨ ▨

Tucked away from the hustle and bustle of nearby Kensington High Street, this comfortable neighbourhood restaurant offers sound modern English cooking at affordable prices. Attracting a loyal local clientele, the short *carte* and set menu list a successful combination of dishes, with choices for both the traditionalist and the more adventurous. A simple yet delicious dish of home-made noodles tossed with wild asparagus, Parmesan and truffle oil started our inspection meal well. Main course salmon was pan fried and served with béarnaise sauce and good fresh vegetables. Choices also included roast saddle of hare wrapped in pancetta with chicken and herb mousse, seared scallops with tomato and rocket tart and basil butter, and sea bass with rhubarb dressing. Desserts range from lemon and ricotta cheesecake with blueberry coulis, and strawberry and chocolate roulade, to tip-top farmhouse cheeses and ice creams. Excellent home-made breads. Service is quiet and professional.

Directions: Just south of Kensington Palace. Between Gloucester Road and High Street Kensington Tubes

Leith's Restaurant 🏵🏵🏵

Track down Leith's for a taste of quality modern British cooking. The restaurant is on the ground floor of a Notting Hill Victorian town house and once you have found your way in, via the hidden-away side entrance, an ambience of Georgian minimalism takes hold. As you enter, staff with big smiles appear, ready to take your coat and offer you a drink from the stylish cocktail bar. The clientele is eclectic – few are here for a quick business lunch – and many guests appear to be on first-name terms with the manager. That said, everyone is heartily welcomed by the friendly staff, who at times make you wonder whether you've met them before. Our inspector enjoyed a winter lunch that started with a stunning little cappuccino of mushrooms and chives, followed by goats' cheese and red onion spring rolls with a tomato tapenade. The main course, of roasted guinea fowl with 'lovely' truffle mash and café au lait sauce, arrived with surreal spontaneity. Dessert was a baked chocolate pudding with pistachio ice cream and hot vanilla anglaise sauce. Dinner is a more elaborate affair, with choices from the *carte* ranging from sauté of guinea fowl with artichokes, oysters and a morel mushroom sauce, to a vegetarian dish of layers of crispy potato with wild mushrooms, roast sweetcorn brandade and a red wine and shallot dressing. The wine list is succinct, with a selection at lunch time that perfectly matches the short set menu, while for dinner the doors to the extensive cellar are thrown wide.

Signature dishes: Roast langoustine and coriander ravioli with lemon grass consommé; sea scallops with spiced lemon couscous, fennel and turmeric; grilled spiced fillet of beef with onion beignet and cardamom

Directions: 500 yds north of Notting Hill Gate

92 Kensington Park Road W11 2PN
Map GtL: C3
Tel: 0171 2294481
Fax: 0171 2211246
Chef: Alastair Ross
Owners: Sir Christopher Bland, Caroline Waldegrave, Alex Floyd, Nick Tarayan
Cost: *Alc* £40, fixed-price L £16.50/D £27.50 (both 2 courses). H/wine £15.50
Times: 12.15-2.15pm/7-11.30pm. Closed L Sat & Mon, all Sun, 2 wks Xmas & New Year
Additional: No children under 7; 🍴 dishes
Seats: 70. Private dining room 36
Smoking: No pipes & cigars; Air conditioning
Credit cards: ▄▄ ▄▄ ▄▄ ▄▄ ▄▄ ▄▄ ▄▄ JCB

Shortlisted for
AA Wine Award-see page 16

Leith's Soho ❁❁

Leith's second restaurant occupies the old Atelier site, now unrecognisable in its new guise. There's a polished wood floor and walls with an almost verdigris effect: one made up of a cunning glass screen to divide the room up for private parties. The *carte* offers an eclectic range of dishes and the aim is to keep the style unpretentious, to offer something for everyone – for the clientele is equally eclectic, ranging (at lunch) from business suits to shoppers and tourists. Early reports are positive about this new venture, with perfect balance and timing being the keynotes in one inspection meal that took in a terrine of poulet noir with sweetbreads and leeks, a main course of sea bass, squid and mussels in a coconut and Thai green curry broth and fine noodles, and banana Tatin with caramel sauce and sultana ice cream. The basket of bread includes ciabatta, brown with rye, strong white and sun-dried tomato. Staff are good, attentive, approachable and professional. The wine list is short but interesting with over thirty choices by the glass.

Directions: Nearest Tube – Piccadilly

41 Beak Street W1R 3LE
Map: D4
Tel: 0171 2872057
Chef: Alex Floyd
Owner: Leith's School of Food & Wine
Cost: *Alc* £35, fixed-price L £19.50. H/wine £11.75
Times: Noon-last L 2.30pm/6-last D 11pm. Closed Sun
Additional: Children welcome; 🍴 dishes
Seats: 50. Private dining room 20
Smoking: Air conditioning
Credit cards:
■ ■ 🐦 ⌶ ▦ 🅱 🄿 JCB

Lemonia ❁

A bustling modern Greek restaurant on a well-heeled parade, Lemonia's large conservatory lends a light, open and informal air. There's a selection of cold and hot mezze. Main courses range from simple chargrilled tuna with delicious fried potatoes to subtly spiced fresh moussaka. The baklava is worth every honey-soaked calorie.

Additional: Children welcome; 🍴 dishes
Smoking: No cigars & pipes; Air conditioning
Credit cards: ■ ■ 🐦 ⌶ 🅱 JCB

Directions: Nearest Tube – Chalk Farm. 200 metres from Primrose Hill Park

89 Regent's Park Road NW1 8UY
Map GtL: C3
Tel: 0171 5867454
Fax: 0171 4832630
Chefs: A Evangelou, A Mitas
Owners: Mr A & Mrs M Evangelou
Cost: *Alc* £16.50, fixed-price L £7.95/D £12.25. ☺ H/wine £10.50
Times: Last L 3pm/last D 11.30pm. Closed L Sat, D Sun, 25, 26 Dec

Lexington ❁

Fun, lively hotel restaurant with live jazz three nights a week. The popular set menu is good value, but for more choice go for the carte, which offers Med dishes such as lemon and sweet garlic risotto with pine nuts, and queen scallop and bacon hash topped with a poached egg.

Directions: Nearest Tubes – Oxford Circus, Tottenham Court Road, Piccadilly Circus

45 Lexington Street W1R 3LG
Map: D3
Tel: 0171 434 3401
Fax: 0171 287 2997
Please telephone for further details

Lindsay House ❁❁❁

The arrival of Richard Corrigan has transformed Lindsay House, a traditional four storey 1740s town house in the heart of Soho. Restored to its original beauty, the interior features dark wood floors, cream walls and marble fireplaces. Two main dining rooms make up the restaurant, where Corrigan's unique interpretation of modern European cooking runs along the lines of grilled mackerel with sweet potato and lime pickle, or baked fillets of place with broad beans and sorrel beurre blanc, and monkfish wrapped in ham and served with green olives

21 Romilly Street W1V 5TG
Map: D3
Tel: 0171 4390450
Fax: 0171 4377349
Chef: Richard Corrigan
Owners: Searcy & Corrigan Restaurants Ltd
Cost: Fixed-price L £21/D £34. H/wine £14.95

and fennel juices. His sense of balance and judgement is also evident in starters such as a delicate dressed Cornish crab with avocado and pink grapefruit, a gutsy sautéed veal kidney with stuffed pig's trotter and broad bean salad, and the striking combination of beetroot bavarois with cured sea bass and caviar. The highlight of a recent meal was a mouth-watering starter of lightly chargrilled, thinly sliced tuna dressed with a super Japanese vegetable relish in a sweet-and-sour sauce. This had been preceded by a 'trendy' demi-tasse of cappuccinoed Jerusalem artichoke soup with a drizzle of truffle oil. A main course, daube of pork with apricots and stir-fried cabbage chiffonade, was followed by a sound chocolate fondant with clementine sorbet. Other desserts include rhubarb and mascarpone trifle, and pineapple with chilli, coriander and coconut cream. The lengthy wine list covers both the Old and New Worlds, and there are several good vintages by the glass.

Times: Noon-last L 2.15pm/6-last D 10.45pm. Closed L Sat, all Sun, last 2 wks Aug, Bhs
Additional: Children welcome; 🖐 dishes
Seats: 60. Private dining room 20
Smoking: No pipes & cigars; Air conditioning
Credit cards: 🔳 🔳 🔳 🔳 🔳 🔳

Directions: Nearest Tube-Leicester Square

Livebait ❀❀

With its chequered tiles and closely packed tables, the no-nonsense style is as refreshingly honest as the fathom-deep bourride that is a staple of the lunchtime menu. Much the same goes for the industrious service with a complimentary bowl of prawns banged down almost before you are seated; a precursor of rapid-fire delivery that makes a snappy lunch a real possibility. Necessarily, the raw materials are first class and the more familiar accompaniments such as aïoli and rouille are, for once, faithfully prepared. The menu extends well beyond these familiar boundaries and reads like a global collection of imaginative (some might say outrageous) things to do with fish. Cod, for instance, has been known to arrive packaged in a spiced banana and almond crust alongside a gumbo of okra. Those who like their seafood straight can settle for lavish mixed platters or generous bowls of whelks and cockles. Wines are fish friendly with a good selection by the glass. Another branch of Livebait, run on similar lines, is to be found at 21 Wellington Street, WC2, tel: 0171 8367161.

43 The Cut SE1 8LF
Map: E3
Tel: 0171 9287211
Fax: 0171 9282279
Chef: Manu Feildel
Owner: Groupe Chez Gerard
Cost: Alc £32, fixed-price L & D (pre- & post-theatre only) £14.50 (2 courses). ☺ H/wine £11.75
Times: Noon-last L 2.45pm/5.30-last D 11.30pm. Closed Sun, Xmas & New Year
Additional: Children welcome
Seats: 100
Smoking: No-smoking area; No pipes & cigars
Credit cards: 🔳 🔳 🔳 🔳 🔳 🔳 JCB

Directions: Near Old Vic Theatre

Lola's ❀❀

You're never far from antiques in this part of Islington, and Lola's (handy for the Business Design Centre and Angel tube) occupies the first floor of an old tram shed over an arcade of objets d'art. It's a bright space with understated, modern decor, a daily changing *carte*, and a set menu. Italy provides much of the inspiration behind a modish collection of dishes that also exhibits French and Middle Eastern influences and tends towards complexity. Original, 'very nice' brown bread with pine kernels and prunes started an inspection meal, the highlight of which was a starter of salt cod drizzled with truffle oil and served with rocket and bruschetta. Tender pork fillet came with lentils and mustard sauce for the main course, and pudding was rhubarb and pistachio trifle, served with the components placed separately on the plate. The wine list, ordered by price, contains several choices by the glass.

359 Upper Street Islington N1
Map GtL: D3
Tel: 0171 3591932
Fax: 0171 3592209
Chef: Juliet Peston
Owners: Carol George, Morfudd Richards
Cost: Alc £25, fixed-price L £16.50. ☺ H/wine £9.75
Times: Noon-2.30pm (till 3pm Sat & Sun)/6.30pm-11pm (till 10pm Sun). Closed 25-26 Dec, 1 Jan
Additional: Sunday L; Children welcome; 🖐 dishes
Seats: 80
Smoking: Air conditioning
Credit cards: 🔳 🔳 🔳 🔳 🔳 🔳 🔳 JCB

Directions: Nearest Tube – Angel

London Hilton
on Park Lane

There is an exciting, international buzz about this well-established Park Lane hotel. The prize location is undoubtedly the Windows Bar and Restaurant, on the top floor of this great high-rise block, and the prize tables those giving on to the sweeping vistas over Hyde Park and the city. The view, however, does not detract from the cooking, which, under Jacques Rolancy, produces precise dishes described as 'bourgeois légére'. Our inspection dinner started with nicely seared scallop and warm potato salad plus a dandelion leaf salad, went on to beautifully cooked venison medallions with that lovely velvety texture that really gets the taste buds going The meat came with an unusual thick coating of chunky, nibbed roasted almonds – a novel and successful touch – and accompanied by a good rich jus. Fun fruit truffles coated in chocolate and iced for dessert were a great idea, but were served over-iced and we needed to wait for them to thaw before the flavours came through and they could be eaten with ease. Staff are friendly and attentive.

Signature dishes: Wild mushroom ravioli with a morel and asparagus sauce; rack of lamb with vegetables cooked 'en cocotte'; monkfish, pot roasted with potatoes, artichokes, baby onions and bacon; scallops marinated in Alba oil and lemon juice on a celeriac mash.

Directions: Nearest Tube – Hyde Park Corner. Restaurant on 28th floor of hotel

22 Park Lane W1A 2HH
Map: C3
Tel: 0171 4938000
Fax: 0171 2084142
Chef: Jacques Rolancy
Owner: Ladbroke Hotels
Cost: *Alc* £60; fixed-price L £39.50/D £44.50 (5 courses). H/wine £15.50
Times: 12.30-last L 2.30pm/7.30-last D 10.30pm. Closed L Sat, D Sun
Additional: Bar food; Sunday brunch; Children welcome; ♨ dishes
Seats: 90. Jacket & tie preferred at D
Smoking: No pipes; Air conditioning
Accommodation: 446 en suite
Credit cards: 💳 💳 💳 💳 💳 💳 💳 JCB

London Kensington Hilton,
Hiroko Japanese Restaurant

The Japanese eating option at this modern West London hotel. Friendlier and less formal than most of the Japanese restaurants in town, and with kinder prices too. The menu includes sushi, sashimi, shabu shabu, teriyaki, Kirin and Osaho dishes giving it broad appeal.

Directions: Holland Park Tube

Holland Park Avenue W11 4UL
Map GtL: C3
Tel: 0171 6033355
Fax: 0171 6029397
Owner: Hilton International Kensington
Telephone for further details

London Marriott
Grosvenor Square Hotel ❀

See Where London Meets Section page 153

The Lowndes Hyatt Hotel ❀❀

The chic atmosphere of Brasserie 21 makes it a good meeting-place throughout the day. In the summer, visitors can dine on the terrace overlooking Lowndes Square. There is a wide choice of eclectic 'international' dishes, such as mussel chowder, Caesar salad, crab cakes, wild mushroom and tomato risotto, and grilled chicken breast with mashed potato and fresh herb sauce. The Knightsbridge Special Sandwich features smoked salmon, avocado, shrimps and quails' eggs on granary toast – but then it does cost £8.95. A good selection of freshly

21 Lowndes Street
SW1X 9ES
Map: B2
Tel: 0171 8231234
Fax: 0171 2351154
Chef: Gary Henden
Owner: The Lowndes Hyatt Hotel
Cost: *Alc* £25, fixed price L £13.95 (2 courses)/D £17. ☺ H/wine £12.50.
Times: 11.30am-last D 11pm

The Lowndes Hyatt Hotel

Additional: Bar food L; Sunday L;
Children welcome; ❹ dishes
Seats: 36. Private dining room 20
Smoking: No pipes or cigars in dining
room; Air conditioning
Accommodation: 78 en suite

squeezed juices and health drinks includes apple and mango,
carrot and fennel – ideal for restoring energy levels after
shopping till you drop.

Credit cards: ▆ ▆ ▆ ▆ ▆ ▆ JCB

Directions: Knightsbridge Tube, from Sloane Street take first L
into Lowndes Square, located on the bottom right hand corner

Maison Novelli 🏵🏵🏵

29 Clerkenwell Green
EC1R 0DU
Map GtL: D3
Tel: 0171 2516606
Fax: 0171 4901083
Chef: Richard Guest
Owner: Jean-Christophe Novelli
Cost: *Alc* £40. H/wine £16.50
Times: Noon-last L 3pm/6.30-last
D 11.15pm. Closed L Sat, all Sun
Additional: Children welcome;
❹ dishes
Seats: 80. Private room 35
Smoking: No pipes & cigars
Credit cards: ▆ ▆ ▆ ▆ ▆ ▆ JCB

Smart, bright decor matches the smart, bright clientele; the
blue-purple walls (Jean-Christophe Novelli's signature colour),
big mirrors and masses of fresh flowers create a room with
great panache. The imaginative cooking pioneered by Novelli
is now in the capable hands of head chef Richard Guest,
although Novelli classics such as stuffed braised pig's trotter
and hot-and-cold chocolate pudding are still on the menu. First
courses of goats' cheese and aubergine ravioli, pepper and sun-
dried tomato juice, and pressed celeriac, potato and foie gras
terrine, pan-fried with hazelnut oil just passed muster, but
main courses were better judged. Gilt-head sea bass was
beautifully fresh and well-timed, served on a coriander risotto
with lime oil, sweet chilli caramel and crispy carrot ribbons,
and bay leaf brochette of lamb, scallops and shiitake with
confit of onions and Marsala sauce proved an exciting and
innovative combination. Combinations can be daring:
carpaccio of tuna with bean sprouts, oyster beignet and soy
ginger dressing; roast jumbo quail with soft poached egg,
fondant potato, lentils du Puy, morels and crispy Ventreche;

blueberry 'financier', toasted lemon verbena sabayon, mascarpone ice cream. A concise, mainly French, list has few halves and only the house wine is available by the glass.

   Signature dishes: Pyramid of tomato aspic, white crab, quails' eggs and chive oil; halibut shallot cappuccino, celeriac fondant and diced apple; stuffed quail.

Directions: Nearest Tube – Farringdon

Mandarin Kitchen

Spacious, bustling, cosmopolitan modern Chinese with all-day opening. The kitchen specialises in fish, but a wide variety of meat dishes encompass most Far-Eastern cuisines. Authentic starters include deep-fried soft-shell crabs, and a quality shark fin soup. Many of the main courses compensate for western tastes: pork in yellow bean sauce, and whole steamed cod with honey and soy, for example.

Additional: Children welcome; ❹ dishes
Smoking: Air conditioning
Credit cards: ▆▆ ▆▆ ▆▆ 匚 ▆▆ 【 ▆ JCB

14 Queensway W2 3RX
Map: C3
Tel: 0171 727 9012
Fax: 0171 7279468
Chef: Mr Man
Owner: Mrs Helen Cheung
Cost: *Alc* £20, fixed-price L/D £9.90.
☺ H/wine £8.90
Times: Noon – last D 11.30pm.
Closed 25-26 Dec

Directions: Opposite Queensway Tube; a few yards from Bayswater Tube

Mandarin Oriental Hyde Park, The Park Restaurant ❀❀❀❀

The Park, the revamped principal restaurant at the much-vaunted Mandarin Oriental Hyde Park, enjoys enviable leafy views across the park. Chef David Nicholls leads a confident crew, producing superbly light, subtle food with fastidiously sourced ingredients. Nicholls' positive approach in the kitchen is evident in the way delicate, subtle flavours are brought out in dishes such as roast sea bass with sweet pepper compote and fried fennel, and confit of duck with mustard mash and buttered sea kale. The highlight of a recent meal was a 'feather-light' dish of seared scallop ravioli with Dublin Bay prawns, surrounded by a light cappuccino-style parsnip cream. Hot on the heels of this 'delightful' starter was a main course of steamed fillet of turbot topped with foie gras and truffle mousse. Accuracy of composition as well as stunning presentation was evident in a crab cake topped with a piece of lobster and set on a dice of tomato and black olive – which added a well-judged sweetness and bite – offset by a light, frothy mustard cream sauce and garnished with spinach leaves with a delicate walnut dressing. Pink, tender French pigeon breast, bursting with flavour, was served with a confit of the leg and cooked en croûte, all set on finely shredded truffled cabbage, Puy lentils, wild mushrooms and a creamy gratin dauphinoise. Desserts of pannacotta with fresh berry compote, raspberry soufflé with crème fraîche and tangerine sorbet, lemon tart set off by an intense blackcurrant sorbet in a delicate pineapple tuile, and a passion fruit soufflé, show the strength of the pastry work.

66 Knightsbridge SW1X 7LA
Map: B2
Tel: 0171 2352000
Fax: 0171 2354552
Chef: David Nicholls
Cost: *Alc* £50, fixed-price L £23.50/D £27. H/wine £22
Times: Noon-last L 2.30pm/6-last D 11pm
Additional: Bar food; Sunday L; Children welcome; ❹ dishes
Seats: 80. Private room 200
Smoking: No-smoking area; Air conditioning
Accommodation: 198 en suite
Credit cards: ▆▆ ▆▆ ▆▆ 匚 ▆▆ 【 ▆ JCB

Directions: Nearest Tube – Knightsbridge

Mas Café ❀

A smart, arty hang-out which comes to life in late evening. There's a large bar for mingling, while modern English and Spanish dishes are served to a backdrop of loud music. Try fresh linguine with shiitake and oyster mushrooms and rocket, or pan-fried tuna steak with a spicy caper butter.

Additional: Sunday L; Children welcome (weekend brunch); ♨ dishes
Credit cards: 🔲 🔲 🔲 🔲 JCB

Directions: Between Ladbroke Grove & Westbourne Park Tube stations. Parallel to Portobello Road

6-8 All Saints Road W11 1HA
Map GtL: C3
Tel/Fax: 0171 2430969
Chef: Frederico Wazinger
Owners: Ian Alexander,
Michael White, David Stacey
Cost: Alc £21, fixed-price D £15. ☺
H/wine £9.50.
Times: Last L 4.30pm/D 11.30pm
(10.30 Sun). Closed L Mon-Fri, 25-26
Dec, 1 Jan, Carnival

Mash ❀ NEW

Pacy, sleek micro-brewery-cum-bar-cum-restaurant complete with state-of-the-art mirrored loos. Great for weekend brunch – a pick-n-mix of the likes of eggs Benedict and vanilla French toast. Otherwise try suckling pig with spring cannellini stew, gutsy pasta dishes and terrific, imaginative pizzas from the wood-fired oven.

Seats: 140. **Smoking:** Air conditioning
Credit cards: 🔲 🔲 🔲 🔲 🔲 🔲 🔲

Directions: Nearest Tube – Oxford Circus. At the Oxford Street end of Great Portland Street

19-20 Great Portland Street
W1 5DB
Map: C3
Tel: 0171 6375555
Fax: 0171 6377333
Chef: Craig Grey
Owner: Oliver Peyton
Cost: Alc £25. ☺ H/wine £12.50
Times: 8am-noon (breakfast)/last L
3pm/6pm-last D 11pm. Closed Bhs
Additional: Bar food; Sunday L;
Children welcome; ♨ dishes

Matsuri ❀❀

The Japanese expats frequenting this enjoyable teppan-yaki (hot-plate grilled) restaurant are a clue to the quality and authenticity of the cooking, but do not be intimidated. Staff here are particularly helpful and pleased to guide newcomers around the menu. Matsuri means festival in Japanese and the restaurant is decorated with various artefacts from the various festivals held throughout the year in Japan. The set Taiko menu, named after the huge ceremonial Japanese drum, includes assorted Japanese hors d'oeuvre, chawan mushi (savoury custard), sashimi, wonderful tempura of prawns and vegetables, seafood in rice vinegar, a side salad, grilled vegetables, rice, miso soup and pickles plus a choice of teppan-yaki such as lobster and other seafood or beef and teppan-grilled asparagus and carrot. Dipping sauces include a sweet soy-based concoction and a lemony cream number that provided good sharpness for the seafood. Fresh fruit is available for dessert and there is a comprehensive selection of sakés.

Directions: From Green Park Tube, walk towards Piccadilly Circus, turn right into St James', 1st left into Jermyn St. 1st right is Bury St

15 Bury Street SW1Y 6AL
Map: D3
Tel: 0171 8391101
Fax: 0171 9307010
Chef: Kanehiro Takase
Owner: ORK (UK) Ltd
Cost: Alc £35, fixed-price D £35
(5 courses). H/wine £20
Times: Noon-last L 2.30pm/6pm-last
D 10pm. Closed Sun, Bhs
Additional: Children welcome;
♨ dishes
Seats: 133. Private dining room 18
Smoking: Air conditioning
Credit cards: 🔲 🔲 🔲 🔲 🔲 🔲 JCB

The Mayfair Inter-Continental London, Opus 70 ❀❀

Opus 70 is the smart new restaurant attached to the Mayfair Inter-Continental, a fashionable hotel favoured by stars from showbiz. Stylish and modern, the restaurant is filled with bold

Stratton Street W1A 2AN
Map: C3
Tel: 0171 3447070
Fax: 0171 3447071
Chef: Michael Coaker

***The Mayfair Inter-Continental
London, Opus 70***

Cost: *Alc* £30, fixed-price L £16.50
(2 courses). ☺
Times: Noon-last L 2.30pm/6-last D
11pm. Closed L Sat
Additional: Sunday L; Children
welcome; ✦ dishes
Seats: 85. Private room 12
Smoking: No pipes & cigars; Air
conditioning
Accommodation: 290 en suite
Credit cards: ▬ ▬ ▬ ▬ ▬ ▬ ▬ JCB

paintings and vases of orchids. The large square tables are laid
with white linen, and there are alcoves for intimate dining.
Chef Michael Coaker has cooked for everyone, Mel Gibson
included, so expect quality British meals updated with
international flavours. Typical starters from the set lunch menu
include confit of rabbit with truffle oil, grilled goats' cheese
with pesto and nut crust, and Caesar salad with chargrilled
chicken or Mediterranean prawns. Mains from the dinner *carte*
continue the theme; look out for roast halibut with sesame
seeds, linguine and coriander, and pan-fried calves' liver with
crispy bacon and creamy polenta. Desserts range from banana
and rum bread-and-butter pudding to frothy coffee brûlée with
raspberries.

Directions: From Hyde Park Corner, turn left off Piccadilly just
below Green Park tube station.

McClements' Restaurant

The small neighbourhood restaurant stands on the corner
opposite Twickenham station. Get through the doors and you
find that tables are small too, prettily displayed with candles
and fresh flowers. John McClements has made his mark here,
and his cooking, which can often have a slight angle to it,
shows taste. Witness a demi-tasse of lobster soup, presented to
our inspector on arrival. Lovely flavour and quite rich 'for a
kick-off soup', the little plate of canapés went down well too,
as did the bread. A plate of hors d'oeuvre – foie gras, bass
fillet, salmon on rösti, scallop on chicory, rabbit balantine, quail
in pastry – were of excellent quality, well presented and
accurately cooked, quite an achievement as all six items were
vying for attention on the plate. Top-quality roast monkfish
followed, accompanied by scallops with saffron and vegetable
jus, an 'absolutely excellent dish'. A selection of desserts –
miniature lemon mousse, chocolate tart, raspberry sorbet in a
tiny tuile basket, coconut ice cream on apple tart, praline
parfait – produced in a small kitchen with just three cooks,
were more in keeping with the production from a large hotel
or restaurant with a pastry orientated section: Mr McClements
is to be congratulated on the standards he achieves. The wine
list is reasonably priced.

2 Whitton Road Twickenham
Map GtL: B2
Tel: 0181 7449598
Chef/Owner: John McClements
Please telephone for further details

Directions: In a small parade of shops next to Twickenham
station

Memories of China Restaurant

There's a cool sophistication about this restaurant, with open screens dividing up the room and ancient Chinese poems written on the walls. Asterisks alongside items on the menu guide people towards those dishes that will ensure they experience the full range of flavours and textures of what's on offer, which picks up influences from Peking, Canton, Szechuan and even Mongolia. A starter of clear-flavoured braised aubergine with a dice of sweet peppers appears alongside mussels in black-bean and chilli sauce, five-spiced spare ribs, and soups. Follow that with perhaps tender, succulent lamb quickly fried with spring onions and garlic, with a side order of bite-sized 'quarters' of perfectly cooked Chinese greens in oyster sauce. Alternatively, go for minced prawns and chicken in lettuce puffs, or sizzling beef, with spicy bean curd casserole and deep-fried French beans. Set menus include a Gastronomic Tour of China and a Lobster Feast. Another branch is at 353 Kensington High Street, London W8, tel: 0171 6036951.

67 Ebury Street SW1W 0NZ
Map: C2
Tel: 0171 7307734
Fax: 0171 7302992
Chef/Owner: Kam Po But
Cost: *Alc* £25, fixed-price L £19/D £28. ☺ H/wine £13.50
Times: Noon–last L 2.30pm/7–last D 11pm. Closed L Sun, Bhs
Additional: ❸ dishes
Seats: 100. Private dining room 20
Smoking: Air conditioning
Credit cards: ▪▪ ▪▪ ▪▪ ▪ ▪▪ ▪ ▪ JCB

Directions: At the junction of Ebury Street and Eccleston Street. Nearest Tubes – Sloane Square & Victoria

Le Meridien Picadilly – The Oak Room, Marco Pierre White ✿✿✿✿✿✿

Marco Pierre White's principal restaurant had something of a holding entry in the 1998 edition of Best Restaurants. This was because he announced he was moving premises as we went to press. He has now settled into his new surroundings, the Oak Room of the Meridien Hotel. The room is very opulent 'very rococo-style decor'; in other words lots of gold and chandeliers. In this setting, the addition of modern art is somewhat baffling, but then Marco Pierre White has never been easy to fathom. Tables are well spaced to the point of leaving one inspector feeling rather exposed, and table lamps can impede conversation, but at least all this generous space is devoted to the service of food in much comfort. There are 'loads of flunkies to attend every need', and the menu is full of foie gras, truffles, morels, caviar and oysters. If one were to be critical, the repetition of ingredients is a starting point, but then each dish is so different in its own way; the intensity for which Marco is famed, the self-contained assurity, is there in spades. A report from a trio of inspectors suggests this and much more. That dinner began with *amuse-bouche*: a small cup of soup, vegetable based and very subtle, a hint of garlic with a few sea-fresh mussels, and divine scallops, soft, gentle and fresh as a daisy, and topped with deep-fried calamari, crisp and sweet – a delightful mix of textures and quite superb ingredients. First courses were oysters en gelée, spot-on, served with a couple of watercress leaves (which gave a refreshing element) and a shallot cream, terrine of foie gras with peppercorns and a quite superb finely chopped Sauternes jelly and freshly toasted brioche, and ballotine of wild salmon poached in milk 'very deep in flavour' with a salad of crayfish and caviar with fromage blanc. This was a prelude to a braised pig's trotter 'Pierre Koffmann', delightfully light, with chopped sweetbreads adding an extra texture, morel essence intense but not overpowering, and pommes purée 'as smooth as they

21 Piccadilly W1V 0BH
Map: D3
Tel: 0171 4370202
Chef/Owner: Marco Pierre White
Cost: Fixed price L £29.50/D £80. H/wine £20
Times: Noon–2.30pm/7–11.15pm. Closed L Sat, all Sun, 2 wks Xmas, 2 wks Aug, Bhs
Additional: Children welcome; ❸ dishes
Seats: 70
Smoking: No pipes & cigars; Air conditioning
Credit cards: ▪▪ ▪▪ ▪▪ ▪ ▪▪ ▪

come', escalope of sea bass with lashings of caviar and a
superbly executed velouté of champagne, and bressoles of
Bresse pigeon with foie gras, which required exact cooking and
proved to be accomplished, with very pink pigeon and melting
foie gras – it was wrapped in Savoy cabbage and cut like
butter. Puddings were exactly as they should be: a perfect
caramel soufflé, caramelised apple tart, but the sensation was
roasted pineapple, caramelised and spiked with vanilla pods
and chilli. It was superb, with fromage-blanc ice cream giving
that extra sharp edge. Petits fours were bliss. Is this the
ultimate in luxury and perfection?

Signature dishes: Salad of lobster with herbs, tomato confit,
sauce cocktail; escalope of sea bass with caviar, cromesquis of
oysters, croquante of fennel, velouté of champagne; braised
pig's trotter 'Pierre Koffmann', pommes mousseline, essence of
morels; caramelised pineapple with vanilla.

Directions: At the Piccadilly Circus end of Piccadilly

Le Meridien Waldorf

Now celebrating its ninetieth year, Le Meridien Waldorf goes
from strength to strength. The Palm Court Lounge remains an
institution, with weekend afternoon tea dances as popular as
ever, and Friday's not-to-be-missed Chocolate Buffet.
Imaginative dishes with vibrant textures and flavours are
served in the Palm Court's romantic setting, and could include
starters such as pan-roasted pigeon breast with pesto rösti,
roasted sweet pepper risotto with garlic tuile, and cured
Scottish salmon with pink peppercorns, frisée salad and lemon
confit. At a meal in April our inspector tried pink bream with
glazed beetroot and an escabeché dressing, followed by red
mullet with seared scallops and olive tapenade. The main dish
of rabbit leg stuffed with foie gras and a raisin and pear
chutney was served with caramelised shallots, plus tomato and
garlic purée. Desserts range from a simple red fruit tart to
Japanese tea mousse with caramelised pear.

Aldwych WC2B 4DD
Map: E4
Tel: 0171 8362400
Fax: 0171 8367244
Chef: Mark Harris
Cost: *Alc* £30. ☺ H/wine £19
Times: Noon-2.30pm/6-11.15pm.
Closed L Sat
Additional: Sunday jazz brunch;
Children welcome; ❹ dishes
Seats: 100
Smoking: No-smoking area
Accommodation: 292 en suite
Credit cards: ■■ ■■ ■■ ■■ ■■ ■ ■ JCB

Directions: Nearest Tube – Covent Garden

Mezzo

From Swinging London to Cool Britannia, this address has
come a long way since it was the Marquee Club back in the
60s. The vast, super-stylish restaurant has lost some of its
fashionability and cutting edge; tables are perhaps more
obtainable than once they used to be. Tablecloths seem
randomly distributed amongst the closely packed tables, tilted
mirrors afford everyone a view of the *passegiata* up and down
the great cantilevered staircase. The choice is wide with grilled
red mullet with leeks à la greque, a roast Bresse pigeon with
polenta and sage, and glazed sweetbreads, spinach and morel
jus representing the European wing, and Japanese glazed
mackerel, spinach and sesame seeds, or cannelloni of fresh
crab, ginger and spring onion, and five spice suckling pig with
lemon are typical of the Oriental influences the restaurant has
always espoused. Caviar, oysters and crustacea remain
hallmarks of this and other Conran eateries. Iced pineapple
soufflé with liquorice is one of the better desserts.

100 Wardour Street W1V 3LE
Map: D3
Tel: 0171 3144000
Fax: 0171 3144040
Chef: Tom Meenaghan
Owner: Conran Restaurants
Cost: *Alc* £40, fixed-price L £12.50
(2 courses). Pre-theatre D £14. ☺
H/wine £12.50
Times: Closed L Sat, 25, 26 Dec
Additional: Bar food L; Sunday L;
Children welcome; ❹ dishes
Seats: 350. Private room 40
Smoking: Air conditioning
Credit cards: ■■ ■■ ■■ ■■ ■■ ■ ■ JCB

Directions: Nearest Tube – Piccadilly Circus

Millenium Britannia Mayfair

The elegance of the Britannia is exactly in keeping with its location bang in the middle of Mayfair. Adams Restaurant provides a traditional and formal setting for some modern cooking, with a more relaxed atmosphere in the Best of Both Worlds Café. More surprising is to find that this is also the home of a Japanese restaurant, its rough-hewn stone walls in what appears to be an old underground wine cellar making a good contrast to the typical minimalism of London's other Japanese restaurants. But stark it isn't, with some decorative touches and racks of kyudo archery arrows separating tables. Start with a trio of appetisers – an fish egg roll, smoked salmon, and noodle salad — and go on to chicken yakitori and prawn and vegetable tempura before a main course of sashimi of tuna, salmon, sole, bream, mackerel and yellowtail, accompanied by cereal-scented rice, miso and a good variety of pickles. Finish with fresh fruit.

Directions: Nearest Tubes – Bond Street, Green Park

Grosvenor Square W1A 3AN
Map: C3
Tel: 0171 6299400
Chef: Neil Gray
Owner: Millenium & Copthorne Hotels
Cost: *Alc* £32, fixed-price D £26. ☺
H/wine £14.50
Times: Noon-3pm/6-10pm
Additional: Bar food; Sunday L; Children welcome; ◑ dishes
Seats: 100. Private dining room 85
Smoking: No-smoking area; Air conditioning
Accommodation: 319 en suite
Credit cards: 🔲 🔲 🔲 🔲 🔲 🔲 🔲

Millennium Chelsea

Close to Harrods and surrounded by exclusive designer stores, this chic Sloane Street hotel offers a varied menu featuring dishes that have more than a hint of fusion in their concept; however, good knowledge of ingredients and balance prevents this becoming confusion cooking. At inspection, very good bread preceded grilled sole on chive potato purée with red pepper and a light carrot essence, and a precisely cooked breast of maize-fed chicken with mushrooms and asparagus. For dessert, crème brûlée was enhanced by a good orange sorbet and berry coulis with pistachios. The short *carte* and fixed-price menu may also feature seared scallops with mango salsa, braised chicken with red wine and bacon, ragout of seafish in parsley cream, or pork fillet on apple and celeriac Tatin with fig gravy.

Directions: Two minutes from Knightsbridge tube

17 Sloane Street Knightsbridge
SW1X 9NU
Map: B2
Tel: 0171 2354377
Fax: 0171 2353705
Chef: Paul Bates
Owner: C D L Hotels
Cost: *Alc* £25, fixed-price L & D £18 (2 courses). ☺ H/wine £12.50
Times: Noon-last L 2.30pm/6-last D 11pm. Closed all Sat, D Sun,
Additional: Bar food; Sunday brunch; Children welcome; ◑ dishes
Seats: 90
Smoking: Air conditioning
Accommodation: 224 en suite
Credit cards: 🔲 🔲 🔲 🔲 🔲 🔲 🔲 JCB

Mims ❀ ❀

Even on a quiet night, when our inspector was the only customer, they don't take short cuts. Maybe there weren't enough brave souls around to try the sauté of cuttlefish with black pancake, chilli and tomato, or grilled mackerel with roasted vegetables, that night. Chicken stuffed with rice, tandoori style, however, ought to have appealed to a wider audience, and there's nothing intimidating about grilled lemon sole with fondant potatoes and buttered vegetables, especially when the cooking is as good as it is here. Roast guinea fowl with mashed potato, French beans and deep-fried parsnips was distinguished by immaculate presentation and succulent, well-flavoured meat. A delicious banana ice cream with slices of caramelised banana was enjoyed by our inspector in her solitary splendour.

Directions: On East Barnet Road, opposite Sainsbury's

63 East Barnet Road EN4 8RN
Map GtL: C4
Tel/Fax: 0181 4492974
Chef: Mr A Al-Sersy
Owners: Ms Azarfar, Mr Al-Sersy,
Cost: Fixed-price L £10.50 (2 courses)/D £16 (2 courses). ☺ H/wine £9.50
Times: Noon-last L 3pm/6.30pm-last D 11pm. Closed L Sat, all Mon
Additional: Sunday L; No children under 7; ◑ dishes
Seats: 45
Smoking: No-smoking area; No pipes & cigars
Credit cards: 🔲 🔲 🔲 🔲

Mirabelle   ❀❀❀   NEW

56 Curzon Street W1Y 8DL
Map: C3
Tel: 0171 4994636
Fax: 0171 4995449
Chefs: Lee Bunting, Charlie Rushton
Owners: Marco Pierre White,
Jimmy Lahoud
Cost: *Alc* £31, fixed-price L & D
£17.95. ☺ H/wine £16.50
Times: Noon-last L 2.30pm/6-last
D midnight. Closed 25 Dec, 1 Jan
Additional: Sunday L; Children
welcome; ❹ dishes
Seats: 110
Private dining rooms 26, 40
Smoking: No pipes; Air conditioning
Credit cards:

Impeccably conceived, Marco Pierre White's latest (at the time of going to press!) London adventure leaves nothing to chance. Wit and intelligence characterise both the surroundings and the menu, and the overall impression is more akin to a restaurant refined by years of careful adjustment, than one taking its first uncertain steps. The interior, a masterpiece of soft-hued discretion, offers just the merest hint of irony in its unfailing good taste. Just as carefully choreographed is the menu, which, consciously or otherwise, sees some MPW trademark dishes taking their place amongst the culinary classics. Thus omelette Arnold Bennett and veal escalope Holstein stand shoulder to shoulder alongside the ink risotto with calamari, and foie gras terrine with Sauternes gélée familiar from elsewhere in the empire. The overall effect is a harmonious one, dismissing frippery and rarely going a flavour to far. The same principles that gave us the quintessential combinations of fresh asparagus with sauce mousseline or Bayonne ham with celeriac remoulade are apparent throughout the MPW canon. The rub, of course, is in the execution, and the evidence of early meals is of a steady hand. Take the aforementioned foie gras terrine 'as elegant as ever', judiciously light and crusted with intense amber jelly, or the ink risotto shining like fresh cut anthracite and strewn with strips of pale calamari. Pork cheeks with ginger and spices have found particular favour, combining melting tenderness with robust flavour in a dish 'heaven sent ' according to one inspector. Desserts provide the only hint of a chink in the armour with a slightly clumsy edge creeping into the caramelised pineapple with glacé fromage blanc, and a dish of biscuit glacé with raspberry coulis that lacked a little subtlety. Packed to the gunwales already, the lunch menu is an undoubted bargain, and whilst the doorstopper of a wine list offers the opportunity to take out a second mortgage, there is plenty of good drinking to be had at the more modest end.

Directions: Nearest Tube – Green Park

Mitsukoshi   ❀❀

Dorland House
14-20 Lower Regent Street
SW1Y 4PH
Map: C3
Tel: 0171 9300317
Fax: 0171 8391167
Chef: Mr Y Motohashi
Owner: Mitsukoshi Restaurant (UK) Ltd
Cost: *Alc* £30, fixed-price L £25
Times: Noon-last L 2pm/6-last D
9.30pm. Closed Sun, Xmas, Easter
Additional: Children welcome;
❹ dishes
Seats: 90. Private dining rooms 12, 20
Smoking: No pipes & cigars; Air
conditioning
Credit cards: JCB

'Amongst the most authentic of London's Japanese restaurants' commented a well-travelled inspector of this tranquil and discreet basement operation. With soft Japanese music in the air, sand strewn floors, and extravagant flower arrangements in elegant vases, the ambience is gently seductive. Whilst the menu offers some of the more inaccessible aspects (to western tastes) of Japanese food, skilful staff – in kimonos and tails – are well used to guiding the uninitiated towards a representative and balanced selection. The set-piece classics – sashimi, tempura, sushi, yakitori and miso soup – are all present but here they are consistently distinguished by a precision and freshness that has few rivals in the capital. Set menus are a sensible option with ten-course, pre-ordered kaiseki served in private rooms on delicate chinaware or bento presented in lacquered boxes laden with deep-fried and grilled fish, simmered seasonal vegetables, pickles and fruit. Saké is an appropriate, and relatively cheap accompaniment, but be prepared for a substantial bill overall.

Directions: One minute's walk from Piccadilly Circus

Miyama Restaurant ❀

A smart Mayfair venue known for its reasonably-priced mainstream Japanese food. Set lunches are particularly good value, and could include sashimi of salmon, sole and yellowfin tuna, sushi of marinated cooked octopus, blanched shrimp and raw tuna, or beef teriyaki with bean sprouts.

Additional: Bar food; Children welcome; ❹ dishes
Smoking: Air conditioning
Credit cards: ▬ ▦ ✖ ⌐ ▦ ◐ ▣ JCB

Directions: Nearest Tube station Green Park

38 Clarges Street W1Y 7PJ
Map: C3
Tel: 0171 4992443
Fax: 0171 4931573
Chefs: Mr Miyama & Mr Miura
Owner: Mr Miyama
Cost: *Alc* £25, fixed-price L £12
(4 courses)/D £34 (6 courses). ☺
H/wine £10
Times: Last L 2.30pm/last D 10.30pm.
Closed L Sat & Sun

Momo ❀

Lively off-Regent Street hang-out. Moroccan-style interior is stunning – straight out of Casablanca. Menu offers a rough approximation of a great North African cuisine, rounding up all the usual suspects – pastilla au pigeon (a traditional sweet and spicy pie with pigeon, almonds and cinnamon), tagines and couscous, as well as grilled red mullet, and marinated, minced lamb kebabs. The loos are worth a visit.

Credit cards: ▬ ▦ ✖ ⌐ ▦ ◐ ▣ JCB

Directions: Nearest tube Piccadilly. Heddon St is opposite Disney store on Regent St

25 Heddon Street WIR 7LG
Map: D3
Tel: 0171 4342011
Fax: 0171 2870404
Chef: Abdullah El Rgrachi
Owner: Momo Mazouz
Cost: *Alc* £32, fixed-price L £12.50.
☺ H/wine £13.50
Times: Last L 2pm/last D 11.30pm.
Closed L Sat, all Sun
Additional: Children welcome;
❹ dishes
Smoking: Air conditioning

Momo ❀

Busy, neighbourhood Japanese, always friendly. The usual staples are all here – tempura, teriyaki and sushi – but so too are a number of more adventurous Japanese dishes. Try deep-fried shell crab with ponzu sauce, tender skewers of yakitori, or chawan mushi – steamed egg custard served in small cups.

Additional: Children welcome; ❹ dishes
Credit cards: ▬ ▦ ▦ ▣ JCB

Directions: Opposite North Ealing Tube station

14 Queens Parade
W5 3HU
Map GtL: B3
Tel/Fax: 0181 9970206
Chef/Owner: Toyosaku Asari
Cost: *Alc* £25, fixed-price L from
£7.20 (2 courses)/D from £23.50
(5 courses). ☺ H/wine £9
Times: Last L 2.30pm/last D 10pm.
Closed Sun, 1 wk Aug, 1 wk after
Xmas

Monkey's ❀❀

In keeping with its name, anthropomorphic monkeys feature in the pictures and prints that decorate the twin cosy dining rooms of this long established restaurant on Chelsea Green. Staff are pleasant and polite but Tom Benham, in chef's jacket taking orders and generally dispensing bonhomie, is the presence around which the restaurant revolves. Two fixed-price menus (you can mix-and-match) changes only to accommodate a good range of game in season so you can be sure of finding Tom's excellent foie gras terrine (served in generous slabs and available for home dinner parties), home-potted shrimps, hot foie gras salad and duck confit salad among the starters, and such mains as grilled sea bass, sautéed calves' kidneys with Madeira and mustard, and roast rack of lamb diablé – ours was beautifully tender and cooked exactly as ordered. Familiar endings include crème brûlée, chocolate mousse and a good tart au citron. Well-chosen, mainly French, wines include a decent selection of half-bottles

1 Cale Street Chelsea Green
SW3 3QT
Map: B1
Tel: 0171 3524711
Chef: Tom Benham
Owner: Mr. & Mrs. T. Benham
Times: 12.30pm-last L
2.30pm/7.30pm-last D 11pm.
Closed D Sun, Xmas, Easter,
3 wks Aug
Additional: Sunday L;
Children welcome.
Seats: 40
Smoking: No pipes in dining room;
Air-conditioning
Credit cards: ▬ ▦ ✖ ⌐

Directions: Corner of Cale St &
Markhay St, 5 mins from Sloane Square

Mon Plaisir

There's no modern minimalism about this long-established, very French restaurant in the heart of Covent Garden. Sit at tightly-spaced tables in one of a number of cosy, picture-lined rooms to enjoy classic bourgeois cooking: cassolette d' escargots à l'ail, scallops meunière, entrecôte grillée allumettes, roast chicken chasseur, tarte maison du jour.

Additional: Children welcome; ❸ dishes
Smoking: Air conditioning
Credit cards: 💳 💳 💳 💳 💳 💳 💳 JCB

Directions: Off Seven Dials. Nearest Tubes – Covent Garden, Leicester Square

21 Monmouth Street, WC2
Map: D4
Tel: 0171 8367243/2403757
Fax: 0171 2404774
Chef: Frédéric Meurlet
Owner: Alain Lhermitte
Cost: *Alc* £35, fixed-price L £14.95/D £19.95. ☺ H/wine £9
Times: Last L 2.15pm/last D 11.15pm. Closed L Sat, Sun, 10 days Xmas, Bhs

Monsieur Max

A quirky bistro serving simple, honest French fare with a few frills. Max Renzland has a loyal following from his Fulham days, and the restaurant is always bustling. The decor is simple, with closely packed cafeteria-style tables and chairs, and the overall feel is very French. There is a keenly-priced, short lunch menu which is replaced at night by a fuller, meatier, more enticing *carte*. Typical starters include rillette of pork and duck with pear chutney, Cantabrian anchovies with shallots and échiré butter, and salad lyonnaise with smoked herring, egg and crisp romaine lettuce. A winter meal started with roast goats' cheese with tabouleh, green beans and red pepper, followed by crisply roasted mullet with parsley tagliatelle and thyme beurre blanc. The short wine list is fun and recherché, but most people seem to bring their own – there's a £5 corkage.

Directions: On E side of Bushy Park

133 High Street
Hampton Hill TW12 1NJ
Map: C2
Tel: 0181 9795546
Fax: 0181 9793747
Chefs: Alex Bentley, Morgan Meunier
Owner: Max Renzland
Cost: Fixed-price L £14/D £19.50. ☺ H/wine £12.50
Times: Noon-2.30pm (3pm wknds)/7-10.30pm (11pm wknds). Closed L Sat, 25, 26 Dec
Additional: Sunday L; Children welcome; ❸ dishes
Seats: 90. Private dining room 20
Smoking: No pipes & cigars; Air conditioning
Credit cards: 💳 💳 💳 💳 💳 💳

The Montcalm-Hotel Nikko London

Great Cumberland Place W1A 2LF
Map: B4
Tel: 0171 4024288
Fax: 0171 7249180
Chef: Peter Robinson
Cost: *Alc* £22.50, fixed-price L £18.50 (2 courses)/D £22.50. ☺ H/wine £12

Old-fashioned courtesy and style remain the hallmarks of this dignified Georgian hotel. Relax in the airy surroundings of the Crescent restaurant and let the professional staff take care of you. Our inspector did just that, and enjoyed a late spring meal of goats' cheese and pumpkin tart with red onion marmalade, followed by roast fillet of sea bass with saffron and tarragon, accompanied by shelled broad beans. Other dishes from the modern English menu might include roast pumpkin and sweet pimento soup with crème fraîche and bacon, rare tuna with kibun, seaweed and noodle salad, and snails with rocket and garlic sauce. Light snacks are served all day (between 11am and 11pm) and include crispy rolls stuffed with Brie and Parma ham, avocado, crab and mozzarella toasted muffins, and minute steak with rocket and horseradish. For those staying the night, the Japanese breakfast menu is a must.

Directions: 2 blocks N of Marble Arch

Times: 12.30-last L 2.30pm/6.30-last D 10.30pm. Closed L Sat, all Sun, L Bh Mon
Additional: Bar food; Children welcome; dishes
Seats: 65. Private dining room 16-60
Smoking: No-smoking area; No pipes & cigars; Air conditioning
Accommodation: 120 en suite
Credit cards: ▆ ▆ ▆ ▆ ▆ JCB

Moro ❀❀

'Understated in decor' writes one of the proprietors, an understatement in itself for a restaurant of bare surfaces, bare tables set closely together, ceiling fans, and a long bar running the length of the room with mirrors behind it angled so that those seated at table can see who's propping it up. The espresso machine hisses, staff bustle around, conversation hums and the place buzzes. 'Moro' means 'Moor', and the style derives from the meeting-point of Spain, North Africa and the Middle East. Sit at the bar, have some tapas and ask advice about which sherry goes with them. Sit at a table for a full meal, choose a bottle from the Mediterranean-based list (plenty to choose from by the glass too) and order: marinated pork loin with deep-fried green peppers – 'wonderful, deep-flavoured, excellent' enthused an inspector – then perhaps wood-roasted cod with tahini sauce, caramelised onions and broad bean pilaff, all 'fresh, full of flavour'. Cinnamon-spiked chunky almond and orange torte makes a fitting dessert. Otherwise, there may be salt-cod and potato soup, roast duck with tabouleh, pomegranate and walnut sauce, and chocolate and apricot tart. Good bread with olive oil, excellent espresso, and helpful, efficient staff all contribute to the enjoyment.

Directions: Exmouth Market is on the corner of Rosebery Avenue and Farringdon Road.

34-36 Exmouth Market EC1R 4QE
Map: E5
Tel: 0171 8338336
Fax: 0171 8339338
Chefs: Samuel Clark, Samantha Clark, Jake Hodges
Owners: Samuel Clark, Samantha Clark, Jake Hodges, Mark Sainsbury
Cost: Alc £24. ☺ H/wine £9.50
Times: 12.30-last L 2.30pm/7-last D 10.30pm. Closed Sat, Sun, Xmas, Bhs
Additional: Bar food; Children welcome; 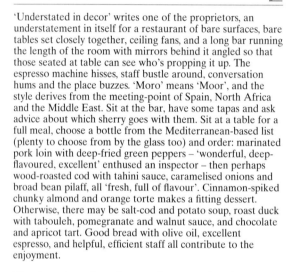 dishes
Seats: 80 (+12 outside)
Smoking: No pipes & cigars; Air conditioning
Credit cards: ▆ ▆ ▆ ▆

Moshi Moshi Sushi ❀

Conveyor belt sushi is great fun, and the quality is sound at this highly unusual Japanese sushi bar offering decent, great-value meals at Liverpool Street station. Miso soup and drinks are served by tee-shirted staff, otherwise help yourself to colour-coded plates – the amount you accumulate dictates how much you pay. Hard to find.

Additional: Bar food L; No children under 5; dishes
Smoking: No-smoking area
Credit cards: ▆ ▆ ▆ ▆

Directions: Inside Liverpool St Station (upper walkway level)

Unit 24 Liverpool Street Station EC2M 7QH
Map: G4
Tel: 0171 3691160
Fax: 0171 2481807
Chefs: Ravi Shiveendran, Sui Hong
Owner: Caroline Bennett
Cost: ☺ H/wine £8.80
Times: L only, 11.30am-3pm. Closed Sat, Sun, Bhs

The Mountbatten ❀

See Where London Meets Section page 153

MPW ❀❀

A bright, light crescent-shaped room with ash and pine floors and cream-painted walls is the decor at this easterly outpost of Marco Pierre White's empire. The attractively priced set-dinner menus may entice people who otherwise would never visit Canary Wharf: three choices at each stage, among them perhaps a potage of mussels and clams, brochette of chicken and Alsace bacon, and lemon croustillant. At virtually the same price as the whole set menu, that brochette crops up again on the main *carte*, where 'modern French' makes a change from 'modern British'. Here we find terrine of foie gras and duck, Bayonne ham with salade remoulade and truffle oil, and baked sea scallop à la croque. A main course of braised beef and dumplings is dubbed bourguignonne, and calves' liver comes à l'anglaise; on the other hand, honey-roast parsnips and braised red cabbage accompany plainly roasted venison. Bread-and-butter pudding is made with – what else? – brioche. Around half-a-dozen wines are sold by the glass; executives on expenses should look at the back of the list for fine vintages running into three-figure prices.

Directions: Docklands Railway; main shopping mall of Canary Wharf

Second Floor Cabot Place
East Canary Wharf E14 4QT
Map GtL: E3
Tel: 0171 5130513
Fax: 0171 5130557
Chef: Robert Arnott
Owners: Jimmy Lahoud,
Marco Pierre White
Cost: *Alc* £28, fixed-price D £12.95
(2 courses). ☺ H/wine £10
Times: Noon-2.30pm/5.30-9pm.
Closed Sat, Sun, 25-26 Dec
Additional: Children welcome;
❹ dishes
Seats: 150. Private dining room 30
Smoking: No pipes; Air conditioning
Credit cards: 🔲 🔲 🔲 🔲 🔲 🔲 🔲

Mulligan's of Mayfair ❀

A rogue's gallery of famous Irish faces lines the walls of this sophisticated bar and restaurant situated amongst the antique shops and jewellers of a quiet Mayfair street. The food is Irish with some contemporary twists and includes several ways with oysters, black and white puddings, Donegal salmon and Wicklow lamb with a whiskey sauce.

Credit cards: 🔲 🔲 🔲 🔲 🔲 🔲 🔲 JCB

Directions: Cork Street is between Burlington Gardens and Clifford Street.

13-14 Cork Street W1X 1PF
Map: C3
Tel: 0171 4091370
Fax: 0171 4092732
Chef: Jason Whomersley
Owner: Balls Brothers of London
Cost: *Alc* £20, fixed-price L £13.50
(2 courses). ☺ H/wine £10
Times: Last L 3pm/last D 9.45pm.
Closed L Sat, all Sun, Bhs
Additional: Bar food; ❹ dishes
Smoking: Air conditioning

Museum Street Café ❀❀

A clean-cut, plain interior, with closely spaced unclothed tables, offers views of St George's church through the skylight, and of the kitchen, open to the rear of the restaurant. The lunchtime menu is brief and concisely described, and vegetarian, except for occasional fish dishes such as smoked salmon and dill tart. It is mostly structured around salads, risottos, tarts and frittata – frittata with spinach, sweet potato, walnuts and roasted red onions, or salad with taleggio and two bruschetta, and saffron risotto with asparagus and grilled courgettes. Spinach and Parmesan soup was beautifully balanced, lifted by a generous seasoning of nutmeg, and a tomato, aubergine and basil tart was freshly made. A chargrilled salmon with red wine and shallot butter arrived a bit dried out on top, but it did have a particularly moreish sauce. Valrhona chocolate cake has all the flavour you might expect; otherwise there's home-made caramel ice cream or cheeses from Neal's Yard Dairy.

Directions: Off Bloomsbury Way, near British Museum, between Tottenham Court Road

47 Museum Street WC1A 1LY
Map: D4
Tel/Fax: 0171 4053211
Chefs/Owners: Gail Koerber,
Mark Nathan
Cost: *Alc* £16. H/wine £9.50
Times: L only, Noon-last L 3pm.
Closed Xmas & Easter
Additional: Children welcome;
❹ dishes.
Seats: 40
Smoking: No smoking restaurant
Credit cards: 🔲 🔲 🔲 🔲 🔲 🔲

Neal Street Restaurant

Dominated by a magnificent Edouardo Paolozzi wood carving, the interior here has changed little since it opened as Sir Terence Conran's first restaurant venture 26 years ago. It is though Antonio Carluccio's presence that is most strongly felt, with the cherubic proprietor's dual passions signalled in the lavish basket of wild mushrooms that grace the entrance, and the rack of carved walking-sticks that symbolise his love of the countryside. Not surprising then to find the menu built solidly on fungal foundations; mycological pilgrims will find it hard to resist the mixed fungi of the day – simply sautéed with garlic butter and parsley – but wild mushroom soup and warm mushroom and bacon salad offer other options amongst the starters. Foragers might be further inspired by nettle gnocchi with Dolcelatte – excellent comfort food – or tagliolini with wild herb sauce. Desserts are strong and have included a perfectly executed pannacotta with plum sauce.

26 Neal Street WC2H 9PS
Map: D4
Tel: 0171 8368368
Fax: 0171 2403964
Chef: Nick Melmoth-Coombs
Owner: Antonio Carluccio
Cost: *Alc* £40, fixed-price L £27. H/wine £11
Times: 12.30-last L 2.30pm/6-last D 11pm. Closed Sun, 24 Dec-1 Jan, Bhs
Additional: ❁ dishes
Seats: 65. Private dining room 24
Smoking: Air conditioning
Credit cards: ▆▆ ▆▆ ▆▆ ▆ ▆▆ ▆ ▆ JCB

Directions: 2 minutes walk from Covent Garden Tube

New World

'A real Chinese gastrodome' enthused our inspector on a first visit to this triple-floored, 600 seater Chinatown restaurant. Lucky red and gold abounds in decoration drawn from the time of the Empress Dowager and, with waitresses parading the floor with steaming carts piled high with delicacies, the atmosphere for dim sum is quite electric. You'll need to get there early on a Sunday lunch as tables are hard to come by after midday and they open the doors at 11am. A myriad of tiny delights are on offer from 'superior' braised chicken feet with chilli, through cha siu bao (steamed bread with tangy pork), shiu mei (steamed dumplings with shrimp) to perfectly formed parcels of sticky rice in lotus leaves. Other morsels include mini-spring rolls, spare ribs and a host of other titbits, marked up as you go. Chinese tea is the best accompaniment, and a range of sticky desserts, including delicate custard tarts, rise above the merely token.

1 Gerrard Place W1
Map: D3
Tel: 0171 4342508
Fax: 0171 2873994
Chef: Lap Diep
Owners: Edward Liu, Tong Ng
Cost: *Alc* £8.50, fixed-price L & D £11.50. ☺ H/wine £7.50
Times: Open all day, 11.30am-11.30pm. Closed 25-26 Dec
Additional: Sunday L; Children welcome; ❁ dishes
Seats: 650. Private dining room 100
Smoking: Air conditioning
Credit cards: ▆▆ ▆▆ ▆▆ ▆ ▆▆ ▆ ▆ JCB

Directions: In Chinatown, just south of Shaftesbury Avenue

Nico Central

Mirrors and Picasso paintings lend a stylish air to this well-established restaurant, now part of a mini-chain that includes Manchester and Brussels. Anything bearing the Nico name has to have a French orientation and good bourgeois dishes include fish soup with croûtons, braised shin of veal with Madeira sauce, and rib-eye of beef with shallots confit and French beans. Lighter ones take in crab ravioli, bok choi, spring onions and chive velouté, and roasted fillet of salmon with pressed spiced vegetables. It is worth waiting the extra 15 minutes for chocolate blinis with caramelised apple nougat glace.

Credit cards: ▆▆ ▆▆ ▆▆ ▆ ▆▆ ▆ ▆ JCB

Directions: Oxford St end of Portland St. 5 mins walk from Oxford Circus Tube

35 Great Portland Street W1N 5DD
Map: C4
Tel: 0171 4368846
Fax: 0171 4363455
Chef: Jean-Philippe Patruno
Owner: The Restaurant Partnership
Cost: Fixed-price L £25/D £27. H/wine £13
Times: Noon-last L 2pm/7-last D 11pm. Closed L Sat, all Sun, 5 days Xmas, Bhs
Additional: No children under 10; ❁ dishes
Seats: 60. Private dining room 12
Smoking: No pipes & cigars; Air conditioning

Nicole's

As stylish as one might expect, the basement restaurant of Nicole Farhi's designer store is as precisely tailored to the

158 New Bond Street W1 9PA
Map: D4
Tel: 0171 4998408
Fax: 0171 4090381

clientele as the haute couture in the shop above. Cream walls, natural wood and cool leather provide the elegant backdrop and importantly the cooking includes figure friendliness amongst its many merits. Equally appropriate is the attention to detail displayed in dishes such as a pancake of smoked fish with crème fraîche, potato sticks and a 'sensational' green leaf salad dressed with lemon and capers. Plenty of evidence of an earthier approach though, with a duck confit with a mash of white bean sauce and roasted clementines just one example of more rustic fare on offer. Delicate balances of textures and flavours are the trademark throughout, nowhere more so than in a rhubarb and Amaretti sponge with frozen yoghurt that provided just the right contrast between the sweet and the sharp.

Directions: Nearest tube – Green Park or Bond St

Chef: Annie Wayte
Owner: Stephen Marks
Cost: Alc £35. ☺ H/wine £10.95
Times: Noon-last L 3.30pm (Sat 4pm)/6.30-last D 10.45pm.
Closed D Sat, all Sun, Bhs
Additional: Bar food L; Children welcome; ❸ dishes
Seats: 70
Smoking: No pipes & cigars; Air conditioning
Credit cards: ▄▄ ▄▄ ▄▄ ▄▄ ▄▄ ▄▄ ▄▄ JCB

Nobu ❀❀

'Is this the coolest place in London?' wondered our inspector, calculating that the combination of 'A-list' personalities, Phillipe Starck-like interior and 'damn good cooking' add up to a pretty irresistible package. Maybe so, with New York-style service and spiced-up Japanese cooking, Nobuyuki Matsuhisa brings the full range of his pan-American experience (restaurants in the USA, travels in South America) to bear on the first floor of The Metropolitan Hotel. Fusion it may be, but it's the Japanese that wins out in the end with the typical notes of the cuisine chiming throughout a June inspection meal. The set menu 'Omakase' eases the burden of decision making and is likely to reward throughout six or seven dishes of razor sharp clarity, that might include a sparkling sashimi salad with Matsuhisa soy sauce dressing and 'spectacularly fresh' black cod in miso. Desserts cater for western habits and are often strikingly successful, with both a set cream with coconut and chilli pineapple and a 'superb' sesame ice cream winning plaudits.

Directions: Nearest Tubes – Hyde Park/Green Park

Metropolitan Hotel 19 Old Park Lane W1Y 4LB
Map: C3
Tel: 0171 4474747
Fax: 0171 4474749
Chefs: Nobuyuki Matsuhisa, Mark Edwards
Owners: Nobuyuki Matsuhisa, Robert de Niro, Como Holdings
Cost: Fixed-price L £22.50 (4 courses)/D £60 (5 courses). H/wine £14.50
Times: Noon-last L 2.15pm/6-last D 10.15pm. Closed L Sat & Sun
Additional: Sushi bar; Children welcome; ❸ dishes
Seats: 150. Private dining room
Smoking: No-smoking area; Air conditioning
Accommodation: 155 en suite
Credit cards: ▄▄ ▄▄ ▄▄ ▄▄ ▄▄ ▄▄ ▄▄ JCB

Novelli EC1 ❀

A simple, modern restaurant run by a team of cosmopolitan young staff. Food arrives briskly. An early summer meal might take in steamed wild mushroom gâteau with crêpes, porcini oil and Parmesan crackling, spiced honey-glazed knuckle of lamb with chickpea salsa, and caramelised rice pudding with fresh rhubarb compote.

Clerkenwell Green EC1 0DU
Map: F5
Tel: 0171 2516606
Fax: 0171 4901083
Chefs: Jean Christophe Novelli, Igor Timchishin
Owner: Jean Christophe Novelli
Cost: Alc £25
Times: Last L 3.30pm/last D 11.15pm (midnight on Sat). Closed L Sat, all Sun
Additional: Children welcome; ❸ dishes
Credit cards: ▄▄ ▄▄ ▄▄ ▄▄ ▄▄ ▄▄

Novelli W8 ❀❀

Fronted by a tiny patio, this outpost of the Jean-Christophe Novelli empire (see Maison Novelli) is quite small so booking is advisable. From a good-length menu, the starters sampled at our last meal included a robust pressed cassoulet terrine (a Novelli signature dish), well-flavoured aubergine soup (given an extra dimension by the ratatouille and red mullet garnish), and a salad of mixed tongues with beetroot marmalade and pancetta. Main courses showed equally good skills and imagination: blanquette of salmon layered with Parmesan; sea bass with cep powder, mushroom froth and port sauce; and poached rabbit leg stuffed with polenta. From the desserts, which come with lots of sugar 'springs' and chocolate decoration, we tried a good apple tart with accompanying sorbet, tiramisu, and a chocolate plate 'Liz McGrath' that included a superb dark chocolate pudding filled with melting fondant. Attentive, efficient service.

Directions: Nearest Tube – Notting Hill Gate

122 Palace Gardens Terrace
W8 4RT
Map GtL: C3
Tel: 0171 2294024
Fax: 0171 2431826
Chefs: Jean-Christophe Novelli, Mike Bird
Owner: Jean-Christophe Novelli
Cost: *Alc* £35. ☺ H/wine £11.50
Times: Noon-3pm (Sun 12.30-3.30pm)/6-10.30pm (Sun 7.30pm). Closed L Mon
Additional: Children welcome; ❀ dishes
Seats: 60
Smoking: Air conditioning
Credit cards: ▬ ▬ ▭ ▭ ▬ ▭

Oak Lodge Hotel ❀

*See **Where London Meets Section** page 153*

Oceana ❀❀

Bright basement restaurant where menu descriptions are fashionably minimalist and concepts are modern middle-of-the-road: roast quail, grilled ceps and aubergine purée; roast wild salmon and lobster mash; pan-fried calves' liver, herb dauphinoise and black pudding; braised shank of pork with Puy lentils. However, our inspection got off to a poor start with stale-tasting bread and a tired, though pretty-looking, first course of bouillabaisse terrine made with John Dory, scallops and bass with leeks wrapped in a red pepper jacket with gazpacho and rouille. More successful was breast of duck with beetroot and onion marmalade with a reduced red wine jus. Sorbets and ice cream feature in most of the desserts; look out for saffron poached pear, orange and cardamom ice cream and rhubarb tart, with vanilla ice cream and a 'very palatable' stylish lemon tart with lime sorbet.

Directions: Nearest Tube – Bond Street. Opposite St Christopher's Place

Jason Court 76 Wigmore Street
W1M 6BE
Map: C3
Tel: 0171 2242992
Fax: 0171 4861216
Chef: Pierre Khodja
Owners: Tony Kitous, Pierre Khodja
Cost: *Alc* £24, fixed-price L & pre theatre D £12.50 (2 courses). ☺ H/wine £9.70
Times: Noon-last L 3pm/6-last D 11.15pm. Closed L Sat, all Sun
Additional: Bar food L; Children welcome; ❀ dishes
Seats: 85. Private room 8-18
Smoking: No-smoking area; Air conditioning
Credit cards: ▬ ▬ ▭ ▭ ▬ ▭ ▭ JCB

O'Conor Don-Ard-Ri Dining Room ❀

A taste of the Emerald Isle in the heart of the West End. Simple Irish dishes are the order of the day, with beef and Guinness casserole and hot buttered oysters still popular. A winter meal could start with butternut squash and thyme soup, followed by traditional Irish lamb stew with pearl barley.

Additional: Bar food; Children welcome; ❀ dishes
Credit cards: ▬ ▬ ▭ ▭ ▬ ▭

Directions: Nearest Tube – Bond Street

88 Marylebone Lane W1M 5FJ
Map: C3
Tel: 0171 9359311
Fax: 0171 4866706
Chef: John Gallagher
Owners: The O'Callaghan Family
Cost: *Alc* £19, fixed-price L&D £19. ☺ H/wine £9.75.
Times: Last L 2.30pm/last D 10.30pm. Closed L Sat, Sun, Bhs, 25 Dec, Good Friday

L'Odéon   ❀❀❀

65 Regent Street W1R 7HH
Map: C3
Tel: 0171 2871400
Fax: 0171 2871300
Chef: Anthony Demetre
Owners: Pierre & Kathleen Condou
Cost: Alc £30, fixed-price L/D £18. ☺
H/wine £14.
Times: Noon-last L 2.30pm/5.30pm-
last D 11.30pm. Closed Bhs
Additional: Bar food; Sunday L;
Children welcome; ♨ dishes
Seats: 220. Private dining room 20
Smoking: No-smoking area;
No pipes & cigars; Air conditioning
Credit cards: 🔲 🔲 🔲 🔲 🔲 🔲 🔲 JCB

Chic and cosmopolitan, the best seats in the house have fabulous views over Regent Street, where the hubbub of daily life takes its course. The urbanely-designed *carte* is spare in its descriptions, giving little hint of the technical input behind the scenes, as in the best stage tradition, although some of the staff need to learn their lines a little better when it comes to content. Anthony Demetre draws on a wide range of European ideas, and gives them a spin, tuna carpaccio with seaweed salad and tahini dressing, for example, or rabbit leg saltimbocca with grilled vegetables and aged Balsamic vinegar. A terrine of foie gras, pear and spices with toasted brioche stood out for texture, flavour, seasoning and skill of preparation, although a walnut dressing was too low-key to make much impact on a dish that didn't need it anyway. Out of a dozen main courses, ranging from monkfish osso buco with mussels, tomato and saffron to pot-au-feu of beef with sauce verte, our inspector chose roast breast and confit of duck with honey and Szechuan pepper – a good choice, pink, tender and full of flavour – served with braised fennel and parsnip purée. Chocolate tart – rich, glossy – was a diet-wrecker. The wine list is colour orientated and reasonably priced, although is perhaps more bistro than refined restaurant in pitch. The espresso coffee is good, but you have to pay extra for the chocolates.
Signature dishes: Tuna tartare with lime pickled ginger and sesame seed tuile; gazpacho with lobster and basil guacamole; roast veal chop, sweetcorn and girolle risotto, jus with marjoram; braised pork knuckle on boulangère potatoes, apple sauce

Directions: Piccadilly Circus, entrance in Air Street, opposite Café Royal

Odettes   ❀❀

A really charming Primrose Hill restaurant that attracts a strong loyal following. Gilt mirrors of all shapes and sizes cover the walls of the dining room, while the downstairs wine bar is more colonial in style. The menu provides half-a-dozen choices at each turn, and it's instantly recognisable that chef David Kennedy isn't afraid to take risks. His modern English cooking translates into dishes such as monkfish wrapped in Parma ham, served on a bed of roasted red peppers, and roast neck of lamb with soft polenta and spring greens. One winter meal began with an accomplished selection of white, brown

130 Regents Park Road NW1 8XL
Map: C4
Tel: 0171 5865486/8766
Fax: 0171 5862575
Chef: David Kennedy
Owner: Simone Green
Cost: Alc £25, fixed-price L £10.
H/wine £10.95
Times: 12.30-2.30pm/7-11pm. Closed
(rest) L Sat , all Sun, 1 wk Xmas, Bhs
Additional: Wine bar; Sunday L;
Children welcome; ♨ dishes

Odettes

Seats: 60. Private dining rooms 8, 30
Smoking: No pipes & cigars;
Air conditioning
Credit cards:

and olive loaves, the latter sumptuously veined with rich olive purée. Then foie gras terrine with tarragon jelly and toasted brioche was followed by fresh grilled sea bass, served with tossed watercress and sautéed kale. The meal finished with a delicious chocolate tart that had great texture and a deep, luxurious flavour.

Directions: By Primrose Hill. Nearest Tube – Chalk Farm

Odin's Restaurant

The restaurant bears all the hallmarks of other restaurants in the Michael Caine/Richard Shepherd group. The cooking is sound, ingredients are fresh and dishes prepared well. Efficient service is by helpful and attentive staff. A purée of well-flavoured mushrooms filled the excellent, light brioche which started our meal. The standard was maintained with nicely roasted guinea fowl with wild rice and bacon, the latter two elements providing good extra flavour. Typical dishes include supreme of salmon with roast fennel and lemon, navarin of lamb with spring vegetables, and roast pork with prune and brandy sauce. But there are also some interesting ideas in grilled black bream with a juniper and rock salt crust, and hot smoked eel with potato and spring onion salad. Homage to the late Peter Langan's mother comes in the form of Mrs Langan's chocolate pudding. The filter coffee needs to be improved.

Directions: At Marylebone High Street end of Devonshire Street. Nearest Tube – Baker Street

27 Devonshire Street W1N 1RJ
Map: C4
Tel: 0171 9357296
Fax: 0171 4938309
Chef: Shawn Butcher
Owners: Richard Shepherd &
Michael Caine
Cost: Fixed-price L £23.95 (2
courses)/D £25.95. H/wine £11
Times: 12.30-2.30pm/6.30-11pm.
Closed Sat, Sun, Bhs
Additional: Children welcome;
❸ dishes
Seats: 64
Smoking: Air conditioning
Credit cards: ▨▨ ▨ ▨ ▨ ▨ ▨ JCB

Olivo ❀

Decorated in electric blue and bright yellow, reminiscent of sea and sand, this ever-busy little place near Victoria Station offers Mediterranean cooking with a Sardinian influence. Look out for grey mullet roe and marinated swordfish carpaccio; otherwise there's clam and couscous soup, and rabbit with polenta and roasted raddichio.

Additional: Children welcome; ❸ dishes
Smoking: No pipes & cigars; Air conditioning
Credit cards: ▨▨ ▨ ▨ ▨ ▨ JCB

Directions: From Buckingham Palace Road, opposite Victoria Station, turn into Eccleston Street. Olivo is on L

21 Eccleston Street SW1W 9LW
Map: C3
Tel: 0171 7302505
Fax: 0171 8248190
Chefs: Marco Mellis, Giuseppe Sanna
Owners: Mauro Sanna, Jean-Louis
Journade
Cost: Alc £22, fixed-price L £16.
H/wine £10
Times: Last L 2.30pm/last D 11pm.
Closed L Sat & Sun, Bhs

One Lawn Terrace

1 Lawn Terrace SE3 9LJ
Map GtL: D3
Tel: 0181 3551110
Fax: 0181 3550111
Chef: Sanjay Owivedi
Owners: Nick Hall, Annie Gibson-Hall
Cost: *Alc* £26, fixed price L £16.50/D
£17.50 (Mon-Thu 6-7.30pm). ☺
H/wine £12.95
Times: Last L 2.15pm/last D 10.30pm.
Closed L Sat & Mon, 25-26 Dec,
1 Jan
Additional: Sunday L; Children
welcome; ☙ dishes
Smoking: No pipes & cigars;
Air conditioning
Credit cards: 🟥 🟥 🟥 🟥 🟥 🟥 JCB

Since opening, One Lawn Terrace has hit the ground running.
It's an unusual place, very modern with open stirs up to the
first-floor restaurant; the ground floor is a reception area with
contemporary art work for sale. Cool notes of vanilla and
natural wood outline the minimalist thinking behind the
design, and space, light, and clean lines dominate. The menu is
intriguing. The kitchen is prepared to experiment and is not
afraid of flavour. Oven-baked red pepper and aubergine soup
had tremendous depth, for example, and Thai-spiced crab and
prawn risotto with sweet soy sauce was all the confident spicing
and really hard-hitting flavours that this delicate dish needed.
Highlight of the main courses was a beautifully balanced
teriyaki marinated salmon with udon noodles, enoki
mushrooms and aubergine pickle. If it's on the menu, go for
the blood orange and strawberry trifle. Although some things
at our test meal were a bit hit-and-miss, on the whole this is
up-beat cooking in safe hands. We can't stress enough how
excellent and helpful we found the staff.

Directions: Turn R out of Blackheath BR station, then 2nd
turning on R. Less than 1 min walk from station.

L'Oranger

5 St James's Street SW1A 1EF
Map: C3
Tel: 0171 8393774
Fax: 0171 8394330
Chef: Marcus Wareing
Owner: A-Z Restaurants
Cost: Fixed-price L £23.50/D £33.50.
H/wine £15
Times: Noon-last L 3pm/6pm-last
D 11pm. Closed L Sun
Additional: Children welcome;
☙ dishes
Seats: 65. Private dining room 20
Smoking: No pipes & cigars;
Air conditioning
Credit cards: 🟥 🟥 🟥 🟥 🟥 🟥 🟥

*As we went to press Marcus Wareing left L'Oranger and the
restaurant was temporarily closed.*
   The subtle but warm colours of the interior are enhanced by
natural light streaming through a skylight. On a warm summer

evening a small number of tables are set outside in the adjacent courtyard, but otherwise the feel of the sun comes through the cooking. The modern French *carte* may kick off with lentil soup with truffles, fine slices of marinated tuna rolled in crushed black pepper and served with white radish and salad, or a pressed terrine of corn-fed chicken, pheasant and ox tongue with a game jus vinaigrette. Fish dominates: pavé of cod seasoned with curry, sautéed courgettes and a creamed curry sauce; roast salmon with sautéed aubergines, cos lettuce, vinaigrette of clams and pepper confit. Flavours can be hit-or-miss, powerful, pungent in a crab bisque perfumed with lemongrass, a little adrift on a sampled grilled fillet of brill with sauce vierge. Meaty main courses might include pan-fried loin of pork and Toulouse sausage with a piquant and mustard grain sauce, or roast rump of lamb, gratin of turnips, baby onions and rosemary jus. In true French style there are a few salad starters - chicory with hazelnut oil dressing, chives and tomatoes, and asparagus with sliced fennel, new potatoes and grain mustard dressing - but that's about it. Desserts are classic - warm apple tart with vanilla ice cream and caramel sauce, or pistachio parfait with dark chocolate sorbet. Cheeses are French. A good choice of Bagatelle bread includes olive, sun-dried tomato, onion, walnut and wholemeal. Staff serve the sophisticated clientele with great skill, dexterity and unflagging courtesy

Directions: Nearest Tube – Green Park. St James's Street is accessible by car via Pall Mall

The Orerry ✿✿✿

An Orrery, we understand, is a mechanical model of the solar system, and sure enough the etched glass screen at the far end of the restaurant depicts the Earth in relation to the sun and other planets. This latest satellite in the Conran universe may not be on the same gastrodomic scale as some of its peers, but with arched windows, a length of the room roof lit, and a sweeping curved ceiling, the pedigree of the interior design is unmistakable. With chef Chris Galvin having migrated from Mezzo, the cooking too displays many of the family characteristics. Drawn predominantly from a classic French and Italian palette, the sturdy flavours and carefully selected produce add up to a menu studded with enticing combinations: smoked mullet escabeche with vegetables à la Grecque, 'fantastically rich' duck confit salad with honey and grain mustard dressing, calves' sweetbreads wrapped in Bayonne ham with a truffle jus, to name but three. Sophistication and 'technical excellence' were also apparent in main courses of perfectly timed roast sea bass served on creamed salsify with a glossy sauternes jus, and sweet seared scallops on a garlic mash with a rich, velvety chive beurre blanc. Desserts are well up to the mark with offerings such as 'exquisite' plump roast figs with mascarpone ice cream, and a tarte Tatin with crème fraîche anglaise that was the best our inspector had tasted in many a moon. Service is refreshingly amicable and courteous without seeming stuffy.

Directions: Nearest Tubes – Baker Street, Regents Park

55-57 Marylebone
High Street W1M 3AE

Map: B4
Tel: 0171 6168000
Fax: 0171 6168080
Chef: Chris Galvin
Owners: Conran Restaurants Ltd
Cost: *Alc* £35, fixed-price L £26.50.
H/wine £13
Times: Noon-last L 2.30pm/7-last
D 11pm. Closed some Bhs
Additional: Bar food; Sunday L;
Children welcome; ♦ dishes
Seats: 80
Credit cards: ▭ ▭ C ▭ D JCB

Orsino

Understated on the outside, within it is all bright and spacious with terracotta walls. Eat Tuscan soup, roast sea bass with leeks, roast peppers and capers, or large pasta shells filled with leek, Ricotta with cream and Fontina. Must try the pizza specialities that taste as if air-lifted straight from Italy.

Additional: Children welcome; 🌣 dishes
Smoking: No-smoking area; Air conditioning
Credit cards: ▆ ▆ ▆ ▆ ▆

Directions: Nearest Tube – Holland Park

119 Portland Road W11 4LN
Map GtL: C3
Tel: 0171 2213299
Fax: 0171 2299414
Chef: Anne Kettle
Owners: Orsino Restaurants Ltd
Cost: *Alc* £30, fixed-price L £15.50.
☺ H/wine £11.50
Times: Noon- last D 11.15pm.
Closed 24-25 Dec

Orso Restaurant

Look for a small doorway with the name Orso above (it's easy to miss) to find this lively basement restaurant on the edge of Covent Garden. Randomly placed tables and relaxed, chatty staff all help to create a cheerfully informal atmosphere. A big basket of delicious focaccia and ciabatta bread with virgin olive oil for dipping gets things started while choosing from a menu that ranges from pasta and pizzas to the likes of slow-roasted duck with pine nuts and herbed potatoes. Our last meal included a good risotto with wild clams, mussels, rock shrimp and courgettes, well-sauced saddle of hare with roasted black figs and a nicely balanced dish of roast sea bass with artichokes, shallots and potato tart. There's an interesting Italian wine list with over half of the bottles at less than £20. Also note the good value fixed-price Sunday brunch and pre-theatre menus.

Directions: 1 block in from The Strand, 2 blocks down from Royal Opera House

27 Wellington Street WC2E 7DA
Map: D3
Tel: 0171 2405269
Fax: 0171 4972148
Chef: Martin Wilson
Cost: *Alc* £25, fixed-price L (Sat & Sun only) £16/pre-theatre (to 6.45pm) £15
Times: Noon-last D 12.45am.
Closed 24, 25 Dec
Additional: Sunday L; Children welcome; 🌣 dishes
Seats: 100
Smoking: No-smoking area; Air conditioning
Credit cards: ▆ ▆ ▆ ▆ ▆

Osteria Antica Bologna

Sit in the bay window or, in summer, take a pavement table at this rustic high street Italian with a loyal following. The daily set menu offers brilliant value and fresh flavours (features, also, of the extensive carte). Enjoy platters of olives and bruschetta with prosecco, excellent fresh pasta and vegetarian dishes, simply sauced meats, super desserts and coffee.

Additional: Sunday L; Children welcome; 🌣 dishes
Smoking: Air conditioning.
Credit cards: ▆ ▆ ▆ ▆ ▆ ▆

Directions: Off Battersea Rise, between Wandsworth and Clapham Commons

23 Northcote Road
SW11 1NG
Map GtL: C2
Tel: 0171 9784771
Chef: Aurelio Spagnuolo
Owners: Aurelio Spagnuolo, Rochelle Porteous
Cost: *Alc* £18, fixed-price L £7.50 (2 courses). ☺ H/wine £7.90.
Times: Last L 3pm/D 11pm (Noon-11.30pm Fri & Sat, 10.30pm Sun). Closed 10 days Xmas-New Year

Osteria le Fate 🌣

This corner of Italy (it's an outpost of a restaurant in Genoa) is to befound in a smart residential area not far from the bustle of the King's Road. Expect the cuisine of Liguria – herbs, seafood, the local olive oil and an all-Italian wine list.

Directions: On corner of Draycott Ave and Bray Place. Nearest Tube – Sloane Square

5 Draycott Avenue SW3
Map: A1
Tel: 0171 5910070
Fax: 0171 5813140
Please telephone for further details

Oxo Tower ❀❀

A doorman stands in the rather bleak courtyard directing customers to the lift that expresses you to the eighth floor, where there are stunning, sweeping river vistas taking in the city and St Paul's. Lunch is better value than dinner. Dishes are drawn from a now familiar global melting pot of influences: grilled lambs' kidneys with merguez sausages, couscous, harissa and minted yogurt; grilled escalopes of salmon, smoked chilli and mango salsa, guacamole and creme fraîche. In the evening there are more classic interpretations in amongst the fusion food: open ravioli of creamed morels and wild mushrooms and a poached egg; pan-fried fillet of John Dory and scallops, fines herbs risotto and Champagne sauce. The sommelier is particularly helpful on matching wine with food, either by the glass or the bottle.

Directions: Nearest Tube – Blackfriars. In between Blackfriars Bridge and Waterloo Bridge

8th Floor Oxo Tower Wharf Barge House Street SE1 9PH
Map: E3
Tel: 0171 8033888
Fax: 0171 8033812
Chef: Simon Arkless
Owners: Harvey Nichols Restaurants Ltd
Cost: Fixed-price L £24.50. ☺ H/wine £12.50
Times: Noon-last L 3pm/6-last D 11.15pm. Closed L Sat, 25 Dec
Additional: Children welcome; ❀ dishes
Seats: 137
Smoking: No pipes; Air conditioning
Credit cards: ▆▆ ▆▆ ▆▆ ▆ ▆▆ ▆ ▆ JCB

Le Palais du Jardin ❀

Seafood is the speciality of this French-style brasserie with all-day oyster bar and pavement tables perfect for people-watching. Typical dishes include smoked salmon terrine with crab salad on parsley sauce, roast lamb with herb crust, lamb sausage ragout and pickled cabbage, and jellied terrine of summer fruits. Good filter coffee.

136 Long Acre WC2E 9AD
Map: D3
Tel: 0171 3795353
Fax: 0171 3791846
Chef: Miles Matthews
Owner: Le Palais du Jardin Ltd
Cost: Alc £30. ☺ H/wine £8.50
Times: Last L 3.30pm/last D 11.45pm. Closed 25, 26 Dec
Additional: Bar food; Oyster Bar open all day; ❀ dishes
Smoking: No pipes & cigars; Air conditioning
Credit cards: ▆▆ ▆▆ ▆▆ ▆ ▆▆ ▆ ▆ JCB

Directions: Nearest Tubes – Covent Garden and Leicester Square

The Park Lane Hotel ❀❀

Major refurbishment has restored much of the former glory of this hotel overlooking Green Park. The Art Deco ballroom is particularly fine, and the Palm Court the perfect place to take afternoon tea to the sound of a harp. There's a choice of eating (the Brasserie on the Park provides the less formal option) but our Rosette award is for Bracewell's Restaurant which boasts Louis XIV-style oak-wood panelling that once graced the home of financier Pierpoint Morgan. From the predominately English-style menu, our last meal began with a dish of tender roast squab with green lentils and little onion ravioli, before steamed fillet of brill on spinach with ink risotto-stuffed squid and a good saffron liquor sauce. The finale was an imaginative two-layered hot lemon soufflé served with mascarpone and fig ice cream. The good selection of moist, crusty breads was also noted.

Directions: On Piccadilly, between Hyde Park Corner and Green Park Tube stations

Piccadilly W1X 8BX
Map: C3
Tel: 0171 2907350
Fax: 0171 4991965
Chef: Andrew Bennett
Cost: Alc £30, fixed-price L £19.50 (2 courses). H/wine £15
Times: Noon-last L 2.30pm/6.30-last D10.30pm. Closed L Sat, all Sun, Bhs
Additional: No children under 10; ❀ dishes
Seats: 60. Jacket & tie preferred
Smoking: No-smoking area
Accommodation: 300 en suite
Credit cards: ▆▆ ▆▆ ▆ ▆▆ ▆ JCB

The Peasant ✹

Ornate corner pub with a traditional feel to the ground floor, sophisticated modern restaurant minimalism upstairs in the light, bright Room 204. The same menu is served throughout, so choose your atmosphere. Sound cooking with a strong Mediterranean rustic streak based on honest flavours takes in the likes of a broad bean and sage risotto, lamb casserole with green beans and root vegetables, and strawberry and ginger fool.

Smoking: No pipes & cigars. **Credit cards:** ▉▉ ▉▉ ▉▉ ▉ ▉▉ ▉

Directions: Nearest Tube – Farringdon or Angel

24 St John Street EC1 4PH
Map: E4
Tel: 0171 3367726
Fax: 0171 2514476
Chef: Renato Porceddu
Owners: Michael Kittos, Craig Schorn
Cost: *Alc* £20, fixed price D £20. ☺
H/wine £9.50
Times: Last L 3pm/last D 11pm.
Closed L Sat, Sun, 2 wks Xmas
Additional: Bar food; Children
welcome; ✿ dishes

The People's Palace ✹✹

The restaurant runs along the entire frontage of the Royal Festival Hall, giving splendid views of the Thames. Pre-theatre dinners that include field mushroom and sage risotto, and mint marinated rump of lamb with red pepper polenta cake and tomato jus will stop stomachs rumbling through the third act, but go easy on the coconut steamed pudding with spiced rum custard or your attention might wander. Those with a little more time can enjoy warm chicken livers with chorizo, baby spinach and walnut dressing, Thai spiced mussels, sauté of rabbit with pancetta, baby onions, broad beans and smoked paprika cream, and hot buttered lobster with caviar, spring vegetables and herbs.

Directions: Level 3 of the Royal Festival Hall

Royal Festival Hall Belvedere Road
SE1 8XX
Map: E3
Tel: 0171 9289999
Fax: 0171 9282355
Chefs: Darby Brookes, Pat Lynch
Owner: David Levin
Cost: *Alc* £21.50, fixed-price L £17/D
£20. ☺ H/wine £11.50
Seats: 220
Smoking: No-smoking area;
Air conditioning
Credit cards: ▉▉ ▉▉ ▉ ▉▉ ▉

Pharmacy Restaurant & Bar ✹ NEW

From the outside this heavily-hyped restaurant designed by Damien Hirst, looks like Boots circa 1950. Enter through automatic doors into the downstairs bar, a loud affair for drinks and snacks. The restaurant proper is upstairs – expect modern fusion dishes such as fish carpaccio with nobu dressing, and ultra-fashionable roast suckling pig with roasted apples. Weekends are great for kids.

150 Notting Hill Gate W11
Tel: 0171 486 7340
No details provided so please telephone

Pied à Terre ✹✹✹✹

34 Charlotte Street W1P 1HJ
Map: C4
Tel: 0171 6361178
Fax: 0171 9161171
Chef: Tom Aikens
Owners: Tom Aikens, David Moore
Cost: *Alc* £45, fixed-price L £19.50
(2 courses)/D £33 (5 courses). H/wine
£15
Times: 12.15-last L 2.15pm/7-last
D 10.45pm. Closed L Sat, Sun, last
2 wks Aug, 2 wks Xmas-New Year
Additional: Children welcome;
✿ dishes
Seats: 36. Private dining room 14
Smoking: No pipes & cigars; Air
conditioning
Credit cards: ▉▉ ▉▉ ▉▉ ▉ ▉▉ ▉ ▉ JCB

Cellular and urbane within, seriously understated without, the surroundings here offer little distraction from the cooking. Deliberate perhaps, appropriate certainly. This is

studied and increasingly artful food that deserves full
attention, and the confidence to set it on such a spare canvas
is far from misplaced. In at the deep end following Richard
Neat's departure a couple of years back, there is a feeling
that Tom Aikens is just coming up for air. Foie gras and
shellfish may be dominant but there is little doubt that
hardwork and perfectionism are the key ingredients in this
man's repertoire. Already he has a classic in the bag. Pig's
heads come and go, but there are surely few worthier
epitaphs than the intricate reworking on offer here. In many
ways this serves as a good definition of Aikens' unifying style,
with a plateful of disparate elements all given equal
treatment: braised cheeks and tongue are intense with
casserole tenderness, whilst the deep-fried brain and ears
offer crispness without and creaminess within; a steamed
trotter puts the pied on the terre. Also typical is the
wonderfully fragrant quail consommé bobbing with breast,
wild mushroom ravioli and poached quail's egg, each a
perfect parcel of flavour and texture. Only occasionally is
there the suggestion of an ingredient a degree or two out of
place – a silky artichoke and foie gras terrine, for example,
might have found better company than a slightly soggy
celeriac remoulade – but given the ambition, incongruity is
impressively rare. Desserts also take the variations-on-a-
theme approach, five chocolate miniatures include a nod to
Nico Ladenis's 'negus', and both poached fig and caramelised
apple are served with accurate sorbet reflections. In this
company interludes and baubles must work to justify
themselves, but pre-dessert crème brûlée was undoubtedly of
premier quality. Bruno Asselin's wine list offers few
compromises on sourcing, but doesn't neglect the under £20
bracket. Punchy bins such as Villard Sauvignon Blanc from
Chile (£15.50) offer heaps of character for relatively little
cash.

Signature dishes: Sea bass with chilled vichysoisse and caviar
sauce; ballotine of duck confit; braised pig's head.

Directions: Nearest Tube – Goodge Street. S of BT Tower

Pied à Terre

AA Shortlisted for Wine Award-see page 16

Le Pont de la Tour ❀❀

On the banks of the Thames, dominated by Tower Bridge, this
large, elegant and surprisingly intimate restaurant forms part
of Sir Terence Conran's Gastrodome. It draws the crowds for
modern Mediterranean food, and for the spectacular views
from the riverside terrace – on a warm summer evening the
best alfresco eating in town. Longish menus include a set lunch
choice, pre- and post-theatre selections and an interesting *carte*
that features seafood specialities such as Irish rock oysters and
lobster mayonnaise among the starters. Main course options
range from roast sea bass with herbs and lemon olive oil, and
grilled Dover sole, to venison with rösti, ceps and Madeira,
calves' liver with salsa verde and Suffolk bacon, and roast
truffled pigeon Rossini. For dessert there might be rhubarb
and mascarpone parfait and warm chocolate tart with Chantilly
cream and mango. Bread comes from the restaurant's own
bakery. The range of the wine list is exceptional, with a sound
selection of house wines.

Directions: SE side of Tower Bridge

The Butlers Wharf Building
36d Shad Thames SE1 2NQ
Map: G3
Tel: 0171 4038403
Fax: 0171 4030267
Chefs: David Burke, Andrew Sargent
Owners: Sir Terence Conran &
David Burke
Cost: *Alc* £70, fixed-price L £28.50.
☺ H/wine £11.95
Times: Noon-last L 3pm (Sun 12.30-
2.30pm)/6-last D 11.30pm (Sun till
11pm). Closed L Sat, 25-26 Dec,
Good Fri
Additional: Bar food;
Children welcome; ◑ dishes
Seats: 120. Private dining room 20
Credit cards: 💳 💳 💳 💳 💳 💳 💳 JCB

The Popeseye

A small bistro, simply decorated and well supported. An open-plan kitchen lets you see the chef chargrilling steaks, for that is all that is on offer: popeseye (rump), sirloin and fillet, all Aberdeen Angus and of excellent flavour, in four different weights and served with chips. No starters and a handful of puddings of the sticky toffee type.

Directions: Nearest Tube – Hammersmith. Restaurant located behind Olympia

108 Blythe Road W14
Map GtL: C3
Tel: 0171 6104578
Chef/Owner: Ian Hutchison
Cost: Alc £25. ☺ H/wine £11.50
Times: D only, last D 10.30pm.
Closed most Aug
Additional: Children welcome
Credit cards: None

La Porte des Indes

32 Bryanston Street W1H 7AE
Map: D4
Tel: 0171 2240055
Fax: 0171 2241144
Chef: Mehernosh Mody
Owners: Blue Elephant International Group
Cost: Alc £30, fixed-price L £15/D £21. ☺ H/wine £10.50.
Times: Last L 2.30pm (3pm Sun)/last D midnight (Sun 6-10.30pm).
Closed L Sat
Additional: Sunday L; ♨ dishes
Smoking: Air conditioning
Credit cards: ▬ ▬ ➰ ▭ ▦ ◖ ◙ JCB

Stylish Indian restaurant on two floors with a 40ft-high Mogul waterfall descending amid carved sandstone balustrades. Lunch is the business, a spectacular buffet affair, and one of the best-value deals in the area. Dishes to look out for are poulet rouge, an Indo/French dish, and the mushroom pilau. Not your average curry house. Highly recommended.

Directions: Nearest Tube – Marble Arch. Behind Cumberland Hotel

The Prince Bonaparte

A converted Victorian pub, as the name suggests, with an informal atmosphere and blackboards listing country wines and the twice-daily changing menu. There's a Mediterranean influence evident in dishes that are otherwise as varied as the clientele.

Directions: Corner Chepstow and Talbot Roads. Nearest Tubes: Notting Hill Gate, Westbourne Park.

80 Chepstow Road W2 5BE
Map GtL: C3
Tel: 0171 2295912
Fax: 0171 7920911
Please telephone for further details

Purple Sage

NEW

An impressive frontage of large arched windows and purple paint work make this bright, airy restaurant stand out. Part of the Red Pepper/Green Olive mini-chain – so expect simple decor, great pizzas from the wood-fired oven, pastas and risottos. First-class espresso, and a short list of predominantly Italian wines.

Smoking: Air conditioning
Credit cards: ▬ ▬ ➰ ▭ ▦ ◖ ◖

Directions: Nearest Tube – Bond Street

92 Wigmore Street W1H 9DR
Map: C3
Tel: 0171 4861912
Chef: Paolo Zanca
Cost: Alc £18. H/wine £9
Times: Noon-2.30pm/6-10.30pm.
Closed Sun
Additional: Children welcome; ♨ dishes
Seats: 120

Putney Bridge

Amongst the Victorian buildings, Putney Bridge stands out as an award-winning exemplar of contemporary design. Large expanses of glass ensure river views for most, and the split-level interior makes much use of wood and metal. The menu is magpie-like in its various components, assembly-line in concept. Honey and soy roast quail with spiced vegetables, tarte Tatin of endive, or game terrine with caperberries, and stuffed breast of pheasant with ceps, bacon, shallots and celeriac purée, are typical, but although the cooking is mostly sound, there is not always the capacity to live up to the promise of the dishes described. A crayfish risotto, for instance, lacked discernible flavour, as did a well-intentioned mustard-crumbed Bath chap with tomato and pickled walnut salad. The dessert menu is short and straightforward. As well as a particularly fine chocolate tarte, there may be passion fruit gratin or apricot cheesecake. The children's lunch menu includes fish and chips and banana split.

Directions: Nearest tube – Putney Bridge. Walk out of station and across bridge. Restaurant is the first building on R, facing onto river

The Embankment SW15 1LB
Map GtL: C2
Tel: 0181 7801811
Fax: 0181 7801211
Chef: Paul Hughes
Owner: Trevor Gulliver
Cost: Alc L £26/D £35.
Times: Noon-3pm/6pm-11pm
Seats: 152
Smoking: Air conditioning
Credit cards: ▬ ▬ ▬ ▬ ▬ ▬ ▬ JCB

Quaglino's ✿✿

Quags is still glam, even if the beau monde has moved on. It's always a thrill to make an entrance down the staircase – and to order rock oysters with a little Beluga on the side. Rotisserie dishes include spiced lamb with tabouleh, or from the grill there could be calves' liver and bacon with frites, perhaps feta salad niçoise, and some asparagus hollandaise amongst the first course choices. Main courses range from good old fish and chips with tartare sauce to modern classics such as seared salmon, beetroot compote and rocket. As well as desserts – passion fruit pavlova and tarte Tatin are recommended – Mrs Kirkham's Lancashire is commendably listed in the cheese selection.

Seats: 267. Private dining room 40
Smoking: Air conditioning
Credit cards: ▬ ▬ ▬ ▬ ▬ ▬ JCB

Directions: Bury St is off Jermyn St

16 Bury Street St James's
SW1Y 6AL
Map: C3
Tel: 0171 9306767
Fax: 0171 8392866
Chef: Henrik Iversen
Owner: Sir Terence Conran
Cost: Alc £26, fixed-price L & D £19.
☺ H/wine £11.75
Times: Noon-last L 3pm/5.30-midnight Mon-Thu (till 1pm Fri-Sat, 11pm Sun). Closed D 24 Dec, all 25 Dec, 26, 31 Dec & 1 Jan
Additional: Bar food; Children over 14, in bar only; ♨ dishes

Quality Chop House ✿

High-backed mahogany booths and etched windows and mirrors maintain the 19th-century atmosphere at this well-established Victorian dining room. The menu offers great British traditional dishes such as jellied eels; there are oysters and monkfish from the new seafood bar, as well as Toulouse sausages, mash and onion gravy, confit of duck, and Beluga caviar with blinis.

Additional: Sunday brunch; Children welcome; ♨ dishes
Smoking: No-smoking area; No pipes & cigars; Air conditioning
Credit cards: None

Directions: On the south side of Farringdon Road, from its junction with Rosebery Avenue. Nearest Tube – Farringdon or King's Cross

94 Farringdon Road
EC1 3EA
Map: E4
Tel: 0171 8375093
Chef/Owner: Charles Fontaine
Cost: Alc £25. ☺ H/wine £10
Times: Last L 2.55pm/last D 11.25pm. Closed L Sat, 1 wk Xmas-New Year

Quincy's Restaurant ❀❀

A popular neighbourhood restaurant with dark green walls, pine furniture and an intimate atmosphere. The mood is relaxed, with owner David Wardle providing charming service while chef David Philpott creates great-value dishes in the kitchen. A typical selection from the concise *carte* could include rack of lamb with cabbage haggis and swede mash, roast rabbit with green olives, cannellini beans and gremolata, and duck breast with Chinese vegetables and hoisin sauce. At a meal in late spring, our inspector decided against a starter of tarte Tatin of onion with Gorgonzola, and instead tried the asparagus risotto, which was well-timed and came with good local granary bread. The main dish of roast cod with braised endive was served with a well-balanced honey and mustard sauce. Desserts range from orange and polenta cake with coconut sorbet, to mango cheesecake with cherry jus. The wine list features three-dozen bottles chosen for quality and value.

675 Finchley Road NW2 2JP
Map GtL: C4
Tel: 0171 7948499
Chef: David Philpott
Owner: David Wardle
Cost: Fixed-price D £25. H/wine £10
Times: D only, 7-11pm. Closed Xmas
Additional: Children welcome; dishes
Seats: 30
Smoking: No pipes & cigars; Air conditioning
Credit cards:

Directions: Situated between Hendon Way & Cricklewood Lane on the Finchley Road

Quo Vadis ❀❀❀

First things first. The food is very good. So, notwithstanding your view on Damien Hirst's molecular model of DNA, or the flayed bovine heads (thankfully in the upstairs bar rather than the restaurant), don't flinch from booking. Whatever the surroundings (and this is some contrast to, say, The Criterion) it is Marco Pierre White's menu that truly defines his operations. The style is at once classic and cosmopolitan. The *carte* is peppered with gastronomic formalities – sauce Bercy, pomme Biarritz, sauce diable – and at the same time covers all bases, with a broad sweep of dishes ranging from the Japanese-style clarity of salmon carpaccio with oriental dressing, to a studied foie gras terrine with Sauternes jelly and toasted brioche. This is wonderfully concise cooking. Nowhere more so than in an exemplary pot-au-feu of young chicken with truffle oil and vegetable broth that involved absolutely 'no mucking about' according to an inspector impressed by the honest flavours and flawless technique in this 'brilliant summer dish'. The kitchen rarely misses a beat and whilst many of the concepts are familiar, inspired reworkings – stunningly presented peach melba – and perfect execution – lemon tarte en surprise – breathe new life into old favourites. The wine list, of epic proportions, is thankfully prefaced by the relative brevity of a sommelier's selection offering bins of real character for around the £20 mark.

26-29 Dean St W1V 6LL
Map: D4
Tel: 0171 4379585
Fax: 0171 4349972
Chef: Phil Cooper
Owners: Marco Pierre White, Jonathan Kennedy, Jimmy Lahoud
Cost: *Alc* £35, fixed-price L & D £17.95. ☺ H/wine £13.50
Times: Noon-last L 3pm/6-last D 11.30pm (Sun till 10.30pm). Closed L Sat & Sun, 25 Dec, 1 Jan
Additional: Children welcome; dishes
Seats: 100. Private dining room 16
Smoking: Air conditioning
Credit cards:

Directions: Nearest Tube – Leicester Square

The Radisson Edwardian Hotel ✸

See Where London Meets Section page 153

The Radisson SAS Portman Hotel ✸✸

Tucked away on the first floor of the hotel, the wood-panelled Library Restaurant, hung with tapestries, is charmingly small and serene, seating just 20 people. Modern cooking makes a contrast with the decor – fashionable towers appear in several starters, especially in a marinated scallop and gravad lax tower with salmon roe and dill pesto. Alternatively there is Thai chicken soup with red chilli and tiger prawns, or smoked salmon carved at the table. A short but sensible list of daily-changing main courses includes thyme-roasted rump of lamb with grilled niçoise vegetables and a light sorrel sauce, and pan-fried monkfish with roasted fennel and seafood beurre blanc.

Directions: Off Oxford St. Close to Marble Arch. Nearest Tube – Marble Arch

22 Portman Square W1H 9FL
Map: B3
Tel: 0171 2086000
Fax: 0171 2086001
Chef: Brian Kerr
Cost: Alc £35. H/wine £13.50
Times: D only, 6.30-last D 10.30pm.
Closed Sun, Bhs
Additional: Bar food;
Children welcome; ✿ dishes
Seats: 20. Private dining rooms 4-400.
Jacket & tie preferred
Smoking: Air conditioning
Accommodation: 279 en suite
Credit cards: ▬ ▆ ▚ ▆ ▐ ▣ JCB

The Raj Vogue ✸

Owner Abed Choudhury provides charming service and creates a very comfortable atmosphere at this most traditional of Indian restaurants. The menu includes favourites from every region of the sub-continent plus some Persian dishes. Drink Sunny beer or chilled lassi.

Directions: Nearest tube – Archway. Opposite to The Whittington Hospital

34 Highgate Hill N19 5NL
Map GtL: C4
Tel: 0171 2729091
Fax: 0171 2811485
Please telephone for further details

Rani ✸✸

'Habitat goes colonial' describes the feel of Rani, a vegetarian Gujerati restaurant just off Finchley Lane. No meat, fish or eggs are allowed in the kitchen; instead, emphasis is placed on fresh vegetables, yogurt, rice and pulses. Typical starters include aloo tiki – deep-fried lentil and pea mix rolled in mash potato topped with tamarind and yoghurt, and lasarn bateta – deep-fried baby potatoes with garlic and red chilli. Main courses include chana bateta, chick peas and potatoes cooked with onions, green chillies and tamarind, and banana methi, with fresh fenugreek leaves and cooked with a richly spiced tomato gravy. Poppadums come with stunning home-made chutneys, and the excellent range of breads includes stuffed paratha, mithi roti and hand-rolled chapatis. The Richmond branch is designed along the same cool, modern lines and serves a similar selection of vegetarian Indian dishes. It is located at 3 Hill Street. Tel: 0181 332 2322.

Directions: 5 min walk from Finchley Central Station

7 Long Lane Finchley N3 2PR
Map GtL: C4
Tel/Fax: 0181 3494386
Chef: Sheila Pattni
Owner: Jyotindra Pattni
Cost: Alc £13, fixed-price D £11.45
(2 courses). ☺ H/wine £9.70
Times: D only, 6-last D 10pm.
Closed 25 Dec
Additional: Sunday L (12.15-2.30pm);
Children welcome; ✿ dishes
Seats: 70. Private dining room 12
Smoking: No smoking in dining room
Credit cards: ▬ ▆ ▚ ▙ ▆ ▐

Ransome's Dock ✸✸

A feeling of cool industry remains at this former ice works with its bold, blue walls and attractively cluttered decor. Owners Martin and Vanessa Lam can both be found at the

35-37 Parkgate Road
Battersea SW11 4NP
Map GtL: C2
Tel: 0171 2231611
Fax: 0171 9242614

stove delivering an enterprising menu that travels all the way from potted Morecambe shrimps to fusion-style mussels with Thai spices. Flavours are up-front, and an extra element of bite (seared scallops with celeriac purée came with some fiery chorizo) is often an inspired addition. Raw materials are carefully sourced (organic meat comes from Cirencester), and there is a seasonal sensitivity to the menu with ingredients given the room to speak for themselves. Hence the high point of one inspector's main course was the quality of a fine piece of calves' liver paired with garlic mash, crisp pancetta. Apple and Calvados tart, and prune and Armagnac soufflé have both featured amongst some indulgent desserts, all of which are complemented by an enticing selection of pudding wines from a smashing list of high-quality wines arranged by grape variety and style.

Additional: Sunday L; Children welcome; 🍴 dishes.
Seats: 55
Smoking: No pipes; Air conditioning
Credit cards: ▉ ▉ ▉ ▉ ▉ ▉ ▉ JCB

Directions: Between Albert and Battersea Bridges. Nearest tube – Sloane Square

Chef: Martin Lam
Owners: Martin & Vanessa Lam
Cost: Fixed-price L £11.50 (2 courses). H/wine £12
Times: Noon-last D 11pm (D from 6pm). Closed D Sun

AA Wine Award–see page 16 Shortlisted for

Rasa ❀❀

At first, Rasa looks decidedly modern with its strident pink walls and metal chairs, but the Indian instrumental music and gleaming brass artefacts are customary and carefully chosen by the chef-patron to help educate customers about his native Kerala. The painstakingly researched vegetarian cooking places prime importance on fresh ingredients and, if you order your meal with an adventurous attitude, you will be amply rewarded. Uncommon delights include the starters of cashew nut pakoda with coconut and ginger chutney, and Mysore bondi – a potato ball delicately spiced with ginger, curry leaves, coriander and black mustard. The superb main course, beet pachadi, is a mix of fresh beetroot, yogurt, roasted coconut and spices and best accompanied by lemon rice. Coconut rice is the considered accompaniment to bagar baingan – aubergines cooked in a paste of roasted onions, coriander, chillies and tamarind with a cashew nut sauce. The desserts are also excellent and include unusually moreish carrot halva. Another branch of Rasa has opened in central London at 6 Dering Street, W1. Tel: 0171 6291346

55 Stoke Newington Church Street
N16 OAR
Map GtL: D4
Tel: 0171 2490344
Fax: 0171 2498748
Chef/Owner: Sivadas Sreedharan
Cost: Alc £15, fixed-price L & D £15.
☺ H/wine £7.95
Times: Noon-last 2pm/6pm-last D 11pm. Closed L Mon, 25-26 Dec
Additional: Children welcome;
🍴 dishes
Seats: 45
Smoking: No smoking in dining room; Air conditioning
Credit cards: ▉ ▉ ▉ ▉ ▉ ▉ ▉ JCB

Directions: Bus no 73 from Oxford St, Angel, Kings Cross, Euston, BR from Liverpool St to Stoke Newington High St

Redmond's ❀❀

Housed in a former shop in a smart, leafy residential area, Redmond's is a stylish place, a great neighbourhood restaurant, with bright, sunny yellow walls, bold contemporary paintings, bare boards, and white clothed tables. Expect a really buzzy atmosphere (especially in the evenings and at Sunday lunch). Redmond Hayward cooks very well indeed, and produces simple, set monthly-changing lunch and dinner menus of imaginative modern food based on fresh seasonal ingredients. A typical meal may start with fennel, smoked haddock and star anise chowder, followed by corn-fed chicken breast with confit of leeks, mash and vanilla and orange sauce. A lemon and poppy seed cheesecake with blueberry sauce, or a selection of Neal's Yard cheeses may be among the choice of

170 Upper Richmond Road West
SW14 8AW
Map GtL: B2
Tel: 0181 8781922
Fax: 0181 8781122
Chef: Redmond Hayward
Owners: Redmond & Pippa Hayward
Cost: Fixed-price L £21/D £24. ☺
H/wine £14
Times: Noon-last L 2pm (Sun till 2.30pm)/7-last D 10.30pm.
Closed L Sat, D Sun, 1st wk Jan, Bhs (not Good Fri)
Additional: Sunday L; Children welcome; 🍴 dishes

desserts. Good olives precede and decent espresso rounds off the meal. There's always a warm welcome from Pippa Hayward who runs front of house with great panache.

Directions: Located half way between Putney and Richmond on the South Circular Road at the Barnes end of Sheen

Seats: 54
Smoking: No pipes & cigars; Air conditioning
Credit cards:

The Red Pepper

Lively, close-packed Italian-style neighbourhood hang-out, simply decorated with an informal atmosphere. 'Designer' pizzas from the wood-fired oven feature strongly on the short menu, as do more traditional Med dishes – linguine al pesto with roasted pine kernels, tagliatelle ai frutti di mare with asparagus, and risotto with taleggio cheese. Great fun.

Additional: Sunday L; No very young children; 🌢 dishes
Smoking: No pipes & cigars; Air conditioning
Credit cards:

8 Formosa Street W9 1EE
Map: C4
Tel: 0171 2662708
Fax: 0171 7227702
Chef: Paolo Zanca
Owner: Bijan Behzadi
Cost: Alc £17.50
Times: Last L 3.30pm/last D 10.45pm. Closed L Mon-Fri, 25, 26 Dec, 1 Jan

Directions: Nearest Tube – Warwick Ave

Restaurant 192 ❀

Wine bar-cum-bistro with an eclectic menu. Highlights of our most recent meal were delicate tempura-style prawns and vegetables with a chilli and a soy sauce dip, and a gargantuan wedge of 'chocolate nemesis', a kind of roulade garnished with dark chocolate sauce and vanilla ice cream in a biscuit basket.

Additional: Bar food L; Sunday L; Children welcome; 🌢 dishes
Smoking: No-smoking area
Credit cards:

192 Kensington Park Road W11 2ES
Map GtL: C3
Tel: 0171 2290482
Fax: 0171 2293300
Chef: Michael Knowlson
Owners: Groucho Club plc
Cost: Alc £22, fixed-price L £10.50 (2 courses). ☺ H/wine £10
Times: Last L 2.30pm/last D 11pm. Closed Aug Bh, 25-26 Dec, 1 Jan

Directions: 5 mins from Ladbroke Grove Tube station, 10 mins walk from Notting Hill Tube station.

Rhodes in the Square ❀❀   NEW

In a follow up to his first successful venture, City Rhodes in the business heart of the capital, Gary Rhodes has expanded his empire to a more discreet residential area – the large, extremely smart restaurant, located in the Dolphin Square luxury apartment and hotel complex in Pimlico, is quite something. An early inspection meal in the lovely room (within weeks of opening), showed great promise. But why change the formula? Rhodes' cooking has always had a slight angle to it or something interesting, nor is he afraid to work with daring combinations, and the reworking of traditional English dishes is a speciality. The menu of modern British dishes is good, reads wells and features all the old TV favourites, plus some new exciting Rhodes' creations. Of the dishes sampled, a richly flavoured, smooth-textured chicken liver and foie gras parfait pleased for its sense of balance, an open omelette which came with juicy chunks of lobster had an outstanding Thermidor sauce with cheese crust, and glazed duck served with a bitter orange jus, mash and spinach was just 'perfectly cooked'. For pudding, a simple seared 'carpaccio' of pineapple oozed flavour. Great espresso to finish.

Dolphin Square
Chichester Street
SW1V 3LX
Map: D1
Tel: 0171 7986767
Fax: 0171 7985685
Chefs: Gary Rhodes, Roger Gorman
Owner: Gardner Merchant & Dolphin Square Trust Ltd
Cost: Alc £37, fixed-price L £19.95/ Sunday L £21.50. ☺ H/wine £15.95
Times: Noon-2.30pm/7-11pm. Closed L Sat, Bhs
Additional: Sunday L, Children welcome; 🌢 dishes
Seats: 90
Credit cards:

Directions: Nearest Tube – Pimlico

Richmond Gate Hotel

Richmond Hill Richmond-upon-
Thames TW10 6RP
Map GtL: B2
Tel: 0181 9400061
Fax: 0181 3320354
Chef: Sidney Bond
Owner: Securicor Hotels
Cost: *Alc* £28, fixed price L £18.50/D
£25.50. H/wine £14.95
Times: Last L 2.30pm/last D 10pm.
Closed L Sat
Additional: Bar food L; Sunday L;
Children welcome; dishes
Smoking: No smoking in dining room;
Air conditioning
Accommodation: 66 en suite.
Credit cards: ▄ ▄ ▄ ▄ ▄ ▄

A Georgian country house on the crest of Richmond Hill,
close to the Royal Park. The restaurant, Gates on the Park,
serves up a mix of international dishes. A candlelit supper
might start with grilled tuna salad with roasted red pepper
salsa, followed by pan-fried medallions of kangaroo with a
Yalumba Cabernet sauce.

Directions: At top of Richmond Hill
opposite Star & Garter & just outside
Richmond Park

Ristorante L'Incontro

87 Pimlico Road SW1W 8PH
Map: C1
Tel: 0171 7303663/6327
Fax: 0171 7305062
Chefs: Danilo Minuzzo, Simone
Rettore
Owner: Gino Santin
Cost: *Alc* £38.50, fixed-price L
£20.50. ☺ H/wine £18.50
Times: 12.30-last L 2.30pm/7-last
D 11.30pm (Sun till 10.30). Closed
L Sat & Sun, 25-26 Dec, some Bhs
Additional: Children welcome;
dishes
Seats: 65. Private dining room 35.
Jacket & tie preferred
Smoking: No pipes; Air conditioning
Credit cards: ▄ ▄ ▄ ▄ ▄ ▄ ▄ JCB

The decor may be cool, metropolitan chic, but as far as the
cooking is concerned, L'Incontro wears its Venetian heart on
its sleeve. Subdivided into antipasti, pasta, fish and meat, the
direct wording of the menu is a fair reflection of a down-to-
earth approach on the plate. Combinations are simple and, in
north-east Italian terms, classic. Thus scallops come adorned
with lemon and parsley, potato gnocchi with tomato and basil,
mussels with white wine and garlic. Raw materials have the
freshness and quality to cope with the spare approach, and
pasta, most importantly, is top-notch. Some tender cuttlefish
paired with 'as good as it gets' polenta were amongst the
highlights of a recent inspection lunch, that also turned up an
'earthy and authentic' osso buco. Apart from the ubiquitous
tiramisu, desserts major on tarts with the almond biscotti
variety being a mainstay. Wines, predominantly Italian, are
enthusiastically marked-up.

Directions: From Lower Sloane Street, left into Pimlico Road,
restaurant is on R. Nearest Tube – Sloane Square

Ritz Hotel ❀❀

150 Piccadilly W1V 9DG
Map: C3
Tel: 0171 4938181
Fax: 0171 4932687
Chef: Giles Thompson
Cost: Alc £50, fixed-price L £34/
D £41. H/wine £19.50
Times: 12.30-last L 2.30pm/6-last
D 10.45pm
Additional: Palm Court; Sunday L;
Children welcome; ❀ dishes
Seats:120. Private dining room 14.
Jacket & tie preferred
Smoking: Air conditioning
Accommodation: 130 en suite
Credit cards: 💳 💳 💳 💳 💳 💳 💳 JCB

A legend among the great metropolitan hotels, the Ritz is
synonymous with magnificent style and sumptuous decor.
The dining room frequently described as the most beautiful
room in Europe, is decorated in Louis XVI style with
exquisite chandeliers, and the famous trompe l'oeil that
sweeps across the ornate ceiling. Splendid floor-to-ceiling
terrace doors open on to views of Green Park. Typical dishes
from the cosmopolitan menus are sprinkled with luxuries,
and built on a firm base of classical training: supreme of brill
soufflé with champagne and lobster sauce, for example, or
noisette of new season lamb with wild mushrooms, and
poached breast of corn-fed chicken with truffle and sauce
supreme. A summer meal, enjoyed alfresco on the terrace,
might start with pan-fried crab cake and wild rocket leaves,
followed by risotto of asparagus and morels with truffle
sabayon. Afternoon tea in the famous Palm Court –
cucumber sandwiches, baked scones and strawberry jam – is
as popular as ever, with hundreds of visitors flocking to take
part in this most English of rituals.

Directions: Nearest Tube – Green Park

Riva Restaurant ❀❀❀

169 Church Road Barnes SW13 9HR
Map GtL: C3
Tel/Fax: 0181 7480434
Chef: Francesco Zanchetta
Owner: Andrea Riva
Cost: Alc £26. H/wine £9.95
Times: Noon-last L 2.30pm/7-last D
11pm. Closed L Sat, Xmas, Easter, Bhs
Additional: Children welcome;
❀ dishes
Seats: 50
Smoking: No pipes & cigars;
Air conditioning
Credit cards: 💳 💳 💳 💳 💳 💳 💳 JCB

Slate blue and wheat coloured walls, architectural prints and
giant flower arrangements give this excellent small restaurant
an air of the class it deserves. Riva's classic northern Italian
cooking is the sort of food that has worked its way deep into
the culture of the British middle class; here it is done with the
understanding, feel and flair lacking in many a more
pretentious establishment. It's a breath of fresh air in culinary
terms. Owner Andrea Riva and chef Francesco Zanchetta
simply know what they are about. Ciabatta, and carrot with
herb bread, arrive within seconds of sitting down, there are no
nibbles or olives to spoil the appetite for the huge portions
ahead. Stuzzichini is a tempting sampler of, perhaps, fresh
mozzarella draped with delectable anchovies, bruschetta with
well-flavoured tomatoes and basil, and smoked sturgeon and
robiola on focaccia. Pasta can be taken as a starter or main
course and sauces are alluring, papardelle with herbed hare
ragout, for example, or linguine with clams, rucola and
bottarga. Fish is beautifully cooked and, as well as more
familiar dishes such as sea bass with rucola sauce and mashed
potatoes, there may be unusual regional dishes such as misto

pesce 'in saor' – scallops, red mullet and cod pan-fried in raspberry vinegar with beans, peppers, tomatoes and radicchio. Feisty meat dishes include 'porchetta' with roast potato, pumpkin and caramelised onions, and pan-fried calves' liver with soft polenta and porcini. Pannacotta is the hit of the dessert chart, followed closely by tiramisu; but excellent as they are it's worth trying others such as crêpes of prunes and blueberries stewed in grappa with cinnamon ice cream, or maize and almond crumble soaked in vin santo with mascarpone.

Signature dishes: Artichoke with cheese fondue; perch in salsa verde; polenta and porcini; goose with white truffles.

Directions: Junction of Church Rd with Castelnau Rd. Nearest Tube – Hammersmith

River Café ❀❀❀

You've seen the TV show, bought the book and – given that the tee-shirt is not yet available – why not come and judge for yourself whether The River Café's simple, rustic Italian cooking is really worth the hype and these kind of prices. Our inspector's report is in the the affirmative, based primarily on the quality of ingredients and knowledgeable service. That meal included ravioli stuffed with spinach and buffalo-milk ricotta tossed in butter flavoured with sage, basil and thyme flowers, a delicious and perfectly cooked generous main course of wood-roasted turbot served on a bed of red and green chard and topped with capers, oregano and marjoram, and a first-class light, zesty lemon tart and pannacotta with caramelised oranges in grappa. However, a high-quality bresaola was marred by some harsh-tasting boiled, salted lemons. An impressive choice of cheese plates is available, and these may include Taleggio, Gorgonzola, fresh Pecorino or the little-known Ubriaco. The menu changes twice daily but survey the designer-clad crowd (which includes the designers themselves) pushing salad around their plates and drinking mineral water and you too may be left wondering who is really here for the food. Understandably, the wine list is Italian and offers a number of half-bottles as well as several wines by the glass and a lip-smacking prosecco and fruit aperitif that starts the meal on the right note.

Directions: Off Fulham Palace Rd. Junction of Rainville Road and Bowfell Road. Nearest Tube – Hammersmith

Thames Wharf Studios Rainville Road W6 9HA
Map GtL: C3
Tel: 0171 3818824
Fax: 0177 3816217
Chefs: Rose Gray, Ruth Rogers
Owners: Rose Gray, Ruth Rogers, Richard Rogers
Cost: *Alc* £60
Times: Noon-last L 2.45pm/7-last D 10.30pm (11.20pm Fri & Sat). Closed D Sun, Bhs
Additional: Children welcome; dishes
Seats: 100
Smoking: No pipes & cigars
Credit cards: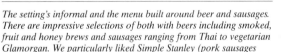

R.K. Stanleys ❀

The setting's informal and the menu built around beer and sausages. There are impressive selections of both with beers including smoked, fruit and honey brews and sausages ranging from Thai to vegetarian Glamorgan. We particularly liked Simple Stanley (pork sausages with onion gravy, kale and champ mash). Good pud too.

Additional: Bar food; Children welcome; dishes
Smoking: No-smoking area; Air conditioning
Credit cards: ▆ ▆ ▆ ▆ ▆ ▆ JCB

Directions: Nearest Tube – Oxford Circus

6 Little Portland Street W1
Map: B3
Tel: 0171 4620099
Fax: 0171 4620088
Chef: Robert Gutteridge
Owner: Fred Taylor
Cost: *Alc* £18. ☺ H/wine £10.50
Times: Last L 3.30pm/last D 11.30pm. Closed Sun, Xmas, Bhs

Royal China ❀

A striking place with a large Chinese following. The lunch menu offers one plate noodle dishes and dim sum – after 4pm the dinner menu takes over. Try fried egg-noodles with shredded pork, bean sprouts and oyster mushrooms, or lightly fried chicken breast with lemon sauce. Service can be slow at busy times.

Directions: N from traffic lights in Putney High Street, Chelverton Road is 2nd L. Nearest Tube – East Putney

3 Chelverton Road SW15 1RN
Map GtL: C2
Tel: 0181 788 0907
Please telephone for further details

Royal China ❀❀

Bustling, colourful Chinese restaurant with a great reputation. A meal just before Christmas proved to be fairly hectic, but the quality of food – fried crispy spring rolls, roast pork cheung fan, and crab meat dumpling just a few examples of the dim sum served till 5pm – made up for the sometimes brisk service. Our inspector followed this with a dish of 'delicate' sautéed oysters with ginger and spring onions, served with seafood fried rice. Set menus for two or more people are worth considering as they are more imaginative than most. The seating is well arranged, and prompt, efficient service can be expected.

Directions: Between Queensway & Bayswater Station.

13 Queensway W2 4QJ
Map: A3
Tel: 0171 221 2535
Fax: 0171 221 2535
Please telephone for further details

Royal Garden Hotel ❀❀❀

There's no missing the Royal Garden, as it stands sentinel to the entrance to Kensington Palace. But by the time you've whizzed up to the tenth floor one can be forgiven for forgetting this is a hotel. The aptly named Tenth is a stylish, contemporary restaurant with brilliant views over Kensington Gardens and Hyde Park. Food here is massively eclectic, with perhaps more nods towards the Far East than any other region. But Derek Baker is also capable of turning out a well-executed classic dish such as the pigeon with red wine jus, correctly cooked turnip, caramelised shallot, baby leeks and carrot and interestingly textured 'mate fame potato', tried at one winter dinner. That meal also produced a highly rated confit of duck with bold ginger and chilli, served in a crispy pancake with a honeyed sauce, a basket made from crisp plantain filled with bitter leaves and some excellent seared scallops garnished with a daring, greeny pesto-type sauce and a drizzle of orange oil,

2-24 Kensington High Street W8 4PT
Map GtL: C3
Tel: 0171 3611910
Fax: 0171 3611921
Chef: Derek Baker
Owner: The Goodwood Group
Cost: Alc £40. Fixed-price L £21. ☺ H/wine £13.75
Times: Noon-last L 2.30pm/5.30-last D 11pm. Closed L Sat, all Sun, 1-9 Jan
Additional: Children welcome. ❹ dishes.
Seats: 80
Smoking: No-smoking area; Air conditioning
Accommodation: 400 en suite
Credit cards: ▆ ▆ ▆ ▆ ▆ ▆ ▆ JCB

and superb langoustine tails seared with choy sum, green noodles with a touch of nam pla chilli jam and a caramel soy sauce. A spring lunch brought courgette and goats' cheese charlotte with mizuna and tomato verjus, fillet of red mullet, cucumber couscous and a sauce antiboise, plus a seriously good caramel mousse chiboust with lime chutney. Ancillaries are in keeping with the ambition of the place, with good canapés, petits fours and a variety of well-made breads.

Directions: Next door to Kensington Palace. Nearest Tube – High Street Kensington

Royal Lancaster Hotel, Nipa Thai ❀❀

Lancaster Terrace W2 2TY
Map GtL: C3
Tel: 0171 2626737
Fax: 0171 7243191
Chef: Nongyao Thoopchoi
Owner: The Lancaster Landmark Hotel Co Ltd
Cost: Alc £30, fixed-price L & D £23. ☺ H/wine £17
Times: Noon-last L 2pm/6.30-last D 10.30pm. Closed L Sat, all Sun
Additional: Children welcome; ◑ dishes.
Seats: 60
Smoking: Air conditioning
Accommodation: 418 en suite
Credit cards: ▬ ▦ ◥ ▭ ▦ ▣ JCB

Inspired by the original Nipa Restaurant in the Landmark Hotel, Bangkok, this hotel dining room is situated within the luxurious Lancaster Gate hotel and overlooks Kensington Gardens. It's smartly teak-panelled and decorated with traditional Thai furnishings, and there's charming service from staff who are attired in native costume. We sampled some good Thai cooking at a recent inspection meal. Soft and well-favoured fishcakes came with a vinegar dipping sauce, while stir-fried duck with ginger was really fragrant and served with superior plain steamed rice and a glass noodle salad that was hot with lime juice, chilli and galangal. For pudding, steamed bananas in coconut milk. Well-balanced set menus and a pricy cosmopolitan wine list.

Directions: Next to Hyde Park on the Bayswater Road. Nearest Tube – Lancaster Gate

Royal Lancaster Hotel, Park Restaurant ❀❀

Lancaster Terrace
W2 2TY
Map GtL: C3
Tel: 0171 2626737
Fax: 0171 7243191
Chef: Nigel Blatchford
Owners: The Lancaster Landmark Hotel Co. Ltd
Cost: Alc £23.50, fixed-price L & D £19.50 (2 courses). ☺ H/wine £17

Situated in the high-rise Royal Lancaster Hotel, the smart Park Restaurant, one of three restaurants at this luxuriously appointed establishment, offers modern British cooking, against a backdrop of panoramic views over Hyde Park and Kensington Gardens from the full length windows. Both the fixed-price menus and the *carte* offer a good choice of dishes. A typical meal may feature foie gras and duck liver parfait with fig chutney for starters, followed by a medley of seafood,

Royal Lancaster Hotel,
Park Restaurant

Times: 12.30-last L 2.30pm/6.30-last
D 10.30pm. Closed L Sat, Sun
Seats: 60. Jacket & tie preferred
Smoking: Air conditioning
Accommodation: 418 en suite
Credit cards: ■ ■ ■ ■ ■ ■ JCB

Directions: Next to Hyde Park on the
Bayswater Road. Nearest Tube –
Lancaster Gate

including lobster, tiger prawns, langoustines, monkfish and
mussels, in a creamy Thermidor sauce, accompanied by a good
spaghetti of vegetables. A well-made lemon tart may be among
the range of desserts displayed on the well-stocked trolley.

RSJ, The Restaurant on the
South Bank 🏵🏵

Occupying an old stable belonging to the Duchy of Cornwall,
the split-level, family-owned restaurant has a comfortably
warm but contemporary interior. Vivid vegetarian dishes
particularly catch the eye – roast beetroot stuffed with goats'
cheese and mushroom, deep-fried tofu, crispy carrots and pea
sauce, for example. Seasonal ingredients are used in intriguing
combinations, such as saddle of rabbit with risotto of lobster,
sautéed rabbit kidneys, baby asparagus, tarragon jus, but there
are also delicious-sounding, more mainstream pairings such as
tenderloin of pork with apple and celeriac purée, spinach, baby
carrots, apple and Calvados sauce.

Directions: On the corner of Coin St and Stamford St; near
National Theatre and LWT studios

13a Coin Street SE1 8YQ
Map: E3
Tel: 0171 6330881
Fax: 0171 4012455
Chef: Peter Lloyd
Owner: Nigel Wilkinson
Cost: Alc £25, fixed-price L & D
£16.95.☺ H/wine £10.95
Times: Noon-3pm/6-11pm.
Closed L Sat, all Sun, Bhs
Additional: Children welcome;
🍴 dishes
Seats: 80. Private dining room 20
Smoking: No pipes & cigars;
Air conditioning
Credit cards: ■ ■ ■ ■ ■

Rules 🏵🏵

Opposite the Vaudeville Theatre, this is one of London's oldest
eating places (owned by only three families since 1798), Rules
offers traditional British fare, notably excellent game obtained
from the owner's Scottish estate. The unique, civilised interior
– almost a museum of London's literary and theatrical history
– has long been a favourite with actors and theatre-goers, and
the pre-theatre dinner continues to offer good value for
money. A recent inspection meal commenced with a well-made
ravioli of wild mushrooms with a delicate glazed sauce,
followed by moist and tender breast of Gressingham duck,
served with a good confit of the leg and a rich sauce flavoured
with five spice. Caramelised vanilla and banana tart, topped
with banana ice cream, and good aromatic coffee rounded off
a successful meal. Further great British dishes range from
Stilton and walnut tart, and smoked Scottish salmon, to steak
and kidney pudding, and herb-crusted rack of lamb. Pleasant
and efficient service from smartly attired staff.

Directions: Nearest Tube – Covent Garden

35 Maiden Lane Covent Garden
WC2E 7LB
Map: D3
Tel: 0171 8365314
Fax: 0171 4971081
Chef: David Chambers
Owner: John Mayhew
Cost: Alc £30, fixed-price L (Sat &
Sun only) £17.95 (2 courses)
Times: Open all day, noon-last
D 11.30pm
Additional: Bar food
Seats: 130. Private dining rooms 64
Smoking: Air-conditioning
Credit cards: ■ ■ ■ ■ ■

Sabras ❀❀

The setting is unassuming, the décor bright and cheerful, the atmosphere that 'of someone's home rather than a High Street restaurant' and the food some of the best Indian vegetarian to be found in London. Starters might include banana and methi pakoda (bananas and chopped fenugreek leaves with a spicy gram flour coating) and delicately flavoured samosas, while mains range from Bombay potato dhosa served with coconut and coriander chutney to a dish of orange pumpkin and green cluster beans with cracked fenugreek seeds, aniseed and fresh spices. To drink there's a cosmopolitan list of beers, a few wines or cool refreshing lassi (salt, sweet or mango). Unhurried service keeps pace with a kitchen where everything is freshly cooked. All this and low prices too; worth seeking out.

Willesden High Road NW10 2RX
Map GtL: C3
Tel: 0181 4590340
Chefs/Owners: Hemant & Nalinee Desai
Cost: Alc £15. H/wine £9.95
Times: 6.30pm-10.30pm. Closed Mon
Additional: Children welcome;
❀ dishes
Seats: 32
Smoking: No-smoking area;
No pipes & cigars
Credit cards: None

Directions: Nearest tube – Willesden Green

Saint George's ❀

The hotel's restaurant is on the 15th floor and offers superb views across the city. The menu has something for everyone, with grills of steaks and Dover sole, deep-fried camembert and raspberry salsa, and lamb cutlets with a chicken and tomato mousse, minted sautéed potatoes and port wine sauce.

Langham Place
Regents Street W1N 8QS
Map: C4
Tel: 0171 5800111
Fax: 0171 4367997
Chef: David Constant
Owner: Forte Hotels
Cost: Alc £26.50, fixed price L £15 (2 courses)/D £21.50. ☺ H/wine £13.95
Times: Last L 2.30pm/last D 10pm

Additional: Bar food; Sunday L; Children welcome; ❀ dishes
Smoking: No pipes & cigars; Air conditioning
Accommodation: 86
Credit cards: 💳 JCB

Directions: Langham Place is N end of Regent St

St John ❀

Close to Smithfield Market, this stark, plain restaurant is housed in a former smokehouse, has its own bakery in a covered courtyard, and bar in the old smoke hole. Extraordinary menu with winkles and samphire, for example, or duck gizzard, broad beans and pea leaf, and chitterlings with turnip greens, and dishes arrive exactly as described. Try Eccles cake with Lancashire cheese, or Dorset apple cake.

26 St John Street
EC1M 4AY
Map: F5
Tel: 0171 2510848/2514998
Fax: 0171 2514090
Chef: Fergus Henderson
Owners: Trevor Gulliver Ptrs: Fergus Henderson, Jon Spiteri
Times: Noon-last L 3pm/6pm-last D 11.30pm. Closed L Sat, all Sun, Xmas/New Year

Additional: Bar meals; Children welcome; ❀ dishes
Seats: 100. Private dining room 22
Credit cards: 💳 JCB

Directions: 3 mins walk from Farringdon Tube & BR stations. The restaurant is 100 metres from Smithfield Market on N side

St Quentin Brasserie ❀❀

From the smart wood panelling down to the professional but aloof service, this is the quintessential French brasserie, a piece of Paris in Knightsbridge. The set menu and the *carte*, which change seasonally, focus on simple dishes faultlessly executed. You will find French classics such as onion soup, confit, and boudin blanc and, of course, excellent crusty baguette, but more up-beat ideas come in the guise of the deepest, richest green nettle soup served in a large individual tureen and

243 Brompton Road SW3 2EP
Map: B2
Tel: 0171 5898005
Fax: 0171 5846064
Chef: Malcolm John
Owner: Groupe Chez Gerard
Cost: Alc £35, fixed-price L & D £12.50 (2 courses). H/wine £10
Times: Noon-last L 3pm/6.30-last D 11pm

smelling like the essence of spring. Main courses may include leek and Gorgonzola risotto, pig's trotters stuffed with morels, or Scotch fillet with tarragon sauce and French-cut chips. Ask for salad and you will receive a big bowl of fresh assorted greens perfectly dressed in classic vinaigrette. Prune and Armagnac mousse is a perfectly balanced dessert choice, tarte Tatin a popular alternative. The extensive wine list is exclusively French.

Directions: Nearest Tube: South Kensington. Opposite The Brompton Oratory

Additional: Children welcome; ❹ dishes
Seats: 55. Private dining room 18
Smoking: No pipes; Air conditioning
Credit cards: 💳 💳 💳 💳 💳 💳 💳 JCB

Salloos ❁

Long-standing Pakistani restaurant in a charming Knightsbridge mews. Tandoori grills and specialities such as chicken karahi (from the Khyber region) and haleem akbari (shredded lamb cooked in whole wheatgerm, lentils and spices), pilaff rice (cooked in lamb stock), and various kormas, masalas, and koftas are all freshly prepared.

Additional: No children under 6, ❹ dishes
Smoking: No pipes & cigars; Air conditioning
Credit cards: 💳 💳 💳 💳 💳 💳 💳

Directions: Nr. Hyde Park Corner – take 1st L into Wilton Place, 1st R opposite Berkeley Hotel. Nearest tube – Knightsbridge

62-64 Kinnerton Street SW1X 8ER
Map: B2
Tel: 0171 2354444
Fax: 0171 2595703
Chef: Abdul Aziz
Owner: Mr Muhammad Salahuddin
Cost: *Alc* £25, fixed-price L £16/D £25 (4 courses). ☺ H/wine £12.50.
Times: Last L 2.30pm/last D 11.15pm. Closed Sun, 25-26 Dec

San Lorenzo Fuoriporta ❁

Worple Road Mews SW19 7PA
Map GtL: C2
Tel: 0181 9468463
Fax: 0181 9479810
Please telephone for further details

Solid rustic fare continues to pull in the crowds at this popular Italian. A small door leads into an attractive walkway with greenery and flagstoned floor, where friendly staff take you to your table. Dishes from the one-page menu might include mushroom risotto, grilled sea bass and braised shank of lamb with polenta.

Directions: Bottom of Wimbledon Hill Road, right into Worple Road, then first right into Worple Road Mews

Santini ❁

'Showroom' windows make this slick, professional Italian a place in which to be seen. 'Perfect' spinach and ricotta ravioli in a lemon and basil butter sauce, and tender osso buco with saffron risotto, set a

29 Ebury Street SW1W 0NZ
Map: C1
Tel: 0171 7304094/7308275
Fax: 0171 7300544
Chef: Giuseppe Rosselli

Santini

Owner: Gino Santin
Cost: Alc £37.50, fixed-price
L £19.75. ☺ H/wine £15. 75
Times: Last L 2.30pm/D 11.30pm
(10.30pm Sun). Closed L Sat, L Sun,
some Bhs, 25-26 Dec
Additional: Children welcome;
🍃 dishes
Seats: 65
Smoking: No pipes in dining room;
Air conditioning
Credit cards: ▅▅ ▆▆ ▅▅ ▆ ▆▆ ▆ 🖻 JCB

fast, modern pace. Heart-stopping espresso, great Italian pastries, but pricey wine list.

Directions: On corner of Ebury Street and Lower Belgrave Street, 2 mins walk from Victoria Station

Sartoria ❀❀

The Saville Row location provides inspiration for the name (Italian for tailor, and a clue to the style of food) and for some of the decor: a button motif is engraved on glass and chinaware, a bundle of cutting patterns hang on a hook, and some obese tailors dummies stand sentinel as you enter ('and make you think of skipping dessert'). Otherwise, neutral colours – 'safari-suit' beige marble floor, 'business suit' grey walls, chairs and banquettes. Good Italian bread comes with extra virgin olive oil, then there's the likes of rabbit risotto with borlotti beans and rosemary, pan-fried scallops with fresh broad beans, peas and mint, and chunky roast potatoes. Green tomato tart with zabaglione had to be tried for dessert, and was surprisingly good with a flavour similar to apricots, it came with a rich zabaglione. This is good, sophisticated cooking, similar in style to the River Café (from where the chef hails). Espresso comes with Amaretti di Saronno, and there are over twenty grappas to chose from.

Directions: Nearest Tube: Piccadilly

20 Saville Row W1X 1AE
Map: D3
Tel: 0171 5347000
Chef: Darren Simpson
Owner: Conran Restaurants
Cost: Alc £50. H/wine £14
Times: Noon-3pm/6.30-11pm.
Closed D Sun
Additional: Sunday L;
Children welcome; 🍃 dishes
Seats: 120
Smoking: Air conditioning
Credit cards: ▅▅ ▆▆ ▅▅ ▆ ▆▆ ▆ 🖻 JCB

Les Saveurs de Jean-Christophe Novelli ❀❀❀

Back in the *Guide* after a brief period of unrest and uncertainty, this luxurious basement restaurant in the heart of Mayfair is now under the guidance of Jean-Christophe Novelli. Blond wood and the softest of pale colours, well-spaced tables covered in resolutely white linen and gleaming crystal tend to create a rather sterile atmosphere, and conversations tend to be in hushed tones. Jean-Christophe Novelli takes a more executive role these days (what with a mini-empire to run), but the kitchen interpret his ideas well. Novelli has always revelled in seafood and a pair of dishes sampled at inspection proved the point; one was the absolute highlight of the meal, a piperade of squid and langoustine with a red pepper jus that just burst forth with big Mediterranean flavours, it was positively 'sun-drenched in feel'. Again, roast sea bass with a

37a Curzon Street W1A 7AF
Map: C3
Tel: 0171 4918919
Fax: 0171 4913658
Chef: Jean-Christophe Novelli,
Nick Wilson
Owner: Jean-Christophe Novelli
Cost: £40. H/wine£15.50
Times: Noon-last L 2.30pm/6-last
D 10.30pm. Closed L Sat & Mon, all
Sun
Additional: 🍃 dishes
Seats: 60. Private dining room 12
Credit cards: ▅▅ ▆▆ ▅▅ ▆

confit of aubergine, couscous coriander and sun-dried tomato sauce produced big flavours working well together. Technique is not in question, but the kitchen does occasionally miss a beat, and timing is not all it should be. A signature hot and cold plate of white and dark chocolate was no more than a great chocolate fondant with a white chocolate ice cream that was too heavy on the rest of the ingredients, and a strawberry Tatin really missed the mark. The waiting staff are very French and charming.

Directions: Nearest Tube – Green Park. Next to Curzon Cinema

The Savoy Grill ❀❀

Strand WC2R 0EU
Map: E3
Tel: 0171 8364343
Fax: 0171 2406040
Chef: Simon Scott
Owner: The Savoy Group plc
Cost: *Alc* £50
Times: 12.30-last L 2.30pm/6-last D 11.30pm. Closed L Sat, all Sun, Aug
Additional: Bar food L; No children under 14; ❂ dishes
Seats: 100. Jacket & tie preferred
Smoking: No pipes; Air conditioning
Accommodation: 207 en suite
Credit cards: ▬ ▬ ▬ ▬ ▬

For decades the Savoy has been frequented by the great and the good, the rich and the famous, and as the 20th century comes to a close, it shows no sign of giving up its enviable position as one of the country's leading hotels. The yew-panelled Savoy Grill, with its army of waiters providing polished service, is the business community's preferred choice for dining, and has an atmosphere to suit. The menu still features traditional British favourites such as roast beef or steak and kidney pie, but alongside these a growing choice of modern dishes vie for your attention. Pappardelle with woodland mushrooms and mascarpone, and pan-fried scallops with parsnip cream and baby leeks, are just a couple of the dozen or so main courses on offer. Our inspector enjoyed a spring lunch of crisp red onion tart with rocket salad and goats' cheese, followed by a well-constructed dish of roast wood pigeon with peas and bacon. The wine list is shared with the River Restaurant (see entry below).

AA Wine Shortlisted for Award-see page 16

Directions: From Embankment Tube, you can walk east through the riverside gardens to the hotel

The Savoy, River Restaurant ❀❀❀

'The place was absolutely packed and had a real buzz and air of excitement about it', was the comment of an inspector, enjoying the popular Saturday night 'stomping' evening. 'I suspect that everyone who eats here does so with a level of high excitement and expectation, so the place naturally has a user friendly feel.' Coveted tables, whether for the Saturday dinner dance, or the more restrained weekdays, are by the windows overlooking the Thames. On that evening (tucked

Strand
WC2R 0EU
Map: E3
Tel: 0171 8364343
Fax: 0171 2408749
Chef: Anton Edelmann
Owner: The Savoy Group plc
Cost: *Alc* £45,fixed-price L £28.50/D £39.50 (£43.50 Fri & Sat). H/wine £18.50

The Savoy, River Restaurant

Times: 12.30-last L 2.30pm/7.30-last D midnight
Additional: Sunday L; ❹ dishes
Seats: 150. Private rooms 200-250. Jacket & tie preferred
Smoking: Air conditioning
Accommodation: 207 en suite
Credit cards: ▬ ▬ ▬ ▬

alone behind a pillar) we tried the set gourmet menu – four courses plus *amuse-bouche*, petits fours and a different wine with each course, and found it excellent value. Quality purchasing and skilled execution shone through. Lobster ravioli, topped by a large lobster claw came with a delicate beurre blanc, was followed by turbot with morels, then the centrepiece, a well-flavoured fillet of lamb, topped with a mint crust, accompanied by a potato cake and a charlotte of vegetables. To finish, a well-risen cappuccino soufflé served with an exceptional thyme ice cream. The *carte* mixes a classic tournedos Rossini with an up-to-date whole lobster in lemongrass flavoured sauce on a tarragon purée. The set lunch could bring wonderfully traditional daily specials of roast saddle and best end of lamb with herbs and glazed fennel, steak, kidney and oyster pudding, and a Sunday roast sirloin of beef with Yorkshire pudding. The wine list (shared with the Grill Room, see entry above) shows a strong affinity to France with the emphasis on top-end Burgundies and clarets with prices to match. Having said that, a good list of house wines keeps the price below £20, and there is plenty to choose in the £30 bracket.

Signature dishes: Asparagus with summer truffles and balsamic vinegar; courgette flower filled with seafood; partridge breast with black pudding, goose liver, wild mushrooms ravioli and ceps; roasted guinea fowl filled with pistachios and two cabbages.

Directions: From Embankment Tube, you can walk east through the riverside gardens to the hotel

AA Wine Award–see page 16
Shortlisted for

Scotts ❀

Themed in the style of a thirties luxury liner, Scotts has a sophisticated air. Popular classics get a modern look with favourite choices from the mainly seafood menu taking in whitebait with yogurt and lime dip, steamed mussels with leek and rosemary, and roast skate with mustard mash and brown nut caper butter. Formal, very professional service.

Additional: Bar food; Sunday L; ❹ dishes
Smoking: No-smoking area; No pipes & cigars; Air conditioning
Credit cards: ▬ ▬ ▬ ▬ ▬ ▬ ▬ JCB

Directions: Mount St runs between Park Lane and Berkeley Sq. Nearest Tube – Green Park

20 Mount Street W1Y 6HE
Map: C3
Tel: 0171 6295248
Fax: 0171 4998246
Chef: Nigel Davis
Owner: Groupe Chez Gerard plc
Cost: *Alc* £35, fixed-price L £23-£25. H/wine £13.25
Times: Last L 3pm/last D 11pm. Closed some Bhs

Searcy's Brasserie ❀❀❀

Library Floor Barbican Centre
Silk Street EC2Y 8DS
Map: F4
Tel: 0171 5883008
Fax: 0171 3827247
Chef: Tom Ilic
Owner: Searcy's Tansley & Co Ltd
Cost: £35, fixed-price L & D
£21.50. ☺ H/wine £10.50
Times: Noon-2.30pm/5-10.30pm (till
6.30 Sun). Closed L Sat
Additional: Bar food; Sunday L;
Children welcome; ♨ dishes
Seats: 120
Smoking: No-smoking area;
Air conditioning
Credit cards:

Much frequented by actors from the RSC at the Barbican, the decor reflects the light, modern and fresh style of European cooking. Former sous chef, Tom Ilic, has taken over the stove from Richard Corrigan (see entry, Lindsay House), and he has settled down to the job well. His *carte* is a model of brevity without sacrificing interest or explanation. Excitingly original dishes show that he has learnt well from one of our most creative chefs, and includes the likes of monkfish tartare, chorizo and olive oil, and sauté of sweetbreads with carrots and cardamom, both revealing a mastery of balance. Unusual vegetables are used to striking effect – wild mushroom and salsify gratin with rocket leaves, baked John Dory with black cabbage, shrimp croquette and coriander, and breast of Gresingham duck with sweet potato and bok choi. But overall simplicity rules, and dishes such as steamed sole, baby vegetables and saffron bouillon, and sauté of pork fillet, polenta, anchovy and paprika sauce are notable for the restraint used in the kitchen, allowing the quality of fresh ingredients to sing out. Note that the black dining chairs with different coloured seats belie their somewhat austere look. The fifty or so wines are carefully chosen and prices fairly reflect quality throughout.

Signature dishes: Rack of kid, aubergine and goats' cheese cannelloni; monkfish tartare, chorizo, olive oil; wild mushroom and salsify gratin, rocket; pork fillet, polenta, anchovy and paprika sauce

Directions: Nearest Tubes – Barbican and Moorgate

Selsden Park Hotel ❀   NEW

See Where London Meets Section page 153

755 Fulham Road ❀❀

Not having to remember the address is just one of the many merits of this sprightly Parsons Green restaurant. This is an energetic show, with the brilliant yellow walls and up-beat service signalling an eager tone that extends to the lively mix of a broadly modern French menu. No shortage of imagination in a *carte* that often introduces an unexpected element to classic dishes, but the innovation is consistently handled with intelligence and there is rarely a flavour out of place. This is not so much fusion, more a blurring of the culinary borders.

755 Fulham Road SW6 5UU
Map: A1
Tel: 0171 3710755
Fax: 0171 3710095
Chef: Alan Thompson
Owners: Alan & Georgina Thompson
Cost: Fixed-price L £10 (2 courses)/D
£18 (2 courses). H/wine £9.50
Times: 12.30pm-last L 2.30pm/7pm-
last D 10.45pm. Closed D Sun, all
Mon, Xmas, Easter, summer

755 Fulham Road

Additional: Sunday L; Children welcome; 🌢 dishes
Seats: 60. Private dining room 35
Smoking: No pipes & cigars; Air conditioning
Credit cards: ■ ▰ ▚ ▱ ▤ ◧

Directions: Nearest Tube – Parsons Green

Witness galantine of quail with a mousseline of the bird and 'quite brilliant' scotch quails' eggs, foie gras griddled with Yorkshire pudding and Madeira, or roast poussin with a confit of the leg and a Mediterranean-style tomato and courgette galette. Some familiar names on the dessert front including a lemon curd brûlée 'creamy and intense', and a coconut parfait that arrived with a praiseworthy banana ice cream. The wine list offers heaps of character in a short list and mark-ups show genuine restraint.

Shepherds ❀❀

The drawn images of the owners, Michael Caine and Richard Shepherd, adorn the walls and menus, and the studded banquettes and partitions add an almost saloon-style atmosphere. The menu takes in many of the adventurous ideas of the 80s, and although it now seems a bit dated, it still offers plenty of variety. There are several 'nursery' dishes such as home-made bangers-and-mash, as well as classic oysters, and roast rib of beef with Yorkshire pudding. The kitchen is sure-footed; green pea and bacon soup was based on a fine-flavoured stock, and potted duck was skilfully made. Wilted spinach, tomato and capers made a good foil to seared fillet of sea bass, and grilled calves' liver was tender and bloody as requested, served with melting fondue onions, a rich but light jus and excellent back bacon. A particularly light toffee pudding was packed with dates. There are good cheeses and Welsh rarebit savoury.

Directions: Near Tate Gallery and Westminster Hospital. Nearest Tube – Pimlico

Marsham Court
Marsham Street SW1P 4LA
Map: D2
Tel: 0171 8349552
Fax: 0171 2336047
Chef: James Rice
Owners: Richard Shepherd & Michael Caine
Cost: Fixed-price L £21.95 (2 courses)/D £23.95. H/wine £12
Times: 12.30-2.45pm/6.30-11pm. Closed Sat, Sun, Bhs
Additional: Bar food; Children welcome; 🌢 dishes.
Seats: 90. Private room 32
Smoking: Air conditioning
Credit cards: ■ ▰ ▚ ▱ ▤ ◧ ▣ JCB

Sheraton Park Tower, Restaurant One-O-One ❀❀❀

Although Pascal Proyart's seafood menu continues to hone in on scallops and sea bass as signature dishes, there is no trace of the ocean theme in One-O-One, which sits on the terra firma of the Knightsbridge pavement. The cooking is thoroughly enjoyable, and young French waiters are eager to please; this is a nice diversion from Harrods and Harvey Nicks round the corner. Simplicity, no complications, with good focus on the prime element and an unwavering adherence to freshness are all hallmarks here. Note a February dinner that opened with

William St Knightsbridge
SW1X 7RN
Map: B2
Tel: 0171 2907101
Fax: 0171 2356196
Chef: Pascal Proyart
Owner: Sheraton
Cost: Alc £40, fixed-price L £25/D £42. H/wine £17
Times: Noon-last L 2.30pm/7-last D 10.30pm

sweet, melt-in-your-mouth scallops, thinly sliced, teamed with wild mushrooms, truffle jus and two creamy shavings of foie gras that hit the right balance of flavour without being too overpowering. 'Juicy, fresh, just cooked' sea bass followed, topped with caviar, excellent shallot sauce and one small potato thinly sliced and five baby leeks beneath the fish. Bitter chocolate tart was paired with a superb orange ice cream, smooth, creamy without being cloying, hugely refreshing 'it smacked of the most perfumed mandarins'. Meat dishes bring feuillantine of Bresse pigeon with foie gras and truffle and ruby port sauce, or persillade of chicken with girolles and morels. A choice of five breads includes a delicate spinach flavour. There's a good choice of some 16 wines by the glass.

Additional: Sunday L; Children welcome; 🌢 dishes
Seats: 86
Smoking: No-smoking area; Air conditioning
Accommodation: 289 en suite
Credit cards: 💳 💳 💳 💳 💳 💳

Directions: Knightsbridge Tube station, E, just after Harvey Nichols

Simply Nico ❀❀

As monikers go this one is hard to argue with. Simplicity pervades every aspect of this reassuringly straightforward operation. Side-street location and shop-front exterior give way to a similarly unassuming dining room where the mustard walls, wooden floor and closely set tables all contribute to an air of relaxed conviviality. The cooking, too, is perfectly in tune with the surroundings. Elemental and uncluttered, first-class ingredients, sure-footed execution and distinct flavours are the undoubted virtues of lunch and dinner menus that (with the exception of a slight increase in price) are almost interchangeable. The style is undoubtedly conservative (perhaps a dangerous adjective this close to Parliament) but why change when dishes as fundamental and satisfying as cassoulet of duck with Toulouse sausage continue to pack them in? Chin-greasingly moist confit, great chunks of pork belly and a mound of steaming beans made this the heavyweight highlight of one inspection lunch, which also turned up a worthy gâteau of salt cod and new potatoes. Cherry clafoutis with vanilla crème fraîche finished off a sturdy springtime meal. Branches of Simply Nico, run on similar lines, can be found at the Barbican, 7 Goswell Road, EC1, tel: 0171 3367677, and also at 7 Park Walk, SW10, tel: 0171 3498866.

48a Rochester Row SW1P 1JU
Map: D2
Tel: 0171 6308061
Fax: 0171 8288541
Chef: Richard Hugill
Owner: The Restaurant Partnership
Cost: Fixed-price D £27
Times: Noon-last L 2pm/7-last D 11pm. Closed L Sat, all Sun, 1 wk Xmas, Easter
Additional: No children under 12; 🌢 dishes
Seats: 45
Smoking: No pipes & cigars; Air conditioning
Credit cards: 💳 💳 💳 💳 💳 💳 💳 JCB

Directions: Corner of Emery Hill Street. Nearest Tube – Victoria

Simpsons in the Strand ❀❀

Little has changed at this venerable English eating house since it was established in 1828. The aura of tradition pervades the handsome panelled dining room, with its antique high-backed chairs, grand fireplace, ornate chandeliers, and famous silver carving trolleys which continue to wheel around the 23 roast saddles of lamb and the 25 roast sirloins of Scotch beef that are served daily. The menu, or 'Bill of Fare' entertains with anecdotes and historical facts and figures, as well as listing such classics as Irish stew, steak and kidney pudding and boiled silverside with pease pudding and caraway dumplings. Menu choices extend to lobster soup, potted shrimps, poached wild salmon with asparagus and hollandaise, and those hallowed English puddings of treacle sponge, Bakewell tart and savouries such as Welsh rarebit and Scotch woodcock. Breakfast here is also recommended.

100 Strand WC2R 0EW
Map: D3
Tel: 0171 8369112
Fax: 0171 8361381
Chef: Nigel Boschetti
Owner: The Savoy Group
Cost: Alc £30, fixed-price L & D £15 (2 courses). ☺ H/wine £15
Times: Noon-last L 2.30pm/5.30-last D 11pm. Closed 25-26 Dec
Additional: Sunday L; 🌢 dishes
Seats: 240. Private dining room 80
Smoking: Air conditioning
Credit cards: 💳 💳 💳 💳 💳 💳 JCB

Directions: Nearest Tube – Charing Cross. In the middle of the Strand between Charing Cross & Waterloo Bridge. Next to the Savoy Hotel.

Singapore Garden

A family-run affair in a parade of shops: two rooms, one with a bar, decorated in pale green with flowers on the tables, paper napkins and friendly service. The menu lists some fairly standard Chinese dishes, so hit the specials and the Singaporean and Malaysian specialities for what the house excels at. Singapore laksa is a substantial, creamy soup gently flavoured with curry containing beansprouts, prawns, rice vermicelli, spongy squares of fishcake and coriander – the best dish of a meal for one inspector. Chilli sings out of a main course of succulent chicken stir-fried with spring onions and lemongrass, and other authentic dishes include nonya fried beansprouts (Penang dried salt fish), pig's trotter braised in soy, garlic, five spices and star anise, and rojak (fruit and vegetables tossed in shrimp paste). Choose a beancurd or a vegetable dish, straw mushrooms with broccoli, say to accompany. There may be lychees or fresh fruit to finish.

Directions: Off Finchley Road, on R before Belsize Park roundabout. Nearest Tube – Swiss Cottage or Finchley Road. No parking restrictions

83/83a Fairfax Road
NW6 4DY
Map GtL: C4
Tel: 0171 3285314
Fax: 0171 6240656
Chef: Siam Kiang Lim
Owners: The Lim Family
Cost: Alc £22.50, fixed-price L £6.25 (2 courses)/D £17.50 (5 courses). ☺ H/wine £10.95
Times: Noon-2.45pm/6-10.45pm (Fri & Sat till 11.15pm). Closed 1 wk Xmas
Additional: Children welcome; 🍴 dishes
Seats: 100. Private dining room 50
Smoking: No pipes & cigars; Air conditioning
Credit cards: 🃏 🃏 🃏 🃏 🃏 🃏 🃏 JCB

Snows-on-the-Green

The bright, inviting look of the restaurant matches the unstuffy welcome. There is a warm, rather Tuscan feel to the interior, achieved through bare woods, and vast floral displays with contorted willow. The menu comes straight to the point: spring green gazpacho, goats' cheese fritters, marinated vegetables and chilli salsa, braised knuckle of lamb in brioche crumbs, flageolet beans and spinach, and roast plaice with green risotto and basil dressing, all featured on a spring menu. A chicken liver parfait was generously portioned, the silky smooth richness tempered with pickled grapes and neatly striped toasted brioche. Daube of beef with bacon and chestnuts had a sauce sweetened with carrot and orange and was served with pumpkin ravioli and perfect, wilted spinach. Our inspector ended a very satisfying meal with chocolate marquise and praline ice cream which came with a sauce so glossy you could see your face in it.

Directions: Nearest Tube – Hammersmith/Goldhawk Road. Opposite Brook Green

166 Shepherd's Bush Road
Hammersmith W6 7PB
Map GtL: C3
Tel: 0171 6032142
Fax: 0171 6027553
Chef/Owner: Sebastian Snow
Cost: Alc £20, fixed-price L £15.50. ☺ H/wine £9.75.
Times: Noon-last L 3pm/6pm-D 11pm. Closed Sat L, Sun D, Xmas, Bhs
Additional: Sunday L; Children welcome; 🍴 dishes
Seats: 75. Private dining room 35
Smoking: Air conditioning
Credit cards: 🃏 🃏 🃏 🃏 🃏 🃏 🃏 JCB

Soho Soho ❀

In the heart of Soho, the bustle of the street tumbles into the popular downstairs brasserie, while upstairs a more formal atmosphere prevails. Great dishes include grilled tuna steak topped with sage and spicy salsa, and grillade of scallops with chicory and pickled walnuts. The wine list is well balanced and offers a good range under £20.

Directions: Nearest Tubes – Tottenham Court Road, Leicester Square

11 Frith Street W1V 5TS
Map: D4
Tel: 0171 494 3491
Fax: 0171 437 3091
Please telephone for further details

Sonny's Restaurant ✿✿

The room just narrowly avoids a stark, minimalist look, and the lively daily menu gets it just right with smoked haddock, saffron and chive risotto, and marinated scallops with tomato, herbs and sweet lemon vinaigrette amongst the pacy starters. Classics are reworked with roast sea bass given a sharp lift with dandelion leaves, sweet Dijon mustard and Jersey potatoes, and garlic leaves lend an interesting dimension to pan-fried calves' liver with grilled pancetta and red onions. The café menu includes grilled chicken and mango sandwich with frites, Caesar salad and steamed fillet of plaice on carrot and Parmesan risotto. The intriguing pudding menu includes a highly recommended lemongrass crème brûlée and warm rhubarb Bakewell tart.

Directions: From Castlenau end of Church Road, on left by shops. Nearest Tube – Hammersmith

94 Church Road Barnes SW13 0DQ
Map: C3
Tel: 0181 7480393
Fax: 0181 7482698
Chef: Leigh Diggins
Owners: Rebecca Mascarenhas, James Harris
Cost: Alc £28, fixed-price L £12 (2 courses). ☺ H/wine £9.50
Times: 12.30-last L 2.30pm/7.30-last D 11pm. Closed D Sun, Bhs
Additional: Sunday L; Children welcome; ✿ dishes
Seats: 103. Private dining room 20
Smoking: No pipes & cigars; Air conditioning
Credit cards: ■ ■ ■ ℂ ■ ℙ

Sotheby's, The Café ✿✿

Located inside the auction house, visitors can roam through the galleries, view and attend sales either before or after (or maybe between) their lunchtime cream of celeriac, greens and potato soup, grilled fillet of haddock, spinach and grilled pepper relish, and baked caramel brownie cheesecake. A great place for breakfast muesli and Scottish smoked salmon and scrambled eggs (buy Sotheby's house-blend tea as a present), and an equally engaging spot for afternoon tea – toasted tea cakes, cucumber sandwiches, home-made cakes and all. Mobile phones are not permitted – so you can't bid whilst scoffing the scones.

Directions: Nearest Tube – Bond Street

34 Bond Street W1A 2AA
Map: D4
Tel: 0171 2935077
Chef: Caroline Crumby
Owner: Alfred Taubman
Cost: Alc £25
Times: L only, noon-last L 3pm. Closed Sat, Xmas, New Year, Easter, last 2 wks Aug
Additional: Sunday L
Seats: 45
Smoking: No smoking in dining room; Air conditioning
Credit cards: ■ ■ ■ ℂ ■ ◗ ℙ

Spiga ✿   NEW

In true Soho style this Italian newcomer from the Zafferano stable (see entry) buzzes with activity, and the noise level is high. The kitchen works flat out to produce a promising menu with pizzas (from a wood-fired oven) at its core. Light pasta meals and simple meat and fish dishes, monkfish with sweet and sour sauce, for example, are transformed into great dishes. Memorable desserts include lemon and mascarpone tart.

Credit cards: ■ ■ ■ ℂ ■

Directions: At the Shaftesbury Avenue end of Wardour Street

84-86 Wardour Street W1V 3LS
Map: D4
Tel: 0171 7343444
Fax: 0171 7343332
Chef: Michele Franzolin
Owner: A-Z Restaurants
Cost: Alc £20. ☺ H/wine £9
Times: Last L 3pm/last D 11pm. Closed Xmas, Bhs
Additional: Children welcome; ✿ dishes
Smoking: Air conditioning

La Spighetta ✿   NEW

Lively, bustling, modern Italian with an open wood-burning oven producing a range of great pizzas. Wild mushrooms layered with asiago cheese and wrapped in Savoy cabbage works well, and lasagnette of fresh vegetables and basil is surprisingly intense. Home-made ices are a speciality – try the gianduia.

Credit cards: ■ ■ ■ ℂ ■

Directions: Half way down Baker St towards Oxford St turn L into Blandford St. Nearest tube – Baker St

43 Blandford Street W1H 3AE
Map: B4
Tel/Fax: 0171 4867340
Chef: Franco Parisi
Owners: Franco & Lee-Ann Parisi
Cost: Alc £16. ☺ H/wine £9
Times: Last L 2.30pm/last D 10.30pm (Fri & Sat till 11)
Additional: Children welcome; ✿ dishes
Smoking: No-smoking area; No pipes & cigars; Air conditioning

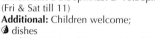

The Square ✸✸✸✸

Modern restaurant minimalism is taken only so far here: big, partially etched windows allow light to flood in; the floor is parquet; there's some colour in the careful use of browns and orange; splendid, bold abstracts draw the eye; tables are well spaced; chairs comfortable; service top-notch. Philip Howard's cooking displays an assured confidence, and he deals in strong, clear flavours from an amuse-bouch of intense parsley soup with truffle oil and a soft-centred quail's egg to a sauté of John Dory with a lasagne of tomato and sardines. Or take the boldness displayed in a signature dish of sauté of langoustines and scallops, the earthy garnish of morels, thyme and garlic working really well with the sweet seafood and the heady floral notes from the thyme adding extra dimension. Classics are reworked with a seafood bisque set off by a courgette flower stuffed with a subtle, delicate scallop mousse, and pot-roasted chicken updated with a tortellini of chanterelles and tarragon – the balance of the wonderfully light chicken broth, spot-on pasta parcels and the right tarragon notes being a modern classic in itself. Other success have included terrine and consommé of duck with toasted raisin bread, roast cod with Savoy cabbage and button onions, and herb-crusted saddle of lamb with white bean purée and garlic. The pastry work is special: a great tarte Tatin with Marsala ice cream 'rivalled Marco's for the depth of skill and flavour, the ice cream was fabulous and reminiscent of zabaglione' and a gâteau Opéra, served with chocolate sauce and vanilla ice cream has been much approved. Great breads and room temperature butter say it all.

Signature dishes: Roast foie gras with caramelised endive and Muscat grapes; roast pigeon from Bresse with pommes Rossini; lemon and lime soufflé and coconut ice cream.

6 Bruton Street W1X 7AG
Map: C3
Tel: 0171 4957100
Fax: 0171 4957150
Chef: Philip Howard
Owner: Nigel Platts-Martin
Cost: Fixed-price D £45. H/wine £18.50
Times: Noon-3pm/6.30-10.45pm (10pm Sun). Closed L Sat, L Sun
Additional: 🌢 dishes
Seats: 70. Private dining room 18
Smoking: No pipes & cigars; Air conditioning
Credit cards: 🔳 🔳 🔳 🔳 🔳 🔳 🔳

Directions: Nearest Tube – Bond Street

The Stafford ✸✸

Tucked away in exclusive St James's, The Stafford is a jewel among top-class luxury hotels, elegant and charming with courteous, professional service. The American Bar, famous for its collection of sporting ties and caps, and the ancient wine cellars, described as 'quite wonderful', are used for private dinners and wine tastings. Top-quality ingredients and technical accomplishment are the hallmarks of the kitchen. Eating off the *carte*, an inspector loved a starter of Parma ham with rocket and grilled figs, and wild mushroom risotto with Parmesan was no less impressive. Mushrooms might make

16-18 St James's Place SW1A 1NJ
Map: D4
Tel: 0171 4930111
Fax: 0171 4937121
Chef: Chris Oakes
Owner: Shire Inns
Cost: *Alc* £38.50, fixed-price L £23.50/D £26.50. H/wine £17.50
Times: 12.30-last L 2.30pm/6-last D 10.30pm. Closed L Sat
Additional: Bar food; Sunday L; Children welcome; 🌢 dishes
Seats: 50. Private room 44; Jacket & tie preferred
Smoking: No-smoking area; No pipes & cigars; Air conditioning
Accommodation: 81 en suite
Credit cards: 🔳 🔳 🔳 🔳 🔳 🔳 🔳

Directions: Nearest Tube – Green Park. 5 mins St James's Palace

another appearance as a main course, this time grilled, filled with goats' cheese and topped with tomato concasse and garlic breadcrumbs and served with parisienne potatoes and runner beans; there might also be plainly grilled Dover sole or a unique version of osso buco. Banana and chocolate chip steamed pudding – 'as light as a feather' – with chocolate sauce has been among successes on the dessert menu. The wine list is a massive tome: stick to the house wines or seek guidance.

Star of India ❀❀

154 Old Brompton Road SW5 0BE
Map: A1
Tel: 0171 373 2901
Fax: 0171 373 5664
Chef: Veneet Bhatia
Please telephone for further details

Wedged in a small parade of shops on the Old Brompton Road, the Star of India has a fairly unassuming exterior. Inside, however, you will find cutting edge Indian cooking, amongst the best in London. The menu is unlike any other: inventive main courses take in baby lamb chops steeped in cream cheese and ginger marinade; soft-shelled crabs enveloped in a carom seed, lemon and chilli marinade; and boned quails stuffed with chicken mince and dried fruits. The highlight of a recent meal was an 'outstanding' baked fillet of sea bass coated in lemon grass, coriander, mint and dill masala, which had 'stunning flavours'. Imaginative desserts include dum malai chikki – steamed milk pudding scented with nutmeg and cardamom, 'chocomosa' – marbled white and plain chocolate with chenna and roasted almonds, and a wonderful dish of roasted pineapple flavoured with saffron and fennel seed and cooked in the tandoor.

Directions: Nearest Tube – Gloucester Road

Stephen Bull Restaurant ❀❀

5-7 Blandford Street W1H 3AA
Map: B4
Tel: 0171 4869696
Fax: 0171 4903128
Chef: Robert Jones
Owner: Stephen Bull
Cost: *Alc* £35. H/wine £12.95
Times: 12.15-last L 2.30pm/6.30-10.30. Closed L Sat, Sun
Additional: Children welcome;
❀ dishes
Seats: 55
Smoking: Air conditioning
Credit cards:

The longest standing of all the three Stephen Bull Restaurants. Stark yellow walls contrast with turquoise ones – the only two colours in this place where 'the stylish crowd were all wearing shades of grey, black and navy'. It's not large, mirrored walls create some illusion of space, but tables are close. New blood in the kitchen comes with a good pedigree and early reports are very positive about the cooking. Sardine and roast pepper tart with pesto was exactly as it sounds, with good flaky pastry and clear fresh fish flavour. Braised neck of lamb with butter beans, chorizo, and artichokes was a nicely composed dish with the excellent flavoured lamb getting good back-up from all the other elements. Pudding was a pear feuilleté topped with chopped fruit in a butterscotch sauce. Staff are solicitous, the place is obviously popular (booking is recommended) and there's a well-chosen selection of wines by the glass.

Directions: Off Marylebone High St, 75 yards down on the left. Nearest Tube – Bond Street

Stephen Bull Smithfield ❀❀

71 St John Street EC1 4AN
Map: E5
Tel: 0171 4901750
Fax: 0171 4903128
Chef: Danny Lewis
Owner: Stephen Bull
Cost: *Alc* £22. ☺ H/wine £11.50
Times: Noon-2.30pm/6-10.30pm.
Closed L Sat, all Sun, 1 wk Xmas, Bhs

Perhaps the most informal of Stephen Bull's trio of restaurants, this Smithfield branch is spacious with strong colours, wooden floor and closely arranged tables; the L-shaped room, however, means most diners have no view. You are unlikely to come out of any of Stephen Bull's restaurants feeling unpleasantly bloated. His is a style that is simple and light, with menus short and to the point. Leek and white wine soup, risotto nero, ceviche of queen scallops with honey, mint and lime, lamb shank tagine with couscous and crispy okra, show a typical range of modern influences. Other dishes, such as stuffed Devon hen with grilled potatoes and olive dressing are a fresh, balanced updating of old-fashioned concepts. Desserts might include ginger crème brûlée and warm raspberry muffin with crème fraîche, and a poire William parfait with warm caramelised pears. Front-of-house staff need a pep talk.

Directions: Halfway between Clerkenwell Rd & Smithfield Market

Additional: Children welcome;
 dishes
Seats: 120
Smoking: No-smoking area; No pipes & cigars; Air conditioning
Credit cards: ■ ▩ ⌷ ▦

Stephen Bull
St Martin's Lane ❀❀

Done out in neutral tones, this long, narrow restaurant in the heart of London's Theatreland has a real sense of style backed up by smooth service from on-the-ball staff. The interesting *carte* (our inspector would have been happy to order anything on the menu) offers well-balanced dishes characterised by complementary textures and flavours. There are about eight choices at each stage, with starters such as marjolaine of foie gras with cured duck and mango salad, fennel gnocchi with sauce vierge and shaved Parmesan, and stuffed loin of rabbit with cassoulet sauce. Among the mains we particularly enjoyed pheasant en cocotte with sweet raisins and tarragon – an interesting concept that worked well. Other options included a panaché of sea bass, monkfish and John Dory with fresh pasta and marinière sauce, and boned skate wing with Jersey royals, broad beans and roast chicken cream. An already good meal ended on a high with a brilliant brown sugar meringue with bananas, ice cream and hot fudge sauce.

Directions: Nearest Tube – Leicester Square. Top of Upper St Martin's Lane

12 Upper St Martin's Lane WC2H 9DL
Map: D3
Tel: 0171 3797811
Fax: 0171 8363855
Chef: Jon Bentham
Owner: Stephen Bull
Cost: *Alc* £25. H/wine £10.75. ☺
Times: Noon-2.30pm/5.45pm-11.30pm. Closed L Sat, Sun, 1 wk Xmas, Bhs
Additional: Children welcome;
 dishes
Seats: 70
Smoking: No pipes & cigars; Air conditioning
Credit cards: ■ ▨ ⚡ ⌷ ▦

The Stepping Stone ❀❀

'Jacket and tie not allowed' was the firm response to our enquiry on dress code at this easy-going south London restaurant. The sartorial requirements may be strictly tongue-in-cheek, but it does say something about the breezy, no-nonsense style that characterises both the atmosphere and the cooking. Stone-tiled floors, terracotta, and splashes of primary colour give something of an upbeat Mediterranean feel to the surroundings and the menu too has southern European leanings. Bresaola, crostini and feta salad have all featured amongst the starters, but a spring visit started with a vibrant dish of sea bass with fried pak choi, chilli oil and soy sauce, in a simple but 'eminently effective' combination. Meats (all organic and free-range) are carefully purchased and sensibly the kitchen is easy on the saucing. Main courses tend to the rustic and can include a 'sweet and tender' rack of lamb with a shallot and rocket mash or roast chicken served with Caesar salad. Half-a-dozen desserts are on offer with some excellent pannacotta making a fine partner for an intense blackcurrant compote.

Directions: Nearest Tube – Clapham Common. From Lavender Hill/Wandsworth Road crossroads, head up Queenstown Road towards Chelsea Bridge. Restaurant on L after 0.5 mile

123 Queenstown Road SW8 3RH
Map GtL: C2
Tel: 0171 6220555
Fax: 0171 6224230
Chef: Peter Harrison
Owner: Best Groom Ltd
Cost: *Alc* £23, fixed-price L £10.75 (2 courses). ☺ H/wine £9
Times: Noon-2.30pm/7-last D 11pm. Closed L Sat, D Sun, 5 days Xmas, Bhs
Additional: Sunday L; Children welcome; dishes
Seats: 56
Smoking: No-smoking area; No pipes & cigars; Air conditioning
Credit cards: ■ ▨ ⚡ ⌷ ▦ ▣ ▥

Stratfords ❀

7 Stratford Road W8 6RF
Map GtL: C3
Tel: 0171 9376388
Fax: 0171 9383435
Chef: Alain Patrat
Owner: Edna P Martin
Cost: Alc £30, fixed-price L/D £12. ☺
H/wine £10.50
Times: Last L 3pm/last D 11pm
Additional: Sunday L; Children
welcome; ⑤ dishes
Smoking: No pipes & cigars
Credit cards: ▄ ▄ ▄ ▄ ▄ ▄ ▄

Directions: Nearest Tube – High
Street Kensington

*The crisp nautical interior of this small restaurant reflects the
seafood menu highlighting fresh fish from Poole. A typical meal
could start with succulent garlic prawns, followed by John Dory with
a light butter sauce or pan-fried sole with parsley butter. Aim for a
window table to take in the area's village atmosphere.*

The Sugar Club ❀❀

A move to new premises, and a more central location for Peter
Gordon. The philosophy remains the same however, from a
man who does not believe less is more: at the ultra-fashionable
Sugar Club, more is more, at least when it comes to hot,
powerful spicing. A signature dish of grilled scallops with
sweet chilli sauce and rich crème fraîche had superbly fresh
queen scallops, but was overwhelmed by searingly hot sauce.
Again, there was no disputing the provenance of top quality
grilled halibut, but gingered turnip tops and wilted spinach
with fiery roasted potatoes proved relentless, with little on
hand to temper the heat, other than the cool demeanour of the
staff. The *carte* is cutting-edge fusion food – so with the roast
Trelough duck breast expect grilled bok choi, cassava chips and
pear chutney, whilst deep-fried tuna is served with shiso leaf
and nori roll with pickled daikon, wasabi-soy dressing and
flying-fish roe. Try terrine of Cointreau-marmalade, roast
banana and cardamom and ginger chocolate-chip ice cream for
an unusual dessert experience.

21 Warwick Street W1
Map GtL: C3
Tel: 0171 4377776
Chef: Peter Gordon
Owners: Ashley Sumner,
Vivienne Hayman,
Cost: Alc £40. ☺
Times: 12-last L 2.30pm/6-last
D 10.30pm.
Additional: Sunday L;
No children under 14; ⑤ dishes.
Seats: 85. Private dining room 30
Smoking: No pipes & cigars;
Air conditioning
Accommodation: 4 en suite
Credit cards: ▄ ▄ ▄ ▄ ▄ ▄ ▄

Directions: Nearest Tube – Oxford Circus

Suntory Restaurant ❀❀

Part of a world-wide chain of restaurants, the Suntory offers
typical Japanese cooking at surprisingly reasonable prices,
especially at lunchtime. Set dinners might include sashimi,
deep-fried minced prawns, thinly sliced beef cooked in hot
broth with vegetables, beancurd and special sauces and
sashimi. In the teppan-yaki corner, choose from turbot,
scallops, foie gras and sirloin with prawns.

Smoking: No pipes & cigars; Air conditioning
Credit cards: ▄ ▄ ▄ ▄ ▄ ▄ ▄ JCB

Directions: At the bottom of St James's Street. Nearest Tube –
Green Park

72 St James's Street SW1A 1PH
Map: C3
Tel: 0171 4090201
Fax: 0171 4990208
Chef: K Kanno
Owner: Suntory Ltd
Cost: Alc £50, fixed-price L £15/D
£49.80. H/wine £17
Times: Noon-last L 2pm/6-last D
10pm. Closed L Sun, Xmas, L Bhs
Additional: No children under 6;
⑤ dishes
Seats: 130. Private dining rooms to 30

Supan Thai Restaurant ❀

*Thai women in traditional dress greet diners at this popular
neighbourhood restaurant. Good-value dishes are offered from wide
ranging menus, mostly authentic but occasionally bowing to Western
tastes. Flavours are bold and clear; stuffed chicken wings, steamed
open dumplings, and green beef curry are highly recommended.*

Credit cards: 🔲 🔲 🔲 🔲 🔲

Directions: At Harrow Road end of Fernhead Road, at its
junction with Elgin Avenue

4 Fernhead Road W9 3ET
Map: B3
Tel: 0181 9699387
Chef/Owner: Mr Adul Piempreecha
Cost: Alc £15. ☺ H/wine £7.50
Times: D only, last D 10.45pm.
Closed Mon, Xmas
Addditional: Children welcome;
🍴 dishes

Swallow International Hotel ❀

See Where London Meets Section page 153

Tamarind ❀❀

20 Queen Street W1X 7PJ
Map: C3
Tel: 0171 6253561
Fax: 0171 4995034
Chef: Atul Kochhar
Owner: Halcyon Hotel
Cost: Alc £30, fixed-price L £16.50.
H/wine £13.50.
Times: Noon-last L 3pm/6pm-last
D 11.30pm. Closed Sat L
Additional: Sunday L;
Children welcome
Seats: 100
Smoking: No-smoking area;
Air conditioning
Credit cards: 🔲 🔲 🔲 🔲 🔲 🔲

The trendy name, chic locale and contemporary decor leave
you in no doubt – this is no ordinary curry house. Tamarind's
menu is Delhi-based and ranges from an unusual dish of wild
mushrooms in pickled mango dressing to the more familiar
lamb rogan josh, all executed with fresh spicing and a sure
hand. Several dishes are excellent, such as jalpari chaat
(tandoori prawns and scallops with sour grapes and mint)
featured as an appetiser. The menu also offers a selection of
tandoori kebabs, curries and vegetable dishes. Machchi sofiyani
(monkfish marinated in saffron and yogurt) was served with a
creamy black lentil dahl that matched it perfectly. Less
impressive was the saag paneer, a bland, soupy mixture of
spinach and Indian cottage cheese, and the gajar ka halwa, or
carrot fudge. Good coffee comes with petits fours.

Directions: From Green Park Tube head for Hyde Park, and turn
4th R into Half Moon St and walk to end (Curzon St). Turn L,
and Queen St is 1st R

La Tante Claire

*As we went to press the five AA Rosetted chef Gordon Ramsay left
Aubergine to open his own restaurant in the premises previously
occupied by La Tante Claire, 68 Royal Hospital Road SW3 4HP,
tel: 0171 3524441*

Tatsuso Restaurant ❀❀❀

One of the best, but also one of the most expensive Japanese restaurants in London, styled in traditional manner with slatted wooden screens separating tables, and silk paintings and gilded screenwork on the walls. This is much frequented by city traders as well as Japanese business men. In the upstairs teppanyaki room, with each table seating seven, you don a white pinnie and watch the chef at work throwing a few tasty morsels on what is basically a hot plate. Downstairs, set menus are recommended (unless you're an expert in the cuisine), for they do away with the difficulties of decision making from the long *carte*. However, the selection contains the familiar: sushi, sashimi, and sukiyaki, as well as a grand parade of dishes such as Japanese clear soup, vegetables or meat braised in soup, grilled salted salmon or beef marinated in miso, grilled eel in special sauce with rice, sliced beef in a casserole, pickles and vinegared relishes. Those trying to impress order the overpriced wine, but kirin is a much better accompaniment. Tea, of course, is best for the digestion.

Directions: Ground floor of Broadgate Circle. Nearest Tube: Liverpool St Station

32 Broadgate Circle EC1M 6BT
Map: G4
Tel: 0171 6385863
Fax: 0171 6385864
Chef: Nobuyuki Yamanaka
Owner: Terutoshi Fujii
Cost: *Alc* £35, fixed-price L £35/D £45. H/wine £13
Times: 11.30am-last L 2.45pm/6-last D 10pm. Closed Sat, Sun
Additional: No children under 12; ❀ dishes
Seats: 150. Private dining room 5, 8. Jacket & tie preferred
Smoking: No pipes & cigars; Air conditioning
Credit cards: ▆ ▆ ▆ ◪ ▆ ◖ ▆ JCB

Teatro ❀❀ NEW

A trendy newcomer, much hyped when it opened in early 1998. The restaurant is on the first floor and overlooks Greek Street, and the decor is designer minimalist with plain neutral walls, stylish leather chairs, blonde wood floors and Conranesque metal ashtrays. Typical starters from the *carte* include sweet corn ravioli with truffle oil and chanterelles, and pan-fried crispy pig's trotter with frizzy salad and fine chopped green beans. Main courses are more substantial, and could include roasted fillet of cod with crushed potatoes, lemon grass tomato concasse cockles and tiny mussels; and breast of guinea fowl with duxelle peas and braised lettuce. Desserts range from hazelnut parfait with chocolate sauce and poached apricots, to warm chocolate cake with white chocolate sorbet. Despite its Shaftesbury Avenue/Greek Street corner location, Teatro is so understated that it can prove difficult to find.

Directions: Nearest Tubes – Leicester Square, Piccadilly Circus

93-107 Shaftesbury Avenue W1V 8BT
Map: C3
Tel: 0171 4943040
Fax: 0171 4943050
Chef: Stuart Gillies
Owner: Lee Chapman
Cost: *Alc* £30, fixed-price L (pre-theatre D) £18. ☺ H/wine £11
Times: Noon – last L 2.45pm/6-last D 11.30pm. Closed Sat L, all Sun, Bhs
Additional: Children welcome; ❀ dishes
Seats: 100
Smoking: Air conditioning
Credit cards: ▆ ▆ ▆ ◪ ▆ ◖ ▆ JCB

The Thai Garden ❀

Simple vegetarian and seafood restaurant on two floors. The carte is well described and keenly priced. Beware the red peppers (whole chillies complete with seeds!). There are subtler dishes with mixed fish and cellophane noodles, and good use is made of coconut, galangal and lemongrass.

Additional: Children welcome; ❀ dishes
Smoking: No-smoking area
Credit cards: ▆ ▆ ▆ ▆

Directions: 2nd left off Roman Road (1-way street); nearest Tube: Bethnal Green

249 Globe Road E2 0JD
Map GtL: D3
Tel: 0181 9815748
Chef: Mrs Napakorn Duff
Owners: Suthinee and Jack Hufton
Cost: *Alc* £15, fixed-price L £7.50/D £21. H/wine £7.50
Times: Last L 2.45pm/last D 10.45pm. Closed L Sat, L Sun, Bhs

Thailand ✿

'Just like eating in someone's home' was one inspector's comment on this tiny proprietor-run restaurant. It might be a standard dish, but the chicken curry with coconut was smooth and fragrant with Thai flavours at their best. Don't miss the fennel-flavoured fishcakes. Drink Singha beer and note the impressive list of malt whiskies.

Additional: ✿ dishes
Smoking: No smoking in dining room; Air conditioning
Credit cards: ▪▪ ▄ ▄ ▄

Directions: Opposite Goldsmiths' College. Nearest Tubes – New Cross, New Cross Gate

15 Lewisham Way SE14 6PP
Map GtL: D3
Tel: 0181 6914040
Chef/Owner: Mrs Kamkong Herman
Cost: Alc £18. Fixed-price D £20. ☺
H/wine £8.75.
Times: D only, 6pm-last D 10pm.
Closed Sun, Mon, 25 Dec

33 St James's Restaurant ✿✿

33 St James Street SW1 1HD
Map: C3
Tel: 0171 9304272
Fax: 0171 9307618
Chef: Kristian Smith-Wallace
Owner: Vincenzo De Feo
Cost: Alc £33, fixed-price L £18.95 (2 courses)/D £24.95 (2 courses). H/wine £17
Times: Noon-last L 2.30pm/6-last D 11.30pm. Closed L Sat, all Sun, Bhs
Additional: Children welcome;
✿ dishes
Seats: 70. Private dining room 30
Smoking: No-smoking area;
No pipes; Air conditioning
Credit cards: ▪▪ ▄ ▄ ▄ ▄ ▄ ▄

Large still-life murals of fruit and game on sunshine yellow walls, and huge Italian-style statues dominate the interior of this stylish, glass-fronted restaurant. Interesting menus, including a gourmet *carte*, feature sound modern British dishes that attract an eclectic mix of diners. At dinner, risotto of Finnan haddock and horseradish with a lime and ginger hollandaise, or steamed five fish salad with lobster oil, may precede lamb cutlets with tapenade mash potato and rosemary sauce, or a tender fillet of ostrich with wilted rocket and a well-flavoured chervil vinaigrette. To finish, there may be lemon tart with citrus kiwi sauce and raspberry sorbet, or a traditional summer pudding with a minted berry sauce. Expect home-made rolls, and rich espresso coffee is served with petits fours.

Directions: Nearest Tube – Green Park

Thistle Cannizaro House ✿✿

Gilded mirrors, oil paintings and tapestry chairs take you back to another age, when people dressed for dinner and the butler served Pimms on the lawn. As you dine, piano music gently wafts in from the drawing-room, staff are attentive to your every need – it's all immensely comforting when done as well at it is here. The Georgian mansion is a luxurious haven on the Common; prices are high, and the *carte* is like a city banker's shopping basket, full of truffles, foie gras, lobster, polenta and Parma ham. Crystal-clear mushroom consommé with

West Side Wimbledon Common SW19 4UE
Map GtL: C2
Tel: 0181 8791464
Fax: 0181 8797338
Chef: Christopher Harper
Owners: Thistle Hotels
Cost: Alc £35, fixed-price L & D £28 75. H/wine £16.95.
Times: Noon-last L 2.30pm/7-last D 10.30pm

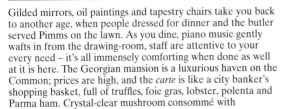

Additional: Sunday L;
No children under 8; ❹ dishes
Seats: 45. Private dining room up to
80. Jacket & tie preferred
Smoking: No-smoking area;
No pipes & cigars
Accommodation: 46 en suite
Credit cards: ▬ ▬ ▬ ▬ ▬ ▬ ▬ JCB

mushroom dumplings proved an excellent first course choice, tender, well rested loin of lamb followed – and if the accompanying ratatouille, crisp spinach, lemon couscous and olives cluttered up the plate, at least they tasted good. Dessert did not quite fulfil its potential – chestnut charlotte with liquorice, garnished with marron glacés and fresh raspberries suffered from an intensity of liquorice flavour. Fab petits fours.

Directions: From A3 (London Rd) Tibbets Corner, take A219 (Parkside) right into Cannizaro Rd, then R into West Side

The Thistle Tower ❀

See Where London Meets Section page 153

Tui Restaurant ❀

A simply decorated, popular Thai restaurant. Pork dumplings came with a crisp water chestnut topping and dark soy sauce, and the chicken broth with a charcoal burner imparting the flavours of sweet basil, kafir lime leaves and lemon grass. Beef curry was tempered by a cooling coconut sauce.

Additional: No children under 5; ❹ dishes
Smoking: No pipes & cigars; Air conditioning
Credit cards: ▬ ▬ ▬ ▬ ▬ ▬ ▬ JCB

Directions: Nearest Tube – South Kensington. On corner of Thurloe Place & Exhibition Road

19 Exhibition Road SW7 2HE
Map: A2
Tel: 0171 5848359
Chefs: Mr & Mrs Kongsrivilai
Owner: Mr E Thapthimthong
Cost: *Alc* £25, fixed-price L £10 (2 courses). ☺ H/wine £9.15.
Times: Last L 2.15pm (2.45pm Sun)/last D 10.45pm (10.15pm Sun).

Turners Restaurant ❀❀❀

The 80s can sometimes seem more dated than, say, the 60s – not far back enough to be retro and rediscovered, too recent for us not to notice. Turners belongs to the era of yuppies and Thatcherism; neither the decor (yellow rag-rolled walls, ruched blinds, floor length tablecloths), nor the *carte* (roast young pigeon on a bed of red cabbage with shallot and red wine sauce, roast rack of English lamb with herb crust, or seared skate wing with asparagus and a shrimp butter sauce) have moved on much since then, despite the inclusion of dishes such as Scottish salmon pan-fried with herb butter and Mediterranean vegetable sauce. That matters less than it might imply – it is an extremely comfortable, intimate, professionally-

87-89 Walton Street SW3 2HP
Map: A1
Tel: 0171 5846711
Fax: 0171 5844441
Chef: Charlie Curran
Owner: Brian Turner
Cost: *Alc* £41.90, fixed-price L £15/D £29.50. H/wine £13.50
Times: 12.30-last L 2.30pm/7.30-last D 11.15pm. Closed L Sat, Bhs, 1 wk Xmas
Additional: Sunday L;
No Children under 11 at D; ❹ dishes
Seats: 56. Private dining room 6

run restaurant, and the reliable cooking holds no hidden terrors. Constantly busy, with or without the presence of TV chef/patron Brian Turner, it can often be hard to get a table, especially at lunch, when there is a set menu of incredibly good value (£12.50 for two courses) offering, say, seared tuna with capers and lemon vinaigrette, and pan-fried breast of chicken with courgettes and aubergines and garlic jus. Our inspection meal began with crab sausage in a cream sauce of green peas, densely textured, but with indistinct flavours, but things got back on course with a perfect breast and leg confit of duck with a glossy port and thyme sauce and garlic potato. Vegetables come on a little side plate (of course). Pudding was a decent chocolate and hazelnut terrine with toasted hazelnut caramel sauce. Good coffee comes with petits fours, including a nostalgic coconut ice.

Smoking: Air conditioning
Credit cards: ▬ ▬ ▼ ⌷ ▬ ◖ ▣ JCB

Directions: South Kensington or Knightsbridge tube stations; behind Harrods

Union Café ❀❀

Food is available all day, starting with breakfast at 9.30am and finishing with dinner. But this plain, spacious place, designed on clean lines with beechwood furnishings and open-to-view kitchen, is more restaurant than traditional café. Friendly service and a short, hand-written, daily-changing menu enhances the relaxed style of the place. Soups are a particular forte and may include carrot and ginger, or a hearty Tuscan white bean, rosemary and tomato soup with basil oil. Imaginative, satisfying dishes extend to steamed mussels in coconut, lime, chilli and coriander, or chargrilled monkfish with saffron mash, trompettes and parsley oil, and honey and soy-glazed poussin with stir-fried bok choi. Main courses can be accompanied by fresh green leaves drizzled with balsamic vinegar. Chocolate and hazelnut cake, French apple tart, and tropical fruit salad are typical puddings. Good breads are offered and there's always a choice of two vegetarian dishes.

96 Marylebone Lane W1M 5FP
Map: C3
Tel: 0171 4864860
Chef: Caroline Brett
Owners: Caroline Brett & Sam Russell
Cost: Alc £25. ☺ H/wine £11
Times: 12.30-3pm/6.30-last D 10.30pm. Closed Sun
Additional: Children welcome; dishes
Seats: 70
Smoking: No pipes & cigars
Credit cards: ▬ ▬ ▼ ⌷ ◖ JCB

Directions: Nearest Tube – Bond Street

Vama ❀ NEW

North-west frontier is the style of cooking at this smart Indian newcomer. There are plenty of vegetarian dishes, some interesting tandoori variations, and chef's daily specials. Dishes to try might be mahi tikka – cubed salmon with mustard – or escalope of chicken stuffed with a purée of cashews and mince.

Additional: Children welcome; dishes
Smoking: No-smoking area; No pipes & cigars; Air conditioning
Credit cards: ▬ ▬ ▼ ⌷ ▬

438 King's Road SW10 0LJ
Map: C3
Tel: 0171 3514118
Fax: 0171 5658501
Chef: B S Narula
Owners: Ms Ritu Dalmia, Mr A Varma
Cost: Alc £30, fixed-price L £9.95 (2 courses). ☺ H/wine £9.75
Times: Last L 2.30pm/last D 11.15pm

Directions: *Telephone for directions*

Vasco & Piero's Pavilion ❀

Long-standing Soho Italian with charming staff and engaging clientele. Umbrian abstracts adorn the walls and the chairs are by Angus McBear. At inspection, home-made tortelloni and grilled

15 Poland Street W1V 3DE
Map GtL: D4
Tel: 0171 4378774
Fax: 0171 2872577
Chef: Vasco Matteucci

breast of guinea fowl were both full of flavour, and the fresh fruits
topped with a grappa-flavoured sabayon were first class.

Directions: On corner of Great Marlborough Street & Noel
Street. Nearest tube: Oxford Circus

Vasco & Piero's Pavilion

Owners: Vasco Matteucci, Tony
Lopez
Cost: *Alc* £28, fixed-price D £14.50
(2 courses). ☺ H/wine £9.50
Times: Last L 3pm/D 11pm. Closed
Sat (exc D once a month), Sun, Bhs
Additional: No children under 5;
🕭 dishes
Smoking: No pipes; Air conditioning
Credit cards: 🔲 🔲 🔲 🔲 a

The Veeraswamy Restaurant ❀

99-101 Regent Street
W1R 8RS
Map: C3
Tel: 0171 7341401
Chef: Gowtham Kumar
Owner: Ms Namita Panjabi
Cost: *Alc* £20, fixed price L (& D after
theatre) £11.50 (2 courses). ☺
H/wine £9.95
Times: Last L 2.30pm/last D 11.15pm.
Closed D Wed, D 25 Dec
Additional: Sunday L;
Children welcome; 🕭 dishes
Smoking: Air conditioning
Credit cards: 🔲 🔲 🔲 🔲 🔲 🔲 🔲 JCB

London's oldest Indian restaurant now has an interior blending
minimalist chic with the Asian love of vibrant colours. The new
menu's also far from traditional: rustic dishes with bold flavours
include rasmali – tomato and coriander soup – and avadhi rogan
josh – shank of lamb served with curried peas and black-eyed beans.

Directions: Entrance near junction of Swallow St & Regent St,
located in Victory House. Entrance in Swallow Street.

Veronica's ❀❀

The Victorian stucco building overlooks a leafy London square,
and in summer there are a few terrace tables. Within, the
restaurant divides into two rooms: the front one is urban-smart
terracotta, gold and green, whilst the other is decorated as a
rustic period kitchen with scrubbed tables and antique
kitchenalia. Veronica Shaw specialises in British historical food,
and the menu is interestingly annotated. Devilled herring roes,
bacon and mushrooms and Tweed Kettle make 19th-meet-20th
century starters, and main courses include chargrilled halibut
Samuel Pepys-style, salmi of duck, Reform cutlets, and Hindle
Wakes chicken. Puddings are intriguing – try the Elizabethan
pikelets. Surprisingly, vegetarian dishes are well represented.

3 Hereford Road Bayswater W2 4AB
Map GtL: C3
Tel: 0171 2295079/2291452
Fax: 0171 2291210
Chefs: Antonio Feliccio, Veronica
Shaw
Owners: Veronica & Philip Shaw
Cost: *Alc* £25, fixed-price L & D
£16.50. ☺ H/wine £9.50
Times: Noon-last L 2.30pm/6-last
D 11.30pm. Closed L Sat, all Sun,
2 days Xmas, Bhs
Additional: Children welcome;
🕭 dishes

Directions: Nearest Tubes: Bayswater & Queensway. Hereford Rd runs parallel to Queensway in between Bayswater Rd and Westbourne Grove.

Villa

All our inspector needed was a dancing partner at this bank-of-the-Thames Italian which offers live music and river views as part of its vibrant mix. The Saro family have been at the helm for 34 years, nurturing a convivial atmosphere with attentive staff and an upbeat menu of Italian favourites. The in-house pasta, as one might hope, is the star of the show, winning praise for its texture in a satisfying combination with Parma ham, asparagus, pine nuts and a vivid tomato concasse. Main courses are split evenly between fish and meat, the former including aromatic tuna served with wild mushroom jus and steamed leeks. Precisely timed fillet of lamb came with sun-dried tomato pesto and a verdant parsley sauce, in a partnership as successful as it was unexpected. Amongst the desserts, sorbets are a highlight, with a lambrusco variety making an excellent marriage with pear and almond tart.

Villandry

Enter through the Great Portland Street entrance and browse your way through the foodstore before taking a seat in the restaurant; in the evening, when the shop is closed, use the Bolsover Street entrance. Either way, you'll find yourself in bright and airy, buzzy surroundings, with a tiled floor, white walls, simple wooden tables and chairs. The daily-changing menu doesn't stray too far from the Mediterranean, with gazpacho ('excellent, just like in Barcelona' writes an inspector), tuna carpaccio, a plate of charcuterie, escabéche of sole, scallops and mussels, and pork and chicken ragout, although there's something comfortingly British about asparagus with scrambled egg and toast. Breads are well reported, as is the timing of seared beef – tender and rare – and pan-fried red mullet with an intensely flavoured tomato and herb sauce. Pastry-making skill shows up in tarts of spiced apple or nectarine and almond. Five house wines, including champagne, are sold by the glass.

Directions: Nearest Tube – Great Portland Street. Restaurant entrance at 91 Bolsover St

Veronica's

Seats: 60. Private dining room 30
Credit cards: ▆ ▆ ▆ ⬚ ▆ █ ▆ JCB

135 Grosvenor Road SW1
Map: C1
Tel: 0171 8349872/8287453
Fax: 0171 8287453
Chef: Roberto Perini
Owner: Luisa Saro
Cost: *Alc* £35. ☺
Times: D only, 7.30-last D 11.30pm. Closed Sun, Bhs
Additional: Bar food D; No children under 12; ⬧ dishes
Seats: 150
Smoking: Air conditioning
Credit cards: ▆ ▆ ▆ ⬚ ▆ █ ▆

Directions: On the north bank of the Thames between Vauxhall & Chelsea Bridge.

170 Great Portland Street W1N 5TB
Map: C4
Tel: 0171 6313131
Fax: 0171 6313030
Chefs: Ros Carrarini & Steve Evenett-Watts
Owners: Jean-Charles & Ros Carrarini
Cost: *Alc* £25. ☺ H/wine £10
Times: 12.30-last L 3pm/7-last D 10pm. Closed Sun, Bhs
Additional: Children welcome; ⬧ dishes
Seats: 90. Private dining room 20
Smoking: No smoking in dining room; Air conditioning
Credit cards: ▆ ▆ ▆ ⬚ ▆ █

Vong ❀❀

Vong's entrance, near the Minema cinema, may be discreet and the decor simple and minimalist but the chef's modern Far Eastern flavour combinations are exciting. If you can't decide between the tempting list of starters, go for the black plate, a sampler dish including the marvellous quail rubbed with Thai spices, prawn satay with oyster sauce, crab spring roll, lobster daikon roll and raw tuna and vegetables wrapped in rice paper. These are served on wonderfully dressed green salad leaves sparkling with freshness. Our inspector's main course was sea bass with Oriental spices and vegetables on a lemony verjus sauce. Jasmine rice came on the side. Other choices include tamarind duck breast and roast monkfish with baby leeks and spiced almond sauce. Dessert was inspired by English cooking: an apple crumble with apple sorbet and cardamom ice cream, the latter delicately spiced and particularly good. Staff are attentive, and there are plenty of them.

Directions: Nearest Tubes – Hyde Park Corner, Knightsbridge

The Berkeley Hotel Wilton Place
SW1X 7RL
Map: B2
Tel: 0171 2351010
Fax: 0171 2351011
Chefs: Jean-Georges Vongerichten
Owners: Jean-Georges Vongerichten, Savoy Group plc
Cost: *Alc* £40, fixed-price L £20/ D £45 (7 courses). ☺ H/wine £19
Times: Noon-last L 2.30pm/6-last D 11.30pm(Sun till 10.30).
Closed L Sun
Additional: Bar food D; ❹ dishes
Seats: 130
Smoking: No-smoking area;
Air conditioning
Credit cards: 💳 💳 💳 💳 💳 💳 💳

Wagamama ❀

Wagamama is a Japanese noodle bar with attitude. Once seated the service is fast and efficient, but expect queues during peak periods. Try yaki udon – thick white noodles with prawns and chicken fried tofu – and gyoza – grilled vegetable dumplings filled with cabbage, carrot and water chestnuts. A second branch, run on the same lines, is at 10a Lexington Street W1R 3HS, tel: 0171 292 0990

Smoking: No smoking restaurant
Credit cards: 💳 💳 💳 💳 💳 💳 JCB

Directions: Nearest Tube – Tottenham Court Road

4A Streatham Street
WC1A 1JB
Map: D4
Tel: 0171 3239223
Fax: 0171 3239224
Chef: David Chia
Cost: *Alc* £7, fixed-price L £8 (2 courses). ☺ H/wine £8.50
Times: Noon (Sun 12.30pm)-last D 10pm
Additional: Children welcome; ❹ dishes

The Washington Mayfair Hotel ❀

See Where London Meets Section page 153

Westbury Hotel ❀❀

Bond Street W1A 4UH
Map: C3
Tel: 0171 6297755
Fax: 0171 4951163
Chef: Jon McCann
Cost: *Alc* £35, fixed-price L £21/D £23.75. ☺ H/wine £15.50
Times: Noon-last L 2.15pm/6-last D 10.15pm. Closed L Sat, Sun & Bhs
Additional: Bar food;
Children welcome; ❹ dishes
Seats: 60. Private dining rooms 15-80
Accommodation: 244 en suite
Credit cards: 💳 💳 💳 💳 💳

A hard day shopping in Bond Street? The cool, calm dining-room of the Westbury is just the place for a relaxing lunch. Deep-fried Parma ham salad with fresh figs and Pecorino cheese made a good start to a recent meal that continued with a well-made lobster Thermidor. For desert we enjoyed a fabulous, silky smooth chocolate truffle mousse with coconut ice cream and chocolate sauce from a list that also included crème brûlée and sticky toffee pudding. The super selection of breads included home-made olive and sun-dried tomato and a dish of olive oil to dip them in. Good petits fours too.

Directions: Nearest Tubes: Oxford Circus, Piccadilly Circus, Bond Street

The White House Hotel ❀

See Where London Meets Section page 153

The White Onion ❀❀

Smart, simple decor with wood flooring and plain walls identify this Islington newcomer with its sister restaurants Green Olive, Red Pepper, and latest addition, Purple Sage. Chef Eric Guignard has a light touch and understanding of fresh, clean flavours which are evident in modern Med dishes such as grilled tuna with vegetable chutney and red pepper coulis, and magret of duck with warm potatoes, pine nuts and garlic sauce. Our inspector sampled a light lunch of spicy Puy lentil soup, followed by a delicate dish of marinated lamb salad with chicory, beetroot and lemon confit. For dessert, a skilful terrine of oranges and grapefruit with kumquat chutney. Dinner offers a bit more ambition and technical skill as in pressed smoked duck terrine, pan-fried foie gras on a warm mozzarella and rocket salad, and pastilla of guinea fowl with caramelised shallots and port sauce.

Directions: Close to Almeida St between Angel and Highbury & Islington tubes

297 Upper Street N1 2TU
Map GtL: D3
Tel/Fax: 0171 3593533
Chef: Eric Guignard
Owner: Bijan Behzadi
Cost: Alc £23.50, fixed-price L £10 (2 courses)/D Sun only £15 (2 courses). ☺ H/wine £9.50
Times: Noon-last L 2.30pm/6.30-last D 10.45pm(Sun 7-10). Closed L Mon, 25-26 Dec, 1 Jan
Additional: Sunday L, Children welcome; ❹ dishes
Seats: 63
Smoking: No pipes & cigars; Air conditioning
Credit cards: ▨ ▨ ▨ ▨ ▨

Wilson's ❀❀

One of Brook Green's best-kept secrets, this charming, unassuming restaurant *du quartier* has been providing satisfying food in a relaxed atmosphere for many years. Tartan curtains and the kilted patron give a Scottish flavour, but thistle kitsch is not overdone. The cooking is reasonably straightforward but does not lack interest. Witness cream of wild mushroom soup, a Finnan haddock pudding with spinach and bacon salad, salmon fishcakes with parsley sauce, and grilled lamb cutlets with redcurrant and mustard sauce, which have all be been soundly delivered. Athol brose with strawberries is full of alcohol but happily not oversweet.

Directions: Nearest Tube – Hammersmith

236 Blythe Road W14 0HJ
Map GtL: C3
Tel: 0171 6037267
Fax: 0171 6029018
Chef: Robert Hilton
Owners: Robert Hilton, Robert Wilson,
Cost: Alc £20. ☺ H/wine £9.50
Times: Noon-last L 2.30pm/7.30-last D 10pm. Closed L Sat, D Sun
Additional: Sunday L; Children welcome; ❹ dishes
Seats: 46
Smoking: Air conditioning
Credit cards: ▨ ▨ ▨ ▨

Wiltons ❀❀

With its comforting English country-house atmosphere, a mixture of booths and tables, green-plush upholstery and sporting, piscatorial and other prints and photographs on the walls, Wiltons is something of an institution, where captains of industry are greeted by name by the long-serving staff. The

55 Jermyn Street
SW1Y 6LX
Map: C3
Tel: 0171 6299955
Fax: 0171 4956233
Chef: Ross Hayden
Owners: The Hambro Family

Wiltons

Cost: *Alc* £50, fixed-price L £40.
H/wine £16.50
Times: 12.30-last L 2.30pm/6.30-last
D 10.30pm. Closed Sat, 25-26 Dec,
1 Jan
Additional: Bar food; Sunday L;
No children under 12; ❹ dishes
Seats: 80. Private dining room 18.
Jacket & tie preferred (except Sun)
Smoking: No-smoking area; Air
conditioning
Credit cards: 🟦 🟫 📷 💳 📧 🅱 📱 JCB

menu is resolutely British, and grills and fish are what it does best, from Dover sole meunière to poached turbot, and Scotch fillet or sirloin steaks to grilled lambs' kidneys. Raw materials are of the highest quality, and luxuries abound, with lobster prepared in four different ways, and also popping up as a starter cocktail, as a bisque, and as a cold main-course salad; then there's Beluga caviar, foie gras and langoustines too. Some more modern ideas have surfaced in recent times, so there may be chargrilled tuna with a salad of tomato, coriander and red onion, or salmon fishcake on spinach purée with mustard sauce. The number of savouries – including angels on horseback and anchovies on toast – printed at the foot of the menu, is just short of the number of puddings, no doubt a better match for vintage ports.

Directions: Opposite Turnbull & Asser (shirtmakers), and near Piccadilly Circus & Ritz Hotel. Nearest Tube – Green Park

The Windmill
on The Common ❀

Southside Clapham Common
SW4 9DE
Map GtL: C2
Tel: 0181 6734578
Fax: 0181 6751486
Chef: Stephen Doyle
Owners: Young & Co Brewery plc
Cost: Fixed-price D £16.95. ☺
H/wine £9.95
Times: D only, last D 10pm.
Closed Sun, Bhs
Additional: Bar food;
Children welcome; ❹ dishes
Smoking: No pipes & cigars;
Air conditioning
Accommodation: 29 en suite
Credit cards: 🟦 🟫 📷 💳 📧 🅱 📱

A pub since 1729, skilfully extended to create hotel accommodation. There are three bars, a bistro, small lounge and wood-panelled restaurant. Enthusiastic cooking delivers a daily chef's pasta, and dishes such as lemon sole with tomato sauce and grilled polenta, and Toulouse sausage with onion marmalade.

Directions: Nearest Tubes – Clapham Common or Clapham South

Woodlands Restaurant

Established South Indian vegetarian restaurant, part of a family chain with over 20 in India. This is the older sibling of three in London. The range of dosas, with about 10 fillings on offer, and uthappams (the South Indian pizza) are popular. The thali and good-value set lunches are worth trying.

Additional: Sunday L; Children welcome; 🍴 dishes
Smoking: No pipes & cigars; Air conditioning
Credit cards: ▬ ▬ ▬ ☐ ▬ ▬ ▬

Directions: Nearest Tube – Bond Street

77 Marylebone Road W1M 5GA
Map: C3
Tel: 0171 4863862
Fax: 0171 4874009
Chef: Radha Krishna
Owner: Mr Sood
Cost: *Alc* £13, fixed price L £7.95
(2 courses). ☺ H/wine £9
Times: Last L 2.45pm/last D 10.45pm.
Closed 25-26 Dec

Yas NEW

An Iranian restaurant with a large blue-tiled tandoor that attracts the eye of passers-by and produces all their own flat bread. In addition to the Iranian and Persian dishes on the regular menu, consider the daily specials for something a little different. Mondays, for example, it's chicken with sweet rice containing candied orange peel, pistachio and almond slivers.

Credit cards: ▬ ▬ ▬ ☐ ▬ ▬

Directions: Kensington (Olympia) Tube

7 Hammersmith Road W14 8XJ
Tel: 0171 6039148/3980
Fax: 0171 6033320
Owners: Sohrab Eshraghi,
Najaf Abadi
Cost: *Alc* £15. H/wine £8. ☺
Additional: Children welcome;
🍴 dishes
Smoking: No-smoking area

YMing

35-36 Greek Street W1V 5LN
Map: D4
Tel: 0171 7342721
Fax: 0171 4370292
Chef: Mr S Luo
Owner: Christine Yau
Cost: *Alc* £10, fixed-price D £10. ☺
H/wine £9.50.
Additional: Children welcome;
🍴 dishes.
Seats: 60. Private dining room 35
Smoking: No-smoking area;
Air conditioning
Credit cards: None

Directions: Off Shaftesbury Ave,
behind Palace Theatre

Ming has had a change of ownership since our last visit, hence YMing, but supporters of this excellent Chinese need not concern themselves – the new owner is the former maitre d', Christine Yau, and Mr Luo remains the chef. The restaurant itself offers a haven of peace and tranquillity in this frenetic area of Soho (behind the Palace Theatre and opposite the famous Coach and Horses pub), tables are well spaced and service is courteous and helpful. The cooking is predominantly from the north around Beijing, plus some regional Szechuan dishes. An early spring dinner took in aubergine delight, delicate parcels incorporating bacon and a very light sauce, crab with spring onions and ginger – a whole crab, very fresh and 'smashed' into pieces – that was 'very messy to eat but well worth the effort', and a spicy duck with black beans and hot plum sauce, accompanied by steamed greens (pak choi et al) and steamed rice. Desserts are fairly standard fare, lychees

and the like, but tea is higher than average quality. The wine
selection is appropriate for the style of cuisine, a gutsy
Echeverria Sauvignon, for example, was a good foil to the
duck, although the house wine could be improved.

Yo! Sushi ❀

*Hi-tech Japanese restaurant with sushi dishes, on colour coded
plates, revolving on a 60-metre conveyor belt, and robotic drinks
trolleys providing hot saké and tea. Mineral water is dispensed by
tap at the table. Over 100 sushis are served, ranging through
asparagus nigiri, tuna maki, and yellow tail sashimi.*

Smoking: No smoking in dining room; Air conditioning
Credit cards: ▇ ▇ ▇ ⌐ ▇ **C** ▣ JCB

Directions: Nearest tube – Oxford Circus

52-53 Poland Street W1V 3DF
Map: C4
Tel: 0171 2870443
Fax: 0171 2872324
Chef: Nacer Arab
Owner: Simon Woodroffe
Cost: *Alc* £14. ☺
Times: Noon-midnight. Closed Xmas
Additional: Bar food, Sunday L;
Children welcome; ❸ dishes

Yumi Restaurant ❀❀

A 'low-key' Japanese restaurant with friendly staff and
neighbourhood ambience. The food is straightforward
Japanese fare along the lines of fillet of beef with teriyaki
sauce and sashimi, miso soup, and smoked salmon and
Camembert tempura. The highlight of a late summer meal was
a Japanese take on shumai dumplings with excellent edamame
soy beans, steamed with salt and served cold. Other dishes to
look out for include minced tuna burgers, grilled mango
topped with rice cake and miso paste, and oshitashi – spinach
salad with soy dressing. A modest sushi bar and several low
tatami tables with bright cushions occupy the ground floor,
while the main restaurant is in the basement together with a
number of private rooms for ceremonial kaiseki banquets.
Service is some of the most courteous and gentle that the
Japanese can offer.

110 George Street W1H 5RL
Map: B4
Tel: 0171 935 8320
Fax: 0171 224 0917
Please telephone for further details

Directions: A few yards east of the
junction of George Street with
Gloucester Place. Nearest Tube –
Marble Arch

Zafferano ❀❀❀

Giorgio Locatelli's discreet, stylish Belgravia restaurant is
always busy, but there's no pressure to speed up or leave. It is
an immediately likeable restaurant, from the simple decor,
with the colour coming from textile wall hangings and
dramatically arranged flowers, to the exciting modern Italian
menu. The finely-tuned repertoire includes the likes of pork
fillet with black cabbage and cannellini beans, flat spaghetti
with sweet chilli, garlic and crab, and chargrilled eels with
herbs. Locatelli cares about sourcing his ingredients – hand-
made buffalo mozzarella, served perhaps with baked
aubergine, is left dramatically whole – you can almost see the
finger marks. Grey mullet roe is served with fennel salad, wind-
dried tuna in a salad with French beans and tomato. Some
traditional Emilia-Romagna dishes include stuffed tortellini in
clear broth, roasted duck with pearl spelt and balsamic vinegar
and baked pike with vegetables and herbs. A sweet-and-sour
skate salad was an unusual and delicate contrast of tastes and
textures, and minced pork, wrapped in Savoy cabbage leaves
with pan-fried risotto, refined a basic dish whilst not sacrificing
any of the rustic earthiness. Desserts range round the
peninsula, from Sicilian cannoli to Neapolitan ricotta
cheesecake with orange sauce. Espresso coffee hits the spot

15 Lowndes Street SW1X 9EY
Map: B2
Tel: 0171 2355800
Fax: 0171 2351971
Chef/Owner: Giorgio Locatelli
Cost: *Alc* £30-£50, fixed-price L
£19.50 (2 courses)/D £28.50.
H/wine £10.70
Times: Noon-last L 2.30pm/7-last
D 11pm. Closed Sun
Additional: Children welcome;
❸ dishes
Seats: 55
Smoking: Air conditioning
Credit cards: ▇ ▇ ▇ ⌐ ▇ **C**

Directions: Off Knightsbridge –
around corner from The Sheraton
Park Tower Hotel. Nearest Tube –
Knightsbridge

perfectly. All-Italian service is zealous. Dinner prices are a bargain (not that much more than lunch) given the location and quality of the ingredients bought fresh daily.

Signature dishes: Sea bream with balsamic vinegar; ravioli of pheasant and truffle; roast rabbit polenta

Zen Central ✿✿

Stylish, with black leather and chrome chairs, white walls and extensive wall mirrors, the cool, ultra-modern interior helps to maintain the calm, contemplative frame of mind which must be adopted when paying the bill – prices are steep and note the 15% service charge added to the final bill. However, from an extensive and varied menu drawn from most Chinese regions, we sampled the dim sum package which included dumplings filled with crisp, good flavoured prawns, and Peking ravioli with chilli sauce. To follow, tender, paper-wrapped chicken with oyster sauce was accompanied by wild mushrooms and thinly sliced bamboo shoots in chilli sauce, although a hint more chilli could have enhanced the dish considerably.

Directions: Off Curzon Street, near Curzon Cinema, and behind London Hilton/Dorchester hotels. Nearest tube – Green Park

20-22 Queen Street W1X 7PJ
Map: C3
Tel: 0171 6298103/8089
Fax: 0171 4936181
Chef: Chris Kwan
Owner: Tealeaf Ltd
Cost: *Alc* £25. ☺ H/wine £15
Times: 12.15-last L 2.30pm/6.30-last D 11.15pm. Closed 24-25 Dec
Additional: Sunday L; Children welcome; ❹ dishes
Seats: 90. Private dining room 20
Smoking: No pipes & cigars; Air conditioning
Credit cards: ▬ ▬ ▨ ▯ ▨ ▐ ▨ JCB

Zen Garden ✿✿

Cheong sams and djsí mark the staff out from the customers at this smart, welcoming Mayfair restaurant serving classical Cantonese food. The menu, apart from a couple of items such as chicken with cashews, is not particularly geared towards conventional Western taste. Birds nest soup, sharks fin, braised fish cheek and other more exotic (and expensive) delicacies, however, are worth exploring, and it may be worth pushing the boat out to share a top-of-the-range banquet, featuring whole pigeon in soy sauce, even at £138 per person. Roasted whole suckling pig at £150 requires 48 hours' notice. On a more modest budget, our inspector enjoyed excellent deep-fried shredded squid with peppercorn salt, assorted seafood dim sum, and freshly-made, piping-hot chicken with shallots, spring onions and dried mushrooms in a clay pot. Special fried rice and aromatic crispy duck were standard offerings. Try the chilled mango pudding for a refreshing dessert.

Directions: Off Berkeley Square, opp Mayfair Hotel. Nearest Tube – Green Park

15-16 Berkeley Street
W1X 5AE
Map: C3
Tel: 0171 4931381
Fax: 0171 4912655
Chef: Cheung Hong
Owner: YH Cheung
Cost: *Alc* £35, fixed-price L £13.50/D £38 (6 courses). H/wine £15
Times: Noon-last L 2.30pm/6pm-last D 11pm
Additional: Sunday L; Children welcome; ❹ dishes
Seats: 95. Private dining room 30
Smoking: No-smoking area; Air conditioning
Credit cards: ▬ ▬ ▨ ▯ ▨ ▐ ▨ JCB

ZENW3 ✿

Strikingly different in design, with its atrium frontage extending the height of two floors, this sleek, ultra-modern Chinese restaurant specialises in the likes of cuttlefish wrapped in lettuce with herbs, and aromatic duck pancake, although the menu extends to steamed sea bass with black bean sauce, and lamb with spiced honey sauce.

Seats: 130. Private dining room 24
Smoking: Air conditioning
Credit cards: ▬ ▬ ▨ ▯ ▨ ▐ ▨ JCB

Directions: 2 mins down hill from Hampstead Tube next to P.O.

83 Hampstead High Street
NW3 1RE
Map GtL: C4
Tel: 0171 7947863
Fax: 0171 7946956
Chef: Kwok-Lee Tang
Owner: Tealeaf Ltd
Cost: *Alc* £25, fixed-price L £12.50/D £27.50 (4 courses). ☺ H/wine £12
Times: Last L 2.45pm/last D 11pm. Closed Xmas
Additional: Children welcome; ❹ dishes

Zinc Bar & Grill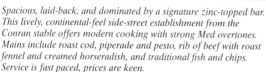

Spacious, laid-back, and dominated by a signature zinc-topped bar. This lively, continental-feel side-street establishment from the Conran stable offers modern cooking with strong Med overtones. Mains include roast cod, piperade and pesto, rib of beef with roast fennel and creamed horseradish, and traditional fish and chips. Service is fast paced, prices are keen.

Additional: Bar food; Sunday L; Children welcome; dishes
Smoking: Air conditioning
Credit cards: ▆ ▆ ▆ ▆ ▆ ▆ ▆ JCB

Directions: Nearest Tube – Piccadilly Circus

21 Heddon Street W1R 7LF
Map: D4
Tel: 0171 2558899
Fax: 0171 2558888
Chef: Paul Gatterson
Owner: Conran Restaurants
Cost: *Alc* £17. fixed-price L £8.95 (2 courses). ☺ H/wine £9.95
Times: Noon-11pm (11.30pm Thur-Sat, Noon-6pm Sun). Closed D Sun; 25-26 Dec

Zoe

Just off Oxford Street (in a side square full of cosmopolitan shops and eateries), Zoe consists of a bar, café and basement restaurant with a trendy atmosphere and Mediterranean-influenced menu. Duck livers with pancetta and sage, polenta terrine and confit of duck with flageolet beans show the style.

Directions: Nearest Tube: Bond Street. Entrance at junction of Barrett St & St James St

3-5 Barrett Street W1M 5HH
Map: C4
Tel: 0171 2241122
Fax: 0171 9355444
Please telephone for further details

Zujuma's

A bright, informal, unusual Indian café offering a simple menu of modern Indian cooking. The kitchen team can be seen through a hatch, coolly preparing dishes such as tali machi – shallow-fried fillet of haddock with ginger, and narangi dopiaza – diced fillet of lamb cooked with oranges and lemon. Inexpensive and should not be missed.

Additional: Children welcome; dishes
Seats: 60
Smoking: No-smoking area; Air conditioning
Credit cards: ▆ ▆ ▆ ▆

Directions: From A3 take Tibbetts Corner exit, follow signs for Wimbledon; through Wimbledon village, at 2nd mini-r/bout take 2nd exit. Located on R, 0.5 mile down road. Train station 200 yds, on R

58a Wimbledon Hill Road
SW19 7PA
Map GtL: C2
Tel: 0181 879 0916
Fax: 0181 944 0861
Chef/Owner: Zuju Shareef
Times: Noon – last D 11pm

Where London meets

The hotel listed below are dedicated to building their reputations on what happens in their restaurants and all hold our coveted one rosette award for food. Although not the most obvious choice as a meeting place, for a working lunch, or just to wind down and relax over dinner, we think these hotels are amongst London's best kept secrets.

Baileys Hotel ✸

Olives Restaurant at this late 19th-century hotel is a smart, trendy place serving modern Med dishes with the occasional oriental twist. Look out for gutsy dishes along the lines of chorizo risotto and pan-fried calves' liver with red onion sauce. The concise wine list includes several favourites by the glass.

140 Gloucester Road SW7 4QH
Map: A2
Tel: 0171 373 6000
Fax: 0171 370 3760
Please telephone for further details

Directions: Opposite Gloucester Road tube station

Bardon Lodge Hotel ✸

Perfectly placed for the Millennium celebrations, this small hotel restaurant offers imaginative food in the Lamplight Restaurant. Good choices on the short set-price menu include warm seafood salad, Lancashire hot-pot and gooseberry and lime tart. Soups, pâtés and breads are all home-made too. Look for the daily specials.

Accommodation: 31 en suite. **Credit cards:** 🔲 ▦ 🏧 £ 🔳 🄲

Directions: Blackheath/Greenwich exit from A2. Left at 1st roundabout, last exit from 2nd roundabout

15-17 Stratheden Road
Nr Greenwich SE3 7TH
Map GtL: C2
Tel: 0181 8534051
Fax: 0181 8587387
Chef: Mark Sylvester
Cost: Alc £25, fixed-price D £17.50.
☺ H/wine £8.95
Times: D only, last D 9.30pm
Additional: Children welcome;
🍴 dishes
Smoking: No smoking in dining room

Basil Street Hotel ✸

A genteel country house-style hotel in the middle of Knightsbridge. The restaurant has traditional Edwardian decor, with fine paintings and a grand piano (which is played every evening). We enjoyed smoked haddock salad, chargrilled calves' liver, and a pear Bakewell tart selected from the sweet trolley.

Smoking: No pipes & cigars
Accommodation: 93 rooms (82 en suite)
Credit cards: 🔲 ▦ 🏧 £ 🔳 🄲 💳 JCB

Directions: Nearest Tube – Knightsbridge

Basil Street Knightsbridge SW3 1AH
Map: C3
Tel: 0171 5813311
Fax: 0171 5813693
Chef: James Peake
Owners: Mrs M Beeching, Mrs S Crofton-Atkins
Cost: Alc £27, fixed-price L £10 (2 courses)/D £19.50. ☺ H/wine £13.75
Times: Last L 2.15pm/last D 10pm
Additional: Bar food; Sunday L; Children welcome; 🍴 dishes

The Berkshire ✸

Ascot's Restaurant at the Berkshire offers a calm oasis amidst the hustle and bustle of Oxford Street. The menu is predominantly British with influences from around the world. Main courses include chicken breast with fig and apricot couscous, and tempura of lemon sole with mange-tout salad and buttered new potatoes.

Smoking: No-smoking area; Air conditioning
Accommodation: 147 en suite
Credit cards: 🔲 ▦ 🏧 £ 🔳 💳 JCB

Directions: Opposite Bond Street Tube station

Oxford Street W1N 0BY
Map: C3
Tel: 0171 6297474
Fax: 0171 6298156
Chef: Dorian Breakspear-Coyle
Owner: Radisson Edwardian
Cost: Alc £30, fixed price L £18.50 (2 courses)/D £22.50. ☺ H/wine £15.50
Times: Last L 2.30pm/last D 10.30pm.
Closed L Sat, L Sun
Additional: Bar food;
Children welcome; 🍴 dishes

Conrad International ❀

Chelsea Harbour SW10 0XG
Map GtL: C2
Tel: 0171 8233000
Fax: 0171 3516525
Chef: Ray Neve
Owner: Conrad International London
Cost: Alc L £30/D £40.
H/wine £19.50
Times: Last L 2.30pm/last D 10.30pm
Additional: Bar food; Sunday brunch;
Children welcome; ❸ dishes
Smoking: No-smoking area;
No pipes & cigars; Air conditioning
Accommodation: 160 en suite
Credit cards: ▬ ▆ ☐ ▆ ▆

*Overlooking the marina, the Brasserie is within the ocean liner-like,
all-suite hotel at Chelsea Harbour. The menu offers a range of
vibrant, well-executed dishes from which Oriental seafood noodles
with lime leaves and lemongrass, corn-fed chicken on stir-fried
vegetables and sticky toffee pudding might constitute a typical meal.*

Directions: Nearest Tube – Fulham Broadway or Earls Court

Copthorne Tara ❀

*Classic British dishes are on the menu at this smart hotel off
Kensington High Street. A typical meal served in the wood-panelled
Jerome restaurant might start with grilled Somerset goats' cheese,
followed by Cumberland sausage with mashed potatoes and onion
gravy. Desserts range from fresh fruit Pavlova to rich chocolate
mousse.*

Scarsdale Place Wrights Lane W8 5SR
Map GtL: C3
Tel: 0171 9377211
Fax: 0171 9377100
Chef: Klaus Hohenauer
Cost: Alc £35, fixed price L & D £18.
☺ H/wine £12.10
Times: Last L 2.30pm/last D 10.45pm

Additional: Bar food; Children welcome; ❸ dishes
Smoking: No-smoking area; Air conditioning
Accommodation: 825 en suite
Credit cards: ▬ ▆ ☒ ☐ ▆ ☐ ▆ JCB

Directions: Nearest Tube – High Street Kensington

Crowne Plaza London – Heathrow ❀

*Colourful contemporary restaurant, the Concha Grill, with Art
Deco-style railings and platforms and views across the hotel lobby.
A comprehensive carte offers grills, such as pork 'stincotto' on
steamed bok choi, specialities from the pizza oven, spit-roasts from
the rotisserie and plenty of seafood, including a shellfish platter.*

Stockley Road UB7 9NA
Map GtL: A2
Tel: 01895 445555
Fax: 01895 445122
Chef: Michael Glynn
Cost: Alc £24. ☺ H/wine £13.95
Times: Last L 2.30pm/last D 11pm

Additional: Bar food; Sunday L; Children welcome; ❸ dishes
Smoking: No-smoking area; Air conditioning
Credit cards: ▬ ▆ ☒ ☐ ▆ ☐ ▆ JCB

Directions: 2 miles N of junction 4 M4/A408

The Gloucester Hotel ❀

4-18 Harrington Gardens SW7 4LH
Tel: 0171 3736030
Fax: 0171 3730409
Chef: Graham Riley
Cost: *Alc* £14. ☺ H/wine £14.50
Times: Open all day, noon-last
D 10pm
Additional: Sunday L;
Children welcome; ❹ dishes
Smoking: No pipes & cigars;
Air conditioning
Accommodation: 610 en suite
Credit cards: 🔲 🔲 🔲 🔲 🔲 🔲

Directions: 1 minute from Gloucester
Road Tube station

Smart, cosmopolitan hotel close to Gloucester Road Tube. The
Conservatory offers a globally inspired menu. Look out for chicken
and coconut soup with deep-fried chillies, grilled salmon marinated
in lime juice with pak choi and pickled ginger salad, and steamed
rhubarb, peppered strawberries and honey anglaise.

The Hampshire ❀

Surrounded by the bustle of the West End, this stylish period hotel
offers a peaceful haven in its plush, intimate Celebrities restaurant.
There's a modern-style carte (backed-up by a keenly priced table
d'hôte) and service that manages to combine formality with
friendliness.

Credit cards: 🔲 🔲 🔲 🔲 🔲 🔲 🔲

Directions: S side of Leicester Square on corner with St Martin's
Street

Leicester Square WC2H 7LH
Map: C3
Tel: 0171 8399399
Fax: 0171 9308122
Additional: Sunday L; Bar meals;
Children welcome; ❹ dishes;
Smoking: No-smoking area; Air-
conditioning
Accommodation: 124 en suite
Please telephone for further details

The Hogarth ❀

33 Hogarth Road Kensington
SW5 0QQ
Map GtL: C3
Tel: 0171 3706831
Fax: 0171 3736179
Chef: Chris Moxon
Owners: Marston Hotels
Cost: H/wine £11.9. ☺
Times: 10am-10pm
Additional: Bar food; Sunday L;
Children welcome; ❹ dishes
Smoking: No-smoking area;
Air conditioning
Accommodation: 85 en suite.
Credit cards: 🔲 🔲 🔲 🔲 🔲 🔲 🔲 JCB

Convenient for Earls Court, this friendly modern hotel offers all-day
dining in the Terrace restaurant. There's a choice of dishes to suit all
budgets and appetites, from sandwiches to full three-course meals.
Familiar options like Caesar salad and chocolate truffle cake are
supplemented by more interesting Mediterranean inspired offerings
from the daily specials board.

Directions: 150 yds from Earl's Court tube station

Holiday Inn Mayfair ❀

3 Berkeley Square W1X 6NE
Map: C2
Tel: 0171 4938282
Fax: 0171 6292827
Chef: Barry Brewington
Cost: *Alc* £25, fixed price L & D £16
(2 courses). ☺ H/wine £12
Times: Last L 2.30 pm/last D
10.30pm. Closed L Sat
Additional: Bar food;
Children welcome; 🌢 dishes
Smoking: No-smoking area;
No pipes & cigars; Air conditioning
Accommodation: 186 en suite
Credit cards: ▬ ▬ ▨ ▄ ▬ ▬ ▣ JCB

Directions: Nearest Tube – Green
Park

*Cosy, elegant hotel restaurant tucked discreetly between Piccadilly
and Berkeley Square. The short menu offers some experimentation
and suggests things are likely to keep improving. Try the very good
monkfish tempura, surprising sesame risotto, or iced Grand Marnier
soufflé. There are also old favourites such as simple grills and oak-
smoked salmon with bread.*

The Langham Hilton ❀

*The capital's first 'grand' establishment when it originally opened in
1865, now a smart, international hotel. Indeed, Memories restaurant
has a grand-style old atmosphere, although now the setting for some
up-to-date cooking. Game ragout in puff pastry, guinea fowl or
simple pan-fried langoustine with roquette salad, show the range.*

Accommodation: 379 en suite. **Credit cards:** ▬ ▬ ▄ ▬ ▣ JCB

Directions: Nearest Tube – Oxford Circus

1 Portland Place W1N 4JA
Map: C4
Tel: 0171 6361000
Chef: Georg Fuchs
Cost: *Alc* £26. Fixed-price L/D
£17.50. ☺ H/wine £17
Times: Last L 2.30pm/last D 10.30pm
Additional: Bar food; Sunday L;
Children welcome; 🌢 dishes
Smoking: No-smoking area; Air
conditioning

London Marriott
Grosvenor Square Hotel ❀

Grosvenor Square W1A 4AW
Map: C3
Tel: 0171 4931232
Fax: 0171 4913201
Chef: Nick Hawkes
Cost: *Alc* £25, fixed price L £9.50/D
£9.95 (5-7pm only). ☺ H/wine
£16.25
Times: Noon-last D 10.30pm.
Closed L Sat, 26 Dec
Additional: Bar food; Sunday L;
Children welcome; 🌢 dishes
Smoking: No-smoking area;
Air conditioning
Accommodation: 221 en suite
Credit cards: ▬ ▬ ▨ ▄ ▬ ▬ ▣ JCB

Directions: Bond Street Tube. Hotel
entrance is on Duke St, off Oxford St

*Popular modern hotel in the heart of Mayfair where the Diplomat
Restaurant offers interesting dishes based on good ingredients.
Expect pan-fried fillets of Dover sole with bubble and squeak,
roasted loin of lamb with hazelnut and pea crust, and traditional cod
in beer batter and chips. Desserts come from the trolley, backed up
by a selection of British farmhouse cheeses.*

The Mountbatten

A stylish Seven Dials hotel restaurant well placed for theatre-goers and a popular business choice. The brasserie-style menu is great value, and a typical autumn meal might start with smoked salmon soup, followed by Cajun chicken with roasted aubergines, and finish off with a light treacle tart with traditional custard.

Monmouth Street WC2H 9HD
Map: E3
Tel: 0171 836 4300
Fax: 0171 240 3540
Please telephone for further details

Oak Lodge Hotel ✸

80 Village Road Bush Hill Park
EN1 2EU
Map GtL: D5
Tel: 0181 3607082
Chef: Mark Lees
Owners: John & Yvonne Brown
Cost: *Alc* £25. ☺ H/wine £11.
Times: D only, 7.30-9pm.
Closed D Sun
Additional: Bar food L; Sunday L
(1pm); dishes
Smoking: No smoking in dining room
Accommodation: 6 en suite
Credit cards: ▆▆ ▆▆ ▆▆ ▆ ▆▆ ▆ ▆ JCB

Small hotel run with great professionalism by totally dedicated owners. Seasonal menus offer the likes of noisette of English spring lamb with redcurrant and mint jelly, or honey roasted Aylesbury duckling, plus a good choice of fish dishes.

Directions: Exit 25 M25, turn 2nd right signed Enfield; hotel 1 mile from railway station and A10

The Radisson Edwardian Hotel

Henleys Restaurant is the luxurious dining option at this international airport hotel. Good choice from the various menus – one based around reduced calorie dishes – that focus on modern English cuisine with classical touches. The largely French wine list includes a good sprinkling of half-bottles.

Additional: Bar food L; Children welcome; ✿ dishes
Smoking: No-smoking area; Air conditioning
Accommodation: 459 en suite.
Credit cards: ▆▆ ▆▆ ▆▆ ▆ ▆▆ ▆ ▆ JCB

Bath Road Hayes UB3 5AW
Map GtL: C2
Tel: 0181 7596311
Fax: 0181 7594559
Chef: Jean-Claude Sandillon
Owner: Radisson Edwardian Hotels
Cost: *Alc* £35, fixed-price L £21/D £30. H/wine £13
Times: Last L 2.30pm/last D 10.30pm.
Closed L Sat & Sun, Bhs

Directions: On the A4, eastbound side

Selsden Park Hotel ✸

Jacobean mansion set in 205 acres of parkland, with a large restaurant in the grand style. Full-flavoured and honest dishes might include honey roast smoked belly of pork with bubble-and-squeak and balsamic jus, and ragout of monkfish cheeks, skate knobs and lobster knuckles with a tarragon risotto.

Smoking: No smoking in dining room; Air conditioning
Accommodation: 204 en suite.
Credit cards: ▆▆ ▆▆ ▆▆ ▆ ▆▆ ▆

Addington Road
Sanderstead CR2 8YA
Map 4: TQ36
Tel: 0181 6578811
Fax: 0181 6516171
Chef: Stephen Cane
Cost: *Alc* £38, fixed-price L 19.50/D £24.95. ☺ H/wine £10.50
Times: Last L 2pm/last D 9.30pm
Additional: Bar food; Sunday L;
Children welcome; ✿ dishes

Swallow International Hotel

Blayneys is a well-kept, professionally run operation, the more serious of the two restaurants at this modern hotel. The menu holds much promise, and the kitchen delivers the goods with confidence. Expect pan-fried sea bass fillet, crab brandade and mussel and tarragon broth, and fillet of beef poached in consommé.

Additional: Bar food; Sunday L; Children welcome; 🍴 dishes
Smoking: No-smoking area; Air conditioning
Accommodation: 421 en suite
Credit cards: 🔲 🔲 🔲 🔲 🔲 🔲 🔲

Directions: Nearest tube stations: Gloucester Road & Earls Court

Cromwell Road SW5 0TH
Map: A2
Tel: 0171 9731000
Fax: 0171 2448194
Chef: Bernhard Engelhardt
Cost: Alc £31.50, fixed-price D £22.50. ☺ H/wine £15.50
Times: D only, last D 11pm. Closed 23-27 Dec

The Thistle Tower ✿

The hotel's Princes Room restaurant has amazing views over Tower Bridge. There is a set-price menu gastronomic, and an ambitious carte with dishes such as roast cod with spinach, fennel risotto and anchovy fritters, and steamed corn-fed chicken with tarragon cream and oyster mushroom galette.

Additional: Bar food; Children welcome; 🍴 dishes
Smoking: No-smoking area; Air conditioning
Accommodation: 800 en suite
Credit cards: 🔲 🔲 🔲 🔲 🔲 🔲 🔲 JCB

Directions: Adjacent to Tower of London and Tower Bridge on North shore of River Thames

St Katharine's Way E1 9LD
Map: G3
Tel: 0171 4812575
Fax: 0171 4805487
Chef: Jerry Davies
Cost: £35.50, fixed-price D £29.95. H/wine £18
Times: D only, last D 10.30pm. Closed Sun, Bhs

The Washington Mayfair Hotel ✿

Smart hotel in the heart of Mayfair with elegant public areas and a modern brasserie-style menu offering a range of dishes with Mediterranean or Pacific influences. Typical choices may take in Thai fishcakes with red pepper coulis, beef medallions with ginger soy dressing, and Dover sole with crab and lemon grass.

Additional: Bar food; Sunday L; Children welcome; 🍴 dishes
Smoking: No pipes & cigars; Air conditioning
Accommodation: 173 en suite
Credit cards: 🔲 🔲 🔲 🔲 🔲 🔲 JCB

Directions: Nearest Tube – Green Park

5-7 Curzon Street W1Y 8DT
Map: C3
Tel: 0171 4997000
Fax: 0171 4097183
Chef: Dirk Phillips
Cost: Alc £21, fixed-price L £14.95. ☺ H/wine £12.95
Times: Last L 2.30pm/last D 10pm

The White House Hotel ✿✿

Pleasant hotel in a smart listed building carved out of a converted apartment block. A traditional daily roast from the carving trolley vies for attention with more modern offerings such as spiced oriental salmon on a bed of sesame noodles, stir-fried vegetables and mushrooms.

Additional: Bar food; Children welcome; 🍴 dishes
Smoking: No-smoking area; Air conditioning
Accommodation: 582 en suite
Credit cards: 🔲 🔲 🔲 🔲 🔲 🔲 JCB

Directions: Nearest Tube – Great Portland Street

Albany Street NW1 3UP
Map: D4
Tel: 0171 3871200
Fax: 0171 3880091
Chef: Clinton Lovell
Owner: Lomondo Ltd
Cost: Alc £35, fixed-price L £22.75/D £23.50. ☺ H/wine £14
Times: Last L 2.30pm/last D 10.30pm. Closed L Sat, all Sun

ENGLAND
BEDFORDSHIRE

ASPLEY GUISE,
Moore Place Hotel 🏵🏵

The Square MK17 8DW
Map 4: SP93
Tel: 01908 282000
Fax: 01908 281888
Chef: Clive Southgate
Owner: Conference Hotels Ltd
Cost: Alc £25, fixed-price L £14.50/D £20.95. ☺ H/wine £10.95
Times: 12.30-last L 1.45pm/7.30-last D 9.45pm. Closed Sat
Additional: Bar food; Sunday L; Children welcome; 🌑 dishes
Seats: 75. Private dining room 6-40
Smoking: No smoking in dining room
Accommodation: 54 en suite
Credit cards: ▆ ▆ ▆ ▆ ▆ ▆ ▆

Due credit must go to any restaurant that provides an additional menu for guests with special dietary needs – vegetarians, vegans and coeliacs, as well as those wishing to avoid butter, cream or alcohol. On the main *carte*, there are some interesting variations on traditional themes such as Hindle Wakes, here with the breast of chicken stuffed with prunes, then cooked in Earl Grey tea and served cold with a mint tea sauce. Other dishes show a more French influence, such as fricassée of scallops, langoustines and monkfish with sweet pepper sauce, topped by a poached Devon oyster. Desserts tend to the richly indulgent, but there's always the fresh fruit salad for those who can't or won't.

Directions: In centre of village

BEDFORD, Knife & Cleaver 🏵

Fresh fish is the speciality of this attractive conservatory restaurant attached to the former 17th-century village inn. Extensive menus may feature bouillabaisse, turbot and leek en croûte, or meaty items like ham and parsley terrine, and succulent pork fillet stuffed with prunes with a red wine sauce.

The Grove Houghton Conquest MK45 3LA
Map 5: TL04
Tel: 01234 740387
Fax: 01234 740900
Chef: Steven Linsner
Owners: Pauline & David Loom
Cost: Alc £24, fixed-price L £11.95 (2 courses)/D £20. ☺ H/wine £10.50
Times: Last L 2.30pm/last D 9.30pm. Closed L Sat, D Sun, 26-30 Dec
Additional: Bar food; Sunday L; Children welcome; 🌑 dishes
Smoking: No smoking in dining room; Air Conditioning
Accommodation: 9 en suite
Credit cards: ▆ ▆ ▆ ▆ ▆ ▆ ▆ JCB

Directions: M1/J12/13, between A6 & B530. 2m N of Ampthill, 5m S of Bedford

BEDFORD,
Woodlands Manor Hotel

Secluded manor house in wooded grounds, yet only two miles from Bedford centre. Set dinners, of two, three or four courses, feature terrine of salmon and sole on smoked salmon and dill salad, and pork cutlets with honey cloved apples, sauerkraut and cider cream sauce.

Smoking: No smoking in dining room
Accommodation: 33 en suite
Credit cards: ▅▅ ▅▅ ▅▅ ▅ ▅▅ ▅

Directions: 2 miles N of Bedford, in Kettering direction on A6

Green Lane Clapham
MK41 6EP
Map 5: TL04
Tel: 01234 363281
Fax: 01234 272390
Chef: Rae Johnson
Owners: Pageant Hotels
Cost: *Alc* £25, fixed-price L £12.50/D £23.75. ☺ H/wine £11.75
Times: Last L 2pm/last D 9.30pm.
Closed L Sat
Additional: Bar food; Sunday L; Children welcome; ✦ dishes

DUNSTABLE,
Old Palace Lodge Hotel

Ivy-clad Victorian residence, now a charming hotel, handy for M1/J11, yet close to the town centre. The menu offers a good selection of dishes, a well made bouillabaisse, perhaps, or tender lamb kashmiri with clear spiced flavours.

Smoking: No-smoking area; air conditioning
Accommodation: 68 en suite
Credit cards: ▅▅ ▅▅ ▅▅ ▅ ▅▅ ▅ ▅ JCB

Directions: From M1/J11 take Dunstable exit at roundabout. At 2 miles road passes under bridge. Hotel on R opposite church.

Church Street LU5 4RT
Map 4: TL02
Tel: 01582 662201
Fax: 01582 696422
Chef: Arif Huseyin
Owner: Andrew Weir Hotels
Cost: *Alc* £30, fixed-price L&D £19.75, ☺ H/wine £10.95.
Times: Last L 1.45pm/D 11.30pm.
Additional: Sunday L; Bar meals; Children welcome; ✦ dishes

FLITWICK, Flitwick Manor

Church Road MK45 1AE
Map 4: TL03
Tel: 01525 712242
Fax: 01525 718753
Chef: Richard Salt
Owner: Menzies Hotels
Cost: *Alc* £40, fixed-price L £24/D £25. ☺ H/wine £15
Times: Noon-last L 1.30pm/7-last D 9.30pm
Additional: Sunday L; No children under 6; ✦ dishes
Seats: 55. Private room 16. Jacket & tie preferred

This gracious Georgian manor house continues to draw praise from inspectors, whether it be the welcome from the staff, the picturesque setting, or the excellent food. Richard Salt's cooking is direct and to the point, founded on classic tradition yet with the confidence to experiment with the likes of oriental seasoning and Mediterranean flavours. Home-made boudin noir with sage-infused mash and Meaux mustard cream, or a chilled pressed terrine of Mediterranean fish with a roast pepper dressing, poached supreme of local chicken in a light marjoram-scented butter, and a classic pot-au-feu show the variety of a short menu. A test dinner at a tricky time of year 'just before spring's bounty and after a long tired winter', opened on a high note with canapés with intent – salmon mousse, carrot quiche and mini pizza – and duck leg confit with ginger and chilli noodles kept the aspirations high. Red mullet followed, with squid ink risotto and a saffron nage with lightly poached vegetables, plus (early) rhubarb tarte Tatin with vanilla ice cream to finish. Ancillaries are good too: bread rolls straight from the oven, and delicately crafted petits fours. Style and service are in keeping with a country hotel. The wine list has broad scope in price and range, with some depth in Bordeaux, and a short selection of half-bottles.

Smoking: No smoking in dining room
Accommodation: 17 en suite
Credit cards: ▆ ▆ ▆ ▆ ▆ ▆ ▆ JCB

Directions: On A5120, two miles from M1 junction 12

WOBURN,

Paris House Restaurant ✿✿

Woburn Park
MK17 9QP
Map 4: SP93
Tel: 01525 290692
Fax: 01525 290471
Chef/Owner: Peter Chandler
Cost: *Alc* £43, fixed-price L £26/D £47 (5 courses). H/wine £12
Times: Noon-last L 2pm/7pm-last D 9.30pm. Closed D Sun, Mon, Feb
Additional: Sunday L; Children welcome, ◑ dishes
Seats: 45. Private dining room 14
Credit cards: ▆ ▆ ▆ ▆ ▆ ▆ ▆

Directions: On A4012, 1.5 miles out of Woburn towards Hockcliffe, through huge archway

Built for the Paris Exhibition of 1878 (hence the name), this ornate black-and-white mock-Tudor confection is now located in the deer park of the Duke of Bedford's estate at Woburn. In fine weather take aperitifs on the patio and watch for the Barra Singha deer. For the last 15 years the place has been home to chef-patron Peter Chandler's own brand of modern French cooking. Cervelas of salmon with leek coulis, French onion soup, poussin au pot and dumplings, rack of lamb dijonnaise, salted red snapper with Chinese cabbage, Grand Marnier soufflé and tarte Tatin show the range. In addition to the *carte* there are daily-changing 'Gastronomic' and set lunch menus. The wine list is a comprehensive tour of the French vineyards with useful tasting notes and the proprietor's own favourites highlighted. Families are well catered for with reductions for children, high chairs, and they have even been known to produce a Marmite sandwich on occasion.

BERKSHIRE

ASCOT, The Berystede ✿

Substantial Victorian mansion set in 9 acres of landscaped grounds. Its period public rooms convey a truly Victorian atmosphere, but the restaurant is modern and airy. Anglo/French cooking offers salmon rillette with spring onions and coriander and a sweet mustard dressing, confit of duck leg with an apricot port sauce, and iced mango pudding.

Bagshot Road Sunninghill SL5 9JH
Map 4: SU96
Tel: 01344 23311
Fax: 01344 872301
Please telephone for further details

Directions: M3/J3, follow signs for Ascot.

ASCOT, Jade Fountain ❁

Smack in the middle of Sunninghill, this predominantly Cantonese restaurant offers the usual fare, plus a few extras not found on the average Chinese menu. Look out for bean curd with Chinese mushrooms and bamboo shoots, grilled dumplings with pork and vegetarian fillings served on ginger vinegar, and steamed sea bass with spring onion and ginger sauce, and Singapore noodles. Drink jasmine tea.

Directions: 1.5 miles from Ascot

38 High Street Sunninghill
Ascot SL5 9NE
Map 4: SU96
Tel: 01344 27070
Please telephone for further details

ASCOT,
The Royal Berkshire Hotel ❁❁

London Road Sunninghill SL5 0PP
Map 4: SU96
Tel: 01344 623322
Fax: 01344 627100
Chef: Paul Sutcliffe
Owner: Hilton
Cost: *Alc* £24.75, fixed-price L
£24.75 (4 courses)/D £34.50. H/wine
£16.85
Times: Last L 2pm/last D 9.30pm.
Closed L Sat

This is upmarket territory and the prices reflect the location of the well-restored Queen Anne mansion. But for your money you might get fillets of Dover sole, braised leeks and fennel with Beluga caviar, or roast breast of pheasant with roast shallots and chestnuts and mulled wine sauce.

Additional: Bar food; Sunday L; Children welcome; ❹ dishes
Smoking: No smoking in dining room
Accommodation: 63 en suite
Credit cards: ▬ ▭ ▜ ▢ ▭ ▨ JCB

Directions: M4/J10, or A30, follow A329 through Ascot. Hotel is on L after 1.5 miles. From M3/J3 take A322

BRACKNELL,
Coppid Beech Hotel ❁❁

Although the hotel carries an alpine theme, this does not extend fully to the decor or menu of Rowan's restaurant. Instead, the menu boasts an eclectic blend of traditional and modern foods: there is confit of duck, but it is served with sautéed pak choi and a black pepper and pineapple jus. Or there is béarnaise sauce, but it comes over eggs poached in red wine. Fresh Cornish crab is available, but dressed with a mix of avocado and red pepper. Other fine choices are roast saddle of venison on glazed salsify and parsnip served with pears, redcurrants and peppered red wine sauce. Desserts, some of which are offered from a trolley, are a particular strong point

John Nike Way RG12 8TF
Map 4: SU86
Tel: 01344 303333
Fax: 01344 301200
Chef: Neil Thrift
Cost: *Alc* £30, fixed-price L £15.95
(2 courses)D £20.95. ☺
H/wine £12.50
Times: Noon-last L 2.15pm/7-last
D 10.15pm. Closed L Sat
Additional: Bar food; Sunday L;
Children welcome; ❹ dishes
Seats: 80

Coppid Beech Hotel

Smoking: No-smoking area; Air conditioning
Accommodation: 205 en suite
Credit cards:

and include lemon tart and crème brûlée. To accompany, there is a serious wine list offering a decent selection of bottles and around ten wines available by the glass. Service is friendly and professional.

Directions: From M4/J10, follow A329 (M) to 1st exit. At roundabout take 1st exit to Binfield; hotel 300 metres on R

BRACKNELL,
Stirrups Country House ❀ NEW

Originally an old English inn dating back to the 17th century, Stirrups is now a modern hotel where guests can expect first-class hospitality and service. Our inspector enjoyed a winter meal, served in the Tudor-style beamed restaurant, of French onion soup followed by roast loin of lamb with apricot and sage cream sauce.

Additional: Bar food; Sunday L; Children welcome; dishes
Smoking: No smoking in dining room
Accommodation: 24 en suite
Credit cards: JCB

Directions: Telephone for directions

Maidens Green RG42 6LD
Map 4: SU86
Tel: 01344 882284
Fax: 01344 882300
Chef: John Sinnerton
Owner: Colin Reed
Alc £23.50, fixed-price L & D £18.25.
H/wine £ 9.50
Times: Last L 2pm/last D 10pm

BRAY, **Chauntry House** ❀❀ NEW

'Chauntry House has a welcoming feel to it as one enters the front door' remarked an inspector of this 18th-century house in the centre of Bray. The dining room is all lemon, pinks and light green, with limed-oak furniture and a feeling of space. The cooking is good and notable for generous portions. Witness a winter dinner that took in an imaginative plum-marinated duck with winter leaves, a perfectly cooked chargrilled salmon on a lime leaf mousseline with vegetables including beans wrapped in paper-thin ham and chargrilled, and lemon meringue with raspberry coulis, plus clotted cream 'to ensure you don't leave the table hungry'. The wine list offers a reasonable selection from around the wall; prices, however are more than reasonable 'for this part of the world'.

SL6 2AB
Tel: 01628 673991
Fax: 01628 773089
Please telephone for further details

BRAY, The Fat Duck 🏮🏮🏮

High Street Maidenhead SL6 2AQ
Map 4: SU97
Tel: 01628 580333
Fax: 01628 776188
Chef: Heston Blumenthal
Owners: Heston & Susanna Blumenthal
Cost: *Alc* £42.50, fixed-price L £21.50. H/wine £14.50
Times: Noon-2pm (Sun till 2.30)/7-9.30pm. Closed D Sun, all Mon
Additional: Children welcome; 🍃 dishes
Seats: 50
Credit cards: ▬ ▬ ⚛ ░ ▓ ▐

Heston Blumenthal is a man of controlled passion with an iconoclastic bent for challenging perceived wisdoms of the classical canon. He has a true intuitive mind, a keen intellect and extraordinary committment – the complexity of many of his labour-intensive dishes means a daily 7am start. Bold simplicity is not the style – in lesser hands many of his ideas would not work, and even in Blumenthal's impressively skilled ones the individualistic cooking can achieve great heights or go awry in the course of a single meal. Dishes which have worked exceptionally well include a signature crab feuillantine with marinated salmon, crystalised seaweed, roast foie gras and oyster vinaigrette, and veal sweetbread, roasted in a saltcrust and marinaded' in hay with sugary parsnips, the most delicious clams and truffle cream oil. Roast spiced cod was dominated by a liquorice flavour, topped with a splodge of runner bean purée, sweet-sour Puy lentils and nutty carrot brunoise plus a cockscomb sauce. Puddings are the weakest link – a chocolate delice with griottines 'defied description' but was basically a Black Forest gâteau deconstructed and rebuilt in an architectural sort of way. The restaurant itself is a lively, modern minimalist place with laminated topped tables, coir carpets, copper-fronted patchwork bar and iron frame chairs. Service is excellent.

Signature dishes: Piquillos peppers stuffed with truffled brandade, red mullet, with cocos beans and olive oil from Mausanne; fillet of lamb cooked in salt crust with hay, gratin of potatoes and Epoisses, clams a la plancha; lasagne of langoustines with pigs' trotters and truffles; Parfait of haricots blancs, chestnut cream, syrop de vin de noix

Directions: M4 J8/9 (Maidenhead), take A308 towards Windsor. turn L into Bray. Restaurant in centre of village on L

BRAY, Monkey Island Hotel 🏮

Privately owned hotel that enjoys an idyllic location on an island in the Thames, with access by footbridge or boat. Changes in the kitchen as we went to press, but early reports on the short menu of modern British cooking indicate standards have been maintained.

Additional: Bar food; Sunday L; No children under 5; 🍃 dishes
Smoking: No-smoking area; No pipes and cigars
Accommodation: 26 en suite
Credit cards: ▬ ▬ ⚛ ░ ▐ ▨

Directions: M4/J8/9, A308 (M) (Windsor) 1st L to Bray, 1st R into Old Mill Lane, hotel at end

SL6 2EE
Map 4: SU97
Tel: 01628 623400
Fax: 01628 784732
Chef: Chris Coubrough
Owner: NGH Properties Ltd
Cost: *Alc* £33, fixed price L £21/D £29.50. H/wine £14.50
Times: Last L 2.30pm/last D 9.30pm. Closed L Sat

BRAY, Waterside Inn ❁❁❁❁

It is more than 25 years since they were first introduced, but
The Waterside Inn and its peerless riverbank location continue
to be a perfectly matched couple. Summer aperitifs taken by
the Thames are a prelude that takes some living up too, but
when the main event is as lovingly produced as it is here, a
sense of anticlimax is unlikely. The atmosphere is unfailingly
relaxed but this is the kind of easy ambience that can only be
attained through sheer hard work and attention to detail.
These virtues (together with the small matter of sheer talent)
are surely the watchwords of Michel Roux's achievement.
True, one might rarely be taken aback, or caught unawares by
some unexpected twist or interstellar flavour, but at the
Waterside that really isn't the point. Whilst others are applying
bold strokes, the Waterside style remains one of painstaking
attention to detail and when words like 'delicate' are used on
the menu (as in shellfish minestrone) you can be sure it means
a jeweller's precision. Some of the most striking dishes are
perfectly cut, little gems of simplicity such as a finely balanced
and seductively aromatic reduction of chicken and lemongrass
consommé. Or there are assemblages of more varied parts, but
the combinations are always classic and as such, rarely
anything less than harmonious. Take for instance a superbly
timed poached goujons of sole, accompanied by a seamless
sauce of pistachio and Sauternes, or pale-pink saddle of milk-
fed lamb stuffed with morels and served with a sensitively
minted hollandaise. Perhaps the apotheosis of the style is to
be found in the desserts where the mastery of technique is the
most visible in dishes such as Amaretto parfait with a white
chocolate sorbet, or warm golden plum soufflé. Lunch
continues to offer set-price good value, but on a summer
afternoon don't bank on getting back to the office.
Signature dishes: Selle d'agneau de lait farcie aux morilles,
sauce paloise; l'assiette de grenadins, rouelle de rognon et
pithiviers de ris de veau à son jus; gibier de saison aux
chataignes et salsifis meunière; daube de boeuf à la Beaujolais.

Ferry Road SL6 2AT
Map 4: SU97
Tel: 01628 620691
Fax: 01628 784710
Chefs: Michel Roux, Mark Dodson
Owner: Michel Roux
Cost: *Alc* £75, fixed-price L £29.50
(£44.50 Sat, Sun)/D £67.50 (5
courses). H/wine £20
Times: Noon-last L 2pm (2.30pm
Sat/Sun)/7-last D 10pm. Closed L Tue,
D Sun (1 Oct-30 Apr), all Mon, 26
Dec-28 Jan, 5-8 Apr
Additional: Sunday L; No children
under 12; ✈ dishes
Smoking: No pipes & cigars
Seats: 75. Private dining room 8
Accommodation: 9 en suite
Credit cards: 💳 💳 💳 💳 💳 💳 💳 JCB

Directions: On A3089 towards
Windsor, turn L before M/way
overpass for Bray. Restaurant clearly
signposted.

COOKHAM DEAN,
The Inn on the Green ❁ NEW

The Old Cricket Common
SL6 9NZ
Map 4: SU88
Tel: 01628 482638
Fax: 01628 487474
Chef: Adrian Hutchinson
Owners: Mr & Mrs A J Taylor,
Mr N Grice, Mr T Saunderson-
Wilson, Mr A Hutchinson
Cost: *Alc* £20, fixed price L & D
£15.95. ☺ H/wine £9.50
Times: Last L 2.30pm/last D 10pm
Additional: Bar food L; Sunday L;
Children welcome; ✈ dishes
Accommodation: 8 en suite
Credit cards: 💳 💳 💳 💳 💳 💳

*A cosy village inn with some parts dating back 300 years, although the
bright conservatory is brand-spanking new. The excellent wine list
includes first-growth clarets and fine Burgundies, all the better to enjoy
alongside classics such as grilled venison with sauce bordelaise. Lovely
passion fruit cheesecake and coffee to complete a charming meal.*

Directions: Telephone for directions

MAIDENHEAD,
Fredrick's Hotel ❀❀❀

Shoppenhangers Road
SL6 2PZ
Map 4: SU88
Tel: 01628 635934
Fax: 01628 771054
Chef: Brian Cutler
Owner: Fredrick W Lösel
Cost: *Alc* £49, fixed-price L £23.50/D £33.50. H/wine £15
Times: Noon-last L 2pm/7-last D 9.45pm. Closed L Sat, Xmas & New Year
Additional: Bar food; Sunday L; Children welcome; ❹ dishes; Jacket & tie preferred
Seats: 60. Private dining rooms up to 130; Jacket & tie preferred
Smoking: No cigars & pipes; Air conditioning
Accommodation: 37 en suite
Credit cards: ▆ ▆ ▆ ▆ ▆ JCB

Soothing elegance is the hallmark of this hotel-restaurant, where traditional and contemporary elements combine to satisfy the business dignitaries that form the bulk of the clientele. The well-trained staff will wheel out an old-fashioned trolley for orders of roast rib of Aberdeen Angus or duck, and the desserts, but modern favourites such as pesto, wild mushrooms, Parma ham and linguine are dotted throughout the menu. The cocktail bar, lined with subtle erotic art, or the hotel's winter garden, are the places to begin and end the meal, with super canapés including smooth salmon mousse and deep-fried balls of goats' cheese, and popular petits fours such as truffles and tartlets. In the well-appointed dining room, which boasts quality china and charming hand-painted walls, our inspector particularly enjoyed the starter of butter bean soup with parsley pesto and morels, plus a tempting selection of home-made breads including a smashing tomato and olive variety. Another trump card was the skate stuffed with crab and ginger and served with mussels in saffron broth, though sadly no sauce spoon was supplied to drink the flavoursome liquid. A good selection of vegetables featuring roast butternut squash accompanied the turbot poached in coconut milk with lemongrass and topped with excellent fried scampi. Desserts included a well-presented dark chocolate soufflé that unfortunately contained too much egg white but was accompanied by a pleasing white chocolate ice cream served in a brandy snap basket.

Signature dishes: Skate stuffed with ginger and crab and mussels in saffron broth; lobster, asparagus and girolle salad in a lime butter sauce; noisettes of venison glazed with Roquefort; medallions of veal with grilled ceps and truffled linguine.

Directions: From A404M exit Cox Green, turn L at roundabout; from A308 take next turning to station bridge.

MAIDENHEAD,
Ye Olde Bell Hotel

An attractive inn, built in 1135 as a guest house for the nearby monastery, which retains much of its historic charm. The wood-panelled restaurant features views over well-tended lawns and offers interesting menus. Accurately cooked dishes may include an onion tart with pesto sauce, and lamb noisette with rosemary sauce.

Additional: Bar food; Sunday L; Children welcome; ♨ dishes
Accommodation: 47 en suite
Credit cards: 💳 💳 💳 💳 💳 💳

Directions: Take A4130 to Henley, at East Arms pub turn R into Hurley village. Hotel 800 yds down road

Hurley SL6 5LX
Map 4: SU88
Tel: 01628 825881
Fax: 01628 825939
Chef: Adrian Offley
Owners: Jarvis Hotels plc
Cost: Fixed-price L £17.95/D £23.50.
Times: Last L 2.30pm/Last D 9.30pm.

NEWBURY,
Donnington Valley Hotel

The fine, galleried restaurant is reason enough to want to eat here, especially as the range has improved notably. Tried at inspection was a pretty dish of scallops with shallots and little gem lettuce, a chicken consommé with ginger, wild mushrooms and noodles, a well-sauced noisettes of lamb on a bed of rösti and spinach. However timing can sometimes go awry, as in beef with coriander dumplings. Best main course sampled was a duo of plaice and salmon with fennel and tomatoes. Chocolate cappuccino cup topped with marshmallow triggered a burst of second childhood in our inspector.

Directions: Exit M4/J13, take A34 S/bound and exit Donnington Castle. Turn R over bridge then L

Old Oxford Road
Donnington RG14 3AG
Map 4: SU46
Tel: 01635 551199
Fax: 01635 551123
Chef: Kelvin Johnson
Cost: *Alc* £35, fixed-price L £19.50/D £21.50. ☺ H /wine £11.50
Times: Noon-last L 1.45pm/7-last D 9.45pm
Additional: Bar food; Sunday L; Children welcome; ♨ dishes
Seats: 120. Private dining rooms 40. Jacket & tie preferred
Smoking: No smoking in dining room; Air conditioning
Accommodation: 58 en suite
Credit cards: 💳 💳 💳 💳

NEWBURY,
Hollington Country House

See Highclere, Hampshire

NEWBURY,
Regency Park Hotel ❀❀

Bowling Green Road
Thatcham RG18 3RP
Map 4: SU46
Tel: 01635 871555
Fax: 01635 871571
Chef: Paul Green
Cost: *Alc* £30, fixed price L £13.95/D £22. ☺ H/wine £11.95
Times: 12.30pm-last L 1.50pm/7-last D 9.50pm
Additional: Bar food; Sunday L; Children welcome; ❀ dishes
Seats: 60. Private dining room 20
Smoking: No smoking in dining room; Air conditioning
Accommodation: 45 en suite
Credit cards: ▬ ▭ ➹ ▢ ▤ ▣ ▨ JCB

Within easy reach of the M3 and M4 motorways, yet peacefully situated in five acres of grounds, the Regency Park is a popular conference venue. It was built in 1904, extended in the 1980s and has an interior decorated in pastel shades. The Terraces restaurant is spacious and light, and looks out on to a terraced garden. Here, daily set menus and a *carte* offer a varied choice of modern English dishes cooked with notable skill. Consommé of spring vegetables was found to be 'very enjoyable, tangy and savoury' by one inspector. Wild salmon with shallot butter sauce and wild mushrooms was a flamboyantly presented main course, garnished with saffron potatoes, various herbs and tomato concasse. Save space for desserts, where culinary expertise is most evident in dishes such as an excellent hot toffee soufflé with citrus sauce. Breads are baked on the premises, and petits fours accompany the coffee.

Directions: From Thatcham A4, towards Newbury, turn R into Northfield Road, then L at mini roundabout. Hotel is on R

NEWBURY, # The Vineyard at Stockcross

NEW

Stockcross RG20 8JU
Map 4: SU46
Tel: 01635 528770
Fax: 01635 528398
Chef: David Sharland
Cost: *Alc* £60, fixed-price D £70 (7 courses)
Times: Noon-last L 1.45pm/7-last D 9.45pm
Additional: Sunday L; ❀ dishes
Seats: 50. Private dining room 30-40. Jacket & tie preferred
Smoking: No-smoking area; No pipes & cigars; Air conditioning
Accommodation: 15 luxury suites
Credit cards: ▬ ▭ ➹ ▢ ▤ ▨

A grand classical hotel that takes its name and inspiration from the Peter Michael Winery in the mountains of northern California. David Sharland updates classical recipes with west-coast influences, and early reports are encouraging. One meal praised a grey mullet broth that successfully combined Bayonne ham, meaty grilled pieces of mullet and a vegetable broth in three totally distinct flavours and textures, and a duo of chocolate iced parfaits (dark and white) with a passion fruit coulis. Another satisfying meal took in tartare of yellow fin tuna with a chicory salad, tender langoustine spring roll, breast of duck topped with foie gras, medallions of sweetbreads set on a pea purée with truffles, sage and a light red wine sauce, and cherry ravioli in a cherry sauce with vanilla ice cream.

The six-course fixed-price menu 'Todays Fusion of Wine and Food' matches Californian wines with each course.

Directions: Take A34 Newbury by-pass to A4 Bath Road interchange, then take B4000 to Stockcross, hotel on R

PANGBOURNE, **Copper Inn** ❀❀

Church Road
RG8 7AR
Map 4: SU67
Tel: 0118 9842244
Fax: 0118 9845542
Chef: Stuart Shepherd
Owner: Michel Rosso
Cost: *Alc* £25, fixed-price L £14.95/D £17.95. ☺ H/wine £12.50
Times: Noon-2.30pm/7-9.30pm (10pm Fri & Sat)
Additional: Bar food; Sunday L; Children welcome; ❹ dishes
Seats: 65. Private dining room 50
Smoking: No-smoking area; No pipes
Accommodation: 22 en suite
Credit cards:

The former Georgian coaching inn has recently had a Designers' Guild makeover – wooden ceilings, tapestries and yellow-green colours give the restaurant a provençale look, emphasised by a menu that includes excellent fish-rich bouillabaisse with garlic croûtons and rouille, a 'Grand Antipasto' of cured meats and pickled condiments, or wild mushroom and saffron risotto, complemented by main courses such as rack of lamb roasted with minted honey served with timbale of couscous and aubergine wafers. Roasted boned quails filled with spinach forcemeat served with Muscat grape sauce, and veal cutlet with morel mushrooms, cream sauce and 'Meme Rosso's green noodles' speak, however, of other times and climes. Poached fruits in warm cinnamon syrup with Amaretto bavarois made a delightful dessert, but it's hard to resist the delectable looking British cheeseboard. One of the pleasures of the place is that there is no pressure to order more than one dish, even a starter – but it would be a wasted opportunity.

Directions: 5 miles from M4/J12, at junction of A329 Reading/Oxford and A340; next to parish church.

SHINFIELD, **L'Ortolan** ❀❀❀❀❀

Church Lane RG2 9BY
Map 4: SU73
Tel: 0118 9883783
Fax: 0118 9885391
Chef/Owner: John Burton-Race
Cost: *Alc* £85, fixed-price L £39.50/D £39.50 (ex D Sat). H/wine £18

John Burton-Race's distinctive restaurant has seen changes since our last visit. A completely new front-of-house team has been received with enthusiasm by inspectors who have all reported a more relaxed air, a willingness 'to have a laugh and a chat', and menus have been streamlined in terms of dish composition, with the food far less complex than it used to be. However, the *carte* describes a remarkable range. A November lunch exemplified some of Burton-Race's skills. A crab trio comprising a consommé of amazing clarity until disturbed by the two small morsels of mouth-watering crab flesh, a roulade (crab flesh encased in the thinnest sliver of Parma ham), and fine spring rolls, was followed by a signature dish of tournedos of venison, rare and tender, served on a delicate cauliflower purée, with wonderfully sweet blackberries, and a rich, glossy port sauce, a marvellously understated dish, even down to the extremely fine green beans simply presented on a side dish. A huge, hot pistachio and chocolate soufflé ended the meal, perfectly timed and served, an effective half-half division of flavours with a faultless colour balance mirrored perfectly by a some chocolate sorbet and pistachio ice cream. Inspectors also

AA Wine Award–see page 16
Shortlisted for

reported well on dinner, enjoying mille-feuille of crab and mussels with a light curry sauce vierge, a boudin of oyster and scallop with a warm tarragon vinaigrette, a superb whole baby red mullet, boned and stuffed with parsley breadcrumbs and bone marrow, served with baby leeks and pommes boulangère, and pig's trotter stuffed with veal sweetbreads, ham, and tongue, served with caramelised juices and a gribiche garnish of egg, parsley, gherkin and caper. Puddings were spot-on, a signature dôme de mousse caramel brûlée was stunning, and île flottante aux mures et pommes was brilliant – soft meringue timbale, stuffed with a compote of slightly sharp apple and blackberry, and floated on a cappuccino-like lake of thin vanilla custard, a witty reworking of apple and blackberry pie with custard. As usual, a great cheese trolley, all in peak condition; as one old hand reported 'one of the two best cheeseboards I have seen, the other being at Le Gavroche'. Great attention is also paid to minor details such as bread, canapés, and petits fours.

Signature dishes: Queue de homard roti, sauce Sauternes et ses petits legumes de printemps; tranche de saumon en papillotte; suprême de pigeoneau en robe de chou et son ravioli girolles; tournedos de chevreuil aux mures et purée Dubarry.

Directions: From M4/J11, take A33 (Basingstoke). At roundabout L to Three Mile Cross, L towards Shinfield, R opposite The Hungry Horse pub. Restaurant on L, 1 mile.

Times: Noon-2.30pm/7-10pm. Closed D Sun, all Mon
Additional: Sunday L; Children welcome; 🍴 dishes
Seats: 65. Private dining room 26
Smoking: No pipes and cigars
Credit cards: ▨ ▨ ▨ ▨ ▨ ▨ ▨

SONNING, **The French Horn** ✹✹

RG4 6TN
Map 4: SU77
Tel: 01189 692204
Fax: 01189 442210
Chef: Gille Company
Owners: The Emmanuel Family
Cost: *Alc* £45, fixed-price L £19.50/D £32. H/wine £13.50
Times: Noon-last L 2pm/7pm-last D 9.30pm. Closed Good Fri.
Additional: Sunday L; Children welcome; 🍴 dishes
Seats: 70. Private dining room 24
Smoking: No pipes in dining room
Accommodation: 20 en suite
Credit cards: ▨ ▨ ▨ ▨ ▨ ▨

Superbly located next to the still, serene waters of the Thames, this luxurious restaurant's view of weeping willows across the river imparts a relaxing sense of well-being to visitors. Decorations and table settings are opulent: swags and tails adorn the windows while the tables feature comfortable seating, neatly starched cloths and silver water goblets. The menu is French-driven and excels at sweet things. Particularly good is a melt-in-the-mouth chocolate tart with spiced banana sauce, a rich combination of bold flavours executed with a perfect sense of balance. Superb petits fours such as crisp almond tuiles, fruit tartlets and chocolate-caramel squares come with delicious coffee. Amongst the savouries there's plenty of seafood, including starters of crab tian and lobster salad and mains such as confit of salmon cooked in duck fat and red mullet bavarois. Meat lovers will find roast beef, rack of lamb and a house speciality of spit-roast duck with traditional sauces.

Directions: M4 exit 8/9 & A4, village centre, on the river

STREATLEY,
Swan Diplomat Hotel ❀❀

High Street RG8 9HR
Map 4: SU58
Tel: 01491 873737
Fax: 01491 872554
Chef: Damian Bradley
Cost: Alc £35, fixed-price D £32.
H/wine £12
Times: D only, last D 9.30pm.
Closed D Sun
Additional: Bar food; Sunday L
(12.30-2pm); Children welcome;
❸ dishes
Smoking: No pipes & cigars
Accommodation: 46 en suite
Credit cards: ▨ ▨ ▨ ▨ ▨ ▨

The pavilion-style restaurant takes full advantage of the hotel's prime riverside location. Now that Damian Bradley has settled in (and revamped the whole brigade) inspectors have noted improvement in standards all round, with the menu full of fashionable touches, but based firmly on sound technique. A summer dinner opened with an amuse bouche of scallop with Parma ham in a lime/soy dressing, was followed by a vibrant, professional looking terrine of leeks and foie gras with vanilla basil-scented oil, then loin of tender veal with buttered spinach, rösti potatoes, a ragout of wild mushrooms and Marsala wine sauce, and finished with coffee and chocolate mousses in the shape of a cup.

Directions: Follow A329 from Pangbourne, on entering Streatley turn R at traffic lights. The hotel is on L before bridge

WINDSOR, Aurora Garden Hotel ❀

Bolton Avenue SL4 3JF
Map 4: SU97
Tel: 01753 868686
Fax: 01753 831394
Chef: Denton Robinson
Cost: Alc £18.50, fixed-price L
£7.95/D £12.95. ☺ H/wine £9.50
Times: Last L 2pm/last D 9.30pm
Additional: Bar food; Sunday L;
Children welcome; ❸ dishes

What could be more pleasant than a summer evening meal overlooking the floodlit terrace and water garden at this charming hotel? Our inspector enjoyed a starter of smoked fish terrine, followed by pan-fried breast of chicken on apricot couscous with coriander pesto. The wine list features several good-value bottles.

Smoking: No smoking in dining room
Accommodation: 19 en suite. **Credit cards:** ▨ ▨ ▨ ▨ ▨ JCB

Directions: From M4 take A308 (Staines); at 3rd roundabout take 3rd exit (Bolton Ave). Hotel is 500yds on R

WINDSOR, The Castle Hotel ❀❀

High Street SL4 1LJ
Map 4: SU97
Tel: 01753 851011
Fax: 01753 621560
Chef: Andrew Barras
Owner: Forte Hotels
Cost: Alc £25. H/wine £16
Times: 12.30-last L 2.15pm/7-last D
9.45pm
Additional: Bar food; Sunday L;
Children welcome; ❸ dishes

This aptly named hotel (it's in the shadow of its more historical namesake) is popular with locals and tourists alike. If the menu in the restaurant (traditional elegance in here, with chandeliers, carved beams and arches) is anything to go by, it's not hard to see why. Gutsy, rustic dishes – duckling faggot with five-bean stew, partridge and pheasant terrine, and braised oxtail, for instance – mingle with the likes of Thai fishcakes, kipper and salmon spring roll, and mushroom and beetroot risotto. A meal could start with cabbage and ham broth, go on

The Castle Hotel

Seats: 50. Private dining room 24
Smoking: No smoking in dining room
Accommodation: 111 en suite
Credit cards: ▦ ▦ ⚑ ▢ ▦ ▣ ▣

to monkfish wrapped in Parma ham served with parsley sauce, and end with precisely cooked lemon tart or apple and prune charlotte. A white and red Côtes du Rhône head up a list of around two-dozen bottles.

Directions: In town centre, opposite Guildhall

WINDSOR, **Oakley Court Hotel**

Windsor Road Water Oakley
SL4 5UR
Map 4: SU97
Tel: 01753 609988
Fax: 01628 637011
Chef: Murdo MacSween
Cost: *Alc* £40. H/wine £14.95.
Times: 12.30-last L 1.45pm/7-last D 9.45pm
Additional: Bar food; Sunday L; Children welcome; ⓓ dishes
Seats: 70. Private dining room 200; Jacket & tie preferred
Smoking: No smoking in dining room
Accommodation: 115 en suite
Credit cards: ▦ ▦ ▢ ▦ ▣

The Victorian Gothic hotel, once the location for Hammer horror films, has been much extended, and as well as the smart Le Boulestin restaurant, lighter meals can be taken in Boaters Brasserie. Our inspector ate in the stately surroundings of the former, sampling a fine starter of scallop, langoustine and lobster tossed in pesto, and served on tomato and herb broth, before going on to cod served with both a béarnaise sauce and a full-bodied jus. Amaretto and banana brûlée brought the meal to a sound conclusion. There are more straightforward dishes on the *carte*, duck liver parfait with red onion chutney and Cumberland sauce, perhaps, or grilled Dover sole.

Directions: Beside the Thames, off the A308 between Windsor and Maidenhead.

YATTENDON, **Royal Oak** ✿ ✿ ✿

The Square RG18 0UF
Map 4: SU57
Tel: 01635 201325
Fax: 01635 201926
Chef: Robin Zavou

The setting is a wisteria-clad country inn with all the accoutrements of old beams, comfortable furnishings, and a pretty garden, plus far better food and wine than usual. Bar

Owner: Regal Hotel Group
Cost: *Alc* £25, fixed price D £32.50.
H/wine £9.95
Times: Noon-last L 2pm/7-last D
9pm. Closed L Sat & Mon, D Sun
Additional: Bar food; Sunday L;
◑ dishes
Seats: 25. Private dining room 8.
Jacket & tie preferred
Smoking: No smoking in dining room
Accommodation: 5 en suite
Credit cards: ▬ ▬ ▨ ▨ ▤ ▨ JCB

snacks may fit into the received idea of pub cooking, but they
also push back the boundaries. However, it is in the stylish
restaurant that Robin Zavou shows his real talent. The
approach is up to date with the watchwords being simplicity,
good accurate flavours, and timing. Dishes range from a simple
chargrilled salad of red mullet and scallops with sauce vierge,
or a roast rack of lamb with braised red cabbage, wild
mushrooms and a tomato jus, to roast wild duck breast with its
confit leg, creamy spinach and sauce diable, and a galantine of
foie gras and Barbary duck with rabbit rillette and sloe gin
preserve. Execution is faultless. A test dinner opened with a
simple but beautifully produced whole-roasted wood pigeon
with celeriac velouté and a Madeira jus, went on to
caramelised sea bass served with fresh tagliarini and a citrus
beurre sauce, and finished with a hot chocolate fondant that
came almost as a collapsing soufflé with such a gooey, runny,
moreish centre 'you wonder how anyone could possibly choose
anything else when this is on offer'.The wine list is desirable,
though pricy away from the house recommendations. Some
interesting wines by the glass, though. Among the dozen or so
on offer on our visit was a tempting Viognier, Vin du Pays
d'Oc, J d'Alibert 1996, not often seen by the glass, which made
up for the fact that half-bottles are no longer stocked.

Directions: M4/J12 follow signs towards Pangbourne turn L for
Yattendon; in centre of the village

BRISTOL

BRISTOL, **Aztec Hotel** ⊛

*A bright, modern feel to the menu in Quarterjacks bustling
restaurant with plenty of Med influences and well-chosen fish.
Scallops come sweet and judiciously seared with a well-judged
yellow pepper risotto. Similar accuracy was evident in a moist
chicken breast pan-fried with crunchy asparagus and a saffron
sauce. Pastry is a strength and a crisp Normandy apple tart is highly
recommended.*

Accommodation: 108 en suite
Credit cards: ▬ ▬ ▨ ▨ ▤ ▨

Directions: On Aztec West Business Park at interchange of
M4/M5

NEW

Aztec West Business Park
Almondsbury BS12 4TS
Map 3: ST57
Tel: 01454 201090
Fax: 01454 201593
Chef: Mark Sorrell
Owner: Shire Inns Ltd
Cost: *Alc* £25, fixed price L £15.95/D
£23. ☺ H/wine £10
Times: Last L 2pm/last D 9.45pm.
Closed L Sat & Bhs
Additional: Bar food; Sunday L;
Children welcome; ◑ dishes
Smoking: No smoking in dining room

BRISTOL, **Bells Diner**

Moroccan/African influences abound at this charming, casual neighbourhood hang-out. The short, set menu (with some supplements) changes daily, and offers rustic food with restrained seasoning rather than robust. This translates as fish soup, crab cakes, rillettes, cod with Seville orange, chorizo, lentils and harissa, and apricot almond tart with farm cheese.

Additional: Sunday L; Children welcome; dishes
Smoking: No smoking in dining room
Credit cards:

Directions: Corner premises in York Road, Montpellier

1 York Road BS6 5QB
Map 3: ST57
Tel: 0117 9240357
Fax: 0117 9244280
Chef/Owner: Christopher Wicks
Cost: *Alc* £16.75, fixed-price D £15.50. ☺ H/wine £8.95.
Times: Last L 3pm/D 10.30pm. Closed L Sat, D Sun, L Mon, 24-30 Dec

BRISTOL, **Berkeley Square Hotel**

Nightingales Restaurant is an apt name for this smart Georgian hotel set in a peaceful square close to the university, art gallery and Clifton village. A lighter, more varied approach to the cooking is paying off. Duck liver pâté, lamb cutlets with minted pear and sweet basil sauce, and rich chocolate pudding have all been endorsed.

Additional: Bar food; Children welcome; dishes
Accommodation: 42 en suite
Credit cards: JCB

Directions: Top of Park Street turn L at traffic lights into Berkeley Square, hotel on R

15 Berkeley Square Clifton BS8 1HB
Map 3: ST57
Tel: 0117 9254000
Fax: 0117 9252970
Chef: Tim Shaw
Cost: *Alc* £18, fixed-price D £19.95. ☺ H/wine £9
Times: D only, last D 9.30pm

BRISTOL, **Blue Goose**

Casual restaurant, known for its buzzing atmosphere and modern European cooking. Inside, the bright blue walls and bold abstracts create an exciting venue for dishes such as fillet of salmon with saffron, mussels and cream, and duck breast with a beetroot and orange compote and brandy sauce.

Additional: Children welcome; dishes
Smoking: No-smoking area; No pipes & cigars; Air-conditioning
Credit cards:

Directions: From city centre, A38 N (Stokes Croft) approx 2 miles to Horefield. On L, corner of Ash & Gloucester Rds

344 Gloucester Road
Horfield BS7 8UR
Map 3: ST57
Tel: 0117 9420940
Fax: 0117 9444033
Owner: Arne Ringner
Cost: Fixed-price D £15. ☺ H/wine £8.95
Times: D only, 7pm – last D 10pm. Closed Bhs

BRISTOL, **Bristol Marriott Hotel**

Large city-centre hotel with a smartly styled restaurant complete with comfortable chairs and well-spaced tables. Main courses might include best end of lamb with herb crust, or escalope of salmon poached in red wine. Desserts, such as pear Belle Hélène are carefully presented.

Additional: Bar food; Children welcome; dishes
Smoking: No-smoking area; Air conditioning
Accommodation: 289 en suite
Credit cards:

Directions: Close to Bristol city centre, at the Old Market, opposite castle ruins

Lower Castle Street BS1 3AD
Map 3: ST57
Tel: 0117 9294281
Fax: 0117 9276377
Chef: Joe Beaver
Cost: Fixed-price D £19.50. ☺ H/wine £11.55
Times: D only, 7.30pm-last D 10.30pm. Closed Sun, Bhs

BRISTOL,
Glass Boat Restaurant ❀❀

Welsh Back BS1 4SB
Map 3: ST57
Tel: 0117 9290704
Fax: 0117 9297338
Chef: Michel Lemoine
Owner: Arne Ringner
Cost: Alc £28, fixed-price L £10.95 (2 courses)/D £17.50 (3 courses). ☺
H/wine £9.95
Times: Noon-last L 2.15pm/6.30-last D 9.45pm. Closed L Sat, all Sun, L Bhs
Additional: Children welcome; ④ dishes
Seats: 90. Private dining room 40
Smoking: Air conditioning
Credit cards: ▥ ▥ ▥ ▥ ▥

Adjacent to Bristol Bridge and in the heart of Bristol's rejuvenated dockland area, is a lovingly restored, permanently moored boat. Nothing very flashy, could be described as straightforward and down-to-earth decor-wise, but the cooking is up beat and modern. It tips its hat to most current fashions: fish soup Spanish-style; sautéed potato gnocchi in butter with sliced garlic, sage, tomato strips and Reggiano Parmesan; seared free-range chicken flavoured with Thai herbs and spices and garnished with crispy rice noodles and popped rice; slow-cooked duck with a caramelised kumquat and orange segment sauce. Fish is a strength, imaginatively partnered in the likes of pan-fried fillet of salmon with a coconut crust with sautéed Chinese leaves, peppered pineapple and a sweet-and-sour sauce or steamed fillet of sea bass, fresh seaweed and chive butter sauce. The wine list is good, well-priced and intercontinental.

Directions: By Bristol Bridge in the old centre of Bristol

BRISTOL, Harveys ❀❀❀

12 Denmark Street
BS1 5DQ
Map 3: ST57
Tel: 0117 9275034
Fax: 0117 9275001
Chef: Daniel Galmiche
Owners: John Harvey & Sons
Cost: Alc £42.85, fixed-price L £17.95/D £39.95. H/wine £14
Times: Noon-last L 2pm/7-last D 10.30pm. Closed L Sat, all Sun, 3rd wk Feb
Additional: No children under 8; ④ dishes
Seats: 60. Private dining room 40
Smoking: No pipes and cigars; Air conditioning
Credit cards: ▥ ▥ ▥ ▥ ▥ ▥ ▥ JCB

Interior design might not seem much of a reason for drinking dangerous amounts of cream sherry, but so striking are the hundreds of empty Harveys' blue bottles packed into the windows of this cellar restaurant, that one's drinking habits could easily change. Many other reminders of the company's principal trade are also to be found (not least the adjacent wine museum) but the viniculture theme is not overdone and bright contemporary prints are the main feature of the restaurant walls. Basement it may be but this is no crowded bistro; tables are well-spaced service smart, professional and handled with a discretion well suited to Daniel Galmiche's immaculately understated cooking. Extravagant flourishes are eschewed in favour of a depth of flavour and lightness of touch that are handled with rare skill. Witness 'brilliantly assembled' rissoles of langoustine, gently marinated in truffle oil and paired with a balsamic dressed spaghetti of vegetables, judiciously spiked with chilli oil. Further evidence comes in the shape of a fat, shining fillet of sea bass, roasted to moist perfection and perfectly at ease with candied tomatoes and basil-leaf tempura. Many combinations are distinctly classic, but when new life is breathed into simple medallions of lamb with garlic and rosemary it's obvious that something special is going on. Desserts are similarly well tuned whether its an unctuous warm honey and pear cake complementing an exemplary spiced crème brûlée or a raspberry sable with fig purée and a suitably sharp rhubarb coulis. The wine list is as voluminous as might be expected with a 'Sommeliers Choice' offering a usefully abbreviated selection.

Signature dishes: Smoked salmon paupiette with sevruga caviar; roasted sea bass with candied tomatoes, olive and balsamic vinegar; roasted farm pigeon with sautéed potatoes with sea salt, jus with herb and sherry vinegar

Directions: City centre off Unity Street at bottom of Park Street, opposite City Hall and Cathedral; follow signs for Harveys Wine Museum

BRISTOL, Howards Restaurant ❀❀

1A-2A Avon Crescent Hotwells
BS1 6XQ
Map 3: ST57
Tel: 0117 9262921
Fax: 0117 9255585
Chef: David Short
Owner: Christopher Howard
Cost: *Alc* £25, fixed-price L £15/D £16.50. ☺ H/wine £8.25.
Times: Noon-last L 2.30pm/7pm-last D 11pm. Closed L Sat, Sun, Bhs
Additional: Children welcome; ⓓ dishes
Seats: 65. Private dining room 27
Smoking: No-smoking area
Credit cards: ▆ ▆ ▆ ▆

Not far from the SS Great Britain, this bistro has a regularly changing menu that takes advantage of seasonal produce. Dishes are primarily French and English with some interesting touches, such as home-smoked fish and duck. Sauces are a selling point. Starters may include warm brioche filled with a ragout of pigeon in rich Madeira sauce and a nice mix of woodland mushrooms. Cod baked with parsley in a filo parcel comes with chive butter sauce, and there's béarnaise for the oyster-filled fillet steak. Generous side vegetables include excellent red cabbage and super dauphinoise potatoes. Vegetarians are well catered for with their own blackboard menu. Of the desserts, the lemon tart has a thick layer of sharp-sweet filling and shredded peel adding texture, accompanied by a tuile of red fruit compote. The wine list includes decent *crus* as well as cheaper options and a selection of half-bottles is offered on a blackboard.

Directions: 5 mins. from city centre following signs for M5/Avonmouth, On the dockside over a small bridge, close to SS Great Britain.

BRISTOL, Hunt's Restaurant ❀❀

Focused Modern English cooking with French overtones is the idiom for this excellent restaurant just off the city centre. Cornish fish is used in dishes such as fricassée of monkfish, saffron and turbot with seared sea scallops and lemon sauce. Fish soup with aïoli, rouille and garlic croûtons vies with smoked chicken and Gruyère salad as a first course choice. A sweet-sour flavour dimension is explored in medallions of venison with sweet dill gherkins and sour cream, and veal noisette with sweet-and-sour peppers and potato galette. Classic desserts include crème brûlée with langue du chat biscuits and chocolate St. Emilion, but the choice of hand-made cheeses is true Brit.

26 Broad Street BS1 2HG
Map 3: ST57
Tel/Fax: 0117 9265580
Chef/Owner: Andrew J Hunt
Cost: *Alc* £30, fixed-price L £20. H/wine £9.95
Times: Noon-2pm/7-10pm. Closed L Sat, all Sun, Mon, 1 wk Easter, 2 wks Aug, 10 days Xmas
Additional: Children welcome; ❸ dishes
Seats: 40. Private dining room 26.
Credit cards: ▬ ▬ ➰ ⌷ ▬ JCB

Directions: City centre, 25 yds from St John's Arch

BRISTOL, Markwicks ❀❀

43 Corn Street BS1 1HT
Map 3: ST57
Tel/Fax: 0117 9262658
Chef: Stephen Markwick
Owners: Stephen & Judy Markwick
Cost: *Alc* £28.50, fixed-price L £16.50/D £23.50. H/wine from £10.50
Times: Noon-2pm/7-10pm. Closed L Sat, all Sun, Mon, Xmas, Easter, 2 wks Aug
Additional: Children welcome; ❸ dishes
Seats: 40. Private dining rooms 6-16
Credit cards: ▬ ▬ ➰ ⌷ ▬ ⌷ ⌷ JCB

There's a Mediterranean feel to the *carte*, and dishes to light up a grey day include scallops with sun-dried tomato risotto, pesto and Parmesan, and noisettes of lamb with garlic confit, ratatouille and thyme jus, although too many competing flavours can sometimes confuse. Also tried were confit of duck with galette potato and Chinese plum sauce, and fillet of turbot in cider with tomato, mustard and thyme. Dishes are served with an interesting selection of vegetables – a medley of minted peas, beans and smoked bacon was singled out for praise. Amongst the desserts, apricot and mascarpone tart is a clear winner.

Directions: Top end of Corn Street beneath Commercial Rooms

BRISTOL, **Red Snapper**

1 Chandos Road Redland
BS6 6PG
Map 3: ST57
Tel: 0117 9737999
Fax: 0117 9247316
Chef: John Raines
Owners: John & Joanna Raines
Cost: *Alc* £21.50, fixed-price L £12.
☺ H/wine £9.50
Times: Last L 1.45pm/last D 9.45pm.
Closed D Sun, all Mon
Additional: Sunday L; Children
welcome; ❹ dishes
Smoking: No pipes & cigars
Credit cards: ▬ ▦ ▧ ▢ ▦ **C**

*Tucked away in a residential area, this is a modern minimalist
restaurant with wooden floors, bright walls and tartan drapes. The
food is British with Med overtones. Expect dishes such as chargrilled
tuna with roasted peppers and olives, pan-fried duck breast with
sherry vinegar and apricot sauce, and whole black bream with
capers and fennel.*

Directions: Telephone for directions

BRISTOL, **Riverstation** ❀❀   NEW

'Very avant garde, a large edifice, all steel and highly polished
wood' notes an inspector of Bristol's hottest new place. On
the river, of course, with a casual, ground-floor bistro and a
more upbeat restaurant upstairs, where a large bar spans the
entire length. Chef/owner Peter Taylor has transplanted many
of his old staff from his previous restaurant, Bell's Diner (see
entry), and retained his distinctive style of cooking –
innovative, unusual combinations with a strong
Mediterranean slant. He tends not to muck around too much
with things on the plate, so that flavours and contrasts really
stand out. Note an inspection meal that took in a vibrant wild
garlic soup with sour cream and croûtons, bresaola with
rocket and spiced pears, 'real comfort food' smoked haddock
risotto with gremolata, gnocchi with roasted plum tomatoes,
Gorgonzola and rocket, and marmalade frangipane tart.
Super home-made coarse breads and an excellent selection of
wines by the glass.

The Grove BS1 4RB
Map 3: ST57
Tel: 0117 9144434
Fax: 0117 9349990
Chef: Peter Taylor
Owners: Shirley Anne Bell, Peter
Taylor, John Payne
Cost: *Alc* £22, fixed price L £10.50/D
£12.95 (both 2 courses). ☺ H/wine
£9
Times: Noon-last L 2.30pm/6-last D
10.45pm. Closed L Sat, 25-28 Dec
Additional: Sunday L; Children
welcome; ❹ dishes
Seats: 130
Smoking: No-smoking area;
No pipes and cigars
Credit cards: ▬ ▦ ▧ ▢ ▦ **C** ▣

Directions: Telephone for directions

BRISTOL, **Swallow Royal Hotel** ❀❀

The Palm Court restaurant stretches up three storeys to a
spectacular stained glass roof, the walls lined by Romeo and
Juliet-style false mini-balconies. A test dinner (accompanied by
a harpist in full flow), produced duck soup with beetroot,
followed by soundly cooked venison with salsify, stuffed figs
and blackberry jus, although presentation was terribly busy,
not quite the pretty picture the chef was obviously trying for.
Unfortunately, out of season, unripe strawberries adorned a
dessert of otherwise excellent strawberry sorbet and
strawberry mille-feuille – good, wafer-thin pastry sandwiched
with strawberry flavoured whipped cream.

College Green
BS1 5TA
Map 3: ST57
Tel: 0117 9255100
Fax: 0117 9251515
Chef: Giles Stonehouse
Owner: Swallow Hotels
Cost: *Alc* £24, fixed-price D £26.50.
H/wine £12
Times: D only 7.30-last D 10.30pm.
Closed Sun, some Bhs
Additional: ❹ dishes
Seats: 80

Swallow Royal Hotel

Smoking: No-smoking area; Air conditioning
Accommodation: 242 en suite
Credit cards: ▆ ▆ ▆ ▆ ▆ ▆ JCB

Directions: City centre, next to cathedral

BUCKINGHAMSHIRE

ASTON CLINTON, **The Bell Inn**

Aylesbury HP22 5HP
Map 4: SP81
Tel: 01296 630252
Fax: 01296 631250
Chef: Colin Woodward
Owner: Michael D G Harris
Cost: *Alc* £29.50, fixed-price L
£14.50. ☺ H/wine £13.50
Times: 12.30-last L 1.45pm/7.30-last
D 9.30pm
Additional: Bar food L; Sunday L;
Children welcome; ✇ dishes
Seats: 90. Private room 12 & 20
Smoking: No smoking in dining room
Accommodation: 20 en suite
Credit cards: ▆ ▆ ▆ ▆ ▆ JCB

That the Bell was built as a coaching inn is clear from its
position on the Buckingham-London road and its layout (what
were the stables around the courtyard are now bedrooms).
The flagstone-floored bar, with its sporting pictures and brass
ornaments, is a reminder of its origins; the dining-room is
distinctive for murals of the seasons and a collection of glass
handbells. The menu's description of a main course of 'fillet of
English beef simply roasted accompanied by a light foie gras
sausage, crushed potato, confit shallots and pink peppercorn
sauce' is typical of the complicated but generally successful
ideas on offer. Canapés are served before a starter of perhaps
roulade of smoked chicken sushi, or marinated mussels with
potato and green bean salad. Thyme risotto accompanies
chicken wrapped in leek and crayfish mousseline, while the
signature dish of roast Aylesbury duck is still very much part of

the Bell's tradition. Beautifully presented desserts of almond bavarois with raspberry coulis, or chocolate 'teardrops' with Muscat syrup and rum and raisin ice cream round things off. Classy French producers are the backbone of the 24-page wine list, although three pages of house recommendations make choosing easier.

Directions: In the centre of the village on the A41, 4 miles from Aylesbury. 10 mins M25/J20

ASTON CLINTON,

West Lodge Hotel ❀❀

London Road Nr Aylesbury
HP22 5HL
Map 4: SP81
Tel: 01296 630362
Fax: 01296 630151
Chef: Philippe Brillant
Owners: Irene & Jeff Burlinson
Cost: Alc £31.95, fixed-price L £25 (2 courses)/D £30. H/wine £15
Times: D only, 7.30-last D 9.30pm. Closed Sun-Thu
Additional: Bar food; No children under 12; ❹ dishes
Seats: 26. Jacket & tie preferred
Smoking: No smoking in dining room; Air conditioning
Credit cards: 🟦 🟥 📇 💳 🟦 🟦 🟦

There's plenty of hot air around here – a commercial balloon flight business is run from the hotel, and the Montgolfier restaurant has a ballooning theme. The eponymous inventors would probably feel at ease with classic French dishes such as puff pastry case of langoustines with Pernod and fennel herb sauce, and medallions of fillet of pork served with a sharp caper sauce. A more modern French style is shown in the confit of duck with salad leaves and tarragon potato rösti and the fillet of lightly smoked salmon with parsley crust and saffron sauce. Desserts go straight to lift-off with bitter chocolate terrine with praline and coffee sauce and caramelised apple tart with prune and Armagnac ice cream.

Directions: On A41 between Aylesbury and Hemel Hempstead.

AYLESBURY,

Hartwell House ❀❀❀

Oxford Road HP17 8NL
Map 4: SP81
Tel: 01296 747444
Fax: 01296 747450
Chef: Roger Barstow
Owner: Historic House Hotels
Cost: Alc £27.50, fixed-price D £42. H/wine £12.90
Times: 12.30-1.45pm/7.30-9.30pm.
Additional: Buttery (7.30am-3pm); Sunday L; No children under 8; ❹ dishes
Seats: 60. Private dining rooms. Jacket & tie preferred at D

Compared to the other ornate public rooms of this grand country mansion, the principal dining room is an essay in understated neo-classicism. It's a jacket-and-tie venue, with waiting staff formally kitted out in waistcoats and tails, providing immaculate and discreet service. A pianist, just outside the room, means guests don't have to speak in muted whispers, but can also enjoy companionable silences. The three-course set price menu starts with an appetiser, perhaps deliciously creamy and smoky chicken mousse drizzled with balsamic, followed by starters such as shelled grilled langoustines with mussel cream, a dish that shone for its simplicity. Another first course, foie gras terrine (although not

Hartwell House

Smoking: No smoking in dining room
Accommodation: 46 en suite
Credit cards: 🟦 🟦 🟦 🟦 🟦 🟦

much more than a thin sliver), had a smooth, creamy flavour. Roger Barstow showed his skills in a main course of pan-fried monkfish and Parma ham, with braised tomatoes, creamed polenta and an excellent red wine sauce. Fillet of venison perhaps lacked the definitive velvety flavour but was very enjoyable, served with leeks, wild mushrooms, purée of root vegetables, cranberry and sage jus. A collection of apple puddings suffered from a little too much ambition, the desire to produce five miniatures resulting in one or two being less than perfect, despite the beautiful presentation. A lemon and cardamom bavarois, although not as dramatic, was creamy and neatly prepared, served with lemon and pistachio shortbread.

The wine list excites, offering a fine fist French wines and classy New Worlds, but at first glance it is also impressively priced. Investigation produces more approachable prices with house wine starting at £12.90.

AA Shortlisted for
Wine Award-see page 16

Directions: 2 miles from Aylesbury on A418 (Oxford)

BUCKINGHAM,

Villiers Hotel ✿

3 Castle Street MK18 1BS
Map 4: SP63
Tel: 01280 822444
Fax: 01280 822113
Chef: Paul Stopps
Owner: Dawnpark Ltd
Cost: *Alc* £23.25, fixed price D
£23.25. ☺ H/wine £11.95.
Times: D only, last D 10pm.
Closed D Sun
Additional: Bar food L; Sunday L;
Children welcome; 🍴 dishes
Smoking: Air conditioning
Accommodation: 38 en suite
Credit cards: 🟦 🟦 🟦 🟦 🟦 🟦 🟦

Visitors have been accommodated at this town centre coaching inn since Cromwell billeted his troops here in 1643. Nowadays, the menu is thoroughly up-to-date and might offer seared loin of yellow fin tuna with coriander and lime pesto, Moroccan spiced chicken breast with tabouleh, and tarte Tatin with English custard.

Directions: Town centre – Castle Street is to R of Town Hall near main square.

BURNHAM,

Burnham Beeches Hotel

Georgian house where Thomas Gray wrote his elegy, and originally a hunting lodge for Windsor Park. Spinach soufflé, langoustine soup or home-made pasta might be followed by fresh fish and good quality beef. Desserts, such as a champagne and passion fruit jelly are skilfully prepared.

Smoking: No-smoking area; No pipes & cigars
Accommodation: 78 en suite
Credit cards: ▮▮ ▦ ▰▱ ▯ ▦ ▮ ▣ JCB

Directions: Off A355 via Farnham Royal roundabout

Grove Road SL1 8DP
Map 4: SU98
Tel: 01628 429955
Fax: 01628 603994
Chef: Ronnie Senior
Owner: County Hotels Ltd
Cost: *Alc* £26, fixed-price L & D
£22.50. ☺ H/wine £12
Times: Last L 2pm/last D 10pm.
Closed L Sat
Additional: Bar food; Sunday L;
Children welcome; ◑ dishes

BURNHAM BEECHES,

Grovefield Hotel

NEW

Comfortable bar and lounge area precede the restaurant, picture windows provide views over the gardens. In all, a relaxing place for lunch and dinner. The kitchen pride themselves on making as much as possible, this includes breads, desserts, and chocolates with coffee. recommended is brill on saffron linguine with parsley sauce.

Taplow Common Road SL1 8LP
Tel: 01628 603131
Fax: 01628 668078
Please telephone for further details

CHENIES, **Thistle Bedford Arms**

A super hotel, only minutes from the M25, yet very peacefully positioned. Ambition drives the kitchen with exemplar Dublin Bay prawns roasted with herbs and garnished with chive and potato ravioli, deliciously crisp roast Aylesbury duck with apple sauce and port wine reduction, and pear tart, setting the pace.

WD3 6EQ
Map 4: TQ09
Tel: 01923 283301
Fax: 01923 284825
Chef: Emil Forde
Owner: Thistle Hotels plc
Cost: *Alc* £30. H/wine £11.50
Times: Last L 2pm/D 10pm.
Closed Sat L
Additional: Bar Food; Sunday L;
Children welcome; ◑ dishes
Smoking: No pipes or cigars in dining room
Accommodation: 10 en suite
Credit cards: ▮▮ ▦ ▰▱ ▯ ▦ ▮ ▣ JCB

Directions: M25, J18/A404 towards Amersham, turn R to Latimer/Chenies, hotel is visible 200yds

DINTON, **La Chouette**

The name of this large white cottage restaurant means the owl, and walls lined with bird paintings and photographs reflect the chef-patron's love of ornithology. Situated at the end of a quiet road in a pretty village, La Chouette has a relaxed, friendly atmosphere and, with the chef handling the bar, cooking and serving all by himself, things are not too formal. The cooking appears to be French but is actually Belgian. Dishes include a salad of sweetbreads, bacon and beans, roast monkfish in a sauce of cream and mustard, turbot with a fennel-scented

Westlington Green Nr Aylesbury
HP17 8UW
Map 4: SP71
Tel/Fax: 01296 747422
Chef/Owner: Frédéric Desmette
Cost: *Alc* £30, fixed-price L £10/D
£26.50 (4 courses). ☺ H/wine £10.50
Times: Noon-last L 2pm/7pm-last
D 9pm. Closed D Sat, Sun
Additional: Children welcome
Seats: 40

lobster sauce. An impressive array of vegetables is carefully prepared and full of flavour. The surprise dessert comes with instructions not to ask what it is; our inspector enjoyed a delicious rich sabayon over tiny scoops of raspberry sorbet. Details matter here – excellent bread served on wooden carving boards, crisp linen napery, good glassware and fine filter coffee complete a pleasant experience.

Directions: On the A418 at Dinton

Smoking: No pipes or cigars in dining room
Credit cards: 💳 💳 💳 💳

IVINGHOE, **The King's Head** ❀

LU7 9EB
Map 4: SP91
Tel: 01296 668388/668264
Fax: 01296 668107
Chef: Patrick O'Keeffe
Owner: Granada-Distinctive Restaurants
Cost: Alc £40, fixed-price L £13.95/D £25.95. ☺ H/wine £15.95
Times: Last L 1.45pm/D 9.15pm. Closed D Sun & D 25 Dec
Additional: Sunday L; Children welcome; ❸ dishes
Smoking: No smoking in dining room; Air conditioning
Credit cards: 💳 💳 💳 💳 💳 💳

A deceptively large, low-beamed old place in a hamlet. The menu is mostly traditional but makes a few nods to fashion. Highlight of lunch was top-class pan-fried cod on creamed potatoes with olive oil and tomato concasse, which followed simple, well-made cheese and onion tart. Puddings from a trolley.

Directions: From M25/J20. Take the A41(M) towards Tring. Turn R, B488 (Ivinghoe). Hotel on R at the junction with B489

MARLOW, **The Compleat Angler** ❀

Marlow Bridge SL7 1RG
Map 4: SU88
Tel: 01628 484444
Fax: 01628 486388
Chef: Alan Swinson
Owner: Forte Hotels
Cost: Alc £35, fixed-price L £19/D £29. ☺ H/wine £15
Times: 12.30pm-last L 2pm/7pm-last D 10pm
Additional: Bar food; Sunday L; Children welcome; ❸ dishes
Smoking: No-smoking area
Accommodation: 65 en suite
Credit cards: 💳 💳 💳 💳 💳 💳 JCB

Well-known hotel (named after Isaak Walton's famous book) on the banks of the Thames. The Riverside Restaurant makes the best of the setting and offers such modish dishes as tomato and mozzarella tart with pesto and crispy onions plus a few classics like Chateaubriand béarnaise. Good selection of wines by the glass.

Directions: From junction 8/9 of M4 or junction 4 of M40 take A404; hotel is on south bank of river by bridge

MARLOW, **Danesfield House**

Henley Road SL7 2EY
Map 4: SU88
Tel: 01628 891010
Fax: 01628 890408

Chef: Michael Macdonald
Cost: *Alc* £40, fixed-price L £24.50/D £35.50 (4 courses). H/wine £18.50
Times: Noon-last L 2.30pm/7-last D 10pm
Additional: Bar food (brasserie); Sunday L; Children welcome; ❧ dishes
Seats: 45. Private dining room up to 110
Smoking: No smoking in dining room; Air conditioning
Accommodation: 87 en suite
Credit cards: ▬ ▬ ➹ ▢ ▬ 🄲 ▣ JCB

Perched high above a sweep of the River Thames, Danesfield House is a grand Victorian-Tudor mansion surrounded by formal gardens. Splendid public rooms are in keeping with the building and include its Oak Room restaurant with its mellow panelling, ornate plaster ceiling and glittering silver and glassware on immaculately set tables. The seasonally changing menu is equally rewarding, with a spring menu offering seafood such as seared Devon scallops with sweet pepper and squid ink sauce, or meatier options along the lines of quail pithiviers with a light hazelnut jus, medallion of Suffolk venison and red wine sauce infused with liquorice, and tian of chicken with pommes Anna and morel sauce. The wine list majors on France with lots of famous names at serious prices but little choice below the £20 mark.

Directions: M40/J4, A404 to Marlow, then A4155 to Henley. Hotel 2 miles on L

STOKE POGES,
Stoke Park

NEW

Park Road SL2 4PG
Map 4: SU98
Tel: 01753 717171
Fax: 01753 717181
Chef: Paul Groves
Cost: *Alc* £40. ☺ H/wine £12
Times: 12.30-last L 2pm/7-last D 9.30pm. Closed L Sat & Sun
Additional: Bar food L; Sunday L (Carvery); No children under 8; ❧ dishes
Seats: 50. Private dining room 18
Smoking: No pipes; Air conditioning
Accommodation: 20 en suite
Credit cards: ▬ ▬ ▢ ▬ ▣ JCB

'An Englishman's home is his castle' said Sir Edward Coke at the time of the gunpowder plot. Stoke Park was his home and the restoration of the property has recaptured some of its former glory and opulence. It is now a luxury hotel, set in the centre of a 27-hole golf course. Stokes brasserie is more modern in style than the main house, but the atmosphere is warm and inviting. Here a summer dinner took in spinach soufflé with anchovy sauce, fillet of tender lamb ('you could almost cut it with the back of a knife') served with mint sauce, ratatouille and new and dauphinoise potatoes, with a simple trifle based on home-made raspberry jelly, sponge and fresh raspberries for dessert. Other choices included bangers and mash and grilled fresh lobster amongst the main courses, Knickerbocker glory and crêpes Suzette with the desserts. The wine list is the hobby of general manager Mark Rawlings Lloyd who prides himself on sourcing the popular and the best from the world over. Twenty or so pages long, mark-ups on the pricy wines are to the customer's advantage.

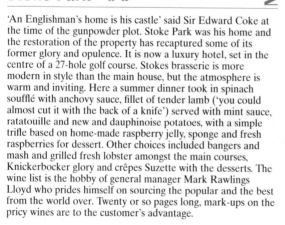

Directions: Exit M4/J6, take A355 (Beaconsfield). After 2.5 miles turn R at double mini roundabout onto B416 (Park Road). Hotel is 1.25 miles on R

TAPLOW, Cliveden Hotel, Waldo's Restaurant ❀❀❀❀

Maidenhead SL6 0JF
Map 4: SU98
Tel: 01628 668561
Fax: 01628 661837
Chef: Gary Jones
Cost: Alc £55, fixed-price L £28/D £39 (4 courses). H/wine £19
Times: Waldo's D only, 7.30pm–last D 9.15pm. Closed Sun, Mon
Additional: Sunday L (Terrace); Children welcome; ❀ dishes
Seats: Waldos's 26. Terrace 65. Private dining rooms 55 & 12
Smoking: No smoking in dining room
Accommodation: 38 en suite
Credit cards: 💳 💳 💳 💳

Shortly before we went to press we learned that four AA Rosetted chef Gary Jones had left Homewood Park (see entry, Somerset) to take up the position of head chef at Waldo's Restaurant. Inspectors have been enthusiastic about Gary's cooking at Cliveden. Indeed, given the short space of time he had been in the kitchen when we had our first meal, he appears to have hit the ground running. That evening saw a 'fantastic dish' of scallop and oyster chowder lightly scented with lemongrass and accompanied by coriander raviolis plump with scallop mousseline that just exploded with flavour; a beautifully crafted braised pig's trotter, nicely caramelised and stuffed with ham hock and sweetbreads and served with a rosemary jus, a dish that revealed richness tempered by a light touch; and a 'sensuous' poached pear on vanilla blini with fromage blanc sorbet. An *amuse-gueule* of artichoke, asparagus and tomato was a brilliant taste of summer, and bread and petits fours are considered outstanding. This is probably one of the grandest settings in the country, and the style is perfectly matched in Waldo's by attentive young staff

Directions: On the B476, 2 miles north of Taplow

CAMBRIDGESHIRE

BYTHORN,
Bennett's Restaurant ❀

A rural village inn serving modern classics and well-chosen wines in a traditional setting. Hearty portions of rich game terrine and steak and kidney pudding will suit the hungry traveller. For dessert indulge yourself with a spectacular chocolate and rum parfait, topped with shavings of white chocolate.

Smoking: No smoking in dining room
Credit cards: 💳 💳 💳 💳 💳 💳

Directions: Between Kettering & Huntingdon on A14/A1-M1 link road

The White Hart
Huntingdon PE18 0QN
Map 4: TL07
Tel/Fax: 01832 710226
Chef/Owner: Bill Bennett
Cost: Alc £25
Times: Last L 2pm/last D 10pm. Closed D Sun, Mon, 26 Dec, 1 Jan
Additional: Bar food; Sunday L; Children welcome; ❀ dishes

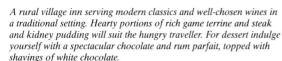

CAMBRIDGE, Arundel House ❀

With both a restaurant and a more informal conservatory, plus a wide selection of dishes on various menus, visitors to this popular riverside hotel have much freedom in where and what to eat. In the former try supreme of chicken with ham and apricot mousse, or grilled Dover sole with orange butter, in the latter, venison pie or poached salmon salad.

Chesterton Road CB4 3AN
Map 5: TL45
Tel: 01223 367701
Fax: 01223 367721
Chefs: Mark Searle, Simon Patten
Cost: Alc £22, fixed-price L £10.95/D £15.95. ☺ H/wine £9.50
Times: Last L 1.45pm/last D 9.30pm. Closed 24-26 Dec
Additional: Bar food; Sunday L; Children welcome; ❀ dishes
Smoking: No smoking in dining room; Air conditioning
Accommodation: 105 rooms (102 en suite)
Credit cards: ▆ ▆ ▆ ▆ ▆ ▆ ▆

Directions: On A1303, overlooking River Cam

CAMBRIDGE, Cambridge Garden House Moat House ❀

Modern hotel in a peaceful setting in its own grounds overlooking the River Cam. Various menu, with choices such as Cullen skink, chicken in wild mushrooms with rich port sauce (served with a good selection of plainly cooked vegetables), and burnt Cambridge cream.

Accommodation: 130 en suite
Credit cards: ▆ ▆ ▆ ▆ ▆ ▆ ▆ JCB

Directions: City centre, from Trumpington Street past Fitzwilliam Museum, L into Mill Lane

Granta Place Mill Lane CB2 1RT
Map 5: TL45
Tel: 01223 259988
Fax: 01223 316605
Chef: John Gardner
Cost: Alc £19, fixed-price D £17.95. ☺ H/wine £12.95
Times: Last L 2pm/last D 10pm
Additional: Bar food; Sunday L; Children welcome; ❀ dishes
Smoking: No smoking in dining room; Air conditioning

CAMBRIDGE,
Midsummer House ❀❀❀

A bright and airy conservatory is the main focus of this restaurant that is going from strength to strength. Anton

Midsummer Common CB4 1HA
Map 5: TL45
Tel: 01223 369299
Fax: 01223 302672
Chef: Anton Escalera
Owners: Russell Morgan, Anton Escalera
Cost: Fixed-price L £23/D £39.50. H/wine £11.95
Times: Noon-last L 2.15pm/7-last D 10.15pm. Closed L Sat, D Sun, all Mon.
Additional: Sunday L; Children welcome; ❀ dishes
Seats: 35. Private dining room 15
Credit cards: ▆ ▆ ▆ ▆ ▆ ▆ JCB

Escalera is a supremely confident young chef, and a summer inspection revealed cooking so fine tuned that concepts, balance, timing, quality of produce, and seasoning were indisputable. Not only were technical skills unfaulted but there were enough twists on the norm to make one consider it had potential for greater things. Witness an appetiser of lightly set consommé with a morsel of poached salmon within and topped with tiny cucumber concasse and caviar and a coffee spoon size of crème fraîche. Or artichoke terrine jam-packed with freshly roasted Mediterranean veg, alive with flavour and colour, with a small, just cooked saddle of rabbit sliced on top. Then roasted sea bass of really fresh quality, in the centre a risotto with clams and mussels radiating so much colour and vibrancy that it was almost a paella, all offset by a simple but effective bouillabaisse sauce. A deep chocolate tart of mousse-like consistency, topped with fat roasted hazelnuts, all set on extra fine pastry, was simply 'gorgeous' with great vanilla cream and superb rich, deep raspberry coulis. Excellent flavoured breads and great petits fours march in tune with the rest of the meal.

Signature dishes: Rack of lamb wth white beans, Toulouse sausage and smoked belly of pork; ravioli of skate, pan-fried langoustine, anchovy butter sauce; foie gras, escabeché of vegetables.

Midsummer House

Directions: Park in Pretoria Road, off Chesterton Road, then walk across footbridge to restaurant

DUXFORD,
Duxford Lodge Hotel ❀❀

Ickleton Road CB2 4RU
Map 5: TL44
Tel: 01223 836444
Fax: 01223 832271
Chef: Kevin Bingham
Owners: Ronald & Suzanne Craddock
Cost: *Alc* £24.25, fixed-price L & D £19.50. ☺ H/wine £10
Times: Noon-last L 2pm/7pm-last D 9.30pm. Closed L Sat, 25-30 Dec
Additional: Bar food L; Sunday L; Children welcome; ♦ dishes
Seats: 46. Private dining rooms 26.
Smoking: No-smoking area; Air conditioning
Accommodation: 15 en suite
Credit cards: ▤ ▧ ▨ ▣ ▤ ▥ ▨ JCB

Birds of Paradise and bomber aircraft seem an unlikely combination, yet paintings of the former decorate the dining room and memorabilia of the hotel's historic connections with the nearby Imperial War Museum fill the bar. The cooking at the cheerful, red-brick hotel takes two tacks – the 'International' *carte* features Thai-style red curry prawns served with a coconut and sesame seed roti, and baked breast of chicken filled with banana and tarragon, served with a spiced mango cream. The 'Gourmet' *carte,* on the other hand, includes chargrilled peppered medallions of venison on a bed of braised chicory endive with fresh thyme sauce, and fresh foie gras and duck liver parfait served with a Cox's apple and sweet wine coulis. International gourmet desserts include an extremely good rich bitter chocolate and ginger layer cake with clementine coulis.

Directions: M11/J10, take A505 eastbound then 1st turning R to Duxford; take R fork at T-junction, entrance 70 yards on L

ELY, **Lamb Hotel**

Centrally located hotel noted for friendly service that manages a good mix of the formal and informal. The kitchen caters for most tastes, from simple, plain typical hotel dishes to the more imaginative. Duck and pork terrine came with a zingy, fruity kumquat and grape chutney, tender beef fillet strips with a dark, spicy sauce, and Baileys cheesecake had a good mango coulis.

Additional: Bar food; Sunday L; Children welcome; ❸ dishes
Smoking: No smoking in dining room
Accommodation: 32 en suite.
Credit cards: ▰ ▰ ▰ ▰ ▰ ▰ ▰

Directions: Follow A10 to Ely, then city centre signs. Hotel on corner of High St adjacent cathedral

2 Lynn Road CB7 4EJ
Map 5: TL58
Tel: 01353 663574
Fax: 01353 662023
Chefs: Stephen Mather, Ian Hudson
Owners: Mr & Mrs R Lilley
Cost: *Alc* £22, fixed-price L £10.95/D £16.95. ☺ H/wine £8.75
Times: Last L 2.30pm/last D 9.30pm

ELY, **Old Fire Engine House** ❀

A charming 18th-century brick farmhouse, opposite St Mary's church. Sound country cooking is served up in the small dining room, where pine tables and polished floors create a warm ambience. A summer meal might start with cold smoked mackerel with horseradish, followed by casserole of rabbit with mustard and parsley.

Additional: Children welcome; ❸ dishes
Smoking: No smoking in dining room.
Credit cards: ▰ ▰ ▰ ▰

Directions: Facing St Mary's Church in town centre

25 St Mary's Street
CB7 4ER
Map 5: TL58
Tel: 01353 662582
Fax: 01353 666282
Chef: Terri Kindred
Owners: Ann & Michael Jarman
Cost: *Alc* £22. ☺ H/wine £8.
Times: Last L 2pm/D 9pm. Closed D Sun, 2 wks from 24 Dec, Bhs

FOWLMERE,
The Chequers Inn ❀

Royston SG8 7SR
Map 5: TL44
Tel: 01763 208369
Fax: 01763 208944
Chef: Louis Gambi
Owners: Norman & Pauline Rushton
Cost: *Alc* £16.80. ☺ H/wine £9.30
Additional: Children welcome;
❸ dishes
Credit cards: ▰ ▰ ▰ ▰ ▰ ▰ ▰

The diarist Samuel Pepys once stayed here and there are strong links with the nearby wartime airfield. Today's visitors are attracted by the 16th-century galleried restaurant and dishes as varied as grilled oysters with tarragon garlic butter, roast salmon on green noodles with basil and white wine sauce, and boiled ham hock with mustard sauce.

Directions: Between Royston & Cambridge, B1368 turn off the A10

HUNTINGDON,
The Old Bridge Hotel ❀❀

The brilliant wine list alone makes this hotel-restaurant a worthy destination. Thoughtfully compiled, its 11 pages distinguish between 'good value' and 'top class' wines, all with clear tasting notes to encourage experimentation and confidence. The kitchen produces interesting modern cooking to a high standard, and any meal in the buzzing brasserie-style restaurant begins with a choice of excellent home-made breads. The game terrine is predominately bird with a centre of pheasant breast and a coating of bacon. It comes served on toasted brioche with a sweet-sour tomato chutney and deliciously dressed salad leaves. Breast of pigeon is delivered rare, tender and gamey on a bed of creamed leeks with well-made rösti and a jus of red wine and thyme. Dates and treacle pack the sticky toffee pudding, the slightly bitter flavour of its molasses-based toffee sauce contrasting well with a dollop of extra thick cream. There's eager, attentive service too. Be sure to book.

Smoking: No smoking in dining room. **Accommodation:** 24 rooms. **Credit cards:** ▉ ▉ ▉ ▉ ▉ ▉ ▉ JCB

Directions: Off A1 near junction with A1-M1 link and A604/M11

PE18 6TQ
Map 4: TL27
Tel: 01480 452681
Fax: 01480 411017
Chefs: Nick Steiger, David Bevan
Owner: Huntsbridge Ltd
Cost: *Alc* £22. ☺ H/wine £9.45.
Times: Noon-last L
2.30pm/6pm(Terrace)-last D
10.30pm. Closed D 25 Dec
Additional: Sunday L; Bar meals;
Children welcome; ❸ dishes
Seats: 32 + 70. Private dining room 28

Shortlisted for
AA Wine Award-see page 16

KEYSTON, **Pheasant Inn** ❀❀

Huntingdon PE18 0RE
Map 4: TL07
Tel: 01832 710241
Fax: 01832 710340
Chef: Martin Lee
Owner: John Hoskins
(Huntsbridge Ltd)
Cost: *Alc* £20, fixed-price L £11.75.
☺ H/wine £9.45
Times: Noon-last L 2pm/6pm-last D
10pm (7pm Sun). Closed D 25-28
Dec
Additional: Sunday L; Children
welcome; ❸ dishes
Seats: 120.
Smoking: No smoking in dining room
Credit cards: ▉ ▉ ▉ ▉ ▉ ▉ ▉ JCB

To say this is a formula, is to misrepresent the blueprint behind the reinvention of this inn (and others in the regional Huntsbridge chefs' partnership – see entry above). The informal foodie pub-brasserie-restaurant has much to commend it. Thatched roof, oak beams, open fires and simple wooden furniture in a rural setting also belie a *carte* that is punchy and modern European in outlook, peppered with ingredients such as linguine, pesto, saffron, truffle oil and rösti. A test meal took in shiitake mushrooms filled with a delicate chicken and fennel mousse with a red wine sauce, and cod with mash and stir-fried shredded vegetables – a powerhouse of a main course, complete with an 'in your face' dressing of salsa verde vinaigrette with lots of baby capers. A fruity cinnamon and raspberry sauce contrasted beautifully with a frozen nougat glacé that was simultaneously nutty, creamy and crunchy.

Directions: In the village centre, clearly signposted off A14

Shortlisted for
AA Wine Award-see page 16

MADINGLEY,
Three Horseshoes ❀❀

Expect gusty, robust cooking and punchy flavours to emerge from the kitchen of this foodie inn not far from Cambridge. The wide-ranging menu makes good use of flavours and ingredients from all over the globe: chargrilled rump of lamb with tabouleh, grilled squash, baby beetroot and harissa; carrot and coriander terrine with wasabi, soy, mooli and mirin; roast grey mullet with asparagus, mashed potato, black pudding and oyster mushrooms. Our last meal comprised a good, herby pork and bacon terrine with roasted red onions and mustard vinaigrette, saddle of wild rabbit with girolles and balsamic dressing, and bread-and-butter pudding with candied fruit and crème fraîche. An equally catholic taste is evident in the interesting list of wines, organised according to style, with plenty of choice by the glass. Eager, youthful service.

Directions: Telephone for directions

High Street CB3 8AB
Map 5: TL36
Tel: 01954 210221
Fax: 01594 212043
Chef: Richard Stokes
Owner: Huntsbridge
Cost: Alc £20
Times: Noon-2pm/6.30-9.30pm
Additional: Children welcome;
❀ dishes
Smoking: No smoking in dining room
Credit cards: ▰ ▰ ▢ ▰ ▣

MELBOURN, Pink Geranium ❀❀

Floral chintz is alive and flourishing at The Pink Geranium, co-ordinating with the rustic beams and setting. The cooking occasionally puts visual adornment ahead of flavour and harmony, but this is complex, sophisticated cooking nonetheless. Norfolk duckling is served roasted with black cherries, Cassis sauce and the confit leg, and local sole is steamed in a soufflé, wrapped with leek, filled with a horseradish mousseline and served with ratatouille and bouillabaisse sauce. Steaming is also used to good effect in rabbit loin noisettes bound with Bayonne ham accompanied by a sage and garlic risotto with a thyme infused veal reduction. Beautifully displayed desserts include mille-feuille of ginger crème brûlée and rhubarb Napolitaine.

Directions: On A10 between Royston and Cambridge. In centre of the village, opposite the church

Station Road SG8 6DX
Map 5: TL34
Tel: 01763 260215
Chefs: Steven Saunders, Mark Jordan
Owners: Sally & Steven Saunders
Times: Noon-last L 2pm/7-last D 10pm. Closed Sun, Mon
Additional: Children welcome;
❀ dishes
Seats: 65. Private dining room 20
Smoking: No smoking in dining room
Credit cards: ▰ ▰ ▰ ▢ ▰ ▣ JCB

MELBOURN, Sheene Mill ❀❀

Station Road SG8 6DX
Map 5: TL34
Tel: 01763 261393
Fax: 01763 261376
Chefs: Steven Saunders/Alex Williams
Owners: Steven & Sally Saunders
Cost: Alc £20. H/wine £10
Times: Noon-last L 2pm/6.30-last D 10pm
Additional: Bar food L; Sunday L; Children welcome; ❀ dishes
Seats: 120. Private dining room 60
Smoking: No-smoking area; No pipes & cigars
Accommodation: 8 en suite
Credit cards: ▰ ▰ ▰ ▢ ▰ JCB

Now under the same ownership as the nearby Pink Geranium (see entry), the cooking at the historic watermill takes a decidedly modern route. The style is cosmopolitan and upbeat, as is the bright blue and yellow setting. Fragrantly warm salad of lamb fillet is marinated in fresh basil pesto then seared, calves' liver is lightly chargrilled with sweet-and-sour onions, garlic mash, Parmesan crisps and pimento salsa sauce. Mash of basil, spinach and the like, accompanies confit salmon with chive velouté, and turmeric fried sea bass with yellow tomato juices. Vegetables get treated royally with lasagne of wild mushrooms with poppy seed pancakes, baby spinach and red pimento coulis.

Directions: Take 2nd exit from A10 Melbourn by-pass signed Melbourn. Sheen Mill is 300yds down Station Road on R

PETERBOROUGH, Orton Hall

Rambling historic country house, set in twenty acres of parkland. Meals in the oak-panelled Huntly Restaurant have an international flavour. Main courses could include sirloin of beef with a red wine jus, escalope of salmon with a mousseline sauce, and breast of chicken with wild mushrooms. For dessert try the chocolate marquise.

Additional: Bar food; Sunday L; Children welcome; ❹ dishes
Smoking: No smoking in dining room
Accommodation: 66 en suite
Credit cards: ▆▆ ▆▆ ▆▆ ▆ ▆▆ ▆ ▆

Directions: Telephone for directions

Orton Longueville PE2 7 DN
Map 4: TL19
Tel: 01733 391111
Fax: 01733 231912
Chef: Mark Jones
Cost: *Alc* £24, fixed-price L £12.95/D £17.95. ☺ H/wine £9.95
Times: D only, last D 9.30pm. Closed D Sun, Xmas-New Year

SIX MILE BOTTOM,
Swynford Paddocks Hotel

A gracious, comfortable hotel, once the home of Byron's half-sister, at the heart of racehorse country. The long menus offer a good mixture of styles and flavours, from seafood mousseline or minty courgette soup to lamb's liver with bacon and champ, or eastern-style sea bass, perhaps followed by sherry trifle.

Additional: Bar food; Sunday L; Children welcome: ❹ dishes
Smoking: No smoking in dining room
Accommodation: 15 en suite
Credit cards: ▆▆ ▆▆ ▆ ▆▆ ▆

Directions: On A1304 6 miles S-W of Newmarket

Newmarket CB8 0UE
Map 5: TL55
Tel: 01638 570234
Fax: 01638 570283
Chef: Patrick Collins
Cost: *Alc* £27, fixed-price D £26.50 (4 courses). H/wine £11.95
Times: Last L 2pm/last D 7pm. Closed L Sat, 4 days Xmas, 1 Jan

STILTON, Bell Inn Hotel

Rustic coaching inn strong on beams, open fireplaces and candles. Ambition drives the kitchen, with up-to-date dishes such as griddled scallops with garlic mash and sauce vierge, pan-fried duck with fondant potato, stuffed Savoy cabbage and cumin and basil sauce, and orange tart setting a strong pace. Sound, good value wine list.

Smoking: No-smoking area
Accommodation: 19 en suite
Credit cards: ▆▆ ▆▆ ▆▆ ▆ ▆▆ ▆ ▆ JCB

Directions: From A1 follow signs to Stilton. Hotel on High Street in centre of village

Great North Road PE7 3RA
Map 5: TL18
Tel: 01733 241066
Fax: 01733 245173
Chef: James Trevor
Owner: Liam McGivern
Cost: Fixed-price L&D £19.95. ☺ H/wine £9.95
Times: Last L 2pm/D 9.30pm
Additional: Sunday L; Bar meals; Children welcome; ❹ dishes

WANSFORD, Haycock Hotel ❀

Old historic house next to the A1 that has been a hostelry for hungry travellers for centuries. It rightly continues to be popular for the formal restaurant, which combines traditional favourites like roasts from the carving trolley with more vibrant cosmopolitan dishes. The Orchards conservatory brasserie is also available for lighter meals.

Directions: In village centre between A1 & A47

PE8 6JA
Map 4: TL09
Tel: 01780 782223
Fax: 01780 783508
Chef: Neil Smith
Owners: Arcadian Hotels
Please telephone for further details

WISBECH,
Crown Lodge Hotel ❀

Imaginative, appealing cooking at this popular hotel. A weekly set-price menu offers a good choice of dishes, such as warm chicken and Stilton mousse, with leaf spinach and a poached egg, and rump steak with creamed kidney mille-feuille, with rösti potato.

Times: last L 2pm/last D 10pm. Closed 25 Dec, 1 Jan
Additional: Bar food; Sunday L; Children welcome; ❹ dishes
Accommodation: 10 en suite
Credit cards: 💳 💳 💳 💳 💳 💳 💳 JCB

Directions: Five miles SE of Wisbech on A1122 close to junction with A1101

Downham Road Outwell
PE14 8SE
Map 5: TF40
Tel: 01945 773391
Fax: 01945 772668
Chef: Mick Castell
Owners: Bill & Rebecca Moore
Cost: *Alc* £18.50. Fixed-price L
£9.95/D £14.75. ☺ H/wine £7.95.

CHESHIRE

ALDERLEY EDGE,
Alderley Edge Hotel ❀❀

An enviable raised location ensures fine views from the conservatory restaurant over the Cheshire Plain. The menu offers several alternatives – the *carte*, the market menu, and

Macclesfield Road SK9 7BJ
Map 7: SJ87
Tel: 01625 583033
Fax: 01625 586343
Chef: Nicholas J Walton
Owner: J W Lees (Brewers) Ltd
Cost: *Alc* £35, fixed-price L £16.50/D
£23.95. ☺ H/wine £12.95
Times: Noon-last L 2pm/7-last D
10pm
Additional: Bar food L; Sunday L;
Children welcome; ❹ dishes
Seats: 80. Private dining rooms 18,
25. Jacket & tie preferred
Smoking: No pipes; Air conditioning
Accommodation: 46 en suite
Credit cards: 💳 💳 💳 💳 💳 💳

'signatures', a lengthy choice. The style of cooking suits the well-heeled environs: individual beef fillet Wellington baked on a rich claret and thyme sauce; grilled delice of turbot sprinkled with a citrus gremolata and a sweet red-pepper syrup; veal cutlet pan-fried in porcini oil on juniper tagliatelle topped with fried quails' eggs and bordelaise sauce. The cheese menu varies monthly and includes excellent British artisan cheeses and unpasteurised French ones.

Directions: A538 to Alderley Edge, then B5087 Macclesfield road

BOLLINGTON,
Mauro's Restaurant ❀❀

Chef-patron Vincenzo Mauro is enthusiastic about his food and cooks in view of the dining room, as well as helping his daughter to take the orders in this friendly establishment. In addition to a largely mainstream Italian menu it is always worth taking note of the daily specials, recited at the table, which is where the day's fish dishes are to be found – red snapper, scallops, mussels, John Dory and sea bass were all on offer on a recent visit. To start there's a good choice of fresh pasta, or consider the hors d'oeuvre trolley laden with all manner of delicacies including hot dishes such as squid stuffed with capers, olives and breadcrumbs and topped with a simple tomato sauce flavoured with oregano. Good Italian wine list featuring regional producers and Enzo's selection of Grappas.

Directions: Situated on the main street of the village, at the Pott Shrigley end

88 Palmerston Street SK10 5PW
Map 7: SJ97
Tel: 01625 573898
Chef/Owner: V Mauro
Cost: Alc £18. ☺ H/wine £10.
Times: 12.15pm-last L 2pm/7pm-last D 10pm. Closed Sun (except L 1st Sun of month), Mon, L Sat
Additional: Bar food L; Children welcome; ❀ dishes
Seats: 50.
Smoking: No pipes and cigars in dining room
Credit cards: ▬ ▬ ▧ ▢ ▬ JCB

BROXTON,
Broxton Hall Hotel ❀

An impressive half-timbered Tudor Hall with an elegant restaurant overlooking the gardens. Rich bread-and-butter pudding was a great finale to a meal that opened with mussels in a herb and butter sauce, and was followed by grilled pork with a mustard, onion and gherkin sauce.

Additional: Bar Food L; Sunday L; Children welcome; ❀ dishes
Smoking: No cigars or pipes
Accommodation: 10 en suite
Credit cards: ▬ ▬ ▧ ▢ ▬ ▢

Directions: On A41 halfway between Whitchurch and Chester, at Broxton roundabout

Whitchurch Road CH3 9JS
Map 7: SJ45
Tel: 01829 782321
Fax: 01829 782330
Chef: James Makin
Owners: Rosemary & George Hadley
Cost: Alc £20, fixed-price L £15.90/ D £25.50 (4 courses). ☺ H/wine £11.
Times: Last L 2pm/D 9.30pm Closed 25-26 Dec, 1 Jan

CHESTER,
The Chester Grosvenor ❀❀❀

The restaurant is hung with horse pictures, and there is gleaming silver and highly polished tables, male staff wear tails, and a pianist plays in the library bar; it makes for a formal atmosphere unless, of course, you're celebrating a win at Chester races. However, Paul Reed has departed, and 3 AA Rosetted chef, Simon Radley (ex Nunsmere Hall, Sandiway,

Eastgate CH1 1LT
Map 7: SJ46
Tel: 01244 324024
Fax: 01244 313246
Chef: Simon Radley
Cost: Alc £52.50, fixed-price L £25/D £40 (5 courses).
H/wine £11.50

The Chester Grosvenor

Times: Noon-2.30pm/7pm-9.30pm.
Closed D Sun, L Mon, 25 Dec-2 Jan
Additional: Bar food L; Sunday L;
Children welcome; 🖤 dishes
Smoking: No smoking in dining room;
Air conditioning
Seats: 45. Private dining room 150.
Jacket & tie preferred
Accommodation: 85 en suite
Credit cards: ▉ ▉ ▉ ▉ ▉ JCB

see entry) has taken over the kitchen. Early reports are encouraging. First courses might include a 'pressing' of pencil leeks and Scottish lobster with a sweet pepper and basil dressing, or stuffed pig's trotter with Puy lentils, Alsace bacon and wild mushrooms. Main courses of carved loin of tender veal with a tian of beetroot, button onions, button mushrooms and thyme essence, or cutlets of salt marsh lamb with Savoy cabbage and artichokes, are well conceived dishes, making a fine balance between the traditional and contemporary. From the dessert list, baked vanilla brioche with a mandarin soufflé and orange sauce hits the spot. A very serious wine list is notable for the selection of halves, large bottles, Burgundies and high prices.

Directions: City centre adjacent to the Eastgate Clock and Roman Walls

CHESTER,
Crabwall Manor Hotel ✿✿✿

Parkgate Road Mollington
CH1 6NE
Map 7: SJ46
Tel: 01244 851666
Fax: 01244 851400
Chefs: Kevin Woods, Michael Truelove
Owner: Carl Lewis
Times: Noon-last L 1.45pm/7-last D 9.45pm
Additional: Sunday L; Children welcome; 🖤 dishes

The Manor is a lovely 17th-century house, a replacement of an earlier building that was mentioned in the Domesday Book. Time moves on, the house is now a grand hotel but the necessary extension has been done in a sympathetic manner. Kevin Woods heads the brigade, but ex head chef and now general manager, Michael Truelove, is still actively involved from time to time. Dishes are quite complicated, skilfully executed without slavishly following fashion, yet with an ability to stay in touch. Comments have been very favourable about the cooking this year. Very good canapés of light, crisp prawn beignets, pastry tartlet of cherry tomato with pesto and Parmesan shavings and perfectly formed roulade of cream cheese and smoked salmon opened a May dinner. Ravioli of wild mushrooms surrounded by girolles and ceps in a tangy reduction of Madeira preceded a simple pan-fried tuna set on a confit of aubergine enclosing slightly sweet red and yellow pepper flesh with courgettes – when cut the aromas just burst out like opening a bottle of champagne – and accompanied by pearls of carrots, courgettes and white turnip in a soy and basil dressing. Pudding was a perfect roast pear tartlet with a Calvados sauce chosen from a list that included an intriguing gâteaux marjolaine layered with dark chocolate mousse and vanilla cream served with a Banyuls syrup. The comprehensive wine list (a passion of the owner) covers a very wide price bracket and range.

Seats: 80. Private room 100. Jacket & tie preferred
Smoking: No pipes & cigars; Air conditioning
Accommodation: 48 en suite
Credit cards:

Directions: From A56 take A5117 then A540. Set back from the A540 north of Chester

CHESTER, **Curzon Hotel**

A small, welcoming hotel a mile from the city centre and racecourse, where friendly Swiss-born proprietors provide food influenced by the cuisine of their homeland. Melted Raclette cheese accompanies boiled potatoes with pickles, and strips of pork and mushrooms with white wine and cream come with rösti potatoes.

Additional: Children welcome; ❸ dishes. **Seats:** 40
Smoking: No smoking in dining room
Accommodation: 16 en suite
Credit cards:

52-54 Hough Green
CH4 8JQ
Map 7: SJ46
Tel: 01244 678581
Fax: 01244 680866
Chef: Markus Imfeld
Owners: Markus & Yvonne Imfeld
Cost: Fixed-price D £16. ☺
H/wine £8.75.
Times: D only, 7-9pm.
Closed 2 wks Xmas

Directions: From M53 take A483 Wrexham/Chester, turning R towards Chester. At 3rd roundabout take 2nd L onto A5104 (Saltney). Hotel 500yds on R.

CHESTER,
Gateway To Wales Hotel

Welsh Road Deeside
CH5 2HX
Map 7: SJ46
Tel: 01244 830332
Fax: 01244 836190
Chef: Chris Thompson
Owners: Mr & Mrs W G Corbett

The name of the hotel seems to imply one-way traffic, nonetheless, it is close to the border, although the *carte* points in a more continental direction. Elaborate descriptions indicate high technical skill and fine aspirations, but more simplicity on

the plate and less 'napping' on the page would help focus the kitchen in a more positive way. Fruit and meat combinations are favoured: duck breast, pan-fried pink, with a strawberry and fig sauce topped with sweet kumquats; roast quail stuffed with chestnut and orange forcemeat on a bed of roasted ginger-flavoured celery flavoured with raspberry dressing. Fish is cooked less elaborately; grilled cod comes with split green pea purée topped with straw potatoes. Plain steaks are also available.

Directions: From Chester follow signs for Deeside/Queensferry taking A548. Turn R at roundabout, to 2nd roundabout, where hotel can be seen. Near RAF Sealand

Cost: *Alc* £27, fixed-price L £15 (2 courses)/D £17.50 (5 courses). ☺ H/wine £8.95
Times: 12.30-last L 2.30pm (Sun noon-9pm)/7-last D 9.30pm
Additional: Bar food; Sunday L; Children welcome; ❹ dishes
Seats: 40. Private dining room 12
Smoking: No smoking in dining room
Accommodation: 39 en suite
Credit cards: ■■ ■■ ⊼ ⊆ ■■ ⊆ ⊇

CHESTER,
Grosvenor Pulford Hotel ✿

A wooden floor and antique tables give a warm feeling to the restaurant at this Edwardian property near Chester. A recent meal highlighted delicately flavoured Japanese-style shellfish, chicken breast stuffed with sun-dried tomato mousse accompanied by praiseworthy vegetables, then caramelised pear crème brûlée.

Additional: Bar food; Sunday L; Children welcome; ❹ dishes
Smoking: No-smoking area; No pipes and cigars
Accommodation: 42 en suite
Credit cards: ■■ ■■ ⊼ ⊆ ■■

Directions: Telephone for directions

Wrexham Road
Pulford CH4 9DG
Map 7: SJ46
Tel: 01244 570560
Fax: 01244 570809
Chef: Brian Tookey
Owners: Mr & Mrs H G Nelson
Cost: *Alc:* £20. ☺ H/wine £9.50
Times: Last L 2.30pm/last D 10pm

CHESTER,
Mollington Banastre Hotel ✿

Extended Victorian mansion conveniently located between the city and the M6, offering good leisure and conference facilities. Menus in the Garden Room Restaurant may feature pan-fried scallops with gazpacho dressing, beef fillet with cep risotto and port wine jus, and prune and Armagnac parfait. The brasserie is more informal.

Additional: Bar Food L; Sunday L; Children welcome; ❹ menu
Smoking: No smoking in dining room; Air-conditioning
Accommodation: 63 en suite
Credit cards: ■■ ■■ ⊼ ⊆ ■■ ⊇

Directions: Bear L at end of M56 onto A5117, L at roundabout onto A540, the hotel is 2 miles on R

Parkgate Road CH1 6NN
Map 7: SJ46
Tel: 01244 851471
Fax: 01244 851165
Chef: David Hadfield
Owner: Arcadian Hotels.
Cost: *Alc* £28, fixed price L £18/D £21. H/wine £11.50
Times: Last L 2pm/last D 9.45pm. Closed L Sat

HANDFORTH,
Belfry Hotel ✿

The welcoming restaurant at this modern hotel is the venue for some great dishes and a worth-a-detour wine list. A typical winter meal could start with duck and chicken liver parfait, followed by roast rack of lamb basted in heather honey. Fresh fish is a speciality – check out the pan-fried river trout served with nut brown butter and roasted almonds.

Stanley Road SK9 3LD
Map 7: SJ88
Tel: 0161 4370511
Fax: 0161 4990597
Chef: Martin Thompson
Owners: Andrew Beech & Family
Cost: *Alc* £30, fixed-price L £16.50/D £19.50 (4 courses). ☺ H/wine £13

Smoking: No-smoking area
Accommodation: 80 en suite
Credit cards: 💳 💳 💳 💳 💳 💳 💳

Directions: A34 to Handforth, at end of village

KNUTSFORD, **Belle Epoque** ✺

Lavishly decorated town-centre brasserie with marble pillars, heavy drapes and Venetian glass floor. It offers a good-value lunch menu and extensive evening choice. A light and creamy chicken, lemon and tarragon risotto, followed by a generous portion of seared salmon served on a yellow pepper purée, perhaps.

Smoking: No-smoking area; No pipes & cigars
Accommodation: 7 en suite
Credit cards: 💳 💳 💳 💳 💳 💳 💳

Directions: Two miles off A50/2 miles from M6/J19

KNUTSFORD, **Cottage Restaurant** ✺

Smart, country-style open-plan restaurant with a few private corners. Good modern cooking. Look out for poached langoustine, red onion salad, or fresh asparagus, lambs' sweetbreads and wild mushrooms, sweet garlic cream and puff pastry pillow, and chilli vinaigrette, new-season lamb with spring vegetables.

Smoking: No smoking in dining roomn
Accommodation: 12 en suite
Credit cards: 💳 💳 💳 💳 💳 💳

Directions: On A50 halfway between Knutsford and Holmes Chapel

KNUTSFORD, **Cottons Hotel** ✺

A successful, well-appointed business and leisure hotel, ideally located for both the M6 and M56. The menu has a noticeable Cajun influence with dishes such as grilled bay shrimp and crab cake with chilli jam and aïoli, seafood risotto, and lemon tart with crème anglaise. Very efficient, friendly service, Good wine list.

Directions: From M6 exit 19/A556 (Stockport). Turn R at lights (A50 to Knutsford). Hotel 1.5 miles on R

Belfry Hotel

Times: Last L 2pm/last D 10pm
Additional: Bar food L; Sunday L; Children welcome; 🍴 dishes

Shortlisted for AA Wine Award-see page 16

60 King Street WA16 6DT
Map 7: SJ77
Tel: 01565 633060
Fax: 01565 634150
Chef: David Mooney
Owners: Nerys & Keith Mooney
Cost: Alc £25, fixed-price L £9.95. ☺ H/wine £10.50
Times: Last L 2pm/last D 10.30pm. Closed L Sat, all Sun, Bhs
Additional: Children welcome; 🍴 dishes

London Road
Allostock WA16 9LU
Map 7: SJ77
Tel: 01565 722470
Fax: 01565 722749
Chef: Steve Burell
Owners: W F Fletcher, C Lowe
Cost: Fixed-price L £10.95/D £14.95 (2 courses). H/wine £9.75
Times: Last L 2pm/last D 9.30pm. Closed D Sun
Additional: Bar food L; Sunday L; Children welcome; 🍴 dishes

Manchester Road WA16 0SU
Map 7: SJ77
Tel: 01565 650333
Fax: 01565 755351
Please telephone for further details

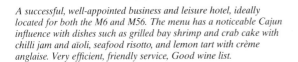

KNUTSFORD,
Dick Willett's ☘

Open to non-residents only three nights a week (as we go to press), Dick Willett's offers an exclusively vegetarian menu with dishes ranging from saffron noodle cake with wild mushroom ragout to potato gnocchi with tomato sauce. The hotel has been created out of a former dairy dating back over 400 years.

Additional: Bar food D; ☘ menu only
Smoking: No smoking in dining room
Accommodation: 10 en suite
Credit cards: ▬ ▭ ✈ ⬜ ▤ ▣ JCB

Directions: One mile S of Knutsford on A50

Toft Hotel Toft Road WA16 9EH
Map 7: SJ77
Tel: 01565 634443
Fax: 01565 632603
Chef: Jean Davies
Owners: Jean & Tony Davies
Cost: Alc £21.95. ☺ H/wine £9.50
Times: D only, last D 9.30pm.
Closed Sun-Wed

KNUTSFORD,
Longview Hotel ☘

Once a Victorian merchant's house, Longview Hotel is now home to a comfortable restaurant serving a good range of modern European dishes. Main courses include fillet of lamb wrapped in smoked bacon with a delicate red wine and garlic sauce, and roast breast of duck, served with a sauce of thyme, roast garlic and Parma ham.

Directions: From M6 junc 19, A556 (Chester, Northwich). Turn L at lights (Knutsford), L again at roundabout, A50. Hotel 200yds on R

55 Manchester Road WA16 0LX
Map 7: SJ77
Tel: 01565 632119
Fax: 01565 652402
Chef: James Falconer-Flint
Owners: Pauline & Stephen West
Cost: Alc £18.95. ☺ H/wine £9.25
Times: D only, last D 9pm.
Closed Sun, 24 Dec-5 Jan
Additional: Bar food D; Children welcome; ☘ dishes
Smoking: No smoking in dining room
Accommodation: 23 en suite
Credit cards: ▬ ▭ ✈ ▣

LYMM, **Lymm Hotel** ☘

Refurbished hotel in the heart of the village, yet handy for the M6/J 20. Window seats in the restaurant overlook a patio, but sit anywhere to enjoy carefully cooked dishes such as duck terrine with red onion and banana salsa, haggis roundels with turnip and nutmeg cream, rib eye steak with périgourdine sauce, and haddock fillet with herb crust and citrus butter sauce.

Additional: Bar food; Sunday L; Children welcome; ☘ dishes
Smoking: No smoking in dining room; Air conditioning
Accommodation: 63 en suite
Credit cards: ▬ ▭ ✈ ⬜ ▤ ▣ ▥

Directions: Near the village centre

Whitbarrow Road
WA13 9AQ
Map 7: SJ68
Tel: 01925 752233
Fax: 01925 756035
Chef: Duncan Mackintosh
Owners: Macdonald Hotels
Cost: Fixed-price L £13.95/D £21.95.
☺ H/wine £11.95
Times: Last L 2pm/last D 9.30pm

NANTWICH,
Churche's Mansion ❀❀

The Grade I Elizabethan building has two dining-rooms, one fully panelled, the other half-timbered. The place is reputed to be haunted, but the ghosts are friendly ones. The menu changes monthly and reads like an index on contemporary trends: pressed terrine of pork belly and duck livers garnished with a vegetable and peanut salad with blueberry dressing; monkfish tail on braised root vegetables and chorizo sausage oil; breast of Gressingham duck on a blackberry and apple compote with a Chinese five-spice sauce. Banana tart topped with rum and raisin ice cream on a light rum and caramel sauce offers sweet temptation.

Directions: M6/J16, follow A500 towards Nantwich. At T junction turn R. Car park is on L immediately before next roundabout

Hospital Street CW5 5RY
Map 7: SJ65
Tel: 01270 625933
Fax: 01270 627831
Chef: Michael Lea
Owner: Amanda Simpson
Cost: Fixed-price L £18.95/D £28.50. H/wine £11.50
Times: Noon-last L 2.30pm/7-last D 9.30pm. Closed Mon, Tue, 2 wks Jan
Additional: Sunday L; No children under 10 at D; ♣ dishes
Seats: 50. Private dining rooms 20, 48
Smoking: No smoking in dining room
Credit cards: ▬ ▩ ⚛ ⏚ ⬛ ▨ JCB

NANTWICH, **Rookery Hall** ❀❀

Rookery Hall is an imposing Victorian château-style country house with an early Georgian heart. It's a place of great charm and comfort. This is apparent in the mahogany-panelled dining room which manages to avoid the stuffiness associated with many fine country house hotels. The cooking is good, with the kitchen well-versed in modern techniques and ideas. A spring dinner was notable for langoustine ravioli on a bed of cucumber, leek and asparagus with a well-balanced dressing of lemon oil and tomato water, wood pigeon, rich celeriac purée, potato fondant and a sweet garlic and herb tuile, plus a warm lemon and lime tart with yogurt and vanilla ice cream layered between confit of lemons as an accompaniment. Wine list has depth and a good selection by the glass.

Directions: On the B5074 north of Nantwich; situated 1.5 miles on right towards Worleston village

Worleston CW5 6DQ
Map 7: SJ65
Tel: 01270 610016
Fax: 01270 626027
Chef: Craig Grant
Owners: Arcadian Hotels
Cost: Alc £38, fixed-price L £18.50/D £38 (4 courses). H/wine £16
Times: Noon-last L 2pm/7pm-last D 9.30pm
Additional: Sunday L; Children welcome; ♣ dishes
Seats: 30. Private dining room 30
Smoking: No smoking in dining room
Accommodation: 45 en suite
Credit cards: ▬ ▩ ⚛ ⏚ ⬛ ▨

PRESTBURY,
White House Restaurant ❀❀

An attractive building in the centre of the village with a bar (offering informal meals) fronting the restaurant proper which occupies three rooms to the rear. While the decor features a display of antique Macclesfield lace and silk, the kitchen is thoroughly up-to-date with both Far Eastern and Mediterranean influences evident on the modern English *carte* and fixed-price menus. Starters might include tempura prawns with chilli jam and coconut cream, and our moist, flavoursome aubergine charlotte that came with hot ciabatta bread and salad. Mains range from roast leg of new season's lamb with a minted leek and white bean casserole to monkfish on a tomato broth with smoked prawn wun-tuns. The daily 'Blue Plate Specials' are described as 'restyled old favourites' and dishes designated Spa Cuisine are low in oil, butter and cream. Hotel accommodation is just down the road at the White House Manor.

Directions: Village centre on A538 N of Macclesfield

SK10 4HP
Map 7: SJ87
Tel: 01625 829376
Fax: 01625 828627
Chefs: Ryland Wakeham, Mark Cunniffee
Owners: Ryland & Judith Wakeham
Cost: Alc £25, fixed-price L £12.95/D £17.95. ☺ H/wine £12.50
Times: Noon-last L 2pm/7-last D 10pm. Closed D Sun, L Mon, 25 Dec
Additional: Bar food L; Sunday L; Children welcome; ♣ dishes
Seats: 75. Private dining room 28
Smoking: No pipes & cigars
Accommodation: 11 en suite
Credit cards: ▬ ▩ ⚛ ⏚ ⬛ ▨

PUDDINGTON, **Craxton Wood**

Parkgate Road L66 9PB
Map 7: SJ37
Tel: 0151 3394717
Fax: 0151 3391740
Chef: James Minnis
Owner: Macdonald Hotels plc
Cost: *Alc* £30, fixed-price L & D £25
(5 courses). ☺ H/wine £13
Times: Noon-last L 2pm/7-last D
9.45pm.
Additional: Bar food; Children
welcome; ♨ dishes
Seats: 80. Private dining rooms 25.
Jacket and tie preferred
Smoking: Air conditioning
Accommodation: 14 en suite
Credit cards:  JCB

A splendidly run hotel that knows exactly what its customers
want – civilised dining in comfortable surroundings. The fixed-
price menu changes seasonally, but there is also a wide choice
of dishes from the *carte*. The cooking is mostly French classical,
as precise and polished as the service, with salmon and prawn
soufflé and lobster sauce, or sliced breast of guinea fowl with
goose liver, noodles, courgettes, spinach and celeriac, and
whole roast quails wrapped in bacon with grape and Madeira
sauce, setting the pace. Oriental influences make a sudden,
startling appearance in dishes such as grilled strips of soya
sauce-marinated brill dressed on seaweed rolled with rice and
served with oyster sauce, rice and stir-fried vegetables.
Accomplished dissecting skills are displayed by waiters boning
out Dover sole and carving pheasant. Praiseworthy was a
crème brûlée, rich and creamy, counterpointed by a side dish
of summer fruits.

Directions: From end of M56 (direction N Wales) take A5117
(Queensferry). R at 1st roundabout onto A540 (Hoylake). Hotel
200 yds after next traffic lights.

SANDBACH, **Chimney House** ✿

*Eight acres of garden and woodlands surround this fine looking,
half-timbered Tudor-style hotel. The modern menu is built around
fresh produce and can offer the likes of local game terrine with
apple and ginger chutney, and sea scallops and smoked bacon with
braised cabbage, rösti potato and saffron and cider sauce.*

Additional: Bar food; Sunday L; Children welcome; ♨ dishes
Smoking: No smoking in dining room
Accommodation: 48 en suite
Credit cards: ▇ ▇ ▇ ▇ ▇ ▇ ▇

Congleton Road CW11 4ST
Map 7: SJ76
Tel: 01270 764141
Fax: 01270 768916
Chef: Thomas Burns
Owner: Regal Hotels
Cost: *Alc* £30, fixed-price L £12/D
£18 (both 4 courses). ☺ H/wine
£10.95
Times: Last L 2pm/last D 10pm

Directions: M6/J17 follow A534 to Congleton. Hotel 0.5 mile on R

SANDIWAY,

Nunsmere Hall Hotel ✿✿✿

All change at this Edwardian pile, as Simon Radley leaves for
pastures new – the Chester Grosvenor (see entry) – and his
position is taken by former sous chef, Duncan Mitchell. Early

Tarporley Road Oakmere Northwich
CW8 2ES
Map 7: SJ67
Tel: 01606 889100
Fax: 01606 889055

Nunsmere Hall Hotel

Chef: Duncan Mitchell
Owners: Julie & Malcolm McHardy
Cost: Alc £38. Fixed-price L £17.50
(2 courses). H/wine £15.50
Times: Noon-last L 1.45pm/7pm-last
D 9.30pm
Additional: Bar food L; Sunday L;
No children under 10; ◈ dishes
Seats: 60. Private dining rooms 45
Smoking: No smoking in dining room
Accommodation: 36 en suite
Credit cards:
▉ ▉ ▉ ▉ ▉ ▉ ▉ JCB

reports are positive about the new regime. The menu is short, allowing the team to concentrate on getting the balance between straightforwardness and clever ideas, and to work on the exact but rounded flavours that are brought out. Typical might be a dish of three components, each with something to say: best end of lamb, for example, with a tian of Mediterranean vegetables and a thyme-infused sauce; roasted sea bass with crushed potatoes and sauce vierge. There's a classic background to the cooking, but the interpretation is thoroughly upbeat and modern, built around some Rolls-Royce ingredients (the factory is not far away): terrine of ham knuckles and foie gras, served with a hazelnut and Muscat grape salad, and ravioli of crab, ginger and coriander comes with a lemongrass scented butter. The *carte*, admirably restrained in its descriptions, includes some more familiar ideas such as grilled Barbary duck breast is served with a pithiviers of the braised leg meat and with blackberry juices, and steamed fillet of brill accompanied by braised fennel and a light truffled bisque to which scallops have been added. Chilled white chocolate and lime tart with a milk chocolate quenelle is as rich as its sounds. Mille-feuille of baby leeks, asparagus and broad beans with a light chervil butter sauce is amongst the choices on the separate vegetarian menu.

Directions: From Sandiway take the A49, one mile on left.

TARPORLEY, **The Wild Boar** ❀

A former 17th-century hunting lodge, this impressive black and white timbered building has been extended over the years to create a substantial hotel. In the beamed restaurant expect to find good local produce in dishes such as goats' cheese mille-feuille, home-made venison and rabbit sausage and crêpes Suzette.

Additional: Bar food; Sunday L; Children welcome;
◈ dishes
Smoking: No-smoking area
Accommodation: 37 en suite
Credit cards: ▉ ▉ ▉ ▉

Directions: Two miles from Tarporley on A49 towards Whitchurch

Whitchurch Road Beeston CW6 9NW
Map 7: SJ56
Tel: 01829 260309
Fax: 01829 261081
Chef: Stuart Darer
Owner: Pageant Hotels
Cost: Alc £26, fixed-price L £14.50 (5 courses)/D £24 (5 courses). ☺ H/wine £10.95
Times: Last L 2pm/last D 9.30pm

WARRINGTON,
Daresbury Park Hotel

Modern hotel, handy for M56/J11 with a civilised restaurant and super staff. An ambitious kitchen produces the likes of salad of marinated duck served with crisp deep-fried leeks and hoisin vinaigrette, roulade of salmon roasted with tarragon, with anchovies and red wine sauce, and warm black cherry and apple Bakewell served with a chilled cheesecake cream.

Smoking: No-smoking area; air conditioning
Accommodation: 140 en suite
Credit cards: ▆ ▆ ⬜ ▆ ▆ JCB

Directions: M56/J11 onto A56 to Warrington. Just on L off roundabout

Daresbury WA4 4BB
Map 7: SJ68
Tel: 01925 267336
Fax: 01925 265615
Chef: David Chapman
Owners: De Vere Hotels Ltd
Cost: *Alc* £30, fixed-price L £15/D £30. ☺ H/wine £12.95.
Times: Last L 2pm/D 10pm. Closed L Sat
Additional: Sunday L; Bar meals L&D; Children welcome; ✿ dishes

WARRINGTON,
Park Royal International ✸

Large, modern, peacefully situated hotel, yet handy for both M56 and Manchester Airport. Pancake-wrapped seafood terrine with a good tangy lemon and basil dressing, tikka marinated breast of chicken with creamy saffron sauce, and lemon tart with fresh thyme and an intense mango sauce, formed part of one autumn meal.

Directions: M56/J10, follow A49 signed Warrington, R towards Appleton Thorn at 1st lights; hotel 200 yds on R

Stretton Road Stretton WA4 4NS
Map 7: SJ68
Tel: 01925 730706
Fax: 01925 730740
Chef: Tom Rogers
Cost: *Alc* £25, fixed-price L £12.95/D £16.95. ☺ H/wine £9.80.
Times: Last L 2pm/D 10pm
Additional: Bar food; Sunday L; Children welcome; ✿ dishes
Smoking: No-smoking area; Air-conditioning
Accommodation: 142 en suite
Credit cards:
▆ ▆ ▆ ⬜ ▆ ▆ ▆ JCB

WARRINGTON, **Rockfield Hotel** ✸

A small, personally run hotel located close to the Manchester Ship Canal, offering authentic Swiss cuisine in the attractively furnished restaurant. Expect soundly prepared dishes such as salmon with lime and cumin flavoured hollandaise, and sautéed pork with mushrooms and a white wine and cream sauce, accompanied by a good rösti.

Additional: Sunday L (Noon-3pm); Children welcome; ✿ dishes
Smoking: No smoking in dining room
Accommodation: 12 en suite
Credit cards: ▆ ▆ ▆ ⬜

Directions: From M6/J20 take A50 (Warrington) to fork with A56 (1.50 miles). Turn L into Victoria Rd. Alexandra Rd is 60 yds on R.

Alexandra Road
Grappenhall WA4 2EL
Map 7: SJ68
Tel: 01925 262898
Fax: 01925 263343
Chef: Thomas Züger
Owners: Thomas & Esther Züger
Cost: *Alc* £16, fixed-price D £16. ☺ H/wine £8.95
Times: D only, 7pm-last D 9pm.

WILMSLOW, **Bank Square** ❀❀

4-6 Bank Square
SK9 1AN
Map 7: SJ88

Tel: 01625 539754
Fax: 01625 539813
Chef: Michael Dodds
Owners: David Rivett, Janet Rivett
Cost: *Alc* £22, fixed price L £5 (2
courses)/D £12.50 (2 courses). ☺
H/wine £11.95
Times: Noon-last L 2.30pm/6.30-last
D 11pm. Closed Sun
Additional: Bar food L; Children
welcome; ✿ dishes
Seats: 50
Smoking: No-smoking area; Air
conditioning
Credit cards: ▆ ▆ ▆ ▆ ▆ ▆ ▆

The setting is a converted bank with a simple café-bar on the
ground floor; the restaurant on the first floor, however, has
high aspirations. It aims to be informally smart in a modern
style. The short menu is noted for sound execution and spot-on
accuracy. The repertoire is eclectic encompassing everything
from a straightforward pot-au-feu of young chicken and
chargrilled Aberdeen Angus ribeye with hand-cut chips
(although that is enlivened by a smoked chilli butter), to more
complex grilled Aylesbury duckling with a risotto of beetroot
plus roast red onion and aged balsamic jus, and steamed fillet
of cod with saffron glazed potatoes and a sauce of broad beans
and chives. Puddings include a hot black cherry soufflé with
vanilla ice cream. The short wine list is reasonably priced and
majors on France and the New World.

Directions: Telephone for directions

WILMSLOW, **Stanneylands** ❀❀

Stanneylands Road SK9 4EY
Map 7: SJ88
Tel: 01625 525225
Fax: 01625 537282
Chef: James Lally
Owner: Gordon Beech
Cost: *Alc* £28, fixed-price L £13.50/D
£32 (7 courses). ☺ H/wine £12
Times: 12.30-last L 2pm/7-last D
10pm. Closed D Sun
Additional: Bar food; Sunday L;
Children welcome; ✿ dishes
Seats: 80. Private dining room 100.
Jacket and tie preferred
Accommodation: 32 en suite
Credit cards: ▆ ▆ ▆ ▆ ▆ ▆

Outstanding technique and flair are the hallmarks of this up-
and-coming kitchen brigade. The restaurant is part of a
peaceful, relaxing country house hotel and the menu consists
of a short carte and 'gourmande' selection. Dishes bound to
delight include the open ravioli of lobster and young spinach
with a jus of creamed ginger tried at inspection – an excellent
balance of flavours and each component perfectly cooked.
Main course of duckling was tender and full of flavour,
accompanied by a tasty pan jus, good quality diced black

pudding and parsnip crisps. Our inspector described the steamed coconut sponge pudding as 'simply brilliant', very light with wonderful coconut flavour. It came topped with a tangy mango ice and garnished with fresh mango. Add top-quality coffee, excellent home-made breads and a good choice of petits fours and you will have a meal to remember.

Directions: From M56/J5 follow Wilmslow/Moss Nook. At traffic lights R, through Styal, L at Handford sign – follow into Stanneylands Rd

WILMSLOW, Pinewood Thistle ❀

The first-floor Terrace Restaurant offers a good choice of well-presented dishes based on quality produce. Grilled goats' cheese salad with warm figs and a peppery redcurrant preserve, griddled halibut with asparagus, dill and orange butter sauce, and banana-stuffed chicken breast in puff pastry with brandy and peppercorn sauce show the range. Good home-made puds too.

Additional: Bar food L; Sunday L; Children welcome; ❀ dishes
Smoking: No smoking in dining room; Air conditioning
Accommodation: 58 en suite
Credit cards: ▬ ▬ ▨ ▢ ▨ ▣ ▨ JCB

180 Wilmslow Road
SK9 3LG
Map 7: SJ88
Tel: 01625 529211
Fax: 01625 536812
Chef: Ian Mitchell
Owners: Thistle Mount Charlotte Hotels
Cost: *Alc* £25, fixed-price L £12.50/D £18. ☺ H/wine £9.90
Times: Last L 1.45pm/last D 9.45pm

Directions: 3 miles from M56/J5 turn off A34 onto B5358 towards Wilmslow. Hotel on L before Handforth Station

CORNWALL & ISLES OF SCILLY

ALTARNUN, Penhallow Manor ❀

A Georgian vicarage, now a delightful, personally run small hotel. Cooking is good with an emphasis on fresh produce, especially local meat, game and fish; the excellent bread is also made locally. Home-made meringues, crispy on the outside an chewy on the inside, filled with clotted cream are worth saving room for. Well balanced wine list with a good choice of half-bottles.

Penhallow PL15 7SJ
Map 2: SX28
Tel: 01566 86206
Fax: 01566 86179
Please telephone for further details

Directions: From Launceston A30 8 miles; 1 mile after B3257 take slip road to Altarnun, hotel near church

BRYHER, Hell Bay Hotel ❀

Located on the smallest of the inhabited islands, this small, friendly hotel offers total peace, marvellous sea views and, on the interesting fixed-price menu, fresh local and regional produce. Follow gâteau of sea trout and lobster with Dartmoor venison steak and Burgundy sauce, then round off a satisfying meal with baked rhubarb charlotte.

Times: 7.15-last D 8.45pm. Closed Nov-Mar
Smoking: No smoking in dining room
Accommodation: 13 en suite
Credit cards: ▬ ▬ ▨ ▢ ▣

Isles of Scilly TR23 0PR
Map 2: SW17
Tel: 01720 422947
Fax: 01720 423004
Chef: David Edge
Cost: Fixed-price D £21. ☺
Additional: Bar food L; No children under 5; ❀ dishes

Directions: By boat from main island of St Mary's

BUDE, **Atlantic Hotel**

It certainly lives up to its name with panoramic views down the valley to the River Neet and to the sea and breakwater beyond. The food is straightforward, but based on fresh produce cooked with care. This translates as mushroom soup with Madeira, roast loin of pork with rosemary flavoured gravy, lovely vegetables, and a wonderful sweet table laden with home-made desserts and a selection of English cheeses.

Additional: Bar food; Children welcome; 🖐 dishes
Smoking: No smoking in dining room
Accommodation: 13 en suite
Credit cards: 🔲 💳 🔳 🔳 🔳

Directions: From M5/J31, follow A30 past Okehampton. Then A386 (Bude) to join A3072 (Holsworthy & Bude)

17-18 Summerleaze Crescent
EX23 8HJ
Map 2: SS20
Tel: 01288 352451
Fax: 01288 356666
Chef: Georgina Cole
Owners: Mr & Mrs Cole
Cost: Fixed-price D £14 (4 courses).
☺ H/wine £6.95
Times: Closed L Sat

CALLINGTON,

Thyme and Plaice

If you don't mind limited choice, dinner here is amazing value at £19.95. The cooking is bold, bright and flavour-driven, but there is only a choice (of two) for the main course. We dined well on breast of pigeon with spiced couscous and redcurrant dressing, followed by tartare of raw marinated scallops with dill, lime and virgin olive oil. Between the roast breast of corn-fed chicken with grain mustard and green peppercorn sauce, and the fillet of Cornish beef with Madeira sauce and straw potatoes, our inspector plumped for the latter and was not disappointed. After a selection of well-kept cheeses, it was time to mainline with hot chocolate soufflé with cocoa sorbet. The former baker's shop is extensively candlelit, and the furniture has draped, rather than fitted, covers.

Directions: Follow signs to Callington. Turn L at traffic lights and R into Church St

3 Church Street PL17 7AN
Map 2: SX36
Tel/Fax: 01579 384933
Chef: Matthew Dixon
Owners: Matthew Dixon & Alison Britchford
Cost: Fixed-price D £19.95 (5 courses). ☺ H/wine £7.50
Times: D only, 7-last D 9.30pm. Closed Sun-Wed, 3 wks Jan
Additional: No children under 8; 🖐 dishes
Seats: 20
Smoking: No smoking in dining room
Credit cards: 🔲 💳 🔳 🔳 JCB

CALSTOCK,

Danescombe Valley ✿✿

A fine 19th-century plantation-style house perched above the Tamar with splendid views, now only open to the public two evenings a week, the other five nights are for residents. The setting might be rural tranquillity, but the kitchen takes a more pacy, modern view of things. The no-choice, four-course menu allows innovation without being outlandish, and the repertoire takes in such starters as salad of sautéed mixed mushrooms with a honey and mustard seed dressing, or avocado with sun-dried tomatoes and crisp prosciutto salad. Main courses could be fillet of salmon with olives, capers and lime, or breast of duck with a plum and chilli glaze served with spiced plums. Cheeses are unpasteurised West Country farmhouse, and pudding could be a simple poached pears and figs in red wine with mascarpone. The wine list is thoughtful, well annotated and noted for its Italian range.

Directions: 0.5 mile west of Calstock village along lane next to river

Lower Kelly PL18 9RY
Map 2: SX46
Tel: 01822 832414
Fax: 01822 832446
Chef: Chris Dew
Owners: Martin & Anna Smith
Cost: Fixed-price D £30 (4 courses). H/wine £9.30
Times: D only, 7.30 for 8pm. Closed Sun-Thu, Nov-Mar
Additional: No children under 12; 🖐 dishes
Seats: 12
Smoking: No smoking in dining room
Accommodation: 5 en suite
Credit cards: 🔲 💳 🔳 🔳 🔳 🔳 🔳

CONSTANTINE,
Trengilly Wartha Inn ✿✿

Popular with visitors and locals alike, the dark-wooded bar is always busy and does a good line in bar food, especially the daily fish dishes that can also be ordered from the bright blue and yellow restaurant. The cooking is modern English, strongly focused and vibrantly flavoured. Warm slices of roast venison fillet, for example, are served as a starter salad on a potato and red cabbage cake with port and redcurrant sauce, and wild rabbit meat is emphatically enhanced by a sweet-and-sour balsamic vinegar glaze. Vegetarian dishes include butternut 'tortelli' and twice-baked leek and cheese soufflé. As well as the fine West Country cheeseboard, puddings include the fab-sounding baked gooey dark chocolate cake with cool orange sauce. Great selection of wines by the glass from a keenly chosen wine list – prices are never less than reasonable and there's a wide range of malt whiskies too.

Additional: Bar food; Sunday L; Children welcome; ✿ dishes
Seats: 25. **Accommodation:** 8 rooms
Credit cards: ▬ 🔳 ⇗ ⌂ ▦ 🅒 🄿 JCB

Directions: In Constantine village turn L at top of hill, follow signs for Gweek, one mile out of village turn L, follow signposts to hotel.

Nancenoy TR11 5RP
Map 2: SW87
Tel/Fax: 01326 340332
Chef: Mike Maguire
Owners: Mike & Helen Maguire, Nigel & Isabel Logan
Cost: Fixed-price D £21.50. ☺
H/wine £8.20
Times: Noon-last L 2.15pm/6.30-last D 9.30pm. Closed 25 Dec

AA Shortlisted for *Wine* Award-see page 16

CONSTANTINE BAY, # Treglos Hotel ✿

If you can tear yourself away from bridge in the lounge and the coastal views, the five-course dinners offer plenty of choice. Simple tastes, local Dover sole grilled with lime and Maldon salt, and fancier ideas, baked loin of pork in Calvados and cider jus with caramelised apricots and apples, are both well catered for.

Additional: Bar food L; Sunday L; No children under 7 at D; ✿ dishes
Smoking: No smoking in dining room; Air conditioning
Accommodation: 44 en suite
Credit cards: ▬ 🔳 ⌂

Directions: Take B3276 (Constantine Bay). At village stores turn R, hotel is 50 yards on L

Padstow PL28 8JH
Map 2: SW87
Tel: 01841 520727
Fax: 01841 521163
Chef: Paul Becker
Owner: Mr J Barlow
Cost: Alc £28, fixed-price L £11.50/D £22 (5 courses). H/wine £9.50
Times: Last L 1.30pm/last D 9.15pm. Closed 8 Nov-11 Mar

FALMOUTH,
Falmouth Beach Resort ✿

Ospreys is the formal restaurant of this personally-run beachside hotel. Smartly uniformed staff and proper service go along with dishes such as citrus-crusted cod on ratatouille with garlic and herb sauce, and fillet steak glazed with Stilton and cream. There is also a less formal carvery.

Smoking: No smoking in dining room
Accommodation: 127 en suite
Credit cards: ▬ 🔳 ⇗ ⌂ ▦ 🅒 🄿

Directions: From A39 to Falmouth follow signs to seafront and Gyllyngvase Beach. Hotel opposite Gyllyngvase Beach

Gyllyngvase Beach
TR11 4NA
Map 2: SW83
Tel: 01326 318084
Fax: 01326 319147
Chef: Simon Spackman
Owner: David Evans
Cost: Alc £25, fixed price D £13. ☺
H/wine £7.60
Times: D only, last D midnight
Additional: Bar food; Sunday L; Children welcome; ✿ dishes

FALMOUTH, Greenbank Hotel

Kenneth Graham wrote 'The Wind in the Willows' here and Florence Nightingale, after whom the restaurant is named, stayed in 1907. The spacious dining room overlooks the harbour and seafood is well represented on a menu that might also include duck with orange, beef Stroganoff (cooked at the table) and various grills.

Smoking: No-smoking area; No pipes and cigars
Accommodation: 61 en suite
Credit cards: ▆ ▆ ▆ ▆ ▆ ▆

Directions: 500yds past Falmouth Marina overlooking the water

Harbourside TR11 2SR
Map 2: SW83
Tel: 01326 312440
Fax: 01326 211362
Chef: Richard Kevern
Owner: CN Gebhard
Cost: *Alc* £26.70, fixed-price L £10.50/D £18.95. ☺ H/wine £7.95
Times: Last L 2pm/last D 9.45pm. Closed 24 Dec-15 Jan
Additional: Bar food; Sunday L; Children welcome; ✿ dishes

FALMOUTH, Penmere Manor

Located in a quiet residential area of town in five acres of gardens and grounds, Penmere Manor, a Grade ll listed building, has both an indoor and a heated outdoor swimming pool. The Fountains Bar is ideal for informal meals, while Bolitho's Restaurant is the venue for serious dining. Freshly made tomato soup, drizzled with olive oil and garnished with basil and Parmesan, makes a simple but tasty starter, while a salad of prawns, smoked salmon and quail's egg in pesto dressing is no less effective. A main course of chicken breast, fanned on spinach purée flavoured with nutmeg and turmeric, has been commended, as have the vegetables served with it. Braised breast of pheasant in port and redcurrant sauce may be offered in season, or there could be monkfish in ginger and orange cream. Tiramisu, attractively presented with a pool of coffee-flavoured custard, was so scrumptious an inspector could have eaten a second slice. The long wine list, arranged alphabetically by country, is noteworthy for its full page of reasonably priced house wines.

Directions: Turn L into Mongleath Road off A39 1 mile after Hill Head roundabout

Mongleath Road TR11 4PN
Map 2: SW83
Tel: 01326 211411
Fax: 01326 317588
Chef: Martin Jones
Owners: Andrew Pope, Elizabeth Rose
Cost: *Alc* £24, fixed-price D £22 (5 courses). ☺ H/wine £8.50
Times: D only, 7-last D 9pm. Closed 24-26 Dec
Additional: Bar food; Children welcome; ✿ dishes
Seats: 60. Private dining room 40
Smoking: No smoking in dining room; Air conditioning
Accommodation: 37 en suite
Credit cards: ▆ ▆ ▆ ▆ ▆ ▆ ▆

FALMOUTH,
Pennypots Restaurant

Teddy bears dotted around the room (there's even one in the ladies loo, peering naughtily over the door) are a strangely quirky touch at this otherwise non-gimmicky restaurant

Maenporth Beach TR11 5HN
Map 2: SW83
Tel/Fax: 01326 250251
Chef: Kevin Viner
Owners: Jane & Kevin Viner

decorated in pine and deep blues. The place is only open at night, but a new, downstairs café now provides daytime casual eating, so the terrific views over the beach and Falmouth Bay can be enjoyed throughout the day. In the restaurant, the food is the thing, starting with a basket of warm bread and crostini of hummus and Jerusalem artichoke. Fish and seafood are always first-rate – scallops in a warm salad with Parma ham and balsamic dressing tasted just how scallops are supposed to taste, as did sautéed langoustine tails with fresh pasta in a Madeira and rosemary jus. Pan-fried fillets of mullet and sea bass with capers and lemon parsley butter were a mega-portion but light. Saucing plays an important part in Kevin Viner's cooking, complementing rather than overwhelming superb quality meat in a duo of grilled duck breast and confit of the leg with cherry and Armagnac sauce. Red wine and shallot sauce is classically paired with a chargrilled fillet of beef. A more contemporary edge comes through in dishes such as pan-fried fillet of sea bass in a coriander and oriental warm dressing. In a plate of five choice cheeses, a 'stunning' fresh local goats' cheese stood out. Caramelised orange tart, an interesting rendition of the more ubiquitous lemon variety, was so exquisitely executed it practically trembled on the plate; Grand Marnier soaked oranges were a perfect finishing touch.

Signature dishes: Cornish lamb on a thyme and port jus; grilled lobster in a herb and garlic butter; venison fillet, roasted on a Cognac and prune sauce; bread-and-butter pudding with clotted cream.

Directions: 3 miles S of Falmouth, follow signs for Maenporth

Cost: Fixed-price D £28.50. H/wine £9.50
Times: D only, 7-9.30pm. Closed Sun, Mon, 4 wks winter
Additional: Children welcome; dishes
Seats: 40
Smoking: Air conditioning
Credit cards: ■ ■ 🐾 💳 ■ 🅒 🅿 JCB

FALMOUTH, **Powell's Cellars** ❀

Surprisingly spacious, with arched walls and an Art Deco theme, this cellar restaurant creates an intimate atmosphere. Home-made breads, fresh fish and great desserts are the main features of an imaginative menu. Expect the likes of chargrilled tuna, or Mediterranean red fish with roasted vegetables and provencale-style sauce.

Additional: Children welcome; dishes
Credit cards: ■ ■ 🐾 💳 🅒 JCB

Directions: Follow signs to 'Town Centre' and park in 'The Moor' car park. Short walk along Webber St to High St – turn L and look for signs

29 High Street TR11 3AD
Map 2: SW83
Tel: 01326 311212
Fax: 01326 311805
Chef: Nicholas Hodges
Owners: Mr Nicholas Hodges, Mrs Sarah Hodges
Cost: *Alc* £23. H/wine ☺ £8.95
Times: D only from 7pm. Closed D Mon in winter, 25-26 Dec, 1 Jan

FALMOUTH, **Royal Duchy Hotel** ❀❀

Cliff Road TR11 4NX
Map 2: SW83
Tel: 01326 313042
Fax: 01326 319420
Chef: Des Turland
Owner: Brend family
Cost: *Alc* £25, fixed-price L £9.95/D £20 (4 courses). ☺ H/wine £8.50.
Times: Noon-last L 2pm/7pm-last D 9pm
Additional: Bar food L; Sunday L; Children welcome; dishes
Seats: 100. Jacket and tie preferred
Accommodation: 44 en suite
Credit cards: ■ ■ 🐾 💳 ■ 🅒 🅿

Warm hospitality and professional, attentive service ensure plenty of return visitors to this sea-front hotel. Fish is a particularly good choice, roast bream with warm spinach salad with lemon chervil sauce, or grilled fillet of bass with herb noodles and white wine and lime sauce, for example. There is a slightly dated 'Grand Hotel' air to much of the *carte*, starting with the ubiquitous selection of chilled fruit juices, moving onto honey roasted gammon with onion and parsley gravy, past a cold buffet selection with Russian and Waldorf salads, and ending with the likes of caramelised lemon tart with crème Chantilly. These sit alongside contemporary ideas such as seared fillet of vanilla scented salmon with couscous and curry oil dressing and iced aniseed parfait with sablé biscuits and blackberry compote.

Directions: Hotel is at Castle end of Promenade

FOWEY, **Food for Thought** ❀❀

The setting is perfect: a former custom-house right on the quay, ideal for the kind of personally run seafood restaurant that the Billingsleys have made a feature in Fowey for two decades. Fish is the business here, although not exclusively so, with terrine of foie gras, rack of lamb roasted with a herb crust, and Barbary duck breast with red onion marmalade and a rich Cassis sauce, equally at home on the menu. Lobster comes from their own tank, oysters are from the River Fowey, and local Dover sole is grilled with lime butter. Salad gourmande is a stunning dish of langoustine, crabmeat, fresh asparagus, smoked duck, and thin strips of smoked salmon, all in a tarragon dressing, by contrast, sea scallops are simply cooked in olive oil with roasted red peppers, garlic and basil. Freshness is the keynote here, coupled with the confidence to let natural flavours shine through.

Directions: Walk down to the quay from the town centre car park

The Quay PL23 1AT
Map 2: SX15
Tel: 01726 832221
Fax: 01726 832077
Chef/Owner: Martin Billingsley
Cost: *Alc* £25, fixed-price D £19.95.
☺ H/wine £8.95
Times: D only, 7-9.30pm.
Closed Sun, Jan, Feb
Additional: No children under 12;
❁ dishes
Seats: 40
Credit cards: ▬ ▭ ▢

FOWEY, **Fowey Hotel** ❀❀

Completely refurbished, this 'Grand Old Lady' of a hotel is perched on the slopes above the estuary and enjoys marvellous marine views from many of the bedrooms and the public rooms, including the restaurant where window tables are favourite. Wherever you sit expect some imaginative meals that make interesting use of local produce. Highlights of our most recent dinner included the good ham and cheese bread (horseradish flavour was the other option) and a starter of scallops around a mound of fresh crab with potato salad and mixed leaves. The main course of three cuts of lamb (cutlet, rump and liver) was perfectly complemented by vegetables (turned courgette, potato and carrot with asparagus spears) served in a puff pastry case as an integral part of the dish. The finale was a tangy lemon tart with elderflower and lemon grass syrup. Wines include a nicely varied selection of half-bottles.

Directions: Telephone for directions

The Esplanade PL23 1HX
Map 2: SX15
Tel: 01726 832551
Fax: 01726 832125
Chef: David Swade
Cost: Fixed-price D £23.95 (4 courses). ☺ H/wine £10
Times: Noon-last L 2.30pm/7-last D 9.30pm
Additional: Bar food L; Sunday L; Children welcome; ❁ dishes
Seats: 60. Private dining room 30. Jacket & tie preferred
Smoking: No smoking in dining room
Accommodation: 21 en suite
Credit cards: ▬ ▭ ▨ ▢ ▦ ▢

FOWEY, Marina Hotel ❀

Originally the Bishop of Truro's summer retreat, this Georgian hotel offers good food and friendly service in the Waterside Restaurant. Typical starters include smoked Scotch salmon with brown bread and butter, and scallops seared with bacon and garlic butter. Spectacular views across the River Fowey.

Additional: Children welcome; ◈ dishes
Smoking: No smoking in dining room
Accommodation: 11 en suite
Credit cards: [card symbols]

Directions: From A38 Dobwalls take A390 to St Austell. At Lostwithiel take B3269 to Fowey

Esplanade PL23 1HY
Map 2: SX15
Tel: 01726 833315
Fax: 01726 832779
Chef: Stephen Vincent
Owner: John Roberts
Cost: *Alc* £25, fixed-price D £18. ☺ H/wine £9.95
Times: D only, last D 8.30pm

GILLAN, Tregildry Hotel ❀❀

Personally run by Huw and Lynne Phillips, Tregildry enjoys a stunning view across Gillan Creek to the Helford River, Falmouth Bay and beyond, while a private path leading down to the cove below gives access to the Cornish coastal path. Another of the attractions is Huw's French-inspired modern British cooking. The daily-changing, fixed-price menus (sensibly limited to three choices at each stage) are well balanced and imaginative. Starters might include an avocado, melon and strawberry salad with a fresh lime and coriander dressing, and a roast-tomato soup with basil, before such mains as lemon roast chicken with sweet potatoes and fresh herbs, and salmon baked with a saffron couscous crust and served with a salsa 'rossa'. Hot puddings are a speciality, a crumble of brandy-marinated plums with clotted cream was a particular hit on our last visit, or you can always finish with some Cornish farmhouse cheeses. Short, but well-chosen, list of wines.

Directions: A3083 from Helston (Lizard Road), take 1st L for St Keverne. Follow signs for Manaccan and Gillan

Gillan TR12 6HG
Map 2: SW52
Tel: 01326 231378
Fax: 01326 231561
Chef: Huw Phillips
Owners: Huw & Lynne Phillips
Cost: Fixed-price D £23 (4 courses). ☺ H/wine £10.50
Times: D only, 7pm-last D 8.30pm. Closed Nov-Feb
Additional: No children under 8; ◈ dishes
Seats: 30
Smoking: No smoking in dining room
Accommodation: 10 en suite
Credit cards: [card symbols] JCB

GOLANT, Cormorant Hotel ❀

The setting is perfect – perched on a hill with splendid river views. The kitchen makes the most of local produce. Fish is obviously a feature, whole bass grilled with fennel and provençale herbs, for example, but prime fillet steak dijonnaise comes from a Cornish protected herd, or there's rack of Cornish lamb with rosemary and black pepper crust.

Accommodation: 11 en suite
Credit cards: [card symbols] JCB

Directions: Turn from A390 St Austell Rd onto B3269 to Fowey. Turn L to Golant. Go to end (almost to water's edge), entrance on R

Fowey PL23 1LL
Map 2: SX15
Tel/Fax: 01726 833426
Chefs: John Keen & George Elworthy
Owners: Mr & Mrs G Elworthy
Cost: *Alc* £25, fixed-price D £18 (4 courses). ☺ H/wine £9.05
Times: Last L 2pm/last D 9pm
Additional: Bar food L; No children under 7; ◈ dishes

HELSTON, Nansloe Manor ❀❀

A long, tree-lined drive leads you to the relaxed, family-run Georgian manor, newly refurbished following a change of ownership. You can't be in Cornwall and not have excellent fish and seafood; here crab with tomato makes the filling for

Meneage Road TR13 0SB
Map 2: SW62
Tel: 01326 574691
Fax: 01326 564680
Chef: Howard Ridden
Owners: The Ridden Family

ravioli on seared provençale vegetables with red pepper and balsamic dressing and grilled red mullet comes with lime scented couscous and chilli and sweetcorn kernel dressing. Duck with orange gets a new twist when marinated with rosemary, is oven-baked and served on orange polenta with coriander salsa. Desserts, such as roasted apple and pear bound in a toffee and dried fruit sauce, topped with almond ice cream, have clotted cream as an optional extra.

Nansloe Manor

Cost: *Alc* £27, fixed-price L £15/D £20. ☺ H/wine £10.40
Times: Noon-last L 1.30pm/7-last D 8.30pm
Additional: Bar food L; Sunday L; No children under 10; ✇ dishes
Seats: 40. Jacket & tie preferred
Smoking: No smoking in dining room
Accommodation: 7 rooms (6 en suite)
Credit cards: 🖃 🖃 ✈ 🖃 🄲 JCB

Directions: 300yds from junction of A394 and A3083 down a well-signed drive

---

LAUNCESTON,

Percy's at Coombeshead ❀❀

The emphasis at this West Country restaurant is on fresh local produce – the ethos is very much 'if it's fresh, it's in'. This zeal for freshness can lead to some exciting dishes. A plot of land next to the restaurant supplies fifteen different types of salad leaf, and most meat and vegetables are produced organically. Occasionally local fishermen turn up with freshly-caught sea bass or Cornish cod, which in hours will be the feature of that evening's *carte*. Main courses could include poached conger eel with a sorrel sauce, bacon-wrapped breast of chicken filled with leek and tarragon mousse, and grilled fillet of turbot with fennel and a white wine and saffron sauce. Desserts range from steamed hazelnut pudding with rich chocolate sauce to lemon ice cream with fresh fruits and blackcurrant coulis.

Directions: Follow signs to restaurant from Gridley Corner A388 (St Giles on the Heath) or at Metherell Cross, B3218 (Okehampton-Bude)

Virginstowe EX21 5EA
Map 2: SX38
Tel: 01409 211236
Fax: 01409 211275
Chef: Tina Bricknell-Webb
Owners: Tony & Tina Bricknell-Webb
Cost: *Alc* £22.50, fixed-price D £22.50. ☺ H/wine £8.95
Times: Noon-2pm/6.30-9pm
Additional: No children under 12; ✇ dishes
Seats: 44. Private dining room 18
Smoking: No smoking in dining room
Accommodation: 8 en suite
Credit cards: 🖃 🖃 ✈ 🖃 🄲

LISKEARD,
Pencubitt House Hotel ❀❀

Station Road PL14 4EB
Map 2: SX26
Tel/Fax: 01579 342694
Chef: Michael Kent
Owners: Michael & Claire Kent
Cost: *Alc* £16.50, fixed-price D £20
(5 courses). ☺ H/wine £10
Times: D only, 7-8.30pm
Additional: No children under 12;
◈ dishes
Seats: 30
Smoking: No smoking in dining room
Accommodation: 8 en suite
Credit cards: ▬ ▦ ◥

Built as a local wool merchant's residence in 1898, the house stands in an elevated position on the edge of town. From the well-balanced set menu (the price depends on how many courses you take) you might start with fresh cod fishcakes with lemon mayonnaise, followed by pan-fried fillet of venison with celeriac purée, red wine and black treacle sauce. Cornish clotted cream takes rightful pride of place alongside a lemon tart with red berry sauce, and excellent West Country farmhouse cheeses are generously offered, though they may have also featured in first courses such as grilled Harbourne goats' cheese with roasted red peppers, basil oil and balsamic vinegar. No problem for cheese lovers.

Directions: Follow BR Park & Ride signs. Hotel signs visible 250 yds from rail station on B3254

LISKEARD, **Well House Hotel** ❀❀❀

St Keyne PL14 4RN
Map 2: SX26
Tel: 01579 342001
Fax: 01579 343891
Chef: Cameron Brown
Owners: Nick Wainford, Ione Nurdin
Cost: Fixed-price L & D £26.95.
H/wine £8.95
Times: 12.30-last L 1.45pm/7-last D
8.45pm
Additional: Sunday L;
No children under 8 at D; ◈ dishes
Seats: 34
Smoking: No-smoking area;
No pipes & cigars
Accommodation: 9 en suite
Credit cards: ▬ ▦ ◥ ▢ ▦ ◖ ▣ JCB

A late 19th-century tea planter's house, built on the side of the East Looe Valley, with charm and tranquillity in spades. Cameron Brown's repertoire is wide, based on a style that is carefully considered and built around soundly sourced fresh produce. Interesting combinations are explored in dishes in which the Mediterranean is never far away. Note grilled red mullet with a tapenade crust on a niçoise salad; roast panaché of monkfish, brill and salmon with langoustine and squid ink risotto, poached baby fennel and a mussel and saffron velouté; rump of lamb topped with a rosemary and truffle crust, oven-baked peppers, timbale of couscous and a quenelle of spiced aubergine and courgette purée. A report on a May dinner reads as a litany of enthusiastically received dishes: an outstanding gnocchi Romagna on a brioche croûte with creamed leeks and smoked bacon with truffle oil; a delicate pan-fried fillet of sea bass with herb potatoes and a dressing of white truffles and leeks; a perfect cheese soufflé; light, full of flavour, warm cherry clafoutis with vanilla anglaise. Perfect attention to small details is seen in canapés of tomato, mozzarella and garlic brochettes, tiny duck samosas, and delicate cheese-courgette pizzas, great home-made bread, and petits fours made from top-quality chocolate.

Directions: At St Keyne Church follow signs to St Keyne Well, the restaurant is 0.5 miles further

MARAZION, **Mount Haven Hotel** ✱

Former coaching inn with stunning views across Mount's Bay towards St Michael's Mount. In the split-level restaurant, fresh local produce (including fish from nearby Newlyn) is the starting point for dishes such as chicken liver parfait, monkfish and scallops with balsamic cream sauce, and honey-roasted guinea fowl.

Turnpike Road TR17 0DQ
Map 2: SW53
Tel: 01736 710249
Fax: 01736 711658
Chef: Yorick Steiner
Owners: John & Delyth James
Cost: Alc £20, fixed-price L £9/D £19. ☺ H/wine £9.50
Times: D only, last D 9pm (8.30pm Oct-Apr). Closed Xmas
Additional: Bar food D; Sunday L (noon-2pm); Children welcome; ✿ dishes
Smoking: No smoking in dining room
Accommodation: 17 en suite
Credit cards: ▬ ▭ ▨ ▢ ▬ ▣

Directions: Through village to end of built-up area

MAWNAN SMITH,
Budock Vean Hotel ✱✱

Smartly updated, this early 18th-century house retains a strong sense of history, as well as a magnificent setting – in 65 acres leading down to the Helford River. The cooking this year has brought praise from our inspectors who have been impressed by the total honesty and simplicity of the kitchen's style. A summer dinner elicited praise for a double-baked Cheddar cheese soufflé, served with spinach, a locally caught, pan-seared sea bass with saffron mash and a splendid hollandaise accompanying vegetables, as well as a tuile of exotic fruits served with a smooth orange and mango sabayon. A comprehensive selection of West Country cheeses is another plus, as is the lovely flavoured bread – tomato, cheese and onion, and walnut, on our visit. The extensive wine list is notable for its selection of half-bottles, as well as being a useful guide regarding sweetness/suitability of various wines with certain dishes.

Falmouth TR11 5LG
Map 2: SW72
Tel: 01326 250288
Fax: 01326 250892
Chef: Darren Kelly
Owners: Mr & Mrs E Barlow
Cost: Alc £32, fixed-price D £24. ☺ H/wine £9.50
Times: Last L 2.15pm/last D 9pm
Additional: Bar food L; Sunday L; No children under 7; ✿ dishes
Smoking: No smoking before 10 pm
Accommodation: 58 en suite
Credit cards: ▬ ▭ ▨ ▢ ▣ ▨

Directions: Three miles S of Falmouth. Straight on at Mawnan Smith for 1.5 miles. Hotel on L

MAWNAN SMITH,

Meudon Hotel ❀

Falmouth TR11 5HT
Map 2: SW72
Tel: 01326 250541
Fax: 01326 250543
Chef: Alan Webb
Owner: Harry Pilgrim
Cost: *Alc* £18, fixed-price L £15 /D
£25 (6 courses). H/wine £11
Times: 7.30pm-last D 9pm. Closed
Jan-Feb
Additional: Bar food only L Mon-Sat;
Sunday L; Children welcome;
❸ dishes
Accommodation: 29 en suite
Credit cards: ▬ ▬ ▰ ⌐ ▦ ◖ ⊡

Family-run hotel of long standing with its own beach plus nine acres
of sub-tropical garden. Local seafood stars in the conservatory
restaurant: poached loin of monkfish with a lobster and grape
ragout, scallops in brandy with spring onions, crab Thermidor.
Steaks come from local beef stock. Children's high tea.

Directions: Take A39 towards Falmouth. Leave Hillhead
roundabout & follow signs to Maenporth Beach; hotel on L after
1 mile

MAWNAN SMITH,

Trelawne Hotel ❀❀

TR11 5HS
Map 2: SW72
Tel: 01326 250226
Fax: 01326 250909
Please telephone for further details

This is a hotel with a lot going for it: lovely garden; super views
over the coastline from St Mawes to the Lizard; owners of
long-standing who put a great deal into the welcome and
comfort of their guests. The kitchen makes the most of the
West Country's bountiful larder. Seafood is there in plenty, but
breast of chicken with chargrilled vegetables and a coriander
pesto, or magret of duckling with port and lime sauce and
roasted plums widen the options. Desserts are well reported.
The wine list offers a sound, comprehensive range.

Directions: Three miles S of Falmouth on coast road to Mawnan
Smith

MOUNT HAWKE,

Tregarthen Country Cottage

Lovely cottage-style hotel in pleasant rural surroundings on the edge of the village. There's a loyal regular following for the good home-cooking based on fresh ingredients and simple concepts such as soups, roasts and fruit tarts served with lashings of whipped double cream. Short wine list of some 9 bottles.

Directions: From the A30 turn off at Three Burrows roundabout onto the B3277 St Agnes road, take first left and follow signs to Mount Hawke, approx 2m

Map 2: SW56
Tel: 01209 890399
Fax: 01209 891041
Please telephone for further details

MOUSEHOLE, **Cornish Range**

Once a pilchard press, this smuggler's haunt of a place is now a serious seafood restaurant – there are a couple concessions to incorrigible carnivores. The freshest of seafood is respectfully treated in dishes such as crab salad, and roasted monkfish with sun-dried tomatoes, red peppers and olive oil. Short, well-chosen wine list. Booking advisable.

Additional: Sunday L (Nov-Easter); Children welcome;
 dishes
Smoking: No-smoking area
Credit cards: 🔲 🔲 🔲 💳 💳 JCB

Directions: Mousehole is 3 miles from Penzance, via Newlyn

6 Chapel Street TR19 6SB
Map 2: SW42
Tel: 01736 731488
Chef: David Rashleigh
Owner: Susan Perry
Cost: Alc £20. ☺ H/wine £9.50
Times: D only, last D 9.30pm. Closed D Sun (all year), Mon-Wed (Nov-Easter)

MOUSEHOLE,

Old Coastguard Inn

Splendid, informally run inn on the edge of the village (with good parking). A popular bar menu is backed up by some sound country cooking in the bare-boarded restaurant. Check the blackboard for the daily fish specials, otherwise there's grilled goats' cheese with red pepper dressing, and pan-fried duck breast with port wine sauce.

Directions: From Penzance take coast road through Newlyn. Inn 1st large building on L as you enter the village, just after public carpark

The Parade TR19 6PR
Map 2: SW42
Tel: 01736 731222
Fax: 01736 731720
Chefs/Owners: A Wood, M Kitchen, K Terry
Cost: Fixed-price D £17.95. ☺ H/wine £7.95.
Times: Last L 2.30pm/D 9.30pm.
Additional: Bar meals L&D; Children welcome; dishes
Smoking: No smoking in dining room
Accommodation: 21 en suite
Credit cards: 🔲 🔲 🔲 💳

NEWQUAY, **Corisande Manor**

More German than Cornish in style – the house was built for an Austrian count over a century ago – it has wonderful sea views. There are a couple of choices at each of four courses, smoked eel salad perhaps, and turkey escalope with orange and honey sauce.

Smoking: No smoking in dining room
Accommodation: 12 en suite. **Credit cards:** ▬ ▦ ▰ ▢

Directions: Off the main road down the Pentire headland, left at Newquay Nursing Home into Pentire Crescent, then R into Riverside Avenue

Riverside Avenue Pentire TR7 1PL
Map 2: SW86
Tel: 01637 872042
Fax: 01637 874557
Chef: Chris Grant
Owners: David & Chris Grant
Cost: Fixed-price D £19.50
(4 courses). ☺ H/wine £9.50
Times: D only at 8pm
Additional: Children welcome;
🍴 dishes

NEWQUAY, **Headland Hotel** NEW

Large Victorian hotel on a headland with the sea on three sides. The main restaurant is the place to enjoy the sunset and sound cooking from a varied menu. (From the less formal, all-day Fistral restaurant watch surfers on the eponymous beach.) Don't miss the mouth-watering display of home-made puds. Staff are smart and well trained and a serious wine list caters for all pockets.

Smoking: No smoking in dining room
Accommodation: 100 en suite
Credit cards: ▬ ▦ ▰ ▢ ▦ ▣ ▣

Directions: Telephone for directions

Fistral Beach TR7 1EW
Map 2: SW86
Tel: 01637 872211
Fax: 01637 872212
Chef: David Connolly
Owners: John & Carolyn Armstrong
Cost: Alc £25, fixed-price D £17.50.
☺ H/wine £10.95
Times: D only, last D 9pm.
Closed Xmas
Additional: Bar food (garden room);
No young children at D in restaurant;
🍴 dishes

NEWQUAY, **Hotel Bristol**

Well-established, traditional seaside hotel. Menu offers quite a blast-from-the-past with dishes such as smoked fish pâté with Melba toast, tournedos Rossini, poached supreme of chicken princesse, lemon pancakes, and banana split.

Directions: From A30 take A39 then A392. Turn R onto A3058 and follow signs for seafront hotels for 2.5 miles along Henver Road and Narrowcliff

Narrowcliff TR7 2PQ
Map 2: SW86
Tel: 01637 875181
Fax: 01637 879347
Chef: Malcolm Jackson
Owners: The Young Family
Cost: Alc £18.50, fixed-price L £11
(4 courses)/D £18.50 (5 courses). ☺
H/wine £9
Times: Last L 1.45pm/last D 8.45pm
Additional: Bar food L; Sunday L;
No children under 4; 🍴 dishes
Smoking: No smoking in dining room
Accommodation: 74 en suite
Credit cards: ▬ ▦ ▰ ▢ ▦ ▣ ▣ JCB

NEWQUAY, **Porth Veor Manor** NEW

19th-century stone-built manor house whose associations with the nearby RAF station are reflected in the choice of names for the Aviators Bar and the Officers Mess restaurant. Mostly classic

Porth Way TR7 3LW
Map 2: SW86
Tel: 01637 873274
Fax: 01637 851690
Chef: Mrs Elizabeth Slyfield

English dishes such as smoked mackerel mousse, lamb with sherry and mushroom sauce, chocolate pudding, and local cheeses. Booking recommended.

Additional: Bar food L; Sunday L; Children welcome; ♿ dishes
Smoking: No smoking in dining room
Accommodation: 22 en suite
Credit cards: ■ ▦ ▚ ▢ ▦ ◧ JCB

Directions: Leave Newquay on A3058. After 1 mile turn L onto B3276 (Padstow Coast Rd). Hotel is on L at bottom of hill

Owners: Paul & Ann Harknett
Cost: Alc £19.75. Fixed-price L £7.95 (4 courses)/D £13.90 (6 courses). H/wine £7.45. ☺
Times: Last L 1.45pm/last D 8.30pm. Closed (non residents/non reservations only) D Sun, Mon, Tue

PADSTOW,
Old Custom House Inn ❀

South Quay
PL28 8ED
Map 2: SW97
Tel: 01841 532359
Fax: 01841 533372
Please telephone for further details

Central location alongside the harbour for this great little hotel. The bar is popular with locals and visitors, and the restaurant offers a good-value fixed-price menu and short carte majoring in locally caught fish, perhaps gratin of flaked crab and local prawns with a tarragon cream. Meat options include griddled chicken breast in lime, coconut and coriander sauce. Sound, straightforward wine list.

Directions: From Wadebridge take A389 (Padstow). Second turning on R after Padstow school, go round sharp bend at bottom of hill. Restaurant is opposite entrance to harbour car park

PADSTOW, ## St Petroc's House ❀❀

4 New Street PL28 8EA
Map 2: SW97
Tel: 01841 532700
Fax: 01841 532942
Chef: Alistair Clive
Owner: Rick & Jill Stein
Cost: Fixed-price L&D £19.95. ☺
Times: Noon-last L 2pm/7pm-last D 9.30pm. Closed Mon, 20 Dec-1 Jan
Additional: Sunday L; Children welcome
Seats: 35. Private dining room 12
Smoking: No smoking in restaurant
Accommodation: 13 en suite
Credit cards: ■ ▦ ▚ ▢ ◧

Simpler, cheaper sibling to Rick Stein's Seafood Restaurant. While seafood is well represented, the menu is not exclusively fishy being rooted in the staples of French bistro cooking. Shortish three-course menus – you can have just a single course if you want – might include grilled goats' cheese with beetroot salad, or mussel, leek and saffron soup, before mains such as whole grilled lemon sole with prawn butter, or fillet steak with salsa verde and pommes frites. Round off with a homely sticky toffee pudding or Berkswell cheese with pear and rocket. Short but well-chosen wine list with several offerings by the glass. Service is relaxed and friendly from a young team, decor simple and modern with contemporary paintings.

Directions: Follow one-way around harbour, take 1st L, situated on the R

PADSTOW,
The Seafood Restaurant ❀❀❀

Riverside PL28 8BY
Map 2: SW97
Tel: 01841 532700/532485
Fax: 01841 532942
Chef: Rick Stein
Owners: Mr & Mrs C R Stein
Cost: Alc £50, fixed-price L £28/D £34. H/wine £12.95
Times: Noon-last L 1.30pm/7-last D 10pm. Closed Sun, Xmas, 1st May

The weight of TV fame always rests heavily upon any restaurant. The pressure to perform is (in both senses) a mixed blessing, but it does ensure a full house, and chez Rick Stein, a splendidly buzzing atmosphere. The setting is metro-smart, in other words, stark white walls with wooden parquet floor, spotlights, and artwork hung around the room. Prices reflect the popularity in the foodie pilgrimage stakes, and other than some olives, there are no frills in the way of canapés or titbits, but then the appetite is not spoilt for dishes of real imagination and flair. The choice is difficult. Should it be crab, ginger and coriander broth, or perhaps hot shellfish with olive oil, garlic and lemon juice, then again, stir-fried mussels with black beans, coriander and spring onions? Main courses such as chargrilled sea bass with tomato, butter and vanilla vinaigrette, roast cod with saffron potatoes and tapenade, and fillets of lemon sole with ciabatta breadcrumbs and salsa verde mayonnaise are equally tempting. Beautifully simple dishes include fillet of turbot with hollandaise, and grilled Dover sole with sea salt and lime, cooked unskinned so that the skin is deliciously crisp. Lobsters, oysters and fruits de mer platters are devoured with gusto. There is usually one meat dish, perhaps an entrecote steak, but please note, this is a vegetarian-free zone. Desserts range from steamed ginger pudding to pannacotta with stewed rhubarb – inspirations are never less than eclectic. The wine list matches the *carte* for prices, and is heavily weighted towards New World selections.

Additional: No children under 6
Seats: 110
Smoking: No pipes and cigars in dining room
Accommodation: 27 en suite
Credit cards: ▓ ▒ ▓ ▒ ▐

Directions: Situated on South Quay

PENZANCE, Tarbert Hotel ✿

Former sea captain's house, now a personally run hotel. Dinner in the candle-lit restaurant emphasises regional produce on a regularly changing menu. Expect stuffed Cornish mackerel with citrus fruits, and loin of Cornish lamb with a honey and red wine sauce.

Additional: No children under 10; ✦ dishes
Smoking: No smoking in dining room
Accommodation: 12 en suite
Credit cards: ▓ ▒ ▐ ▓ ▐

11-12 Clarence Street TR18 2NU
Map 2: SW43
Tel: 01736 363758
Fax: 01736 331336
Chef: Philip Thomas
Owners: Patti & Julian Evans
Cost: *Alc* £19, fixed-price D £15. ☺ H/wine £8
Times: D only 7pm-last D 8.30pm. Closed 22 Dec-7 Jan

Directions: At top of Market Jew St continue into Alverton St. At traffic lights turn R into Clarence St

PENZANCE, Ward's Brasserie ✿✿

Simple furnishings, a bare wooden floor and a friendly atmosphere: what could be more appropriate for a brasserie. The quality of the cooking at Ward's, on one of the main thoroughfares leading to the seafront, raises it above the humdrum. An inspector was impressed by a lunchtime starter of mixed mini-dishes of tiny monkfish and salmon terrines wrapped in seaweed, chicken liver and pork pâté on a croûte, and goats' cheese and tomato salsa, also on a croûte. Perfectly cooked roasted cod accompanied by mash with tomato butter sauce followed, while creamy and light lemon posset concluded the meal. Dinner could see starters of Stilton and almond soufflé, or confit of quail, and main courses of saddle of local lamb with herb filling on redcurrant sauce, rabbit sautéed with cider and cream, and griddled mixed seafood surrounding red rice with an oriental dressing. Potted West Country cheese with apple and celery is an appropriate way to finish, or go for something chocolatey like Grand Marnier and chocolate mousse. A short list of wines fits the bill.

12-13 Chapel Street TR18 4AW
Map 2: SW53
Tel: 01736 363540
Chef/Owner: Alan Ward
Cost: *Alc* £11.50, fixed-price L £5 (2 courses). ☺ H/wine £6.50
Times: Noon-last L 2pm/7-last D 9.30pm. Closed 15 Jan-13 Feb, D Sun-Wed (Oct-Apr)
Additional: No children under 8; ✦ dishes
Seats: 45
Smoking: No-smoking area; No pipes and cigars
Credit cards: ▓ ▒ ▓ ▐

Directions: In town centre

POLPERRO, **The Kitchen** ✿✿

Park your car in the obligatory car park (tourism is a major industry at this well-preserved little fishing village) and walk down to the Batesons' charming restaurant. You will find much to please. Cornish crab soup requires no explanation, but Cornish hog pudding is a version of black pudding , served here with garlicky flageolet bean purée, or there are forays further afield with vegetable samosas served with home-made mango and ginger chutney. Main courses explore the global influences more thoroughly: Thai chicken, a Goan dish of chicken cafriel, or a Malaysian coconut and lime lamb, as well as offering the likes of salmon florentine and a good selection of vegetarian dishes. The wine list is very reasonably priced.

Directions: Between the harbour and the car park

The Coombes PL13 2RQ
Map 2: SX25
Tel: 01503 272780
Chefs/Owners: Ian & Vanessa Bateson
Cost: Alc £20. ☺ H/wine £9
Times: D only, 7-9.30pm. Closed Sun, Mon, Oct-Easter
Additional: No children under 12; ❹ dishes
Seats: 24
Smoking: No smoking in dining room
Credit cards: ▬ ▬

POLZEATH,
Cornish Cottage Hotel ✿✿

Spectacular cliff paths and the beach are but a short walk away from this engaging, small hotel. Further attractions are the welcoming staff, and the restaurant's serious approach to food, which becomes apparent from the sophisticated *carte* and set menus. A complimentary starter of monkfish in a light tempura batter with a chilli and parsley oil, began our test meal well. The chosen starter, salmon tartlet, featured chunks of well-flavoured fish and was surrounded by a butter and chive sauce. Baked rack of Cornish lamb, the main course, produced a well-trimmed cutlet cooked pink, with a powerfully flavoured mustard and herb crust, garlic and onion potato cake, and red wine jus. Dessert of assiette of chocolate was a chocoholic's dream. The trappings – enticing canapés, a choice of own-made bread, petits fours and a sound wine list – also confirm the Cornish Cottage's exacting standards.

Directions: From Wadebridge/Camelford pass the 'Bee Centre' and take the R fork. The hotel is 300 yds on R.

New Polzeath Nr Rock PL27 6UF
Map 2: SW97
Tel: 01208 862213
Fax: 01208 862259
Chef: Martin Walker
Owners: Mr & Mrs D Faulkner
Cost: Alc £35, fixed price D £29.50 (6 courses). H/wine £10.50
Times: D only, 7-9pm
Additional: Sunday L (noon-2pm); No children under 12; ❹ dishes
Seats: 36
Smoking: No smoking in dining room
Accommodation: 15 en suite
Credit cards: ▬ ▬ ▬ ▬ ▬

PORT GAVERNE,
Headlands Hotel ✿   NEW

Spectacular views over the north Cornish coastline are to be had from an unrivalled position overlooking the tiny port. Local produce, especially fish, influences the menu – look out for locally smoked fish, and Port Isaac crab and lobster. Otherwise there's cream of dill cucumber soup, and oriental pork with sesame sauce.

Port Isaac PL29 3SH
Map 2: SX08
Tel: 01208 880260
Fax: 01208 880885
Chef: Anna Harris
Owners: Chris & Anna Harris
Cost: Alc £22, fixed-price D £16.50. ☺ H/wine £8.50

Times: D only, 7pm-9.30pm. Closed Jan
Additional: Children welcome; ❹ dishes
Smoking: No smoking in dining room
Accommodation: 11 en suite
Credit cards: ▬ ▬ ▬ ▬ ▬ ▬ ▬ JCB

Directions: B3319 to Port Isaac. Hotel is 0.5 mile E of Port Isaac on unclassified road

PORT GAVERNE,
Port Gaverne Hotel

Port Isaac PL29 3SQ
Map 2: SX08
Tel: 01208 880244
Fax: 01208 880151
Chef: Ian Brodey
Owner: Midge Ross
Cost: *Alc* £19.95. ☺ H/wine £7.60
Times: Last L 2pm/last D 9pm.
Closed D Sat, early Jan-mid Feb
Additional: Bar food; Sunday L;
No children under 7; ◑ dishes
Smoking: No smoking in dining room
Accommodation: 17 en suite
Credit cards: ▆▆ ▆▆ ▆▆ ▆ ▆▆ ▆ JCB

Directions: Signposted from B3314 2
miles from Delabole

*Retaining much of its original character and charm, this 17th-
century coastal inn has been presided over by Mrs Ross for over 30
years. The friendly restaurant offers an uncomplicated menu with
the emphasis on fresh local produce. Look out for crab soup, rack
of lamb with rosemary and garlic, or Chateaubriand béarnaise.*

PORT ISAAC, The Castle Rock NEW

*Great views over the sea and cliffs are enjoyed from this hotel
restaurant. Menus are comprehensive, but fish and seafood are a
speciality. Home-made crab and shrimp bisque may be followed by
Pacific and jumbo tiger prawns cooked with Thai spices. The lemon-
lime brûlée is also recommended.*

Accommodation: 17 en suite
Credit cards: ▆▆ ▆▆ ▆▆ ▆▆ ▆

Directions: From A39 take B3314 then B3267 to top of Port
Isaac village

4 New Road PL29 3 SB
Map 2: SW98
Tel: 01208 880300
Fax: 01208 880219
Chef: Keith Vernon
Owners: June Hotchkiss, Derek Mann
Cost: *Alc* £25, fixed price D £16. ☺
H/wine £7.50
Times: Last L 2pm/last D 9.30pm
Additional: Bar food L; Sunday L;
No children under 5; ◑ dishes
Smoking: No smoking in dining room

PORTHLEVEN,
Critchards Seafood Restaurant

*In a lovely spot right on the harbour front, this is a converted old
mill with plenty of nautical character. Typical starters include fresh
Helford mussels in white wine, garlic and butter, creamy seafood
chowder, and deep-fried baby squid, served with a garlic dip. Fresh
local fish and other Cornish produce feature heavily on the carte.*

Smoking: No smoking in dining room
Accommodation: 2 en suite
Credit cards: ▆▆ ▆▆ ▆

Directions: Overlooking the harbour

The Harbour Head TR13 9JA
Map 2: SW62
Tel: 01326 562407
Fax: 01326 564444
Chef: Jo Critchard
Owners: Steve & Jo Critchard
Cost: *Alc* £25. ☺
Times: D only, last D 9.30pm.
Closed Sun
Additional: No children under 6 in
main restaurant; ◑ dishes

PORTREATH, Tabb's Restaurant ❀❀

An informal bistro-style atmosphere pervades this friendly
restaurant, housed in an old forge close to the harbour. Well-
spaced tables, local paintings and an original Cornish range

Railway Terrace TR16 4LD
Map 2: SW64
Tel: 01209 842488
Chef: Nigel Tabb
Owners: Nigel & Melanie Tabb

characterise the relaxing, stone-walled interior. Chef/proprietor, Nigel Tabb, uses quality local ingredients, in particular fresh fish, in preparing the varied and imaginative range of dishes listed on both the *carte* and fixed-price dinner menu. An enjoyable spring inspection meal commenced with a refreshing vegetable pâté with Indian spices and lentils, accompanied by good home-made bread. This was followed by a well-cooked chicken breast topped with garlic tapenade and served with a red pepper sauce, and imaginative vegetables – a mix of Mediterranean and Oriental in flavour. A deliciously light chocolate marquise with a not-too-zesty orange sauce rounded off the meal. Comprehensive wine list with an emphasis on regional French.

Directions: At the centre of the village, under the viaduct

Cost: *A/c* £20, fixed-price D £13.50.
☺ H/wine £8.50
Times: D only, 7-last D 9pm. Closed Tue, 2 wks Jan, Nov
Additional: Sunday L (noon-1.45pm); Children welcome; ✿ dishes
Seats: 35
Smoking: No pipes & cigars
Credit cards: ▬ ▬ ▬

PORTSCATHO, Roseland House Hotel ✿

NEW

Rosevine TR2 5EW
Map 2: SW83
Tel: 01872 580644
Please telephone for further details

A charming hotel that has a lot going for it: set on a cliff top overlooking the Roseland peninsula with its own private beach, comfortable lounges filled with antiques, and good food. The pretty dining room offers a set-price, five-course menu of traditional English cooking prepared by owner Carolyn Hindley.

Directions: Off A3078, hotel signed on R, 2 miles after Ruan High Lanes

---

PORTSCATHO, **Rosevine Hotel** ✿

Porthcurnick Beach TR2 5EW
Map 2: SW83
Tel: 01872 580206
Fax: 01872 580230
Chef/Owner: Ian Andrew Thomson Picken
Cost: Fixed-price D £22 (5 courses).
☺ H.wine £8
Times: D only, 7.15pm-last D 8.30pm. Closed Nov-March

Delightful views over the garden to the sea from this hotel restaurant. The menu roams the world for inspiration, taking in the likes of conchiglette in brodo (clear Italian soup with pasta), buckra passandra chawal basmati (lamb curry), and grilled Fowey sea trout.

Additional: Bar food L; Children welcome; ✿ dishes
Smoking: No pipes & cigars in dining room
Accommodation: 15 en suite
Credit cards: ▬ ▬ ▬ ▫

Directions: Off A3078, hotel signed on R, 2 miles after Ruan High Lanes

---

REDRUTH, **Penventon Hotel** ✿

TR15 1TE
Map 2: SW64
Tel: 01209 214141
Fax: 01209 219164
Chef: Calvin Trevend
Owners: Pascoe family
Cost: *A/c* £16, fixed-price L £10.50/D £15.10. ☺ H/wine £8.50.
Times: Last L 2pm/last D 9.30pm
Additional: Bar food L; Sunday L; Children welcome; ✿ dishes
Smoking: No smoking in dining room; Air conditioning
Accommodation: 50 en suite
Credit cards: ▬ ▬ ▬ ▫ ▬ ▬

A short walk from the town centre, this extended Georgian mansion has been run by the Pascoe family for many years. An extensive menu of international cooking takes in tournedos Rossini, boeuf 'bourguinon', as well as Newlyn grilled sole and Cornish crab. Dinner is often accompanied by a pianist playing in the background.

Penventon Hotel

Directions: On Redruth intersection of A30, 1 mile S of town centre

RUAN HIGH LANES,
The Hundred House Hotel ❀

TR2 5JR
Map 2: SW93
Tel: 01872 501336
Fax: 01872 501151
Chef: Kitty Eccles
Owners: Mike & Kitty Eccles
Cost: Fixed price D £23 (4 courses).
☺ H/wine £9
Times: D only, 7.30-8pm.
Closed Nov – Feb
Additional: No children under 8;
❸ dishes
Smoking: No smoking in dining room
Accommodation: 10 en suite
Credit cards: ▬ ▬ ▬

A tastefully furnished Edwardian building with a real country-house party atmosphere. The daily-changing menu offers a choice of starters and sweets, the main course being fixed, and results on the plate are both accomplished and imaginative. Begin with crab tart, then roast loin of pork, and round off with lemon crunch pie, and excellent local cheeses.

Directions: On A3078 4 miles after Tregony on R

ST AUSTELL,
Boscundle Manor Hotel ❀

Small 18th-century manor house peacefully set in secluded grounds and personally run by resident proprietors. A short daily changing menu is offered in the attractive dining room. Fresh produce is used in such traditional dishes as crab Mornay, duck with cherry and brandy sauce, and rhubarb fool. Extensive wine list.

Additional: Children welcome
Smoking: No smoking in dining room
Accommodation: 12 en suite
Credit cards: ▬ ▬ ▬ ▬ ▬ JCB

Tregrehan PL25 3RL
Map 2: SX05
Tel: 01726 813557
Fax: 01726 814997
Chef: Mary Flint
Owners: Andrew & Mary Flint
Cost: Fixed price D £25 (4 courses).
H/wine £9.50
Times: D only, last D 8.30pm
Closed Sun to non-residents

Directions: 2 miles E of St Austell, off A390 on road signposted Tregrehan

ST AUSTELL, Carlyon Bay Hotel

Hotel of long-standing set in a stunning location with extensive leisure activities and wide range of menu choices. There's a strong Thai influence in some of the dishes, seared scallops dressed with

Sea Road Carlyon Bay PL25 3RD
Map 2: SX05
Tel: 01726 812304
Fax: 01726 814938
Chef: Paul Leakey

Carlyon Bay Hotel

Owners: Brend Hotels
Cost: *Alc* £28, fixed-price L £12.50/D
£24 (4 courses). ☺ H/wine £8.50.
Times: Last L 2pm/D 9pm
Additional: Bar food L; Sunday L;
Children welcome; 🍃 dishes
Accommodation: 72 en suite
Credit cards: ▆▆ ▆▆ ⚡ ▢ ▆▆ ▆ ▣

*cumin, chervil and star anise for instance, and Thai crab soup. More
straightforward is roasted fillet of beef with mashed potato.*

Directions: A390 towards St Austell; from town follow
Charlestown then Carlyon Bay/Crinnis. Hotel at end of Sea
Road near Cornwall Coliseum

ST IVES, Chy-an-Dour Hotel ❀

*Turn-of-the-century family hotel, with excellent views across the
beach and harbour. The daily-changing dinner menu includes a
good selection of continental dishes. An early spring meal might
start with cream of parsnip and apple soup, followed by honey roast
tenderloin of pork, stuffed with apricots and served in a Madeira
sauce.*

Smoking: No smoking in dining room
Accommodation: 23 en suite
Credit cards: ▆▆ ▆▆ ⚡ ▢ ▆ JCB

Directions: Hotel on main road into St Ives, A3074

Trelyon Avenue TR26 2AD
Map 2: SW54
Tel: 01736 796436
Fax: 01736 795772
Chef: David Watson
Owners: Mr & Mrs Watson
Cost: Fixed-price D £17.50
(4 courses). ☺ H/wine £6.25
Times: D only, last D 8.30pm
Additional: Bar food L; 🍃 dishes

ST IVES, Garrack Hotel ❀

Higher Ayr TR26 3AA
Map 2: SW54
Tel: 01736 796199
Fax: 01736 798955
Chef: Ben Reeve
Owners: Frances, Michael &
Stephen Kilby
Cost: *Alc* £24.10, fixed-price D
£19.50 (4 courses). ☺ H/wine £8.05.
Times: D only, 7pm-last D 8.30pm
Additional: No children under 4;
🍃 dishes
Smoking: No smoking in dining room
Accommodation: 19 en suite
Credit cards: ▆▆ ▆▆ ⚡ ▢ ▆▆ ▆ ▣

*The hotel stands in extensive grounds and offers superb views over
Porthmeor beach. The kitchen makes excellent use of home-grown
produce and locally caught seafood, especially lobsters – done every
which way. Otherwise, mussels in white wine and basil-pesto cream
sauce, and Chateaubriand with Madeira jus show the style.*

Directions: Follow signs for 'Porthmeor Beach and Car Parks'

ST IVES,
Mermaid Seafood Restaurant

A fabulous collection of local photos, wine bottles suspended from the ceiling and church-pew seating make for an atmospheric setting in one of St Ives' oldest buildings. International seafood dishes are listed on a daily changing chalk board menu. These might include coquilles St Jacques, Dover sole and local lobster.

21 Fish Street TR26 1LT
Map 2: SW54
Tel: 01736 796816
Fax: 01736 799099
Chef: Helen Scott-Smith
Owners: Trevor & Helen Scott-Smith
Cost: *Alc* £20. ☺ H/wine £7.95
Times: D only, last D 10pm. Closed Sun, 2 wks Feb
Additional: No children under 7; ☻ dishes
Smoking: No-smoking area; No pipes & cigars; Air conditioning
Credit cards: ▨ ▨ ▨ ☐ ▣

Directions: Along Harbour Street towards the Sloop Inn, turn L. Restaurant is at top of street on R.

ST IVES, **Pig 'n' Fish** ❀❀

The restaurant is in a quiet part of St Ives, overlooking the rooftops and the bay. Formally a net loft – it still has the thick Cornish-stone walls, wooden floors and high beams for hanging nets – the ground floor was used for salting pilchards that were wheeled up in barrows from the harbour to the old 'Pudding Bag Lane'. Paul Sellars is a professional, he takes no short-cuts, the cooking is simple but deceptively accomplished. Fish is a speciality with often just one meat dish on the short *carte*. The latter reads well with delicious combinations such as a light crab soup with chilli, lemongrass and coriander, warm mussel salad with new potatoes and parsley pesto, or grilled fillet of bass with a confit of fennel and bourride sauce. Other recommendations have included roast cod with cannellini beans, capers and a warm mayonnaise, and citrus tart with a lightly whipped cream. Service is friendly and relaxed, with Debby Sellars looking after front of house.

Norway Lane TR26 1LZ
Map 2: SW54
Tel: 01736 794204
Chef: Paul Sellars
Owners: Debby & Paul Sellars
Cost: *Alc* £25, fixed-price D £21.50. ☺ H/wine £10
Times: 12.30-last L 1.30pm/7-last D 9pm (Telephone for Nov-Feb times). Closed Sun, Mon, Xmas
Additional: No children under 2
Seats: 25
Smoking: No smoking in dining room
Credit cards: ▨ ▨ ☐

Directions: 300 yards from St Ives Tate Gallery

ST IVES, **Skidden House**

Skidden Hill TR26 2DU
Map 2: SW54
Tel: 01736 796899
Fax: 01736 798619
Chef: CD Stoakes
Owners: M Hook, CD Stoakes
Times: D only, 7-8.30pm
Additional: Bar food L; ☻ dishes
Smoking: No smoking in dining room
Accommodation: 7 en suite
Credit cards: ▨ ▨ ▨ ☐ ▨ ▣ ▣ JCB

Town centre location for Skidden House, which dates back many centuries and is reputed to be the oldest hotel in St Ives. The intimate dining room offers fixed-price menus and a carte built around fresh local produce, with dishes prepared in a classic French-style.

Directions: A30 to St Erth roundabout, then A3074 to St Ives; follow to railway/coach station, then first R. Hotel is 30 metres on R

ST KEYNE,
Old Rectory House Hotel ❀❀

Liskeard PL14 4RL
Map 2: SX26
Tel: 01579 342617
Fax: 01579 342293
Chef: Glen Gatland
Owners: John & Pat Minifie
Cost: Fixed-price D £21.50. ☺
H/wine £9.50
Times: D only, 7-last D 8.45pm.
Closed D Sun
Additional: Sunday L; No children under 12; ❹ dishes
Seats: 28. Private room 24
Smoking: No smoking in dining room
Accommodation: 7 en suite
Credit cards: ▬ ▬

Smashing little place with acres of garden and seclusion, that's going from strength to strength. Consistent cooking with the kitchen committed to local produce and a simple approach that allows natural flavour to shine through. Bright, vibrant soups such as cream of carrot and cardamom, or celery and Stilton, and great home-made bread have all been endorsed. Also enjoyed have been roast rack of lamb with pea purée in a flaky pastry case, and caramelised tangy lemon tart. Other choices from the short, good value dinner menu could be tenderloin of pork wrapped in filo pastry with peppered Cornish Yarg, or pan-fried local skate with beurre noir and fresh herbs.

Directions: 3 miles from Liskeard on B3254

ST MARTIN'S,
St Martin's on the Isle ❀❀❀

TR25 0QW
Map 2: SW28
Tel: 01720 422092
Fax: 01720 422298
Please telephone for further details

Carved out of a cluster of cottages tucked into the shelter of the hillside, this island hotel, with its sense of timelessness, is the quintessential retreat. There is an unrivalled panorama of the sea and surrounding islands, and the place offers its own beach, jetty and yacht – it can only be reached by a 20 minute boat ride. The dining room has a sun/sea decor, 'guests move towards poll position (window views) as they near the end of their stay; tough on us one nighters'. The cooking has many fine qualities of accuracy and discretion – the heart is classic French cuisine, the pulse modern. Fish is naturally the mainstay of the menu. The amuse-bouche, perhaps smoked salmon on sweet little blinis, start a meal well. To follow, perhaps quail with its leg boned and stuffed with a duxelle and set beside a garlic bulb in tempura and accompanied by a

St Martin's on the Isle

smooth, reduced jus with truffle slices. Next, an oven-roasted fillet of sea bass with a beetroot mousse and a good parcel of asparagus and beurre blanc coloured by scallop corals. To finish, have fun with French toast – two rounds of light, fluffy, eggy bread flavoured with Calvados, with similar rings of apple and a lovely, distinct apple sorbet and a little crème anglaise. The wine list continues to offer reasonable prices with breadth rather than depth being the most distinguishing feature.

Directions: 28 miles from Penzance via helicopter, steamship or aircraft, then 20-minute launch boat ride
Isles of Scilly

ST MARYS, **Star Castle Hotel** ✵

A late 16th-century castle, now a smart hotel, in a commanding position offering magnificent views over the island and the sea. There's ambition in the kitchen, which offers a menu built around fresh produce, notably fish.

Directions: Flights available from Lands End, Plymouth, Exeter, Bristol & Southampton. Helicopter or ferry from Penzance. Hotel taxi meets all guests from airport or quay

The Garrison TR21 0JA
Map 2: SW28
Tel: 01720 422317
Please telephone for further details

ST MAWES, **Idle Rocks Hotel** ✵✵

Harbour Side TR2 5AN
Map 2: SW83
Tel: 01326 270771
Fax: 01326 270062
Chef: Alan Vickops
Owners: Mr & Mrs E K Richardson
Cost: Fixed-price D £23.75. ☺
H/wine £9.75
Times: Noon-last L 3pm/7-last D 9.15pm
Additional: Bar food L; Children welcome
Seats: 60
Smoking: No smoking in dining room
Accommodation: 24 en suite
Credit cards: 📷 📷 📷 📷 📷 📷

Built right on the quayside, this smart, well-run hotel couldn't have a more typically Cornish setting looking over the small harbour and the open sea. The waterside terrace is popular at lunchtimes for bar food: expect baguettes, toasted sandwiches, perhaps cod, salmon and parsley fishcakes, and Malaysian chicken with mushrooms; a minnows' menu for small fry is also available. Enjoy the setting in the evening with dinner at the appropriately named Water's Edge restaurant. The kitchen takes full advantage of local produce, from early-season fruit and vegetables to meat and fish. Seared scallops stuffed with basil and sun-dried tomatoes in a tartlet, or crab and Parmesan gâteau might crop up among the starters, and fillet of West Country beef with a Stilton and herb crust, or vanilla-marinated monkfish on noodles flecked with smoked river trout among the main courses. A savoury like deep-fried goats' cheese or farmhouse cheeses could make a change from desserts such as bread-and-butter pudding. Seven house wines include a pudding wine, with the full list running to 50-odd bottles.

Idle Rocks Hotel

Directions: Take the A3078 to St Mawes. Hotel is on L as you enter the village, at water's edge

ST MAWES,
Rising Sun Hotel ❀

Situated by the harbour at St Mawes, not surprisingly seafood is the speciality of the hotel's brasserie. Examples are mussels steamed with rosé wine and garlic, lobster Thermidor, and grilled bass and salmon served on a lemon-flavoured spaghetti with beurre blanc sauce.

Additional: Bar food; Sunday L; Children welcome; ❹ dishes
Smoking: No smoking in dining room
Accommodation: 6 en suite
Credit cards: ▰ ▱ ▰ ▱ ▰

Directions: On harbour front

Truro TR2 5DJ
Map 2: SW83
Tel: 01326 270233
Fax: 01326 270198
Chef: Paul Naylor
Owner: R J Milan
Cost: *Alc* £19.50, fixed-price D £19.50. ☺ H/wine £9.50
Times: Last L 2pm/last D 9.45pm

ST MELLION,
St Mellion Hotel ❀❀

Straightforward cooking at this purpose-built, time-share, golfing and leisure complex will suit most tastes. Curried chicken with mango, orange and lime salsa on chickpea risotto is one of the more adventurous starters, along with salmon and mixed pepper hash in a dry sherry and olive oil sauce, but main courses are mostly along the lines of tenderloin of pork with caramelised onions and red cabbage, grilled Dover sole, grilled sirloin steak garni. The occasional venture into other realms surfaces as a breast of chicken with bok choi, smoked bacon, egg noodles and soy and olive oil sauce. The crèche has its own kitchen facilities.

Additional: Sunday L (12.30-2pm); Children welcome; ❹ dishes
Seats: 70. Private dining room 10-90
Smoking: No smoking in dining room; Air conditioning
Accommodation: 57 en suite
Credit cards: ▰ ▱ ▰ ▱ ▰ ▰ ▰ JCB

Directions: On the A388 about 4 miles N of Saltash

Saltash PL12 6SD
Map 2: SX36
Tel: 01579 351351
Fax: 01579 350537
Chef: Ian Crook
Owner: American Golf (UK) Ltd
Cost: *Alc* £26. ☺ H/wine £10.40
Times: D only, 7-last D 9.30pm

ST WENN, **Wenn Manor** ❀

Former vicarage complete with deep well in the bar, a crystal grotto in the garden and a resident ghost. Strong local following, attracted by the robust cooking of generously portioned dishes such as prawn and red pepper pâté, roast duck with black cherry sauce, and whole Dover sole with parsley and butter.

Smoking: No-smoking area; No pipes and cigars;
Air conditioning
Accommodation: 4 en suite
Credit cards: ▆ ▆ ▆ ▆ ▆ JCB

Directions: Halfway between A30/A39, next to church in village

Bodmin PL30 5PS
Map 2: SW96
Tel: 01726 890240
Fax: 01726 890680
Chef: Jo Stretton-Downes
Owners: Paul & Jo Stretton-Downes
Cost: Alc £21.50. ☺ H/wine £9.50
Times: Last L 1.45pm/last D 9.15pm.
Closed Sun
Additional: Bar food L;
No children under 12; ❀ dishes

TALLAND BAY,
Allhays Country House ❀

Mrs Spring loves to cook and her Aga is the centre of the kitchen. Local or home-grown produce make up a simple menu that offers a set starter and a choice of main course and dessert. We tried a platter of assorted smoked fish, lamb cutlets on a bed of leeks with port, redcurrant and caper sauce, and apple pie with clotted cream.

Accommodation: 7 rooms
Credit cards: ▆ ▆ ▆ ▆ ▆ ▆ ▆ JCB

Directions: From Looe A387 (Polperro), after 2.5 miles L at hotel sign. 1st large house on R

Nr Looe PL13 2JB
Map 2: SX25
Tel: 01503 272434
Fax: 01503 272929
Chef: Lynda Spring
Owners: Brian & Lynda Spring
Cost: Fixed-price D £16.50. ☺
H/wine £9
Times: D only at 7pm
Additional: Bar food L; No children under 10; ❀ dishes
Smoking: No smoking in dining room

TALLAND BAY, **Talland Bay Hotel** ❀

Dating from the 16th century, this stone-built manor house has a tropical influence, with lovely views over the gardens to the sea beyond. Seafood figures strongly, with dishes such as crab cakes with lime and pineapple salsa, and grillade of seafood with roasted red pepper and saffron butter sauce.

Smoking: No smoking in dining room
Accommodation: 19 en suite
Credit cards: ▆ ▆ ▆ ▆ ▆ ▆ ▆

Directions: Follow A387 Polperro road from Looe, hotel signed from crossroads

Near Looe PL13 2JB
Map 2: SX25
Tel: 01503 272667
Fax: 01503 272940
Chef: Paul Kingswood
Owners: Barry & Annie Rosier
Cost: Alc £31, fixed price D £21. ☺
H/wine £8.75
Times: Last L 2pm/last D 9pm.
Closed Jan
Additional: Bar food L; Children welcome; ❀ dishes

TINTAGEL, **Trebrea Lodge** ❀

A haven of peace and tranquillity, parts of this imposing Cornish manor house date back over 600 years. Dinner in the candlelit, oak-panelled dining room is served at 8pm. A typical set menu might comprise curried parsnip soup, mustard and paprika baked chicken breast, and vanilla meringues and toffee sauce, with Cornish Yarg and farmhouse Cheddar to finish.

Accommodation: 7 en suite
Credit cards: ▆ ▆ ▆ ▆ ▆

Directions: From Camelford (A39) follow signs to Tintagel. 1 mile before village turn R for Trenale

Trenale PL34 0HR
Map 2: SX08
Tel: 01840 770410
Fax: 01840 770092
Chef: Sean Devlin
Owners: John Charlick, Sean Devlin
Cost: Fixed-price D £21 (4 courses).
☺ H/wine £9.50
Times: D only, last D 8pm. Winter closing
Additional: No children under 12;
❀ dishes
Smoking: No smoking in dining room

TRESCO, **The Island Hotel**

Local fish and shellfish are staples on the daily changing menu, especially the local Tresco lobster served cold with fresh Bryher crab, or poached in white wine and saffron, and main courses such as chargrilled tail of monkfish served with ratatouille and fresh chive oil. Island eating, at this splendid hotel set amidst lushly rich gardens, also includes pan-fried escalope of Dorset veal glazed with smoked cheese, served with Parma ham and honey and whole grain mustard sauce. Desserts are a little dated sounding – brandy snap basket filled with strawberry ice cream, for example – but the selection of seasonal West country cheeses is outstanding.

Accommodation: 48 en suite
Credit cards: ▅ ▆ ▇ ▉ ▆ ▆ JCB

Directions: Situated on north-eastern tip of island

Isles of Scilly TR24 0PU
Map 2: SW17
Tel: 01720 422883
Fax: 01720 423008
Chef: Peter Hingston
Owner: Robert Dorrien-Smith
Cost: Alc £40, fixed-price D £32.50 (5 courses). ☺ H/wine £10.50
Times: Noon-last L 2.15pm/6.45-last D 9.30pm. Closed Nov-Mar
Additional: Bar food L; Sunday L; Children welcome; ❹ dishes
Seats: 110. Private dining room 12
Smoking: No pipes & cigars

TRESCO, **New Inn** ✿

Quality local ingredients, notably the freshest of fish, highlight the well-balanced set menu at this most welcoming hostelry, which forms the hub of social life on this delightful island. Expect leek and sweet potato soup, baked herb-crusted cod with fish juices, or pork fillet with apple rösti, cider and Calvados sauce.

Smoking: No smoking in dining room
Accommodation: 15 en suite.
Credit cards: ▅ ▆

Directions: 250 yds from the harbour (private island, contact hotel for details)

Isles of Scilly TR24 0QQ
Map 2: SW17
Tel: 01720 422844
Fax: 01720 423200
Chef: Graham Shone
Owners: Tresco Estate
Cost: Fixed price D £20. ☺ H/wine £7.50
Times: D 6.45-9pm
Additional: Bar food; Sun L; Children welcome; ❹ dishes

TREYARNON BAY,
Waterbeach Hotel ✿

The Etherington's run the sort of welcoming hotel that sees guests return year after year. Local produce dictates the six-course Aga sagas – splendid dinners of country-style cooking. Note smooth salmon pâté surrounded by smoked salmon, real minestrone soup (proper stock base), roast loin of pork, gravy, apple sauce, and moist sage and onion stuffing, and chocolate and orange mousse gâteau. There's a cheeseboard if you can manage it.

Smoking: No smoking in dining room
Accommodation: 21 rooms
Credit cards: ▅ ▆ ▇ ▉ ▆ ▆

Directions: 4 miles from Padstow on coastal road to Newquay

PL28 8JW
Map 2: SW87
Tel: 01841 520292
Fax: 01841 521102
Chef: Mrs V Etherington
Owners: Mr & Mrs A Etherington
Cost: Fixed-price D £15 (6 courses). ☺ H/wine £7.50
Times: D only, 7.30pm-8.15pm
Additional: Children welcome: ❹ dishes

TRURO, **Alverton Manor** ✿✿

You can get married in the striking converted chapel of this former convent, standing in six acres of picturesque grounds, yet within easy walking distance of the city centre. The peachy-pink dining-room has an intimate air, tables are both well spaced and sized. Some dishes tend to be a touch over-garnished, but local ingredients are generally used to good

Tregolls Road TR1 1XQ
Map 2: SW84
Tel: 01872 276633
Fax: 01872 222989
Chefs: Nick Cassidy, Robert Brandreth
Owner: Mr M Sagin
Cost: Alc £25, fixed-price L £16.25/D £19.50 (4 courses). ☺ H/wine £9.50

Alverton Manor

Times: Noon-last L 1.45pm/7-last D
9.30pm. Closed 26 Dec-4 Jan
Additional: Bar Food; Sunday L;
Children welcome; ✪ dishes
Seats: 45. Private dining rooms for 25,
90, 120
Smoking: No smoking in dining room
Accommodation: 34 en suite
Credit cards: ▆▆ ▆▆ ▆▆ ▆ ▆▆ ▆ ▆ JCB

effect. Seafood and shellfish steamed with white wine, saffron and herbs made a fresh, crisp starter, and the kitchen clearly was going all out to dispel any lingering memories of nouvelle cuisine with a king-size portion of chargrilled cushion of veal with prune and Armagnac sauce. When available, there's whole fresh local lobster with sweet herb lobster oil and cream sauce. A trio of chocolate dessert (which arrived straight out of the freezer) was, when eventually defrosted, delicious.

Directions: from the Truro by-pass, take A39 to St Austell. Just past the church on L.

TRURO, Oliver's Restaurant ✿✿

Although located below a 'civilised' pub near the Law Courts, Oliver's is run quite separately. Brightly decorated with yellow walls, blue plates and linen (and patterned red carpet), the menu changes daily, depending on what produce is available. Typical dishes might include chargrilled medallions of calves' liver stacked on a 'bed' of sweet potato and onion with red cabbage and a light cider jus, and breast of duck with a wild berry and rosemary reduction. Fish features strongly on the menu – 'cassoulette' of fish and shellfish was robust and chunky with a smooth, winey liquor. Desserts, such as an iced duo of chocolate parfaits with dew drops of orange sauce, allow the kitchen full rein to its artistic instincts.

Directions: Below Law Courts in the city centre

Castle Street TR1 3DP
Map 2: SW84
Tel/Fax: 01872 273028
Chef: Colin Hankins
Owners: David & Serena London
Cost: *Alc* £20.50, fixed-price L £16
(2 courses)/D £19. ☺ H/wine £8.50
Times: Noon-last L 2.30pm/7-last D
10pm. Closed D Sun
Additional: Bar food; Sunday L;
Children welcome; ✪ dishes
Seats: 30
Smoking: No pipes and cigars
Credit cards: ▆▆ ▆▆ ▆▆ ▆ ▆

VERYAN, The Nare Hotel ✿

Overlooking Gerrans Bay, the Nare Hotel is a long, attractive building set in five acres of lawns and gardens on the cliff edge. An early summer meal in the restaurant might include a starter of cream of asparagus soup, followed by pan-fried fillet of John Dory with sherry dressing. Fresh local seafood is a speciality.

Additional: Bar food L; Sunday L; Children welcome; ✪ dishes
Smoking: No smoking in dining room
Accommodation: 38 en suite
Credit cards: ▆▆ ▆▆

Directions: Through village passing New Inn on L, continue 1 mile to sea

Carne Beach TR2 5PF
Map 2: SW93
Tel: 01872 501279
Fax: 01872 501856
Chef: Malcolm Sparks
Owner: Mrs T N Gray
Cost: *Alc* £32, fixed price L £13/D
£29 (5 courses). H/wine £11
Times: Last L 2pm/last D 9.30pm.
Closed 3 Jan-1 Feb

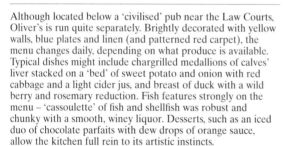

CUMBRIA

ALSTON, Lovelady Shield

CA9 3LF
Map 12: NY74
Tel: 01434 381203
Fax: 01434 381515
Chef: Barrie Garton
Owners: Peter & Marie Haynes
Cost: Fixed-price D £28 (5 courses). H/wine £9.75
Times: Noon-last L 2pm/7-last D 8.30pm. Closed Jan
Additional: Bar food L; Sunday L by arrangement; No children under 7
Seats: 30
Smoking: No smoking in dining room
Accommodation: 12 en suite
Credit cards: ▀▀ ▀▀ ▀▀ ▚ ▀▀ ▐ JCB

The hotel is set high in the remote north Pennines in stunning scenery. Within, it is all well and truly decorated, the restaurant full of swags and tails. The kitchen shows ambition, and tries hard to get things right. Reports have praised dishes such as a vibrant, well-conceived tian of black pudding with an apple and vine tomato confit, and a very clean flavoured roast loin of lamb with redcurrants. Desserts are a highlight, especially the hot fig pudding with butterscotch sauce served with crème fraîche in a chocolate tuile that so bowled our inspector over. Staff are knowledgeable, and ready to give help with menu suggestions and wine recommendations.

Directions: Off the A689, 2.5 miles from East Alston; signposted at top of drive

AMBLESIDE, Borrans Park Hotel

Once a Georgian farmhouse, Borrans Park is now a friendly family-run hotel. An autumn meal in the intimate candlelit dining room started with carrot and coriander soup, and was followed by grilled chicken breast with a mustard sauce. Desserts are theatrically presented at the table, and include traditional favourites such as steamed spotted Dick.

Borrans Road LA22 0EN
Map 7: NY30
Tel: 015394 33454
Fax: 015394 33003
Chef: Kate Lewis
Owner: Andrew Whitehead
Cost: Fixed-price D £18.50 (4 courses). ☺ H/wine £9.95
Times: D only, at 7pm. Closed Xmas week

Additional: No children under 7; ❹ dishes
Smoking: No smoking in dining room
Accommodation: 12 en suite
Credit cards: ▀▀ ▀▀ ▀▀ ▚ ▐ JCB

Directions: Turn L off A591 at Waterhead traffic lights to Ambleside, hotel 0.5 miles, opposite rugby field

AMBLESIDE,
Fisherbeck Hotel

Relaxing, friendly hotel handy for the attractions of Ambleside and south Lakeland. In the kitchen an ambitious chef works well with fresh local produce. Rack of lamb with a herb crust comes with a

Lake Road LA22 0DH
Map 7: NY30
Tel: 015394 33215
Fax: 015394 33600
Chef: Michael J Wilson

robust, rustic garlic and rosemary pan gravy. Desserts are something of a speciality – try the white and dark chocolate roulade with cherry compote.

Additional: Bar food; No children under 5; 🌡 dishes
Smoking: No smoking in dining room
Accommodation: 18 en suite
Credit cards: 🔲 🔲 🔲 🔲

Directions: Telephone for directions

Owners: B Barton, R Lane, G Lane
Cost: Fixed-price D £17.95 (5 courses). ☺ H/wine £7.95
Times: Last L 2pm/last D 8.30pm.
Closed Jan

AMBLESIDE,

The Glass House 🏵🏵

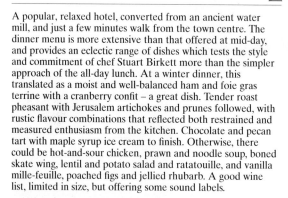

A popular, relaxed hotel, converted from an ancient water mill, and just a few minutes walk from the town centre. The dinner menu is more extensive than that offered at mid-day, and provides an eclectic range of dishes which tests the style and commitment of chef Stuart Birkett more than the simpler approach of the all-day lunch. At a winter dinner, this translated as a moist and well-balanced ham and foie gras terrine with a cranberry confit – a great dish. Tender roast pheasant with Jerusalem artichokes and prunes followed, with rustic flavour combinations that reflected both restrained and measured enthusiasm from the kitchen. Chocolate and pecan tart with maple syrup ice cream to finish. Otherwise, there could be hot-and-sour chicken, prawn and noodle soup, boned skate wing, lentil and potato salad and ratatouille, and vanilla mille-feuille, poached figs and jellied rhubarb. A good wine list, limited in size, but offering some sound labels.

Rydal Road LA22 9AN
Map 7: NY30
Tel: 015394 32137
Fax: 015394 31139
Chef: Stuart Birkett
Owner: Adrian Sankey
Cost: Alc £22. ☺ H/wine £11.95
Times: Noon-5pm, 6.30-10pm.
Closed Xmas
Additional: Sunday L;
Children welcome; 🌡 dishes
Seats: 80
Smoking: No smoking in dining room
Credit cards: 🔲 🔲 🔲 🔲

Directions: Telephone for directions

AMBLESIDE, **Nanny Brow**
Country House 🏵🏵

Don't arrive at this curiously named hotel-restaurant expecting nursery food; the kitchen concentrates on elegant French-style cuisine and service is attentive and precise. Classical music and superb views over the Langdale valley provide a soothing atmosphere in which to survey the various menus while enjoying canapés such as smoked salmon and tapenade en croûte, Parmesan and poppy seed tuiles, and filo parcel of wild mushroom quiche. The chef is at his best concentrating on simple flavour combinations – a refined terrine of rabbit and leeks was slightly overpowered by the accompanying onion salsa and piccalilli. Better was the main course of salmon pavé in pastry lattice served with a light white wine and shallot sauce, fresh okra and duchesse potatoes. Such classicism was cast aside when it came to dessert. Although the intriguing deep-fried chocolate ravioli with sweet pasta and crème anglaise sounded like a trendy affection, the plate was a brilliant combination of chocolate, mascarpone and posh custard.

Clappersgate LA22 9NF
Map 7: NY30
Tel: 015394 32036
Fax: 015394 32450
Chef: Mark Joyce
Owners: Michael & Carol Fletcher
Cost: Fixed-price D £27.50 (5 courses). ☺ H/wine £11.99.
Times: D only, 7.30-last D 8.45pm
Additional: No children under 12 at D; 🌡 dishes
Seats: 32. Private dining room 12.
Jacket and tie preferred
Smoking: No smoking in dining room
Accommodation: 18 en suite
Credit cards:
🔲 🔲 🔲 🔲 🔲 🔲 🔲 JCB

Directions: One mile from Ambleside on the A593 to Coniston

AMBLESIDE, **Rothay Manor**

Long-established Regency-style hotel set in landscaped gardens within walking distance of the town centre. The short, carefully chosen menu might offer fresh asparagus wrapped in Cumberland ham, served with a yogurt and dill dressing, and rack of lamb with green peppercorn sauce and mint jelly.

Additional: Sunday L; No children under 6 at D; 🍴 menu
Smoking: No smoking in dining room; Air conditioning
Accommodation: 18 en suite
Credit cards: 💳 💳 💳 💳 💳 💳

Directions: Quarter of a mile out of Ambleside on the Coniston road

Rothay Bridge LA22 0EH
Map 7: NY30
Tel: 015394 33605
Fax: 015394 33607
Chefs: Jane Binns, Colette Nixon
Owners: Nigel & Stephen Nixon
Cost: Fixed-price L £13.50/D £28. ☺
H/wine £12.50
Times: Last L 2pm (Sun till 1.30)/last D 9pm. Closed 3 Jan-5 Feb

AMBLESIDE, **Wateredge Hotel**

Family-run hotel on the shores of Lake Windermere. Seasonal produce inspires the set menu, with simple honest dishes such as goats' cheese soufflé with a sun-dried tomato dressing, tomato and courgette soup, grilled lemon sole with lemon butter and asparagus, and chocolate terrine, setting the pace. Excellent staff.

Directions: From A591 N to Ambleside, fork L at traffic lights after Ambleside sign. Skirt lake for few hundred yards, hotel is on L

Borrans Road Waterhead
LA22 0EP
Map 7: NY30
Tel: 015394 32332
Fax: 015394 31878
Chef: Mark Cowap
Owners: Mr & Mrs D Cowap
Cost: Fixed-price D £26.90
(5 courses). H/wine £12.50
Times: D only, last D 8.30pm.
Closed mid Dec-mid Jan
Additional: Bar food L;
No children under 7; 🍴 dishes
Smoking: No smoking in dining room
Accommodation: 22 en suite
Credit cards: 💳 💳 💳 💳 💳 💳 JCB

APPLEBY-IN-WESTMORLAND,
Appleby Manor ⊛   NEW

Stately Victorian mansion situated high above the town and enjoying delightful views of the castle and valley. The kitchen is daring by design. Interesting dishes include chicken and peanut brochettes, roast lamb shank with coriander, and sumptuous white and bitter chocolate mousse. Friendly staff and an extensive wine list.

Additional: Bar food; Sunday L; Children welcome; 🍴 dishes
Smoking: No smoking in dining room
Accommodation: 30 en suite
Credit cards: 💳 💳 💳 💳 💳 💳 💳 JCB

Directions: From N: M6/J40, then A66 (Brough), take Appleby turning. Turn R continue for 0.5 mile. From S: M6/J38 then B6260 (Appleby), through town to T junction, L then 1st R and follow road for 0.75 mile.

Roman Road CA16 6JB
Map 12: NY62
Tel: 017683 51571
Fax: 017683 52888
Chef: David Farrar
Owners: Nick & Rachel Swinscoe
Cost: Alc £21. ☺ H/wine £9.95
Times: Last L 2pm/last D 9pm

APPLEBY-IN-WESTMORLAND,
Royal Oak Inn

Bongate CA16 6UN
Map 12: NY62
Tel: 017683 51463
Fax: 017683 52300
Chef: J Stuart Good
Owners: CF & HK Cheyne
Cost: *Alc* £16. ☺ H/wine £8
Times: Last L 2pm/last D 9pm.
Closed 25 Dec
Additional: Bar food; Sunday L;
Children welcome; ⚅ dishes
Smoking: No-smoking area; no pipes
or cigars
Accommodation: 9 en suite
Credit cards:
▨ ▨ ▧ ▨ ▨ ▨ ▨ JCB

Busy traditional inn with a fine local reputation. The menu offers a diverse selection of traditional and contemporary dishes complemented by blackboard specials. Potted brown shrimps, Bongate lamb pudding with sweet leeks, and herrings baked with onions and sour cream are typical dishes. Look out for the rich Belgian chocolate tart.

Directions: On A66 13 miles from M6 junction 40 (Penrith) and 38 miles from Scotch Corner. Appleby rail station on Leeds-Settle-Carlisle line

APPLEBY-IN-WESTMORLAND,
Tufton Arms Hotel ✾

Market Square CA16 6XA
Map 12: NY62
Tel: 017683 51593
Fax: 017683 52761
Chef: David Milsom
Owners: Mr & Mrs W D Milsom &
Sons
Cost: *Alc* £15, fixed-price D £21.50.
☺ H/wine £9.50
Times: Last L 1.45pm/last D 9.15pm
Additional: Bar food; Sunday L;
Children welcome; ⚅ dishes
Accommodation: 21 en suite
Credit cards:
▨ ▨ ▧ ▨ ▨ ▨ ▨ JCB

Stylish hotel in the centre of picturesque Appleby. Meals are served in the elegant conservatory restaurant, which overlooks the cobbled courtyard. Our inspector enjoyed a summer dinner of sautéed chicken livers flamed in whisky, followed by chargrilled tuna steak, marinated in olive oil and served with noodles and soy sauce.

Directions: In centre of Appleby on B6260, 12 miles from M6/J38

BASSENTHWAITE,
Armathwaite Hall ✾✾

Stately 17th-century mansion surrounded by woodland and close to Bassenthwaite Lake. Indeed, there are spectacular views of the lake and Skiddaw mountain from the oak-panelled dining room. This year inspectors have reported positively on cooking that is fresh, vibrant and honest with clean flavours blending well together. At our most recent inspection carpaccio

Keswick CA12 4RE
Map 11: NY23
Tel: 017687 76551
Fax: 017687 76220
Chef: Kevin Dowling
Cost: *Alc* £40, fixed price D £32.95
(6 courses). H/wine £11.95
Times: Last L 1.45pm/last D 9.30pm

of duck breast came with a light spiced chutney, steamed fillet of halibut was accompanied by home-made Thai noodles and mussels in a delicate, clear fish consommé, and a teardrop of bitter chocolate filled with an iced praline parfait with a black cherry coulis was as good as it gets. Good bread and petits fours show the kitchen is firmly on the ball. The wine list offers a little of everything and staff are keen to help.

Directions: From M6/J40 take A66 to Keswick then A591 towards Carlisle. Turn L by Castle Inn, 8m to hotel.

Additional: Bar food L; Sunday L; Children welcome; dishes
Smoking: No smoking in dining room
Accommodation: 43 en suite
Credit cards:

BASSENTHWAITE, Castle Inn Hotel

Modern-styled hotel with indoor and outdoor leisure facilities, popular with both conferences and tourists. Two stylish restaurants, but the Thomas de Quincy offers the more exciting, innovative cooking. Delicate flavours and well-made sauces are noteworthy, but room should be left for the dessert platter containing a sample of all the desserts available.

Directions: On the A591 6 miles north of Keswick

Keswick CA12 4RG
Map 11: NY23
Tel: 017687 76401
Fax: 017687 76604
Please telephone for further details

BASSENTHWAITE, Overwater Hall Hotel

Stately Victorian dining room – tapestry hangings, sweeping drapes, crisp napery, candles – with the dessert display as a centrepiece. Chicken terrine, brill with smoked salmon mousse on yellow pepper sauce, and braised lamb on boulangère potatoes with tomato and basil jus, give a flavour of the five-course menu.

Accommodation: 12 en suite. **Credit cards:**

Directions: Take A591 from Keswick to Carlisle, after 6 miles, turn R at the Castle Inn. Hotel is signposted after 2 miles.

Ireby CA5 1HH
Map 11: NY23
Tel/Fax: 017687 76566
Chef: Adrian Hyde
Owners: Adrian & Angela Hyde
Cost: Fixed-price D £23 (5 courses). ☺ H/wine £8.75
Times: D only, last D 8.30pm
Additional: Sunday L (12.30-1.30pm); No children under 3; dishes
Smoking: No smoking in dining room

BORROWDALE, Borrowdale Gates Hotel

Grange Keswick CA12 5UQ
Map 11: NY21
Tel: 017687 77204
Fax: 017687 77254
Chef: Wendy Lindars
Owners: Terry & Christine Parkinson

Diners in the modestly elegant, open-plan restaurant can aptly look out upon the 'Jaws of Borrowdale', one of Lakeland's most spectacular views, as they work their way through the daily-changing four-course dinners. Avocado and wood pigeon salad or deep-fried skate knobs in tempura batter make an ambitious start; cream of fennel soup or seared tuna with a spicy salad appear next, followed by ballotine of wild rabbit or supreme of corn-fed guinea fowl with a Marsala and crème fraîche sauce. Cappuccino crème brûlée and double chocolate ice cream parfait number amongst the desserts. Farmhouse cheeses can be taken as an extra course. Expect to be pampered in a courteous, traditional and wholly delightful way.

Directions: B5289 from Keswick. After 4 miles turn R over double humpback bridge to Grange village. Hotel 400yds through village on R

Cost: Fixed-price D £26 (4 courses). H/wine £12
Times: 12.15-last L 1.30pm/7-last D 8.45pm. Closed Jan
Additional: Bar food L; Sunday L; No children under 6; 🌢 dishes
Seats: 60. Jacket & tie preferred
Smoking: No smoking in dining room
Accommodation: 28 en suite
Credit cards: 🔳 🔳 🔳 🔳 🔳 🔳

BRAMPTON, **Farlam Hall Hotel** ❀❀

Hallbankgate CA8 2NG
Map 12: NY56
Tel: 016977 46234
Fax: 016977 46683
Chef: Barry Quinion
Owners: Quinion & Stevenson families
Cost: Fixed-price D £29 (4 courses)
Times: D only, 8pm for 8.30pm. Closed 25-30 Dec
Additional: No children under 5; 🌢 dishes on request
Seats: 45. Private dining room 24.
Smoking: No pipes or cigars in dining room
Accommodation: 12 en suite
Credit cards: 🔳 🔳 🔳 🔳

Directions: On the A689 Brampton to Alston road. Not in Farlam Village

Luxurious and lavish Victorian restaurant with honest, unpretentious cooking concentrating on classic flavour combinations. The menu incorporates a range of fresh fish and prime cuts. Lovely bread includes apricot and nut bloomer plus the usual brown and white options. The starter of crispy grilled sea bass comes with a chunky ratatouille. Chargrilling provides a contemporary twist to the traditional mix of venison and nicely reduced red wine and shallot sauce. Side vegetables are simply prepared. A modest cheeseboard with all the trimmings is followed by a tempting choice of desserts, including a hearty chocolate and pecan pie served with milk chocolate sauce and crème anglaise. There's a wide and wonderful selection of teas plus filter coffee served in the lounge after dinner. Intelligent and discreet staff enhance the pleasure of a meal here. The hotel also offers good breakfasts and some delicious cakes for afternoon tea.

CARLISLE, **Crosby Lodge Hotel** ❀❀

Built in 1802, this impressively crenellated pile is notable for its antiques and period furnishings, a quiet and relaxed atmosphere, and its parkland setting looking over the River Eden. A grand fireplace is the focal point of the elegant dining room, done out in reds and golds and with floor-to-ceiling windows. A starter of grilled goats' cheese with Parma ham on a croûte with home-made chutney impressed an inspector for its robust flavours. Seafood Thermidor – shrimps, salmon and scallops – came next, then peppered noisettes of lamb with 'superb' mint jelly and pan juices and a selection of 'great' vegetables. Toffee and banana

High Crosby CA6 4QZ
Map 11: NY35
Tel: 01228 573618
Fax: 01228 573428
Chef: James Sedgwick
Owners: Michael & Patricia Sedgwick
Cost: Alc £30, fixed-price L £16.50 (4 courses)/D £28.50 (5 courses). ☺ H/wine £12.50
Times: 12.15-last L 1.30pm/7.15-last D 8.45pm. Closed 24 Dec-mid Jan

Crosby Lodge Hotel

cheesecake, its base made of pecan nuts, was declared 'delicious'; along with other desserts, it was served off the trolley with much wielding of silver cutlery. The kitchen has a fondness for fishy starters, shellfish in particular, but is equally at ease turning out main courses of escalopes of venison in Madeira or roast farm duckling with orange sauce. House wines on the extensive list, encouragingly annotated, are served by the glass, carafe or bottle. The rest of the well-spread list is cannily chosen with prices fairly reflecting quality throughout

Additional: Bar food L; Sunday L; No children under 5; 🍴 dishes
Seats: 50. Private dining room 16. **Smoking:** No smoking in dining room. Jacket & tie preferred. **Accommodation:** 11 en suite
Credit cards: 💳 💳 💳 💳 💳 💳 JCB

AA Wine Shortlisted for *Award–see page* 16

Directions: 3 miles from M6/J44 on A689 towards Carlisle Airport/Brampton. R at Low/High Crosby sign, 1 mile on R

CARLISLE, **Crown Hotel** ❀

Former farmhouse, dating from the 18th century, with a conservatory restaurant overlooking well-tended gardens. Typical dishes are terrine of locally smoked chicken and ham hock, and a chef's speciality, monkfish and tiger prawns on a spring onion mash with garlic, coriander and white wine sauce.

Smoking: No smoking in dining room
Accommodation: 51 en suite. **Credit cards:** 💳 💳 💳 💳 💳 💳 💳

Directions: Take J42 of M6 and in Wetheral follow signs for conference centre at Post Office

Wetheral CA4 8ES
Map 11: NY35

Tel: 01228 561888
Fax: 01228 561637
Chef: Martin Strand
Owner: Shire Inns
Cost: *Alc* £23.50, fixed price L £10.50 (2 courses)/D £20. H/wine £11.45
Times: Last L 2pm/last D 9.30pm. Closed L Sat
Additional: Bar food; Sunday L; Children welcome; 🍴 dishes

CARTMEL, **Aynsome Manor Hotel** ❀

Expect warm hospitality, a relaxed atmosphere and good food at this lovely 16th-century manor house, set in carefully tended gardens. Honest home-cooked food is well prepared by a dedicated kitchen team. The short menu may feature mushroom and apple soup, duck with cranberry and Cointreau sauce, and strawberry mousse.

Accommodation: 12 en suite.
Credit cards: 💳 💳 💳 💳 💳 💳 JCB

Directions: Leave A590 signed Cartmel. Hotel is 0.5 mile N of Cartmel village on R

Grange-over-Sands LA11 6HH
Map 7: SD37
Tel: 015395 36653
Fax: 015395 36016
Chef: Victor Sharratt
Owners: P Anthony, Margaret Varley
Cost: Fixed-price D £15.50. ☺ H/wine £8
Times: D only, 7-8.30pm. Closed D Sun, Jan
Additional: Sunday L for 1pm
Smoking: No smoking in dining room

CARTMEL, Uplands Hotel ❀❀

The dining room has taken on a new look in shades of pale yellow and ivory, but the uninterrupted views towards the Leven Estuary continue to draw guests back. The format remains constant: one sitting and a substantial four-course meal. Go easy on the loaf of oven-fresh bread on each table, ahead, there may be fresh Morecambe Bay shrimps in lightly curried mayonnaise with Charantais melon, and broccoli cheese soup, as well as braised guinea fowl with prune and bacon roll and port wine sauce. In the Tovey tradition, there are excellent vegetables, such as grated beetroot with orange. Finish with chocolate Grand Marnier mousse.

Smoking: No smoking in dining room
Seats: 28
Accommodation: 5 en suite
Credit cards: ▇ ▇ ▇ ▇

Directions: 1 mile up road signed Grange opposite the Pig & Whistle pub in Cartmel

Haggs Lane
Grange-over-Sands LA11 6HD
Map 7: SD37
Tel: 015395 36248
Fax: 015395 36848
Chef: Tom Peter
Owners: Tom & Diana Peter
Cost: Fixed-price L £15.50/D £27 (4 courses). H/wine £9
Times: 12.30 for 1pm/7.30 for 8pm. Closed Mon, L Tue & Wed, Jan, Feb
Additional: Sunday L; No children under 8; ✿ dishes

CLEATOR, Ennerdale Hotel ❀ NEW

Solidly built Cumbrian country house in peaceful surroundings. The kitchen delivers the likes of game terrine, fillet of Orkney Gold beef Madeira and truffle, and profiteroles with chocolate sauce.

Smoking: No smoking in dining room
Accommodation: 30 en suite
Credit cards: ▇ ▇ ▇ ▇ ▇ ▇

Directions: Please telephone for directions

CA23 3DT
Map 11: NY01
Tel: 01946 813907
Fax: 01946 815260
Chef: Kenneth Gerrie
Owner: Feathers Hotel Group
Cost: Fixed-price L £10.95/D £18.50 (4 courses). ☺ H/wine £9.95
Times: Last L 2pm/Last D 9.30pm
Additional: Bar food; Sunday L; Children welcome; ✿ dishes

CONISTON, The Old Rectory Hotel ❀

Family-run Victorian house, two miles south of Coniston, with three acres of gardens surrounded by farmland. Dinner at 7.30pm is the main occasion, with a set four-course menu of country-house cooking – haddock smokies, fillet of pork Normandy, raspberry vacherin and a selection of cheeses, for example.

Accommodation: 8 en suite. **Credit cards:** ▇ ▇ ▇ ▇ JCB

Directions: 2.5 miles south of Coniston on the A593, just before Torver

Torver LA21 8AX
Map 7: SD39
Tel: 015394 41353
Fax: 015394 41156
Chef: Carolyn Fletcher
Owners: Paul & Carolyn Fletcher
Cost: Fixed-price D £17 (4 courses). ☺ H/wine £9.25
Times: D only at 7.30pm
Additional: Children welcome; ✿ dishes
Smoking: No smoking in dining room

CROOKLANDS, Crooklands Hotel ❀

Situated on the first floor of this 18th-century farm house, the Hayloft Restaurant is a suitably rustic setting for some great English fare. Main courses include fillet of beef with a rich mushroom and port wine sauce, fine strips of pork sautéed with asparagus and paprika, and breast of chicken, cooked in a lobster sauce with prawns.

Smoking: No-smoking area; Air conditioning
Accommodation: 30 en suite
Credit cards: ▇ ▇ ▇ ▇ ▇ ▇

Directions: 1.5 miles from M6/J36; 4 miles from Kendal A65

Milnthorpe Near Kendal LA7 7NW
Map 7: SD58
Tel: 015395 67432
Fax: 015395 67525
Chef: Colin Scot
Owners: Neil & Hedda Connor
Cost: Alc £19.50. ☺ H/wine £8.95
Times: D only, last D 9pm. Closed Sun, Mon
Additional: Bar food; ✿ dishes

CROSTHWAITE, **The Punchbowl**

The low-beamed ceiling and three open fires of this 17th-century coaching inn remain but there's little else to suggest it was once a pub. People come here to drink in both the atmosphere and the good value wines, and tuck into the tasty modern British menu. Crowd pleasers such as leek and potato soup, gravad lax, chicken schnitzel and grilled steak are complemented by more experimental dishes such as chargrilled tuna steak served with a sauté of Oriental veg, wholewheat noodles and a soy, ginger, olive oil and sesame dressing. Our inspector enjoyed a lentil and bacon soup with crusty rolls and a delightfully cooked whole red mullet served with herby Mediterranean vegetables. Save room for dessert – the lemon tart with lemon mascarpone ice cream is excellent – and chocolate lovers have a choice of puddings. There's a selection of fine British cheeses served with biscuits and oatcakes.

Directions: M6/J36 (Kendal). L onto A540 (Barrow). R at Jaguar dealership and follow A5074 until Crosthwaite sign. Top of lane on L next to church

Kendal LA8 8HQ
Map 11: SD49
Tel: 015395 68237
Fax: 015395 68875
Chefs: Duncan Collinge, Steven Doherty
Owners: Steven & Marjorie Doherty, Alan Bell, Lionel Yates
Cost: Alc £15. ☺
Times: Noon-last L 2pm/6pm-last D 9pm. Closed 25 Dec
Additional: Sunday L; Children welcome; ❹ dishes
Seats: 80
Smoking: No-smoking area
Accommodation: 3 en suite
Credit cards:

ESKDALE GREEN,
Bower House Inn

A former farmhouse-cum-country inn with a characterful dining room of Jacobean origin. Good old-fashioned cooking offers the likes of robust mushroom soup packed with flavour, creamy, light oeufs en cocotte, hake portugaise, and a calorie-laden chocolate pot for dessert.

Holmrook CA19 1TD
Map 6: NY10
Tel: 019467 23244
Fax: 019467 23308
Chef: Margaret Johnson
Owners: Derek & Beryl Connor
Cost: Alc £19.50. Fixed price D £21.50 (4 courses). ☺ H/wine £7.95.
Times: Last L 2pm (bar)/D 7-8.30pm
Additional: Bar food; Children welcome; ❹ dishes
Smoking: No smoking in dining room
Accommodation: 24 en suite
Credit cards:

Directions: 4 miles from A595 coast route at Holmbrook.

GRANGE-OVER-SANDS,
Clare House ❀   NEW

Family-run hotel with delightful views over Morecambe Bay. An ambitious team produces exemplary cooking that takes in caramelised onion and garlic tart, roast loin of pork with sweet-and-sour tartlet, apple sauce and 'gorgeous' crackling, and sticky toffee pudding. Superb sun-dried tomato and granary rolls, as well. One to watch.

Accommodation: 17 en suite
Credit cards: None

Directions: From motorway Park Road follows the shore line. Hotel on L

Park Road LA11 7HQ
Map 7: SD47
Tel: 015395 33026
Chef: Andrew Read
Owners: DS & J Read
Cost: Fixed-price D £20 (5 courses). ☺ H/wine £10.
Times: D only, 6.45-7.15pm. Closed end Oct-April
Smoking: No smoking in dining room

GRASMERE, **Gold Rill Hotel** ✿

With glorious views across the lake and surrounding fells, especially
from the attractive restaurant, this personally run hotel offers warm
hospitality and a good standard of cooking. Our inspector enjoyed a
well balanced Stilton and onion broth, herb-crusted sea bream with
lemon beurre blanc, and an excellent sticky toffee pudding.

Smoking: No smoking in dining room; air conditioning
Accommodation: 25 en suite. **Credit cards:** 🟦 🟧 ⓒ

Directions: M6/J36 then A590/591: Red Bank Road in centre of
village opposite St Oswalds Church. Hotel 200yds on L

Red Bank Road LA22 9PU
Map 11: NY30
Tel: 015394 35486
Fax: 015394 35097
Chef: Ian Thompson
Owner: Paul Jewsbury
Cost: Alc £25. Fixed-price D £18.50
(4 courses). ☺ H/wine £9.80
Times: D only, 7.30pm-8.30pm.
Closed mid Dec-mid Jan
Additional: Bar food L; No children
under 3; ✿ dishes

GRASMERE, **Grasmere Hotel** ✿

A pleasant Victorian country house next to the river Rothay, just a
couple of minutes' walk from the village centre. Interesting, unusual
dishes are served in the restaurant – try blackened leg of lamb,
guinea fowl in red wine and wild mushroom sauce, or sautéed
turkey breast with black olives and basmati rice.

Broadgate LA22 9TA
Map 11: NY30
Tel/Fax: 015394 35277
Chef: Gretchen Riley
Owners: Paul & Gretchen Riley
Times: D only, last D 8.30pm.
Closed Jan
Additional: No children under 10;
✿ dishes
Smoking: No smoking in dining room
Accommodation: 12 en suite
Credit cards: 🟦 🟧 ⓒ 🟥 ⓒ JCB

Directions: Off A591, a short distance
from the village centre, by the river

GRASMERE, **Michael's Nook** ✿✿✿✿

Splendid country house hotel with the restaurant overlooking
gardens and the distant fells. Decor is bold red and green, with
polished tables, crisp linen, good glass and gleaming silver – a
perfect backdrop for Will Drabble's food. This is a chef with real
talent, one who is capable of producing some quite exceptional
dishes; the hand-over from Mark Treasure has been seamless.

Ambleside LA22 9RP
Map 11: NY30
Tel: 015394 35496
Fax: 015394 35645
Chef: William Drabble
Owner: Mr R S E Gifford
Cost: Fixed-price L £34.50 (4
courses)/D £45 (5 courses). H/wine
£14.50

Buying, for example, is first-class, despite the hassle of getting quality produce in such a relatively remote location. Luxuries are common: foie gras, lobster, morels and truffles, but incorporated into dishes that have obviously been thought about. Dinner is a short menu, classically based and simply executed. Thus, an appetiser of confit of duck with foie gras and truffles, proved to be bursting with flavour, you could really taste each ingredient. That winter dinner also produced a stunning ravioli of lobster with tender, sweet roasted scallops and asparagus, noteworthy for accurate flavours that were balanced and in complete harmony. The best part of the dish, and one which demonstrated excellent skills, was the construction and execution of the ravioli – it was paper thin yet retained a detectable 'bite' (and incredibly, detectable flavour). Great cauliflower soup with truffle sabayon followed, delicate, rich, with the flavour of the truffle (as part of the sabayon, which just melted into the soup) adding a further rich dimension. The centrepiece of the meal was a wonderfully sweet and tender best end of lamb served with roasted sweetbreads. The addition of confit tomatoes, onions and garlic made the dish quite robust, yet there was nothing clumsy in terms of execution – flavours and balance were quite delicate. A classic lemon tart was all flavour, tangy, sharp, sweet, with delicate pastry that was thin, buttery and of great lightness, the whole presented with 'no garnish, no cream, nothing – superb'. All the details – canapés, bread and petits fours – are excellent. Best canapé was foie gras wrapped in truffle, covered in a Madeira jelly (warm), with a quail's egg and hollandaise sauce. Breads included a light textured, yeasty cep bread. The wine list, in true Reg Gifford style, is lively and interesting with some depth and expensive numbers.

Times: 12.30-1pm/7.30-8.30pm
Additional: No children under 7
Seats: 50. Private dining room 35.
Jacket & tie preferred
Smoking: No smoking in dining room
Accommodation: 14 en suite
Credit cards: ■■ ■■ ■■ ■■ ■■ ■■ ■■ JCB

Directions: On N side of Grasmere. From A591, turn uphill at The Swan, bear L for 400yds.

GRASMERE,

Rothay Garden Hotel ❀❀

The popular conservatory dining room of this charming hotel has a heavy accent of the colour pink – Queen Anne chairs, tablecloths, napkins and Austrian blinds. Service is personal and attentive, yet keeps a courteous balance. Ambitious cooking with terrines and classic sauces done well, and dishes such as leek and potato broth, and a chocolate marquise with white chocolate sauce winning praise.

Broadgate LA22 9RJ
Map 11: NY30
Tel: 015394 35334
Fax: 015394 35723
Please telephone for further details

Directions: From the south take junction 36 from M6 and follow the A590/A591 to Grasmere. From the north take junction 40 from M6 and follow A66 to Keswick, then A591 to Grasmere

GRASMERE, The Swan ❀

Delightful 300-year-old building, Wordsworth's favourite lakeland hostelry, now offering well-appointed bedrooms, views of the surrounding fells, and a high standard of British cooking. A typical menu may feature kipper pâté, lamb shank with honey and mint sauce, venison with redcurrant sauce, and cappuccino mousse among the puddings.

Accommodation: 36 en suite
Credit cards: ■■ ■■ ■■ ■■ ■■ ■■ JCB

Directions: On the A591

Ambleside LA22 9RF
Map 11: NY30
Tel: 015394 35551
Fax: 015394 35741
Chef: Beverley Holmes
Owner: Forte Hotels
Cost: *Alc* £18, fixed-price L £14 (4 courses)/D £18 (4 courses). ☺
H/wine £13
Times: Last L 2pm/last D 9.30pm
Additional: Bar food, Sunday L; Children welcome; ❦ dishes
Smoking: No smoking in dining room

GRASMERE,
White Moss House ✿✿

Overlooking Rydal Water, real English food is served in the pretty cottage-style restaurant. The cooking is skilful, with careful attention to detail and an assured lightness of touch, with ingredients carefully sourced and the daily changing menu celebrating regional produce. An early May meal brought leek and lovage soup, followed by a soufflé of Wastwater line-caught sea trout with River Eden smoked salmon and Cumbrian smoked cheese, then rack of Westmoreland organic spring lamb roasted with a herb crust with redcurrant, mint and Merlot sauce. Ever-popular desserts include sticky toffee pudding with pecan toffee sauce, or there are British cheeses with White Moss oat biscuits.

Directions: On A591 between Grasmere and Ambleside opposite Rydal Water

Rydal Water Ambleside LA22 9SE
Map 11: NY30
Tel: 015394 35295
Fax: 015394 35516
Chefs: Peter Dixon, Colin Percival
Owners: Sue & Peter Dixon
Cost: Fixed-price D £27.50
(5 courses). H/wine £9.50
Times: D only, at 8pm. Closed Sun
Additional: No children under 8;
⚘ dishes
Seats: 18
Smoking: No smoking in dining room
Accommodation: 8 en suite
Credit cards: 🔲 🔲 🔲 🔲

GRASMERE,
Wordsworth Hotel ✿✿

Ambleside LA22 9SW
Map 11: NY30
Tel: 015394 35592
Fax: 015394 35765
Chef: Bernard Warne
Owner: R Gifford
Cost: *Alc* £32 (4 courses), fixed-price
L £19.50. H/wine £12.75
Times: 12.30-last L 1.45pm/7-last
D 9pm (Fri, Sat till 9.30)
Additional: Bar food; Sunday L;
Children welcome; ⚘ dishes
Seats: 70. Private rooms 14 & 100
Smoking: No smoking in dining room;
Air conditioning
Accommodation: 37 en suite
Credit cards: 🔲 🔲 🔲 🔲 🔲

This impressive Victorian hotel continues to go from strength to strength. Yet despite its seemingly busy central location in a village frequently overrun by tourists, the place has a peaceful air, helped by splendid gardens, terrace and swimming pool. The Prelude Restaurant is decorated in daffodil yellow to honour the Lakeland poet William Wordsworth who is buried in the cemetery across the road. This year inspectors' have reported on a welcome shift of emphasis in the kitchen. The cooking has taken on a more modern outlook, is lighter and simpler in concept. Heartily endorsed dishes have included crab and salmon terrine with rouille and warm potato salad, smoked haddock with a herb crust served in a reduction of the cooking liquid finished with cream, seared duck breast with honey and soy sauce and a spiced confit of the leg, and a dark chocolate and lime mousse with a white chocolate sauce. Five types of 'gorgeous' bread show the kitchen has a firm eye on lesser details, and petits fours finish the meal on a high note. The wine list has been extended to include over 50 half-bottles, whilst the full bottle list is notable for its budgetary and geographical flexibility.

Directions: In the village centre next to the church

HOWTOWN, **Sharrow Bay** ❀❀❀

Sharrow Bay Penrith CA10 2LZ
Map 12: NY41
Tel: 017684 86301
Fax: 017684 86349
Chefs: Juan Martin, Colin Akrigg
Owner: Brian Sack
Cost: *Alc* £29, fixed-price L £35
(4 courses)/D £46 (5 courses)
Times: L at 1pm/D at 8pm. Closed
Dec-late Feb
Additional: Sunday L; No children
under 13; ❀ dishes
Seats: 60. Jacket and tie preferred
Smoking: No smoking in dining room;
Air conditioning
Accommodation: 26 en suite
Credit cards: ▬ ▬ ▣ ▣ JCB

Fifty years ago, with his colleague Brian Sack, the late Francis Coulson invented the country house hotel as we know it today. Sharrow Bay is an enchanting hotel on the shores of Lake Ullswater with, arguably, the best view in England. The kitchen is run by two long-standing members of the team, Juan Martin and Colin Akrigg, along with Philip Wilson, and they maintain the standards that put the hotel on the world map. The cooking goes in for big sweeping statements: duck foie gras on braised pig's trotter and ham shank with pease pudding and shallot and thyme sauce; roast stuffed saddle of rabbit, roast leg of rabbit, bouchette of liver and kidney, Madeira and chive-cream sauce. Terrines with fruity things are favoured, for example, venison, pork and pistachio nuts with pear and saffron chutney, spicy orange and toasted brioche. The grand style is kept up with the likes of fillet of brill with Sauternes and curry sauce, followed by Sharrow fruit sorbet, then noisette of local venison, parsnip and chestnut purée, fried pimentos, rosemary and juniper berry sauce, or breast of duckling, choucroute, gnocchi of duck confit, cider and honey sauce. Lighter dishes might include steamed fillet of salmon served on a risotto of salmon caviar with Champagne sauce. Desserts are triumphant: an old English Regency syllabub with buttery shortbread hearts, miraculously smooth and frothy, and 'La Stupenda Bavarois' created for Dame Joan Sutherland. The wine list is an impressive selection, showing both enthusiasm and knowledge and offering range, fair prices and quality.

AA Wine Shortlisted for
Wine Award-see page 16

Directions: Turn off A592 through Pooley Bridge, turn R (signed to Howtown), hotel 2 miles

KESWICK, **Dale Head Hall** ❀❀

The dining room of this small family-run hotel looking over the waters of Thirlmere is in the original 16th-century building, with oak beams and panelling and large inglenook; most of the bedrooms and two lovely lounges at the front are of a later period. Dinner is a set five courses with normally a choice of two dishes at each except the first – which might be baked avocado with crab, or goats' cheese salad with peppers – and the last, a selection of cheeses. In between come a soup of perhaps white onion, or lentil and thyme broth, with oven-fresh breads, then a main course of breast of guinea fowl stuffed with a mousseline of chicken and basil served with a filo parcel of kidneys ('this was great' noted an inspector), or

Lake Thirlmere CA12 4TN
Map 11: NY22
Tel: 017687 72478
Fax: 017687 71070
Chefs: Warren Goodridge,
Caroline Bonhenburg
Owners: Mr & Mrs A Lowe
Cost: Fixed-price D £27.50
(5 courses)
Times: D only, 7.30-8.30pm
Additional: No children under 10;
❀ dishes
Seats: 18
Smoking: No smoking in dining room

pan-fried sea bass with salsa verde; vegetables come in for praise too. A platter of three desserts – chocolate marquis, lemon tart and a basket of marinated summer fruits – is another dish that illustrates the kitchen's accomplishment. Wines on the fairly extensive list are grouped by style.

Directions: 12 miles M6/J40, half way between Keswick and Grasmere.

Accommodation: 9 en suite
Credit cards: ▩ ▩ ▩ ▩ ▩ ▩

KESWICK, **Swinside Lodge** ❀❀

Newlands CA12 5UE
Map 11: NY22
Tel/Fax: 017687 72948
Chef: Christopher Astley
Owner: Graham Taylor
Cost: Fixed-price dinner £25 (4 courses). ☺
Times: D only, 7.30 for 8pm.
Closed Dec-Jan
Additional: No children under 10
Seats: 18
Smoking: No smoking in dining room
Accommodation: 7 en suite
Credit cards: None

Nestling in its own grounds under Cat Bells, surrounded by lush greenery and delightful views (and Derwent Water just minutes away) Swinside Lodge is in superb walking country – the more sedate can take the launch around the lake. Relax among the deep sofas in the superbly appointed and traditionally styled lounges before moving to the dining room for the set four-course dinner, with no choice until pudding. The first course might be hazelnut and smoked cheese soufflé, or a tart of red onion and caraway. Soup normally comes next, perhaps cream of fennel, accompanied by fine, interesting breads – fig and walnut, say, or plain white twists – and then the main course: roast breast of guinea fowl with brown butter sauce, or salmon with saffron sauce with sun-dried tomato and lemon couscous. Chocolate tart, its pastry exemplary, with light chocolate sorbet, or compote of plums with vanilla ice cream may be among the selection of puddings. The hotel is unlicensed, although you get a glass of sherry before dinner, so don't forget to bring your own wine.

Directions: 3 miles SW of Keswick. Take A66 for Cockermouth, L at Portinscale, follow road to Grange

KESWICK, **Thwaite Howe Hotel** ❀

Thornthwaite CA12 5SA
Map 11: NY22
Tel: 017687 78281
Fax: 017687 78529
Chef: Mary Kay
Owners: Harry & Mary Kay
Cost: Fixed-price D £17.50. ☺
H/wine £8.95
Times: D only at 7pm.
Closed Nov-Feb
Additional: No children under 12

A traditional Victorian residence with panoramic views to the distant fells. Mary Kay offers a five-course dinner built around first-rate ingredients that overcome the fact that there is no choice. A typical meal could be smoked salmon roulade filled with cheese, lime and dill mousse, grilled chicken with oranges, two chocolate parfait. A good range of local cheeses too.

Smoking: No smoking in dining room
Accommodation: 8 en suite
Credit cards: ▩ ▩ ▩ ▩ ▩

Directions: From A66 W of Keswick, follow signs to Thornthwaite Gallery. Hotel signed from there.

KESWICK, **Underscar Manor**

Applethwaite CA12 4PH
Map 11: NY22
Tel: 017687 75000
Fax: 017687 74904
Chef: Robert Thornton
Owners: Pauline & Derek Harrison,
Gordon Evans
Cost: *Alc* £43, fixed-price L £25/D
£30 (6 courses)
Times: Noon-1pm/7-8.30pm
Additional: Sunday L; No children
under 12; **◊** dishes
Seats: 50. Jacket & tie preferred
Smoking: No smoking in dining room
Accommodation: 11 en suite
Credit cards: ■ ▓ ▚ ▢ ▒

The house is Italianate in design and sits on the slopes of
Skiddaw. Indeed, from the conservatory-style restaurant there
are sweeping views over Derwent Valley and the surrounding
fells. Lavish swags and tails, opulent seating and silver table
appointments define the decor here. The cooking is ambitious,
with Robert Thornton leading a talented team. An *amuse-
bouche* of beef kebab with couscous on a spicy tomato sauce
kicked off one test lunch. Swordfish steak came next, grilled
and served with olive oil, tomato and capsicum dressing with
aubergine crisps, then the centrepiece, breast of guinea fowl
with an apricot and onion stuffing, simple spring cabbage and
light, fluffy châteaux potatoes, a dish that was low-key in all
the right places – it worked well. Chocolate and hazelnut tart
with a praline-flavoured ice cream and a pool of crème de
menthe sauce was pronounced excellent. A later diner
reported on a superb selection of breads; an appetiser of
seafood terrine larded with salmon; lobster and king prawn
gâteau; chargrilled beef with foie gras and a well-formed red
wine jus, plus Puy lentils, caramelised shallots and pommes
Anna. Dessert was a grand selection of pecan pie, crème
caramel, crème brûlée, lemon tart, and chocolate mousse
wrapped in a thin chocolate case and honey ice cream with a
little raspberry purée. All this is backed up by good,
professional service.

Directions: From M6/J40, A66
Keswick/Workington for 17miles.
At large roundabout take 3rd exit.
Turn immediate R at signpost for
Underscar; hotel 0.75 mile on R.

KIRKBY LONSDALE, **Cobwebs**

A bright and stylish conservatory dining room, candle-lit at
night with soft lighting. Local reputation dictates that business
is brisk here, and booking is recommended. Although the daily
menu is fixed, guests are told this when they book, however,
Yvonne Thompson is extremely flexible and able to cater for
all needs; she also works alone in the kitchen and 'must work
her socks off' reported our inspector. Brochette of salmon and
prawn with a tomato salsa and a light roasted red pepper
dressing, roast rack of lamb with polenta and a piquant sauce,
and a dark and white chocolate marquise with a brandy
custard sauce formed our most recent, well-reported meal.
The wine list is extensive and Paul Kelly is happy to serve most
wines by the glass.

Leck Cowan Bridge LA6 2HZ
Map 7: SD67
Tel/Fax: 015242 72141
Chef: Yvonne Thompson
Owners: Yvonne Thompson,
Paul Kelly
Please telephone for further details

Directions: From M6/J36 take A65 (Skipton), 8 miles to Cowan
Bridge, L to Leck, hotel on L 200 yds

MUNGRISDALE, The Mill Hotel

Penrith CA11 0XR
Map 11: NY33
Tel: 017687 79659
Fax: 017687 79155
Chef: Eleanor M Quinlan
Owners: Richard & Eleanor Quinlan
Cost: Fixed-price D £26 (5 courses).
☺ H/wine £7.95
Times: D only, 7pm-last D 8pm.
Closed 1 Nov-1 Mar
Additional: Children welcome;
𝅘 dishes
Smoking: No smoking in dining room
Accommodation: 7 en suite
Credit cards: None

Former mill cottage, complete with cosy beamed restaurant, set amidst terrific mountain scenery. The emphasis is on sound country cooking, with dishes such as ragout of venison or roast duckling offered from a limited choice, five-course menu. The dessert trolley is a highlight.

Directions: Mungrisdale is signed on A66 midway between Penrith & Keswick. Hotel 2 miles N of A66

NEWBY BRIDGE, Lakeside Hotel

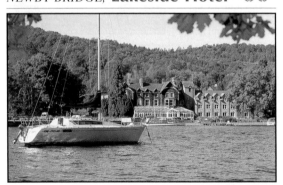

Ulverston LA12 8AT
Map 7: SD38
Tel: 015395 31207
Fax: 015395 31699
Chef: Robert Marshall-Slater
Owner: Neville R Talbot
Cost: Alc £20, fixed-price D £29.50
(4 courses). ☺ H/wine £13
Times: Noon-3pm/7-9.30pm
Additional: Bar food L; Sunday L;
Children welcome; 𝅘 dishes
Seats: 60. Private room 25
Smoking: No smoking in dining room;
Air conditioning
Accommodation: 80 en suite
Credit cards: 💳 💳 💳 💳 💳

Set on the peaceful southern shore of Lake Windermere, next to the steamer dock, this is a spacious hotel where guests can expect high standards of service. Dinner is served in the stately restaurant, but more informal meals can be enjoyed in Ruskin's Brasserie, named after the great Victorian poet and social revolutionary John Ruskin. His passion for Switzerland and Italy is reflected in the menu. Typical dishes include a traditional Swiss soup made with rustic vegetables, pasta and Parmesan, and flash-fried strips of pork with wild mushrooms, sherry and cream. A summer meal in the restaurant might start with Morecambe Bay mussels cooked in champagne and cream, followed by pot-roast of monkfish with Puy lentils, leeks and baby onions. For dessert, perhaps rich chocolate mousse with coffee bean sauce, or hot apple and toffee pudding. The wine list reflects a high calibre cellar, and you pay for the privilege.

Directions: M6/J36 follow A590 to Newby Bridge, R over bridge, follow Hawkshead Road for 1 mile

PENRITH, A Bit on the Side ❀

Both lunchtime bistro and smart restaurant, this stylish split-level eatery, set in a character barn conversion, produces imaginative modern dishes to suit all tastes. An enjoyable inspection lunch included crispy prawn spring rolls with coriander salsa, duck with honey and soy sauce, and a glorious rich chocolate cheesecake.

Smoking: No smoking in dining room
Credit cards:

Directions: Follow town centre from M6 J40 Brunswick Sq is opposite Bluebell Lane car park

Brunswick Square CA11 7LG
Map 12: NY53
Tel: 01768 892526
Chef: Archie Bell
Owners: Archie & Susan Bell
Cost: *Alc* £21, fixed-price L £9.95. ☺ H/wine £8.95
Times: Last L 1.30pm/last D 9pm.
Closed L Sat, Mon, all Sun,
1st 2 wks Jan
Additional: No children under 7;
❀ dishes

RAVENSTONEDALE,
Black Swan Hotel ❀

A friendly hotel in a picturesque village just ten minutes from the M6. Huge oil paintings adorn the walls of the classically decorated restaurant, where good cooking from a bygone era is served by attentive staff. Expect dishes such as grilled fillet of salmon with tomato concasse, and honey glazed breast of duck.

Smoking: No smoking in dining room
Accommodation: 14 en suite.
Credit cards: JCB

Directions: M6/J38/A685 (Brough). Through Kirkby Stephen, then to Ravenstonedale

Near Kirkby Stephen CA17 4NG
Map 12: NY70
Tel: 015396 23204
Fax: 015396 23604
Chefs: Mrs N W Stuart, Mr John Murphy
Owners: Mr & Mrs G Stuart
Cost: *Alc* £20, fixed-price L £9.75/D £25 (4 courses). ☺ H/wine £7.50
Times: Last L 2pm/D 8.45pm
Additional: Bar food; Sunday L; Children welcome; ❀ dishes

TEBAY,
The Westmoreland Hotel ❀

Stunning views over the valley, moors and distant hills from this two-tiered restaurant. A February meal featured open ravioli of Atlantic scallops, followed by an 'accomplished' loin of lamb with garlic and rosemary mousseline. The highlight of an assiette of desserts was the chocolate brûlée.

Westmorland Motorway Services,
Orton, Penrith CA10 3SB
Map 7: NY60
Tel: 015396 24351
Fax: 015396 24354
Please telephone for further details

TEMPLE SOWERBY,
Temple Sowerby House Hotel ❀❀

Popular throughout the region, this 17th-century house welcomes with open log fires, a delightful walled garden and an opulent restaurant serving traditional English dishes with a modern twist. Indeed, visitors can expect to sample a fair degree of creativity from the wide ranging menu. Good use is made of langoustine, foie gras and truffle, and whilst traditional cooking techniques are retained, the kitchen actively and successfully blends a whole host of interesting flavours. Note a summer meal that took in goose terrine stuffed with foie gras and served with lashings of Cumberland sauce, pigeon breast with pickled vegetable, pan-fried corn-fed chicken with langoustine tails, pilau and a saffron cream sauce, and iced milk chocolate parfait.

Directions: On A66 5 miles E of Penrith in village centre

Near Penrith CA10 1RZ
Map 12: NY62
Tel: 017683 61578
Fax: 017683 61958
Chef: Andrew Walker
Owners: Geoffrey & Cecile Temple
Cost: *Alc* £28.50. ☺ H/wine £10.25
Times: Last L 1.30pm/last D 8.45pm
Additional: Bar food L;
Children welcome; ❀ dishes
Smoking: No smoking in dining room
Accommodation: 13 en suite
Credit cards: JCB

TROUTBECK,
Queen's Head Hotel ❀❀

Lakeland hostelry with a very *oldeworlde* feel that boasts a four-poster bed as part of the appropriately named bar. The cooking here is no nonsense: unfussy, uncomplicated, straight from the hip. Dishes enjoyed have included rabbit and leek terrine and citrus chutney, made notable by clean flavours, and served with a doorstep of home-made brown bread that was 'sumptuous'; as well as a superb roast lamb shank on a claret jus with basil pomme purée, in which great rustic flavours came through. Desserts are in true Lake District tradition, served in large portions with the popular sticky toffee pudding accompanied by thick, creamy vanilla anglaise – described by one inspector as the 'real stuff'.

Accommodation: 8 en suite
Credit cards: ▬ ▭ ▧ ▢ ▣ JCB

Directions: On the A592, approx 2 miles from Windermere

Town Head LA23 1PW
Map 7: SD49
Tel: 015394 32174
Fax: 015394 31938
Chef: Wallace Drumond
Owners: Mark Stewardson, Joanne Sherratt
Cost: *Alc* £16. ☺ H/wine £8.95
Times: Noon-last L 2pm/6.30-last D 9pm. Closed 25 Dec
Additional: Bar food; Sunday L; Children welcome; ❹ dishes
Seats: 120. Private room 30
Smoking: No-smoking area

ULVERSTON, # Bay Horse Hotel ❀❀

LA12 9EL
Map 7: SD27
Tel: 01229 583972
Fax: 01229 580502
Chef: Robert Lyons
Owners: John J Tovey, Robert Lyons
Cost: *Alc* £23, fixed-price L £16.75. H/wine £13.95
Times: Noon-last L 1.30pm/7.30pm-last D 8pm. Closed L Mon
Additional: Bar food L; No children under 12; ❹ dishes
Seats: 50.
Smoking: No smoking in dining room
Accommodation: 7 en suite
Credit cards: ▬ ▭ ▧ ▢

Don't be put off by the unprepossessing approach to this 17th-century former coaching inn; part of the reward is a splendid view across the Leven estuary from a water's edge conservatory restaurant. Part-owned by John Tovey, of Miller Howe fame, the driving force behind the cooking here is chef-patron Robert Lyons. A recent lunch began with the arrival of a delicious, crusty mini-loaf fresh out of the oven, and included tomato and apricot soup, braised lamb pie, and chocolate and orange mousse in an almond tuile. The weekly-changing evening menu offers a choice of five dishes at each stage along the lines of duck, pork and Bramley apple rillettes with Cumberland sauce, pan-fried medallions of monkfish in lemon and fresh herb butter with basmati rice, and chicken breast rolled in white peppercorns and coriander with a honey, Calvados and raspberry vinegar glaze. Brown sugar meringue with strawberries and kiwi fruit makes a great dessert. The New World is well represented on a good length wine list where almost nothing except the 'fizz' breaches the £20 barrier.

Directions: From A590 entering Ulverston follow signs for Canal Foot

WATERMILLOCK, **Leeming House**

Penrith CA11 0JJ
Map 12: NY42
Tel: 017684 86622
Fax: 017684 86443
Chef: Adam Marks
Owner: Forte Hotels
Cost: Fixed-price L £13.95/D £31.50
(4 courses).
Times: Noon-last L 2pm/7pm-last
D 9pm
Additional: Sunday L; Bar meals;
Children welcome; ❸ dishes
Seats: 70. Private dining room 26.
Smoking: No smoking in dining room
Accommodation: 40 en suite
Credit cards: ▆ ▆ ▆ ▆ ▆ ▆ ▆

Enjoying superb views over Lake Ullswater and the breathtaking backdrop of the mountain fells, this hotel-restaurant prides itself on its choice of quality suppliers. Leeming House attracts a mixed crowd to its elegant Regency dining room where guests can enjoy a four-course dinner menu for £31.50. The good ingredients are presented in a contemporary British style that fashionably includes Italian, French and Oriental influences as well as hearty English comfort food. A highlight is the beautifully tender shank of Lakeland lamb with kumquat, rosemary and mint glaze served on crisp grilled ratatouille. Fine flavour is also to be found in the passion fruit terrine served with blackcurrant coulis. Weekend lunches bring a tempting selection of hearty salads and filled baguettes, offered in addition to simple starters, mains and desserts. A choice of vegetarian dishes is always available and service from the young staff is charming. History buffs will enjoy looking into the listed building's detailed past.

Directions: 8 miles from M6/J40; 8 miles from Penrith

WATERMILLOCK, **Old Church Hotel**

Penrith CA11 0JN
Map 12: NY42
Tel: 017684 86204
Fax: 017684 86368
Chef: Kevin Whitemore
Owner: Kevin & Maureen Whitemore
Cost: Alc £25
Times: D only, last D 8.15pm.
Closed Sun
Additional: No children under 10
Smoking: No smoking in dining room
Accommodation: 10 en suite
Credit cards: ▆ ▆ ▆ ▆ ▆

An enviable lakeside location is just one of the attractions of this immaculate 18th-century hotel. Another is chef-patron Kevin Whitemore's dinners in which quality ingredients (often locally sourced) and deft skills combine in well-balanced menus. The home-made desserts are a particular treat.

Directions: M6 J40 then take A592 and continue for 2.5 miles south west of Pooley Bridge

WATERMILLOCK,

Rampsbeck Hotel ✿✿✿

The bright, spacious restaurant has been sympathetically designed to capture the regal elegance of this smart Edwardian country house, and huge windows allow all tables to enjoy views of Ullswater and the fells. Despite the formality, the friendly and attentive staff are likely to stop and chat in a manner refreshing in such a setting. Dinner, as is so often the case in the Lake District, is a grand affair, and Rampsbeck is no exception adding canapés, an appetiser, a sorbet course and petits fours. Pre-dinner drinks are taken in the opulent lounge

Penrith CA11 0LP
Map 12: NY42
Tel: 017684 86442
Fax: 017684 86688
Chef: Andrew McGeorge
Owners: T I & M M Gibb,
M J Mac-Dowall
Cost: Fixed-price L £25/D £26-£39
(4 courses). H/wine £11.25
Times: L by prior arrangement (except Sun L noon-1.45pm)/7-last D 8pm.
Additional: Bar food L; Sunday L;
No children under 5; ✿ dishes
Seats: 40. Private dining room 12
Smoking: No smoking in dining room
Accommodation: 21 en suite
Credit cards: ▰ ▰ ▰ ▱

where choice antiques and roaring fires add to the sense of luxurious pampering. Terrine of corn-fed chicken, baby leeks and foie gras with Muscat jelly, shaped in triangular form, made an impressive first course, then came an intermediate course of curried cod chowder. A super piece of sea bass fillet, served with langoustine risotto, tomato confit and warm tomato and basil dressing, proved to be based on wonderful ingredients even if the concept was lavish, but then bold simplicity is not the style here. This is evident in the construction of dishes such as steamed fillet of turbot with grilled fennel, poached Loch Fyne oysters and star-anise flavoured butter sauce, and roasted saddle of venison with creamed celeriac, Parmentier potatoes, glazed button onions, batons of bacon and game jus. Dishes on the set menu are more modestly composed. Symphony of desserts is a good way to encapsulate the entire dessert menu – lemon tart, pistachio ice cream, chocolate delice, apple fritter, poached pear with praline, hot Amaretto soufflé, and white chocolate and passion fruit mousse were thus all wheeled out and, in the name of research, sampled with due diligence.

Signature dishes: Terrine of chicken confit, baby leeks and foie gras with Muscat jelly; baked summer berry clafoutis with an elderflower wine sabayon; roasted fillet of beef with calves' sweetbreads wrapped in Cumbrian air-dried ham.

Directions: M6/J40, follow signs to Ullswater on A592, turn R at lake's edge. Hotel 1.25 miles along lake shore

WINDERMERE,
Beech Hill Hotel ❀❀

Newby Bridge Road
Cartmel Fell LA23 3LR
Map 7: SD49
Tel: 015394 42137
Fax: 015394 43745
Chef: Adrain Lan
Owners: Mr & Mrs E K Richardson
Cost: Fixed-price D £24.50
(5 courses). ☺ H/wine £11.75
Times: Noon-last L 3pm/7-last
D 9.30pm
Additional: Bar food L; Sunday L;
Children welcome; ❹ dishes
Seats: 80. Jacket & tie preferred
Smoking: No smoking in dining room,
Air conditioning
Accommodation: 53 en suite
Credit cards: ▆ ▆ ▆ ▆ ▆ ▆ ▆ JCB

A delightfully positioned hotel on the eastern bank with a
series of terraces leading down eventually to the lake itself,
which means you can watch the sunset on Lake Windermere.
Make the most of the views of lake and fells from the oak-
panelled dining-room (after a day's walking) as you tuck into a
four-course set dinner. Bacon and Stilton, and banana and
walnut breads are a foretaste of what's to come. The first
course might be pan-seared sea bass with a lemongrass beurre
blanc 'as cheeky as it was delightful', according to an inspector.
Then may come monkfish and basil chowder, followed by a
main course of sauté chicken breast with cucumber sauce and a
confit of wild mushrooms – a combination that works well,
with clear, distinct flavours – and after that a dessert of
perhaps chocolate pudding with cappuccino sauce. Those who
have enough room could enjoy truffles, Turkish delight and
candied physalis with their coffee.

Directions: On A592, Newby Bridge 4 miles from
Windermere

WINDERMERE,
Burn How Garden House ❀

*Delightful hotel with a country house feel that nestles in a quite
secluded position within its own well-tended grounds. An ambitious
menu offers warm brioche bun with casserole of queen scallops and
prawns in a Pernod cream sauce, roast leg of lamb with a tarragon
and Marsala cream sauce, and pink gin syllabub with angostura
bitters and a Viennese biscuit.*

Additional: Bar food L; Children welcome; ❹ dishes
Smoking: No smoking in dining room
Accommodation: 26 en suite
Credit cards: ▆ ▆ ▆ ▆ ▆ ▆ JCB

Directions: Exit 36 of M6, 200 yds from Bowness Bay on
Windermere

Back Belsfield Road Bowness
LA23 3HH
Map 7: SD49
Tel: 015394 46226
Fax: 015394 47000
Chef: Michael Milburn
Owner: Michael Robinson
Cost: Fixed price D £19.50
(4 courses). H/wine £12.50
Times: Last L 1.45pm/last D 8.30pm

WINDERMERE,
Fayrer Garden House ✦

Lyth Valley Road LA23 3JP
Map 7: SD49
Tel: 015394 88195
Fax: 015394 45986
Chef: Edward Wilkinson
Owners: Iain & Jackie Garside
Cost: Fixed-price L £14/D £21
(4 courses). ☺ H/wine £10
Additional: No children under 5;
🍴 dishes
Smoking: No smoking in dining room;
Air conditioning
Accommodation: 18 en suite
Credit cards: 🔲 🔲 🔲 🔲 🔲 🔲

Directions: On A5074 1 mile from
town centre

*Beautiful conservatory restaurant overlooking the lake, with a
pianist providing background music. Dishes sampled include quail
filled with a light game mousse, served cold with Cumberland sauce,
and an orange and thyme sauce, and fillet of sea bass with a rösti,
tomato compote and another duo of sauces.*

WINDERMERE,
Gilpin Lodge Hotel ✦✦✦

Crook Road LA23 3NE
Map 7: SD49
Tel: 015394 88818
Fax: 015394 88058
Chef: Christopher Davies
Owners: John & Christine Cunliffe
Cost: *Alc* (L only) £17, fixed-price
D £27.50 (4 courses). H/wine £11.50.
Times: Noon-last L 2.30pm/7-last
D 8.45pm
Additional: Bar food L; Sunday L;
No children under 7; 🍴 dishes
Seats: 65. Private dining rooms 28
Smoking: No smoking in dining room
Accommodation: 14 en suite
Credit cards: 🔲 🔲 🔲 🔲 🔲 🔲 🔲 JCB

There are three different, equally intimate, rooms in this
elegant turn-of-the-century Lakeland house in which to dine.
Chris Davies follows no trend or direction other than his own,
and his eclectic, highly individual style allows a chorus of
vibrant flavours to harmonise to stunning effect. Boldness
defines his approach to cooking. When an inspector describes
a fish dish as 'making me feel as if kissed by a mermaid', then
you know something's really cooking. Such fantasy was
wrought by a warm crab and coriander torte on a mussels
marinière sauce, superbly seasoned with a precise, tightly
disciplined balance of flavours. Charlotte of langoustine and
provencale vegetables with roast cherry tomatoes and
tapenade was also a winner – stunningly fresh with pin-point
accuracy in presentation and flavour combinations. Roast
supreme of salmon with pancetta and watercress sauce was
honest, fresh and vibrant, the last item smelling of 'a freshly
cut hedge'. Fish is obviously handled brilliantly, but among the

Directions: M6/J36 & A590/(Kendal),
then B5284 for 5 miles

listed meat dishes are home-cured bresaola of beef with celeriac remoulade, roast boudin of foie gras on champ with onion sauce, roast breast and confit of Gressingham duckling with butter bean cassoulet and sage sauce. Desserts carry the air of a past era, especially an iced Pina Colada parfait with mango coulis and rum anglaise, but a solid chocolate box contained a good, light chocolate mousse. All the friendly, hovering staff are keenly enthusiastic, as well they might be with this standard of cooking.

Signature dishes; Roast fillet of red mullet on a confit of fennel and orange Pernod beurre blanc; charlotte of charcoal vegetables and langoustines with saffron oil and tapenade

WINDERMERE, Holbeck Ghyll

Holbeck Lane LA23 1LU
Map 7: SD49
Tel: 015394 32375
Fax: 015394 34743
Chef: Jake Watkins
Owners: David & Patricia Nicholson
Cost: *Alc* £15, fixed-price D £29.50. H/wine £13.95
Times: Noon-last L 2pm/7-last D 9pm
Additional: Bar food L; Sunday L; No children under 8 at D; ⑤ dishes
Seats: 50. Private room 18
Smoking: No smoking in dining room
Accommodation: 20 en suite
Credit cards: ▉ ▉ ▉ ▉ JCB

Panoramic vistas stretch across Windermere to the magnificent Langdale Fells beyond: there can be few views from a hotel that are more dramatic. The two dining rooms live up to the luxurious country house image: lots of silver, fresh flowers, oak panelling, mullions, chandeliers. Service is excellent, structured and friendly with good menu knowledge and a keenness to recommend wines with the chosen dishes. The cooking lives up to this setting with a stunning performance from a chef, Jake Watkins, and brigade devoted to their craft. This year things which have satisfied include very clear, fresh canapés of roasted provençale vegetable spring rolls, and a light salmon mousse quenelle on a croûte fried in olive oil; a 'divine' *amuse-bouche* of a white bean soup with roasted chanterelles and truffles; a vibrant parsley and celeriac soup with Périgord truffles and truffle oil; pan-fried foie gras with lentils and pancetta with a light Madeira sauce cappuccino-style; a 'wicked' seared red mullet with a clear tomato juice and basil tortellini; and a braised Charolais ox cheek with parsnip purée and bordelaise garnish – a brilliant dish. The rest of the meal – bread, desserts, sensational petits fours – was pitched perfectly. Wines and the service thereof are reported enthusiastically and the range is good; this is serious drinking. There is an intelligent selection of halves.

Signature dishes: Roasted chump of spring lamb with morels, peas and broad beans; wild salmon with Jersey Royal potatoes and wild asparagus; assiette of local game with roast vegetables and truffles; roasted local pheasant with cep risotto and foie gras.

Directions: 3 miles N of Windermere on A591. Turn R into Holbeck Lane. Hotel is 0.5 miles on L

WINDERMERE, Jerichos

In a county renowned for its traditional country house hotels, here is a new restaurant offering food as sophisticated and contemporary as anywhere in London. The modern style is reflected in the deep purple interior dramatically offset by vases of tiger lilies and lit with low-voltage spotlights, and the open-plan kitchen that exudes enticing aromas. The simple menus offers five choices at each course with dishes showing strong English, Italian and Spanish influences. After sampling the good home-baked rolls, we went on to a delightful seafood risotto that featured tender langoustines and mussels. Roast fillet of cod with Mediterranean vegetables followed, a 'wholesome symphony of flavours'. The warm chocolate mousse for dessert was excellent, and was followed by great cappuccino. The sixty-strong wine list offers wines by the glass and bottle. Business here is understandably brisk.

Birch Street LA23 1EG
Map 7: SD49
Tel/Fax: 015394 42522
Chefs: Chris Blaydes, Chris Dickson
Owners: Chris & Jo Blaydes
Cost: Alc £25. ☺ H/wine £10.75
Times: D only, 6.45-last D 10.15pm. Closed Mon
Additional: No children under 12; ❹ dishes
Seats: 38. Private dining room 20
Smoking: No smoking in dining room
Credit cards: ▆ ▆ ▆ ▆

Directions: In town centre

WINDERMERE,
Langdale Chase

LA23 1LW
Map 7: SD49
Tel: 015394 32201
Fax: 015394 32604

Chef: John Connor

Owners: Philip & Samantha Capon
Cost: Fixed-price L £15.95/D £27. H/wine £9
Times: 12.30-last L 1.45pm/7-last D 8.30pm
Additional: Sunday L; Children welcome; ❹ dishes
Seats: 75. Private dining room 24. Jacket & tie preferred
Smoking: No smoking in dining room; Air conditioning
Accommodation: 29 en suite
Credit cards: ▆ ▆ ▆ ▆ ▆ ▆ ▆ JCB

This fine late-Victorian mansion has a lot going for it: a lakeside setting; splendid gardens and grounds; stunning views. The pillared dining room is a bright, luxurious room, staff are polished and friendly, keen to please. An inspection dinner taken in late autumn was full of praise for dishes such as superb scallops with roasted red peppers, potato and cep cream soup, grilled sea bass on a bed of spiced couscous with a pesto jus, accompanied by accurately cooked dauphinoise potatoes, puréed parsnip, turned carrots, saffron potatoes, and mange-tout. Dessert was an iced banana parfait with a bitter chocolate sauce. Good home-baked breads and petits fours maintained standards. The wine list is eclectic, offering a value-for-money range of New World labels as well as the more classically French.

Directions: On the A591 3 miles N of Windermere, 2 miles S of Ambleside

WINDERMERE, **Lindeth Fell Hotel**

Lyth Valley Road
Bowness LA23 3JP
Map 7: SD49
Tel: 015394 43286
Fax: 015394 47455
Chefs: Diana Kennedy, Wayne Tarney
Owners: Pat & Diana Kennedy
Cost: Fixed-price D £17 (5 courses).
☺ H/wine £7.50
Times: D only, 7.30pm-8.30pm
Additional: Bar Food L; Sunday L;
No children under 7; 🌢 dishes
Smoking: No smoking in dining room
Accommodation: 15 en suite
Credit cards: 💳 💳 💳

Both the Edwardian dining room and the conservatory offer lake and mountain views. The five-course menus provide straightforward choices and exemplify good country cooking. Options might be poached salmon with shrimp butter sauce, or chargrilled calves' liver with onions and bacon jus.

Directions: 1 mile S of Bowness on A5074 Lyth Valley Road

WINDERMERE,
Lindeth Howe Country House

Longtail Hill Storrs Park LA23 3JF
Map 7: SD49
Tel: 015394 45759
Fax: 015394 46368
Please telephone for further details

The former home of Beatrix Potter is a now a charming country house hotel set in six acres of secluded grounds. The daily changing four-course menu makes much use of fresh produce, perhaps salmon and dill fishcakes with saffron and parsley sauce, cream of onion soup, roast loin of lamb with a port wine and rosemary jus, and iced banana parfait.

WINDERMERE,
Linthwaite House Hotel

Crook Road Bowness LA23 3JA
Map 7: SD49
Tel: 015394 88600
Fax: 015394 88601
Chef: Ian Mark Bravey
Owner: Mike Bevans, Handmade
Hotels Ltd
Cost: Alc £15, fixed-price D £33.50
(4 courses). H/wine £14.75
Times: 12.30-last L 1.30pm/7.15-last
D 8.45pm
Additional: Bar food L; Sunday L;
No children under 7; 🌢 dishes
Seats: 42. Private dining room 16
Smoking: No smoking in dining room
Accommodation: 18 en suite
Credit cards: 💳 💳 💳 💳 💳 💳 💳 JCB

Formerly an Edwardian gentleman's residence, Linthwaite is surrounded by delightful gardens and enjoys spectacular views of the lake and surrounding fells from its elevated position. The restaurant, where the cooking is going from strength to strength, retains an opulent period feel with antique tables, heavy burgundy drapes and quality table settings. Clear, well-balanced flavours are the hallmark of adventurous dishes which, on our last visit, included a delicious starter of monk fish tails wrapped in air-dried Cumbrian ham on Burgundy butter sauce, flavourful breast of guinea fowl baked with tarragon and morels with Madeira sauce and fried parsnip shavings, and steamed chocolate sponge with a chocolate fudge centre and vanilla pod ice cream. The meal got off to a good start with nicely varied canapés and a bonne bouche of lobster tail and truffle set in a light Muscadet jelly with a tomato and basil salsa. Lots of half-bottles on an interesting wine list and a good handful available by the glass.

Directions: Take 1st L off A591 at roundabout NW of Kendal (B5284). Follow for 6 miles, hotel is 1 mile after Windermere Golf Club on L

WINDERMERE,

Miller Howe Hotel

Rayrigg Road LA23 1EY
Map 7: SD49
Tel: 015394 42536
Fax: 015394 45664
Chef: Susan Elliott
Owner: Charles Garside
Cost: Fixed-price L £15/D £32 (4 courses). H/wine £15.50
Times: L at 1pm/D at 8pm. Closed Jan
Additional: Sunday L; No children under 8. dishes
Seats: 70. Private room 35
Smoking: No smoking in dining room; Air conditioning
Accommodation: 12 en suite
Credit cards:

The departure of John Tovey marks the end of an era for Miller Howe. But Charles Garside writes to say that any new ideas will be 'implemented gently' as he enters a period of evolution, not revolution. Some things won't change: one of the best sites in the Lake District, with stunning views from lounges, conservatory and dining-room over Lake Windermere and the fells, the comfort, the relaxing atmosphere, the quality of the food. In time-honoured tradition, the set four-course dinner, with no choice until pudding, remains, although plans are afoot to offer a wider choice as well as vegetarian dishes. Meanwhile, guests are ushered in, rather theatrically, to the dining-room at 8 o'clock before the lights are dimmed. A first course of plum tomato, seared to intensify its sweetness, on papardelle cooked in white wine and crème fraîche with shaved Parmesan might be followed by thick gravad lax on smooth hummus with crisp asparagus spears — a good blend of textures and flavours. A main course of breast of Gressingham duck, pink, its skin properly crisp, gets the thumbs up for its tenderness and flavour, the usual proliferation of interesting vegetables accompanying. Ginger crème brûlée, smooth and properly topped, steals the show among desserts. Choose one of the New World wines from the pedigrees on the list.

Directions: On A592 between Windermere and Bowness

WINDERMERE, **Old England Hotel**

*A modern menu and fine views can both be enjoyed at this elegant
Georgian hotel whose gardens run down to the edge of the lake.
Thai chicken noodle soup, loin of pork with sage and onion stuffing,
chicken fettucine with cream and basil sauce, and Greek yogurt
brûlée demonstrate the range.*

Smoking: No-smoking area. **Accommodation:** 76 en suite
Credit cards: 💳 💳 💳 💳 💳 💳 💳

Directions: M6/J36, W on A592, hotel is behind St Martins
Church at Bowness Bay

Church Street Bowness LA23 3DF
Map 7: SD49
Tel: 015394 42444
Fax: 015394 43432
Chef: Andy Hipwell
Owner: Forte
Cost: Alc £18. H/wine £13.95
Times: D only, last D 9.45pm
Additional: Bar food L; Sunday L
12.30-2.30pm; Children welcome;
dishes

WINDERMERE,
Quarry Garth Hotel

NEW

*Smart country house hotel with a French-style restaurant noted for
ambitious cooking. Two menus provide ample choice and value for
money. Our most recent meal included a lavish celery and Stilton
soup, grilled delice of fresh sea bass with a chive butter sauce, and a
delicious baked almond tart with sauce anglaise. Good petits fours.*

Smoking: No smoking in dining room
Accommodation: 13 en suite. **Credit cards:** 💳 💳 💳 💳 💳

Directions: Telephone for directions

Troutbeck Bridge LA23 1LF
Map 7: SD49
Tel: 015394 88282
Fax: 015394 46584
Chef: John Male
Owner: KJ Maclean
Cost: Alc £20, fixed-price L £11.75/D
£25.95 (5 courses). ☺ H/wine £11.95
Times: Last L 2pm/last D 9pm
Additional: Bar food; Sunday L;
No children under 8; dishes

WINDERMERE, **Roger's Restaurant**

*The Pergl-Wilsons have been pleasing customers at this intimate,
candlelit restaurant for more than sixteen years. Alena's friendly,
knowledgeable service is matched by Roger's good cooking of
French and English dishes like poulet farci à la limousine, roast
Yorkshire grouse with traditional garnish, and grilled wild salmon
with avocado and crème fraîche sauce.*

Credit cards: 💳 💳 💳 💳 💳 💳 💳

Directions: Close to Windermere railway station, opposite
Tourist Information Centre

4 High Street LA23 1AF
Map 7: SD49
Tel: 015394 44954
Chef: Roger Pergl-Wilson
Owners: Roger & Alena Pergl-Wilson
Cost: Alc £22, fixed-price D £16.50
(4 courses). ☺ H/wine £9.80
Times: D only, last D 9.30pm.
Closed Sun
Additional: Children welcome;
dishes
Smoking: No-smoking area;
No cigars & pipes

WINDERMERE,
Wild Boar Hotel

NEW

*A former coaching inn in the peaceful Winster Valley, mid-way
between Kendal and Windermere. Great traditional dining room
with exposed beams, horse brasses and swathes of red velvet. Simple
honest cooking takes in chicken and duck terrine with redcurrant
and orange sauce, grilled fillet of steak with foie gras and Madeira
jus, and mango and chocolate mousse.*

Accommodation: 36 en suite
Credit cards: 💳 💳 💳 💳 💳 JCB

Directions: From M6/J36 take dual carriageway signposted
'South Lakes' for 8 miles. Turn L on to B5284, signed 'Crook &
Hawkshead via Ferry'. Hotel 4 miles on R

Crook LA23 3NF
Map 7: SD49
Tel: 015394 45225
Fax: 015394 42498
Chef: Marc Saunders
Owner: English Lakes Hotels
Cost: Alc £25, fixed-price D £19.95
(4 courses). ☺ H/wine £9.75
Times: Last L 1.45pm/last D 9pm
Additional: Bar food L; Sunday L;
Children welcome; dishes
Smoking: No smoking in dining room
Church Road Grange over Sands

WITHERSLACK,

Old Vicarage Hotel ❀❀

Church Road
Grange-over-Sands
LA11 6RS
Map 7: SD48
Tel: 015395 52381
Fax: 015395 52373
Chef: James Brown
Owners: S Reeve & J Brown
Cost: Fixed-price D £27.50 (4
courses). H/wine £12.50
Times: D only, 7-last D 8.30pm
Additional: Sunday L (12.30-2pm);
Children welcome; ❹ dishes
Seats: 40. Private dining room 14
Smoking: No smoking in dining room
Accommodation: 15 en suite
Credit cards: ▬ ▬ ▨ ▢ ▬ ▣ JCB

Dating back to 1803, this delightful former vicarage enjoys a peaceful location just outside Kendal. Lovely mature gardens include a damson orchard. The experience of dinner, served in what was the original kitchen of the house, is enhanced by friendly, knowledgeable staff. Fresh ingredients are carefully used in dishes such as terrine of roast capsicums with basil beurre blanc, leek and potato soup with rosemary croûtons, baked lemon sole with halibut and prawn mousseline sauce vierge, and grilled breast of Gressingham duck with piperade and chargrilled aubergine. The fixed-price menu includes a cheese course (British farmhouse) and such desserts as steamed orange and sultana sponge pudding, and vanilla bavarois. Wines are well chosen with an interesting Italian selection and a good choice of half-bottles.

Directions: Off A590. Take turning in village signposted to church

DERBYSHIRE

ASHBOURNE,

Callow Hall ❀❀

Mappleton Road DE6 2AA
Map 7: SK14

Food plays an important part of a stay at this hotel; apart from the soundly cooked evening meals served in a choice of dining rooms (intimate red, or fresh, airy lemons and creams), bacon is cured on the premises and sausages are home-made, as are the preserves. Even small details stand out. At our last inspection, fresh, extremely tasty vegetables of sugar snap peas, courgettes with chopped herbs, fennel and both duchesse and new potatoes were singled out for praise, as were canapés of quails' eggs with prawn and a baby sausage, and home-made wholemeal rolls. Otherwise there's fish, or loin of lamb with roasted garlic and mint stuffing, and rice and cinnamon pudding for dessert. There is much enthusiasm in the wine list as well as thought, and prices are very reasonable.

Directions: 0.75 mile from Ashbourne; A515 (Buxton), sharp L by Bowling Green Pub, 1st R Mappleton Road

ASHFORD-IN-THE-WATER,

Riverside House Hotel ❀❀

Inside this Georgian mansion, its gardens fronting the River Wye, is a series of comfortably appointed rooms, including a bright conservatory for light meals, a cosy oak-panelled lounge with an inglenook, a drawing-room and two smart Regency-style dining-rooms. The kitchen uses high-quality produce, prepared with an assured hand. Canapés are out of the ordinary – rabbit and sultana croquette, lamb with wild mushroom duxelles in filo – and bread is baked in-house. A starter of seared scallops is well complemented by a purée of mango and banana, others may be calves' sweetbreads with black pudding and chanterelles. A main course of roasted Scotch salmon, moist and well-flavoured, may be served with lemon risotto and confit of fennel, and corn-fed chicken breast with goats' cheese mille-feuille and aubergine and artichoke fondue. An equally happy amalgam has been a pudding of mascarpone and summer fruit brûlée with intensely flavoured honey ice cream in a brandy snap.

Directions: 2 miles from centre of Bakewell on A6 (Buxton). In Ashford village next to Sheepwash Bridge

Callow Hall

Tel: 01335 343403
Fax: 01335 343624
Please telephone for further details

AA Shortlisted for
Wine Award-see page 16

Fennel Street Bakewell
DE45 1QF
Map 7: SK17
Tel: 01629 814275
Fax: 01629 812873
Chef: John Whelan
Owner: Penelope Thornton Hotels Ltd
Cost: *Alc* £35.50, fixed-price L £18.95/D £33. ☺ H/wine £10
Times: Noon-2pm/7-9.30pm
Additional: Bar food L; Sunday L; No children under 10; ✦ dishes
Seats: 40. Private dining room 24. Jacket & tie preferred
Smoking: No smoking in dining room
Accommodation: 15 en suite
Credit cards: ▬ ▬ ✖ ▭ ▬ ▭ ▭

BAKEWELL, Croft Hotel ❀

Relaxation is assured at this charming, personally run Victorian country house hidden away in its own grounds. Public rooms, including the intimate restaurant, lead off a central galleried lounge. Dinner only is served, with menus built around fresh produce.

Smoking: No smoking in dining room
Accommodation: 9 en suite. **Credit cards:** ▅ ▅ ⌷ JCB

Directions: A6 from Bakewell towards Buxton, 1.7 miles turn R (A6020). After 0.75 miles turn L signed Great Longstone. Hotel on R in village.

Great Longstone DE45 1TF
Map 8: SK26
Tel: 01629 640278
Chef: Lynne Macaskill
Owners: Robert Allan & Lynne Macaskill
Cost: Fixed-price D £23.50 (4 courses). ☺ H/wine £8.75
Times: D only at 7.30pm. Closed Jan-early Feb
Additional: ✿ dishes

BAKEWELL,
Renaissance Restaurant ❀

French owned and run restaurant converted from an old barn with plenty of old beams and stone walls to create a striking impression. Lovely classic dishes include duck confit served on a bed of potatoes and caramelised onions, veal tournedos wrapped in bacon accompanied by a rustic mustard sauce, and crêpes Suzette with fresh orange sauce. Short, mainly French wine list.

Smoking: No smoking in dining room
Credit cards: ▅ ▅ ⌷

Directions: From Bakewell roundabout in town centre take A6 Buxton exit. 1st R into Bath Street (one-way).

Bath Street DE45 1BX
Map 8: SK26

Tel: 01629 812687
Chef: Eric Piedaniel
Owners: E & C Piedaniel, D Beraud
Cost: *Alc* £20.45, fixed-price L & D £18.95. ☺ H/wine £9.80
Times: Last L 1.30pm/last D 9.30pm. Closed D Sun, all Mon, 1st 2 wks Jan, 1st 2 wks Aug
Additional: Bar food L; Sunday L; Children welcome; ✿ dishes.

BAKEWELL, Rutland Arms ❀   NEW

Jane Austen stayed at this 18th-century hotel while writing 'Pride and Prejudice'. Almost two centuries later, and the Rutland Arms is now home to some fine English cooking. In the Four Seasons restaurant starters range from black pudding with roasted shallots and smoked bacon, to glazed goats' cheese on toasted brioche.

Accommodation: 36 en suite. **Credit cards:** ▅ ▅ ⌷ ▅ ▅

Directions: Telephone for directions

The Square DE45 1BT
Map 8: SK26
Tel: 01629 812812
Fax: 01629 812309
Chef: Martyn Noon
Cost: Fixed price L £11.50/D £17.95. ☺ H/wine £10
Times: Last L 2pm/last D 9pm
Additional: Bar food; Sunday L; Children welcome; ✿ dishes
Smoking: No smoking in dining room

BASLOW, Cavendish Hotel ❀❀

Part of the great Chatsworth estate, the sense of formality spills over into the restaurant. Concepts are interesting – a spinach mousseline with scallops, Parmesan wafers and beurre blanc sauce was a good idea, but a main course of roast sea bass with red wine sauce, strawberries, capers, beansprouts and gratin dauphinoise was considered over the top. Other typical dishes might include confit of duck with a duck and green peppercorn sausage, soused tomato, apple and raisin salad with chive potatoes, and pan-fried smoked salmon fishcake with sesame-seeded chicken and scallops, lemon and smoked oil juices. Orange soufflé pudding and blood orange sabayon for dessert, but a savoury alternative might be mushrooms and anchovies on brioche toast, or the British cheese of the month.

Directions: In the centre of Baslow village

Bakewell DE45 1SP
Map 8: SK27

Tel: 01246 582311
Fax: 01246 582312
Chef: Nick Buckingham
Owner: Eric Marsh
Cost: Fixed-price D £37.75. ☺ H/wine £17.50
Times: 12.30pm-last L 2pm/7pm-last D 10pm.
Additional: Bar food; Sunday L; Children welcome; ✿ dishes
Seats: 50. Private dining room 16
Smoking: No smoking in dining room
Accommodation: 24 en suite
Credit cards: ▅ ▅ ▅ ⌷ ▅ ▅

BASLOW,
Fischer's Baslow Hall 🏵🏵🏵

Calver Road DE45 1RR
Map 8: SK27
Tel: 01246 583259
Fax: 01246 583818
Chef: Max Fischer
Owners: Max & Susan Fischer
Cost: Fixed-price L £24/D £42
(4 courses). H/wine £12.50
Times: Noon-last L 1.30pm/7-last
D 9.30pm. Closed D Sun (except
residents), 25-26 Dec
Additional: Café Max L & D; Sunday
L; No children under 12 at D;
🍴 dishes
Seats: 40. Private dining rooms 12-24.
Jacket & tie preferred
Smoking: No smoking in dining room
Accommodation: 6 en suite
Credit cards: 🟦 🟦 🟥 🟦 🟦 🟦 🟦

Max Fischer's refined, beautifully crafted cuisine is worth travelling some distance for, and there probably isn't a better, or more committed chef for miles around. Public rooms centre around the restaurant, and the slightly more casual Café Max with its brasserie-style menu. The efficient team of smart staff exude friendly hospitality, and visitors can relax before dinner in the attractive lounge with its log fire and convivial drinks trolley. Canapés are soon demolished, especially when the selection includes a bite-sized piece of cod in crisp batter (but where was the chip?), a little croûte with a super fresh ravigote topping, and smoked fish mousse on toast and filo parcels. At the table, an *amuse bouche,* perhaps white bean cappuccino with truffle oil, precedes first courses such as sea bass with pepper and aubergine compote, coriander pesto, or sea scallops, briefly seared rather than heavily caramelised to enhance their natural flavour, served with sauté potato truffle and sherry vinaigrette. Fish dishes often include a meat element such as monkfish in pancetta with morel mushrooms. Luxury ingredients, however, are not just there for effect, but served in generous quantity, as in the popular pan-fried foie gras with citrus sauce – pickled ginger, lime and orange juice are thickened with the fat from the foie gras, which is set on caramelised mango and home-made brioche. Colour plays an important part – vividly hued oils and pepper essences illuminate the plate. Dessert plates are always popular – an apple theme included crème brûlée, sorbet and Granny Smith jus. Strong cafetière coffee and good petits fours round the meal off. The well-balanced wine list features some older vintages as well as good-value bottles.

Signature dishes: Saddle of new season Derbyshire lamb; saddle of rabbit, spaghetti, spinach and mustard sauce; pig's trotter, pommes purée and morel mushrooms; saddle of Chatsworth venison, celeriac purée, game pepper sauce.

AA Wine Award-see page 16 Shortlisted for

Directions: On right of A623
Stockport Road as you leave Baslow
towards Calver.

BELPER, **Makeney Hall Hotel** 🏵🏵

The beautifully restored Victorian mansion stands in six acres of grounds above the River Derwent. Sound country house cooking from a menu that offers the likes of grilled goats' cheese on a walnut croûton with sweet onion and mâche salad, cutlets of English lamb with a tarragon mousse, rosemary scented potato cake and a Madeira and tomato jus, and

Milford DE56 0RS
Map 8: SK34
Tel: 01332 842999
Fax: 01332 842777
Chef: Martyn Yates
Owner: Regal Hotel Group
Cost: Alc £25, fixed-price L
£13.95/£19.50. 🍴 H/wine £10.25

Makeney Hall Hotel

Times: Noon-1.45pm/7-9.45pm. Closed Sat
Additional: Sunday L; Children welcome; 🕭 dishes
Seats: 90. Private dining rooms 150
Smoking: No-smoking area; No pipes and cigars; Air conditioning
Accommodation: 45 en suite
Credit cards: ▰ ▰ ▰ ▰ ▰ ▰ ▰ JCB

Directions: Join A6 N of Derby & turn R into Milford. Hotel is 0.25 miles, just past Garden Centre

coconut and mango soufflé with crème anglaise. A well reported winter dinner opened with a colourful, attractive seafood terrine set in a delicate saffron gelatine, and was followed by ballotine of duck confit set on a creamy curry sauce that gave just enough spicy flavour to be interesting without being overpowering – an unusual combination that worked well. Dessert was a classic raspberry brûlée, served with moreish chocolate chip cookies.

BUXTON, Lee Wood Hotel ❁❁

13 Manchester Road SK17 6TQ
Map 7: SK07
Tel: 01298 23002
Fax: 01298 23228
Chef: Chris Bates
Owner: John C Millican
Cost: Fixed-price L £13.50/D £22. ☺ H/wine £10.95.
Times: 12.15pm-last L 2pm/7.15pm-last D 9.30pm
Additional: Bar food; Sunday L; Children welcome; 🕭 dishes
Seats: 80. Private dining room 20
Smoking: No smoking in dining room
Accommodation: 37 en suite
Credit cards: ▰ ▰ ▰ ▰ ▰ ▰ ▰ JCB

The conservatory restaurant overlooks landscaped grounds and offers an extensive *carte* that can be taken in various permutations, priced by the number of courses chosen. The length of the menu allows for a variety of styles, although dishes read a like a check-list of must-have ingredients and techniques: poached egg wrapped in Parma ham, deep-fried in a tempura batter and served on a tomato salad with purple pesto; sautéed duck livers, tossed with seasonal leaves, asparagus, black pudding and cherry tomatoes, dressed with a sun-dried tomato vinaigrette; brochettes of chicken marinated in soy, garlic and ginger served with a hoisin sauce and coconut-flavoured noodles; seared salmon escalope cooked in butter and served with green-lip mussels set on a red pepper coulis. The 'Speciality Menu' is straightforward by comparison – oak-smoked Scotch salmon and prime Scotch Chateaubriand with béarnaise sauce.

Directions: Follow A5004 Long Hill to Whaley Bridge. Hotel 300 metres beyond the Devonshire Royal Hospital

DERBY, **Mickleover Court Hotel**

Etwall Road
Mickleover DE3 5XX
Map 8: SK33
Tel: 01332 521234
Fax: 01332 521238
Chef: Martin Clayton
Cost: Alc £25. ☺ H/wine £11.50
Times: Noon-last D 10pm
Additional: Bar food; Sunday L;
Children welcome; 🍴 dishes
Smoking: No-smoking area; No pipes
& cigars; Air conditioning
Accommodation: 80 en suite
Credit cards:

*Impressive modern hotel situated on the outskirts of Derby. Guests
have two choices, the informal Stelline Restaurant offering Italian
dishes and the Avesbury Brasserie. In the latter our inspector
particularly enjoyed a very fresh sea bass cooked with baby fennel
and a Pernod sauce, followed by a well- flavoured lemon crème.*

Directions: From Mickleover take A516 (Uttoxeter) hotel is L of
1st roundabout

DOVERIDGE, **The Beeches Farmhouse Hotel** ❀❀

Doveridge DE6 5LR
Map 7: SK13
Tel: 01889 590288
Fax: 01889 590559
Chef: Barbara Tunnicliffe
Owners: Barbara & Paul Tunnicliffe
Cost: Alc £22, fixed-price L £10.95.
☺ H/wine £7.95
Times: Noon-last L 2pm/7-last
D 9pm. Closed 25-26 Dec
Additional: Bar food D; Sunday L;
Children welcome; 🍴 dishes
Seats: 70
Smoking: No smoking in dining room
Accommodation: 10 en suite
Credit cards:

The myriad of small dining rooms continue to be enjoyed by
an appreciative audience at this aptly named hotel: still a
working farm with an excellent standard of accommodation,
roaring open fires, rough hewn wooden tables, low beams,
quarry-tiled or polished floorboards, fresh flowers. Cooking is
robust, rich, dependent on seasonal produce and utterly
traditional. Home-made soups, or potted duck served with
lemon chutney are typical openers to a meal that could go on
to local boneless rib of beef with fresh horseradish and onion
sauce with onion rings, or braised shoulder of lamb on hot-pot
potatoes with oysters. Desserts are from the trolley and there's
English farmhouse cheeses served with exotic fruits.

Directions: From A50 take exit sighposted Doveridge and
follow signs for Waldley. At grass triangle turn R; hotel is 1st L

HATHERSAGE, George Hotel ❀

15th-century stone coaching inn surrounded by stunning Peak District scenery. Inside, traditional and innovative dishes jostle for attention in the elegant restaurant. From the lunch menu try double baked soufflé with mozzarella and spinach, or pot-roasted lamb with mushrooms and rosemary.

Smoking: No smoking in dining room
Accommodation: 19 en suite
Credit cards: ▬ ▨ ▚ ▢ ▨

Directions: In village centre on A625

Main Road S30 1BB
Map 8: SK28
Tel: 01433 650436
Fax: 01433 650099
Chef: Ben Handley
Owner: Eric Marsh
Cost: Alc £30, fixed-price L £14.95/D £19.95. ☺ H/wine £13.50
Times: Last L 3pm/last D 10pm. Open all day in summer
Additional: Sunday L; Children welcome; ❹ dishes

MATLOCK, Riber Hall ❀

Elizabethan manor house beautifully located in the foothills of the Pennines. The menu is typified by grilled turbot on puff pastry with marinated tomatoes and watercress sauce, saddle of rabbit with potato and wild mushroom soufflé and mustard cream, and meringue-glazed lemon tart with honey and lavender ice cream. Separate vegetarian menu.

Tansley DE4 5JU
Map 8: SK35
Tel: 01629 582795
Fax: 01629 580475
Chef: Patrick Salvadori
Owner: Alex Biggin
Cost: Fixed-price L £13 (2 courses)/D £27 (2 courses). H/wine £14.75
Times: Last L 1.30pm/last D 9.30pm
Additional: Bar food L; Sunday L; Children welcome; ❹ dishes
Smoking: No smoking in one dining room
Accommodation: 14 en suite
Credit cards: ▬ ▨ ▚ ▢ ▨ ▣ ▣ JCB

Directions: One mile up Alders Lane and Carr Lane off A615 at Tansley

MELBOURNE, The Bay Tree ❀

Former coaching inn dating from the 17th century, now a smart restaurant with a beamed dining room. The varied menu offers pasta dishes, crab cakes with mango and tomato salsa, and marinated salmon with deep-fried oysters. There's a good selection of cheeses for those not tempted by Cointreau bread-and-butter pudding.

Directions: Town centre

4 Potter Street DE73 1DW
Map 8: SK32
Tel: 01332 863358
Fax: 01332 865545
Please telephone for further details

RIDGEWAY,
The Old Vicarage Restaurant ❀❀❀

Set amidst tranquil countryside, this lovely old house has been lovingly nurtured by the Bramleys. Drinks are taken in the one of several lounges, strikingly decorated in sunset yellows and cobalt blues. The restaurant itself is typically British, a unique theme these days, and includes long flowing starched cloths, Wedgwood and silver candelabras. The dinner menu is a set affair and provides five choices at each course. There's a rustic theme here, with the emphasis on traditional, simple, tried-and

Ridgeway Moor S12 3XW
Map 8: SK48
Tel: 0114 2475814
Fax: 0114 2477079
Chefs: Tessa Bramley, Nathan Smith, Andrew Gilbert
Owners: Tessa & Andrew Bramley
Please telephone for further details

-tested concepts. This could be seen in a late spring meal that opened with an exact, very fresh tasting roasted tail of monkfish wrapped in prosciutto, gratinated with a herb crust and served with basil pesto and a roasted ratatouille. An extra course took in a well-executed wild mushroom ravioli set on a bed of roasted baby leeks. An earthy roast loin of new season lamb followed, served with a parsley mash, sweet corn and chilli pancakes and a pan gravy made from the roasting tray. Banana crème brûlée with caramelised fruits and butterscotch sauce was applauded for its freshness and flavour. Breads, canapés, amuse bouche (gravad lax of salmon with a dill crème fraîche), and petits fours maintain the exact standards. The wine list is fairly modest but encompasses a healthy range to suit both the menu and customer budgets.

Directions: S/E of Sheffield off the A616 on B6054; follow signs for Ridgeway Cottage Industries. Restaurant is 300yds on L

RISLEY, **Risley Hall Hotel**

While parts of the hotel date from 1500, the dining room is Victorian, traditionally decorated and comfortable. There is a good choice of dishes from a combination of menus, supplemented by vegetarian and fish specials. The highlight of a test meal was a 'melt-in-the-mouth' confit of duck.

Smoking: No smoking in dining room
Accommodation: 16 en suite
Credit cards: ■ ▒ ◣ ◻ ▦

Directions: From M1/J25 take road signposted Risley. Up to crossroads, turn R. Hotel is 0.75 mile on R past garage.

Derby Road DE72 3SS
Map 8: SK43
Tel: 01159 939000
Fax: 01159 9397766
Chef: John Molnar
Owners: Mr & Mrs Crosbie
Cost: *Alc* £25. Fixed-price D £15.95. ☺ H/wine £9.95
Times: Last L 2pm/last D 9.30pm. Closed D Sun
Additional: Bar Food L; Sunday L; No children under 10; ◕ dishes

ROWSLEY, **East Lodge Hotel**

Victorian lodge set in ten attractive acres. Good quality produce combined with sound cooking produce dishes such as salmon and pink peppercorn brûlée, oxtail paysanne with horseradish dumplings, confit of duck with sweet braised white cabbage and a bigarade sauce, plus a classic crème brûlée.

Accommodation: 15 en suite
Credit cards: ■ ▒ ◣ ◻ ▦

Directions: Hotel drive access on A6, 5 miles from Matlock and 3 miles from Bakewell

Matlock DE4 2EF
Map 8: SK26
Tel: 01629 734474
Fax: 01629 733949
Chef: Mark Allday
Owners: Sue & Peter Mills
Cost: *Alc* £14.80, fixed-price D £21.95. ☺ H/wine £9.75
Times: Last L 2pm/D 9pm
Additional: Bar food L; Sunday L; Children welcome; ◕ dishes
Smoking: No smoking in dining room

SOUTH NORMANTON, **Swallow Hotel**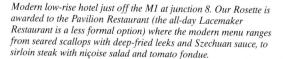

Modern low-rise hotel just off the M1 at junction 8. Our Rosette is awarded to the Pavilion Restaurant (the all-day Lacemaker Restaurant is a less formal option) where the modern menu ranges from seared scallops with deep-fried leeks and Szechuan sauce, to sirloin steak with niçoise salad and tomato fondue.

Accommodation: 160 en suite
Credit cards: ■ ▒ ◣ ◻ ▦ ◼ ◳ JCB

Directions: From M1/J28 – A38 (signed Mansfield). At 100 yards 1st L into car park

Carter Lane East DE55 2EH
Map 8: SK45
Tel: 01773 812000
Fax: 01773 580032
Chef: Alan McGilveray
Cost: *Alc* £22, fixed-price L £15.95/D £22. ☺ H/wine £12
Times: Last L 2pm/last D 10pm
Additional: Bar food L; Sunday L; Children welcome; ◕ dishes

THORPE, **Izaak Walton** ✿

17th-century hotel named after the renowned fisherman and author. The Haddon Hall Restaurant enjoys breathtaking views of Dovedale Valley, where guests can enjoy a spot of fishing on the meandering river. Typical dishes include roast loin of pork glazed with Stilton, and pan-fried veal escalope with Marsala wine.

Smoking: No smoking in dining room
Accommodation: 31 en suite
Credit cards: 🗠 🗠 🗠 🗠 🗠 🗠 🗠 JCB

Directions: One mile W of Thorpe on the Ilam road

Dovedale DE6 2AY
Map 7: SK15
Tel: 01335 350555
Fax: 01335 350539
Chef: Martin Griffith
Owner: The Duke of Rutland
Cost: Fixed-price L £14.50/D £22.75
(4 courses). ☺ H/wine £9.95
Times: D only, last D 9.30pm
Additional: Bar food; Sunday L (noon-2.30pm); Children welcome; ◑ dishes

DEVON

ASHBURTON,
Holne Chase Hotel ✿✿✿

The former hunting lodge is peaceful and calm, set in woodland in the Dart Valley. The cooking is described as 'traditional English with modern influences' and this translates as duck confit sausage with a salad of green beans and orange vinaigrette, pink grapefruit sorbet, and monkfish coated in sesame seeds and served with roast vegetables of pepper, garlic and asparagus in balsamic vinegar and oil. Puddings are a real strength with a passion fruit mousse surrounded by good white chocolate, a chocolate fondant top and some brunoise of exotic fruit. Other choices could include tomato and basil soup, a signature roast saddle of Dartmoor venison on bubble-and-squeak with a game sauce, and glazed rice pudding with fresh fruit. Excellent canapés and petits fours, and good onion, buttermilk and granary rolls show attention to small details.
Signature dishes: Shellfish tagliatelle with a mussel cream; tower of red mullet on wilted spinach with pesto and smoked bacon; tenderloin of pork with an apple and thyme crumble.

Two Bridges Road
Newton Abbot
TQ13 7NS
Map 3: SX77
Tel: 01364 631471
Fax: 01364 631453
Chef: Ross Duncan
Owners: Sebastian & Philippa Hughes
Cost: Alc £29.50, fixed-price L £20/D £25. H/wine £12
Times: Noon-last L-1.45pm/7.15-last D-8.45pm
Additional: Bar food L; Sunday L; No children under 10 at D; ◑ dishes
Seats: 45. Private dining room 12
Smoking: No smoking in dining room
Accommodation: 17 en suite
Credit cards: 🗠 🗠 🗠 🗠 🗠 🗠 🗠

Directions: Travelling from N & E, take 2nd Ashburton turning off A38. 2 miles to Holne Bridge, hotel is 0.25 miles on R. From Plymouth take 1st Ashburton turn

AXMINSTER,
Fairwater Head Hotel ✿

Recently refurbished, this spacious hotel restaurant offers panoramic views of the Axe valley and, at dusk, beautiful sunsets. Fresh local produce cooked in classic style features on the daily changing menu. Try beef with mushroom, onion and red wine sauce, or marinated pheasant with blackcurrant and port. There are pleasing wines too, at reasonable prices.

Accommodation: 20 en suite
Credit cards: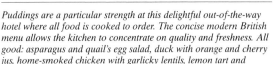

Directions: From Axminster or Lyme Regis take B3165 to Crewkerne. Hawkchurch village is signposted and hotel signs on approach to village

Hawkchurch EX13 5TX
Map 3: SY29
Tel: 01297 678349
Fax: 01297 678459
Chefs: Bob Renshaw, Ian Carter
Cost: *Alc* £20, fixed-price L £11/D £20.50 (4 courses). ☺ H/wine £9
Times: Last L 1.15pm/D 8.45pm. Closed Jan, Feb
Additional: Bar food L; Sunday L; Children welcome; ❹ dishes
Smoking: No smoking in dining room

AXMINSTER, **Lea Hill** ✿   NEW

Puddings are a particular strength at this delightful out-of-the-way hotel where all food is cooked to order. The concise modern British menu allows the kitchen to concentrate on quality and freshness. All good: asparagus and quail's egg salad, duck with orange and cherry jus, home-smoked chicken with garlicky lentils, lemon tart and chocolate mousse.

Accommodation: 12 en suite
Credit cards: ▬ ▬ ▫ ▣

Directions: From Axminster follow A358 towards Chard. After 2 miles turn L to Smallridge and follow signs to Membury. Half mile on R after village.

Membury EX13 7AQ
Map 3: SY29
Tel: 01404 881881/881388
Fax: 01404 881890
Chef: James Hubbard
Owners: Chris & Sue Hubbard
Cost: *Alc* £19.95, fixed-price D £19.95. ☺ H/wine £8.95
Times: D only, last D 8.45pm. Closed D Sun, Jan-mid Feb
Additional: Bar food L; Sunday L (noon-1.45pm); ❹ dishes
Smoking: No smoking in dining room

BAMPTON,
Bark House Hotel ✿✿

Sometimes the best British cooking is unpretentious and wholesome. The daily changing three-course dinner at this charming hotel, set in a beautiful part of the Exe valley, displays such virtues with interesting, nostalgic soups such as cream of mushroom and Madeira, or cream of swede, onion and potato, and some good old-fashioned dishes such as steamed steak and kidney pudding, and braised skate wings with caper butter sauce. Proper puddings are the order of the day – steamed spotted dick with egg custard sauce, or rhubarb ice cream. As an alternative, there is always a selection of West Country cheeses. Low beamed ceilings, log fires and fine views all contribute to the enjoyment.

Directions: 9 miles N of Tiverton on A396

Oakford Bridge Tiverton EX16 9HZ
Map 3: SS92
Tel: 01398 351236
Chef/Owner: Alastair Kameen
Cost: Fixed-price L £13.50/D £19.95. ☺ H/wine £8.50.
Times: L by prior arrangement/ 7.15pm-last D 8.45pm. Closed 1 wk late April, restricted service Nov-Mar
Additional: Bar meals L; Sunday L; No children under 5; ❹ dishes
Seats: 14
Smoking: No smoking in dining room
Accommodation: 5 en suite
Credit cards: None

BARNSTAPLE,
Halmpstone Manor ✿✿

A charming manor house owned by the Stanburys since 1947 and now run by Charles and Jane, the second generation of the family. Meals are served in the 16th-century panelled dining

Bishop's Tawton EX32 0EA
Map 2: SS53
Tel: 01271 830321
Fax: 01271 830826
Chef/Owner: Mrs Jane Stanbury

room, which by candlelight has an intimate atmosphere. Fish, fresh from Bideford Quay, regularly features on the hand-written, five-course set menu. A typical meal might start with salad of warm leaves with avocado, Roquefort and quails' eggs, followed by fillet of monkfish with a seed mustard sauce. At a meal in April, our inspector tried an 'excellent' starter of cheese soufflé, and a tiny fillet of sea bream with layered potato and a wonderfully delicate orange sauce. Rack of lamb followed – 'succulent and tender' – and came with sweet sugar snap peas and creamed mashed swede. After dinner relax in the lounge in front of the log fire with a glass of port.

Cost: Fixed price D £32.50 (5 courses). H/wine £9.80
Times: D only, 7-9pm. Closed Sun, Nov-Jan
Additional: ✪ dishes
Seats: 16. Jacket & tie preferred
Smoking: No smoking in dining room
Accommodation: 5 en suite
Credit cards: 💳 💳 💳 💳 💳

Directions: From Barnstaple take A377 to Bishop's Tawton. At end of village turn L for Cobbaton; sign on R

BARNSTAPLE,

Royal & Fortescue, The Bank

Boutport Street
EX31 1HG
Map 2: SS53
Tel/Fax: 01271 42289
Please telephone for further details

A former coaching inn with a pleasantly appointed restaurant and a popular bistro for all-day meals. In the latter, The Bank, the menu majors in Mexican dishes with a few 'less fiery dishes for the more wimpish'. Enjoy nachos tempered by a generous quantity of tomato salsa, soured cream and guacamole, and vegetable chilli with tortilla chips. Good espresso.

Directions: A361 into Barnstaple, along Barbican Rd signposted town centre; turn R into Queen St & L (one way) Boutport St. Hotel on L

BEER, Anchor Inn ✿   NEW

Seaton EX12 3ET
Map 2: SY28
Tel: 01297 20386
Fax: 01297 24474
Chef: Neil Harding
Owner: Mr DM Boalch
Cost: £20.50. ☺ H/wine £7.50.
Times: Last L 1.45pm/last D 9.30pm.
Closed Xmas

Locally caught fish is the speciality at this very popular, typically English harbour-side inn. The restaurant has a relaxed, informal atmosphere, and offers something for everyone, including fresh oysters and home-smoked salmon, or there might even be roast pheasant, or fusilli with wild mushrooms and herb sauce.

Additional: Bar food; Sunday L; Children welcome; ✪ dishes
Smoking: No smoking in dining room
Accommodation: 8 rooms
Credit cards: 💳 💳 💳 💳

Directions: By the harbour

BEER, Old Steam Bakery ✿   NEW

Fore Street EX12 3JJ
Map 3: SY28
Tel: 01297 22040
Chef: Michael Stride
Owners: Michael Stride,
Sarah Doak-Stride
Cost: *Alc* £22.50, fixed-price
L £13.50. ☺ H/wine £8.95

Converted from a steam bakery and decorated in shades of terracotta. A brook runs past the restaurant down to the sea. Local seafood is bought daily for dishes such as sole and scallop sushi, and herb-crusted cod, which appear alongside braised lamb shank and chargrilled chicken.

Times: Last L 2.30pm/last D 10.30pm. Closed D Mon, L tue, 2nd wk Feb-2nd wk Mar
Additional: Sunday L; No children under 11 at D, ✪ dishes
Credit cards: 💳 💳 💳 💳

Directions: Turn off A3052 (Exeter to Lyme Regis). Beer is 2 miles from Seaton.

BIDEFORD,

Yeoldon Hotel ❀

There's a Victorian theme to the dining room of this ivy-clad hotel overlooking the River Torridge. The menu however, offers innovative dishes such as Libyan lamb, chickpea and couscous soup with soda bread and mint pesto, alongside straightforward roast chicken, grilled salmon or steaks.

Additional: Sunday L (noon-1.30pm); Children welcome; dishes
Smoking: No smoking in dining room
Accommodation: 10 en suite
Credit cards: ▬ ▬ ⌱ ⌱ ▬ ⌱ ⌱ JCB

Directions: Follow A39 towards Bideford from Barnstaple, turn R onto A386 towards Northam at Torridge Bridge roundabout, take 3rd turning on R

Durrant Lane Northam EX39 2RL
Map 2: SS42
Tel: 01237 474400
Fax: 01237 476618
Chef: Kevin Jelley
Owners: Mr & Mrs K Jelley
Cost: Alc £23.50, fixed price
D £21.50 (4 courses). ☺
H/wine £9.50
Times: D only, last D 8.45pm

BOVEY TRACEY,

Edgemoor Hotel ❀❀

Haytor Road TQ13 9LE
Map 3: SX87
Tel: 01626 832466
Fax: 01626 834760
Chef: Edward Elliott
Owners: Pat & Rod Day
Cost: Fixed-price D £22.50. ☺
H/wine £7.95.
Times: Noon-last L 1.45pm/7pm-last D 9pm. Closed 1 wk after Xmas
Additional: Bar food; Sunday L;
No children under 8 in restaurant; ⌱ dishes
Seats: 40. Private dining room 60
Smoking: No smoking in dining room
Accommodation: 17 en suite
Credit cards: ▬ ▬ ⌱ ⌱ ▬ ⌱ ⌱ JCB

Situated in two acres of well-tended gardens on the edge of Dartmoor, the charming, ivy-clad country house was originally built as a school in 1870. The beamed bar has a welcoming open fire on cold days, and the restaurant is stylishly decorated. West country produce is used wherever possible – twice-baked cheese soufflé with Denhay smoked ham and topped with Devon Blue cheese, made a filling start on our recent visit, although the indulgent richness barely left room for the subsequent main course of sole filled with smoked salmon mousse with Vermouth-flavoured cream sauce. Vegetables are served on a help-yourself basis. More creamy calories came with a good banana brûlée, then coffee with cream and home-made clotted-cream fudge. The cooking, on the monthly changing *carte* with daily fish dishes, however, is careful enough to warrant any diet-busting.

Directions: From A38 take A382 (Drumbridges). Cross first mini roundabout & turn L at 2nd roundabout. Bear L towards Haytor. Hotel 0.25 mile on R

BRANSCOMBE, **The Masons Arms**

EX12 3DJ
Map 3: SY18
Tel: 01297 680300
Fax: 01297 680500
Chef: Saul Vicary
Owner: Murray Inglis
Cost: Fixed-price D £22. ☺
H/wine £11
Times: Last L 2.15pm/last D 9.15pm
Additional: Bar food; Children
welcome; 🍴 dishes
Smoking: No-smoking area
Accommodation: 21 rooms (most
en suite)
Credit cards: 🟦 🟦 🟥 🟦

*A 14th-century thatched inn in a chocolate-box village surrounded
by National Trust land. Dressed stone walls and old ships' timbers
are features of the charming two-room restaurant. Dishes might
include pan-fried duck liver with tossed salad and celeriac
rémoulade, steamed sea bass with saffron mash and coriander sauce,
and crème brûlée.*

Directions: Turn off A3052 (Exeter to Lyme Regis) and follow
road through Branscombe

BRIXHAM,
Maypool Park Hotel

NEW

Galmpton TQ5 0ET
Map 3: SX95
Tel: 01803 842442
Fax: 01803 845782
Chef: Brendan Keeley
Owners: Gill & Peter Bennion
Cost: Fixed-price D £20 (4 courses).
☺ H/wine £9.50
Times: Last D 8.30pm. Closed D Sun,
all Mon, Xmas & New Year

*Enjoying views across wooded hills to the River Dart, this delightful
small hotel presents well-executed dishes based on fresh local
produce, notably fish and seafood. Innovative menus may list tartlet
of Dartmoor venison stew, John Dory with herb cream sauce, and
lemon tart with clotted cream. Interesting wine list.*

Additional: Sunday L (noon-2pm); No children under 12;
🍴 dishes
Smoking: No smoking in dining room
Accommodation: 10 en suite
Credit cards: 🟦 🟦 🟥 🟦 🟦

Directions: Turn off A3022 at Churston into Manor Vale Road
for Maypool, pedestrian ferry and Greenway Quay and continue
for 2 miles

BROADHEMBURY, **Drewe Arms**

EX14 0NF
Map 3: ST10
Tel/Fax: 01404 841267
Chef/Owners: Kerstin & Nigel Burge
Cost: *Alc* £23, fixed price L &D £23.
☺ H/wine £9.75
Times: Last L 2pm/last D 9.30pm.
Closed D Sun
Additional: Bar food; Children
welcome; 🍴 dishes

*Steep yourself in history and seafood at this ancient pub-restaurant
named after the family who own the village. The Swedish chef's fishy
forte is not restricted to Scandinavia: prawn gazpacho, crab
Thermidor and John Dory with chanterelles reflect the international
approach. Meat lovers can choose beef or venison. An interesting
selection of local beers complements the setting.*

Smoking: No-smoking area; No pipes & cigars
Credit cards: None

Directions: From M5/J28, 5 miles on A373 Cullompton to
Honiton. Pub 1 mile NE of Broadhembury turning

BURRINGTON,

Northcote Manor

A stone-built manor set in 12 acres surrounded by lovely countryside. Murals depicting the history of the house adorn the hotel's restaurant. Dishes to sample might include light tomato soup with gnocchi and basil, a refreshing elderflower sorbet, and grilled red tilapia fillet with garlic and lemon thyme.

Additional: Bar food L; Sunday L; dishes
Smoking: No smoking in dining room
Accommodation: 13 en suite
Credit cards: ▨▨ ▨▨ ▨▨ ▨ ▨▨ ▨ ▨ JCB

Directions: A377 Exeter to Barnstaple. Turn into private drive opposite Portsmouth Arms railway station (Don't enter Burrington)

Nr Portsmouth Arms Station
EX37 9LZ
Map 3: SS61
Tel: 01769 560501
Fax: 01769 560770
Chef: Jez Hill
Owner: D J Boddy
Cost: Alc £26, fixed-price L £18/D £24.50 (4 courses). ☺ H/wine £12
Times: Last L 2pm/last D 9pm.
Closed L Mon-Fri

CHAGFORD, **22 Mill Street**   NEW

22 Mill Street TQ13 8AW
Map 3: SX78
Tel: 01647 432244
Chef: Duncan Walker
Owners: Amanda Leaman, Duncan Walker
Cost: Alc £17, fixed price L £14.95/D £24.50. ☺ H/wine £9.30
Times: Noon-2pm/7-9pm.
Closed L Mon, all Sun, 2 wks Jan
Additional: No children under 8; dishes
Seats: 30. Private room 12
Smoking: No smoking in dining room
Accommodation: 2 en suite
Credit cards: ▨▨ ▨▨ ▨▨ ▨

A shop-fronted property in the heart of Chagford (street parking can be difficult) has been converted into a restaurant by Duncan Walker and Amanda Leaman. A small hall warmed by a fire and boasting a small sofa is for pre-dinner drinks, 'or a smoke – the only place' gasped one inspector, and the restaurant itself, though small, is light and airy. Duncan worked at nearby Gidleigh Park (see entry) under Shaun Hill, and did time at Keith Floyd's restaurant in Tuckenhay. His style is his own, however, with dishes often offering something interesting: crab, spinach and spring onion lasagne, for example. A well liked, 'great value' May lunch began with excellent canapés – tiny croûton with scrambled egg, smoked salmon and chives, and filo pastry filled with prawn, spinach and fresh ginger. Gorgonzola risotto with a red pepper salad was really creamy and full of the promised flavours. After that came roast Gressingham duck – breast cooked just pink, the 'knuckle end' that much more so and falling off the bone – and good contrast from a layer of pastry topped with endive and red wine sauce. Raspberry soufflé was a strong point, well risen and had an intense raspberry flavour. Short wine list.

Directions: 200 yds on L after turning R out of Chagford Sq

CHAGFORD,

Easton Court Hotel

Evelyn Waugh wrote 'Brideshead Revisited' in the sitting room of this lovely thatched Tudor house, which nestles on the eastern edge of Dartmoor. The dining room has an intimate atmosphere, with old wooden beams, candles and a roaring fire in winter months. Look out for home-made terrines, hearty soups and scrumptious puddings.

Additional: No children under 12
Smoking: No smoking in dining room
Accommodation: 8 en suite
Credit cards: ▨▨ ▨▨ ▨▨ ▨ ▨

Directions: Off A30 on to the A382. Hotel on L near turning to Chagford

Easton Cross TQ13 8JL
Map 3: SX78
Tel: 01647 433469
Fax: 01647 433654
Chef: Ian Wanstall
Owners: Gordon & Judy Parker
Cost: Fixed-price D £22 (5 courses). ☺ H/wine £8.90
Times: D only, last D 8pm

CHAGFORD, Gidleigh Park ❁❁❁❁❁

Newton Abbot TQ13 8HH
Map 3: SX78
Tel: 01647 432367
Fax: 01647 432574
Chef: Michael Caines
Owners: Paul & Kay Henderson
Cost: Fixed-price L £33. H/wine
£17.50
Times: 12.30pm-last L 2pm/7pm-last
D 9pm
Additional: Bar food L;
No children under 5
Seats: 35
Smoking: No smoking in dining room
Accommodation: 14 en suite
Credit cards: ▇ ▇ ▇ ▇ ▇ ▇ ▇ JCB

The well-kept, mock-Tudor house is set in complete seclusion in 45 acres of land within the Dartmoor National Park. The grounds contain streams, intriguing pools and banks, peaceful retreats as well as a choice of sporting pursuits; it is, without doubt, one of the best country house hotels in the country. Michael Caines is known for his ambition and achievement, and his cooking more than lives up to the standards set by the house. He has the ability to season dishes, bringing all the flavours to the fore, with an accuracy that is paramount. A May dinner exemplified some of his skills. Chicken mousse was delicately flavoured and beautifully complemented by fresh asparagus and clearly flavoured morels; a stunning mille-feuille of monkfish and scallops was accompanied by a leek fondue that 'brought the whole dish to life' and a fennel cream sauce that was quite potent in terms of flavour but did not detract from the other ingredients. At that meal other tables were singing the praises of a terrine of foie gras with Madeira jelly and salad with truffle vinaigrette, a lobster fricassée, and the flavour of the organically reared local beef. Local, French and Irish cheeses were served with home-made bread and biscuits, before the near perfection of a chocolate tart of light, crisp pastry and smooth, rich, bitter chocolate filling, served with a stunning coffee-flavoured ice cream and coffee crème anglaise. The wine list is extensive and clearly laid out with a section on every French wine producing area (in depth in Bordeaux and Burgundy). The Italian section is worth studying, as is Alsace, and most of the New World countries are well covered. A Cruvinet machine allows for eight quality wines to be served by the glass.
Signature dishes: Local lamb with a tian of spinach, tomato and aubergine; wild salmon with a dill and caviar butter sauce; terrine of duck confit, foie gras and shallots; roast pheasant with boudin noir and lentils with red wine sauce.

Directions: Chagford Square turn R at Lloyds Bank into Mill Street, after 150 yd R fork, straight across crossroads into Holy Street. Restaurant is 1.5 miles.

**Shortlisted for AA Wine Award –
see page 16**

CHAGFORD,
Mill End Hotel ❁

The substantial 18th-century flour mill sits by the River Teign and the Teign Gorge; the atmosphere is as tranquil as the setting is glorious. The original waterwheel is still in business, now supplying the hotel with its own electricity. The menus change daily and use fresh, local ingredients, indeed, the West Country cheeseboard is a fine sight to behold. Typical dishes include poached venison sausage on leaf spinach with cranberry-infused sauce, medley of south-coast seafood on a red pepper coulis. Breakfasts are wonderful.

Sandy Park TQ13 8JN
Map 3: SX78
Tel: 01647 432282
Fax: 01647 433106
Chef: Alan Lane
Owners: Julian Peck, Mrs Jill Day
Cost: *Alc* £30, fixed-price L £15/ D
£32 (5 courses). H/wine £11.50
Times: 12.30-last L 1.45pm/7.30-last
D 8.45pm

Credit cards: ■ ■ ⌧ ▢ ▤ ▣ JCB

Directions: From Exeter take A30 to Whiddon Down, turn S on A382 (Moretonhampstead) – don't turn into Chagford at Sandy Park; hotel is at Dogmarsh Bridge

Additional: Bar food L; Sunday L; Children welcome; ❸ dishes
Seats: 40. Private dining room 20
Smoking: No smoking in dining room

CHARDSTOCK,
Tytherleigh Cot Hotel ❀

This thatched 14th-century listed building was once a cider house but has been sympathetically converted and extended into a delightful small hotel. The daily dinner menu offers dishes built around fresh local produce. Cooking is noted as much for careful construction as for sound technique.

Directions: From M5/J25 take A358 to Axminster via Ilminster. 4 miles from Chard at Tytherleigh village turn R – Chardstock 1 mile

Axminster EX13 7BN
Map 3: ST30
Tel: 01460 221170
Fax: 01460 221291
Please telephone for further details

CHITTLEHAMHOLT,
Highbullen Hotel ❀

The cellars are the place to meet and dine at this Victorian Gothic mansion, set in lovely countryside. The restaurant's daily changing fixed-price menu offers a good choice, with dishes such as leek and potato soup, chicken with lemon and thyme, and a delicious apricot and hazelnut meringue.

Smoking: No smoking in dining room; Air-conditioning
Accommodation: 35 en suite. **Credit cards:** ⌧ ▢

Directions: At Chittlehamholt, 1 mile through village

Umberleigh EX37 9HD
Map 3: SS62
Tel: 01769 540561
Fax: 01769 540492
Chef: Colette Potter
Owners: Hugh & Pam Neil
Cost: Fixed-price D £20. H/wine £9.50.
Times: Last L 2pm/last D 9pm
Additional: Bar food L; No children under 8; ❸ dishes

COLYFORD, Swallows Eaves ❀

The restaurant at this 1930's 'gentleman's residence' has beautiful oak floors and an interesting collection of Doulton china. The short choice of freshly prepared dishes might include sauté of smoked bacon and mushrooms in red wine, pork braised in cider with prunes and a creamy sauce, and chargrilled strawberries.

Smoking: No smoking in dining room
Accommodation: 8 en suite. **Credit cards:** ■ ■ ⌧ ▢ ▣

Directions: In the centre of the village on the A3082

Swan Hill Road Colyton EX13 6QJ
Map 3: SY29
Tel: 01297 553584
Fax: 01297 553574
Chef: Jane Beck
Owners: Jane & Jon Beck
Cost: Fixed-price D £21 (4 courses). ☺ H/wine £9.95.
Times: D only, 7pm-last D 8.30pm. Closed Dec, Jan, Feb
Additional: ❸ dishes

CROYDE, Kittiwell House Hotel ❀

Thatched, cottage-style hotel with a friendly and relaxed atmosphere. Head for the panelled restaurant for sound cooking from a menu that ranges from avocado vinaigrette and pork Wellington, to zuppa pavese and chicken Romana. Afters include savouries like Welsh rarebit alongside zabaglione and cherries Jubilee.

Smoking: No smoking in dining room
Accommodation: 12 en suite. **Credit cards:** ■ ■ ⌧ ▢ ▤ ▣ JCB

Directions: At top end of Croyde village

St Mary's Road EX33 1PG
Map 2: SS43
Tel: 01271 890247
Fax: 01271 890469
Chef: David Rayner
Owners: Yvonne & James Lang
Cost: Alc £30, fixed-price D £18. ☺ H/wine £9.90
Times: D only, last D 9.30pm. Closed Jan
Additional: Sunday L (noon-2pm); Children welcome; ❸ dishes

DARTMOUTH,

The Carved Angel ❀❀❀

After 25 glorious years, what can you say about a restaurant that deserves to be listed as a national monument? Only that a meal here remains one of life's most memorable and pleasurable experiences. It is the special blend of location facing the River Dart, simple furnishings, open-plan kitchen where staff work in amazing, unflustered silence, and superb local produce that help make the Angel work her magic, plus cooking from Nick Coiley, and (part time now) from Joyce Molyneux, that transcends a one-dimensional listing of ingredients. Fish is always beautifully and carefully cooked to show off its obvious freshness, texture and clarity of flavour: steamed smoked haddock with spinach, quails' eggs and hollandaise was light, full of natural flavours and the sauce, made with fennel, highly elegant. Deep-fried lemon sole in spiced batter with cucumber salad, and a wonderful grilled fillet of brill was of a quality which one rarely finds nowadays. All dishes are presented with total simplicity and without unnecessary garnish or fuss, sauces are clear and flavoursome. These same precepts apply to the meat dishes: roast best end of lamb with shallot tart and thyme sauce; braised venison with bacon, mushrooms and onions, finished with chocolate; a duck plate consisting of breast with plum sauce, liver crostini and leg confit with red cabbage. Desserts are made to equally exacting standards. An iced lemon meringue parfait, full of lemon zest, melted in the mouth, a kumquat ice cream delighted with its unique and subtle scents. Espresso and petits fours, including fudge and a tiny chocolate truffle, are just the icing on the cake. Such earthly delights do not come cheap, but look out for the terrifically good-value set lunches.

Signature dishes: Scallops with Jerusalem artichoke mousseline; strawberry and elderflower jelly; lamb in vine leaves and filo mint sabayon; venison with pig's trotters and Burgundy

2 South Embankment
TQ6 9BH
Map 3: SX85
Tel: 01803 832465
Fax: 01803 835141
Chefs: Nick Coiley, Joyce Molyneux
Owners: Joyce Molyneux, Meriel Matthews, Nick Coiley, Zoë Wynne
Cost: *Alc* £40, fixed-price L £30/D £48. H/wine £15
Times: 12.30-2.30pm/7.30-9.30pm. Closed D Sun, Mon, 6 wks from 1 Jan
Additional: Sunday L; Children welcome; ❹ dishes
Seats: 50. Private dining room 18
Smoking: No smoking in dining room
Credit cards:

Directions: Dartmouth centre, on the water's edge

DARTMOUTH, **Dart Marina** ❀

A comfortable hotel restaurant right on the marina, bearing a nautical theme. There's plenty of fresh local fish in dishes such as cutlets of Dart River sea bass with cream and chive sauce, and alternatives like fillet of pork stuffed with field mushrooms and bacon.

Smoking: No smoking in dining room; Air conditioning
Accommodation: 50 en suite
Credit cards: 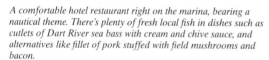 JCB

Directions: A379 from Torbay via Philip car ferry, or A381 from Totnes. By the marina

Sandquay TQ6 9PH
Map 3: SX85
Tel: 01803 832580
Fax: 01803 835040
Chef: Malcolm Whybrow
Owners: Forte Heritage
Cost: *Alc* £25. H/wine £11.95
Times: 10am-6pm/6.30-9.30pm
Additional: Bar food L; Sunday L; Children welcome; ❹ dishes

DARTMOUTH, **The Exchange** ❀❀

The brasserie-style restaurant occupies two floors of the architecturally interesting, 14th-century former mayor's residence near the harbour. Modern European dishes are cleverly presented, yet not over-fussy; mackerel and avocado gâteau with mixed leaves and lime dressing, and coulibiac of salmon with tomato and black olive coulis were excellent

5 Higher Street TQ6 9RB
Map 3: SX85
Tel/Fax: 01803 832022
Chef: Colin Newton
Owner: Sarah Allan
Cost: *Alc* £22. ☺ H/wine £8.95
Times: Noon-last L 2pm/7pm-last D 9pm. Closed Tue, Xmas, Feb

examples of the relaxed style on our visit. Dishes are to the point: duck liver pâté; pan-fried scallops in garlic; poached breast of chicken wrapped in Parma ham and Savoy cabbage; sirloin of beef with red wine and mushroom sauce. The lunch menu includes their 'ultimate' burger, and ribbon pasta with seared salmon. Daily specials get a little more fancy, Brie wrapped in filo pastry with honey and hazelnuts, perhaps, or supreme of duck with a brandy and orange glaze. Dessert of St. Emilion au chocolat was 'out of this world'.

Directions: In town centre near parish church

Additional: No children under 2; dishes
Seats: 46
Credit cards:

EAST BUCKLAND,
Lower Pitt Restaurant ✸

A 16th-century former farmhouse, with old wooden beams and log fires creating a cosy atmosphere. The best of West Country produce is used in modern English dishes such as casseroled pheasant with pancetta and cranberries, Thai-style green curry with prawns and jasmine rice, and steamed escalope of salmon with seafood tagliatelle.

Barnstaple EX32 0TD
Map 2: SS63
Tel/Fax: 01598 760243
Chef: Suzanne Lyons
Owners: Jerome & Suzanne Lyons
Cost: *Alc* £25. ☺ H/wine £8.90
Times: D only, last D 9pm. Closed Sun, Mon, 23, 24 Dec
Additional: No children under 10; dishes
Smoking: No smoking in dining room
Accommodation: 3 en suite
Credit cards:

Directions: Two miles N of the A361 (N Devon Link Road), near East Buckland village church

---

EXETER, **Barton Cross Hotel** ✸✸

Five miles from the city centre, Barton Cross is a beautifully converted 17th-century thatched long-house in a pretty rural setting. Enjoy pre-dinner drinks and appetisers in the comfortable cottagey bar-lounge (with roaring log fire in winter), before moving to the beamed, galleried restaurant. The

Huxham Stoke Canon EX5 4EJ
Map 3: SX99
Tel: 01392 841245
Fax: 01392 841942
Chef: Paul George Bending
Owners: B A & G A Hamilton
Cost: *Alc* £25, fixed-price D £25 (4 courses). ☺ H/wine £9.25
Times: D only, 6.30pm-last D 9.30pm. Closed Sun
Additional: Children welcome; dishes
Seats: 45. Private dining room 16
Smoking: No smoking in dining room
Accommodation: 8 en suite
Credit cards: JCB

Directions: 4 miles N of Exeter on A396. At Stoke Canon, turn R at church

menu makes good use of local produce, as evidenced in starters such as local scallops wrapped in marinated salmon, game terrine with Cumberland chutney, and a good wild mushroom tart topped with foie gras. Mains on an autumn menu included roast partridge with almonds and honey, lobster and monkfish in a cucumber and mustard sauce, and ratatouille lasagne. For those with a sweet-tooth there's sticky toffee pudding, blackberry crêpe soufflé, or our inspectorís 'highly enjoyable' dark chocolate and orange mousse with Cointreau sauce. Home-made bread rolls are excellent. The extensive wine list travels the world, and the French section includes plenty of half-bottles.

EXETER, Buckerell Lodge ❀❀

Topsham Road EX2 4SQ
Map 3: SX99
Tel: 01392 221111
Fax: 01392 491111
Chef: David Grindrod
Owner: Elmville Ltd
Cost: *Alc* £25, fixed-price L £12.50/D £19.95 (4 courses). ☺ H/wine £9.95
Times: Noon-last L 1.50pm/7-last D 9.45pm. Closed L Sat
Additional: Bar food L; Sunday L; No children under 10; ❹ dishes
Seats: 60. Private dining rooms 30. Jacket & tie preferred
Smoking: No smoking in dining room
Accommodation: 53 en suite
Credit cards: 🔲🔲🔲🔲🔲🔲🔲 JCB

Five acres of tall pines, broad lawns and serene gardens surround this pretty white hotel on Exeter's outskirts and make stunning viewing while enjoying a meal in the Raffles restaurant. Fresh local produce is employed on a menu offering a pleasing mix of the contemporary and traditional. Starters may be as familiar as gravad lax or pan-fried calves' liver, but there's also innovative ideas such as plum and tarragon granita with rock melon, or air-dried wild duck breast with pickled vegetables and chicory salad. Steak and ale suet pudding makes a comforting main course for wintry nights, while vegetarians will enjoy vegetable coulibiac with spring onion and tomato butter sauce. Desserts include steamed date pudding with toffee sauce, chocolate tart with pistachio nut cream, and pan-fried banana with rum sabayon and white chocolate and coconut ice cream.

Directions: 5 minutes from M5J30, follow signs for Exeter city centre. Aiport 5 miles, station 2 miles

EXETER, Ebford House Hotel ❀❀

The traditional Georgian dining-room is dominated by a magnificent gilt-edged mirror, and overlooks the pretty garden and rolling Devon countryside. The *carte* is short but there is no shortage of ideas. Ingredients are unconventionally paired, but a sense of balance is retained so that combinations intrigue rather than repel. Local hand-picked scallops are sautéed with mushrooms and garlic and arranged on a trout mousse croûte with sesame seeds, or seared pork tenderloin with chive lemongrass cream sauce is accompanied by a potato basket filled with pickled ginger chutney, and chargrilled fillet of beef

Exmouth Road EX3 0QH
Map 3: SX99
Tel: 01392 877658
Fax: 01392 874424
Chef: Paul Bazell
Owners: Mr & Mrs D Horton
Cost: *Alc* £27.50, fixed-price L £15/D £25.50. ☺ H/wine £9
Times: Noon-last L 1.30pm/7-last D 9pm. Closed L Sat, Sun, Xmas
Additional: Bar food; ❹ dishes
Seats: 30. Private dining room 10

and kangaroo are topped with a seared scallop of mango and served with mange-tout and a rich beef and oyster sauce. Main course fish dishes, however, are the exception rather than the rule. Frisco's bistro serves steaks and home-cooked cider ham.

Directions: On A376 Exmouth road near Topsham

EXETER, **Lord Haldon Hotel**

Just four miles from Exeter and affording glorious views over the Exe Valley, this friendly, family-run hotel provides a generous choice of dishes on its fixed-price menu. Our inspector sampled a full-flavoured and moist roast tenderloin of pork with apple and cider sauce and carefully cooked vegetables, followed by a light tiramisu.

Accommodation: 22 en suite
Credit cards: ▨ ▨ ▢ JCB

Directions: Leave M5/J31, take A30 (Okehampton); follow signs to Ide. Through village for 2.5 mile, L after phone box, follow for 0.5 mile; hotel L after low stone bridge

EXETER, **St Olaves Court Hotel** ❀❀

A short stroll from Exeter's mediaeval cathedral, Golsworthy's offers imaginative food in a stylish but informal setting. Customers are a happy mix of business people, holidaymakers and local foodies who appreciate the pleasant atmosphere, enthusiastic service and choice of light or more formal menus.

Ebford House Hotel

Smoking: No smoking in dining room
Accommodation: 16 en suite
Credit cards: ▨ ▨ ▨ ▢ ▨ ▢

Dunchideock EX6 7YF
Map 3: SX99
Tel: 01392 832483
Fax: 01392 833765
Chefs: Robin Webber, Richard Consterdine
Owner: Michael Preece
Cost: *Alc* £25, fixed-price L £14.50/D £18.50. ☺ H/wine £8.95.
Times: Last L 2pm/last D 8.30pm
Additional: Bar food; Sunday L; Children welcome; ◑ dishes
Smoking: No smoking in dining room; Air conditioning

Mary Arches Street
EX4 3AZ
Map 3: SX99
Tel: 01392 217736
Fax: 01392 413054
Chef: Robert Drakett
Owners: Raymond & Ute Wyatt, James Wyatt

The chef's flair is evident in his choice of nutmeg to flavour a well-judged starter of salmon mousse with crème fraîche and balsamic dressing. Main courses include roast monkfish on saffron risotto, fillet of beef garnished with a forest mushroom soufflé and meltingly moist duck that comes with crispy skin and plum sauce. Vegetarians are well catered for too. A dessert of light, flavoursome vanilla parfait is iced and accompanied by kirsch-soaked cherries. There's good coffee and skilfully produced petits fours. A simply annotated wine list comes with a page of fine bin-end wines at bargain prices. No wonder this restaurant is always busy.

Directions: Follow signs to city centre, then 'Mary Arches P'; hotel is opposite car park entrance

Cost: *Alc* £29, fixed-price L&D £14.50. ☺ H/wine £10.50.
Times: Noon-last L 2pm/6.30-last D 9.30pm. Closed L Sat, L Sun
Additional: Bar food L; Children welcome; ✿ dishes
Seats: 45. Private dining rooms 16, 14 & 8
Smoking: No smoking in dining room
Accommodation: 15 en suite
Credit cards: ▀ ▀ ▀ ▀ ▀ ▀ ▀

GITTISHAM, **Combe House Hotel** ✿

Splendid Elizabethan mansion at the heart of a massive estate. Indeed, the drive winds its way through nearly a mile of meadows and wooded valleys. Changes of ownership occurred as we went to press, although the chef of four years remains; we are certain standards will be retained.

Accommodation: 15 en suite
Credit cards: ▀ ▀ ▀ ▀ ▀ ▀ ▀

Directions: In Gittisham village off A30 & A303 south of Honiton

Honiton EX14 0AD
Map 3: SY19
Tel: 01404 42756
Fax: 01404 46004
Chef: Mark Stansell
Cost: *Alc* L £15, fixed-price D £25. ☺ H/wine £10.
Times: Last L 1.45pm/last D 9.30pm
Additional: Bar food L; Sunday L; Children welcome; ✿ dishes
Smoking: No smoking in dining room

GULWORTHY,
The Horn of Plenty ✿✿✿

PL19 8JD
Map 2: SX47
Tel/Fax: 01822 832528
Chef: Peter Gorton
Owners: Ian & Elaine Gatehouse
Cost: *Alc* D £35.50, fixed-price L £18.50. H/wine £12
Times: Noon-last L 2pm/7-last D 9pm. Closed L Mon, 25, 26 Dec
Additional: No children under 13; ✿ dishes
Seats: 50. Private dining room 12
Smoking: No smoking in dining room
Accommodation: 7 en suite
Credit cards: ▀ ▀ ▀ ▀ ▀ ▀

This gem of a country house is set high above the Tamar Valley with stunning views across to Bodmin Moor. It's a place that draws special praise from inspectors: bedrooms (overlooking a pretty walled garden) are bright and attractive, and public rooms combine elegance and comfort, with personal touches from trinkets and the like. Elaine Gatehouse is a warmly dedicated host, and rightly proud of her restaurant. In the kitchen Peter Gorton heads a dedicated team that scores heavily on freshness and consistency. Colourful ideas and light saucing were apparent in a winter dinner that opened with canapés of chicken tikka, and duxelles with goats' cheese and hollandaise. A brandade of cod followed, quite 'fishcakey' with nice chunky pieces of lobster studded through and topped with

a whole lobster claw, and sauced with a lobstery jus with dice of carrot and discs of asparagus. Next came a 'fab' piece of John Dory, crackling fresh, crisp skinned and resting on a bed of spinach. This was accompanied by asparagus and three lovely pan-fried scallops with a wine and saffron sauce. Pudding was a trio of chocolate mousse cake with a 'blinding' white chocolate ice cream, feuilleté of apple with a ginger crème patissière, and an iced pistachio parfait topped with caramelised banana. Other choices that catch the eye include sauté of foie gras on a potato and parsnip pancake with fresh figs, and pan-fried breast of duck with sweet potato, bok choi and an orange sauce. For the wines, the list continues to offer nine very well-chosen house wines by the glass, as well as an impressive selection that is both informed and informative. Prices are very fair.

Directions: 3 miles from Tavistock on A390. Turn R at Gulworthy Cross, then signed

HAYTOR, Bel Alp House

An elevated position overlooking Exmoor gives diners at this peaceful Edwardian hotel a superb view of the surrounding countryside. No less appealing are dishes such as roast quail with apricot and walnut sauce, cod with red pesto crust, and duck breast with honey and pine nut sauce all offered on a short fixed-price menu. Non-residents should book.

Smoking: No smoking in dining room
Accommodation: 8 en suite
Credit cards: ▅▅ ▩ ▩ ◁ ▩ ▶ ▣ JCB

Directions: 1.5 miles W of Bovey Tracey off B3387 to Haytor

Bovey Tracey TQ13 9XX
Map 3: SX77
Tel: 01364 661217
Fax: 01364 661292
Chef: Ian Davidson
Owners: Jack & Mary Twist
Cost: *Alc* £25, fixed-price L £9.50 (2 courses)/D £20. ☺ H/wine £9
Times: L by arrangement, last D 8.30pm
Additional: Children welcome; ✦ dishes

HAYTOR, Rock Inn

A comfortable village inn, full of olde-worlde character. After a day exploring Dartmoor, return for a hearty supper in the beamed dining room. Expect simple but effective dishes such as chargrilled chicken supreme with asparagus sauce. For dessert don't miss chocolate teardrops with black cherries – out of this world!

Smoking: No smoking in dining room
Accommodation: 9 en suite
Credit cards: ▅▅ ▩ ▩ ◁ ▩ ▶

Directions: In Haytor village on A3387, 3 miles from A382

Haytor Vale Newton Abbot
TQ13 9XP
Map 3: SX77
Tel: 01364 661305
Fax: 01364 661242
Chefs: Philip Hurrell, Steven Bowden, Nick Jones
Owner: Christopher Graves
Cost: *Alc* £25, fixed price D £25. ☺ H/wine £8.25
Times: Last L 2.15pm/last D 9.45pm
Additional: Bar food; Sunday L; No children under 6 months; ✦ dishes

HEDDON'S MOUTH,
Heddon's Gate Hotel

Built in Swiss Victorian style, Heddon's Gate has outstanding views over a wooded valley, best appreciated from the restaurant. Carefully sourced ingredients are cooked in modern English style with Mediterranean overtones. A rustically textured salmon bisque, and flavourful chicken breast in tarragon sauce, were recent offerings on the short daily menu.

Directions: A39 from Lynton. After 4 miles turn R towards Martinhoe and Woody Bay. Take 1st L after half mile and follow signs to Hunters Inn and Heddon's Mouth. Hotel drive on R

EX31 4PZ
Map 3: SX64
Tel: 01598 763313
Fax: 01598 763363
Chef: Robert Deville
Owners: Robert & Heather Deville
Cost: Fixed price D £25 (5 courses). ☺ H/wine £8.90
Times: D only, last D 8.30pm.
Closed Nov-Mar
Additional: Older children welcome
Smoking: No smoking in dining room
Accommodation: 14 en suite
Credit cards: ▅▅ ▩ ◁ ▩

HOLSWORTHY, Court Barn Hotel

Clawton EX22 6PS
Map 2: SS30
Tel: 01409 271219
Fax: 01409 271309
Chef: Sue Wood
Owners: Robert & Sue Wood
Cost: Fixed-price L £13/D £21 (4 courses). ☺ H/wine £7.95
Times: Last L 1.30pm/last D 8.45pm. Closed 2-12 Jan
Additional: Bar food L; Sunday L; Children welcome; ❹ dishes
Smoking: No smoking in dining room
Accommodation: 8 en suite
Credit cards: 🖃 📰 🖳 🖳 🖳 🖸 🖳 JCB

Friendly, family-run hotel with 17th-century origins. The short set menu employs fresh produce with sturdy flavours in dishes like hake with lemon butter sauce, rack of Devon lamb with port and mushroom sauce, and coq au vin. Extensive, informative, good-value wine list includes no less than 17 dessert wines by the glass.

Directions: 2.5 miles S of Holsworthy on A388, next to Clawton church

HONITON, Home Farm Hotel

Wilmington EX14 9JR
Map 3: ST10
Tel: 01404 831278
Fax: 01404 831411
Chef: Barry Bingham
Owners: AJ & EL Cressy
Cost: Alc £20.25, fixed-price L&D £14.50. ☺ H/wine £8.95.
Times: Last L 2.15pm/last D 9.15pm. Closed 25-26 Dec

Tasteful country hotel appeal at this thatched former farmhouse dating from the 16th-century. Simple but effective cooking takes in the likes of avocado stuffed with crab pâté in a beer batter with chilli and tomato salsa, pan-fried escalopes of pork tenderloin filled with Brie and Parma ham, and a light chocolate and rum tart.

Additional: Bar meals; Sunday L; Children welcome; ❹ dishes
Smoking: No smoking in dining room
Accommodation: 13 en suite. **Credit cards:** 🖃 📰 🖳 🖳 🖳 🖸 🖳 JCB

Directions: Three miles E of Honiton in village of Wilmington

HORRABRIDGE,
Overcombe Hotel

Near Yelverton PL20 7RN
Map 2: SX56
Tel/Fax: 01822 853501
Chef: Brenda Durnell
Owners: Maurice & Brenda Durnell
Cost: Fixed-price D £15 (4 courses). ☺ H/wine £9
Times: D only, 7 for 7.30pm

There's a relaxed, informal atmosphere to this friendly small hotel, plus splendid views over Walkham Valley to the high granite tors of Dartmoor beyond. Good country cooking with the short, fixed-price menu offering the likes of spinach and Stilton soup, baked slice of leg of lamb with leeks in a creamy sauce, proper roast potatoes and fresh, soundly cooked vegetables. Smooth lemon tart with clotted cream for dessert.

Additional: Children welcome; ❹ dishes
Smoking: No smoking in dining room
Accommodation: 11 en suite
Credit cards: 🖃 📰 🖳

Directions: Off A386 past Yelverton r/bout, direction Tavistock. 1st L after Horrabridge sign

ILSINGTON,
Ilsington Country Hotel

Set on the southern slopes of Dartmoor, a fine country house in extensive grounds, offering good conference and function facilities. Sound cooking takes in the likes of leek, potato and saffron soup, seared fillet of lamb with grilled figs and port and chervil jus, and redcurrant and vanilla brûlée for dessert.

TQ13 9RR
Map 3: SX77
Tel: 01364 661452
Fax: 01364 661307
Please telephone for further details

IVYBRIDGE, ## Glazebrook House

TQ10 9JE
Map 3: SX66
Tel: 01364 73322
Fax: 01364 72350
Chef: David Merriman
Owners: Fred & Christine Heard
Cost: Alc £27.50, fixed-price L&D £19.50 (4 courses). ☺ H/wine £9.95.
Times: Last L 1.30pm/last D 8.45pm
Additional: Sunday L; No small babies in dining room; ☺ dishes
Smoking: No smoking in dining room
Accommodation: 10 en suite
Credit cards: ▉ ▉ ▉ ▉ ▉ ▉

Personally run hotel with hospitality, service and food all major strengths. Unfussy but accurate cooking was the hallmark of a winter inspection dinner that produced scallops in puff pastry with a chive butter sauce, roast best end of lamb stuffed with walnut and rosemary mousse with a red wine sauce, and chocolate and Tia Maria mousse.

Directions: Follow B&B signs from A38 South Brent to Glazebrook

---

KINGSBRIDGE,
Buckland-Tout-Saints Hotel

Dinner is served in the beautiful Queen Anne panelled dining-room, with coffee in the Great Hall with its comfy sofas and log fire. Although short, the menu is packed with imaginative ideas – ballontine of quail is unusually pot roasted with hay and garnished with a confit of parsnip and plum fondue. Roasted fillet of wild seabass comes with oysters in a Champagne butter sauce on a julienne of vegetables, and honey-roasted root vegetables and a honey jus provide sweet and earthy notes to a magret of duck with pommes Anna. A new variation on an old theme is banana and black treacle bread and butter pudding with whisky and orange sauce and caramelised bananas.

Accommodation: 12 en suite
Credit cards: ▉ ▉ ▉ ▉ ▉

Directions: 2 miles N of Kingsbridge on A381. Through village of Goveton, 500 yds past church

Goveton TQ7 2DS
Map 3: SX74
Tel: 01548 853055
Fax: 01548 856261
Chef: Anton Goodwin
Owner: Mr A P Hardstaff
Cost: Fixed-price D £30 (4 courses). ☺ H/wine £9.75
Times: 12.30-1.45pm/7-9pm. Closed Jan
Additional: Bar food L; Sunday L; No children under 6 at D; ☺ dishes
Seats: 40. Private dining room 18. Jacket & tie preferred
Smoking: No smoking in dining room

KINGSKERSWELL,
Pitt House Restaurant ❀❀

Chocolate-box pretty, the thatched, 15th-century Pitt House is as appealing inside as out. Add friendly service and good cooking, warm provençale tart perhaps, a ragout of rabbit and wild mushrooms, or duck breast on potato and apple rösti with Calvados sauce, plus a glazed lemon tart, and the whole package becomes irresistible.

Additional: Sunday L (some); No children under 8 at D; ❹ dishes
Smoking: No smoking in dining room
Credit cards: ▭ ▭ ▭ ▭

Directions: Torquay road from Newton Abbot, 1st R, follow road to junction & turn L, parish church on R. Take 1st R, restaurant 50yds on L

2 Church End Road
Nr Newton Abbot TQ12 5DS
Map 3: SX86
Tel: 01803 873374
Chefs: Stephen Sanders,
Vanessa Rogers
Owners: Mr A & Mrs J Rogers
Cost: *Alc* £25, fixed-price L £12.95.
☺ H/wine £10.20
Times: Last L 2pm/last D 9pm.
Closed Sun, Mon, 2 wks summer,
wks winter

LEWDOWN,
Lewtrenchard Manor ❀❀

Four hundred-years-old, this is a gloriously atmospheric Jacobean house which enjoys sweeping views across the Lewtrenchard estate and Dartmoor. Inside, stunning ceilings, superb carvings and granite window frames have survived the centuries and bring much character to the building. Guests can look forward to well-executed modern English dishes, served in the refined splendour of the dark panelled dining room. Harmonious combinations of flavours are much in evidence in dishes such as baked fillet of cod with asparagus, broad beans and morel cream, and spiced loin of Tiverton pork with garlic potatoes, smoked ham hock and sage beurre blanc. Our inspector enjoyed an early summer meal of pan-fried Cornish scallops with roasted leeks, followed by roast chump of Devon lamb served on a black olive blini, with roasted fennel tortellini and basil gravy. The wine list is well chosen, and is particularly notable for its South African selection.

Directions: Take A30 for Lewdown, after 6 miles turn L at signpost for Lewtrenchard. Follow signs for 0.75 mile

Okehampton
EX20 4PN
Map 2: SX48
Tel: 01566 783256/783222
Fax: 01566 783332
Chef: David Jones
Owners: Mr & Mrs James Murray
Cost: *Alc* £30, fixed-price D £30.
H/wine £10
Times: D only, 7-last D 9pm
Additional: Bar food; Sunday L (noon-2pm); No children under 8
Seats: 40. Private dining room 16.
Jacket & tie preferred
Smoking: No smoking in dining room
Accommodation: 9 en suite
Credit cards: JCB

LIFTON, **Arundell Arms** ❀❀❀

20 miles of salmon and trout fishing have made this delightful 18th-century inn a Mecca amongst the angling community. A day spent in or by the water encourages healthy appetites, well catered for by Philip Burgess's vibrant yet simple style of cooking. Dishes achieve the rare distinction of actually living up to their description. A salad of pan-fried chicken livers with avocado and a mild garlic dressing could not have been bettered for clutter-free presentation and clarity of flavours. Other starters might include red mullet soup with anchovy toasts or griddled Cornish scallops with celeriac and basil relish. Cornish sea bass makes a regular appearance on the menu, either in a croustade with spinach leaves, sweet peppers and saffron butter sauce, or roasted with coriander and hazelnut crust and warm ratatouille as a main course. Game is handled with care -roasted squab pigeon is stuffed with bacon

PL16 0AA
Map 2: SX38
Tel: 01566 784666
Fax: 01566 784494
Chefs: Philip Burgess, Nick Shopland
Owner: Mrs Anne Voss-Bark
Cost: Fixed-price L £19/D £29.50. ☺
H/wine £10.50
Times: 12.30-last L 2pm/7.30-last D 9.30pm. Closed 2 days Xmas
Additional: Bar food; Sunday L; Children welcome; ❹ dishes
Seats: 70. Private room 30
Smoking: No smoking in dining room
Accommodation: 28 en suite
Credit cards: ▭ ▭ ▭ ▭ ▭ ▭

Arundell Arms

and juniper and served with onion sauce. Fillet of Trelough duckling with baby spring vegetables and a mousseline of chicken, with tarragon sauce epitomised the strengths of the cooking – simple composition, depth of flavour and careful presentation. Desserts are excellent – depending on the season, there may be steamed ginger sponge pudding with lemon and lime sabayon and Cornish clotted cream, or Tamar strawberry shortcake with strawberry ice cream and red berry sauce.

Signature dishes: A casserole of monkfish, sole, turbot and scallops with button onions, baby leeks and nutmeg cream; salad of Cornish lobster, asparagus and summer herbs with a saffron and shallot dressing; tournedos of South Devon beef with celeriac and potato dauphinoise, pan-fried chicken livers and rich red wine sauce; a brace of roasted woodcock with winter root vegetables, bread sauce and game gravy

Directions: Just off A30 in village of Lifton

LIFTON,
Thatched Cottage Hotel ✿

A charming place, a converted 16th-century cottage with bedrooms in former stables. Typical choices from an imaginative menu would be wild boar and pecan nut pâté, tender roasted breast of duck with spiced blackberry sauce, served with fresh vegetables, and sticky toffee pudding with a choice of double cream, clotted cream, or ice cream.

Directions: From A30 at Stowford turn S on C493 2 miles to Sprytown Cross – straight ahead 100yds on R

Sprytown PL16 0AY
Map 3: SX38
Tel: 01566 784224
Fax: 01566 784334
Chefs: Rita Willing, Victoria Bryant
Owners: Mr & Mrs Willing, Miss V T Bryant,
Cost: *Alc* £23.25 Fixed price L £12.50. ☺ H/wine £8.95
Times: Last L 2pm/D 9.30pm
Additional: Sunday L; Bar meals L; No children under 12; ✿ dishes
Smoking: No-smoking area; no cigars & pipes
Accommodation: 5 en suite
Credit cards: ▬ ▬ ✖ ⌐ ▬ ◖ ▣ JCB

LYDFORD, Castle Inn Restaurant ✾

Atmospheric old inn with pretty garden. The flagstone-floored restaurant is cosy and romantic with decor featuring many items of interest. Dishes range from warm pigeon, smoky bacon and Puy lentil salad, and salmon mille-feuille with dill and lemon crêpes to their famed steak and kidney pie with suet crust. Good bar food too.

Additional: Bar food; Sunday L; Children welcome; ♨ dishes
Smoking: No-smoking area; No pipes & cigars
Accommodation: 9 en suite
Credit cards: 💳 💳 💳 💳 💳 💳 💳

Directions: From A30 take A386 towards Tavistock. Lydford signposted to right after 5 miles

EX20 4BH
Map 2: SX58
Tel: 01822 820242
Fax: 01822 820454
Chefs: Mo Walker, Philip Waring
Owners: Mo & Clive Walker
Cost: Alc £22.50, fixed-price L £12/D £15.95. ☺ H/wine £8.65
Times: Last L 2.30pm/last D 9.30pm

LYMPSTONE,
River House Restaurant ✾✾

The Exe estuary is the setting, and provides wonderful views from the first-floor dining room of this agreeable restaurant in a pretty village. Pre-dinner drinks and simple canapés are served in the ground-floor lounge, a country-house style room with local artwork on the walls. Visitors – a well-heeled bunch – then proceed upstairs to spacious table placements and (at dinner) candlelight. An inspector pronounced crab and spinach ravioli to be a 'thoroughly successful' starter. It arrived piping hot with lots of fresh white crab meat and bright green spinach. Main dishes, served with a vast range of vegetables (some from the restaurant's own allotments), included a splendid lemon sole stuffed with herbs and oven baked, as well as roast duck with rum, rhubarb and plum sauce, and a slab of juicy salmon with sorrel sauce. Rich bread-and-butter pudding completed a good meal that was augmented by a notable wine list.

Directions: In Lower Lympstone, approx 2 miles off A376 Exeter-Exmouth road

The Strand EX8 5EY
Map 3: SX98
Tel: 01395 265147
Chef: Shirley Wilkes
Owner: J F Michael Wilkes
Cost: Alc £20, fixed-price L & D £34. H/wine £9.95
Times: Noon-last L 1.30pm/7-last D 9.30pm. Closed Sun, Mon, Bhs
Additional: No children under 6; ♨ dishes
Seats: 54. Private dining room 14
Smoking: No smoking in dining room
Accommodation: 3 en suite
Credit cards: 💳 💳 💳

LYNMOUTH, Rising Sun Hotel ✾✾

Not to be confused with the famous house of ill-repute in New Orleans, this nevertheless historic hotel and restaurant looks out over Lynmouth harbour. A good setting for elegant or romantic occasions, the small oak-panelled dining room

Harbourside EX35 6EQ
Map 3: SS74
Tel: 01598 753223
Fax: 01598 753480
Chef: Neal Heyworth
Owner: Hugo Jeune

features leaded windows, linens and much silverware and a meal here will offer several highlights. Duck liver pâté has pleasing colour and texture and comes with an excellent onion marmalade. Roast rack of Devon lamb with Savoy cabbage and garlic is served pink and moist with perfectly cooked vegetables. Best of all is the crème brûlée with pine nuts, an innovative combination that works perfectly. The petits fours, a selection of clotted cream fudge, gives a nod to the rural Devon location. To accompany your meal, choose from the extensive, interesting wine list, or opt for one of the house wines displayed on the blackboard. The Rising Sun also has a popular bar.

Directions: M5/J23 (Minehead). take A39 to Lynmouth, opposite the harbour

Rising Sun Hotel

Cost: *Alc* £30, fixed-price L £16.50/D £27.50. H/wine £9.75
Times: Noon-last L 2pm/7-last D 9pm
Additional: Bar food L; No children under 7
Seats: 36
Smoking: No smoking in dining room
Accommodation: 16 en suite
Credit cards: JCB

LYNTON,

Chough's Nest Hotel

Built as a private residence by a Dutch millionaire, this beautiful stone house has spectacular views over Lynmouth Bay. The short, daily-changing menu offers excellent country-style cooking. Look out for robust peppered lentil and smoked bacon soup, French roast chicken served with pan juice gravy, cabbage with caraway and cauliflower, and lemon and almond tiramisu.

Additional: No children under 5; dishes
Smoking: No smoking in dining room
Accommodation: 12 en suite
Credit cards: JCB

Directions: From Lynton Parish Church in centre, turn on to North Walk. Last hotel on L.

North Walk EX35 6HJ
Map 3: SS74
Tel: 01598 753315
Chef/Owner: Andrew Collier
Cost: Fixed-price D £19 (4 courses). ☺ H/wine £6.95
Times: D only, last D 8.30pm. Closed Nov-Feb

LYNTON, Combe Park Hotel

A former hunting lodge set in a stunning National Trust owned valley with a 'babbling brook' in front of the main entrance. Many guests return time-after-time for the warm welcome, relaxed atmosphere, and the lovely country cooking. Shirley Barnes cooks in her own style, and second helpings for puddings are a popular feature.

Directions: At Hillsford Bridge, junction of A39/B3223

Hillsford Bridge
EX35 6LE
Map 3: SS74
Tel: 01598 752356
Fax: 01598 753484
Please telephone for further details

LYNTON, Highcliffe House

Honest cooking, fresh ingredients and careful preparation are the watchwords of the kitchen at this former Victorian gentleman's residence, now a delightfully hospitable hotel with a campaigning non-smoking policy. Dinner in the elegant candlelit dining room is not to be missed. We enjoyed the simple yet effective first course of pan-fried red mullet served with well-prepared couscous and a red pepper coulis. Other typical starters are gin tomato soup, and pheasant with braised pearl barley and redcurrant jus. Between the savoury courses sorbet is offered then, to follow, there may be baked cod with chive beurre blanc and diced scallops, or roast duck with lentils and juniper sauce. Good veg, including fine beans, baby carrots, broccoli and garlicky dauphinoise, come on the side. Ensure you save room for the lovely cardamom-flavoured rice pudding served cold with a chilled blueberry coulis. The wine list is kept to a manageable 24 bottles including old and New World wines.

Directions: Turn off the A39 at Lynton; hotel is up Sinai Hill on L

Sinai Hill EX35 6AR
Map 3: SS74
Tel/Fax: 01598 752235
Chef: Steven Phillips
Owners: Steven Phillips, John Bishop
Cost: Fixed-price D £25 (5 courses).
H/wine £9.50
Times: D only, 7.30pm for 8
Additional: dishes
Seats: 14. Jacket & tie preferred
Smoking: No smoking in dining room
Accommodation: 6 en suite
Credit cards: ▨ ▨ ▨ ▨

LYNTON, Lynton Cottage Hotel

Secluded 17th-century hotel affording spectacular views over Lynmouth Bay. A well balanced selection of dishes, listed on the fixed-price menu, show flair. Moist chicken liver pâté, and a perfectly cooked rack of lamb with a rich Madeira and redcurrant sauce, highlighted a recent inspection meal. Delicious puddings.

Additional: Bar food L; Sunday L; No children under 14; ☺ dishes
Smoking: No smoking in dining room
Accommodation: 16 en suite
Credit cards: ▨ ▨ ▨ ▨ ▨ ▨ ▨

Directions: In North Walk off main road through town

North Walk EX35 6ED
Map 3: SS74
Tel: 01598 752342
Fax: 01598 752774
Chef: Stephen Cooper
Owner: Christine Smith
Cost: Alc £26, fixed-price D £21.50.
☺ H/wine £12.50
Times: Last L 3pm/last D 8.45pm

MARTINHOE, Old Rectory Hotel ❀

The restaurant at this comfortable 18th-century hotel is superb – Georgian in style, the room is tastefully finished with antique furniture, and silverware laid on polished mahogany tables. The highlight of a recent meal was a main dish of duck breast with raspberries, followed by strawberry Pavlova for dessert.

Additional: No children under 14; ☺ dishes
Smoking: No smoking in dining room
Accommodation: 8 en suite
Credit cards: None

Directions: R at Blackmore gate onto A39 (Parracombe). Use Parracombe by-pass, take 3rd L at Martinhoe Cross

Parracombe EX31 4QT
Map 3: SS64
Tel: 01598 763368
Fax: 01598 763567
Chef: Geoffrey Wilson
Owners: Dennis Bennett, Geoffrey Wilson
Cost: Fixed-price D £26.50 (4 courses)
Times: D only at 7.30pm

MORETONHAMPSTED,

Blackaller Hotel ❀

Hazel Phillips aims to use only Devon produce for her short, fixed-price dinner menus. A typical choice might be cheese and chive soufflé, mango sorbet, bacon-wrapped chicken breast with spinach

North Bovey TQ13 8QY
Map 3: SX78
Tel/Fax: 01647 440322
Chef: Mrs H Phillips
Owners: Mrs H Phillips, Mr P Hunt

and mushroom stuffing and lemon sauce, and syrup sponge pudding to finish. The setting, on the banks of the Bovey River, is idyllic.

Directions: From M5 – A30 Okehampton Road. Then Marsh Barton sign onto B3212 (Moretonhampstead). Take North Bovey road from there

Blackaller Hotel

Cost: Fixed-price D £21 (4 courses).
☺ H/wine £8.20
Times: D only, last D 8.30pm. Closed Sun, Mon, Jan, Feb
Additional: ✤ dishes
Smoking: No smoking in dining room
Accommodation: 5 en suite
Credit cards: None

PARKHAM,
Penhaven Country House ❀

Former rectory set in 11 acres of gardens and woodland with distant views of Exmoor. The fixed-price menu is strong on local produce, including fish and game, with good options for vegetarians. Dinner could include cannellini bean soup, followed by pork en croûte with Madeira sauce, and bread-and-butter pudding from the trolley.

Bideford EX39 5PL
Map 2: SS32
Tel: 01237 451711
Fax: 01237 451878
Chef: Richard Copp
Owners: Maxine & Alan Wade
Cost: Alc £28, fixed-price D £14.50.
☺ H/wine £11.95.
Times: D only, 7.15-9pm.
Additional: Sunday L;
No children under 10; ✤ dishes
Smoking: No smoking in dining room
Accommodation: 12 en suite
Credit cards: ▬ ▦ ▬ **⊂**

Directions: From A39 at Horns Cross, follow signs to Parkham and turn L after church

PLYMOUTH,
Boringdon Hall Hotel ❀

Attractive Grade I listed building popular with business, leisure and conference delegates. Good selection of home-made breads, soups such as pear and Stilton, with excellent roast rib of beef, Yorkshire pudding flavoured with horseradish and traditional gravy, and ricotta cheesecake with coffee-scented custard showing the style.

Accommodation: 40 en suite
Credit cards: ▬ ▦ ▧ ▢ ▬ **⊂**

Directions: Telephone for directions

Colebrook Plympton PL7 4DP
Map 2: SX45
Tel: 01752 344455
Fax: 01752 346578
Chef: Andrew White
Owner: Paragon Hotels
Cost: Alc £30, fixed-price L £12.50/D £18.95 (4 courses). ☺ H/wine £12.45
Times: Last L 2pm/last D 9.30pm
Additional: Bar food; Sunday L;
Children welcome; ✤ dishes
Smoking: No smoking in dining room

PLYMOUTH, **Chez Nous** ❀ ❀ ❀

13 Frankfort Gate PL1 1QA
Map 2: SX45
Tel/Fax: 01752 266793
Chef: Jacques Marchal
Owners: Jacques & Suzanne Marchal
Cost: Alc £33. H/wine £10.50
Times: 12.30-last L 2pm/7-last
D 10.30pm. Closed Sun, Mon,
3 wks Feb, 3 wks Sep
Additional: No children under 8
Seats: 28
Smoking: No pipes; Air conditioning
Credit cards: ▆ ▆ ▆ ▆ ▆ ▆ ▆

'Chez Nous is located, surprisingly, in a pedestrianised precinct of downtown Plymouth and easy to miss because of its understated exterior and lack of prominent signage', warns an inspector, visiting Jacques and Suzanne Marchal's intimate French restaurant for the first time. The interior is a little piece of France in both decor and atmosphere, and the place is well patronised. Suzanne is very much in charge of front-of-house, and does a superb job, explaining the blackboard items to those customers finding difficulty in understanding either the hand-writing or the French descriptions – or both! Jacques Marchal's cooking is simplicity itself, he describes it as 'cuisine spontanée', and our April lunch certainly lived up to that description. It opened with an appetiser of croûtons with sun-dried tomatoes, red peppers and excellent pain de seigle. Next came a signature dish, coquilles St Jacques au gingembre 'unlike any other bearing that name', consisting of succulent, fat, delicate scallops which melted in the mouth and were beautifully complemented by the simply presented yet effective sauce. The centrepiece was mignons of pork with prunes, again simply presented with a side dish of mange-tout, purée of celeriac, and new potatoes. The prune sauce was 'delicious, with the prunes having been marinated in dry sherry and Madeira to give a flavour combination of both dry and sweet simultaneously. Dessert of grilled pineapple with crème de cacao and vanilla ice cream and grilled black pepper was a stunning combination.

Signature dishes: Cabillaud grillé au pistou; coquilles St Jacques au gingembre.

Directions: Frankfort Gate is a pedestrianised street between Western Approach & Market Avenue

PLYMOUTH, **Duke of Cornwall** ❀ ❀

Small, personally run hotel with a kitchen that is going from strength to strength. Ideas are global, ranging from rosette of Scottish beef on a haggis base with Drambuie infused veal jus, through fresh linguine pasta with olive and sun-dried tomato pesto served on toasted focaccia, to honey and lemon chicken with Asian noodles and shiitake mushrooms. Flavour, however, is a strong point. Note a late spring dinner that opened with a selection of excellent home-made rolls – black olive, poppy seed – and went on to duck liver and Cointreau parfait, a well-presented marmalade and mustard pork loin with crisply fried leeks, sweet potato pancake and tiny pears poached in Chardonnay, and finished with an individual lemon tart. Petits fours with coffee were outstanding.

Millbay Road PL1 3LG
Map 2: SX45
Tel: 01752 266256
Fax: 01752 600062
Chef: Mr C Bailey
Cost: H/wine £10.95 ☺
Times: Last L 2pm (bar only)/last D
10pm
Additional: Bar food L; Sunday L;
Children welcome; ◑ dishes
Smoking: No smoking in dining room
Accommodation: 73 en suite
Credit cards: ▆ ▆ ▆ ▆ ▆ ▆ JCB

Directions: City centre, follow signs
"Pavilions", hotel road is opposite

PLYMOUTH, **Kitley Hotel**

Apparently, the nursery rhyme *Old Mother Hubbard* was composed at Kitley; happily, there are no bare cupboards here these days. Instead, a crimson dining room overlooks the salt-water lake, and the tables groan under the weight of mille-feuille of Devon crabmeat, roasted Gressingham duck breast, with honey and spices and Madeira sauce, and lemon tart with raspberry sauce. Rabbit and foie gras terrine delivered good contrast in flavour and texture, and a plump little roast grouse was gamey and unusually tender. The latter was served on a bed of creamed potatoes with ceps. Chocolate tart had short, buttery pastry, rich cocoa-moist filling and creamy coffee sauce. Service is attentive and youthful.

Smoking: No smoking in dining room
Accommodation: 20 en suite
Credit cards: ▆ ▆ ▆ ▆ ▆

Directions: From Plymouth take A379 (Kingsbridge). Entrance between villages of Brixton & Yealmpton on R (10 mins)

The Kitley Estate Yealmpton
PL8 2NW
Map 2: SX45
Tel: 01752 881555
Fax: 01752 881667
Chef: Christopher Tanner
Owners: Traditional Hotels
Cost: Alc £38, fixed-price L £15.50/D £27.50. H/wine £12.
Times: Noon-last L 2pm/7pm-last D 9.30pm
Additional: Bar food L; Sunday L; ❹ dishes
Seats: 40. Private dining room 24

PLYMOUTH,
Langdon Court Hotel ❀ NEW

A Tudor manor set in woodland, six miles from Plymouth. Good-value meals are served in the bar, while the formal restaurant has a fixed-price menu highlighting fish delivered daily from Barbican market. At inspection, an enjoyably rustic watercress and Stilton soup preceded salmon mille-feuille with a sherry sabayon.

Additional: Bar food; Sunday L; Children welcome; ❹ dishes
Accommodation: 16 en suite
Credit cards: ▆ ▆ ▆ ▆ ▆ ▆ JCB

Directions: Telephone for directions

Down Thomas DL9 0DY
Map 2: SX45
Tel: 01752 862358
Fax: 01752 863428
Chef: Richard Hann
Owners: Ann & Alan Cox, Sheila Barnes
Cost: Alc £23, fixed price L £10.95/D £19.50. ☺ H/wine £7.75
Times: Last L 2pm/last D 9.30pm. Closed D Sun, 25 Dec

ROCKBEARE,
The Jack In The Green Inn ❀❀

'The food here gets better and better' enthused one inspector, won over by the cooking at this busy, unassuming roadside inn. A reception area with comfy chairs leads to the beamed interior, where guests choose between an extensive bar menu and proper restaurant food. The young chef once worked at Gidleigh Park, Chagford (see entry) and the training shows. Starters may include deep-fried almond cheese balls with the pub's own tomato chutney – all very well presented. Main courses are a mix of innovation and old favourites, ranging from bangers and mash or lamb and apricot pie, to a great dish of roast pigeon with Puy lentils and polenta, or excellent Savoy cabbage with bacon (which arrived with pristine vegetables). Sweetness and sharpness were finely balanced in the dessert of white chocolate and passion fruit delice. Local cheeses, monthly wine specials available by the glass, and professional, friendly staff are welcome accompaniments to the peerless pub food.

Directions: 5 miles E of Exeter on the A30

Exeter EX5 2EE
Map 3: SY09
Tel: 01404 822240
Chef: Matthew Mason
Owner: Paul Parnell
Cost: Alc £17.50, fixed-price L/D £16.50. ☺ H/wine £9
Times: Noon-last L 1.45pm/6.30-last D 9.45pm. Closed 25-26 Dec
Additional: Bar food; Sunday L; No children under 10; ❹ dishes
Seats: 60. Private dining room 30
Smoking: No smoking in dining room
Credit cards: ▆ ▆ ▆ ▆ ▆

SALCOMBE, **Bolt Head Hotel**

South Sands TQ8 8LL
Map 3: SX73
Tel: 01548 843751
Fax: 01548 843060
Chef: John Gallagher
Owner: Colin Smith
Cost: Fixed-price D £25 (5 courses).
H/wine £8.95
Times: Last L 2pm/last D 8.45pm.
Closed mid Nov-mid Mar
Additional: Bar food L; Sunday L;
Children welcome; ✪ dishes
Smoking: Air conditioning
Accommodation: 28 en suite
Credit cards:

Superbly positioned overlooking Salcombe Estuary and the sea, the restaurant here makes much use of farm produce and locally landed fish. Salcombe crab may be followed by English lamb cutlets with Stilton and pear butter or Dover sole meunière, then farmhouse cheeses or a pudding from the trolley.

Directions: At Malborough follow National Trust signs for Sharpitor; the hotel is above the beach at South Sands

SALCOMBE,
The Marine Hotel

NEW

Cliffe Road TQ8 8JH
Map 3: SX73
Tel: 01548 844444
Fax: 01548 843109
Please telephone for further details

Unbeatable views over the Dart estuary are complemented by some genuinely sound cooking. Highly recommended is chicken liver parfait, served with onion chutney, mushroom soup with quail, lamb served with an aubergine charlotte, and pear and almond tart for dessert. Good home-made breads – especially the brioche and sage bread,

Directions: From Exeter take A384 to Totnes, then follow A381 to Kingsbridge and Salcombe

SALCOMBE,
Soar Mill Cove Hotel

Soar Mill Cove
Malborough TQ7 3DS
Map 3: SX73
Tel: 01548 561566
Fax: 01548 561223
Chef: Keith S Makepeace
Owner: The Makepeace Family
Cost: A/c L £26, fixed-price D £35
(5 courses). H/wine £13.50
Times: Noon-last L 2.45pm/7.15-last
D 9pm. Closed end Nov-Feb (excl
Xmas & New Year)
Additional: Bar food L; No children
under 5 at D; ✪ dishes

Watch the lobster pots being emptied in the bay, then enjoy the catch served in a saffron sauce with sautéed queen scallops. Fish and seafood are a speciality at this idyllically located hotel and although the freshness of Soar Bay crab needs no more than a crisp leaf salad, the modern West Country cooking also takes in seared veal with ginger and lime butter, and breast of Devonshire chicken with wild mushrooms and a casserole of haricot beans. Desserts include hot blackberry and apple pie, and Cornish Yarg soufflé makes an unusual savoury. A special children's menu is served between 5 and 5.30pm.

Seats: 45
Smoking: No smoking in dining room
Accommodation: 19 en suite
Credit cards: ▆ ▆ ▆ ▆

Directions: A381 to Salcombe, through village follow signs to sea

SALCOMBE, **Tides Reach Hotel**

Salcombe is known for lobsters – they make an excellent starter when served as a salad with yellow tomatoes and grilled peppers, albeit as a special supplement to the fixed price menu. Meals are served in the Garden Room of this ever-popular waterside hotel, and there are good choices, although dishes tread a fine line between original and unusual combinations of flavours: poached fillet of John Dory with saffron rice in a smoked salmon broth; baked guinea fowl breast filled with horseradish mousse served with raspberries and basil; grilled magret of corn-fed duck on chilli and garlic cabbage. Tender best end of lamb on a bed of wild mushrooms and red peppers with a wine flavoured jus was full of marvellous spring lamb flavour but the offer of commercially produced mint sauce was a disappointment. Desserts include chocolate mille-feuille and apple fritters with cinnamon cream.

Directions: Take cliff road towards sea and Bolt Head

South Sands TQ8 8LJ
Map 3: SX73
Tel: 01548 843466
Fax: 01548 843954
Chef: Finn Ibsen
Owners: The Edwards Family
Cost: *Alc* £31.50, fixed-price
D £26.75 (4 courses). H/wine £10.25
Times: D only, 7-last D 9pm.
Closed Dec-Jan
Additional: Bar food L;
No children under 8; dishes
Seats: 90
Smoking: No smoking in dining room
Accommodation: 38 en suite
Credit cards: 🔲 🔲 🔲 🔲 🔲 🔲 🔲

SIDMOUTH, **Brownlands**

Smashing little private hotel that benefits from a regular clientele. Super views from the dining room. Food is good. Bread is made on the premises, for instance, and lunch brings the likes of carrot and coriander soup, liver and onions, and orange and Cointreau soufflé, with a wider choice from a set-price menu for dinner.

Additional: Bar food L; Sunday L; No children under 8;
dishes
Smoking: No smoking in dining room
Accommodation: 14 en suite. **Credit cards:** None

Directions: Take A3052 (Exeter – Sidford), turn R at crossroads past Blue Bull Inn onto Fortescue Rd. Hotel in 1 mile

Sid Road EX10 9AG
Map 3: SY18
Tel/Fax: 01395 513053
Chefs: Laurence J Barber, Janice May
Owners: Peter, Diane & Steven
Kendall-Torry
Cost: Fixed-price D £19.95. H/wine
£8.90
Times: Last L 1.15pm/last D 8pm.
Closed Nov-Mar

SIDMOUTH, **Riviera Hotel**

Elegant Regency surroundings at this sea-front hotel. The restaurant offers traditionally inspired fish and grill dishes along the lines of full-flavoured noisettes of lamb 'Grand Veneur', as well as imaginative ideas such as roulade of marinated salmon with bavarois of leeks.

Directions: In the centre of The Esplanade, overlooking Lyme Bay

The Esplanade EX10 8AY
Map 3: SY18
Tel: 01395 515201
Fax: 01395 577775
Chefs: Mark Leavers, Christian Miguel
Owner: Peter Wharton.
Cost: *Alc* £23.50. Fixed-price L £15
(5 courses)/D £25 (7 courses). ☺
H/wine £10.90
Times: Last L 2pm/last D 9pm
Additional: Bar Food L; Sunday L;
Children welcome; dishes
Smoking: No-smoking area; No cigars
or pipes; Air conditioning
Accommodation: 27 en suite
Credit cards: 🔲 🔲 🔲 🔲

SIDMOUTH, Victoria Hotel ❀

Imposing turn-of-the-century building occupying a prime position on the esplanade. Sound cooking offers the likes of scampi and monkfish in puff pastry with a white wine and dill sauce, medallions of local venison with caramelised walnuts and a red wine sauce, and bread-and-butter pudding. Good selection of half-bottles.

Directions: At the western end of the esplanade

Esplanade EX10 8RY
Map 3: SY18
Tel: 01395 512651
Fax: 01395 579154
Please telephone for further details

SOUTH MOLTON,
Marsh Hall Hotel ❀

Delightful. small, personally run hotel set in lovely grounds. Herbs, vegetables and fruit are home-grown, and the daily changing menu offers good, honest cooking of simply conceived dishes such as tomato and basil soup, sirloin steak with peppercorn sauce, and fruit terrine.

Smoking: No smoking in dining room
Accommodation: 7 en suite
Credit cards: 💳 💳 ⚡ ▫ JCB

Directions: Off A361 signed North Molton; first R, then R again

EX36 3HQ
Map 3: SS72
Tel: 01769 572666
Fax: 01769 574230
Chef: Judy Griffiths
Owners: Tony & Judy Griffiths
Cost: Fixed price D £20 (4 courses).
☺ H/wine £9
Times: D only, last D 8pm
Additional: No children under 12

SOUTH MOLTON,
Whitechapel Manor ❀❀❀

Stunning, remote location for this magnificent Elizabethan manor house hidden in its own gardens and grounds. Period pieces such as a Jacobean oak-carved screen and William and Mary plasterwork and panelling add to the character of the house. Matt Corner makes the most of West Country produce on a short menu that combines assured technique with imaginative combinations. Green bean and chorizo sausage salad with pesto, for example, could be followed by seared wild salmon with a coriander and ginger butter sauce, with an iced lemon parfait with oatmeal meringue for dessert. One spring dinner saw 'great' roast Cornish scallops with a tomato and coriander nage; breast of corn-fed chicken served with a slice of fried Parmesan polenta, decent ratatouille and a drizzle of pesto on the plate; and an apple tarte Tatin with a creamy but suitably bitter caramel ice cream. The primary tastes were all clearly there. Smaller details, bread, canapés, petits fours, are all as they should be.
  Signature dishes: Chicken liver and green bean salad with sesame and soy dressing; roast north Devon sea bass and scallops with fennel purée and bouillabaisse sauce; roast partridge with celeriac, dauphinoise and wild mushroom sauce; hot apple Tatin with caramel ice cream.

EX36 3EG
Map 3: SS72
Tel: 01769 573377
Fax: 01769 573797
Chef: Matt Corner
Owners: Margaret Aris, Charles Brown
Cost: Fixed-price L £20/D £34. H/wine £12
Times: Noon-last L 1.45pm/7-last D 8.45pm
Additional: Children welcome
Seats: 32. Private dining room 10
Smoking: No smoking in dining room
Accommodation: 11 en suite
Credit cards: 💳 💳 ⚡ ▫ 🅱 🅿 JCB

Directions: From Tiverton take A361, Whitechapel signed at roundabout. Right after 0.75 mile

STAVERTON, Sea Trout Inn ❀❀

It used to be called the Church House Inn until a previous landlord changed the name after catching a large sea trout in the River Dart close by. The 15th century inn lies in the lush Dart Valley, and comprises the sturdy, white-painted inn that has over the years extended to adjoining cottages, and a smart,

TQ9 6PA
Map 3: SX76
Tel: 01803 762274
Fax: 01803 762506
Please telephone for further details

Sea Trout Inn

hotel-style accommodation extension. When we visited the car park was filling up at 7pm – this is a popular place. It is a well run, brisk place, but it adheres to good standards. The staff, for instance are plentiful, and the image strives for a stronger country look than most country pubs. Fish dominate the decor in the open plan bar, filling glass cases, and is a strength of the menu in the spacious restaurant, especially the blackboard specials. There are beams, and thick walls but modernisation has taken away any old feel, replacing it with an air of solid, respectable comfort.

Directions: In village centre, from A38 turn onto A384 to Staverton

TAVISTOCK, Bistro 19 ✿

Charming, double-fronted building, a stone's throw from the town centre, serving value-for-money meals. Colourful rear courtyard for alfresco dining, weather permitting. Informal and relaxed atmosphere. dishes range from roasted Barbary duck with fruits of the forest compote and brandy game jus to parsley lamb noisette with a honey glaze.

19 Plymouth Road PL19 8AU
Map 2: SX47
Tel: 01822 617581
Please telephone for further details

THURLESTONE, Heron House Hotel ✿

Family-owned hotel located next to a bird sanctuary and with fabulous views of the South Devon coast. Bird prints adorn a dining room where the short menu might include salmon fishcakes with lobster butter, local pheasant with red wine and herb jus, and roast cod with green noodles, pancetta and red pesto.

Thurlestone Sands
Nr Salcombe TQ7 3JY
Map 3: SX64
Tel: 01548 561308/561600
Fax: 01548 560180
Chef: David Newland
Owner: Pear Rowland
Cost: *Alc* £22.50, fixed-price
L £12.95/D £25. ☺ H/wine £12
Times: Last L 2.30pm/last D 8.30pm
Additional: Bar food L; Sunday L;
Children welcome; ❹ dishes
Smoking: No smoking in dining room
Accommodation: 17 en suite.
Credit cards:  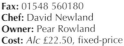 JCB

Directions: From Kingsbridge take Salcombe road (A381) ignoring all signs for Thurlestone; R for Hope Cove, straight on at crossroads, fork R at Galmpton for Thurlestone Sands

THURLESTONE, **Thurlestone Hotel**

Kingsbridge TQ7 3NN
Map 3: SX76
Tel: 01548 560382
Fax: 01548 561069
Chef: Hugh Miller
Owners: The Grose Family
Cost: Fixed-price L £14/D £25
(both 4 courses). H/wine £9.75
Times: Last L 2pm/D 9pm. Closed
4-14 Jan
Additional: Bar food L; Sunday L;
Children welcome; dishes
Smoking: No smoking in dining room;
Air conditioning
Accommodation: 65 en suite
Credit cards:

Owned and run by the Grose family for over a century, this large traditional coastal hotel has some stunning views over a beautiful stretch of Devon coastline. A meal in the elegant restaurant may include Caesar salad with marinade duck and quails' eggs, poached fillet of lemon sole on a crab galette, and apple pie with vanilla custard to finish.

Directions: A381 (Kingsbridge), then A379 (Churchstow), turn onto B3197, then turn into lane signposted Thurlestone

TORQUAY, **Corbyn Head Hotel**

With great views across the harbour, both restaurants at this waterfront hotel offer a great setting for an enjoyable meal. Starters range from asparagus and Brie tartlet to cream of ham and lentil soup. Main courses could include pan-fried fillet of red mullet, and roast supreme of chicken with bacon lardons and a chasseur sauce.

Smoking: No smoking in dining room
Accommodation: 50 en suite.
Credit cards:

Directions: On seafront at Livermead

Torquay Road Seafront
Livermead TQ2 6RH
Map 3: SX96
Tel: 01803 213611
Fax: 01803 296152
Chef: Michael Kuckuzka
Owners: Julian & Anne Cook
Cost: Alc £21, fixed-price D £17.50
(4 courses). H/wine £12.50
Times: Last L 2pm/last D 9pm
Additional: Bar food; Sunday L;
No children under 5; dishes

TORQUAY, **The Grand**

Edwardian seafront hotel retaining the air of that elegant era. Dinner offers sea views and a sensible length, fixed-price menu. Prawn and sun-dried tomato cheesecake with tarragon and dill-dressed leaves, medley of seafood with avocado and cucumber cream, and breast of Guinea fowl with honey-braised red cabbage show the style.

Accommodation: 110 en suite
Credit cards: JCB

Directions: From M5 take A380 to Torquay. At seafront turn 1st right. Hotel on corner 1st on left

Sea Front TQ2 6NT
Map 3: SX96
Tel: 01803 296677
Fax: 01803 231462
Chef: Michel Nijsten
Owner: Great Portland Hotels Ltd
Cost: Alc £30, fixed-price L £15.50/D £23.50 (4 courses). H/wine £10.50
Times: Last L 2pm/last D 9.30pm
Additional: Bar food L; Sunday L;
Children welcome; dishes
Smoking: No smoking in dining room

TORQUAY, **Grosvenor Hotel** NEW

Mima's restaurant at the Grosvenor provides a romantic setting for dinner. From a cosmopolitan menu, a test meal included a starter of spicy Thai fish soup, followed by liver and bacon with a rich onion

Belgrave Road TQ2 5HG
Map 3: SX96
Tel: 01803 294373/215515
Fax: 01803 291032
Chef: Paul Webb

Grosvenor Hotel

Owner: Grosvenor Resorts Group
Cost: *Alc* £25, fixed price D £18.50.
H/wine £8.50
Times: D only, last D 10.30pm
Additional: Bar food L; Sunday L;
Children welcome; ✦ dishes
Accomodation: 45 en suite
Credit cards: ▨ ▨ ▨ ▨ ▨ ▨ JCB

sauce. To finish, a light and zesty lemon torte was accompanied by delicious home-made ice cream.

Directions: Telephone for directions

TORQUAY, **Imperial Hotel** ✿

Park Hill Road TQ1 1DG
Map 3: SX96
Tel: 01803 294301
Fax: 01803 298293
Chef: Austin Mitchell
Cost: *Alc* £35, fixed-price D £25.
H/wine £16
Times: D only, last D 9.30pm
Additional: Bar food L; Sunday L;
Children welcome; ✦ dishes
Smoking: No-smoking area; Air
conditioning
Accommodation: 167 en suite
Credit cards: ▨ ▨ ▨ ▨ ▨ ▨ ▨ JCB

Well-established grand hotel with fabulous views over the harbour. Eat in the splendid Regatta Restaurant or the Haldon Room. The kitchen displays an understanding of good technique in dishes such as seafood ravioli with a fennel and caraway seed stew with sauce vierge, and roasted fillet of lamb, potato galette, sweet potato purée and cocktail olives Casablanca.

Directions: M5 to Exeter, A380 then A3022 to Torquay. Park Hill Road is off Torwood Street/Babbacombe Road, just N of new harbour

TORQUAY, **Mulberry House** ✿

Victorian hotel with a homely dining room where chef-proprietor Lesley Cooper continues to please with her short blackboard menus. On offer is a stylish mix of the familiar with unusual twists. Note chicken liver ramekin with tomato and fennel sauce, smoked ham rissoles with spiced cranberries, and baked marinated salmon with Thai flavours and plum sauce.

Accommodation: 3 en suite. **Credit cards:** None

Directions: From the seafront turn up Belgrave Road, then 1st L into Scarborough Road.

1 Scarborough Road
TQ2 5UJ
Map 3: SX96
Tel: 01803 213639
Chef/Owner: Lesley Cooper
Cost: *Alc* £15, fixed-price L £7.95. ☺
H/wine £9.50
Times: Last L 1.30pm/last D 9pm.
Closed D Sun, (all Mon & Tue except
residents)
Additional: Sunday L; Children
welcome; ✦ dishes
Smoking: No smoking in dining room

TORQUAY, **Orestone Manor**

Rockhouse Lane Maidencombe
TQ1 4SX
Map 3: SX96
Tel: 01803 328098
Fax: 01803 328336
Owner: Bill & Gill Dagworthy
Please telephone for further details

Bill and Gill Dagworthy continue to provide excellent hospitality at their attractive Georgian country house hotel. Enviable views across Lyme Bay are an added attraction, but the draw here is the cooking. Clear flavours, sound technique and prime ingredients were all noted in a well-reported summer dinner. That meal opened with canapés of chicken livers wrapped in bacon and taramasolata tart. Then smooth chicken liver parfait with kumquat chutney was followed by a vibrant fillet of cod baked in tomato sauce with a cheese crust. Orange tart with orange mint sorbet for dessert was perfect, the mint in the sorbet adding an extra taste dimension. Good coffee, petits fours, and home-made breads show that attention to detail extends to lesser points. One to watch.

Directions: Off B3199 Torquay/Teignmouth coastal road, turn R on Watcombe Hill opposite Brunel Manor.

TORQUAY, **The Osborne Hotel**

Hesketh Crescent Meadfoot TQ1 2LL
Map 3: SX96
Tel: 01803 213311
Fax: 01803 296788
Please telephone for further details

The Osborne forms the centrepiece of an elegant Regency terrace and commands superb views over Meadfoot Beach and Torbay. The brasserie serves informal meals and light refreshment; it is the Langtry restaurant that is the more stylish of the two, offering a more formal atmosphere although pleasantly styled with white linen, modern crockery, fresh flowers and candles. The kitchen produces some sound modern cooking. An early summer dinner opened with good home-made bread and canapés, then a quail consommé made notable for the perfectly poached quail egg and slices of quail breast and petit parisienne of vegetables. Breast of Gressingham duck with cabbage and smoked bacon came next, simple, well executed, both in flavour and consistency. A praline pyramid, for dessert was filled with orange, dark and white chocolate mousse and served with a trio of chocolate sauces.

Directions: Follow A3022 to seafront and turn L towards Harbour. At Clock Tower turn L; at next junction/traffic lights turn R. Follow rd over brow of hill and down other side. The gates of Hesketh Crescent and hotel are opposite.

TORQUAY,

The Table Restaurant ❀❀

The key to the success of this small high street restaurant is that Julie Tuckett not only cooks the things she likes to eat herself but also knows she can cook well; it makes for a 'jewel of a restaurant'. Filo pastry parcels, for instance, filled with locally caught crab were bursting with flavour, the pastry cooked to perfection and Exmoor venison fillet with juniper and Madeira jus was outstandingly tender and flavoursome. Other starters might include Sussex goats' cheese with a salad of avocado and mâche, or fish soup with croûtons and rouille. Apart from the 'catch of the day', there may be a choice of braised Scottish hare with red cabbage and buttered herbed gnocchi, or roasted fillet of salmon on a spinach and Pernod sauce. There is also a 'very serious' chocolate terrine with hot plums which deserves all the praise it gets.

Directions: From Torquay follow signs to Babbacombe. Restaurant on L hand side when approached from harbour

135 Babbacombe Road TQ1 3SR
Map 3: SX96
Tel/Fax: 01803 324292
Chef/Owner: Julie T Tuckett
Cost: Fixed-price L £12.85 (2 courses)/D £27.50. H/wine £11.50
Times: 12.15-last L 1.45pm (Sept-Apr only)/7.15-last D 9.45pm.
Closed L Sat, L Sun, 2 wks early Feb, 2 wks end Mar
Additional: No children under 11; ❀ dishes
Seats: 16. Private dining up to 20
Smoking: No pipes and cigars
Credit cards: ▬ ▬ ▬

TORQUAY, **Toorak Hotel** ❀ **NEW**

A quiet location opposite the Torquay Riviera Centre for this well-appointed hotel. The restaurant bustles in season, with a short choice of soundly cooked dishes. Enjoy oriental chicken noodle soup, British beef lasagne in a white wine, mushroom and cream sauce, and a charlotte russe from the fresh, tempting sweet buffet.

Chestnut Avenue TQ2 5JS
Map 3: SX96
Tel: 01803 291444
Please telephone for further details

TOTNES, **Durant Arms** ❀ **NEW**

A very attractive inn dating back to the 18th century. It is immaculately kept with an up-market clientele, situated in an unspoilt village not far from Totnes. Mr and Mrs Ellis are serious about their little inn and the food complements the overall atmosphere which exists here.

Ashprington TQ9 7UP
Map 3: SX86
Tel: 01803 732240
Please telephone for further details

TWO BRIDGES, **Prince Hall Hotel** ❀❀

Expect a warm welcome at the Southwell's hotel in the heart of Dartmoor National Park. Crisp linen, fresh flowers on the table and stunning moorland views are a great back drop to dinner and a daily-changing menu that makes good use of local produce. Brixham crab, Dartmoor venison with rowanberry and port sauce, Chagford pork with apples and Calvados, and local fillet steak marchand de vin, show the style. A May

PL20 6SA
Map 2: SX67
Tel: 01822 890403
Fax: 01822 890676
Chefs: Adam Southwell, Les Pratt
Owners: Adam & Carrie Southwell
Cost: Fixed-price D £24 (4 courses). ☺ H/wine £8.95

dinner took in a lovely procençale tart, then a perfectly cooked fillet of sea bass and John Dory with a salsa verte on a bed of wilted spinach, 'lovely' vegetables, and banana, pineapple, and peach cooked in a rum flavoured syrup with a scoop of Salcombe Dairy ice cream and some clotted cream for dessert. Sound wine list including a good selection of halves.

Directions: From Two Bridges take B3357 Dartmeet Road; hotel is hidden 1 mile on R

Times: D only, last D 8.30pm. Closed Jan
Additional: No children under 8; dishes
Smoking: No smoking in dining room
Accommodation: 9 en suite
Credit cards:

TWO BRIDGES,

Two Bridges Hotel ❀❀

Dartmoor PL20 6SW
Map 2: SX67
Tel: 01822 890581
Fax: 01822 890575
Chef: Andrew Shortman
Owner: Warm Welcome Hotels
Cost: *Alc* £25.50, fixed-price L £14/D £19.95. ☺ H/wine £9
Times: Noon-last L 2.30pm/7-last D 9.30pm
Additional: Bar food; Sunday L; Children welcome; ❀ dishes
Seats: 100. Private room 26
Smoking: No smoking in dining room
Accommodation: 29 en suite
Credit cards:

Set beside the West Dart River, this fine hotel stands next to the two bridges that give the village its name. Full of *olde worlde* character, there are huge log fires, deep, comfortable easy chairs and an impressive collection of memorabilia. Traditional food is served in Saracen's Bar, where meals can be washed down with a pint of locally-brewed Jail Ale. More formal dining takes place in the candlelit restaurant. Hearty dishes include pan-fried collops of beef with a rich mushroom and red wine jus, and fennel and tarragon ratatouille. Our inspector enjoyed an autumn meal of creamy risotto with Parmesan and thin crisps of aubergine, followed by baked loin of lamb with roasted garlic and a rich rosemary jus. For dessert, a 'lovely' bramble apple and rhubarb crumble. After dinner, enjoy coffee in the magnificent Music Room where the baby grand is played most weekends.

Directions: From Tavistock take B3357, hotel at junction with B3312

WHIMPLE, **Woodhayes Hotel** ❀❀

EX5 2TD
Map 3: SY09
Tel: 01404 822237
Fax: 01404 822337
Chefs: Katherine & Michael Rendle
Owners: Frank, Katherine & Michael Rendle
Cost: Fixed-price D £27.50 (6 courses). H/wine £11.50
Times: D only, 7.15 for 7.45pm. Closed 2 wks Xmas & New Year
Additional: No children under 12; ❀ dishes
Seats: 18
Smoking: No smoking in dining room
Accommodation: 6 en suite
Credit cards:

Expect a warm welcome at the Rendles' charming Georgian country house hotel surrounded by four acres of lovely gardens and grounds. Dinner in the elegant, intimate dining room is a no-choice affair (except at the dessert stage) but runs to five courses, seven if you count the appetisers served in the bar and the petits fours with coffee. Our most recent meal was typically well thought out with thinly sliced Parma ham and slices of juicy ripe pear, before a carrot and coriander soup (Michael Rendle's home-made bread deserves more than a passing mention at this point), and then the fish course of fillet of brill with a cheese crust. The centrepiece was tender venison with a moreish cranberry and red wine sauce for which some creamed celeriac and Delmonico potatoes were the perfect complement. From desserts such as crème brûlée, and apple and quince pudding, we chose the selection of ice creams and sorbets (all made from their own fruit) before some West Country cheeses. The carefully constructed wine list includes a good choice of half-bottles.

Directions: On A30 midway Honiton/Exeter. Straight down Whimple Road, first building on R

WINKLEIGH, **Pophams** ✿✿✿

Twelve years ago Melvyn Popham and Dennis Hawkes opened a small deli-cum-bakery. That led to morning coffee, then lunch, initially no more than the likes of carrot soup, smoked trout pâté, and steak and kidney pudding. Now, as a restaurant Pophams is hard to define. It remains open for lunch only, retains an endearing simplicity and lack of licence (BYO is part of the charm). The place remains 'coffin-sized', as all temptation to expand into the dilapidated premises next door is fully resisted, despite being fully booked every day, with a three month waiting list for summer Saturdays. What has grown is Melvyn's cooking. Completely self-taught, he has moved on from the traditional steak and kidney pudding-style and now offers an up-to-date repertoire of butternut squash soup with shaved Parmesan, roast fillet of local beef with oyster mushrooms and Madeira sauce, boned best end of lamb wrapped in puff pastry with spinach and a cream paprika sauce, and perhaps a chocolate marquise with vanilla ice cream and a coffee bean Tia Maria sauce, or a fresh orange tart with orange Grand Marnier sauce, from the dessert list. The dedication is astonishing. The day starts at 6.30am (lunch often begins at 11.30am) and might not finish until 7pm. The cooking may be the initial draw, but Dennis's talent as a front-of-house man means that a meal can often go on until late in the afternoon as tables (there are only three) get chatting. Sourcing is everything. Meat comes from a butcher in Hatherleigh, where possible vegetables are grown in the village, and bread (the only thing not made on the premises), comes from a baker in Okehampton. Vin Sullivan in Crediton, and trips to Exeter, fill the gaps. The translation to dishes in the kitchen is based on a very straightforward approach: for Melvyn 'cooking is the most natural thing to do'.

Castle Street EX19 8HQ
Map 3: SS60
Tel: 01837 83767
Chef: Melvyn Popham
Owners: Melvyn Popham, Dennis Hawkes
Cost: *Alc* £24
Times: L only, noon-last L 3.30pm. Closed Sun, Mon, Tue, Xmas, Feb
Additional: No children under 14; ✿ dishes
Seats: 10
Smoking: Totally no smoking establishment; Air conditioning
Credit cards: ▬ ▬ ▬

Directions: In village centre, about 9 miles from Okehampton

WOOLACOMBE,
Watersmeet Hotel ✿✿

Every table in the restaurant of this smartly appointed North Devon hotel has a view of the sea. It's a popular place, the front-facing bedrooms naturally most in demand, with the sound of the waves crashing in the bay below. Starters on the dinner menu could range from Exmoor game terrine with pear chutney to Greek salad or sautéed lambs' kidneys in filo, while the inspiration for main courses is equally broad-ranging: local venison with mulled fruits on rösti, roast beef with Yorkshire pudding, pan-fried monkfish Thermidor, or Scotch salmon with

Mortehoe
EX34 7EB
Map 2: SS44
Tel: 01271 870333
Fax: 01271 870890
Chef: John Prince
Owners: Brian & Pat Wheeldon
Cost: *Alc* £23.50, fixed-price D £26.50 (5 courses). ☺ H/wine £9.85
Times: Noon-last L 2pm/7-last D 8.30pm

Watersmeet Hotel

Additional: Bar food L; No children under 8; ❸ dishes
Seats: 50. Jacket & tie preferred
Smoking: No smoking in dining room
Accommodation: 25 en suite
Credit cards: ▬ ▬ ▅ ▅ ▅ ▅ ▅

hollandaise. Accompanying vegetables have been well received. Sweet-lovers could opt for Watersmeet's unique bread-and-butter pudding with whisky sabayon, or a tuile of honey ice cream surrounded by fresh fruits; West Country cheeses may appeal to others. Around half of the nine house wines on the list are also sold by the half-bottle.

Directions: M5/J27. Follow A361 to Woolacombe, R at beach car park, 300 yds on R

YARCOMBE, **Belfry Country Hotel** ❀

Victorian village school, now an attractive small hotel with a wood panelled restaurant. Good country cooking with Stilton cream pears, Yarcombe casseroled pheasant, and Devon lamb all justly popular, as are the home-made puddings, especially lemon meringue pie served with lashings of clotted cream.

Additional: No children under 12; ❸ dishes
Smoking: No smoking in dining room
Accommodation: 6 en suite
Credit cards: ▬ ▬ ▅ ▅ ▅ ▅ JCB

Directions: On A30, in village centre, midway between Honiton and Chard

EX14 9BD
Map 3: ST20
Tel: 01404 861234
Fax: 01404 861579
Chef: Jackie Rees
Owners: Jackie & Tony Rees
Cost: Alc £25.45. Fixed-price D £18.95. ☺ H/wine £9.75
Times: D only, 7pm-last D 8.45pm

YELVERTON, **Moorland Links** ❀

Picture windows give diners garden views at this hotel within Dartmoor National Park. The fixed-price menu offers a choice of soundly cooked dishes ranging from simple steaks and vegetable soup with herbs, to confit of duck with tomato concasse, or seared salmon on spinach and mushroom ravioli with Sauternes sauce. Desserts come with a bowl of clotted cream.

Additional: Bar food; Sunday L; Children welcome; ❸ dishes
Smoking: No smoking in dining room
Accommodation: 45 en suite
Credit cards: ▬ ▬ ▅ ▅ ▅ ▅

Directions: On A386, within Dartmoor National Park

PL20 6DA
Map 2: SX56
Tel: 01822 852245
Fax: 01822 855004
Chef: Stephen Holmes
Owner: Forestdale Hotels Ltd
Cost: Alc £21.75, fixed-price L&D £21.75. ☺ H/wine £9.95
Times: Last L 2pm/last D 10pm. Closed L Sat, L Bhs

DORSET

BEAMINSTER,
Bridge House Hotel ❀❀

Good food, reasonable prices, friendly service, the family-owned 13th-century inn scores well on all points. The arrival of a new chef has lifted the quality of the cooking and there is an emphasis on freshly prepared food using local ingredients. The *carte* is kept commendably simple and sensible – fusion food means a platter of smoked mackerel and gravad lax with dill mustard sauce, and balsamic vinegar is about as daring as it gets. Other enjoyable starters might include smoked trout parfait, or pâté of local game with port and orange jelly. Fresh vegetables are served alongside uncomplicated main courses such as Barbary duck breast with raspberry vinaigrette, whole lemon sole with lemon herb butter sauce, and roast rack of local lamb. Pancakes with Grand Marnier sauce (aka crêpes Suzette) make a popular retro dessert – although, one suspects, here, deep in Thomas Hardy country, it may never have gone away.

Directions: On A3066, 200m down hill from town centre

3 Prout Bridge DT8 3AY
Map 3: ST40
Tel: 01308 862200
Fax: 01308 863700
Chef: Simon Clewlow
Owner: Peter Pinkster
Cost: Fixed-price L £11.50/D £21.50.
☺ H/wine £10.40.
Times: Noon-last L 2pm/7pm-last D 9pm
Additional: Sunday L; No children under 12; ◑ dishes
Seats: 36. Private dining room 16
Smoking: No smoking in dining room
Accommodation: 13 en suite
Credit cards: ▆▆ ▀▀ ▀▆ ⌐ ▀▀ ▆ ▨ JCB

BLANDFORD FORUM,
Castleman Hotel ❀❀

Good places to eat in the country on a Sunday evening are still few and far between, so the Castleman scores doubly well. The setting has bags of character, down to the lights flickering on and off due to an unreliable village power supply! The cooking is freshly and competently done with chicken and ham terrine with yellow courgette and pepper chutney, sautéed lambs' kidneys with bacon, mustard and rosemary, braised hare in Beaujolais with glazed shallots and mushrooms, and celeriac purée being typical of the robust dinner-party style menu. Baked lemon and ginger cheesecake is a must for dessert. Details are comforting – locally made bread, superior mashed potato, home-made biscuits with coffee and there is a good selection of wines, including dessert ones by the glass.

Directions: One mile from the A354. Hotel is signposted within village

Chettle DT11 8DB
Map 3: ST80
Tel: 01258 830096
Fax: 01258 830051
Chef: Barbara Garnsworthy
Owners: Barbara Garnsworthy, Edward Bourke
Cost: Alc £20, fixed-price L £14. ☺ H/wine £8.
Times: D only, 7pm-10pm. Closed Feb
Additional: Sunday L (Noon-2pm); Children welcome; ◑ dishes
Seats: 50
Smoking: No smoking in dining room
Accommodation: 8 en suite
Credit cards: ▆▆ ▀▀ ▀▆ ⌐ JCB

BOURNEMOUTH,
Bistro on the Beach ❀ NEW

You cannot eat any closer to the sea than at this unique little bistro, bang on the beach. Not the most prepossessing of buildings, but regulars flock here for good value, excellent cooking, and friendly service; it is essential to book. Expect the likes of sea bass and stir-fried vegetables, and an outstanding bread-and-butter pudding.

Additional: Children welcome; ◑ dishes
Credit cards: ▀▀ ▀▆ ⌐

Directions: Telephone for directions

Solent Promenade
Southbourne H6 4BE
Map 4: SZ09
Tel: 01202 431473
Chef: David Ryan
Owners: Sheila & David Ryan
Cost: Alc £15.25, fixed-price D £13.95. ☺ H/wine £8.25
Times: D only, 7pm-last D 9.30pm. Closed Sun, Mon, Tue, 3wks Nov, 2 wks spring

BOURNEMOUTH,
Carlton Hotel 🏵🏵

Overlooking the bay, the Carlton enjoys one of Bournemouth's most sought-after addresses. Award-winning gardens and leisure facilities keep the guests coming, as do the Anglo/European dishes served in the hotel's smart, formal restaurant. Meals start with a selection of fresh breads – red pepper, white and poppy seed – all baked on the premises. Typical dishes from the *carte* include roast loin of pork with a chunky swede and artichoke purée, breast of chicken with spaghetti tossed with sun-dried tomatoes and oyster mushrooms, and pan-fried red mullet with julienne of vegetables and a lemon and coriander sauce. Starters to look out for include chicken liver and herb parfait with toasted brioche and tomato chutney, and smoked chicken and avocado rillette with walnuts and ground nut oil. Desserts are along the lines of white and dark chocolate mousse with raspberry coulis. The comprehensive wine list has a decent selection of half-bottles.

Directions: M3/M27, follow A338 (Bournemouth). Follow signs to town centre and East Overcliff. Hotel is on seafront

East Overcliff BH1 3DN
Map 4: SZ09
Tel: 01202 552011
Fax: 01202 299573
Chef: Richard Walton
Owner: Menzies Hotels & Leisure Ltd
Cost: *Alc* £25, fixed-price L £16.50/D £23. ☺ H/wine £12.50
Times: 12.30-last L 1.45pm/7-last D 9.45pm
Additional: Bar food; Sunday L; Children welcome; 🍴 dishes
Seats: 130. Private dining room 90. Jacket & tie preferred Sat D
Smoking: No smoking in dining room
Accommodation: 74 en suite
Credit cards: 💳 💳 💳 💳 💳 💳 💳 JCB

BOURNEMOUTH,
Chine Hotel 🏵🏵

Boscombe Spa Road
BH5 1AX
Map 4: SZ09
Tel: 01202 396234
Fax: 01202 391737
Chef: Paul Bingham
Owners: FJB Hotels.
Cost: Fixed-price L £14.50/ D £17.50. ☺ H/wine £11.50.
Times: 12.30pm-last L 2pm/7pm-last D 9.15pm Closed L Sat
Additional: Bar Food; Sunday L; Children welcome; 🍴 menu
Seats: 175.
Private dining rooms 30-130
Smoking: No smoking in dining room
Accommodation: 92 en suite
Credit cards: 💳 💳 💳 💳 💳

Peacefully located in Boscombe, this Victorian hotel is surrounded by three acres of mature gardens from which a path leads down to the promenade. Deep, rich colours create a warm atmosphere in the restaurant, which enjoys views across the gardens to the sea beyond. Fixed-price dinner menus are not long but well balanced with a typical main course choice comprising a ragout of seafood in a pastry case with crayfish sauce, poached brill with a cumin crust on potato purée and wilted watercress, caramelised duck with coconut and banana fritter, rump steak chasseur, and a vegetarian dish based on baby gem lettuce with grilled aubergine and salsa. A very approachable wine list is helpfully organised by style. Good service from caring staff.

Directions: From M27, A31 and A338 follow signs to Boscombe Pier, Boscombe Spa Road is off Christchurch Road near Boscombe Gardens

BOURNEMOUTH, Farthings ❀

5/7 Grove Road BH1 3AS
Map 4: SZ09
Tel: 01202 558660
Fax: 01202 293766
Chef: Andy Sewell
Owners: Mr & Mrs T Porteous
Cost: Alc £25, fixed-price L £16/ D
£25.50 (4 courses). ☺ H/wine £10.75
Times: Last L 2pm/last D 9.30pm.
Closed Xmas
Additional: Bar Food L; Sunday L;
Children welcome; ❹ dishes
Smoking: No-smoking area

Originally an old coach house, with the restaurant based in a large, airy conservatory. Promise in the kitchen, with the likes of salmon and monkfish terrine, medallions of venison with haggis, chicken breast with celeriac and horseradish nest, and mille-feuille of vanilla shortbread and Grand Marnier brûlée, setting the pace.

Accommodation: 5 rooms
Credit cards: ▅ ▆ ▆ ▆ ▆ ▆ ▆

Directions: On roundabout, top of hill on Bath Road going from Pier to Lansdowne

BOURNEMOUTH,
Langtry Manor Hotel ❀

With its timeless sense of well-being, Langtry Manor provides the perfect setting for a romantic break. Brimming with history, original features abound – the magnificent dining hall, for example, has a minstrel's gallery and several enormous Tudor tapestries. The food is pretty good too, and at weekends gourmet Edwardian banquets are held.

Accommodation: 28 en suite
Credit cards: ▅ ▆ ▆ ▆ ▆ ▆ JCB

Directions: On the East Cliff, at corner of Derby and Knyveton roads

26 Derby Road BH1 3QB
Map 4: SZ09
Tel: 01202 553887
Fax: 01202 290115
Chef: Richard Glanville
Owner: Mrs Pamela Hamilton-Howard
Cost: Alc £23.75, fixed-price
D £19.75 (4 courses). H/wine £9.95
Times: D only, last D 9.30pm
Additional: ❹ dishes
Smoking: No smoking in dining room

BOURNEMOUTH, Queens Hotel ❀

On the East Cliff, the Queens has fine sea views and a convenient location for lifts down to the sea front. Dinner might include chicken liver pâté with Cumberland sauce, honey and soy-roasted duck with Cointreau and orange sauce, and salmon with a tomato and chive sauce. Lunch is an extensive hot-and-cold buffet.

Smoking: No smoking in dining room; Air conditioning
Accommodation: 110 en suite
Credit cards: ▆ ▆ ▆

Directions: Follow signs to East Cliff, hotel is one road back from seafront

Meyrick Road East Cliff BH1 3DL
Map 4: SZ09
Tel: 01202 554415
Fax: 01202 294810
Chef: William Summerell
Owners: Mr & Mrs Arthur Young
Cost: Fixed-price D £17.95 (4 courses). ☺ H/wine £9.95
Times: Last L 1.30pm/last D 8.30pm.
Closed L Sat
Additional: Bar food; Sunday L;
Children welcome; ❹ dishes

BOURNEMOUTH,
Royal Bath Hotel ⊛⊛

There's a choice of eating at this large Victorian hotel with its enviable position, surrounded by well-tended gardens, in the heart of town. Our Rosette award is for Oscar's (named after Oscar Wilde who once stayed here) where friendly service goes along with a modernised French menu. Our most recent meal began with a stimulating canapé of smoked salmon with mustard mayonnaise in a lovely short-pastry case, and ended with a first-class apricot and almond tart served with coconut ice cream. In between the choice ranges from pan-seared foie gras on baby spinach leaves with tangy black and redcurrant sauce, and cream of leek and potato soup infused with truffles, to salmon with creamed watercress sauce, and calves' liver on onion marmalade with ginger and lime sauce.

Accommodation: 140 en suite
Credit cards: ▆▆ ▆▆ ▆ ▆▆ ▆

Directions: Follow signs for Bournemouth Pier and beaches

Bath Road BH1 2EW
Map 4: SZ09
Tel: 01202 555555
Fax: 01202 554158
Chef: Gary Paine
Owners: De Vere Hotels
Cost: *Alc* £33, fixed-price L £16.50/D £30 (4 courses). H/wine £11.95
Times: 12.30-last L 2pm/7-last D 10pm. Closed D Sun
Additional: Bar food; Sunday L; Children welcome; ⊕ dishes
Seats: 60. Private dining rooms 10-400. Jacket & tie preferred
Smoking: No-smoking area; No pipes & cigars

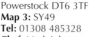

BOURNEMOUTH,
Swallow Highcliff Hotel ⊛

Apt name for this wonderfully located hotel with panoramic sea views. Extensive leisure facilities and a range of business facilities make this an understandably popular place. The kitchen is serious about food. Menus in the Terrace restaurant are built around fresh produce. Staff are cheerful and willing.

St Michael's Road West Cliffe
Map 4: SZ09
Tel: 01202 557702
Fax: 01202292734
Please telephone for further details

BRIDPORT, **Bridge House Hotel** ⊛

18th-century hotel run in friendly fashion by Simon and Trish Badger. Seared salmon fillet with fresh tomatoes, chives and white wine sauce, baked chicken with honey and ginger crust, roast pork with apple and cider sauce, and pan-fried sirloin steak are typical of the main course choice at dinner.

Additional: Bar food D; Children welcome; ⊕ dishes
Smoking: No smoking in dining room
Accommodation: 10 en suite
Credit cards: ▆▆ ▆▆ ▆▆ ▆ ▆▆ JCB

Directions: Into Bridport (East Street). Hotel is 1st Georgian building on R

115 East Street DT6 3LB
Map 3: SY49
Tel/Fax: 01308 423371
Chef/Owner: Simon Badger
Cost: *Alc* £20, fixed price D £15.50. ☺ H/wine £8
Times: D only, last D 9.15pm. Closed Sun

BRIDPORT, **Horseshoes** ⊛

Stone and thatch country inn offering superior pub food and decent wines by the glass. Well worth the tortuous drive down narrow winding lanes for competently prepared dishes, in particular fresh local fish. Typical choices may include rabbit terrine with apple and shallot chutney, monkfish with saffron sauce, and crème brûlée for pudding.

Directions: In the village of Powerstock, 5 miles NE of Bridport, signposted off A3066 Beaminster Road.

Powerstock DT6 3TF
Map 3: SY49
Tel: 01308 485328
Chef: Mark Johnson
Owners: Mark & Sue Johnson
Cost: *Alc* £21. ☺ H/wine £7.95
Times: Last L 2pm/D 9.30pm
Additional: Bar Food; Sunday L; Children welcome; ⊕ dishes
Smoking: No smoking in dining room
Credit cards: ▆▆ ▆▆ ▆▆ ▆

BRIDPORT, **Riverside Restaurant**

West Bay DT6 4EZ
Map 3: SY49
Tel: 01308 422011
Chefs: Mike Mills, Nic Larcombe
Owners: Janet & Arthur Watson
Cost: *Alc* £25. ☺ H/wine £11.95
Times: Noon-last L 2.30pm/6.30pm-
last D 9pm. Closed D Sun, Mon
(except Bhs), Dec, Jan, Feb (times
vary evenings Mar-April, Oct-Nov)
Additional: Children welcome;
 dishes
Seats: 70
Smoking: No pipes and cigars
Credit cards: 〓 〓 〓 ⌐ JCB

Jutting out 'twixt land and water, the Riverside's enviable
location ensures a view from every table. Part restaurant, part
café, the bare wooden tables and paintings by local artists
create a civilised, relaxed atmosphere. Fresh fish is the star –
excellent seafood soup, brandade of cod, hake with provencale
sauce, brilliant brill with sorrel sauce and deep-fried spinach.
Shellfish includes stuffed clams (palourdes) with herb butter,
Atlantic oysters, moules marinière, and local lobster. Red
mullet and John Dory can be ordered, grilled whole, when
available. Daily specials might include brochette of scallops
with couscous and basil pesto, or deep-fried cod in Guinness
batter with home-made mushy peas and chips. Vegetarian
choices might include wild mushroom and red pepper risotto,
and meat-eaters can dig into chargrilled steak or roast chicken.
Desserts are another highlight – crème brûlée and caramelised
banana 'tartelette' with butterscotch sauce have both been
praised.

Directions: In the centre of West Bay by the river

BRIDPORT,
Roundham House Hotel

*Some of the vegetables served at dinner may have been grown in the
acre of gardens that surround this small hotel, an elegant Edwardian
building. Creamed and Parmentier potatoes and broccoli and
cauliflower florets may accompany Lyme Bay plaice meunière, or
perhaps steak and kidney pie, preceded by celery soup and followed
by sherry trifle.*

Smoking: No smoking in dining room
Accommodation: 8 en suite.
Credit cards: 〓 〓 JCB

Directions: From roundabout on A35 S of Bridport take road to
West Bay, then 2nd L into Roundham Gardens

Roundham Gardens
West Bay Road DT6 4BD
Map 3: SY49
Tel: 01308 422753
Fax: 01308 421500
Chef: Jeremy Thomas
Owners: Daphne & Jeremy Thomas
Cost: *Alc* £20, fixed-price D £16.95.
H/wine £8.95
Times: D only, last D 8.15pm.
Closed Jan-Feb
Additional: Sunday L (12.30-3pm);
Children welcome; dishes

CHARMOUTH, **Thatch Lodge**

The charming hotel makes much of its history: a 14th-century
monastic retreat, with thick cobb wall, oak beams and the
splendid thatch that gives the place its name. The cooking

The Street DT6 6PQ
Map 3: SY39
Tel/Fax: 01297 560407
Chef: Andrea Ashton-Worsfold
Owners: Christopher Worsfold,

rejoices in prime fresh produce and the daily changing dinner menu (choice only at starter and pudding) offers much of interest. The repertoire here is mainstream but not tired: first courses include pan-fried chicken livers served with a small dressed salad and topped with Parmesan shavings, and Somerset brie melted over a mixed leaf and apple salad with fresh garden chives; exemplary main dishes include roasted breast of chicken stuffed with ricotta cheese and sun-dried tomatoes, wrapped in bacon and served with a chive and tomato butter sauce, or roasted breast of duck with a rich pear sauce and compote of pear. Thatch spicy apricot bread-and-butter pudding is served with local clotted cream.

Directions: Charmouth is off A35 2 miles east of Lyme Regis. Hotel on R half way up High Street

Andrea Ashton-Worsfold
Cost: Fixed-price D £24.50 (4 courses). H/wine £10.35
Times: D only at 7.30pm. Closed Sun, Mon, mid Jan-mid Mar
Seats: 14
Smoking: No smoking in dining room
Accommodation: 7 en suite
Credit cards: 🃏 🃏 🃏 🃏 🃏 JCB

CHIDEOCK,
Chideock House Hotel ✸

Main Street DT6 6JN
Map 3: SY49
Tel: 01297 489242
Fax: 01297 489184
Chef: Anna Dunn
Owners: Anna & George Dunn
Cost: Alc £23. ☺ H/wine £9.50
Times: D only, last D 9pm. Closed D Sun & Mon, Jan
Additional: Sunday L ; Children welcome
Smoking: No-smoking area
Accommodation: 7 en suite
Credit cards: 🃏 🃏 🃏 🃏 🃏 🃏

The building dates from the 1400s and was, reputedly, headquarters for the Roundheads in 1645. Today it's a friendly hotel whose dining room might offer rack of lamb with port sauce, and chicken with tarragon, plus, on a separate menu, fish dishes like prawn bisque, and salmon with ginger and sultanas.

Directions: 3 miles W of Bridport, fronting onto A35 in centre of village.

CHRISTCHURCH, Avonmouth ✸

Fish specialities highlight the fixed-price menu at this friendly hotel situated alongside Mudeford Quay with wonderful estuary views. Follow lobster bisque with roasted sea bass, pork fillet with horseradish mash and tomato jus, or steak with herb rösti and green peppercorn sauce. Finish with spotted Dick or farmhouse cheeses.

95 Mudeford BH23 3NT
Map 4: SZ19
Tel: 01202 483434
Fax: 01202 479004
Chef: Ian Morton
Owner: Forte UK Ltd
Cost: Fixed-price D £20. ☺ H/wine £10.95
Times: Last L 2pm/last D 8.45pm

Additional: Bar food L; Sunday L; Children welcome; dishes
Smoking: No smoking in dining room
Accommodation: 40 en suite
Credit cards: 🃏 🃏 🃏 🃏 🃏 🃏 🃏 JCB

Directions: Close to the bridge over the Avon on A35 (Bournemouth-Lyndhurst). Mudeford is on the edge of Christchurch Harbour, and the hotel is on the approach to Mudeford Quay

CHRISTCHURCH, **Splinters** ❀❀

12 Church Street BH23 1BW
Map 4: SZ19
Tel/Fax: 01202 483454
Chef: Jason Davenport
Owners: Timothy Lloyd, Robert Wilson
Cost: Alc £30.90, fixed-price L £13.95 (2 courses)/D £27.95. H/wine £12.45
Times: Noon-2.30pm/7-10pm. Closed D Sun, all Mon
Additional: Bar food L; Sunday L; Children welcome; ❹ dishes
Seats: 42. Private dining room 6-22
Smoking: No smoking in dining room
Credit cards: 🔳🔳🔳🔳🔳🔳🔳 JCB

The restaurant itself is a bit of a mish-mash, with several small dining rooms, some with homely pine booths, others in elegant white and indigo blue. The cooking, however, shows much more identity and cohesion and is exceptionally good value for money. Exciting dishes coming out the kitchen have included potato and chive goats' cheese tart with deep-fried tomato sorbet, pan-fried fillet of salmon with crab and coriander ravioli, chilli tomato jam and spring onions salsa, and a 'mango sunflower' made with sun-dried mango with mango sorbet and passion fruit coulis. The restaurant is housed in two period listed buildings on a cobbled street leading up to the gates of the ancient priory.

Directions: Splinters is on L side of cobbled street directly in front of Priory Gates

CHRISTCHURCH,
Waterford Lodge Hotel ❀❀

87 Bure Lane Friars Cliff Mudeford BH23 4DN
Map 4: SZ19
Tel: 01425 272948
Fax: 01425 279130
Please telephone for further details

A friendly hotel for both business and leisure guests with dinner offering a wide choice. Unusually, the *carte* suggests a recommended wine to go with each dish – a jolly good idea other restaurants might like to adopt. A Pouilly Fuissé, for example, is suggested as a match for grilled escalopes of sea bass with lime, butter and vanilla vinaigrette accompanied by Parisienne vegetables, and a Barolo Riserva, Villa Lantra to go with the braised haunch of venison in red wine and juniper berries, plus a red onion marmalade served on Anna potato. There is a choice of three dessert wines to drink alongside desserts such as frozen white chocolate dome with raspberry parfait and marbled chocolate curls.

Directions: From A35 Somerford roundabout take A337 towards Highcliffe, at next roundabout turn R to Mudeford, hotel on L

CORFE CASTLE,

Mortons House Hotel

Elizabethan manor house in a village setting. Traditional English cooking with offerings from around the globe complemented by a thoughtful wine list. Expect the likes of crab and tomato bisque flavoured with sherry, followed by lamb cooked with cumin, apricot and lemon and served with couscous.

Smoking: No smoking in dining room
Accommodation: 17 en suite
Credit cards: ▬ ▬ ▬ ▟ ▬ 🄫 🄿

Directions: In centre of village on A351

East Street BH20 5EE
Map 3: SY98
Tel: 01929 480988
Fax: 01929 480820
Chef: Christopher Button
Owners: Mr & Mrs David Langford
Cost: Alc £22, fixed-price L £15
(4 courses)/D £22.50 (6 courses). ☺
H/wine £11
Times: Last L 2pm/last D 8.30pm
Additional: Bar food L; Sunday L;
Children welcome; ⓥ dishes

CRANBORNE,

La Fosse at Cranborne

Unpretentious restaurant-with-rooms situated in a sleepy village in the heart of Dorset. Choose from the short, good-value fixed-price menus, or from the evening only carte. Interesting dishes on the latter may range from fish soup, stuffed quail with mushroom couscous, to rack of lamb, or monkfish with a spicy Thai coconut sauce.

Directions: M27 – W on to A31 to Ringwood, then to Verwood, then Cranborne

London House
The Square BH21 5PR
Map 4: SU01
Tel: 01725 517604
Fax: 01725 517778
Chefs: M LaFosse, S Hallam
Owners: MJ LaFosse, SV LaFosse
Cost: Alc £20, fixed-price L £6.25
(2 courses)/D £10.95. ☺ H/wine
£9.95
Times: Last L 1.45pm/D 9.45pm.
Closed L Sat, D Sun, all Mon, 26 Dec,
1 Jan
Additional: Sunday L;
Children welcome; ⓥ dishes
Smoking: No smoking in dining room
Accommodation: 3 en suite
Credit cards: ▬ ▬ ▬ ▟ ▬ 🄫 JCB

DORCHESTER, # The Mock Turtle

This former rectory is made up of separate eating-areas on three levels, the one in front of the bar very like someone's sitting-room, with lots of squishy sofas and chairs, all in a shop window-type frontage; an incongruous undertaker's clock dominates one wall. The hand-written lunchtime menus could run from black pudding with a poached egg and potato salad, through a main course of seafood ragout, to sticky toffee pudding, while dinner sees a printed menu backed up by a list of daily specials, largely fish. Well-balanced leek and potato soup was enjoyed on a cold, wet night, as was monkfish and mushroom risotto. An enormous plaice, very fresh and plainly grilled, is typical of the fish main courses, as is a beautifully presented filo parcel of brill and salmon served with beurre blanc; meat dishes might include chicken Stroganoff or rack of

34 High West Street DT1 1UP
Map 3: SY69
Tel: 01305 264011
Chef: Raymond Hodder
Owners: Raymond, Alan & Vivien
Hodder
Cost: Fixed-price L £14.95/D £21.75.
☺ H/wine £8.95
Times: Noon-last L 2pm/7-last
D 9.30pm. Closed L Sat, all Sun,
L Mon, 25 Dec-1 Jan
Additional: ⓥ dishes
Seats: 50
Smoking: No smoking in dining room
Credit cards: ▬ ▬ ▬ ▟ 🄫

lamb. Finish with chocolate and banana pancakes, West
Country farmhouse cheeses, or mango mousse with coconut ice
cream. A fairly priced wine list, featuring some notable
producers, kicks off with house vin de pays.

Directions: Town centre, top of High West Street

DORCHESTER,
Yalbury Cottage ✿

*Oak beams and inglenook fireplaces in the lounge and restaurant
are fitting accoutrements for the conversion of two 300-year-old
thatched cottages. Dinner may kick off with canapés with drinks
before a typical meal of goats' cheese with avocado, sea bass with
home-made tagliatelle, then apple and cinnamon torte.*

Additional: Children welcome; 🍴 dishes
Smoking: No smoking in dining room
Accommodation: 8 en suite
Credit cards: 💳 💳 💳 💳 💳 JCB

Directions: Two miles east of Dorchester, off A35

Lower Bockhampton DT2 8PZ
Map 3: SY69
Tel: 01305 262382
Fax: 01305 266412
Chef: Nick Larby
Owners: Derek & Heather Furminger
Cost: Fixed-price D £21. ☺
H/wine £9.80
Times: D only, last D 9pm. Closed
some Sun in winter, 28 Dec-30 Jan

EVERSHOT, **Summer Lodge** ✿✿✿

They're never short of a cheese dish here – the family
collection of over 300 is arrayed throughout the chintzy, former
dower house, designed in part by Thomas Hardy. French
(anyone-for-tennis) windows open from the dining room into
the garden. Residents are most likely to get the favoured
window tables, but everyone can enjoy Timothy Ford's
polished and assured style of modern English cooking. A salad
of pink, roasted wood pigeon with balsamic vinegar dressing
was a good, light beginning to an inspection meal, as was
smoked salmon on a warm buckwheat blini with sour cream
and caviar – lots of salmon, minuscule caviar. Rather chewy
home-made brown and white bread was served with butter in a
'cute' tomato shape, disdained by our inspector sternly as 'an
unnecessary frippery'. Another first course, torte of duck foie
gras with dressed salad leaves was rich and impressively
constructed; soup, for those with simpler tastes, is served from
a terrine left on the table. Main courses of panaché of
monkfish, lemon sole and sea trout in saffron sauce, and roast
saddle of rabbit with a confit of the leg served on a herb risotto

DT2 0JR
Map 3: ST50
Tel: 01935 83424
Fax: 01935 83005
Chef: Timothy Ford
Owners: Nigel & Margaret Corbett
Cost: *Alc* £42, ficed-price L £12.75/D
£36 (4 courses). ☺ H/wine £12.75
Times: 12.30-last L 2pm/7.30-last
D 9pm
Additional: Bar food L; Sunday L;
No children under 7 at D; 🍴 dishes
Seats: 40. Private dining room 20
Smoking: No smoking in dining room
Accommodation: 17 en suite
Credit cards: 💳 💳 💳 💳 💳 💳 JCB

Directions: 1 mile W off A37,
between Dorchester and Yeovil.
Entrance in Summer Lane

were well-prepared and executed. Mandarin coulis, however, got lost in an iced mango parfait with a 'miniature' fruit salad that practically took over the whole plate. It was pretty to look at though, as was a particularly fine dark chocolate and pecan tart served with pistachio ice cream. Regulars on the country house circuit like to have menus as keepsakes – copies are available at £2.75, but the cheese dishes are not for sale.

Signature dishes: Pink roasted rump of Dorset new season lamb with a sorrel and mint sauce; ragout of West Bay lobster with a twice-baked cheese soufflé; pot-roasted leg of local free-range chicken, stuffed with the breast and wild mushrooms; ravioli of calves' sweetbreads with baby spinach and a morel cream sauce.

GILLINGHAM,
Stock Hill Hotel ❀❀❀

The linen is pristine and highly starched, and the tables are delightfully set with little posies of flowers and candles. This luxurious but intimate setting is much favoured by well-heeled Londoners seeking a weekend retreat. Service is ultra-professional and courteous, and Peter Hauser's cooking continues along its own idiosyncratic path, combining modern ideas with traditional Austrian ones. Seared scallops with squid-ink risotto, beautifully presented on Villeroy and Boch china, was well thought out and deeply flavoured, as was another starter of foie gras and truffle parfait, served with kumquat compote and lemon brioche. Chargrilled artichoke hearts and Marshvale ham with balsamic vinegar, and nuggets of salmon, and codling in brown-beer batter with spiced tomato, may also be listed amongst the first courses. Superbly flavoured deep-fried supreme of chicken with Parmesan and Mediterranean vegetable risotto, was only let down by dryish rice. An interesting cross-cultural offering was local rabbit cooked in coconut milk served with spätzle; another was paupiette of English veal filled with wild mushrooms with courgette flan and Japanese sea vegetable. Of the two desserts sampled, crème caramel with caramel ice cream was enjoyable, but chestnut rice with dates cooked in mulled wine was described as just like eating a boring mound of chestnut and whipped cream, the dates contributing nothing in the way of sweetness. Coffee is served with home-made sweetmeats.

Signature dishes: Hedgerow rabbit in coconut milk and Thai herb; ravioli of lobster and scallops in saffron and lemon pasta; breast of duckling in thyme jus; roast pheasant on fried polenta with wild mushrooms and Madeira sauce

Directions: 3 miles off A303 on B3081

Stock Hill SP8 5NR
Map 3: ST82
Tel: 01747 823626
Fax: 01747 825628
Chef: Peter Hauser
Owners: Peter & Nita Hauser
Cost: Fixed-price L £22/D £32 (4 courses). ☺ H/wine £14.10
Times: 12.30pm-last L 1.45pm/ 7.30pm-last D 8.45pm
Additional: Sunday L; No children under 7; ❤ dishes
Seats: 24. Private dining room 12
Smoking: No-smoking area; Air conditioning
Accommodation: 10 en suite
Credit cards: 🔲 🔲 C

HIGHCLIFFE,
The Lord Bute Restaurant ❀❀

When Lord Bute introduced the cider tax in the 18th century, he became the most hated man in England. He retired disillusioned to Christchurch Bay where he engaged Robert Adam to build him a house. The modern restaurant is tucked discreetly behind one of the original lodges and retains the classical style. The *carte* includes Lord Bute's classic beef Wellington with Madeira, as well as supreme of chicken

Lymington Road BH23 4JS
Map 4: SZ29
Tel: 01425 278884
Fax: 01425 279258
Chef: Christopher Denley
Owners: Simon & Christopher Denley, Stephen Caunter
Cost: Alc £25, fixed-price L £12.95/D £18.95. ☺ H/wine £10.95

sautéed and served on green tagliatelle with Stilton and port sauce, and grilled trout fillets with steamed leeks, saffron cream sauce and asparagus tips. Starters include lobster bisque and avocado, oyster mushroom and mozzarella salad.

Accommodation: 10 en suite
Credit cards: ■■ ■■ ⚞ ⎗ ■■ J

Directions: Follow the A337 to Lymington, situated opposite St Mark's churchyard in Highcliffe

LYME REGIS, **Kersbrook Hotel** ✿

Thatched little hotel attracting a loyal following for splendid, traditional country cooking from good-value fixed-price menus as well as the lengthy carte. Expect course chicken liver pâté, rough-textured pea soup, poached fillet of salmon and a smooth hollandaise sauce, and raspberry mousse.

Directions: Town centre – go along main street (Pound Street), turn R at car park into Pound Road, hotel on L

MAIDEN NEWTON,
Le Petit Canard ✿✿

This is Pacific Rim Dorset-style: tiger prawn brochette on stir-fried snow peas, baby corn, ginger bean sprouts; grilled wood pigeon breast on cured ham sausage, tarragon lentils with crispy celeriac; or roasted rack of lamb on a caramelised onion jus with smoked chilli béarnaise. Multi-elements can lead to culinary confusion but happily the soup 'creation' of the day – banana and shallot velouté with chicken slivers topped with scrambled quails' eggs and tarragon, came together eye-openingly well. Chargrilled tuna, as fresh as can be, was served with corn, red pepper and basil cream, and Hoisin-brushed grilled kangaroo fillet on Chinese greens defied its usual tough image. Desserts are particularly good – an intense orange-chocolate torte with caramel ice cream, and a nectarine and peach Napoleon with crunchy almond wafers both worked wonderfully, with contrasting sweet and sharp, rich and crunchy dimensions. The dining room is understated pale primrose, lit by candles and white fairy lights.

The Lord Bute Restaurant

Times: Noon-last L 2pm/7-last D 10pm. Closed L Sat, D Sun, all Mon
Additional: Bar food L; Sunday L; No children under 9; ⚘ dishes
Seats: 80. Private dining room 20
Smoking: No-smoking area; Air conditioning

Pound Road DT7 3HX
Map 3: SY39
Tel: 01297 442596
Please telephone for further details

Dorchester Road DT2 0BE
Map 3: SY59
Tel/Fax: 01300 320536
Chef: Geoff Chapman
Owners: Lin & Geoff Chapman
Cost: Fixed-price D £23.50.
☺ H/wine £12.75.
Times: D only, 7pm-8.30pm. Closed Sun, Mon, early Jan, 1 wk summer
Additional: No children under 9
Seats: 28
Smoking: No smoking in dining room
Credit cards: ■■ ■■

Directions: In the centre of Maiden Newton 8 miles from Dorchester

POOLE,
Harbour Heights Hotel ✸

*Magnificent maritime views over Brownsea Island and Studland Bay
for this pleasant seaside hotel that caters admirably for a mix of
business and leisure guests. A wide choice of menus is offered in the
popular restaurant, and vegetarians get an interesting selection too.
Cooking is sound, showing assured technique.*

Directions: Midway between Poole and Bournemouth

73 Haven Road Sandbanks
BH13 7LW
Map 4: SZ09
Tel: 01202 707272
Fax: 01202 708594
Please telephone for further details

POOLE, Haven Hotel ✸✸

Banks Road BH13 7QL
Map 4: SZ09
Tel: 01202 707333
Fax: 01202 708796
Chef: Karl Heinz Nagler
Owner: FJB Hotels
Cost: *Alc* £36. H/wine £9.75
Times: D only, 7-last D 10pm.
Closed Sun, Mon, Xmas
Additional: Children welcome;
✿ dishes
Seats: 40. Private room 160
Smoking: No smoking in dining room;
Air conditioning
Accommodation: 94 en suite
Credit cards: ▬ ▬ ▬ ▬ ▬

A hotel with an enviable site and prospect – the views of
Brownsea Island and the Purbeck Hills are magnificent. La
Roche is the hotel's premier restaurant. Here the kitchen
impresses for its market buying – an avocado and crab salad
spiked up with mayonnaise, slices of orange and pink
grapefruit and a piquant citrus vinaigrette, and fresh vegetables
served with main courses, for example – as much for invention
and technique. Note a meal that took in grilled wild boar steak
accompanied by glazed apples, celeriac chips and a Madeira
sauce, and finished with an outstanding orange crème brûlée
topped with a crisp caramel 'cage'. All this is backed up by
smooth, professional service. The wine list is categorised by
degrees of sweet/dry.

Directions: Follow signs to Sandbanks Peninsula; hotel next to
Swanage ferry departure point

POOLE,
Mansion House Hotel ✸✸

Situated just off Poole's busy quay, the smart Georgian hotel is
a calming port of call in the old town. The sense of exclusivity
is heightened by the concept of a 'Dining Club' to which hotel
residents get temporary membership. A wide choice of modern
English dishes includes brasserie-style starters such as mussels
cooked in red wine with bacon lardons, onions and cream, and
Caesar salad with deep-fried sardines and Parmesan. More
upmarket main courses range from loin of venison with
truffled creamed celeriac and shallots to roasted breast of
chicken stuffed with crab meat and served with a ginger,

Thames Street BH15 1JN
Map 4: SZ09
Tel: 01202 685666
Fax: 01202 665709
Chefs: Gerry Godden, Darren Rockett
Owner: Robert Leonard
Cost: Fixed-price L £14.50/D £26.95.
☺ H/wine £12.50
Times: Noon-2pm/7-last D 9.30pm.
Closed L Sat, D Sun, L Bh Mon
Additional: Bar food; Sunday L; No
children under 5; ✿ dishes

Mansion House Hotel

lemongrass and coriander sauce. On Saturdays, there is a roast carved from the trolley.

Seats: 85. Private dining room 36
Smoking: Air conditioning
Accommodation: 28 en suite
Credit cards: ▬ ▬ 🐦 ⬜ ▦ 🅒 💷 JCB

Directions: Follow signs to Channel Ferry/Poole Quay, L at bridge, 1st L is Thames Street

POOLE, **Salterns Hotel** ❀❀

38 Salterns Way
Lilliput BH14 8JR
Map 4: SZ09
Tel: 01202 707321
Fax: 01202 707488
Chef: Nigel Popperwell
Owners: John & Beverley Smith
Cost: *Alc* £21, fixed-price L £15.50
(4 courses)/D £19.50 (4 courses). ☺
H/wine £11
Times: Noon-last L 2pm/7-last
D 9.30pm
Additional: Bar food; Sunday L;
Children welcome; ❧ dishes
Seats: 50. Private dining room 30
Smoking: No-smoking area; No pipes
and cigars; Air conditioning
Accommodation: 20 en suite
Credit cards: ▬ ▬ 🐦 ⬜ ▦ 🅒 💷 JCB

Superb views across the harbour to Brownsea Island are a highlight at this popular, modern hotel, situated in a south-facing position a mere pebble-flip away from Poole Marina. Both a pretty bistro and the more formal Waterside restaurant are housed within, the latter providing *carte* and set menus with plenty of choice. Light, modern dishes dominate the cooking, with fish to the fore, and fruit often paired with meat. Three bean broth with pancetta and herb oil, tian of crab with pickled cucumber, roasted monkfish tail with baby leeks and truffle dressing, and pan-roasted duck with compote of satsuma and cranberry, were recent enticements. Finish a meal with petits fours, an Armagnac from the wide-ranging drinks list (fair-priced house wines and *grand crus* included), and one more look at that view.

Directions: From Poole take B3369 for Sandbanks; after 1.5 miles in Lilliput turn R (Salterns Way). Restaurant on R at end

POOLE, **Sandbanks Hotel** ❀

15 Banks Road
Sandbanks BH13 7PS
Map 4: SZ09
Tel: 01202 707377
Fax: 01202 708885
Chef: Robert Alan Jones
Owner: J G J Butterworth
Cost: *Alc* £29, fixed-price L £14.50/D £18.50. ☺
Times: Last L 2pm/last D 9pm
Additional: Bar food; Sunday L; Children welcome; ❹ dishes
Smoking: No smoking in dining room; Air conditioning
Accommodation: 107 en suite
Credit cards:

A superbly positioned waterside hotel, popular with both leisure and business guests, overlooking Poole Harbour. Variety and interest are high points of the menus, which may range from goats' cheese tart, through turbot poached in white wine, or best end of lamb, to crème brûlée, or passion fruit and apple tart.

Directions: From Poole or Bournemouth, follow signs to Sandbanks Peninsula

SHAFTESBURY,
La Fleur de Lys ❀❀

25 Salisbury Street
SP7 8EL
Map 3: ST82
Tel: 01747 853717
Chefs: D Shepherd, M Preston
Owners: D Shepherd, M Preston, DM Griffin
Cost: *Alc* £30, fixed-price D £23.50. ☺ H/wine £11.
Times: Noon-last L 2.30pm/7pm-last D 10pm. Closed D Sun, L Mon, Jan 2 wks
Additional: Sunday L; Children welcome; ❹ dishes
Seats: 40.
Smoking: No smoking before 10pm
Credit cards:  JCB

The smartly decorated first-floor restaurant describes its style as modern English, but much of the menu is in classical French mode. Saucing skills are to the fore, in the likes of baked avocado and white crab with fennel and Pernod wrapped in bacon with baked garlic in a Madeira sauce, and a chocolate box filled with passion fruit ice cream and fresh raspberries in vanilla sauce anglaise. The cooking is equally discriminating. Asparagus tart with onions, courgettes and spinach in a coriander sauce, and pan-fried calves' liver with fried onions and grain mustard sauce, were both enjoyed on our visit. Delicious granary and white glazed rolls show attention to small details. Try one of the specially selected wines of the month – and raise a toast to the glorious view over Blackmoor Vale.

Directions: Town centre, near the Post Office, on the main road

SHAFTESBURY,

Royal Chase Hotel ❀❀

A former priory located in the heart of Thomas Hardy country, the Royal Chase has been personally run by George Hunt for a quarter of a century. The well-appointed Byzant restaurant (named after an ancient water ceremony enacted in the town) boasts crisply clothed, well-spaced tables and an imaginative menu prepared with flair. A recent meal included three small salmon, crab and ginger fishcakes with a nicely contrasting tomato chutney, peppercorn-dusted fillet of lamb on a bed of garlic potato purée with a rich berry confit, and an apple and ginger crumble to finish. Other dishes that caught the eye were a local pheasant terrine with Cumberland sauce and olive bread, steamed sea bass with a black lentil and tomato ragout, and (one of two vegetarian options) couscous and wild mushrooms flavoured with harissa, wrapped in a Savoy cabbage leaf and accompanied by a soy and black bean syrup. Service is friendly and attentive.

Royal Chase Roundabout
SP7 8DB
Map 3: ST82
Tel: 01747 853355
Fax: 01747 851969
Chef: Andrew Wheatcroft
Owner: George Hunt
Cost: *Alc* £18.50, fixed-price L £5.95 (2 courses). ☺ H/wine £11
Times: 12.30-last L 2pm/7-last D 9.30pm
Additional: Bar food; Sunday L; Children welcome; ❀ dishes
Seats: 65. Private dining room 120. Jacket & tie preferred
Smoking: No smoking in dining room
Accommodation: 35 en suite
Credit cards: 💳 💳 💳 💳 💳 💳 💳

Directions: On roundabout where A350 crosses A30 (avoid town centre)

SHAFTESBURY,

Wayfarers Restaurant ❀❀

This cottage of a restaurant on the A30 towards Sherborne, has been feeding travellers for some years. Mark Newton is a fine cook, enthusiastic for well-defined flavours and inventive dishes. A strong sense of modernism sets the tone, and he surprises with the ambition of his work in such fulsomely

Sherborne Causeway SP7 9PX
Map 3: ST82
Tel: 01747 852821
Chef: Mark Newton
Owners: Mark & Clare Newton
Cost: *Alc* £28, fixed-price L & D £13.95. ☺ H/wine £9.50
Times: Noon-last L 1.30pm/7-last D 9.15pm. Closed L Sat, D Sun, all Mon, 2 wks after 25 Dec
Additional: Sunday L; No children under 7; ❀ dishes
Seats: 35. Private room 20
Credit cards: 💳 💳 💳 💳

described dishes as smoked salmon baked with a stuffing of celeriac cooked in sour cream with deep-fried oysters and chive butter and caviar, or saddle of venison wrapped in prosciutto with sautéed potato and sour-sweet cabbage with walnuts in a juniper-scented sauce. Puddings include a hot dark chocolate fondant soufflé served with white chocolate ice cream, and an iced Italian meringue nougatine with biscuit cornets filled with poached fruits. The comprehensive wine list covers most areas.

Directions: 2 miles W of Shaftesbury on main A30 heading towards Sherborne and Yeovil

Wayfarers Restaurant

SHERBORNE, Eastbury Hotel ✿

Edwardian townhouse hotel with a conservatory-style restaurant overlooking a lovely mature garden. Local ingredients are a feature of an interesting menu that might offer a gamey pigeon and leek sausage, free-range chicken breast wrapped in Parma ham, and a superior summer pudding.

Additional: Bar food; Sunday L; Children welcome; 🍴 dishes
Smoking: No smoking in dining room
Accommodation: 15 en suite
Credit cards: 📇 📇 📇 📇 📇

Directions: 800 metres from Abbey

Long Street DT9 3BY
Map 3: ST61
Tel: 01935 813131
Fax: 01935 817296
Chef: Mark Vaughan
Owners: Mr & Mrs Thomas Pickford
Cost: Alc £22, fixed-price L £11.95/D £16.95. ☺ H/wine £8.45
Times: Last L 2pm/last D 9.30pm

SHERBORNE,
Pheasants Restaurant ✿✿

This is a great enterprise set in a superb location: an imposing Georgian house in the centre of a town that has real charm. Andrew Overhill runs his restaurant-with-rooms with great style. The kitchen delivers food that is complex, light and accurate, a cuisine built of components that has as its starting point prime-quality ingredients. Fine things are to be found on the menu: slices of smoked duck, goose and quail supremes, accompanied by chickpea and onion salad with a plum compote, pork tenderloin marinated in ginger, soy sauce and sesame oil and served with sweet potato and lettuce leaves, or Dover sole with leeks, scallops and a provençale sauce, and poached pears with whisky ice cream. The decent wine list has fair prices and a good selection of half-bottles.

Directions: At the top of the High Street, A30 (Salisbury/Yeovil)

24 Greenhill DT9 4EW
Map 3: ST61
Tel/Fax: 01935 815252
Chefs: Neil Cadle, Darren Lawrence
Owner: Andrew Overhill
Cost: Alc £25, fixed-price L £15/D£23. H/wine £9.20
Times: Noon-last L 1.50pm/6.30-last D 9.50pm. Closed D Sun, all Mon, L Tue-Fri, 2 wks mid-Jan
Additional: Sunday L; Children welcome; 🍴 dishes
Seats: 40. Private 10
Smoking: No pipes & cigars
Accommodation: 6 en suite
Credit cards: 📇 📇 📇 📇 📇

STURMINSTER NEWTON,
Plumber Manor ✿✿

The atmospheric Jacobean country house has been with one family for over 300 years. It is now a hotel with the intimate feel of a restaurant-with-rooms, and offers three dining-rooms and two set menusThe quality of the basic ingredients gives the cooking stellar quality: the prawns that accompanied avocado and melon in light curry sauce were firm and wonderfully briny, rack of lamb with onion soubise sauce was a fine helping of meat, and a smashing piece of beef fillet hardly needed the

Hazelbury Bryan Road
DT10 2AF
Map 3: ST71
Tel: 01258 472507
Fax: 01258 473370
Chef: Brian Prideaux-Brune
Owner: Richard Prideaux-Brune
Cost: D £20.50. ☺ H/wine £10
Times: D only 7.30-last D 9.30pm. Closed Feb

Plumber Manor

Additional: Sunday L only (12.30-last L 2pm); Children welcome; ✪ dishes
Seats: 65. Private dining rooms 26. Jacket & tie preferred
Smoking: No pipes and cigars
Accommodation: 16 en suite
Credit cards: ▆ ▆ ▆ ▆ ▆ ▆

Stilton mousse and Madeira sauce that accompanied it. The 'Gourmet Menu' includes more complex dishes such as boned quail stuffed with wild rice wrapped in filo pastry. The dessert trolley overdoses on mousse-style puddings, but almond meringue with grapes and tiramisu, were both good.

Directions: At Sturminster Newton cross the packhorse bridge, R to Stalbridge (A537). 1st L to Hazelbury Bryan. Two miles on L opposite Red Lion

SWANAGE,

The Cauldron Bistro ❀❀

5 High Street BH19 2LN
Map 4: SZ07
Tel: 01929 422671
Chef: Terry Flenley
Owners: Terry & Margaret Flenley
Cost: *Alc* £22, fixed-price L £10/D £14 (2 courses). ☺ H/wine £12.
Times: Noon-last L 1.30pm/6.30pm-last D 9.15pm. Closed Mon, L Tue & Wed summer (L&D in winter), 2 wks Nov & Jan

With an emphasis on game in winter and seafood in summer, chef-patron Terry Flenley takes great care in sourcing ingredients and will happily discuss their provenance with interested diners. A recent meal included a generous portion of first-class fresh tuna on a bed of pak choi with a prawn 'salsa'. Other items on an unpretentious menu (the vegetarian section is headed 'No Meat') could include oriental leaves with a Caesar dressing, wild boar and apple sausages with soured cream and horseradish, corn-fed chicken marinated in olive oil and herbs with tarragon gravy, and honey-roast confit of duck. Bread-and-butter pudding, caramelised orange and grapefruit in Grand Marnier and cinnamon exemplify the desserts. Simple decor features polished tables separated by settle seating.

Additional: Sunday L; Children welcome; ✪ dishes
Seats: 36
Smoking: No pipes & cigars
Credit cards: ▆ ▆ ▆ ▆ ▆ ▆ ▆

Directions: At lower end of the High Street, opposite The Old Quay.

SWANAGE, **Grand Hotel** ❀

Burlington Road BH19 1LU
Map 4: SZ07
Tel: 01929 423353
Fax: 01929 427068
Owner: WS Bowman
Cost: Fixed price D £17.95
(4 courses). ☺ H/wine £9.50
Times: Last L 1.45pm/ last D 9.30pm
Additional: Bar food L; Sunday L;
Children welcome; ✿ dishes
Smoking: No-smoking area
Accommodation: 30 en suite
Credit cards: ▉ ▨ ☜ ▢ ▦ ▄

There are spectacular views across Swanage Bay from this cliff-top hotel. The Renaissance Restaurant offers an imaginative five-course dinner menu, with good vegetarian options. A starter of smoked haddock kedgeree was the highlight of one meal, followed by rack of lamb, and a berry terrine with crème fraîche.

Directions: From North Beach end of town into Ulwell Road, 2nd on R

WAREHAM, **Kemps Hotel** ❀

Family-owned former rectory surrounded by open countryside. The recently refurbished dining room and conservatory are where to sample the extensive carte or set menus. Warm pigeon salad with bacon and mixed mushrooms was a well-executed starter, while imagination was certainly not lacking in the salmon and chicken with Brie in a filo parcel.

Smoking: No smoking in dining room
Accommodation: 14 en suite. **Credit cards:** ▉ ▨ ▢ ▦

Directions: On A352 midway between Wareham and Wool

East Stoke BH20 6AL
Map 3: SY98
Tel: 01929 462563
Fax: 01929 405287
Chef: Philip Simpkiss
Owners: Paul & Jill Warren
Cost: Alc £22.50, fixed price
L £9.95/D £19.95 (4 courses).
☺ H/wine £8.95
Times: Last L 1.30pm/last D 9.30pm.
Closed L Sat
Additional: Bar food L; Sunday L;
Children welcome; ✿ dishes

WAREHAM, **Priory Hotel** ❀❀

Set in four acres of beautiful gardens running down to the River Frome, this antique-furnished hotel has been lovingly created out of a 16th-century former priory by Stuart and John Turner. At our last inspection, dinner, served in the atmospheric stone-vaulted cellar restaurant, got off to a good start with delicious canapés in the bar (chicken mousse tartlet, mini pizza and smoked salmon with caviar) and the kitchen's attention to detail extends to good home-baked breads and tempting petits fours. The principle dishes did not disappoint either with a good balance of Oriental flavours to a coconut and tiger prawn soup that preceded roasted sea bass with a light sweet-and-sour sauce. Other mains might include rack of venison with celeriac purée and redcurrant sauce, duck with Puy lentils, caramelised apples and Calvados, and beef Wellington. There's a separate vegetarian menu. Clarets are a particular strength on a serious, Francophile wine list.

Directions: Town centre between the church and the River Frome

Church Green BH20 4ND
Map 3: SY98
Tel: 01929 551666
Fax: 01929 554519
Chef: Stephen Astley
Owners: Stuart & John Turner
Cost: Alc £41, fixed-price L £15.95,
D £26.50 (4 courses). H/wine £12.50
Times: 12.30-last L 2pm/7.30-last
D 10pm
Additional: Bar food L; Sunday L;
No children under 8; ✿ dishes
Seats: 46. Private dining room 22.
Jacket & tie preferred
Smoking: No smoking in dining room
Accommodation: 19 en suite
Credit cards: ▉ ▨ ☜ ▢ ▦ ▄ ▢

WEST BEXINGTON,
The Manor Hotel ❀

Beach Road Dorchester
DT2 9DF
Map 3: SY58
Tel: 01308 897616
Fax: 01308 897035
Chef: Clive Jobson
Owners: Richard & Jayne Childs
Cost: *Alc* £22.95, fixed-price
L £16.95/D £22.95. ☺ H/wine £8.95
Times: Last L 2pm/last D 9.30pm.
Closed D 25 Dec
Additional: Bar food; Sunday L;
Children welcome; ❡ dishes
Smoking: No-smoking area
Accommodation: 13 en suite
Credit cards:
▨ ▨ ▨ ▨ ▨ ▨ ▨ JCB

Just a short walk from Chesil Bank, this ancient manor house affords views of the coastline from its oak-beamed lounges and leafy conservatory. An imaginative selection of dishes are served in the restaurant, with fresh fish a feature. Expect crab cakes with chilli dressing, Dover sole with mustard and bacon, pheasant with chestnuts and red wine, and a laden sweet trolley.

Directions: Off B3157 Bridport to Weymouth road, turning seawards at The Bull, Swyre

WEYMOUTH,
Perry's Restaurant ❀❀

Although the menu includes meat dishes such as sauté of calves' liver with seared air-dried ham, glazed shallots, thyme and red wine sauce, and pork spare ribs, caramelised with honey, lemon and garlic, the blackboard-listed local fish and seafood is the true speciality of the cheery, bistro-style restaurant bang on the harbour front. Scallops in champagne butter sauce, crab soup, cod with ratatouille and herb crust, were cooked in that straightforward, unfussy way which meant the quality of the sea-fresh ingredients was not overwhelmed by extraneous detail. A special treat was lobster with chive butter, served in the shell and, as our inspector put it, 'thankfully not cooked to a rubbery texture – worth going back for.' Desserts include baked lemon and cream cheese torte as well as the ever-popular Sharrow Bay sticky toffee pudding and butterscotch sauce.

Directions: On western side of old harbour – follow signs for Brewers Quay

4 Trinity Road
The Old Harbour DT4 8TJ
Map 3: SY67
Tel: 01305 785799
Chef: Andy Pike
Owners: Raymond, Alan & Vivien Hodder
Cost: *Alc* £23, fixed-price L £15. ☺ H/wine £8.95
Times: Noon-last L 2pm/7-last D 9.30pm. Closed D Sun Oct-Easter, L Mon & Sat, 25-26 Dec, 1 Jan
Additional: Sunday L; ❡ dishes
Seats: 60 (summer garden 16). Private dining room 30
Smoking: No cigars or pipes.
Credit cards: ▨ ▨ ▨ ▨ ▨

WEYMOUTH, **The Sea Cow** ⊛

Set directly on the quayside, this well-established, friendly restaurant specialises in fresh local fish and seafood dishes. Crab soup, and lemon sole with garlic butter are typical, but highlights of our last inspection were Mediterranean-style sweet peppers, smoked cod with lemon butter, and rich chocolate mousse with Grand Marnier.

Smoking: No-smoking area; No cigars or pipes
Credit cards: ▆ ▆ ▆ ▆

Directions: On the quay – park in large car parks near town bridge, 5 mins walk to restaurant

7 Custom House Quay
DT4 8BE
Map 3: SY67
Tel: 01305 783524
Chef: Terry Woolcock
Owners: T & S Woolcock
Cost: *Alc* £21. ☺ H/wine £10.35
Times: Last L 2pm/last D 10.15pm. Closed D Sun in winter, 25, 26 Dec, 1 Jan
Additional: Bar food L; Sunday L; Children welcome; ⓭ dishes

WIMBORNE, **Les Bouviers** ⊛⊛

This smart venue is now outfitted in eau-de-nil with burgundy trim, classy high-backed dining chairs and super curtains with an appropriate grape motif, given that the wine list boasts over 400 entries. The result is comfy and this is backed by friendly, efficient service. The extensive menu changes frequently, with typical dishes including tuna carpaccio with peppercorns and basil beetroot dressing and shaved Parmesan (pleasant but lacked 'oomph'), a signature hot cheese soufflé that was delightfully crisp and puffy outside, deliciously gooey inside, and wild duck with sage, Madeira sauce, Parma ham and green peppercorns. An assiette of desserts proved to be a mix of excellent orange and Grand Marnier terrine, a choux bun filled with banana and butterscotch sauce, chocolate and mandarin brandy mousse cake and lavender ice cream. Lovely home-made petits fours. Theme menus have proved popular here and there is a seven-course 'menu surprise' with wines included.

Directions: 0.5 miles south of A31 Wimborne bypass on A349

Oakley Hill Merley
BH21 1RJ
Map 4: SZ09
Tel/Fax: 01202 889555
Chef: James Coward
Owners: James & Kate Coward
Cost: *Alc* £25, fixed-price L £12.75/D £23.95 (5 courses). ☺ H/wine £11.
Times: Noon-last L 2.15pm/7pm-last D 10pm. Closed L Sat, D Sun
Additional: Sunday L; Children welcome; ⓭ dishes
Seats: 60. Private dining rooms 30-12
Smoking: No-smoking area; Air conditioning
Credit cards: ▆ ▆ ▆ ▆ ▆ ▆

WIMBOURNE MINSTER,
Beechleas Hotel ⊛⊛

The location of this fine Georgian house couldn't be betterd: away from the town centre, yet within easy reach of the shops and the Minster. Indeed, our last inspector's enthusiasm ran the risk of turning to effusion, both decorativly when describing the fine conservatory-style restaurant, the winter open fires and the relaxing lounge, to the Aga-saga dinners.

17 Poole Road BH21 1QA
Map 4: SZ09
Tel: 01202 841684
Fax: 01202 849344
Please telephone for further details

Beechleas Hotel

The cooking here is honest and unpretentious, and great care is taken in sourcing prime ingredients, especially from the local organic farm.

Directions: On A349 at Wimborne

DURHAM, COUNTY

BARNARD CASTLE,
Morritt Arms Hotel

NEW

Greta Bridge DL12 9SE
Map 12: NZ01
Tel: 01833 627232
Fax: 01833 627392
Chef: David Bittlestone
Owners: Barbara-Anne Johnson,
Peter J Phillips
Cost: *Alc* £18. Fixed-price D £15.95
(4 courses). ☺ H/wine £8.50
Times: Last L 2.30pm/last D 9.30pm
Additional: Bar food; Sunday L;
No children under 11; ✦ dishes

Charming 17th-century coaching inn by the River Greta. Eat in the garden, bar and bistro, in addition to the oak-panelled, beamed restaurant. Game terrine, roast monkfish with mussels marinière sauce, and caramelised lemon tart with sauce anglaise, show the range.

Smoking: No pipes & cigars in dining room
Accommodation: 20 en suite
Credit cards: ▬ ▬ ▬ ▬ ▬ ▬

Directions: Telephone for directions

BEAMISH, **Beamish Park Hotel**

Beamish Burn Road Marley Hill
NE16 5EG
Map 12: NZ25
Tel: 01207 230666
Fax: 01207 281260
Chef: Clive Imber
Owner: William Walker
Cost: *Alc* £26, fixed-price D £24.50.
☺ H/wine £8.95
Times: Noon-last L 2pm/7-last
D 9.30pm
Additional: Bar food; Sunday L;
Children welcome; ✦ dishes
Seats: 38. Private room 10
Smoking: No smoking in dining room
Accommodation: 47 en suite
Credit cards: ▬ ▬ ▬ ▬ ▬ ▬ ▬

A purpose-built hotel within easy reach of the main north-east business and heritage centres, ideally located for both business people and tourists. Public areas include a spacious lounge bar and a bright conservatory restaurant (steaks, omelettes and cold-meat salads are typical offerings here) as well as an outside pub. Serious dining takes place in the cosy and stylish restaurant, with its set-price dinner menus of artistically presented, imaginative dishes supplemented by a daily dish at each course. Start with perhaps mussels in puff pastry with a curry sauce, or asparagus with roasted peppers and Parmesan, and go on to rosemary-infused roast lamb with honeyed parsnip mash and smoked garlic, or grilled tuna with tomato and chilli jam. Finish with impressive-looking banana and Kirsch mousse with liquorice ice cream in a tuile basket on mango coulis. The annotations to the 40-odd bottles on the wine list should make choosing easier.

Directions: Just off A6076 Newcastle to Stanley road

DARLINGTON, **Hall Garth Hotel**

Hugo's Restaurant occupies two rooms and a conservatory of the 16th-century country house hotel. Dishes sampled include salmon and smoked haddock fishcakes with lemongrass and caper butter, and roast best end of lamb, cooked pink with a crust of black olives and served with ratatouille chutney and basil sauce.

Additional: Bar food; Sunday L; Children welcome; ❹ dishes
Smoking: No smoking in dining room
Accommodation: 41 en suite
Credit cards:

Directions: A1(M) exit 59 (A167) (Darlington), top of hill turn L signed Brafferton, hotel 200 yds on R

Coatham Mundeville DL1 3LU
Map 8: NZ21
Tel: 01325 300400
Fax: 01325 310083
Chef: Kevin Hacking
Owner: Regal Hotel Group plc
Cost: *Alc* £25, fixed-price L £10.95/D £22.95. ☺ H/wine £10.95
Times: Last L 2pm/last D 9.30pm.
Closed L Sat, D Sun, some Bhs

DARLINGTON, **Headlam Hall Hotel**

Delightful Jacobean manor house with a magnificent grand hall. Menu is typically British, with an abundance of fresh fish and seasonal game. Saddle of venison with a red onion confit, typifies the style. Banoffee pie with a bitter chocolate sauce is highly recommended.

Additional: Sunday L; No children under 7; ❹ dishes
Smoking: No smoking in dining room
Accommodation: 36 en suite
Credit cards:

Directions: 1.5 miles north of Gainford, off A67

Headlam Gainford DL2 3HA
Map 8: NZ21
Tel: 01325 730238
Fax: 01325 730790
Chef: Alex MacMurray
Owner: John H Robinson (Headlam Leisure Ltd)
Cost: *Alc* £24, fixed-price L £12.50/D £18.50. ☺ H/wine £7.80
Times: Last L 1.45pm/last D 9.15pm.
Closed L Sat, 24-25 Dec

DURHAM, **Bistro 21**

Aykley Heads House
Aykley Heads DH1 5TS
Map 12: NZ24
Tel: 0191 3844354
Fax: 0191 3841149
Chef: Craig Edmond
Owners: Terence & Susan Laybourne
Cost: *Alc* £24.40, fixed-price L £14.50. ☺ H/wine £9.50
Times: Last L 2.30pm/last D 10.30pm.
Closed Sun, Bhs
Additional: Children welcome; ❹ dishes
Smoking: No smoking in dining room
Credit cards:

A plain French provincial look- whitewashed walls, wooden floors, cosy vaulted bar and open-stone stairway in restaurant – sums up this smashing bistro from the Terry Laybourne stable. Fish soup, spinach and Cheddar soufflé, spicy Thai mussels, chargrilled chicken, pearl barley and wild mushroom risotto, medallions of venison with blue cheese polenta, button onions and pancetta, and banana bread-and-butter pudding with Horlicks ice cream, set a cracking pace.

Directions: Off B6532 from Durham centre, pass County Hall on R and Dryburn Hospital on L; turn R at double roundabout into Aykley Heads

DURHAM, Royal County Hotel

Old Elvet DH1 3JN
Map 12: NZ24
Tel: 0191 386 6821
Fax: 0191 386 0704
Chef: John Cruickshank
Owner: Swallow Hotels Ltd
Cost: *Alc* £28, fixed price L £15.50/D
£24.50. ☺ H/wine £13.
Times: 12.30pm-last L 2.15pm/7pm-
last D 10.15pm
Additional: Bar food L; Sunday L;
Children welcome; ❹ dishes
Seats: 88. Private dining room 30
Smoking: No-smoking area; Air
conditioning
Accommodation: 150 en suite
Credit cards: ▬ ▩ ⚑ ⬚ ▦ ▣ ⬚

There's something of a divide here between a fairly standard, and perhaps rather over long, set menu and more interesting *carte*. From the latter, dishes such as salmon and scallop sausage on buttered spinach with a shellfish bisque, pot-roasted guinea fowl on a casserole of foie gras and white beans with braised cabbage, and chargrilled sea bass with garlic, tomato and Muscadet wine, catch the eye. Several of the desserts – cherries jubilee, crêpes Suzette, strawberry Romanoff – are prepared at the table and it is from the desserts that the most successful element of our latest test meal came: a creamy, just chilling-out hazelnut parfait. The restaurant is part of a hotel that had its origins in a terrace of town houses built in 1630. An all-day brasserie provides a less formal option.

Directions: From A1(M) on to A690. Follow City Centre signs, straight ahead at 1st roundabout, L at 2nd, over bridge, L at lights, hotel on L

HARTLEPOOL, Krimo's Restaurant

Cheery atmosphere and excellent value at this great family-run restaurant. Set lunch is a bargain, and the carte offers soundly cooked old favourites along the lines of pâté mille-feuille, breast of French duckling with apple and blackcurrant sauce, or peppered steak, as well as Algerian dishes such as couscous and lamb.

Additional: No children under 8; ❹ dishes
Smoking: Air conditioning. **Credit cards:** ▬ ▩ ⚑ ⬚

Directions: On A178 two miles from Hartlepool on the seafront

8 The Front Seaton Carew
TS25 1BS
Map 8: NZ53
Tel: 01429 290022
Chef: Krimo Bouabda
Owners: Karen & Krimo Bouabda
Cost: *Alc* £20, fixed-price L £6.50/D
£11.95. ☺ H/wine £8.90.
Times: Last L 1.30pm/D 9pm.
Closed L Sat, Sun, Mon, last 2 wks
Aug

REDWORTH, Redworth Hall ❀❀

An imposing honey-coloured, mullioned-windowed Elizabethan mansion thoughtfully extended to provide an all-encompassing hotel and health club. Within, elegant corridors and staircases and comfortable lounges set the scene. Eat in the Conservatory Restaurant or the quiet and sophisticated surroundings of the Blue Room, in what was originally the drawing room. At inspection, crayfish ravioli with 'superbly chargrilled' scallops and sauce vierge was an impressive starter; this was followed by properly cooked roast turbot with crab beignets and shellfish sauce. Also on the menu might be a

Nr Newton Aycliffe
DL5 6NL
Map 8: NZ22
Tel: 01388 772442
Fax: 01388 775112
Chef: Craig Nicholls
Owner: Scottish Highland Hotels
Cost: Fixed-price D £32.95
Times: The Blue Room - D only,
7-last D 9.45pm. Closed Sun
Additional: No children under 8 in
The Blue Room; ❹ dishes

Redworth Hall

Seats: 40. Private room 15
Smoking: No smoking in dining room
Accommodation: 100 en suite
Credit cards: ■ ▨ ▶ ▢ ▢ ▶ ▶ JCB

terrine of duck, foie gras and leeks, followed by roast rabbit with a ceps sauce, or grilled brill partnered by oysters, caviar and champagne butter sauce. A 'delightful' milk chocolate marquise with bitter chocolate sorbet was the highlight of an inspector's meal, or you could go for hot banana charlotte. The wines on the long, fairly priced list have all been chosen with care.

Directions: From A1(M) take A68. Hotel is on A6072 (off A68) near Newton Aycliffe

ROMALDKIRK,

Rose and Crown ❀❀

Nr Barnard Castle DL12 9EB
Map 12: NY92
Tel: 01833 650213
Fax: 01833 650828
Chefs: Christopher Davy, Dawn Stephenson
Owners: Christopher & Alison Davy
Cost: Fixed-price D £24 (4 courses). ☺ H/wine £9.50
Times: D only, 7.30-8.45pm. Closed D Sun, Xmas, New Year
Additional: Bar food; Sunday L (noon-1.30pm); No children under 6 at D; ❹ dishes
Seats: 24
Smoking: No smoking in dining room
Accommodation: 12 en suite
Credit cards: ▨ ▨ ▶ ▢

The heart of this fine old coaching inn remains its kitchen. The daily changing menu reflects the seasons, with game from the moors, fish from the east coast, beef and lamb from the local butcher and locally grown vegetables and herbs. Regional accents come through loud and clear in dishes such as terrine of Yorkshire venison with three home-made pickles, smoked haddock and potato risotto with poached egg and hollandaise, roast breast of mallard with parsnip and apple purée as well as port and Seville orange sauce, and baked monkfish tails with tarragon and grain mustard. Try the excellent local Cotherstone cheese, or the home-made coffee and pecan nut ice cream.

Directions: On B6277 in the centre of the village, near the church

RUSHYFORD,
Eden Arms Swallow Hotel

DL17 0LL
Map 8: NZ22
Tel: 01388 720541
Fax: 01388 722162
Chef: Michael Reynolds
Owners: Swallow Hotels Ltd
Cost: *Alc* £29, fixed-price L £11.45/D
£21.50 (4 courses). ☺ H/wine £12
Times: Noon-last L 2pm/7-last
D 10pm. Closed L Sat
Additional: Bar food; Sunday L;
Children welcome; ✿ dishes
Seats: 100. Private room 80
Smoking: No-smoking area
Accommodation: 45 en suite
Credit cards:
⬛ ⬛ ⬛ ⬛ ⬛ ⬛ ⬛ JCB

A former coaching inn dating from the 17th-century, is the
setting for modern cooking. A suitably rustic-looking warm
salad of Toulouse sausage with deep-fried leeks made a good
start to our inspection meal. An interesting idea, poached fillet
of beef on a 'hotch-potch' of vegetables and wild mushrooms
topped with Stilton soufflé, had tender, good quality meat in a
powerful stock base, and a rich, though lumbering soufflé, but
vegetables – carrots, mange-tout, broccoli, cauliflower and
lentils – were mostly mirrored in the dish of vegetables served
alongside. Decent summer pudding (although this was April)
with a sweetish port and fruit coulis.

Directions: From A1M/J60, follow A689 towards Bishop Auckland
for 2 miles. Take 2nd exit at large roundabout, hotel is on L

STOCKTON-ON-TEES,
Parkmore Hotel

*A late 19th-century building with high ceilings, ornate coving and
luxurious fabrics. Imaginative dishes are offered from a choice of
menus. Sticky treacle tart was a particular highlight at a test meal,
following a mousseline of chicken with a sweet apple sauce, and
tender fillet steak with a wild mushroom and Madeira sauce.*

Additional: Bar food; Sunday L; Children welcome; ✿ dishes
Smoking: No smoking in dining room
Accommodation: 56 en suite
Credit cards: ⬛ ⬛ ⬛ ⬛ ⬛ ⬛ ⬛ JCB

636 Yarm Road Eaglescliffe
TS16 0DH
Map 8: NZ41
Tel: 01642 786815
Fax: 01642 790485
Chef: Fergus Robertson
Owner: Brian Reed
Cost: *Alc* £22, fixed-price
L £12.75/D £17.25. ☺ H/wine £8.25
Times: Last L 2pm/last D 9pm

Directions: On the A135 between Yarm and Stockton-on-Tees,
almost opposite Eaglescliffe Golf Course

ESSEX

BRENTWOOD,
Marygreen Manor ❀❀

The restaurant at this Tudor manor hotel is a grand baronial hall adorned with tapestries and carvings. A wide-ranging wine list complements a choice of menus that offer the likes of chicken liver parfait, and 'chump and champ', roast whole chump of lamb with champ potatoes.

Times: Last L 2.15pm/D 10.15pm
Additional: Bar food L; Sunday L; ❹ dishes
Smoking: No pipes & cigars; Air conditioning
Accommodation: 44 en suite
Credit cards: ▬ ▭ ◲ ▦ ◖ ◨

Directions: 1 mile from Brentwood town centre, 0.5 mile from M25/J28

London Road CM14 4NR
Map 5: TQ59
Tel: 01277 225252
Fax: 01277 262809
Chef: Theresa Valentine
Owner: S P Pearson
Cost: Alc £30, fixed-price L £17/D £27. ☺ H/wine £14

CHELMSFORD,
Pontlands Park Hotel ❀

The large, airy, attractively muralled restaurant is frequently used for dinner dances. Foxtrot between the steamed mussels in leek and celery broth, and roast breast of chicken with diced bacon and button mushrooms in red wine sauce, then waltz away the baked banana cheesecake with toffee sauce.

Directions: From M25/J28 take A12 then A130; leave by 1st slip road (Great Baddow) and take 1st turning L

West Hanningfield Road Great Baddow CM2 8HR
Map 5: TL70
Tel: 01245 476444
Fax: 01245 478393
Chef: Stephen Wright
Owners: The Bartellas
Cost: Alc £30, fixed-price L&D £21. ☺ H/wine £9.95
Times: Last L 1.45pm/D 9.45pm. Closed L Sat, D Sun, L Mon
Additional: Sunday L; Children welcome; ❹ dishes
Smoking: No pipes and cigars
Accommodation: 17 en suite
Credit cards: ▬ ▭ ⚏ ◲ ▦ ◖ ◨ JCB

COGGESHALL,
Baumann's Brasserie ❀

A wooden floor, wooden venetian blinds on the windows, and walls covered with paintings make an impact as you step into Baumann's. The strikingly large-sized menu may run from butter-bean and red onion soup, through honey-basted goose with peaches and red wine sauce, to iced tea parfait with lemon sauce.

4-6 Stoneham Street CO6 1TT
Map 5: TL82
Tel: 01376 561453
Fax: 01376 563762
Chef: Mark Baumann
Owners: Mark Baumann, Douglas Wright

Baumann's Brasserie

Cost: *Alc* £25, fixed-price L £12.50. ☺ H/wine £9.85
Times: Last L 2pm/last D 9.30pm. Closed L Sat, D Sun, all Mon,
1st 2 wks Jan
Smoking: No cigars & pipes
Credit cards:

Directions: In centre of Coggeshall opposite the clock tower

COGGESHALL,
White Hart Hotel ❀❀

Parts of this historic inn date from 1420, and many original
features are tastefully preserved. Traditional Italian cooking is
featured in the restaurant, with home-made pasta, and risottos
appearing amongst the strong seafood selection. The wine list
includes some interesting halves and Italians. A vast menu is
offered in the bar.

Directions: From the A12 towards Ipswich take the A120,
L towards Braintree; at B1024 crossroads turn L

Market End CO6 1NH
Map 5: TL82
Tel: 01376 561654
Fax: 01376 561789
Please telephone for further details

DEDHAM, Le Talbooth ❀❀

Colchester CO7 6HP
Map 5: TM03
Tel: 01206 323150
Fax: 01206 322309
Chef: Terry Barber
Owners: Gerald & Paul Milsom
Cost: *Alc* £35, fixed-price L £21.50/D
£26.95. H/wine £12.50

Immortalised in a painting by Constable, this 16th-century,
black-and-white timbered former weaver's cottage enjoys a
glorious position alongside the River Stour – go for one of the
parasol-covered terrace tables when the weather allows. The
kitchen leans towards the modern English style which means

dishes such as carpaccio of tuna with guacamole and niçoise salad, and pan-fried salmon and haddock cakes with spinach and chervil butter sauce among the starters, and mains along the lines of pork fillet wrapped in spinach mousseline with spiced pear and white wine gravy, and locally-landed cod on fettucine with wild mushrooms and red pepper pesto. Leave room for some tempting desserts; chocoholics will note the Talbooth's chocolate assiette. A less formal lunch menu includes a daily roast. Burgundy takes the number one spot among the whites on a serious wine list while Bordeaux has the edge among the reds. Of the non-French offerings South African wines make a good showing.

Additional: Sunday L; Children welcome; 🍴 dishes
Seats: 75. Private dining room 30
Smoking: No pipes & cigars
Accommodation: 10 en suite (Maison Talbooth)
Credit cards: ■ ☱ ⚛ 🗋 ☷ 🄲 🄿

Directions: 6 miles from Colchester: follow signs from A12 to Stratford St Mary, restaurant on L before village

Times: Noon-2pm/7-9.30pm.
Closed D Sun in winter

AA Wine Shortlisted for Award-see page 16

FELSTEAD, **Rumbles Cottage** ❀

Braintree Road CM6 3DJ
Map 5: TL62
Tel: 01371 820996
Please telephone for further details

Charming, rustic, very olde worlde cottage strong on homely decor and a mass of beams. Service is friendly and attentive. Good country cooking with chicken and pistachio terrine served with a zippy lime sauce, crisp pastry case of goats' cheese, red onion, rocket and pine kernels plus a simple purée of tomato and red pepper, and Atholl brose with Highland Mist blackberry syllabub showing the range.

Directions: In centre of village, approached by A120 or A130. 15/20 minutes' from M11

GREAT DUNMOW,
Starr Restaurant ❀❀

Market Place CM6 1AX
Map 4: TL62
Tel: 01371 874321
Fax: 01371 876337
Chef: Mark Fisher
Owners: Brian & Vanessa Jones
Cost: *Alc* £24.50, fixed-price L £10
(2 courses)/D from £22.50. 😊
H/wine £10
Times: Noon-last L 2pm/7-last D 9.30pm. Closed D Sun, 1st wk Jan

The setting is a solid, square market town inn. Within there is almost a French feel to the place as a cosy bar-cum-reception area, fresh flowers, white-washed beams, eau-de-nil cloths, and gleaming silver lighten the mood, and is anything but *olde worlde*. The kitchen displays admirable intentions and recipes are inventive. Note starters of pigeon sausage, a purée of butter beans with shallots and tarragon jus, or crispy crab strudel with sweet-and-sour peppers. Main courses take in traditional ideas and rework them, as in Barnsley chop wrapped in pastry with a stuffing of field mushrooms and a pink rosemary sauce, or calves' liver steak with spicy creamed potatoes and caramelised onions and vegetable broth with crushed peppercorns. The wine list offers a good range of everyday drinking with attractive prices to match.

Additional: Sunday L; Children welcome; 🍴 dishes
Seats: 60. Private rooms 12 & 30
Smoking: No smoking in dining room
Accommodation: 8 en suite
Credit cards: ■ ☱ ⚛ 🗋 ☷ 🄲 🄿

AA Wine Shortlisted for Award-see page 16

Directions: M11 exit 8, A120 7 miles eastward towards Colchester. In town centre

GREAT YELDHAM,
White Hart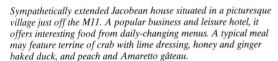

Another successful foodie inn from the small Huntsbridge group, this being very much an informal, relaxed set-up, just good food, wine and great ambience. The menu is quite a bold, eclectic collection, strong on flavours and offering quite hearty fare. Note an autumn dinner that took in a good, rustic pressed ham and shallot terrine served with a zappy spiced home-made piccalilli, a creamy risotto of spring onion and parsley topped with excellent crisp bacon, tenderloin of pork accompanied by a crisp tartlet of spinach and purée of apple, and a meaty, moist roast monkfish with a crisp pancetta overcoat, courgette tagliatelle, hot aubergine purée, and a fresh, tangy tomato salsa. Puddings were no less successful: a warm rice pudding came with a wonderful coconut ice cream, and a well-made dark chocolate and pear pudding with an excellent mint chocolate chip ice cream in a chocolate tartlet. The wine list, compiled, as all Huntsbridge lists are, by Master of Wine John Hoskins, is divided into categories by style, offers good tasting notes, an excellent choice of dessert wines, and is 'worth a detour for the wines alone'.

Halstead CO9 4HJ
Map 5: TL73
Tel: 01787 237250
Fax: 01787 238044
Chef: Roger Jones
Owners: Huntsbridge Ltd
Cost: Alc £25, fixed price L £7.50 (2 courses). ☺ H/wine £9.45
Times: Noon- last L 2pm/6.30-last D £10pm. Closed for D 25-26 Dec & 1 Jan
Additional: Bar food; Sunday L; Children welcome; ◑ dishes
Seats: 90. Private room 28
Smoking: No smoking in dining room
Credit cards: ▆▆ ▆▆ ▆▆ ▆ ▆▆ ▆ ▆ JCB

Directions: On A1302 between Halstead and Haverhill

HARLOW,
Swallow Churchgate Hotel ❀

Sympathetically extended Jacobean house situated in a picturesque village just off the M11. A popular business and leisure hotel, it offers interesting food from daily-changing menus. A typical meal may feature terrine of crab with lime dressing, honey and ginger baked duck, and peach and Amaretto gâteau.

Accommodation: 85 en suite
Credit cards: ▆▆ ▆▆ ▆ ▆▆ ▆

Directions: Take A414 (Harlow) exit M11, turn R on to B183 at 4th roundabout, then L into village street; hotel past church, at bottom of hill

Churchgate Street Village CM17 0JT
Map 5: TL41
Tel: 01279 420246
Fax: 01279 437720
Chef: Lee Acreman
Cost: Alc £25, fixed-price L £18.50/D £19.50. ☺ H/wine £11.50
Times: Last L 2pm/last D 10 pm. Closed L Sat, Xmas
Additional: Bar food L; Sunday L; Children welcome; ◑ dishes
Smoking: No smoking in dining room

HARWICH, The Pier at Harwich ❀❀

A truly nautical restaurant with the main restaurant on the first floor decked out with all kinds of maritime memorabilia. Fish is obviously given pride of place, and may be approached with simplicity as in pan-fried skate wing with lime and capers in butter, or as a more complicated timbale of latticed salmon and Dover sole, filled with lobster and prawn mousseline on a herb and Vermouth sauce. Fish and chips come as cod, haddock, plaice or skate, and steak and kidney pie, or flash-fried calves' liver with smoked bacon, Madeira sauce and rösti potatoes follow a traditional path. Puddings follow suit, with steamed treacle and date pudding with hot butterscotch and pecan nut sauce, or coupe Denmark with vanilla ice cream, whipped cream and hot chocolate sauce, as typical offerings. An informal, family-suited fish bistro, the Ha'penny Pier, is on the ground floor.

Directions: A12 to Colchester than A120 to Harwich town quay front

The Quay CO12 3HH
Map 5: TM23
Tel: 01255 241212
Fax: 01255 551922
Chef: Chris Oakley
Cost: Alc £30, fixed-price L £17.50. ☺ H/wine £9.95
Times: Noon-last L 2pm/6-last D 9.30pm. Closed D 25-26 Dec
Additional: Sunday L; Children welcome; ◑ dishes
Seats: 70
Smoking: No pipes and cigars
Accommodation: 6 en suite
Credit cards: ▆▆ ▆▆ ▆▆ ▆ ▆▆ ▆

MANNINGTREE, **Stour Bay Café**

39-43 High Street CO11 1AH
Map 5: TM13
Tel: 01206 396687
Fax: 01206 395462
Chef: Stas Anastasiades
Owners: Mr & Mrs Mark Bright
Cost: *Alc* £20. ☺ H/wine £9.75
Times: Last L 2pm/last D 9.30pm.
Closed L Sat, all Sun, Mon
Additional: Bar food L;
Children welcome; ♨ dishes
Smoking: No pipes and cigars
Credit cards: ▬ ▦ ▧ ▢ ▦

*Beamed, late 16th-century building featuring bare-boarded floors, a
bright Mediterranean decor, and a short carte highlighting fresh
local seafood such as rock oysters and poached lobster. Further
choices may include chicken liver parfait with port wine jelly,
sea bass with pickled ginger and soy sauce, and beef fillet with
whisky-spiked jus.*

Directions: Town centre (A317 from Colchester to Ipswich) –
large green building in High Street

ROCHFORD, **Hotel Renouf**

Bradley Way SS4 1BU
Map 5: TQ89
Tel: 01702 541334
Fax: 01702 549563
Chef: Melvin Renouf
Owner: Derek Renouf
Cost: *Alc* £30, fixed-price L/D £15.50
(2 courses). ☺ H/wine £10.50
Times: Last L 1.30pm/D 9.30pm.
Closed L Sat, D Sun (except
residents), 26-30 Dec
Additional: Sunday L;
Children welcome; ♨ dishes
Smoking: No smoking in dining room;
Air conditioning
Accommodation: 23 en suite
Credit cards: ▬ ▦ ▧ ▢ ▦ ▢ JCB

*Modern English ideas rub shoulders with classical French cuisine at
this smart, red-brick establishment in the centre of Rochford.
Imaginative food can be enjoyed overlooking the garden: a meal in
late summer meal included tiger prawn salad with balsamic dressing,
and duck rouennaise coated in breadcrumbs and mustard.*

Directions: M25/J29, A127 into Rochford onto B1013

SOUTHEND-ON-SEA,
Schulers Hotel

*A bright spot in an area not known for fine dining, Schulers on the
seafront concentrates on classic French and exciting seafood
numbers such as stir-fried tiger prawns with soy, coriander and
ginger, or scallops with white wine sauce in puff pastry. Fresh and
fruity sherry trifle is a good dessert choice.*

161 Eastern Esplanade
SS1 2YB
Map 5: TQ88
Tel: 01702 610172
Fax: 01702 466835
Chef: Ben Allani
Owners: Claire & Manfred Schuler

Directions: From A13 or A127 into Southend, follow seafront signs. Then E towards Thorpe Bay. Eastern Esplanade (E of pier).

Schulers Hotel

Cost: Alc £25, fixed-price L&D £10.
☺ H/wine £9.50.
Times: Last L 1.45pm/last D 9.30pm.
Closed D Sun, L Mon.
Additional: Sunday L; Children welcome; 🍴 dishes
Accommodation: 9 en suite
Credit cards: 💳 💳 💳 💳 💳 💳 💳

STANSTEAD,

Whitehall Hotel ❀❀

Church End
CM6 2BZ
Map 5: TL52
Tel: 01279 850603
Fax: 01279 850385
Chef: Paula Keane
Owner: Sisyrinchium Ltd
Cost: Alc £35, fixed-price L £19.50/D £37.50 (5 courses). ☺ H/wine £10.50.
Times: 12.30pm-last L 2pm/7.30pm-last D 9.30pm
Additional: Sunday L; Children welcome; 🍴 dishes
Seats: 40. Private dining room 16
Smoking: No pipes and cigars
Accommodation: 25 en suite
Credit cards: 💳 💳 💳 💳 💳

Conveniently situated near Stansted airport, this hotel boasts a very attractive Elizabethan-timbered dining room. The cooking is in a traditional country house hotel style with a few modern touches, and choice seems to be the watchword. Simple dishes feature on the chef's daily changing selection menu; there is also a *carte* and a six-course menu surprise. In the bar you can enjoy *amuse bouches* such as quails' eggs en-croûte, smoked mackerel pâté and lamb kebab. At the table there are appetisers, which may be a chicken and pistachio terrine with potato and chive dressing. Duxelle-style chicken liver crostini comes with excellent home-made plum chutney. Of the main courses, the duck breast features rich honey glazing, honey gravy and roasted figs. A highlight is the plum parfait, its soft iced texture complemented by a warm, spicy plum compote. Good too are the petits fours and here again a wide choice features.

Directions: From M11/J8 follow signs for Stansted Airport and then for Broxted

TOLLESHUNT KNIGHTS,
Five Lakes Hotel ❀

Medieval Camelot-style restaurant set in a striking modern leisure hotel complex in the heart of the Essex countryside. New chef at time of print was promising good things.

Directions: Kelvedon exit A12 follow signs to Tiptree, over staggered crossroads past jam factory, take L fork, approx 2 miles turn R at T junction.

Colchester Road
CM9 8HX
Map 5: TL91
Tel: 01621 868888
Fax: 01621 869696
Please telephone for further details

WETHERSFIELD,
Dicken's Restaurant ❀❀

The *olde-worlde* atmosphere of this countrified restaurant does not extend to the menu, which is a well-judged mix of eclecticism and restraint. A dark Mediterranean fish soup, served with a pungent rouille, was not too rich to be a first course. It was followed by an elegant interpretation of steamed game pudding, the fluffy dough filled with a mélange of venison, hare and pheasant and accompanied by a light jus and finely diced winter roots. Buttery side vegetables included herbed roast potato wedges and fine al dente beans. The raspberry and coconut tart served with vanilla ice cream could have done with less of its almond frangipane filling, and perhaps a stream of raspberry sauce instead of a flood. Tasty petits fours included unctuous orange chocolate ganache, light Turkish delight, a fresh cream choux bun and sugary fudge. The comprehensive wine list is split by style and covers all price brackets.

The Green CM7 4BS
Map 5: TL73
Tel/Fax: 01371 850723
Chef/Owner: W John Dicken
Cost: *Alc* £24.25, fixed-price L £10 (2 courses)/D £19.50. ☺ H/wine £10.25.
Times: 12.30pm-last L 2pm/7.30pm-last D 9.30pm. Closed Sun D, Mon, Tue
Additional: Sunday L; Children welcome; ◕ dishes
Seats: 60. Private dining room 18-36
Credit cards: None

Directions: From M11/Stanstead Airport take A120, bypass Gt Dunmow, towards Braintree. Turn L to Gt Saling then R towards Shalford. Wethersfield is next village

GLOUCESTERSHIRE

ALVESTON, Alveston House Hotel ❀

Near Bristol BS35 2LA
Map 3: ST68
Tel: 01454 415050
Fax: 01454 415425
Chef: Julie Camm
Owners: Bladon Hotels Ltd
Cost: *Alc* £24, fixed-price L & D £18.75. ☺ H/wine £9.50.
Times: Last L 1.45pm/D 9.30pm
Additional: Bar food L; Children welcome; ◕ dishes
Smoking: No pipes & cigars
Accommodation: 30 en suite
Credit cards: 🟦 🟦 🟦 🟦 🟦 🟦 🟦 JCB

Fine period house hotel. Quincey's restaurant is a civilised setting for soundly prepared English and international dishes. Both the pork fillet medallions with a rich au poivre sauce, and an orange and Grand Marnier soufflé, are recommended.

Directions: On A38 at Alveston, 3.5 miles N of M4/M5 junction

BIBURY, **Bibury Court**

Grand country house hotel for which the term 'faded elegance' might have been coined. Eat in the compact, formal but elegant dining room, or amongst the abundant foliage of the bright conservatory. Robust, modish cooking with no shortage of flavours in well-judged combinations: scallop mousseline; pink hearted pigeon breasts with an earthy sage mash and rich red wine sauce; opulent dark chocolate and pistachio tart.

Additional: Bar food; Sunday L (noon-2.30pm); Children welcome; ♨ dishes
Smoking: No smoking in dining room
Accommodation: 19 en suite
Credit cards: ▆ ▆ ℂ ▆ ▣ JCB

Directions: On B4425 between Cirencester & Burford; hotel lies behind the church

Cirencester GL7 5NT
Map 4: SP10
Tel: 01285 740337
Fax: 01285 740660
Chef: Tom Bridgeman
Owners: Mr & Mrs Johnston, Miss Collier
Cost: Alc £24.50, fixed-price L £15. ☺ H/wine £10
Times: Last L 2.30pm/last D 9.30pm. Closed 21-30 Dec

BIBURY, **Swan Hotel** ❀❀

Absolutely nothing of the ugly duckling about this creeper-clad riverside hotel. However, the country inn exterior does little to prepare one for the swan-like elegance of the Signet dining room. Whilst the brasserie bustles at the other end of the long building, the formal restaurant offers a more studied menu that nevertheless retains an uncluttered, modern British feel. Ingredients make much of the local bounty – the trout might have been reeled in through the kitchen window. Stephen Bulmer, formerly of the London restaurant, Atelier – where he won three AA Rosettes – had just taken over the kitchen when we inspected, and the meal reported on here was cooked by the brigade. Witty canapés – mini-versions of shepherd's pie, quiche and pizza – are a taste of the intelligent and understated approach that characterises the cooking. Thus foie gras terrine, buttery and generous, is effectively paired with simple caramelised apples. Similarly, pork confit, bewigged with a slab of golden crackling, shares space with a herby bubble-and-squeak. Pastry is a strength – prune and frangipane tart with a velvety Guinness ice cream is highly recommended. The wine list has recently been in transition, but the good range of wines by the glass is worth investigating. This is a place to watch.

Directions: On B4425 between Cirencester (7 miles) and Burford (9 miles). Beside bridge in centre of Bibury.

Cirencester GL7 5NW
Map 4: SP10
Tel: 01285 740695
Fax: 01285 740473
Chef: Stephen Bulmer
Owners: Mrs E A & Mr J A Furtek
Cost: Fixed-price D £26.50. H/wine £14.75
Times: D only, last D 9.30pm. Closed 21-28 Dec
Additional: Bar food; Sunday L; Children welcome; ♨ dishes
Seats: 60. Private dining room 30. Jacket & tie preferred
Smoking: No smoking in dining room
Accommodation: 18 en suite
Credit cards: ▆ ▆ ⚞ ℂ ▆ ▣ JCB

BIRDLIP,
Kingshead House Restaurant ✿

Judy and Warren Knock are a winning team at this cosy, cottagey little restaurant. Judy's menu might include sea bass with caramelised onions and white wine sauce, and roast loin and casseroled leg of rabbit with rosemary. Warren provides the hospitality and an informative, hand-written wine list that is full of interest.

Smoking: No pipes & cigars. **Accommodation:** 1 en suite
Credit cards: 🔲 🔲 🔲

Directions: A417, then B4070 (Stroud) to village

GL4 8JH
Map 3: SO91
Tel: 01452 862299
Chef: Judy Knock
Owners: Judy & Warren Knock
Cost: *Alc* £18.50 (L only, Tue to Fri), fixed-price D £27.50. H/wine £10.50
Times: Last L 1.45pm/last D 9.30pm. Closed L Sat, D Sun, all Mon, 25-26 Dec, 1 Jan
Additional: Bar food L; Sunday L; Children welcome; ◑ dishes

BLOCKLEY, ## Crown Inn ✿

Mellow, 16th-century inn with a full complement of old beams, log fires and exposed stone walls. The menu, however, includes such up-to-date dishes as pork stir-fry with hoisin sauce, and rack of lamb on celeriac and basil mash alongside traditional steak and kidney pudding. Interesting wines are listed by grape variety.

Accommodation: 21 en suite. **Credit cards:** 🔲 🔲 🔲 🔲 🔲

Directions: A44 W from Moreton-in-Marsh, right on to B4479

High Street GL56 9EX
Map 4: SP13
Tel: 01386 700245
Fax: 01386 700247
Chef: Olivier Broyer
Owners: Messrs Champion
Cost: *Alc* £25. ☺ H/wine £9.95
Times: Last L 2pm/last D 10pm
Additional: Bar food; Sunday L; No children under 2; ◑ dishes

BOURTON-ON-THE-WATER,
Dial House Hotel ✿✿

The Chestnuts
High Street GL54 2AN
Map 4: SP12
Tel: 01451 822244
Fax: 01451 810126
Chef: Calvin Williamson
Owners: Lynn & Peter Boxall
Cost: *Alc* £24, fixed-price L £8.50 (2 courses). ☺ H/wine £9.95
Times: Noon-last L 2pm/7-last D 9pm
Additional: Bar food L; Sunday L; No children under 9; ◑ dishes
Seats: 20. Private dining room 14
Smoking: No smoking in dining room
Accommodation: 12 en suite
Credit cards: 🔲 🔲 🔲 🔲 🔲 🔲

Built of mellow Cotswold stone, the beautifully preserved house stands in the village centre. There are two small, charming dining-rooms, one with an impressive inglenook fireplace. There's plenty of choice on the menu, and an obvious degree of skill and care goes into the cooking. Start with home-smoked Deben duck on an orange and pink peppercorn dressing, or pan-fried chicken livers with grape and Madeira jus, then follow with cannon of lamb with Pernod and ratatouille dressing, or grilled red snapper on a timbale of red wild rice with lime-butter sauce. As well as glazed lemon tart and sticky toffee pudding, there is short, well-selected list of Cotswold cheeses.

Directions: In village centre; A436 from Cheltenham, A40-A424 from Oxford

BUCKLAND. **Buckland Manor** ❀❀❀

Broadway WR12 7LY
Map 4: SP03
Tel: 01386 852626
Fax: 01386 853557
Chef: Kenneth Wilson
Owners: Roy & Daphne Vaughan
Cost: *Alc* £45, fixed-price L £29.50.
H/wine £11.50
Times: 12.30pm-last L
1.45pm/7.30pm-last D 9pm
Additional: Bar food L; Sunday L;
No children under 12; ❀ dishes
Seats: 40. Jacket & tie preferred
Smoking: No smoking in dining room
Accommodation: 13 en suite
Credit cards: 🔳 🔳 🔳 🔳 🔳 🔳

Inspectors always comment on the setting of this 13th-century manor house: Buckland Manor stands on the edge of a secluded village, set in a hillside within extensive but impeccably maintained grounds. Period furnishings and rich, costly fabrics speak of comfort. Ken Wilson had been but a few months in the kitchen when our inspector called, but that early summer meal promised well for the future. Canapés set the standard: light kipper tartlet, mushroom and asparagus quiche, rare chopped beef and truffle en croûte. Bread, too, showed attention to detail, a wide selection that took in poppyseed, olive as well as white and brown. A well-constructed foie gras and chicken liver parfait opened the meal, its counterpart, a grilled goats' cheese, tomato and olive tart with rocket pesto was simple concept but well done. Confit of duck breast was served with a delicate parcel of cabbage, a light and properly seasoned potato and apple cake, sweet beetroot purée, and a delicate honey and cider sauce. Parfait of honey, oatmeal and whisky was all velvety smoothness and a good berry coulis. The cellar book-style of the wine list can be a bit laborious, and there's not enough time to absorb it all over an aperitif, but it offers excellent depth and choice and interesting, descriptive annotation.
Signature dishes: Rack of local lamb; Dover sole; venison; Scotch beef.

Directions: 2 miles SW of Broadway. Take B4632 signposted Cheltenham, then take turn for Buckland. Hotel is through village on R

CHARINGWORTH,
Charingworth Manor ❀❀

Last year we extolled the early promise of Simon Crannage who had been in place for just weeks when our inspector called. Almost before the ink was dry the chef merry-go-round had spun Mr Crannage off to pastures new. This year, our well-timed visit found the kitchen between chefs, and whilst the inspirational note struck last year has diminished, the remaining team are keeping things on an even keel with a sensibly short 'Cotswold Market' menu concentrating on first principles. As it stand, one can expect some sturdy staples such as a good confit of duck with crunchy broad beans, and a milk-sweet chump of lamb with rosemary and garlic. Desserts can

Chipping Campden
GL55 6NS
Map 4: SP13
Tel: 01386 593555
Fax: 01386 593353
Chef: Mark Lawson-Smith
Owner: English Rose Hotels
Cost: *Alc* £40, fixed-price L £17.50/D £37.50. H/wine £20
Times: 12.30pm-last L 2pm/7pm-last D 9.30pm
Additional: Bar food; Sunday L;
Children welcome; ❀ dishes

be painfully sweet but those who like it that way will be rewarded by a banana parfait with honey-glazed bananas. The wine list offers an admirable selection by the glass.

Directions: From A429 Fosse Way take B4035 towards Chipping Campden, hotel is 3 miles on R

Seats: 48. Private dining room 30. Jacket & tie preferred
Accommodation: 26 en suite
Credit cards: ▆ ▆ ▆ ▆ ▆ ▆

CHELTENHAM,

Le Champignon Sauvage 🐾🐾🐾🐾

24 Suffolk Road
GL50 2AQ
Map 3: SO92
Tel/Fax: 01242 573449
Chef: David Everitt-Matthias
Owners: David & Helen Everitt-Matthias
Cost: Fixed-price L £18.50/D £33. ☺
H/wine £9.95
Times: 12.30-1.30pm/7.30-9.15pm.
Closed L Sat, all Sun, 2 wks Xmas,
2 wks summer, Bhs
Additional: Children welcome
Seats: 28
Credit cards: ▆ ▆ ▆ ▆ ▆ ▆ JCB

The restaurant may look out over a fairly unassuming street, but it is the small, intimate dining room that gives a clue to the quality of the food: smartly appointed, well-spaced tables, comfortable high-backed chairs, good artwork. David Everitt-Matthias cooks very well, his menus are short, based on an assured, confident repertoire that owes a lot to France, and the terroir-style of cooking, and each ingredient is used because it works well within the framework of the dish. Thus a duck confit 'sausage' is successfully paired with an acidulated apple tarte Tatin: sweet-and-sour caramelised apples in the thinnest filo case, with a purée of turnips to add a bitter note to the dish. The terroir style came through strongly in a rustic roast monkfish, rolled in cep powder and accompanied by cep gnocchi and sautéed ceps on a bed of wonderfully smooth pumpkin purée, a bit of sauté pak choi acted as a 'cleansing' vegetable. More down-to-earth grouping of elements can be seen in a signature dish of fillet of Wiltshire pork with home-made black pudding, pork dumplings and a cider sauce. That ingredients are carefully sourced goes without saying, and some witty ideas are at work in a lunch menu that takes in lamb dumplings with haggis-filled pasta and a caramelised onion sauce, and chocolate mousse layered between hazelnut meringue, with ginger beer ice cream. Service is excellent.
   Signature dishes: Salted salmon with a pea and bacon risotto, chicken juices; warm pistachio tart, roasted strawberries; spiced pigeon, beetroot, barley risotto, bitter chocolate infused sauce.

Directions: South of town centre, near Boys' College on A40 (Oxford). Please phone for exact details

CHELTENHAM, **Daffodil** 🐾🐾   NEW

The last credits may have rolled in the 1950's but 40 years on this former cinema is putting on a brand new show. Whilst the movie stars have been relegated to portraits on the walls, the stage is now occupied by an open kitchen with Ed Portlock and

18-20 Suffolk Parade
Montpelier GL50 2AE
Map 3: SO92
Tel: 01242 700055
Fax: 01242 700088
Chef: Edward Portlock

his team performing in full view of a bustling restaurant. The concept is narcissus bright and undoubted fun. Much of the Art Deco styling remains, with broad staircases sweeping down from the circle bar to the main restaurant and dramatic evening lighting that adds to the sense of glamour. An early inspection found the food living up to its billing with the brasserie-style menu being an intelligent working of a familiar script. A balanced approach offers, on the one hand, breezy items such as chicken liver and foie gras terrine with a sharp tomato chutney and, on the other, weighty modern British stylings including Cornish pasty with parsley mash. Quality control appears to be a strength with the plate of mini-desserts including a skilled toffee and banana brûlée amongst its well-honed components. In enlightened style the entire wine list is available by the glass.

Owner: Mark Stephens
Cost: *Alc* £21.50, fixed-price L £10 (2 courses). ☺
Times: Noon-last L 3pm,/7-last D 11pm. Closed Sun, 1 wk Xmas
Additional: Bar food; Children welcome; ❹ dishes
Seats: 120
Smoking: No-smoking area; Air conditioning
Credit cards: ▰ ▰ ▰ ▰ ▰

Directions: Please telephone for directions

CHELTENHAM, **The Greenway**

Shurdington GL51 5UG
Map 3: SO92
Tel: 01242 862352
Fax: 01242 862780
Chef: Peter Fairclough
Owners: David & Valerie White
Cost: *Alc* £34.75, fixed-price L £19.50/D £32. ☺ H/wine £13.50
Times: 12.30-last L 2pm/7.30-last D 9.30pm. Closed L Sat
Additional: Sunday L; No children under 7; ❹ dishes
Seats: 50. Private dining room 24
Smoking: No smoking in dining room
Accommodation: 19 en suite
Credit cards: ▰ ▰ ▰ ▰ ▰

The dining room, part conservatory and part oak-panelled, overlooks the sunken garden and lily pond with views to the Cotswold Hills beyond. It is a great backdrop to a menu that explores how best to offer emphatically fresh ingredients with high flavour and balanced combinations. If there is a weakness in the cooking here, it is one shared with many other places of a similar exacting standard: in the course of one meal the food can triumph magnificently or go somewhat awry. One impressive inspection dinner included a fine appetiser of mushroom cappuccino with whole scallops, and was followed by an exactly cooked, superbly flavoured first course of wood pigeon with red onion marmalade and a robust, clear and well-balanced jus. Next came perfectly and simply grilled John Dory fillets served with a single ravioli of langoustine and langoustine nage, both latter items a little underpowered in terms of flavour. A dessert of cheese crème brûlée, a delicate, lightly set cheese, flavoured with crisp potato slices, was served with an over-robust tomato chutney, offsetting the balance of the dish – good idea that it was. An excellent wine list offers quality, breadth and depth.

Signature dishes: Mille-feuille of lamb loin with red onion marinade and foie gras on a rosemary jus; lobster and spring onion risotto with Parmesan crisp and a saffron sauce; seared fillets of John Dory with crushed potatoes and a thyme fish sauce; roasted medallion of Cotswold venison with home-made sausages and a blackberry jus.

Directions: 2.5 miles south of Cheltenham on A46 (Stroud)

CHELTENHAM,
Mayflower Chinese Restaurant

32-34 Clarence Street
GL50 3NX
Map 3: SO92
Tel: 01242 522426/511580
Fax: 01242 251667
Chefs: Mrs M M Kong, Mr C F Kong
Owner: The Kong Family
Cost: Alc £20, fixed-price L £6.50/D £19.50. ☺ H/wine £8.95
Times: Last L 1.45pm/last D 10.30pm. Closed L Sun, 24-26 Dec
Additional: Children welcome; ♨ dishes
Smoking: Air conditioning
Credit cards: ▆ ▆ ▆ ▆ ▆ ▆ ▆ JCB

The Kongs are in their 16th year at this smart 'Regency-oriental'-style Chinese, specialising in Cantonese, Pekinese and Szechuan cooking. Long menu with mainly familiar fare – sizzling dishes are hugely popular, and crispy aromatic duck is a firm favourite. Decent wine list.

Directions: Town centre opposite Eagle Star building

CHELTENHAM,
Le Petit Blanc ❀❀

NEW

The Queen's Hotel
The Promenade GL50 1NN
Map 3: SO92
Tel: 01242 266800
Fax: 01242 266801
Chef: Stephen Nash
Owner: Raymond Blanc
Cost: Alc £30, fixed-price L&D £14. ☺
Times: 11am-11pm (10.30pm Sun). Closed 25 Dec
Additional: Bar food; Sunday L; Children welcome; ♨ dishes
Seats: 152
Credit cards: ▆ ▆ ▆ ▆ ▆ ▆ ▆

Success breed success. This is the second of Le Manoir's offspring and anybody who feels less than well-served by their local restaurant scene might like to lobby Raymond Blanc as further outposts are apparently planned. The Cheltenham version is discreetly located to the side of the Queen's Hotel on the edge of the town centre, and the understated exterior gives some clue to the style of an already well-honed operation. Brasserie-mode certainly, with bench seating, brushed steel tables and breezy, polo-shirted staff, whilst the menu is of the same ilk – plenty of the expected chargrilling and pan-frying – although there is a tad more ambition than sometimes found in the genre. Nevertheless, the success of this approach relies on accuracy with top-notch ingredients, and the evidence of simple but exquisite starters such as sautéed asparagus with rocket and balsamic dressing is that Stephen Nash's team are on target. Main courses offer plenty of heavyweights with a thumping good lunch of braised rabbit leg with cassoulet and mustard tempting one inspector to siesta in nearby Regency Park. Similarly, a lighter sounding roast monkfish turned out to be great rounds of firm white fleshed, wrapped in Parma ham, with a generous nest of irresistible pesto noodles. Desserts can be equally lusty, but frankly lack a little enterprise with offerings such as sticky toffee pudding and apple and rhubarb crumble being worthy rather than exciting.

Directions: To the side of the Queen's Hotel, town centre

CHELTENHAM, **The Queen's**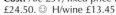

Elegant hotel with a fine Regency façade, prominently located in the centre of town. The dedicated kitchen brigade is noted for respect of flavours, accurate technique and ability to keep any fancy ideas in check. This simple approach translates as seafood tortilla with lemon cream sauce, escalope of pork loin with apple and sultanas and grain mustard sauce, and tarte Tatin.

The Promenade GL50 1NN
Map 3: SO92
Tel: 01242 514724
Fax: 01242 224145
Chef: Tony Harrison
Owners: Forte Hotels UK
Cost: *Alc* £31, fixed price L £15.95/D £24.50. ☺ H/wine £13.45

Times: Last L 2pm/last D 9.45pm. Closed 24-27 Dec except for residents
Additional: Bar food; Sunday L; Children welcome; dishes
Smoking: No smoking in dining room
Accommodation: 79 en suite
Credit cards: ▬ ▭ 🗙 ⌷ ▦ ▣ ▣ JCB

Directions: Town centre

CHELTENHAM,
Regency House Hotel

A quiet location close to the town centre is one advantage of John and Barbara Oates' Regency townhouse, another is Barbara's well-crafted home cooking. Expect some robust flavours in dishes such as smoked cod with orange and caper sauce, stir-fried coq au vin and pork Stroganoff with three mustards.

50 Clarence Square
GL50 4JR
Map 3: SO92
Tel: 01242 582718
Fax: 01242 262697
Chef: Barbara Oates
Owners: John & Barbara Oates
Cost: *Alc* £18.50, fixed-price L&D £12.95. ☺ H/wine £8

Times: Last L 2pm/last D 8pm. Closed L Sun, Xmas-New Year
Additional: Children welcome; dishes
Smoking: No smoking in dining room
Accommodation: 8 en suite
Credit cards: ▬ ▭ ▦

Directions: Clarence Square is in Pittville just N of town centre

---

CHELTENHAM,
Restaurant On The Park

Located within the Hotel On The Park (a town house hotel with a country-house atmosphere) this elegant restaurant is run by chef-patron Graham Mairs with a style as distinctive as it is accomplished. Wonderful black olives and coarse olive bread accompanied the pre-prandial drinks of a recent dinner that began with goats' cheese filo parcels on a bed of fine beans with cucumber relish. Next came a cumin-flavoured cauliflower cappuccino (frothy and delicious), before a main dish of belly of pork with pea fondue and flageolet bean cassoulet. From desserts such as blood orange parfait with nut craquelin, and white chocolate and vanilla crème brûlée, a tarte au citron proved to be a good choice. Interesting wines are listed by grape variety and include a good sprinkling of half-bottles.

38 Evesham Road GL52 2AH
Map 3: SO92
Tel: 01242 227713
Fax: 01242 511526
Chef: Graham Mairs
Owners: Graham Mairs, Donna Fox
Cost: *Alc* £ 27, fixed-price L £14.95/D £21.50. ☺ H/wine £9.75
Times: Noon-last L 2pm/7-last D 9.30pm. Closed 1 wk Jan
Additional: Sunday L; No children under 10; dishes
Seats: 40. Private room 16
Smoking: No smoking in dining room
Accommodation: 12 en suite
Credit cards: ▬ ▭ 🗙 ⌷ ▦ ▣

Directions: A435 (Evesham) from Cheltenham centre, hotel at 3rd lights opposite Pittville Park

CHELTENHAM,
Thistle Golden Valley

*Popular hotel with good conference, business and leisure facilities.
The Burford Room restaurant is the place to try cream of Guinness
and Stilton soup topped with puff pastry, gâteau of sea bass and
salmon filled with spring vegetables with a sweet pepper ratatouille,
and rack of lamb caramelised with an apricot marmalade, with
parsnip purée.*

Gloucester Road GL51 0TS
Map 3: SO92
Tel: 01242 232691
Fax: 01242 221846
Chef: Ronald Pharoah
Cost: *Alc* £32.50, fixed-price L
£15.50/D £23.50. ☺ H/wine £11
Times: Last L 1.45pm/last D 9.45pm
Additional: Bar food; Sunday L;
Children welcome; ❹ dishes
Smoking: No-smoking area;
Air conditioning
Accommodation: 122 en suite
Credit cards: 🟥 🟦 ✈ 💷 🟥 🅲 🔳 JCB

Directions: 2.5 miles from centre of
Cheltenham on A4O (Gloucester).
1 mile M5/J11, towards Cheltenham
(A40), 2nd exit off 1st roundabout.

CHIPPING CAMPDEN,
Cotswold House ❀❀

Step out of this charming house and you will find yourself in
the high street of one of the prettiest Cotswold towns. Inside,
there is a relaxed elegance, promoted by accomplished staff
who combine professional service with an easy informality.
There is a feeling that everything is in its place and this
precision extends to Simon Crannage's cooking. The best dishes
give an impression of a clockwork attention to detail with
flavours laid down in intelligent and striking combinations. An
amuse-bouche of a lightly spiced and cheerfully fat scallop was
an excellent early example, brilliantly seasoned and served
with a spoonful of wild mushroom risotto – a dish that
smacked of genuine inspiration. A starter of artichoke, truffle
and goose liver velouté followed the same lines, and a main
course of venison with a kidney sauce had enough impact in
the principal ingredients to make curried leeks something of an
encumbrance. A sharper approach in all senses was evident in

The Square GL55 6AN
Map 4: SP13
Tel: 01386 840330
Fax: 01386 840310
Chef: Simon Crannage
Owners: Mr & Mrs C Forbes
Cost: *Alc* £29.50, fixed-price
D £21.50. ☺ H/wine £12
Times: D only, 7.15pm-9.30pm.
Closed 3 days Xmas
Additional: Brasserie L&D; Sunday
L (12.30-2pm); Children welcome;
❹ dishes
Seats: 44. Private dining room 20.
Jacket & tie preferred
Smoking: No smoking in dining room
Accommodation: 15 en suite
Credit cards: 🟥 🟦 ✈ 💷 🟥 🅲 🔳 JCB

Directions: 1 mile N of A44 between
Moreton-in-Marsh and Broadway on
B4081

a magnificent apple crème brûlée served with a rhubarb ice cream and a wonderful, verdant Granny Smith sauce. A fairly priced and generally well-sourced wine list offers some worthwhile options, including an honest, velvety Château-Lyonnat Lussac-St Emillion.

CHIPPING CAMPDEN,

The Malt House ❀❀

Julian Brown still single-handedly manages the cooking at this charming small Cotswold hotel. The dining room is delightful, in keeping with the style of the house and tastefully appointed with antiques, polished wood tables and vibrant floral displays. Service is informal, with Julian often taking the orders. His cooking is a treat; simple dishes but with assured flavours offered on a short, modern menu with three choices at each course, and desserts selected at the time of ordering. One successful dinner opened with a creamy butternut squash risotto with Parma ham and chives, followed by Scottish steak – a fine cut of fillet topped with pancetta salad of finely diced red onion, coriander and garlic, accompanied by mixed leaf salad (crisp and colourful) and turned baby roast potatoes (creamy texture inside a golden salt crust). Dessert was a super chocolate tart of melting centre and great taste balanced by a soft, smooth honey ice cream.

Directions: Entering Chipping Campden on A44, turn R for Broad Campden, follow four sharp turns to Malt House

Broad Campden GL55 6UU
Map 4: SP13
Tel: 01386 840295
Fax: 01386 841334
Chef: Julian Brown
Owners: The Brown Family
Cost: *Alc* £27, fixed-price D £27.50. H/wine £18
Times: D only, 7.30-last D 8.45pm. Closed Tue, Wed, 23-28 Dec
Additional: dishes
Seats: 22
Smoking: No smoking in dining room
Accommodation: 8 en suite
Credit cards: ▊ ▊ ▊ ▊ ▊

CHIPPING CAMPDEN,

Noel Arms Hotel ❀❀

The Noel Arms dates from the 14th century when it served to accommodate visiting wool merchants; today, it has the oak-panelled style that visiting American tourists simply adore. After some chopping and changing in the kitchen, things have settled down, and meals are now of a far more consistently high standard. There is a slight Gallic touch to many of the dishes (like as not served by charming Gallic staff), a rillette of salmon and monkfish with a pert spiced mustard sabayon was a cheerful, generous offering, and an unfussy breast of duck with Port sauce was deliciously tender. More elaborate daily specialities tend towards the ornate – fresh oysters, vegetable

High Street GL55 6AT
Map 4: SP13
Tel: 01386 840317
Fax: 01386 841136
Chef: Wayne Hatenboer
Owner: Cotswold Inns & Hotels Ltd
Cost: *Alc* £21.75. Fixed-price D £21.75. ☺ H/wine £9.25.
Times: D only, 7pm-9.30pm
Additional: Bar food; Sunday L (noon-2pm); Children welcome; dishes
Seats: 45. Private dining room 14
Smoking: No smoking in dining room
Accommodation: 26 en suite
Credit cards: ▊ ▊ ▊ ▊ ▊ ▊ ▊ JCB

Directions: Town centre

noodles and Champagne sabayon, or boudin of venison topped with crisp leeks and buttered chives. Desserts include the ubiquitous trio of chocolate with crème anglaise, as well as iced Baileys flavoured soufflé on raspberry coulis.

CHIPPING CAMPDEN,
Seymour House Hotel ❀❀

The 18th-century house, set in the centre of Chipping Campden, has bags of character as well as a vine growing through the centre of the restaurant. The kitchen cooks a set-price menu noted for a strong Italian influence and careful execution. Chicken liver parfait with a peppered raspberry and onion sauce, supreme of chicken set on black noodles in a warm balsamic dressing, thin slices of Scottish fillet steak on a sizzling plate of virgin olive oil, herbs and garlic, and roasted medallion of tuna with creamed potato flavoured with olive oil and garlic with a tomato and sweet red pepper sauce are typical of the style. Risotto all'amarone comes finished with butter and Parmesan, and panzerotti al quattro formaggi is a popular dish of stuffed pancakes baked in a spicy tomato sauce.

Directions: Town centre – along the High Street

High Street GL55 6AH
Map 4: SP13
Tel: 01386 840429
Fax: 01386 840369
Chef: Roberto Stratta
Cost: Alc £26.50, fixed-price L £15.50/D from £24.95. ☺
H/wine £13.50
Times: Noon-last L 2pm/7-last D 10pm
Additional: Bar food; Sunday L; Children welcome; ❀ dishes
Seats: 60. Private room 40
Smoking: No smoking in dining room
Accommodation: 15 en suite
Credit cards: 🔲 🔲 🔲 🔲 🔲 🔲

CIRENCESTER, **Crown of Crucis** ❀

The hotel restaurant creates a relaxed atmosphere, and complements the chef's approach to imaginative, seasonal menus. Typical dishes include sautéed red mullet fillets with a balsamic dressing, and braised shank of Cotswold lamb with honey roasted parsnips and a rosemary jus.

Ampney Crucis GL7 5RS
Map 4: SP00
Tel: 01285 851806
Fax: 01285 851735
Chef: Chris O'Neill
Owners: Mr & Mrs R K Mills
Cost: Alc £16, fixed-price D £16.45.
☺ H/wine £7.75.
Times: Last L 2.30pm/D 10pm.
Closed 25 Dec, hotel only 24-30 Dec
Additional: Bar food; Sunday L; Children welcome; ❀ dishes
Smoking: No-smoking area; No pipes and cigars; Air conditioning
Accommodation: 25 en suite
Credit cards: 🔲 🔲 🔲 🔲 🔲 🔲 🔲

Directions: 3 miles E of Cirencester on A417 to Lechlade

CIRENCESTER, **Harry Hare's** ❀

Forget the 17th-century townhouse setting, Harry Hare's is a lively, upbeat establishment with young polo-shirted staff adding to the buzz. The all-day menu copes with breakfast, brunch and tea while more substantial dishes range from chargrilled tuna and traditional Languedoc cassoulet to fish 'n' chips. Super list of wines by the glass.

Credit cards: 🔲 🔲 🔲 🔲 🔲

Directions: Opposite Cirencester Parish Church, in market place at centre of town

3 Gosditch Street GL7 2AG
Map 4: SP00
Tel: 01285 652375
Fax: 01285 641691
Chef: Ed Portlock
Owner: Mark Stephens
Cost: Alc £18.50. ☺ H/wine £8.95
Times: Open all day, last D 10.30pm.
Closed 1st wk Jan
Additional: Sunday L; Children welcome; ❀ dishes
Smoking: No-smoking area

CIRENCESTER, Polo Canteen

29 Sheep Street
GL7 1QW
Map 4: SP00
Tel: 01285 650977
Fax: 01285 642777
Chef: Paul Welch
Owners: Paul & Carol Welch,
Tina & Brian Mussell
Cost: *Alc* £20. ☺ H/wine £9.50
Times: Last L 2pm/last D 10pm.
Closed Sun
Additional: No children under 6mths;
 dishes
Smoking: No-smoking area;
Air conditioning
Credit cards: ▆ ▆ ▆ ▆ ▆ ▆

Cirencester is the polo capital of England and the game lends both name and theme to this pleasant brasserie-style restaurant. Polo originated in India and all the polo bric-a-brac has been imported from there. Otherwise, emphasis on fresh local produce with calves' liver with soy sauce dressing, smoked haddock and salmon risotto, and paillard of chicken, setting the pace.

Directions: Just off Cirencester ring road, opposite Waitrose

CIRENCESTER,
Stratton House Hotel ⊛

A walled garden provides the view from the restaurant of this 17th-century manor house on the edge of town. A balanced menu, about a dozen choices at each stage, might include grilled chicken breast with red wine and wild mushroom sauce, lambs' liver and bacon, and salmon with lime and coriander.

Gloucester Road GL7 2LE
Map 3: SP00
Tel: 01285 651761
Fax: 01285 640024
Chef: Peter Cuss
Owner: Forestdale Hotels Ltd
Cost: Fixed-price D £18.75
Times: D only, last D 10pm

Additional: Bar food; Sunday L (noon-2pm); Children welcome;
⊕ dishes
Smoking: No smoking in dining room
Accommodation: 41 en suite
Credit cards: ▆ ▆ ▆ ▆ ▆ ▆ ▆

Directions: From A419 (Cirencester), take A417 (Gloucester) for 0.5 mile.

CLEARWELL,
Tudor Farmhouse Hotel ⊛

Exposed stonework, oak beams and wall panelling add to the cosy atmosphere in the public rooms at this ancient former farmhouse. Dinner is a set four-course affair with alternative choices from a grill menu. Recent successes include smoked haddock with Welsh rarebit and pink duck breast accompanied by perfectly cooked local vegetables.

Near Coleford GL16 8JS
Map 3: SO50
Tel: 01594 833046
Fax: 01594 837093
Chef: Dean Wassell
Owner: Richard Neil Fletcher
Cost: Fixed-price D £18.95 (4 courses). ☺ H/wine £8.50
Times: D only, last D 9pm. Closed D Sun, 1 wk Xmas
Additional: No children under 6;
⊕ dishes
Smoking: No smoking in dining room

Accommodation: 13 en suite
Credit cards: ▆ ▆ ▆ ▆ ▆ JCB

Directions: Leave Monmouth to Chepstow road at Redbrook, follow signs Clearwell, turn L at village cross, hotel on L

COLN ST ALDWYNS, **New Inn**

Cirencester GL7 5AN
Map 4: SP10
Tel: 01285 750651
Fax: 01285 750657
Chef: Stephen Morey
Owners: Mr & Mrs Brian Evans
Cost: Fixed-price D £26.50. H/wine
£10.50
Times: Noon-last L 2pm/7pm-last
D 9pm
Additional: Bar food; Sunday L;
No children under 10; ◑ dishes
Seats: 36. Private dining room 20
Smoking: No smoking in dining room
Accommodation: 14 en suite
Credit cards: ▬ ▭ ▨ ▢ ▥ ▣

A leading candidate for misnomer of the millennium, this
'new' inn was a period piece when Wren was building St Paul's
Cathedral. Even staunch republicans would applaud Elizabeth
I's decree that every town should have a coaching house, and
there can be few finer legacies than this terrific country inn.
Creature comforts may have been refined but the charm is
undisturbed, and there remains something of the roadside
hostelry welcome about the excellent hospitality. Stephen
Morey's cooking takes its cue from the down-to-earth
ambience, with both bar and restaurant offering honest
cooking that often belies the admirably unfussy descriptions.
Take a Caesar salad with chargrilled swordfish that included
crackling strips of smoked bacon, crunchy leaves and
triumphantly good fish amongst its components. Whilst starters
major on such breezy offerings, main courses include some
weightier options. No-nonsense dishes, such as a lovingly
intense fricassée of guinea fowl, demonstrates that this is a
kitchen where flavour comes first. Casseroled with a treeful of
olives, smoked bacon and provençale herbs, we found the
melting sweet flesh something of a revelation for a sometimes
dry old bird. Punchy desserts keep up the standard with, for
instance, Calvados-scented apples offering an aromatic and
carefully assembled finale.

Directions: 8 miles E of Cirencester between Bibury (B4425)
and Fairford (A417)

FOSSEBRIDGE, **Fossebridge Inn**

A characterful bar, comfortable lounge, and a breakfast room that doubles as an additional dining-room are found at this Cotswold-stone inn with a garden on the River Coln. Start with cauliflower soup perhaps, and go on to salmon and cod fishcake with notable vegetables, and finish with apple and almond tart.

Additional: Bar food; Sunday L; Children welcome; 🍴 dishes
Smoking: No smoking in dining room
Accommodation: 13 en suite
Credit cards: 💳 💳 💳 💳 💳 💳

Directions: On A429 between Cirencester and Northleach

Northleach Cheltenham GL54 3JS
Map 4: SP01
Tel: 01285 720721
Fax: 01285 720793
Chef: Kevin Hanks
Owners: Tim & Caroline Bevan
Cost: Fixed-price D £15.95. ☺
H/wine £8.95
Times: Last L 2.30pm/last D 9.30pm

FRAMPTON-ON-SEVERN,
Restaurant on the Green NEW

An intimate, candlelit restaurant with a Georgian façade looking out, as the name suggests, on to the village green. The evening menu offers about half-a-dozen choices at each stage, beginning with the likes of goats' cheese and spring onion tartlet with tomato salad, seared salmon on a potato galette, and cream of carrot and orange soup. Mains include crispy duck breast with a sour cherry sauce, grilled lemon sole with sorrel butter, and pan-fried fillet of beef with red wine and mushroom sauce and seared potato scallops. Finish with rich chocolate brandy tart, poached pear with lime caramel sauce, or an enjoyable sticky toffee pudding. There's a short list of wines from around the world.

Directions: From J13 of M5 follow A38 towards Bristol. Turn R at Frampton/Saul signpost, continue for 1 mile, L across village green, restaurant at end, on R

The Green GL2 7DY
Map 3: SO70
Tel: 01452 740077
Cost: Fixed price D £23.95.
H/wine £8.50
Times: Noon-last L 1.30pm/7-last D 9.30pm. Closed Sun, Mon, L Tue
Additional: No children under 10; 🍴 dishes
Seats: 26
Smoking: No smoking in dining room
Credit cards: 💳 💳 💳 💳 💳

GLOUCESTER, **Hatton Court**

Views across the Severn Vale are the draw at this comfortably formal restaurant situated in a 17th-century Cotswold manor. Menus take inspiration from around the world with best choices being boudin of chicken with tarragon butter sauce, tian of lamb with aubergine fritters, and rice pud or pear and caramel mousse.

Directions: Three miles from Gloucester on B4037

Upton Hill
Upton St Leonards GL4 8DE
Map 3: SO81
Tel: 01452 617412
Fax: 01452 612945
Chef: Scott Lawrie
Owners: The Hiscox Family
Cost: Alc £28, fixed-price D £22.50. ☺ H/wine £11.50
Times: Last L 2pm/last D 10pm
Additional: Bar food L; Sunday L; Children welcome; 🍴 dishes
Smoking: No smoking in dining room; Air conditioning
Accommodation: 45 en suite
Credit cards: 💳 💳 💳 💳 💳 💳 💳 JCB

LOWER SLAUGHTER,
Lower Slaughter Manor ❀❀❀

The country mansion stands in effortless tranquillity on the edge of Lower Slaughter (an outstanding pretty village even by Cotswold standards). The immaculate stonework bears the mark of the Strong family, later responsible for St Paul's Cathedral. Such highly developed craftsmanship is reflected in the cooking of Alan Dann, whose studied approach is built on classical foundations no doubt developed in his time at the Waterside Inn (see entry, Berkshire). In dishes such as a breathtakingly accurate combination of Cornish lobster with fennel mousseline, Dann proves that precision is well within his grasp. Seismic flavours are far from absent, with a creamy foie gras terrine dramatically cut with an intense compote of fig and white port jelly. Ingredients are top-notch: roasted breast of chicken (of the Bresse variety) is a welcome reminder of the bird's true flavour, and is classically complemented by crispy bacon and a smoked paprika sauce. Desserts are handled with similar good judgement by chef pâtissier Thomas Gauvrit: note a hot raspberry soufflé, perfectly timed, and set off by raspberry ice. The wine list majors on California and there are some fair mark ups to be found, especially when one considers the opulent surroundings.

GL54 2HP
Map 4: SP12
Tel: 01451 820456
Fax: 01451 822150

Chef: Alan Dann

Owners: Roy & Daphne Vaughan
Cost: *Alc* £38, fixed-price L £16 (2 courses)/D £48 (4 courses). H/wine £15
Times: Noon-last L 1.45pm/7.30pm-last D 9.30pm.
Additional: Sunday L;
No children under 10; ❹ dishes
Seats: 30. Private dining room 22. Jacket & tie preferred
Smoking: No smoking in dining room
Accommodation: 15 en suite
Credit cards: ▨ ▨ ▨ ▨ ▨ ▨

Directions: Off A429, signposted 'The Slaughters'. 0.5 miles into village on R

MORETON-IN-MARSH,
Manor House Hotel ❀❀

High Street GL56 0LJ
Map 4: SP23
Tel: 01608 650501
Fax: 01608 651481
Chef: Richard Smith
Owner: Coral Trend Ltd
Cost: *Alc* £28, fixed-price L £12.50/D £24.50. ☺ H/wine £11.95.
Times: Noon-last L 2pm (2.30 Sun)/7pm-last D 9pm
Additional: Sunday L; Bar food L; Children welcome; ❹ dishes
Seats: 60. Private dining room 20-80
Smoking: No smoking in dining room
Accommodation: 39 en suite
Credit cards: ▨ ▨ ▨ ▨ ▨ ▨ ▨

Quality produce and an emphasis on flavour are the hallmarks of the dining room in this 16th-century Cotswold manor house built from the local honey-coloured stone. Don't hesitate to choose the simpler dishes, such as a starter of rabbit and pork terrine served with a celeriac rösti and chunky home-made piccalilli. Of the main courses, braised lamb shank with broad bean sauce is marvellous – a piece of tender, deeply flavoured lamb with an intense, pungent broth. Crisply coated caramelised banana works particularly well as an accompaniment to the zesty orange-flavoured sponge pudding. Our inspector was less keen on the finale of petits fours and the dull bread that started the meal. The wine list is comprehensive, featuring bottles from worlds Old and New, plus over ten well-priced house wines. A good choice of dishes can be found on the Sunday luncheon menu, great value at £12.95 for four courses.

Directions: On main A429 Stow/Stratford Rd; at crossroads with A44 Evesham/Oxford rd

MORETON-IN-MARSH,
Marsh Goose Restaurant ❀❀

Various eating areas are divided by stone walls adorned with large, bold abstracts jostling for space with the odd still life and landscape. The cooking is fresh and bright, and the *carte* is studded with inventive but well-considered ideas and clean flavours; black coffee jelly, for example, is a marvellous invention. Many of the combinations have a vivid, almost Sicilian/Arabic slant: seared sea bass with sweet-and-sour fennel, beetroot and roasted red pepper purée; calves' liver with spiced aubergine purée, balsamic and raisin jus. Others reveal a more Caribbean lilt: breast of duck with roast sweet potato, spiced cashew nuts and mango salsa; saffron fish cakes with peppered spinach and curry mayonnaise. Fillet of brill with green herb risotto and tomato butter sauce was beautifully judged, as was a warm, inviting and crunchy pear and frangipane tart with vanilla ice cream.

High Street GL56 0AX
Map 4: SP23
Tel: 01608 653500
Fax: 01608 653510
Chefs: Sonya Kidney, Matthew Laughton
Owners: Leo Brooke-Little, Sonya Kidney, Gordon Campbell-Gray
Cost: Fixed-price D £26.50. H/wine £10
Times: 12.30-last L 2.30pm/7.30-last D 9pm. Closed D Sun, Mon
Additional: Sunday L; Children welcome; ❸ dishes
Seats: 60.

Smoking: No smoking in dining room
Credit cards: 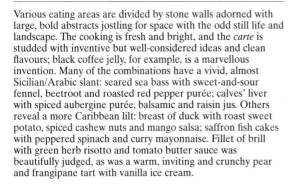 JCB

Directions: In the High Street opposite the war memorial

NAILSWORTH,
Egypt Mill Hotel ❀

Cleverly converted from a 16th-century flour mill, Egypt Mill offers a choice of eating – an informal bar/bistro, and the main restaurant. In the latter, starters such as potted salmon and home-made soup precede the likes of skate wing with tomato salsa, and rack of lamb with rosemary flavoured sauce. Good puds.

Additional: Bar food; Sunday L; Children welcome; ❸ dishes
Smoking: No smoking in dining room
Accommodation: 18 en suite
Credit cards: ▬ ▬ ▬ ▬ ▬ ▬ ▬

Directions: On the A46

GL6 0AE
Map 3: ST89
Tel: 01453 833449
Fax: 01453 836098
Chef: John Sanderson
Owner: Stephen R Webb
Cost: *Alc* £18, fixed-price L £8.45 (2 courses)/D £16.50. ☺
H/wine £8.90
Times: Last L 2pm/last D 9.45pm

NAILSWORTH,
Waterman's Restaurant

Old Market GL6 0BX
Map 3: ST89
Tel: 01453 832808
Chef: Sarah Waterman
Owners: John & Sarah Waterman
Cost: *Alc* £20. ☺ H/wine £8.75
Times: D only, 7-last D 9.45pm.
Closed Sun, Mon
Additional: Bar food; Sat L (noon-last
L 1.45pm); Children welcome;
✿ dishes
Seats: 24. Private dining room 12
Smoking: No-smoking area; No pipes
& cigars
Credit cards: 💳 💳 💳 💳 💳 💳 JCB

If you are over six-feet tall, watch the beams in the Garden
Room – nooks and crannies abound in the 16th-century
Cotswold stone cottage. Wines are carefully chosen and during
the winter there are regular tastings and supper nights. Locally
sourced game is a speciality – venison medallions, for instance,
come with celeriac purée and red onion marmalade. The
cooking is modern but uncluttered: Jerusalem artichoke,
Parmesan and smoked bacon soufflé; rack of lamb with rough
rosemary mash; and walnut tart with caramel sauce, are typical
of the style. Vegetables frequently come from the restaurant's
organic allotment. The 'hidden' courtyard garden, with
fountain and trout stream, is particularly lovely on a warm
summer evening.

Directions: Signposted off A46, in the centre of Nailsworth

NEWENT, # Three Choirs
Vineyards Restaurant

GL18 1LS
Map 3: SO72
Tel: 01531 890223
Fax: 01531 890877
Chef: Antony Warburton
Owners: Three Choirs Vineyards Ltd
Cost: *Alc* L £12 /D £23. ☺
H/wine £7.50

Modern restaurant with exposed brickwork and real fire. Large
picture windows look out over rolling countryside, with rows of
vines in the foreground. Well-done traditional recipes with a
modern twist (mainly Mediterranean) is the underlying theme
behind the cooking. Chargrilled vegetables and rocket salad
with red wine vinaigrette, terrine of ham hock and chicken

livers with home-made chutney, and main courses of roast fillet of cod, lemon mash and chive butter sauce, or loin of venison, spiced roast pear, fresh spinach and port wine sauce are typical choices. Lovely desserts such as pears poached in white wine, and sticky toffee pudding. Short wine list majors, naturally, on the estate wines, all single grape varieties, with some guest reds to make up the shortfall in that area. Prices are very reasonable.

Directions: On B4215, N of Newent

Times: Noon-last L 2.30pm/7-last D 9pm. Closed D Sun-Wed, early Jan
Additional: Children welcome; dishes
Seats: 50. Private dining room 30
Smoking: No smoking in dining room
Credit cards: ▆ ▆ ▆ ▆ ▆

PAINSWICK, **Country Elephant** ❀❀

The building may span the centuries but the dining room is quite minimalist in style, although it lacks nothing in comfort – note high-backed chairs, crisp linen, fresh flowers and, in winter, warming log fires. On the food front chef-patron Robert Rees is maintaining the high standards that have built up a solid reputation for the restaurant over the last few years. Booking is recommended. The emphasis of a sensibly short, monthly-changing menu is on first-rate raw materials used with discretion in well-conceived and satisfying dishes: paillard of moist salmon baked in celery salt and served with a watercress dressing; soufflé Suissesse (which the menu credits to Le Gavroche); a winningly plump Bresse chicken in Sauternes sauce with a wild rice timbale; Cornish cod flaked with truffles and served with parsley potatoes and a wasabi dressing. The wine list, which is full of interest, offers a good selection by the glass, including several dessert wines.

Directions: On the A46 between Stroud and Cheltenham

New Street GL6 6XH
Map 3: SO80
Tel/Fax: 01452 813564
Chef/Owner: Robert Rees
Cost: *Alc* £30, fixed-price D £18. ☺ H/wine £9.60.
Times: Noon-last L 2pm/7pm-last D 10pm. Closed D Sun, Mon, Jan
Additional: Sunday L (special occasions); Children welcome; dishes
Seats: 30
Smoking: No smoking in dining room
Credit cards: ▆ ▆ ▆ ▆ ▆ ▆ ▆ JCB

PAINSWICK, **Painswick Hotel** ❀❀

As Cotswold villages go, Painswick must rank amongst the prettiest. Medieval workers cottage stand shoulder to shoulder with Georgian merchants houses and this Palladian mansion is perched on the edge of the settlement with calming views of the valley beyond. Make an effort to arrive early on a warm evening and an aperitif on the stone balcony or in the well-manicured garden will be an ample reward. In the restaurant generously spaced tables, pale-oak panelling, crisp white cloths and cheerful service add up to a breezy feel, but a glance at the menu is enough to reveal serious intent in the kitchen. A midsummer menu veered between classic France and the

Kemps Lane Stroud GL6 6YB
Map 3: SO80
Tel: 01452 812160
Fax: 01452 814059
Chef: Mark Shelton
Owner: Helen & Gareth Pugh
Cost: *Alc* £30, fixed-price L £13/D £24.50. H/wine £12.50.
Times: 12.30-last L 2pm/D from 7pm
Additional: Sunday L; Children welcome;  dishes
Seats: 60. Private dining room 14
Accommodation: 20 en suite
Credit cards: ▆ ▆ ▆ ▆ ▆ JCB

bright Mediterranean, but with a welcome lightness of touch throughout. Dishes such as rabbit saddle with a roast hazelnut mousse, and a well timed delice of sea bass with saffron butter, are both intelligently composed and skilfully handled. Similar precision is evident in desserts that have included a sturdy pear and almond baked tart with crème anglaise.

Directions: Painswick is on A46, the Stroud/Cheltenham road. The turning into Kemps Lane is near the church

PETTY FRANCE, Petty France Hotel

The pretty walled gardens of this genteel Regency house yield fresh herbs and organic vegetables for the relaxed restaurant. Simple starters and robust main courses feature alongside a good-value wine list. Go for moist roast chicken supreme with potato and celeriac mash and crunchy warm almond and apricot tart.

Additional: Bar food; Sunday L; Children welcome; ❹ dishes
Smoking: No smoking in dining room
Accommodation: 20 en suite
Credit cards: ▆ ▆ ▆ ▆ ▆

Directions: On the A46, 5 miles N of M4/J18

GL9 1AF
Map 3: ST78
Tel: 01454 238361
Fax: 01454 238768
Chef: Jacqui Burton
Owners: W J Fraser, V I Minnich
Cost: *Alc* £23, fixed-price D £17.95.
☺ H/wine £11.95
Times: Last L 1.45pm/last D 9.15pm.
Closed D Sun

RANGEWORTHY,
Rangeworthy Court Hotel

Guests at this creeper-clad 17th-century manor house can enjoy simple, effective country cooking. Expect the likes of roast open mushroom filled with smoked haddock, bacon and onion, and rack of lamb with an almond herb crust with rosemary and mint sauce.

Directions: Signposted off B4058, down Church Lane

Church Lane Wotton Road
BS37 7ND
Map 3: ST68
Tel: 01454 228347
Fax: 01454 228945
Chef: Peter Knight, Andrew Broome
Owners: Lucia & Mervyn Gillett
Cost: *Alc* £23, fixed-price L £9.50. ☺
H/wine £10.50.
Times: Last L 1.45pm/D 9pm (9.30pm Sat)
Additional: Bar food L; Sunday L; Children welcome; ❹ dishes
Smoking: No smoking in dining room
Accommodation: 13 en suite
Credit cards: ▆ ▆ ▆ ▆ ▆ ▆ ▆

STONEHOUSE, Stonehouse Court

This is an exceptional 17th-century Cotswold manor house to suit many occasions. The oak-panelled John Henry restaurant is the setting for sound cooking based on well-sourced local produce and a firm understanding of modern trends. Note dishes such as confit of chicken leg with red onion marmalade and toasted brioche, or sweetbread terrine with spring leaves and grain mustard vinaigrette, main courses of chargrilled

GL10 3RA
Map 3: SO80
Tel: 01453 825155
Fax: 01453 824611
Chef: Martin Osedo
Owner: Pageant Hotels
Cost: *Alc* £30, fixed-price L £12.50/D £24.95. ☺
H/wine £10.50

medallions of pork with linguine, basil, roast chestnuts and peppercorn, or caramelised supreme of duck with beetroot and vanilla vinaigrette. Desserts take in white and dark chocolate terrine with summer berries and a duet of sauces, and caramel-glazed choux buns with Chantilly cream and chocolate sauce.

Directions: M5/J13/A419 (Stroud); 1.5 miles from M-way, 1 mile from Stonehouse

STOW-ON-THE-WOLD, **Fosse Manor**

Lovely, creeper-clad Cotswold-stone manor house set in pleasant gardens. Sound cooking of dishes such as cream of cauliflower and cheese soup, grilled cod with braised mussels and a garlic and garden herb sauce, or baked quails filled with pistachio nut mousse with a redcurrant and port sauce. Short, reasonably priced wine list.

STOW-ON-THE-WOLD,
Grapevine Hotel 🌸🌸

Inspectors rate this light, airy conservatory restaurant with its centrepiece of a century-old gnarled Black Hamburg grapevine. It is set in a charming 17th-century hotel. The kitchen successfully blends the traditional with the modern. On the dinner menu, carpaccio of peppered beef and pickled ginger and soy dressing jostles for attention with timbale of lobster mousse with chargrilled scallops and chive sauce, and roast rack of lamb is served alongside a basil mousse, polenta

---

Times: Noon-last L 1.45pm/7-last D 9.30pm. Closed L Sat
Additional: Bar food L; Sunday L; Children welcome; 🍴 dishes
Seats: 70. Private room 24
Smoking: No smoking in dining room
Accommodation: 36 en suite
Credit cards: ▆▆ 🔤 ≈▇ ⊂ 🔤 J 🔤

Cheltenham GL54 1JX
Map 4: SP12
Tel: 01451 830354
Fax: 01451 832486
Chef: Ted Turner
Owners: Mr & Mrs B Johnston
Cost: *Alc* £25, fixed-price L £15.50/D £25. ☺ H/wine £11.95
Times: Last L 2pm/last D 9pm. Closed 22-29 Dec
Additional: Bar food; Sunday L; Children welcome; 🍴 dishes
Smoking: No smoking in dining room
Accommodation: 17 en suite
Credit cards: ▆▆ 🔤 ≈▇ ⊂ 🔤 J 🔤 JCB

Directions: One mile S of Stow-on-the-Wold on the A429 (Cirencester)

Sheep Street GL54 1AU
Map 4: SP12
Tel: 01451 830344
Fax: 01451 832278
Chef: Adrian Doughty
Owner: Mrs S Elliot
Cost: Fixed-price L £14.95/D £24 (4 courses). ☺ H/wine £10.25
Times: 12.30-last L 2pm/7-last D 9.30pm
Additional: Bar food L; Sunday L; Children welcome; 🍴 dishes
Seats: 60. Private dining room 20
Smoking: No smoking in dining room
Accommodation: 22 en suite
Credit cards: ▆▆ 🔤 ≈▇ ⊂ 🔤 J

and red wine jus, or there is grilled lemon sole meunière with lyonnaise potatoes. Lunch is simpler: potato, goats' cheese and red pepper terrine, pan-fried fillet of salmon with tomato and herb risotto, perhaps bread-and-butter pudding for dessert, from a short choice set menu. The wine list is well chosen and reliable.

Directions: Off Fosseway A429, take A436 Chipping Norton; 150 yards on R facing green

STOW-ON-THE-WOLD,

Old Farmhouse Hotel

Lower Swell GL54 1LF
Map 4: SP12
Tel: 01451 830232
Fax: 01451 870962
Chef: Kena Hawtin
Owner: Erik Burger
Cost: Fixed-price L £9.99/D £17.50.
☺ H/wine £8.95
Times: Last L 2pm/last D 9pm
Additional: Bar food; Sunday L;
Children welcome; ◑ dishes

16th-century listed farmhouse, now a personally run hotel. Good country cooking comes in generous portions with the likes of grilled Barnsley lamb chop with garlic shavings and rosemary jus, baked turkey escalope with a blueberry sauce, and warm Bramley apple slice with cinnamon ice cream, showing the range.

Smoking: No smoking in dining room
Accommodation: 13 en suite
Credit cards: ▬ ▬ ◥ ▢ J JCB

Directions: One mile W of Stow-on-the-Wold, on B4068

STOW-ON-THE-WOLD,

Washbourne Court ❀❀

Lower Slaughter GL54 2HS
Map 4: SP12
Tel: 01451 822143
Fax: 01451 821045

Chef: Kevin Barron

Cost: *Alc* £40, fixed-price L £18
(4 courses)
Times: 12.30pm-last L 2pm/7.30pm-last D 9pm (9.30pm weekends)
Additional: Bar meals L; Sunday L;
◑ dishes
Seats: 60. Private dining room 12.
Jacket & tie preferred
Smoking: No smoking in dining room
Accommodation: 28 en suite
Credit cards: ▬ ▬ ◥ ▢ ▬ ▣ ▣ JCB

The setting, alongside the River Eye is magnificent, but then so is the house: a splendid 17th-century mansion built in honey-coloured Cotswold stone. There's an English country feel to the public rooms, especially in the formal restaurant with its chintz-covered chairs and Wedgwood crockery. Nothing retro about the kitchen however, it is firmly up to date, producing outstanding modern English cooking Sliced roast guinea fowl atop foie gras on a crisp bread croûton with a delicious salsa of trompet, black truffle and red wine vinegar, lamb cutlets wrapped in caul and filled with chicken and basil mousse, and a cherry-chocolate soufflé with chocolate straw, a tuile basket of coconut ice cream and plum purée, show what the kitchen is about.

Directions: Off A429 village centre by the river

STOW-ON-THE-WOLD,

Wyck Hill House Hotel ❀❀

Delightful 18th-century house which enjoys superb views across the Windrush Valley. Although most of the first courses are easy-to-assemble affairs, Parma ham with Caesar salad, for instance, or local oak-smoked salmon with lime and chive cream, and Thai-style marinated mackerel with avocado and red pepper salad, they rely on the outstanding quality of the produce for effect. A good choice of main courses ranges from straightforward grilled cutlets of English lamb with home-made apple and mint jelly, to roast monkfish tail scented with ginger and five spice served on stir-fried vegetables and a sweet-and-sour sauce. All dishes come with fresh vegetables, such as green beans, ratatouille and dauphinoise potatoes. Desserts are worth leaving space for, with hot passion fruit soufflé, rich dark chocolate tart, iced toffee apple parfait with cinnamon shortbread, among the sweet temptations.

Directions: A424 (Burford) 1.5 miles from Stow

Burford Road GL54 1HY
Map 4: SP12
Tel: 01451 831936
Fax: 01451 832243
Chef: Ian Smith
Owner: Lyric Hotels
Cost: Fixed-price L £14.95/D £32.50. H/wine £14.95
Times: 12.30-last L 2pm/7-last D 9.30pm
Additional: Bar food L; Sunday L; Children welcome; ♦ dishes
Seats: 60. Private dining room 40. Jacket & tie preferred
Smoking: No smoking in dining room; Air conditioning
Accommodation: 30 en suite
Credit cards: ▆ ▆ ▆ ▆ ▆ ▆

STROUD,

Burleigh Court ❀

A relaxed 18th-century manor house in a tranquil setting surrounded by several acres of landscaped gardens. In the dining room a balanced menu, supplemented by daily specials, might include chargrilled vegetables with sun-dried tomato bread, quails' eggs Florentine, chicken saltimbocca with Madeira sauce, and rack of lamb with roasted onion and red wine sauce.

Additional: Bar food; Sunday L; Children welcome; ♦ dishes
Smoking: No smoking in dining room
Accommodation: 17 en suite
Credit cards: ▆ ▆ ▆ ▆ ▆ ▆ JCB

Directions: Telephone for directions

Minchinhampton GL5 2PF
Map 3: SO80
Tel: 01453 883804
Fax: 01453 886870
Chef: Chris Perkins
Owners: Ian & Fiona Hall
Cost: Fixed-price L £17.50/D £22.50. ☺ H/wine £10
Times: Last L 1.45pm/ last D 8.45pm. Closed D Sun

STROUD,

Bear of Rodborough ❀

A native of Rodborough Common, this well-known Bear has benefited from some sprucing up in recent months. The kitchen receives every encouragement to make the most of the local Cotswold bounty, and a long list of local cheeses is a welcome sight. Cooking is not over ambitious, but hits the spot in thoughtful dishes such as breast of steamed chicken stuffed with game pâté and accompanied by a chunky ratatouille.

Additional: Bar food; Sunday L; Children welcome; ♦ dishes
Smoking: No smoking in dining room
Accommodation: 46 en suite
Credit cards: ▆ ▆ ▆ ▆ ▆ ▆

Directions: From M5 J13 follow signs for Stonehouse then Rodborough

Rodborough Common GL5 5DE
Map 3: SO80
Tel: 01453 878522
Fax: 01453 872523
Chef: Michael Rooke
Owner: Cotswold Inns & Hotels
Cost: Alc L £19, fixed-price D £19.95. ☺ H/wine £9.75
Times: Last L 2pm/last D 9.15pm. Closed L Sat

STROUD, Fischers ❀❀

NEW

In an area liberally sprinkled with good places to eat, Stroud has been less well served that many of it's near neighbours. Over the years, this stone-built roadside house, has ploughed a relatively lonely furrow, first as Oakes, briefly as the Ivy, and now as the self-titled venture of the Fischer family. An established chef himself, Stephen Fischer has forsaken the stove in favour of dispensing bonhomie and enthusiastic advice front of house, but still oversees a menu which combines enterprise with accurate execution. Lunch offers a good value two or three course table d'hôte which might feature a liberal niçoise salad with seared tuna or smoked haddock risotto with a poached egg as ample starters. In a selection of sturdy main courses an intense confit leg of duck with a rich garlic sauce has found particular favour and an elaborately decorated chocolate fondant with pistachio ice cream offered some excellent flavours amongst the frippery.

Directions: From M5.J13 make for Cheltenham on Stroud ring road. At last roundabout turn R, then 1st L into Slad Rd

169 Slad Road GL5 1RG
Map 3: SO80
Tel: 01453 759950
Chef: Ben Glassonbury
Owners: Stephen & Jacqueline Fischer
Cost: *Alc* £29, fixed-price L £14.85. H/wine £10
Times: Noon-last L 2pm/7-last D 9.30pm. Closed D Sun, all Mon
Additional: Sunday L; No children under 6; ◑ dishes
Seats: 30
Smoking: No smoking in dining room
Credit cards: ▆ ▆ ▆ ▆ ▆

TETBURY,
Calcot Manor ❀❀

Calcot GL8 8YJ
Map 3: ST89
Tel: 01666 890391
Fax: 01666 890394
Chef: Michael Croft
Cost: *Alc* £26, fixed price L £12.50 (2 courses). ☺
Times: Noon-last L 2.30pm/7-last D 9.30pm
Additional: Bar food; Sunday L; Children welcome; ◑ dishes
Seats: 75. Private dining rooms 25
Smoking: No smoking in dining room
Accommodation: 27 en suite
Credit cards: ▆ ▆ ▆ ▆ ▆ ▆

Log fires, flagstone floors and exposed beams help bolster the country-house feel of Calcot Manor (it was once, after all, a farmhouse), but there's also a breezy informality about the place. Nowhere is this more apparent than in the restaurant, which now benefits from a bright conservatory extension. Punchy flavours in well-judged combinations, and much chargrilling, are to be found on the Mediterranean-influenced menu. At a test meal, a starter of seared tuna worked well with chargrilled vegetables. Roasted pork confit – pleasingly crispy, if a little overcooked – was enhanced by a dark and pungent Puy lentil, bacon and shallot sauce . Chargrilling even extends to desserts, which can include still-smouldering pineapple with in-house ice cream. Wines are from around the world, with several available in half-bottles. Well-marshalled service is dispensed by cheery, often French staff in bistro style.

Directions: 4 miles W of Tetbury on A4135 close to intersection with A45

TETBURY, Snooty Fox ❀

Market Place GL8 8DD
Map 3: ST89
Tel: 01666 502436
Fax: 01666 503479
Chef: Stephen Woodcock
Owner: Carlos Alfaro
Cost: *Alc* £19.95, fixed-price L £12.
☺ H/wine £9.95
Times: Last L 2pm/last D 9.30pm
Additional: Bar food; Sunday L;
Children welcome; ❹ dishes
Smoking: No smoking in dining room
Accommodation: 12 en suite
Credit cards: ▬ ▦ ✂ ▢ ▦ ◖ ▣ JCB

Directions: Town centre opposite the
Market Place

A relaxed atmosphere and good value are both to be found at this attractive former coaching inn. Whilst lunch brings a good snack range, it is dinner that earns the Rosette for unpretentious cooking from a carte that offers plenty of choice. Delicious crusty bread and creamy fudge are tasty home-made extras.

THORNBURY,
Thornbury Castle Hotel ❀❀❀

Castle Street BS12 1HH
Map 3: ST69
Tel: 01454 281182
Fax: 01454 416188
Chef: Steven Black
Owner: The Baron of Portlethen &
family
Cost: Fixed-price L £18.50/D £34.50.
H/wine £12
Times: Noon-2pm/7-10pm.
Closed 4 days Jan
Additional: Sunday L; No children
under 12; ❹ dishes
Seats: 60. Private dining rooms 14, 20
& 28. Jacket & tie preferred
Smoking: No smoking in dining room
Accommodation: 20 en suite
Credit cards: ▬ ▦ ✂ ▢ ▦ ◖ ▣

Abandoned, half-built in 1521, as a result of the untimely demise of its founder, the 3rd Duke of Buckingham, there is a sense in which this magnificent castle remains a work in progress. Since 1986, the Baron Portlethen has been an enterprising custodian, steadily creating a fine country house, unique in its adherence to the Tudor tradition. In such faithfully created medieval surroundings, an expectation of unruly banqueting could be forgiven, but potential wassailers will be disappointed. However, food is an important pillar of the whole operation. Stephen Black cooks with meticulous attention to detail, and most dishes are a marriage of several, carefully honed elements, with stuffing, parcelling and crusting being favoured techniques. In the wrong hands, this could be fractious cooking, but the approach is confident and assured, combinations are unfailingly intelligent and sensibly based on twists of classic couplings. If there's a fault, it is the occasional duplication of ingredients – one Saturday night, balsamic reduction featured in both seared king scallops on tomato

fondue topped with 'rockette' salad, and loin of lamb with aubergine caviar, fondant potato and red pepper jus. Goats' cheese wrapped in filo could not be described as cutting edge, but here it came deep-fried, pleasingly pungent and accompanied by a lively, baked vegetable salad. Flavours are up front with, for instance, a fat fillet of grilled brill being a brilliantly seasoned match for a bright tomato fondue and verdant basil mash. New life was breathed into that old favourite, treacle tart, sensibly adorned with nothing more complicated than the finest clotted cream. As well as the classical gardens, the grounds include the castle's own vineyards and the resultant Müller-Thürgau.

Directions: At bottom of High Street turn left into Castle Street. The entrance is to left of St. Mary's Church

UPPER SLAUGHTER,

Lords of the Manor ❀❀❀

GL54 2JD
Map 4: SP12
Tel: 01451 820243
Fax: 01451 820696
Chef: John Campbell
Cost: *Alc* £40, fixed-price L £19.95/D £32.50. H/wine £14.95
Times: L at 12.30pm/7-last D 9.30pm
Additional: Bar food L; Sunday L; No children under 7; ❹ dishes
Seats: 60. Conservatory 20. Jacket & tie preferred
Smoking: No smoking in dining room
Accommodation: 27 en suite
Credit cards: ▆▆ ▆▆ ▆▆ ▆ ▆▆ ▆ JCB

Last year we reported on the early promise of new chef John Campbell who had just taken up the sabatiers following a change of ownership. This year we can confirm that our initial impressions were well founded, with the new team now well settled into this immaculate Cotswold house. The surroundings are faithful to the grand country house tradition, with extravagant grounds that offer an ideal setting for aperitifs. Menu descriptions are of the franglais variety, which is a fair pointer to the classic French and modern British influences that pretty much sum up the style. The approach is not over prissy, with baking and roasting favoured techniques throughout. Dishes are substantial and often robust, with a bright artichoke risotto, for instance, coming with crisp Parma ham, béarnaise, and a poached egg. Puréed vegetables and pulse-based sauces make regular appearances with a garden-pea mash a well-matched partner for a thick fillet of baked turbot, and pot-roast rabbit being served with a lentil sauce. Desserts are equally forthright, especially a steamy warm chocolate fondant of irresistible example. The six-course dégustation menu is the kitchen's chance to show off its capabilities and includes an assiette gourmande of desserts. Those of stout constitution can take advantage of a well kept, entirely British cheeseboard.

Directions: Follow sign towards The Slaughters off A429. The restaurant is in centre of Upper Slaughter

WINCHCOMBE, **Wesley House** ✿✿

High Street GL54 5LT
Map 4: SP02
Tel: 01242 602366
Fax: 01242 602405
Chef: Jonathan Lewis
Owners: Jonathan Lewis,
Matthew Brown
Cost: Fixed-price L £16.50/D £28.50.
H/wine £11.50
Times: Noon-2pm/7-9pm. Closed
D Sun, 14 Jan-14 Feb
Additional: Bar food L; Sunday L;
Children welcome; ❹ dishes
Seats: 55
Smoking: No smoking in dining room
Accommodation: 6 en suite
Credit cards: 🔲 🔲 🔲 🔲 🔲 🔲

The split-level, half-timbered restaurant has become even
more child-friendly since the owner become the father of
twins. Parents can expect to pampered too with saffron soup
served with mussels and garnished with ravioli of celeriac and
ginger, and pan-fried breast of guinea fowl accompanied by
spiced plum chutney. Fresh Cornish crab is sensibly and simply
served with salad leaves and coriander dressing; more
extensive preparation goes into a slow-roast belly of pork with
black beans and ginger on garlic mash. Layers of white and
dark chocolate mousse on coffee sauce, and Tatin of pears with
caramel sauce and Amaretto ice cream will meet the approval
of everyone.

Directions: In the centre of Winchcombe on the main road

GREATER MANCHESTER

ALTRINCHAM, **Bowdon Hotel** ✿

Langham Road Bowdon
WA14 2HT
Map 7: SJ78
Tel: 0161 9287121
Fax: 0161 9277560
Chef: Robert Conway
Owners: Lyric Hotels
Cost: Alc £27, fixed-price L £7.25 (2
courses)/D £17.95. ☺ H/wine £11.50
Times: Last L 2pm/last D 9.45pm.
Closed L Sat
Additional: Bar food; Sunday L;
Children welcome; ❹ dishes
Smoking: No-smoking area; Air
conditioning
Accommodation: 89 en suite
Credit cards: 🔲 🔲 🔲 🔲

*A converted Victorian house handy for M56/J7 and Manchester
airport. Guests can eat either in the stylish Café Continental, which
serves light snacks all day, or in Expressions, an elegant dining room
serving modern English dishes such as pan-fried lamb with roasted
shallots, potato mash and garlic.*

Directions: Leave M56/J7
(Altrincham). At large roundabout
take 3rd exit (Altrincham); at next
traffic lights turn R into Park Rd.
Hotel 1 mile on R

ALTRINCHAM, Juniper ❀❀❀

21 The Downs WA14 2QD
Map 7: SJ78
Tel: 0161 9294008
Fax: 0161 9294009
Chef: Paul Kitching
Owners: Nora & Peter Miles
Cost: *Alc* £32.50, fixed-price L £22.
H/wine £15
Times: Noon-last L 2.30pm/7pm-last
D 10pm. Closed L Sat, Sun, L Mon,
Bhs
Additional: Children welcome
Seats: 50. Private dining room 14
Smoking: No pipes and cigars;
Air conditioning
Credit cards: 💳 💳 💳 💳 💳 💳

Directions: A556 Chester-Manchester
Rd

Juniper is a small but classy restaurant in the busy centre of
Altrincham; its decor makes much use of wood and greenery
and the style is best described as modern simplicity. Menus are
short, with three choices for each course. At inspection, a frothy
cappuccino of truffled chicken broth proved a good introduction
to Paul Kitching's undoubted talent, only just out-paced by a
courgette parfait, spot-on for innovative flavour and texture.
Kitching has a brilliant, sharply-honed eye for presentation, and
a main course of chicken did not disappoint. The bird, cut into
three, with three pools of purée, black pudding and 'lego bricks'
of carrot and swede, was bursting with flavour. Other dishes in
the repertoire might include roast fillet of Scottish beef with
truffle, saffron and onion purée, grilled codling with sautéed
courgette, noodles, morels and Madeira, and roast breast of
duck with a tian of Mediterranean vegetables. Details impress –
special sorbet made from the house champagne (Marie
Demets), home-made breads, strong coffee, and excellent petits
fours. But it is the soufflés that are to die for, especially the
passion fruit with honey ice cream – although the special
tiramisu, or perfect glazed lemon tart with citrus fruit, have their
champions. The wine list is good value for money, easy to read
and understand, and mercifully lacking in flowery descriptions.
   Signature dishes: Cornish lobster bisque; individual glazed
lemon tart; white truffle and noodle bouillon; Juniper's special
coq au vin

ALTRINCHAM,
Woodland Park Hotel ❀

Wellington Road Timperley
WA15 7RG
Map 7: SJ78
Tel: 0161 9288631
Fax: 0161 9412821
Chef: Jeff Spencer
Owners: Brian & Shirley Walker
Cost: *Alc* £26.50, fixed-price
L&D £14.95 (2 courses). ☺
H/wine £10.95
Times: Last L 1.55pm/last D 9.55pm.
Closed Sat L, Sun D
Additional: Bar Food L;
Children welcome; 🍽 dishes
Smoking: No smoking in dining room;
Air conditioning

Country house hotel set in a residential area of Altrincham. Good variety from a sensible, short menu. At a test meal, crisp, full flavoured fishcakes with a creamy Dijon sauce were followed by corn-fed chicken with Puy lentils, with strawberry mille-feuille to finish.

Directions: 300 yds from Metro-Link Station – Navigation Road

Accommodation: 46 en suite
Credit cards: ▉ ▉ ▉ ▉ ▉ ▉ JCB

BOLTON, Egerton House Hotel ✤

The heart of this sympathetically extended hotel is an 18th-century mansion. It stands in woodlands and neat gardens 3 miles north of Bolton. Expect sound British cooking with local items such as salad of Lancashire black pudding, or rillettes of Goosnargh duck. Fillet of baby halibut comes toasted with Welsh rarebit. Service is professional and efficient.

Directions: Hotel 3.5 miles N of Bolton on A666, in Egerton village

Blackburn Road Egerton BL7 9PL
Map 7: SD70
Tel: 01204 307171
Please telephone for further details

BURY, Normandie Hotel ✤✤✤

Standing on a hill, at the end of a winding lane, this popular north-west hotel offers stunning views over the Manchester connurbation. Paul Bellingham cooks in a robust style, one that allows natural flavours to shine through. Dishes such as butter bean soup with spicy chorizo ravioli, and loin of lamb and liver, served, pink, with chive and smoked bacon potatoes, exemplify the style well. Although the repertoire is based on tried and trusted combinations, rather than being adventurous, there are some inspired pairings: terrine of mackerel, smoked haddock, sardine and potato with tapenade dressing, for example, or a roast fillet of brill with a vanilla and lemon dressing. An autumn test meal opened with fillet of red bream, cooked just to the point with moist, translucent flesh and a 'slightly crunchy outer', served on a type of fine ratatouille that had a surprisingly delicate but nicely flavoured red pepper sauce. Its counterpart was a good potato and sorrel soup topped with shredded sorrel and truffle oil. Then came tender braised shoulder of lamb served with a subtly flavoured, smooth garlic mash, and a well-flavoured fillet of Scottish beef (sourced through a local butcher) had an onion and thyme sauce. Iced cinnamon parfait (made using an Italian meringue technique rather than cream) was delicately flavoured, and served with pears properly poached in red wine. Raspberry soufflé, including whole raspberries, came with a champagne sorbet.

Elbut Lane Birtle BL9 6UT
Map 7: SD81
Tel: 0161 7643869/1170
Fax: 0161 7644866
Chef: Paul Bellingham
Owners: Max & Susan Moussa
Cost: *Alc* £25, fixed-price
L £12.50/D £15. ☺ H/wine £9.95.
Times: Noon-last L 2pm/7-last
D 9.30pm. Closed L Sat, Sun, 1 wk
Easter, last wk Dec, 1st wk Jan
Additional: Children welcome;
♦ dishes
Seats: 50
Smoking: No pipes and cigars in
dining room
Accommodation: 23 en suite
Credit cards: ▉ ▉ ▉ ▉ ▉ ▉

Directions: From M66/J2, take A58 –
Bury. After 100yds turn R into Wash
Lane, then 1st R into Willow Street,
R at B6222. After 1 mile L into Elbut
Lane, then up hill 1 mile

MANCHESTER,
Copthorne Manchester ✤

Chandlers restaurant overlooks the waterfront at this modern brick-built hotel on Salford Quays. Starters might include smoked salmon pancake mille-feuille with poached quail's egg and hollandaise sauce. Dishes such as oven roasted Chateaubriand and fresh Dover sole are carved or cooked at table.

Accommodation: 166 en suite
Credit cards: ▉ ▉ ▉ ▉ ▉

Directions: Close to M602

Clippers Quay Salford Quays M5 2XP
Map 7: SJ89
Tel: 0161 8737321
Fax: 0161 8737318
Chef: Ken Tait
Cost: *Alc* £31.50, fixed price L&D
£31.50. ☺ H/wine £13.95
Times: Last L 2.15pm/last D 10.15pm.
Closed L Sat, all Sun
Additional: Bar food L; Children
welcome; ♦ dishes
Smoking: Air conditioning

MANCHESTER,
Midland Crowne Plaza

Peter Street M60 2DS
Map 7: SJ89
Tel: 0161 2363333
Fax: 0161 9324100
Chef: Paul Reed
Cost: *Alc* £40, fixed price D £32.50
(4 courses). H/wine £12.95
Times: D only 7-last D 10.30pm.
Closed Sun
Additional: Children welcome;
❹ dishes
Smoking: No-smoking area;
Air conditioning
Accommodation: 303 en suite
Credit cards:  JCB

No rosettes this year as Paul Reed, AA three Rosetted chef
from the Chester Grosvenor (see entry), took up the position
of executive chef too late for us to assess fairly. However, the
period Edwardian architecture remains as grand as ever,
reflected throughout the hotel including the French
Restaurant, where wood panelling and marble create an
elegant ambience. One to watch.

Directions: City centre, opposite Central Reference Library and
adjacent to G-Mex Centre and Bridgewater Hall

MANCHESTER,
Little Yang Sing ❀

*Now in modern, bright attire, this lower-ground-floor Chinatown
restaurant attracts shoppers and business folk. The extensive menu
includes tender fried sliced duck with winter bamboo shoots in
oyster sauce, and is also notable for dim sum and vegetarian dishes,
stir-fried yam with garlic in spicy sauce, for instance.*

17 George Street M1 4HE
Map 7: SJ89
Tel: 0161 2287722
Fax: 0161 2379257
Chef: Jeff Choi
Owners: LYS Ltd
Cost: *Alc* £18, fixed-price L £10/D
£16.50. ☺ H/wine £11
Times: Noon-last D 11.30pm.
Closed 25 Dec

Additional: Children welcome; ❹ dishes
Smoking: No-smoking area; No pipes and cigars
Credit cards:

Directions: Behind Piccadilly Plaza on the corner of George &
Charlotte Street, on Metrolink route

MANCHESTER,
Manchester Airport Hilton ❀ NEW

*Next time you're waiting for a flight, nip into the Portico restaurant
in the Hilton's airport hotel and enjoy a meal from a good range of
Mediterranean choices. This small but smart restaurant makes
excellent use of fresh produce. Expect a full-bodied langoustine
cappuccino, and fragrant Moroccan spiced poussin with fruity
couscous.*

Outwood Lane Ringway M90 4WP
Map 7: SJ89
Tel: 0161 4353000
Fax: 0161 4353040
Please telephone for further details

MANCHESTER, **Market Restaurant**

104 High Street M4 1HQ
Map 7: SJ89
Tel: 0161 8343743
Chefs: Mary-Rose Edgecombe,
Paul Mertz
Owners: Peter O'Grady, Anne
O'Grady, Mary-Rose Edgecombe
Cost: Alc £24. ☺ H/wine £5.95
Times: D only, 6-last D 9.30pm.
Closed Sun, Mon, Tue, 1 wk
Xmas/Easter, most of Aug
Additional: Children welcome;
❸ dishes
Seats: 48. Private dining room 20
Smoking: No pipes & cigars in dining
room; Air conditioning
Credit cards: 🔲 🔲 🔲 🔲 🔲 🔲 🔲 JCB

Old sewing machines form the bases for tables, house wine is served in antique milk bottles, period posters exhort the consumption of more fruit and veg, in other words the Market is idiosyncratic, with an atmosphere that is both unpretentious and informal. Tables are closely spaced – fun when full, but not the place for intimate confidences. The menu is a complete mix of, say, potted kippers to Georgian kidney bean salad, with Barbary duck with Szechuan peppers thrown in for good measure. Laab, a Thai hot-and-sour beef salad was a nice blend of flavours, while fillets of salmon with a herb crust on braised aubergines with a sweet and slightly hot red pepper dressing, was based on a dish from Sydney's Rock Pool. Chocolate and cherry rum trifle and Sussex pond pudding, are Pudding Club favourites.

Directions: On the corner of Edge St and High St, close to Craft Village. Nearest Metro station – High St

MANCHESTER, **Mash & Air** ❀❀

The proof of the pudding is that London now has its own Mash, for once proving the old adage that what Manchester does today, London does tomorrow! On that basis, expect terrine of sweet potato and Rosary goats' cheese with cherry balsamic dressing, and Barbary duck spring roll with melon mizuna and rucola salad to hit the capital next. Fish is given particularly interesting treatment in the midnight blue and chrome top-floor 'Air' restaurant, centred around the orange neon-lit in-house microbrewry: seared blue-fin tuna is served with new potato and feves salad and mint pesto, and oven-roasted West Coast cod with snow pea and fennel salad with celeriac remoulade. Down below, 'Mash' continues to pack 'em in with wood-fired pizzas and smart salads.

40 Chorlton Street M1 3HW
Map 7: SJ89
Tel: 0161 6616161
Fax: 0161 6616060
Chef: Jason Whitelock
Owner: Oliver Peyton
Cost: Alc £18. ☺
Times: Noon-last D 11.15pm.
Closed 25 Dec
Additional: Bar food; Sunday Brunch;
Children welcome; ❸ dishes
Seats: 120. Private dining room 8
Credit cards: 🔲 🔲 🔲 🔲 🔲 🔲

Directions: City centre on corner of Chorlton Street/Canal Street

MANCHESTER,
Moss Nook Restaurant ❀❀

Long-established restaurant improbably located next to the runway at Manchester Airport (effective secondary glazing keeps any noise at bay). Inside the red plush interior is opulent

Ringway Road M22 5WD
Map 7: SJ89
Tel: 0161 4374778
Fax: 0161 4988089
Chef: Kevin Lofthouse

in traditional style with mirrors, lace tablecloths, Tiffany lamps, and much crystal and silverware. Based on good quality raw materials, the menu relies largely on tried and trusted combinations: pan-fried scallops with deep fried cabbage on a red pepper coulis; melon with mango, papaya and fruit coulis; grilled loin of lamb with basil and tomato; venison with a timbale of wild mushrooms and a red wine sauce. If you would rather leave the choice to long-serving chef Kevin Lofthouse, go for the Menu Surprise (five courses at lunch, seven at dinner – for whole tables only). Hot apple bake, chocolate and chestnut parfait, and toffee and nut tart typify the desserts. The wine list lacks tasting notes but you are encouraged to ask for help and advice.

Directions: Close to Manchester Airport – at junction of Ringway with B5166

Owners: Derek & Pauline Harrison
Cost: *Alc* £37, fixed-price L £16.95 (5 courses)/D £29.95 (7 courses). H/wine £9.50
Times: Noon-last L 1.30pm/7pm-last D 9.30 pm. Closed L Sat, Sun, Mon, 2 weeks Xmas
Additional: No children under 12; ✎ dishes
Seats: 65
Accommodation: One bedroom cottage
Credit cards: ▆▆ ▆▆ 🐾 ▆▆

MANCHESTER,

New Emperor ✸

Large, spacious and always busy and bustling, the restaurant has a more contemporary look than many of its competitors. It also serves better food than most. Try the excellent dim sum, sliced duck with winter bamboo shoots and richly satisfying casseroled bean curd with shredded pork.

Directions: Heart of Chinatown, near Manchester Piccadilly

52-56 George Street M1
Map 7: SJ89
Tel: 0161 2282883
Fax: 0161 2286620
Chef: Tommy Chan
Owner: Johnny Lee
Cost: *Alc* £15, fixed-price L from £3.80/D £15.50 (5 courses). ☺ H/wine £9.90
Times: Noon-midnight
Additional: Children welcome; ✎ dishes
Smoking: Air conditioning
Credit cards: ▆▆ ▆▆ 🐾 ⌑ ▆▆ 🄲 ▆▆

MANCHESTER,

The Thistle Portland ✸

City-centre hotel, converted from a warehouse, with professional and attentive service. There's a brasserie menu in Winston's Restaurant, an alternative to the more formal carte that majors in modern English cooking, (also a lunchtime carvery, cold table and dessert trolley, all fresh and attractively displayed). Lighter meals are served in Mr Manchester's Bar.

Additional: Bar food L; Children welcome; ✎ dishes
Smoking: No-smoking area; No pipes; Air conditioning
Accommodation: 205 en suite
Credit cards: ▆▆ ▆▆ 🐾 ⌑ ▆▆ 🄲 ▆▆

Directions: Opposite Piccadilly Gardens

3-5 Portland Street M1 6DP
Map 7: SJ89
Tel: 0161 2283400
Fax: 0161 2286347
Chef: Neil Riley
Owner: Thistle Hotels
Cost: *Alc* £25. ☺ H/wine £11.50
Times: Last L 1.45pm/last D 10.15pm

MANCHESTER,
Simply Heathcotes 🏵🏵

Jacksons Row
Deansgate M2 3WD
Map 7: SJ89
Tel: 0161 8353536
Fax: 0161 8353534
Chef: Max Gnoyke
Owner: Paul Heathcote
Cost: *Alc* £22.50, fixed-price L
£11.50/D £18.50. ☺ H/wine £10.75
Times: 11.45am-last L 2.30pm/6-last
D 11pm. Closed 25-26 Dec, 1 Jan
Additional: Bar food L; Sunday L;
Children welcome; 🌢 dishes
Smoking: No pipes & cigars; Air
conditioning
Credit cards: 🔳 🔳 💳 🔳 🔳

City slick and brightly lit, Paul Heathcote's Manchester branch gives modern European brasserie food a regional spin in dishes such as green pea soup with black pudding croûtons, and Heathcote's 'Ploughman's terrine' with sweet pickle dressing and potato chips. Most of the menu, however, is pan-European: daube of beef braised with lemons and paprika baked potatoes; lasagne of caponata with pepper coulis and Parmesan tuile; iced nougatine parfait with Kirsch cherries. Clever ideas include potted salmon niçoise and roast breast of Goosnargh duckling with Asian duck consommé. Although ginger cream with lime leaf sorbet and biscotti tempts, it's always hard to resist the signature bread-and-butter pudding.

Directions: M62/J17. Restaurant at the top end of Deansgate

MANCHESTER, **Le Meridien**
Victoria & Albert Hotel 🏵🏵

Theming is infectious at Granada's warehouse hotel that uses TV motifs in its decor. The Sherlock Holmes Restaurant eschews British cooking for more global influences. Aspirations are high – pan-seared sea bass with chargrilled polenta, caponata of seafood, saffron vanilla liquor, roasted duckling with ballotine of leg, pithiviers of livers and griottine jus – but there's a wilful obscurantism in the descriptions and ingredients i.e. lobster rice condé with guana and red pepper dressing. Crab and aubergine tian, with citrus herb infusion looked good, but lacked flavour. Risotto of forest fruits, roasted quail and essence of Madeira hit the spot, and baked turbot on a bed of potato with crab tuiles, had good fish. Coconut and lime cheesecake, cinnamon biscuit and chocolate 'palms' for dessert.

Directions: Head for city centre and follow signs for Granada Studio Tours. Hotel is opposite

Water Street M60 9EA
Map 7: SJ89
Tel: 0161 8321188
Fax: 0161 8342484
Chef: Paul Patterson
Cost: *Alc* £34
Times: D only, 5.30pm-last
D 9.30pm. Closed Sun
Additional: Sunday L;
Children welcome; 🌢 menu
Seats: 50. Private dining room 50
Smoking: No-smoking area;
Air conditioning
Accommodation: 156 en suite
Credit cards: 🔳 🔳 💳 🔳 🔳 🔳 🔳

MANCHESTER, Yang Sing 🌑🌑

Just before Christmas 1997, the famous Yang Sing at 34 Princess Street burned down. Temporary premises have now been set up in nearby Charlotte Street in a building that gives them three floors (including one for banqueting), while the Princess Street site is being rebuilt. Staff were still settling in when we called. They are offering a similar menu and we tried dim sum consisting of steamed beef and ginger with spring onion, Cantonese spring roll, and crabmeat and prawn parcel. Stewed beancurd came with black mushrooms, bok choi and shredded pork, there was full-flavoured barbecued roast duck, and sliced beef with straw mushrooms and sliced carrots. We recommend telephoning for details.

Charlotte Street
(34 Princess Street M1 4JY)
Map 7: SJ89
Tel: 0161 2362200
Fax: 0161 2365934
Chef: Harry Yeung

MANCHESTER AIRPORT,
Bowdon Hotel 🌑

See under Altrincham

MANCHESTER AIRPORT,
Etrop Grange Hotel 🌑🌑

Thorley Lane M90 4EG
Map 7: SJ88
Tel: 0161 4990500
Fax: 0161 4990790
Chef: Hamish Deas
Owner: Regal Hotels
Cost: Fixed-price L £16.50/ D £29.75.
H/wine £11.95
Times: Noon-last L 2pm/7-last
D 10pm. Closed L Sat
Additional: Bar food ; Sunday L;
Children welcome; 🍴 dishes
Seats: 50. Private dining room 6-90
Smoking: No smoking in dining room
Accommodation: 64 en suite
Credit cards:  JCB

Etrop Grange is not your usual run-of-the-mill airport hotel; despite the fact it is only a half-mile from the airport, the Georgian building retains an air of elegant seclusion (as long as you ignore the council estate lapping at the perimeter). A comprehensive dinner menu caters for jet-lagged MDs and newlyweds alike, with main courses such as fillet of salmon baked with a herb and breadcrumb crust with watercress purée, and calves liver, pan-fried pink with a gin and juniper berry sauce and a rissole of bubble and squeak. Vegetarians can choose wild mushrooms, shallots and cream baked in filo pastry with Brandy cream sauce. No self-respecting Northern restaurant can be without its sticky toffee pudding – here served with traditional custard sauce.

Directions: Off M56/J5. At main airport roundabout, take
1st L (to Terminal 2), then 1st R (Thorley Lane), 200yds on R

OLDHAM, **Hotel Smokies Park**

*Modern hotel with an Italian accent to the Cosi Fan Tutti restaurant.
Standard menu of popular trattoria fare that takes in saltimboca alla
romana, filetto Rossini, bistecca Diana, as well as risotto, pasta and
pizza.*

Additional: Sunday L; Children welcome; 🄳 dishes
Smoking: Air conditioning
Accommodation: 47 en suite
Credit cards: ▓▓ ▓▓ ▓▓ ▓ ▓▓ ▓

Directions: On A627 between Oldham and Ashton-under-Lyne

Ashton Road OL8 3HX
Map 7: SD90
Tel: 0161 6336331/6243405
Fax: 0161 6275262
Chef: Kevin Amesbury
Owner: Mr J Fry
Cost: Alc 15.90, fixed-price
D £14.50. ☺ H/wine £9.50
Times: Last L 2pm/last D 11pm.
Closed L Sat, Sun

OLDHAM, **Moorcock Restaurant**

*A stone building set high on the moors, with a keen young chef
keeping the food up to scratch. Cream of cauliflower soup with
Applewood Cheddar, griddled tuna loin marinated in basil and
lemon, and poached chicken with wild rice and sage and onion
cream sauce, set a cracking pace. Look out for Manchester tart with
coconut ice cream and glazed bananas.*

Directions: J21/M62 follow signs for Newhey, then left for
Denshaw

Huddersfield Road Denshaw
OL16 3TG
Map 7: SD90
Tel: 01457 872659
Fax: 01457 875646
Chef: Nigel Philip Skinkis
Owners: Mr & Mrs M J Skinkis
Cost: Alc £25, fixed-price L&D
£14.95. ☺ H/wine £7.95
Times: Last L 2pm/last D 9.30pm
(Noon-5pm Sun). Closed L Sat, Mon,
L Tue
Additional: Bar food; Sunday L;
Children welcome; 🄳 dishes
Smoking: No-smoking area
Credit cards: ▓▓ ▓▓ ▓▓ ▓ ▐

OLDHAM, **White Hart Inn**

Downstairs, the brasserie serves fashionably rustic food in
large bowls, such as roast home-smoked duck breast with
dauphinoise potatoes and lentils; upstairs, it's an altogether
posher affair, with an ambitious monthly changing menu that
teases the imagination. Fresh anchovies flavour a roast rump of
lamb served with saffron spinach risotto; Goosnargh duck
breast comes stuffed with langoustines, Parma ham and
spinach; and roast salsify and asparagus with Parmesan
shavings and a tomato and onion pickle. And it's a while since
we've seen lambs' fries on any menu, even when served with
roast fillet of British beef and leek tagliatelle. Desserts hit the
right note with delicious sounding roasted pears and stewed
blackberries with a sugar biscuit, and warm chocolate tart with
orange compote.

Directions: Take A669 for Oldham town centre; after going
through Grotton turn immediate R after garage at top of hill –
inn is 50 yards on L

51 Stockport Road Lydgate
OL4 4JJ
Map 7: SD90
Tel: 01457 872566
Fax: 01457 875190
Chef: John Rudden
Owners: Charles Brierley, John
Rudden
Cost: Fixed-price L £16 (4 courses)/D
£24.75 (5 courses). ☺ H/wine £12.25
Times: Noon-last L 2.30pm/6-last
D 9.30pm
Additional: Bar food; Sunday L;
Children welcome; 🄳 dishes
Seats: 60. Private dining room 24
Smoking: No smoking in dining room
Accommodation: 5 en suite
Credit cards: ▓▓ ▓▓ ▓▓ ▓ ▓▓ ▐

RAMSBOTTOM,
The Village Restaurant ✪

16-18 Market Place BL0 9HT
Map 7: SD71
Tel: 01706 825070
Fax: 01706 822005
Chef: Ros Hunter
Owners: Ros Hunter, Chris Johnson
Cost: Fixed-price L £9.50/D £19.50
(4 courses). ☺ H/wine £9
Times: L at 12.45pm (Sat at noon &
2pm)/D at 8pm. Closed D Sun, all
Mon, Tue
Additional: Sunday L at 1pm & 3pm
Smoking: No smoking in dining room
Credit cards: ▬ ▥ ▚ ▢ ▥ C ▣ JCB

Directions: From M66 northbound
take J1 and follow signs to
Ramsbottom. Restaurant in centre of
village

*Cosy restaurant set over a fine delicatessen housed in a couple of
cottages dating from the 1820s. The proprietors are passionate about
the integrity of their raw materials and the cooking is simple and
honest. A meal might comprise marinated mushrooms, Pennine hill-
reared beef with organic veg, and Ricotta cheesecake.*

ROCHDALE, **Nutter's** ✪✪

Edenfield Road
Cheesden Norden OL12 7TY
Map 7: SD81
Tel/Fax: 01706 650167
Chef: Andrew Nutter
Owners: Rodney, Jean & Andrew
Nutter
Cost: *Alc* £26.50, fixed price D
£29.50 (6 courses). ☺ H/wine £10.50
Times: Noon-2pm/7 (from 6.45 Sat)-
9.30pm (till 9 Sun). Closed Tue,
1st 2 wks Aug
Additional: Sunday L; Children
welcome; ◖ menu
Seats: 52
Smoking: No smoking in dining room
Credit cards: ▬ ▥ ▚ ▢ ▥

'There's a nutter in the kitchen' the menu playfully quips – not
just any nutter, it might add, but a tabloid TV Nutter. Media
fame brings its own problems – and although Andrew Nutter
certainly knows what he's about in terms of technical prowess
and visual presentation, some may find his combinations too
complicated for comfort. It's hard, though, not to be engaged
by the witty reworking of the local pride and joy – crispy Bury
black pudding wun-tuns. Main courses include pan-seared
salmon topped with a sesame crust with ginger and chive
butter sauce, and caramelised duck breast with its own crispy
confit with hot punch and citrus sauce. The former pub stands
high on the moors overlooking Ramsbottom.

Directions: On the A680 between Rochdale and Edenfield

STANDISH, **Wrightington Hotel** ✪✪

See Wrightington, Lancashire

WIGAN, **Kilhey Court Hotel** ❀❀

Set in 10 acres of well-tended grounds and with its own golf course just a mile away, Kilhey Court has a lot to offer guests. Apart from conference and banqueting facilities, an adjoining leisure centre houses a heated pool and a gym. Choose between eating in an informal brasserie or the Laureate Restaurant, the latter in an attractive split-level Victorian conservatory looking over gardens and lakes. How about a starter of a terrine of foie gras, chicken and haggis with a timbale of neeps and tatties and a dressing of whisky and oats? Alternatively, sample a tart of salmon and asparagus or Lancashire flan (bacon, scalloped potatoes, sausage and cheese) with tomato and black pudding chutney. Breast of Goosnargh duck is a fitting main course for the area – served here with a grape and apple chutney – or go for sea bass with lemon and samphire risotto and seared scallops. You could end dinner with banana and butterscotch flan or lemon tart with ice cream. Virtually all the major wine-producing regions of the world are represented on the extensive wine list.

Chorley Road Wigan
WN1 2XN
Map 7: SD51
Tel: 01257 472100
Fax: 01257 422401
Owner: Macdonald Hotels plc
Cost: *Alc* £30, fixed-price L £13.25/D £23.95. ☺
Times: Noon-last L 2.30pm/7-last D 9.30pm
Additional: Bar food; Sunday L; Children welcome; ❹ dishes
Seats: 90. Private room 26
Smoking: No smoking in dining room; Air conditioning
Accommodation: 62 en suite
Credit cards: 🖃 🖃 🖃 🖃 🖃

Directions: On A5106 at Worthington.

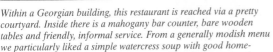

HAMPSHIRE

ALRESFORD, **Hunters** ❀

Within a Georgian building, this restaurant is reached via a pretty courtyard. Inside there is a mahogany bar counter, bare wooden tables and friendly, informal service. From a generally modish menu we particularly liked a simple watercress soup with good home-made bread. The Watercress Line steam railway is just across the road.

Accommodation: 3 en suite
Credit cards: 🖃 🖃 🖃 🖃 🖃 🖃 🖃

Directions: Off A31 – in centre of Alresford

32 Broad Street SO24 9AQ
Map 4: SU53
Tel/Fax: 01962 732468
Chef: Andrew Sherlock
Owner: Martin Birmingham
Cost: *Alc* £35, fixed-price D £15. ☺ H/wine £9.95
Times: Last L 2pm/last D 9.45pm. Closed D Sun
Additional: Sunday L (Sep-May only); No children under 4; ❹ dishes
Smoking: No-smoking area; No pipes and cigars

ANDOVER, **Esseborne Manor** ❀

Hurstbourne Tarrant
SP11 0ER
Map 4: SU34
Tel: 01264 736444
Fax: 01264 736725
Chef: Ben Tunnicliffe
Owner: I C Hamilton
Cost: *Alc* £27, fixed-price L & D £17. ☺ H/wine £13
Times: Last L 2.30pm/last D 9.30pm
Additional: Sunday L; No children under 7; ❹ dishes
Smoking: No-smoking area; No pipes and cigars
Accommodation: 15 en suite
Credit cards: 🖃 🖃 🖃 🖃 🖃 🖃 🖃

Attractive manor house set in well-tended gardens and surrounded by open countryside. Good country house cooking offers the likes of chicken livers with wild mushrooms, fillet of halibut with pesto and grain mustard fritters , and a vibrant champagne and rhubarb terrine with crème anglaise. Interesting wine list noted for value for money.

Directions: H/way between Andover & Newbury on A343, just N of Hurstbourne Tarrant

BASINGSTOKE,

Basingstoke Country Hotel

The restaurant of this popular business hotel has oak panelling and a well-balanced menu of mainstream modern dishes. The highlight of our last meal was a ballotine of duck and rabbit on salad leaves with a beetroot and orange dressing. Fresh coffee came with home-made Turkish delight and dipped fruits.

Additional: Sunday L; Children welcome; 🍴 dishes
Smoking: Air conditioning
Accommodation: 100 en suite
Credit cards: ▬ ▬ ▬ 🄲 🄿 JCB

Directions: On A30 between Nately Scures and Hook

Nately Scures Hook
RG27 9JS
Map 4: SU65
Tel: 01256 764161
Fax: 01256 768341
Chef: Joe Lado
Owner: Andrew Weir Hotels
Cost: *Alc* £25, fixed-price L £14.50 (2 courses)/D £17.50. ☺
Times: Last L 1.45pm/D 9.45pm. Closed D Sun

BASINGSTOKE,

The Thistle Audleys Wood ❀❀

Only a short drive from Basingstoke, this extended Victorian country house hotel is set in seven acres of wooded gardens. Its restaurant, featuring a high-vaulted ceiling, makes a stylish backdrop for the accomplished cooking of the kitchen. Prime quality ingredients are used in a wide variety of dishes on both the *carte* and the daily set menus. Chicken livers and lamb sweetbreads with veal and red wine jus and artichoke panache got an inspection meal off to an impressive start, with clean flavours and laudable execution. A main course of salmon with a rissole of strawberries and black pepper with mint hollandaise also exhibited sound skills in presentation and cooking technique. Standards were maintained in the dessert of pear and Calvados charlotte with caramelised pears, and hospitable staff added to the occasion. Although the wine list has its share of pricy stars, there's also a good choice of wines by the glass.

Directions: M3/J6 & A339 (Alton). Hotel entrance is on R, one third of mile from Venture Roundabout.

Alton Road RG25 2JT
Map 4: SU65
Tel: 01256 817555
Fax: 01256 817500
Chef: Ronnie Wyatt-Goodwin
Owner: Thistle Hotels
Cost: *Alc* £38, fixed price L £17.95/D £19.75. ☺ H/wine £13.85
Times: Noon-last L 1.45pm/7-last D 9.45pm. Closed L Sat, L Bhs
Additional: Bar food; Sunday lunch; Children welcome; 🍴 dishes
Seats: 75. Private room 16-48. Jacket & tie preferred
Smoking: No-smoking area; No pipes and cigars
Accommodation: 71 en suite
Credit cards: ▬ ▬ ▬ 🄲 ▬ 🄲 🄿 JCB

BEAULIEU, **Beaulieu Hotel**

Great country house hotel in the heart of the New Forest, a perfect place to relax. The cosy restaurant offers stylish surroundings and magnificent views. Menus are built around fresh produce, and the kitchen has a firm eye on modern trends, and sound technique.

Additional: Children welcome; dishes
Smoking: No smoking in dining room
Accommodation: 18 en suite
Credit cards: ■ ■ ■ ■ ■ ■ ■ JCB

Directions: On the B3056 between Lyndhurst and Beaulieu, opposite railway station

Beaulieu Road
Lyndhurst SO42 7YQ
Map 4: SU30
Tel: 01703 293344
Fax: 01703 292729
Chef: James Darby
Owner: Care Hotels Ltd
Cost: Fixed-price D £20.50
(5 courses). ☺ H/wine £9.95
Times: D only, 7-last D 8.45pm

BEAULIEU,
Montagu Arms Hotel ❀❀

Creeper-clad hotel in a picturesque setting. The kitchen, in particular pleases, with a menu based on well-sourced local ingredients. The style is 'county house modern British but no worse for that'. Amuse bouche was a mushroom and chicken terrine on our visit, followed by salmon and sole terrine with spring onion and red pepper salad. The main course was a good piece of duck confit, succulent and moist, served with a bubble-and-squeak cake. Crème brûlée as based on mascarpone cheese and it worked well, with the acidity from the cheese cutting the sweetness. Showing that the eye is firmly on the ball, home-made bread was pronounced 'particularly memorable'.The restaurant is a formal room, with hand-painted Italian cover plates and white napery. Great staff.

Directions: From Southampton take A326 (Fawley), follow signs to Beaulieu (B3054). The hotel is on L as you enter village

Palace Lane SO42 7ZL
Map 4: SU30
Tel: 01590 612324
Fax: 01590 612188
Please telephone for further details

BISHOP'S WALTHAM,
Cobblers Restaurant ❀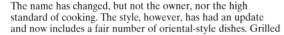

The split-level restaurant, personally supervised by owner Andrew Cobb, has a friendly, relaxing atmosphere. An autumn menu produced succulent pan-fried scallops with gazpacho dressing, pheasant crepinette with spiced pear confit, and an excellent caramel mousse brûlée.

Additional: Bar food L; Children welcome; dishes
Smoking: No-smoking area
Credit cards: ■ ■ ■ ■ ■

Directions: Bishop's Waltham is on B2177, midway between Winchester & Portsmouth/Southampton

The Square SO32 1AR
Map 4: SU51
Tel: 01489 891515
Fax: 01489 891577
Chef: David Heyward
Owners: Andrew & Susan Cobb
Cost: Alc £20, fixed-price L £12.95/D £18.95. ☺ H/wine £9.45
Times: Last L 2pm/last D 9.30pm.
Closed Sun, Mon

BISHOP'S WALTHAM,
The Old Granary ❀❀

The name has changed, but not the owner, nor the high standard of cooking. The style, however, has had an update and now includes a fair number of oriental-style dishes. Grilled

Bank Street SO32 1AE
Map 4: SU51
Tel: 01489 896352
Fax: 01489 896288
Chefs: Lauro Aman, William Spencer

tiger prawns, for example, flavoured with garlic, wrapped with bacon, and set on a bed of vegetable noodles with blackbean butter sauce, or steamed fillet of Scottish salmon with buckwheat noodles, served in a salmon liquor flavoured with shiitake mushrooms. Salmon also featured in a rather complex but successful dish of roasted nuggets of monkfish tails, rolled in fresh herbs with salmon mousse in a choux pastry cage, with a Sauternes and carrot butter sauce. Equally well prepared was a main course of boned rack of English lamb with a provençale crust, served with a timbale of lamb, mushrooms and ham with Reform sauce. White and dark chocolate mousse wrapped in a light sponge, with raspberry sauce, ended the meal on a high note.

Owner: Lauro Aman,
Cost: *Alc* £22, fixed price L £9.90 (2 courses)/D £17.50. ☺ H/wine £8.50
Times: Noon-last L 1.45pm/7-last D 9.45pm. Closed D Sun, all Mon, last 2 wks Jan
Additional: Bar food L; Sunday L; Children welcome; ④ dishes
Seats: 80. Private room 50
Smoking: No-smoking area
Credit cards: ▬ ▭ ▜ ▣ ▤ **G** JCB

Directions: Telephone for directions

BROCKENHURST, Carey's Manor

SO42 7RH
Map 4: SU30
Tel: 01590 623551
Fax: 01590 622799
Chef: Kevin Dorrington
Owner: Greenclose Ltd
Cost: *Alc* £30, fixed price L £14/D £23.50. H/wine £10.95
Times: Last L 1.45pm/last D 9.45pm
Additional: Sunday L; No children under 7; ④ dishes
Smoking: No smoking in dining room
Accommodation: 79 en suite
Credit cards: ▬ ▭ ▜ ▣ ▤

Former hunting lodge that now has a health club, cocktail bar, continental café and a smart restaurant. Local produce is a highlight of the extensive, modish menu. At a recent meal lobster and crevettes came on a base of squid ink noodles and were topped with spaghetti of mooli and carrot, but banana and fudge parfait stole the show.

Directions: M27/J1, follow signs for Lyndhurst and Lymington A337. Railway station 5 minutes from hotel

BROCKENHURST,
Forest Park Hotel

Views over the landscaped garden and outdoor pool are enjoyed from the newly redecorated hotel restaurant. A gigantic portion of bacon hock with pea purée was particularly appreciated by our inspector, in a meal that began with leek, almond and red onion beignets, and finished with a dark chocolate tart.

Additional: Bar food; Sunday L; Children welcome; ④ dishes
Smoking: No smoking in dining room
Accommodation: 38 en suite
Credit cards: ▬ ▭ ▜ ▣ ▤

Rhinefield Road SO42 7ZG
Map 4: SU30
Tel: 01590 622844
Fax: 01590 623948
Chef: Stuart Mallen
Owner: Robin Collins
Cost: Fixed-price L £9.95/D £19.95. ☺ H/wine £8.85
Times: Last L 2pm/last D 10pm

Directions: From A337 to Brockenhurst turn into Meerut Road, follow road through Waters Green; at T junction turn R into Rhinefield Road

BROCKENHURST,
New Park Manor ✦

Lyndhurst Road SO42 7QH
Map 4: SU30
Tel: 01590 623467
Fax: 01590 622268
Chef: Steve Hurst
Owner: Von Essen Hotels
Cost: Fixed-price D £27. H/wine £15
Times: Last L 2pm/last D 9.30pm
Additional: Bar food; Sunday L;
Children welcome; ◑ dishes
Smoking: No smoking in dining room
Accommodation: 24 en suite
Credit cards: ▦ ▦ ▧ ▣ ▦ ▣ ▣ JCB

The favourite hunting lodge of Charles II is now a smart hotel set in acres of parkland with it own equestrian centre. The kitchen delivers the likes of asparagus and wild mushroom terrine with white truffle oil, toasted local scallops with ravioli of lobster with lemongrass and saffron nage and sticky toffee pudding with butterscotch sauce and raisin ice cream.

Directions: Turn of the A337 between Lyndhurst and Brockenhurst and follow the hotel signs.

BROCKENHURST,
Le Poussin Restaurant ✦✦✦

The unassuming restaurant is hidden in a row of High Street shops; the small conservatory-style entrance opens on to flagstone floors with the carpeted dining room smartly appointed in white, cream and dark green. The 'poussin' connection is strong from various pictures down to the salt cellar. 'This year we hope to move to an extra choice of dish per course and change weekly; this should enable us to concentrate on improving our quality,' writes Alex Aitken of his constantly evolving menu. His is up-to-the minute, ambitious cooking with the confidence to handle flavours in an assured manner. A lunch in May produced some top-drawer dishes: a vibrantly flavoured puff pastry pillow filled with fresh asparagus and a tarragon cream sauce; perfect breast of farm-reared chicken with morels simply sautéed and served with an accurate cream sauce and a pile of fresh tagliatelle; rich, bitter chocolate truffle cake set on crème anglaise and well balanced by a white chocolate terrine on a fruit coulis plus a tuile basket filled with a plummy Merlot granite. Attention to small details is impressive – outstanding home-made bread of basic white and granary plus a super rosemary and olive bread with a touch of rock salt, good canapés, and lovely chocolate truffles, tuile and candied orange peel with coffee. The wine list is notable for both quality and depth of vintages, with the real strength lying in Bordeaux and Burgundy.

Directions: Village centre through an archway between two shops

The Courtyard
Brookley Road SO42 7RB
Map 4: SU30
Tel: 01590 623063
Fax: 01590 623144
Chef: Alex Aitken
Owners: Alex & Caroline Aitken
Cost: Alc £30, fixed-price L £15
(2 courses)/D £30. H/wine £12.50
Times: Noon-last L 1.30pm/7-last
D 9.30pm. Closed Mon, Tue
Additional: Sunday L; Children
welcome; ◑ dishes
Seats: 20
Smoking: No smoking in dining room
Credit cards: ▦ ▦ ▣

BROCKENHURST,

Rhinefield House ❀❀

Rhinefield Road SO42 7QB
Map 4: SU30
Tel: 01590 622922
Fax: 01590 622800
Chef: David Whiffen
Owner: Virgin Hotels Ltd
Cost: Fixed-price L £16.95/D £25.50.
H/wine £13.50
Times: Last L 2pm/last D 10pm
Additional: Bar food; Sunday L;
Children welcome; ❀ dishes
Smoking: No smoking in dining room
Accommodation: 34 en suite
Credit cards: ▰ ▰ ▱ ▰ ▱

Formally laid out gardens complete with canals are an added
attraction at this splendid 19th-century mock-Elizabethan
mansion. Eating in the Armada Restaurant (named after the
carving above the fireplace), you could choose, say, seafood
soup, followed by beef fillet with foie gras and truffles, then
ginger mousse encased in chocolate. A summer meal showed
the kitchen's sure hand in giving classical themes a modern
twist. Rabbit and pigeon terrine came with good apricot and
apple chutney, wonderfully fresh scallops were served with
truffle-flavoured black pasta, great sugar-snap peas and a good
butter sauce, and ginger mousse was encased in home-made
chocolate teardrops and a wonderful ginger syrup with
shredded root ginger throughout – a great combination.

Directions: From M27/J1 follow signs to Lyndhurst, then take
A35 to Christchurch. After 3 miles turn L to Rhinefield. Hotel
approx 2 miles on R

BROCKENHURST,

Thatched Cottage Hotel ❀❀

The kitchen admirably credits its suppliers on the menu, and
just to prove they've got nothing to hide, the open-to-view
kitchen lets everyone in on the act. The dining room is pretty
in a country cottage way with beams, swags of dried flowers
and white lace cloths. Japanese connections add an unusual
dimension to the Anglo-French *carte* – a fillet of cod with tofu
sauce, for example. Duck always works well with fruit, here the
richness of a supreme of Dorset duckling is balanced by
Kirsch-flavoured cherry sauce and fondant potatoes. Follow
with a cappuccino ice cream parfait presented like a little cup
of coffee and served with meringue and fruit sauces.

16 Brookley Road SO42 7RR
Map 4: SU30
Tel: 01590 623090
Fax: 01590 623479
Chefs: Michiyo & Martin Matysik
Owners: The Matysik Family
Cost: Fixed-price L £26/D £30.
H/wine £14.50
Times: 12.30-last L 2pm/7.30-
9.30pm. Closed D Sun, all Mon,
Jan, Feb

Additional: Bar food L; Sunday L; No children under 12
Seats: 20
Smoking: No smoking in dining room
Accommodation: 5 en suite
Credit cards: ▰ ▰ ▰ ▱ ▰ JCB

Directions: On A337 in Brockenhurst, turning before level
crossing

BROCKENHURST,
Whitley Ridge Hotel

Beaulieu Road SO4 7QL
Map 4: SU30
Tel: 01590 622354
Fax: 01590 622856
Please telephone for further details

Visitors are likely to be enchanted by the setting of this former royal hunting lodge: the part Georgian, part Victorian country house hotel stands in the heart of the New Forest surrounded by acres of parkland over which deer roam freely. The classically based cuisine manages a modern twist in dishes such as crispy salmon oriental with a ginger, chilli and sweet sherry sauce, and tornedos of pork with a hazelnut crust, caramelised apples and a coarse grain mustard sauce. Otherwise a strongly traditional streak characterises the likes of scallops Whitley Ridge – flambéed and served with a lobster sauce, and breast of duck with crushed peppercorns and a blackcurrant and Cassis sauce. Supreme of chicken Topaz is an intriguing amalgamation of breast of chicken baked with Red Leicester cheese and smoked ham and served with a mild tandoori sauce.

Directions: A337 (from Lyndhurst) turn L towards Beaulieu on B3055, approx 1 mile.

BROOK, Bell Inn 🌸

Lyndhurst SO43 7HE
Map 4: SU21
Tel: 01703 812214
Fax: 01703 813958
Chef: Malcolm Lugg
Owner: Brook Enterprises
Cost: Fixed price D £26.50
(4 courses). H/wine £11.50.
Times: D only, 7.30-last D 9.30pm
Additional: Bar food; Sunday L;
Children welcome; 🍴 dishes
Smoking: No smoking in dining room
Accommodation: 25 en suite
Credit cards:  JCB

A golf club and the New Forest are nearby attractions at this popular hotel. Well-tested cuisine takes centre stage in the cosy oak-beamed bar and restaurant, where best end of lamb might be paired with rosemary sauce, and tarte Tatin with crème Chantilly, on the daily-changing menu.

Directions: M27/J1 (Cadnam) 3rd exit on to B3078, signed Brook, 0.5 mile on right

CADNAM, Bartley Lodge ❀

Lyndhurst Road SO40 2NR
Map 4: SU31
Tel: 01703 812248
Fax: 01703 812075
Chef: Richard Turner
Owner: Care Hotels
Cost: *Alc* £25. Fixed-price D £20.50.
☺ H/wine £9.95
Times: D only, 7pm-last D 9pm
Additional: Bar food L; Sunday L
(12.30pm-2pm); Children welcome;
🍴 dishes

The elegant Crystal Restaurant overlooks the gardens at this 18th-century former hunting lodge. The short daily menu is full of imaginative ideas such as fillet of trout with gremolata crust and avocado and tomato salsa. Leave room for the special dessert, warm pear and chocolate tart.

Smoking: No smoking in dining room
Accommodation: 31 en suite
Credit cards: ▬ ▭ ▰ ▢ ▦ ▣ ▨ JCB

Directions: Telephone for directions

CRAWLEY, Fox and Hounds ❀

SO21 2PR
Map 4: SU43
Tel: 01962 776285
Fax: 01962 776005
Chef: Pierre-Olivier Michel
Owner: Vistro Ltd
Cost: *Alc* £25. H/wine £10.95
Times: Last L 2.15pm/last D 9.30pm.
Closed D Sun, all Mon
Additional: Sunday L;
No children under 7; 🍴 dishes

Sound and well balanced French provincial cooking can be found at this listed 17th-century building, set within a tranquil thatched village. The short carte, offered by French staff, may feature terrine of foie gras, followed by sea bass with onion confit and red wine sauce and, for pudding, pear terrine with crème anglaise.

Smoking: No-smoking area; No pipes and cigars
Credit cards: ▬ ▭ ▰ ▢ ▣ JCB

Directions: Telephone for directions

DENMEAD,
Barnard's Restaurant ❀❀

Hambledon Road PO7 6NU
Map 4: SU61
Tel/Fax: 01705 257788
Chef: David Barnard
Owners: David & Sandie Barnard
Cost: *Alc* £26, fixed-price L £10/D
£12.50 (wknds £17.50). ☺
H/wine £10
Times: Noon-last L 1.30pm/7-last
D 9.30pm. Closed L Sat, all Sun,
Mon, 1 wk Easter, 1 wk Aug
Additional: Children welcome;
🍴 dishes
Seats: 38. Private dining rooms 20, 34
Smoking: No-smoking area
Credit cards: ▬ ▭ ▰ ▢ ▦ ▣ JCB

Green and yellow decor with beautiful flower paintings enliven this small, family-run, country restaurant that serves a mix of English and French food. The style may be a little conservative, but there's nothing wrong with twice-baked Swiss cheese soufflé, and grilled fillet steak with tarragon-flavoured hollandaise sauce when correctly cooked as it is here. Lightly peppered noisettes of lamb are pan-fried and served with a creamy pepper sauce, but the most adventurous ideas are in desserts such as crème brûlée, filled with lychees spiked with peach schnapps and glazed with sugar, as well as the dark and white chocolate mousse with coffee-bean sauce.

Directions: Opposite village church, from A3M/J3/B2150 (Waterlooville)

EMSWORTH, Julies ❀❀

30 South Street PO10 7EH
Map 4: SU70
Tel: 01243 377914
Chef: Kevin Hartley
Owners: Mr & Mrs K A Hartley
Cost: Fixed-price L £18.50/D £24.95.
☺ H/wine £9.95
Times: Noon-last L 2.30pm/7-last
D 9.30pm. Closed L Sat, all Sun,
Mon, 2 wks Jan
Additional: Children welcome;
🍴 dishes
Seats: 28. Private dining room 16
Credit cards: ▬ ▭ ▰ ▢ ▦

A short stroll from the harbour, Julies Restaurant is a charming 17th-century fisherman's cottage with oak beams. The small dining room has a relaxed atmosphere, and dinner is served in one sitting, so guests can enjoy their meals without hurrying. The flavour is modern English with Med overtones: look out for fillet of lamb topped with garlic hazelnut crust and served with rocket and deep-fried parsnip crisps; griddled calves' liver on a bed of crushed potato infused with olive oil, tarragon and green peppercorns; and glazed pork fillet with a garlic chive pesto and spicy prune relish. A summer meal enjoyed by our inspector kicked off with layered chive and sweetcorn pancakes with duck livers and roasted pear. Pan-fried duck followed, served with creamed sorrel and fresh greengages. For dessert choose between traditional spotted Dick and custard, and tart au citron with home-made vanilla ice cream.

Directions: At Emsworth town centre, 1st R after Emsworth Square – South Street. Go 100 yds down towards the Quay. Restaurant on L facing main car park.

EMSWORTH, Spencers ❀❀

Gas lighting, polished tables and racks of books add to the congenial atmosphere of this cosy, first-floor restaurant. As well as a reasonable round-up of brasserie-style dishes along the lines of sautéed calves liver in red wine and onion sauce, confit of duck with red cabbage chutney, salad niçoise, and pasta bolognese, there is an impressive choice of daily fish dishes. More unusual choices include swordfish steak chargrilled with garlic and pimento butter, and grilled tilapia fillet with shallot and coriander dressing. Grilled salmon is jazzed up a little with sage and pink peppercorn butter. Desserts include fresh fruit pavlova and hot chocolate gâteau.

Directions: Following A259 to Emsworth roundabout, turn L into North Street, restaurant is 0.5 mile on left.

36 North Street PO10 7DG
Map 4: SU70
Tel/Fax: 01243 372744
Chef: Denis Spencer
Owners: Denis & Lesley Spencer
Cost: Alc £20
Times: D only, 7.30-last D 10.30pm. Closed Sun, Mon, 25-26 Dec
Additional: Children welcome; ❃ dishes
Seats: 34. Private dining room 10
Smoking: No smoking in dining room; Air conditioning
Credit cards: ▆ ▆ ▆ ▆ ▆ ▆ ▆

EMSWORTH,
36 On The Quay ❀❀❀

At high tide, you feel the sea is practically lapping at your feet. Intimate is the word, however, rather than watery, for this comfortable, citrus green and yellow restaurant housed on the quay overlooking Chichester Harbour. Ramon Farthing's love of food shines through in the cooking, matched by his considerable skill and expertise. Our inspection lunch consisted of a procession of well-executed dishes, each following the other with precision, flair and massive behind-the-scenes effort. Note a warm salad of cod fillet with smooth potato cream and mustard oil, its counterpart a warm salad of boned quail, seared goose liver and crisp Parma ham with sherry vinegar and honey sauce. Then a breast of chicken coated with spice crust served with its boned-out leg braised in a bacon and apple stock, and pan-fried fillets of John Dory with spinach, glazed shallots, crisp bacon and mushroom that came with a light wine sauce spiked with lime juice. Just as much went into the desserts. A lime tart was crisp, neither too sweet nor too sour, a caramel mousse came encased in a circular box of hazelnut biscuit with a little caramel lid, set off perfectly by warm glazed pears and a milk chocolate sauce. As well as the *carte* and set-price menus, there is a six-course gourmet menu which can either be described or come as a complete surprise. Karen Farthing ably runs the front of house, backed up by a friendly and welcoming team. Wines are a high quality global selection, although France tends to dominate with a serious selection of the countries top producers; prices are a little steep for half-bottles – it is worth perusing the bin-end list.
Signature dishes: Fresh scallops wrapped in skate, baby leeks and coral cream with basil; banana ice cream with caramelised banana galette, crisp spice biscuit; breast of wood pigeon with bacon and cabbage tortellinis, rösti potato; 36 speciality apple dessert

47 South Street PO10 7EG
Map 4: SU70
Tel: 01243 375592
Fax: 01243 375593
Chef: Ramon Farthing
Owners: Ramon & Karen Farthing
Cost: Alc £34.45, fixed-price L £19/D £31.95. H/wine £13.50
Times: Noon-last L 1.45pm/7pm-last D 9.45pm. Closed L Sat, Sun, L Mon, 4-18 Jan, 4-12 Oct
Additional: Children welcome; ❃ dishes
Seats: 30. Private dining room 10
Smoking: No-smoking area; No pipes and cigars in dining room
Credit cards: ▆ ▆ ▆ ▆ ▆ ▆ ▆ JCB

Directions: Last building on R in South Street, which runs from the Square in the centre of Emsworth

AA Shortlisted for
Wine Award-see page 16

EVERSLEY, The New Mill ❀❀

New Mill Road RG27 0RA
Map 4: SU76
Tel: 0118 9732277
Fax: 0118 9328780
Chef: Simon Smith
Cost: Alc £30, fixed-price L £12.50/D
£19.50. ☺ H/wine £10
Times: Noon-last L 2pm/7-last D
10pm (Sun noon-9pm). Closed L Sat,
26 Dec
Additional: Grill Room L&D; Sunday
L, Children welcome; ❹ dishes
Seats: 80. Private dining rooms 20, 40
Smoking: No pipes & cigars
Credit cards: ▆ ▆ ▆ ▆ ▆ ▆ ▆

Directions: From Eversley take A327
(Reading), cross river, turn L at cross
roads into New Mill Road

This 16th-century water mill, once used by local farmers to grind corn, is now superbly restored and home to the modern English cooking of chef Simon Smith. The idyllic riverside setting and alfresco dining attract a regular crowd, who come from far and wide to enjoy dishes such as chargrilled breast of duckling with apricot and lovage confit, seared halibut with mango and coriander salsa, and grilled swordfish with aubergines, vine tomatoes and button mushrooms. An early summer meal in the Riverside Restaurant could start with sautéed lambs sweetbreads with mustard and spinach sauce, followed by baked supreme of chicken with rocket pesto, and red pepper and tomato salsa. More informal dining can be enjoyed in the Grill Room, where starters range from steamed mussels with shallots, garlic and sparkling lambrusco wine, to a Greek platter of hummus, taramasalata and tzatziki with olives, pitta bread and salad.

FAIR OAK, Noorani Restaurant ❀

Grand-style Indian restaurant, with alcoves and plush banquettes, in a village roadside setting. The extensive menu includes duck, fish and seafood, plus plenty for vegetarians. Highly spiced karai specials are a feature (cooked in the wok-like karai), as well as traditional Parsee fare and tandoori dishes.

Additional: Sunday L buffet; Children welcome; ❹ dishes
Smoking: No-smoking area; Air conditioning
Credit cards: ▆ ▆ ▆ ▆ ▆ ▆

465 Fair Oak Road Eastleigh
Map 4: SU41
Tel: 01703 601901/601903
Chef: Koyse Miah
Cost: Alc £20. ☺ H/wine £7.95
Times: Last L 2pm/last D 11.30pm

FAREHAM, Lysses House Hotel ❀

Elegant Georgian hotel conveniently located on the edge of the town centre. The formal Richmond Restaurant offers an interesting selection of dishes. A sample meal was notable for the imaginative use of simple ingredients, especially king prawns, fennel and tomato with Pernod and crème fraîche sauce, and almond and pineapple tart.

Accommodation: 21 en suite
Credit cards: ▆ ▆ ▆ ▆ ▆ ▆ ▆

Directions: From M27 exit 11 follow signs to Fareham town centre; hotel is at top of High Street

51 High Street PO16 7BQ
Map 4: SU50
Tel: 01329 822622
Fax: 01329 822762
Chef: Clive Wright
Owner: Prosig Ltd
Cost: Alc £23, fixed-price L £13.95/D
£18.50. ☺ H/wine £9.35
Times: Last L 1.45pm/last D 9.45pm.
Closed L Sat, all Sun, 24 Dec-2 Jan
Additional: Bar food; Children
welcome; ❹ dishes
Smoking: No smoking in dining room;
Air conditioning

FAREHAM, **Solent Hotel**

A split-level restaurant, with a conservatory at one end. The menu ranges from traditional prawn cocktail and peppered steak, to salmon and spring onion fishcakes with 'gravlax' sauce, and roast rump of lamb with couscous and rosemary sauce. Great hospitality from friendly, helpful staff.

Accommodation: 90 en suite
Credit cards: ■ ▒ ▒ ⌨ ▒ ▣ ▣ JCB

Directions: From M27/J9, follow signs to Solent Business Park & Whiteley

Rookery Avenue
Whiteley PO15 7AJ
Map 4: SU50
Tel: 01489 880000
Fax: 01489 880007
Chef: Chris Taylor
Cost: *Alc* £32.50, fixed-price
L £13.95/D £22. ☺ H/wine £10.95
Times: Last L 2pm/last D 10pm.
Closed L Sat
Additional: Bar food; Sunday L;
Children welcome; ❹ dishes
Smoking: No smoking in dining room

FORDINGBRIDGE, **Ashburn Hotel** ✿

Great views over the garden to the New Forest beyond from the dining room of this welcoming hotel. Where possible, local produce is used and dishes from a choice of menus might include carrot and coriander soup, grilled salmon with sorrel sauce, and loin of pork with Stilton sauce.

Accommodation: 20 en suite
Credit cards: ■ ▒ ▒ ⌨ ▒ ▣ JCB

Directions: On the B3078

Station Road SP6 1JP
Map 4: SU11
Tel: 01425 652060
Fax: 01425 652150
Chef: Simon Reed
Owners: Mr & Mrs G Robson
Cost: *Alc* £24, fixed-price D £15.
H/wine £8.50
Times: D only, last D 9.30pm
Additional: Bar food; Sunday L (noon-2.15pm); Children welcome; ❹ dishes
Smoking: No smoking in dining room

FORDINGBRIDGE, **Hour Glass** ✿

Original beams and open fires give this 14th-century cottage restaurant plenty of charm. Imaginative Anglo-French dishes are created by John Collins, who shows his skill in dishes such as ravioli of chicken livers with lemon and garlic, and tender saddle of rabbit with pistachio stuffing and a white wine and mustard sauce.

Smoking: No-smoking area
Credit cards: ■ ▒ ▒ ⌨ ▣ ▣

Directions: On main A338 (Salisbury/Ringwood road) just outside Fordingbridge

Burgate SP6 1LX
Map 4: SU11
Tel/Fax: 01425 652348
Chef/Owner: JM Collins
Cost: *Alc* £19.95. Fixed-price
L £9.95-£11.95/D £9.95 (4 courses).
☺ H/wine £9.95.
Times: Last L 1.45pm/D 9.45pm.
Closed D Sun, Mon, 2 wks Feb,
1 wk Nov
Additional: Sunday L; No children under 5 at L, under 10 at D; ❹ dishes

FORDINGBRIDGE,
The Three Lions ✿✿✿

The Womersley's restaurant-with-rooms is a former 19th-century farmhouse that did time as a pub. In the three years that they have been in residence the restaurant has, in the words of one inspector who knows the place well 'become so much warmer in terms of atmosphere and decor'. The menu is written on a blackboard in the bar and offers around eight choices at each stage. Small touches give encouragement: the home-made brown bread, neatly presented tables, good petits fours, the amiable service. Mike Womersley is a talented cook, not afraid to let the quality of ingredients shine through in dishes of the utmost simplicty. Our test meal began with ravioli of crab with artichoke sauce that showed really good combination of flavours and robust saucing. For main course, fillet of sea bass was judged accurately cooked and with lots of flavour. It came with a well-refined sauce, fish cream flavoured

Stuckton SP6 2HF
Map 4: SU11
Tel: 01425 652489
Fax: 01425 656144
Chef: J M Womersley
Owners: Mr & Mrs J M Womersley
Cost: *Alc* £25, fixed-price L £13.50
(2 courses). ☺ H/wine £15
Times: 12.15-last L 2pm/7-last
D 9.45pm. Closed D Sun, all Mon,
last 2 wks Jan, 1st 2 wks Feb
Additional: Children welcome;
❹ dishes
Seats: 60. Private room 30
Smoking: No smoking in dining room
Accommodation: 3 en suite
Credit cards: ■ ▒ ▒ ⌨ ▣ JCB

with tarragon. Vegetables were well suited to the dish and included new potatoes, courgettes, celeriac purée and green beans, all perfectly timed. A smooth iced lime parfait for dessert, was simply served with some passion fruit that proved a successful partner. The wine list is impressive, reasonably priced with around 150 well-chosen wines from all the major wine growing countries.

Signature dishes: Loin of lamb and crispy bits; Quantock duck with foie gras sauce; vine-roasted partridge and grapes; galette of smoked haddock.

Directions: In the village of Stuckton, near Fordingbridge, half a mile off the A338

HIGHCLERE, **Hollington Country House** ✿✿✿

Woolton Hill
Newbury RG20 9XA
Map 4: SU45
Tel: 01635 255100
Fax: 01635 255075
Chef: Keith Short
Owners: John & Penny Guy
Cost: *Alc* £40.50, fixed-price L £20 (2 courses)/D £29.50. H/wine £18
Times: Noon-last L 1.45pm/7-last D 9.45pm
Additional: Sunday L; Children welcome; ✿ dishes
Seats: 48. Private dining rooms 8-50
Smoking: No smoking in dining room
Accommodation: 20 en suite
Credit cards: ▀▀ ▀▀ 🐦 🗎 ▀▀ 🅒 ▨

Goats' cheese ravioli with marinated peppers and balsamic dressing is destined to become a signature dish at this charming, beautifully restored country house set amidst park and woodland. Remarkably, the cooking appears simultaneously accomplished and relaxed; smoked chicken sausage with a butter bean and oyster mushroom stew and leaf spinach is not an easy dish to get as right as they do here. The kitchen, however, knows when to hold back as well, grilled sea bass is served simply but luxuriously with saffron noodles and caviar. Desserts are a triumph – an assiette of lemon desserts comprised faultless lemon tart, lemon curd ice cream, lemon parfait and a syllabub. Separate children's menus. The fine wine list is interesting and clued-up with good names and vintages throughout. It probably has the best Australian selection in the UK, twentysomething dedicated pages, clearly a passion.

**Shortlisted for AA Wine Award –
see page 16**

Directions: Take A343 (Andover) from Newbury. Follow signs for Hollington Herb Garden, hotel is next door.

LIPHOOK, **Nippon-Kan at Old Thorns** ✿✿

A smartly uniformed chef talks his diners through the dishes as they are prepared in front of them on the teppan. Indeed, teppanyaki is done with considerable style here, but there are

Griggs Green GU30 7PE
Map 4: SU83
Tel: 01428 724555
Fax: 01428 725036
Chef: T Suzuki

other classic Japanese dishes to sample as well. Sushi is superb, we sampled a cracklingly fresh selection of fat belly tuna, mackerel, sweet shrimps, tuna, octopus, cuttlefish and brill. Rice is clean and deliciously cereal-scented. Teriyaki beef is sweetly sauced, vegetable pickles are first-class and miso soup comes with slices of fried tofu and wakame seaweed.

Smoking: No pipes & cigars; Air conditioning
Accommodation: 33 en suite
Credit cards: ■ ■ ▢ ■ ▣ JCB

Directions: Approx 500 yds from Griggs Green exit off A3

Owner: London Kosaido Co Ltd
Cost: *Alc* £35, fixed-price L from £18/D from £20. ☺ H/wine £10.95
Times: Noon-last L 2pm(till 4.30 Sat & Sun)/7-last D 9.30pm(from 6.30 Sat & Sun). Closed Mon, 2 wks from 4 Jan
Additional: Sunday L; Children welcome; ◕ dishes
Seats: 36. Private dining room 80

LIPHOOK, Old Thorns Hotel, Thorns Restaurant ❀

Griggs Green GU30 7PE
Map 4: SU83
Tel: 01428 724555
Fax: 01428 725036
Chef: Geoff Sutton
Owner: London Kosaido Co Ltd
Cost: *Alc* £27, fixed-price D £23.50. ☺ H/wine £10.95
Times: D only, last D 9pm. Closed D Sun, 24-26 Dec
Additional: Bar food L; Sunday L (12.15-2.30pm); Children welcome; ◕ dishes
Smoking: No pipes or cigars
Accommodation: 33 en suite
Credit cards: ■ ■ ▢ ■ ▣ JCB

Directions: Approx 500 yds from Griggs Green exit off A3

After a day on the golf course, or just taking it easy, the menu at this Japanese-owned hotel has something for everyone. Beef and red wine cobbler, grilled steaks, and Japanese-style pork could be the more casual option, lamb with scallops and mango a more formal choice. Treacle tart with white chocolate ice cream for dessert.

LYMINGTON, Gordleton Mill ❀❀❀

Silver Street Hordle
SO41 6DJ
Map 4: SZ39
Tel: 01590 682219
Fax: 01590 683073
Chef: Stephen Smith
Owner: WF Stone
Cost: *Alc* £35, fixed-price L £16.50-£20. H/wine £17
Times: Noon-last L 2pm/7-last D 10pm. Closed D Sun, all Mon, Jan
Additional: Sunday L; No children under 6; ◕ dishes
Seats: 36
Smoking: No smoking in dining room; Air conditioning
Accommodation: 7 en suite
Credit cards: ■ ■ ▅ ▢ ■ ▣ ▣ JCB

Directions: Take A337 to Lymington, at railway bridge mini-roundabout go straight on then 1st R 1.5 miles

'A little piece of Provence nestling in the Hampshire greenbelt, with lily-padded millponds and quaint bridges over the River Avon, ivy-clad terracotta and sunny Mediterranean washes, and provençale tiles bordering a covered terrace'. So mused an inspector, on visiting this delightful old mill, fashioned in the

Provence-style some years ago. We were there for a late test meal to report on Stephen Smith, who had taken over on Toby Hill's departure. It was a Tuesday and that meant a provençale evening: a fixed-set menu with well-chosen accompanying wines. It was brilliantly executed. Fat black olives, herbed white rolls with a good, wholesome texture and taste, and a full-flavoured, garlicky gazpacho in a demi-tasse, got the meal off to a flying start. Velouté of red mullet croûton and rouille was punchy-flavoured and accomplished, the centrepiece of the meal, a confit of duck with red wine fumet was intense, robust, the fumet showing great consistency, sheen and balance. Crème vanille with nutmeg, vanilla and black pepper topped with fine crisp slices of dried-apple glued with splodges of apple sorbet was everything it should be.

Signature dishes: Mille-feuille of sea bream, basil, pomme mousseline, sauce gazpacho; roast sea scallops, celeriac purée, truffle vinaigrette; feullatine of lobster, shellfish velouté; braised pig's trotter, haricot blanc purée, essence of morels.

LYMINGTON,
Stanwell House Hotel NEW

Striking colours create a stylish feel to the restaurant at this Georgian period hotel. For lunch or dinner, choose between the Stanwell Restaurant and the more informal bistro bar, both of which serve excellent modern English cooking. Try fillet of salmon with spicy cabbage and oriental sauce, followed by a roasted hazelnut and chocolate tart.

Smoking: No smoking in restaurant
Accommodation: 29 en suite
Credit cards: ■ ■ ▢ ■ ▣

Directions: 2 miles from M27/J1. Take A337 through the New Forest to the coast

High Street SO41 9AA
Map 4: SZ39
Tel: 01590 677123
Fax: 01590 677756
Chef: Mark Hewitt
Owner: Jane McIntyre
Cost: *Alc* £25.50. Fixed-price L £9.25/D £20. ☺ H/wine £9
Times: Last L 2pm/last D 10pm
Additional: Bar food; Sunday L; Children welcome; ⚘ dishes

LYNDHURST, Crown Hotel

High Street SO43 7NF
Map 4: SU30
Tel: 01703 282922
Fax: 01703 282751
Chef: Stephen Greenhalgh
Owners: Mr & Mrs A Green
Cost: *Alc* £20, fixed-price D £18. ☺ H/wine £10.20
Times: D only, last D 9.15pm
Additional: Bar food; Sunday L; Children welcome
Smoking: No smoking in dining room
Accommodation: 39 en suite
Credit cards: ■ ■ ▨ ▢ ■ ▣ ▣

The Crown celebrated its centenary in 1997, but there has been an inn on this site since the 17th-century. The hotel's airy restaurant overlooks the small garden, and offers a daily-changing menu of modern English dishes. Poached breast of chicken filled with spinach, bacon and hazelnuts is a typical main course.

Directions: Top end of Lyndhurst High Street, opposite church

LYNDHURST, **Parkhill Hotel**

Beaulieu Road
SO43 7FZ
Map 4: SU30
Tel: 01703 282944
Fax: 01703 283268
Please telephone for further details

Be careful not to miss the turn off to Parkhill – it is easy to be distracted by the New Forest scenery. The hotel dates from the 18th century, but today it wears a more modern, elegant look. Cooking is sound based on classical techniques with some modern twists. A test meal produced tuna tartar on a bed of cold roasted Provençale vegetables, lightly roasted lamb saddle, spot-on, with a herby lamb jus, and accurately cooked vegetables, with a strongly flavoured chocolate mousse for dessert. Breads included onion and sun-dried tomato as well as plain brown and white rolls.

Directions: From Lyndhurst take B3056 (Beaulieu), hotel signed 1 mile on R. From Southampton take A35 (Lyndhurst)

MIDDLE WALLOP,
Fifehead Manor

Stockbridge SO20 8EG
Map 4: SU23
Tel: 01264 781565
Fax: 01264 781400
Chef: Frederick Roy
Owner: Fifehead Manor Hotel Ltd
Cost: *Alc* £19.50, fixed-price D £27.
☺ H/wine £11
Times: Noon-2.30pm/7-9.30pm
Additional: Bar food; Sunday L;
Children welcome; 🍴 dishes
Seats: 38. Private room 18
Smoking: No smoking in dining room
Accommodation: 16 en suite. Jacket & tie preferred
Credit cards: 🖃 🖃 🖅 🖸 🖃 🄲 JCB

Dating back to Saxon times, Fifehead retains many original details, especially in the dining room which occupies the main hall. The menu features classical French dishes, all deftly prepared using quality ingredients. Typical starters include pressed terrine of duck confit and foie gras studded with whole caramelised shallots and served with a garnish of potato brunoise and a scattering of lentils, and Fjordling smoked salmon with cucumber salad, keta and a saffron water vinaigrette. Main courses continue the trend – expect dishes such as roast fillet of cod with a basil and red pepper coulis, and roast breast of guinea fowl with garden peas and morels. Puddings range from the grandiose – gâteau Opéra with a slice of chocolate marquise, to the simple – lemon tart with a generous helping of sorbet. The wine list is predominantly French, with a token showing from other countries.

Directions: On the A343, 5 miles S of Andover

MILFORD ON SEA,
Rocher's Restaurant ❀❀

An unassuming sort of place, just 20 covers, with all the work done by owners Rebecca and Alain Rocher – she out front, he at the stove. Indeed, the Rochers have been plying their trade on Milford's High Street for a decade now. The room itself is modern and smart, rather more formal than one would expect in such a location, with a small bar area fronting the dining room proper. A winter dinner produced a good piece of duck confit, suitably melting, served with some well-dressed leaves, then a clean tasting, spot-on monkfish – firm fillets of fish, correctly trimmed with a slightly spiced orange beurre blanc. For dessert, a delicious chocolate fondant whose crisp and sponge-like exterior concealed a devilish heart of molten chocolate. France gets the biggest concentration on the wine list, prices are not high, and there is a more than adequate selection of half-bottles.

69/71 High Street SO41 0QG
Map 4: SZ29
Tel: 01590 642340
Chef: Alain Rocher
Owners: Alain & Rebecca Rocher
Cost: Fixed-price L £14.50/D from £17.95. ☺ H/wine £10.50.
Times: D only, 7.15-9.30pm.
Closed D Sun, Mon, Tue
Additional: Sunday L;
No children under 7
Seats: 24
Smoking: No pipes or cigars in dining room
Credit cards: ▬ ▬ ▆ ◨ ▬ ▐

Directions: On the B3058 3 miles SW of Lymington

MILFORD ON SEA,
South Lawn Hotel ❀

Lymington Road SO41 0RF
Map 4: SZ29
Tel: 01590 643911
Fax: 01590 644820
Chefs: Ernst Barten, David Gates
Owners: Ernst & Jennifer Barten
Cost: *Alc* £22.50, fixed-price L £12/D £18.50. ☺ H/wine £10
Times: Last L 1.45pm/last D 8.45pm.
Closed L Mon, Xmas & New Year
Additional: Sunday L; No children under 7; ◉ dishes
Smoking: No smoking in dining room
Accommodation: 24 en suite
Credit cards: ▬ ▬ ◨

Former dower house with a nice old-fashioned feel, set in four acres of well-tended grounds on the edge of the New Forest. The dining room serves a good range of local produce, especially fish – grilled fillets of locally caught plaice with parsley butter, cod Mornay, trout with toasted almonds. Sautéed calves' liver is recommended.

Directions: A337 from Lymington, L after 3 miles on to B3058; hotel 1 mile on R

MILFORD ON SEA,
Westover Hall Hotel &

Park Lane SO41 0PT
Map 4: SZ29
Tel: 01590 643044
Fax: 01590 644490
Chef: Neil Johnson
Owners: Stewart Mechem,
Nicola Musetti
Cost: *Alc* £21.50, fixed-price L
£21.50/D 22.50. ☺ H/wine £11.95
Times: Last L 2pm/last D 9.30pm
Additional: Bar food L; Sunday L;
Children welcome; ❹ dishes
Smoking: No smoking in dining room
Accommodation: 12 en suite
Credit cards: ■ ▄ ▀◥ ◖ ▦ ▐◖ ▣ JCB

*Lovely hotel, the view alone is enough to cheer anyone up – quite
spectacular. Italian menu with the food a mix of styles, all fairly
traditional and simple – melon with Parma ham, or tomato,
mozzarella and basil salad, and asparagus with melted butter and
Parmesan, for example. Superb sea bass with lemon oil, and good
olive bread.*

Directions: Turn off A337 onto B3058. Hotel is situated just out
of Milford centre, towards clifftop.

NEW MILTON,
Chewton Glen Hotel &&&

Christchurch Road
BH25 6QS
Map 4: SZ29
Tel: 01425 275341
Fax: 01425 272310
Chef: Pierre Chevillard
Owners: Martin & Brigitte Skan
Cost: Fixed-price L £18.50/D £47.50.
H/wine £17.25
Times: 12.30-last L 1.45pm/7.30-last
D 9.30pm
Additional: Bar food L; Sunday L;
Children welcome (no babies);
❹ dishes
Seats: 200. Private rooms 120. Jacket
& tie preferred

Inspectors applaud Chewton Glen for its atmosphere and
elegance; the quintessential country house hotel, it makes a
luxurious and hospitable retreat. Chef of long-standing, Pierre
Chevillard, has made his mark here, offering cooking that is
sure-footed as well as being full of interest, subtlety and aware
of current trends. Note braised pork cheeks and lobster
flavoured with ginger and lemongrass and garnished with baby
root vegetables. Or consider an April dinner that opened with
a well-flavoured, well-timed double-baked Emmental soufflé
served with a delicate fondue sauce, went on to top-quality
roast monkfish wrapped in ham with rösti-style potato and
accompanied by a light sauce flavoured with ham and spring
onions, and finished with a Victoria plum tart of superb pastry

and good sauce anglaise. The style has a classic base, as can be seen in dishes such as beef consommé with poached quails' eggs and julienne vegetables, and pan-fried tournedos of black Aberdeen Angus beef, creamed wild mushrooms with Perigord truffles and Madeira sauce.

Signature dishes: Fine tomato and Raclette cheese tart flavoured with pesto; braised fillet of sea bass with shiitake mushrooms, beansprouts flavoured with ginger and coriander; braised pork cheeks and lobster flavoured with ginger, lemongrass, and garnished with baby vegetables; double-baked Emmental soufflé served with a fondue sauce.

Directions: On A35 (Lyndhurst) turn R through Walkford, then 2nd left into Chewton Farm Road.

Smoking: No smoking in dining room; Air conditioning
Accommodation: 54 en suite
Credit cards:

AA Wine Award-see page 16 Shortlisted for

OLD BURGHCLERE,
The Dew Pond Restaurant ❀❀

The cottage-style restaurant dates from the 16th century and comprises two dining rooms – the Dew Pond Room and Winchester Room. Both have a homely, cosy feel and the place attracts a strong loyal following from the Newbury, Basingstoke and Winchester areas. The kitchen offers a modern style of cooking: risotto of wild mushrooms with Parmesan shavings and garden herbs; seared scallops with linguine and lightly curried mussel cream; Gressingham duck flavoured with ginger, honey and soy, served with a confit of peppers and spiced anise sauce; saddle of roe deer with creamed wild mushrooms and thyme red sauce. Desserts take in mille-feuille of bananas with chocolate sauce and vanilla pod ice cream, and chilled lemon soufflé with pistachios and raspberries. The wine list is large and lists wines by tastes such as full-bodied reds, as opposed to traditional regions.

Directions: Six miles south of Newbury. Take the Burghclere turn off A34 (Winchester), and follow signs for Old Burghclere

Newbury RG20 9LH
Map 4: SU46
Tel/Fax: 01635 278408
Chef: Keith Marshall
Owners: Keith & Julie Marshall
Please telephone for further details

PORTSMOUTH,
Bistro Montparnasse ❀

Enthusiastic new owners for this popular bistro, formerly a Victorian house, just off Southsea's town centre. Warm decor with modern feel and lots of arty prints. Short menu is supplemented by a fresh fish board. Light prawn and crab soufflé, pork fillet with creamed cabbage and bacon, and traditional apple tart show the style.

Additional: Children welcome; dishes
Smoking: No-smoking area; No pipes and cigars
Credit cards:

Directions: Follow brown tourist signs to D Day Museum. Turn L opposite museum (Avenue de Caen). At 1st road junction look for somewhere to park. Bistro across road on R.

103 Palmerston Road
PO5 3PS
Map 4: SZ69
Tel/Fax: 01705 816754
Chef: Gary Coleborn
Owner: Georgette Payne
Cost: Alc £24.45, fixed-price D £14.90. ☺ H/wine £9.50
Times: D only, last D 10pm. Closed Sun, Mon

RINGWOOD,
Moortown Lodge Hotel ❀❀

Expect a warm welcome from Jilly and Bob Burrows-Jones at their small Georgian hotel on the edge of the New Forest. Using local produce whenever possible, Jilly's short dinner menu (priced for three or four courses) is characterised by traditionally prepared dishes and good clear flavours. Floating cheese island (a light soufflé) is a speciality among the starters, while a typical evening's main course selection might comprise salmon with tarragon and vermouth, duck breast with Calvados and apple purée, and a rich casserole of local venison under a puff pastry top. Finish with one of the tempting home-made puds or a selection of British cheeses.

Directions: From Ringwood town centre take B3347 towards Christchurch for about 1.5 miles

244 Christchurch Road
BH24 3AS
Map 4: SU10
Tel: 01425 471404
Fax: 01425 476052
Chef: Jilly Burrows-Jones
Owners: Jilly & Bob Burrows-Jones
Cost: Fixed-price D £17.95. ☺
H/wine £8.95
Times: D only, last D 8.30pm. Closed Sun (non-residents), 24 Dec-mid Jan
Additional: Children welcome; ❹ dishes
Smoking: No smoking in dining room
Accommodation: 6 rooms
Credit cards: ▬ ▧ ▨

RINGWOOD, **Tyrrells Ford Hotel** ❀

Lovely quiet location for pleasant hotel with a wood-panelled restaurant that overlooks the large garden. Expect the likes of prawn and mushroom ramekin with a cheese topping, whole local sole with deep-fried parsley and nut-brown butter, and apple pie.

Avon BH23 7BH
Map 4: SU10
Tel: 01425 672646
Fax: 01425 672262
Chef: Philip Cooper
Owner: Mr I Caplan
Cost: *Alc* £27, fixed-price L £14.95/D £21. ☺ H/wine £10.95
Times: Last L 2pm/D 9pm
Additional: Bar food; Sunday L; ❹ dishes
Smoking: No smoking in dining room
Accommodation: 16 en suite
Credit cards:
▬ ▧ ▨ ▢ ▩ ▣ ▢ JCB

Directions: M27/A31 to Ringwood, B3347 3 miles south to Avon

ROMSEY, **Bertie's** ❀❀

A Georgian-era former workhouse, Bertie's is in the centre of this old market town. The restaurant is filled with highly-polished wooden tables and fresh flowers, and the atmosphere is cosy and intimate. The lunch menu offers a mix of dishes which can be taken either as a starter or main course, together with a range of upmarket sandwiches with fillings such as grilled cheese and mushroom, or avocado, bacon and tomato, and smoked salmon and cucumber with mint yoghurt dressing. Dinner is a more elaborate affair, with modern dishes along the lines of roasted guinea fowl with broad beans and honeyed carrots, perhaps seared breast of chicken with polenta chips and tarragon mayonnaise, and roast wood pigeon scented with rosemary and served with beetroot and pancetta. Desserts include pear tartlet with elderflower sorbet, creamy rice pudding with raisin sauce, and our inspector's choice – a simple chocolate marquise with 'vibrant' orange coulis.

Directions: 200m from Broadlands' gate in the centre of town

80 The Hundred SO51 8BX
Map 4: SU32
Tel/Fax: 01794 830708
Chef: Michael Weir
Owner: David Birmingham
Cost: *Alc* £25. ☺ H/wine £9.50
Times: Noon-last L 2pm/6.30-last D 10pm. Closed Sun, 24 Dec-3 Jan
Additional: Bar food L; Children welcome; ❹ dishes
Seats: 45
Smoking: No-smoking area; No pipes and cigars
Accommodation: 5 en suite
Credit cards: ▬ ▧ ▨ ▢ ▩ ▣ ▢

ROMSEY, **Old Manor House**

21 Palmerston Street SO51 8GF
Map 4: SU32
Tel: 01794 517353
Chef: Mauro Bregoli
Owners: Mauro & Esther Bregoli
Cost: *Alc* £28. H/wine £11.50
Times: Noon-last L 2pm/7-last
D 9.30pm. Closed D Sun, all Mon
Additional: Children welcome
Seats: 16
Smoking: No pipes & cigars
Credit cards:

An impressively ancient, beamed house with loads of character set in the heart of town. Enter straight into a small bar with comfy sofas and an open fire and ponder the menu. This has been simplified since our last visit to some half-a-dozen starters and main courses, but Mauro Bregoli's cooking remains with its heart and soul firmly in Italy. Top-notch produce is used in dishes as diverse as potted duck on a bed of rocket, or warm buffalo cacciotta with crusty olive bread and pancetta, and main courses such as braised wild boar with polenta, or fillet of beef with mustard and peppercorn sauce. A spring dinner began with carpaccio of 'the most superb' foie gras with walnuts, pronounced 'divine', and well-timed fresh asparagus with a light hollandaise sauce. Next up was a lovely piece of roast tuna served with a salsa verde, and perfectly cooked duck breast with morels, white wine and cream. Desserts such as apple tart with sauce anglaise, and orange tart with crème pâtissière show a wish to keep things simple. Great petits fours – truffles, fudge and Italian pastries.

Directions: Opposite the entrance to Broadlands Estate

ROTHERWICK, **Tylney Hall**

Rotherwick Hook
RG27 9AZ
Map 4: SU75
Tel: 01256 764881
Fax: 01256 768141
Chef: Stephen Hine
Cost: *Alc* £45, fixed-price L £21/D
£33. H/wine £15.50

Sixty-six acres of beautiful parkland surround Tylney Hall, a spacious Victorian country house with log fires, and fine ceilings. The gardens, originally laid out by Gertrude Jekyll, have been restored to their former glory and feature lakes and ornamental fountains. The gardens are overlooked by the oak-panelled restaurant, a grand Victorian dining room where modern French cooking is the order of the day. Typical dishes range from roast monkfish with wild mushrooms, fettucine and thyme, to breast of duck with olive and garlic mash. Our inspector enjoyed a late spring meal of hot sole mousse with Mediterranean prawns and asparagus and caviar sauce, followed by saddle of venison with a red wine and bitter chocolate sauce. The dessert list could include lime tart with poached pineapple and coconut ice cream, and caramelised rice pudding with spiced plums. The set menu changes daily, while the *carte* evolves seasonally.

Times: Noon-last L 1.45pm/7-last D 9.45pm
Additional: Bar food ; Sunday L; Children welcome; ⏺ dishes
Seats: 70. Private rooms available
Smoking: No smoking in dining room
Accommodation: 110 en suite
Credit cards:
▮▮ ▨ ▧ ▨ ▨ C ▨ JCB

Directions: M3/J5 take A287 (Newnham). From M4/J11 take B3349 (Hook), at sharp bend L (Rotherwick), L again and L in village (Newnham), 1 mile on R.

SILCHESTER,
Romans Hotel ✺

Little London Road
RG7 2PN
Map 2: SU66
Tel: 01189 700421
Fax: 01189 700691
Chef: Erik Chauffour
Owners: N & M Tuthill
Cost: *Alc* £20, fixed-price L&D £15.50. ☺ H/wine £11.50
Times: Last L 2pm/last D 9.30pm. Closed L Sat, Xmas-New Year

Lovely Elizabethan house set in its own grounds. The kitchen is currently showing good form. Terrine of quail with a compote of grapes is a speciality, and comes garnished with home-grown herbs. Other treats are a good-value three-course lunch which on the day of inspection included a duck breast with raspberry vinegar and a pistachio crème brûlée.

Additional: Bar food; Sunday L; Children welcome; ⏺ dishes
Smoking: No smoking in dining room
Accommodation: 25 en suite
Credit cards: ▮▮ ▨ ▧ ▨ ▨ ▨

Directions: Signposted on the A340 between Basingstoke and Tadley

SOUTHAMPTON,
The Boathouse ✺✺

29 Shamrock Way
Hythe Marina Village
SO45 6DY
Map 4: SU41
Tel: 01703 845594
Fax: 01703 846017
Chef: Ian McAndrew
Owner: Leisure Great Britain (Oakley) Ltd
Cost: *Alc* £24.50. Fixed price L £10.50 (2 courses). ☺ H/wine £9.95
Times: Noon-last L 2.30pm/7pm-last D 10pm. Closed D Sun, Mon, 2 weeks Jan
Additional: Sunday L; Children welcome

There are outstanding views of the Solent, and the luxury boats in the Hythe Marina, so the split-level dining-room goes for the nautical look in jolly yellow and blues with lots of stripped pine. Tables are set simply, with a bottle of olive oil on each, and the *carte* pre-empts the question 'What do you recommend', by starring the chef's choice. This could well be poached fillet of salmon topped with asparagus tips with tomato butter sauce. Lunch offers a more brasserie-led menu with the kitchen really showing its style in the evening. Terrine of confit of pheasant with winter vegetables and spicy lentil dressing was accurately prepared with good balance and depth of flavour, and roast fillet of cod with creamed sweet yellow peppers and spinach was simply spot-on in every respect. A dessert of chocolate tarte with orange-flavoured ice cream slipped down equally pleasurably.

Seats: 50. Private dining room 12
Smoking: Air-conditioning
Credit cards: ▮▮ ▨ ▧ ▨ C

Directions: M27 exit 2 A326 (Fawley). Left to Hythe, in Marina Village

SOUTHAMPTON,

Botleigh Grange Hotel ❀❀

Hedge End SO30 2GA
Map 4: SU41
Tel: 01489 787700
Fax: 01489 788535
Chef: Edward Denovan
Owner: D K Plumpton
Cost: *Alc* £22, fixed price L £13.95/D
£17.95. ☺ H/wine £9.95
Times: Noon-last L 2pm/6-last
D 10pm
Additional: Bar food ; Sunday L;
Children welcome; ❸ dishes
Seats: 150. Private room 24-80
Smoking: No smoking in diningroom.
Jacket & tie preferred
Accommodation: 41 en suite
Credit cards: ▆ ▆ ▆ ▆ ▆ ▆ ▆ JCB

A much-extended mansion standing in extensive grounds near
the village of Hedge End, which is within easy reach of the
M27, Southampton and Portsmouth. The panelled cocktail
lounge, with its ornate ornamental ceiling, leads into the
elegant, comfortable dining-room, where a glass-domed ceiling
gives a light and airy feel. The modern English menu plunders
mainland Europe for ideas, making the occasional foray
further afield. Risotto may come with ratatouille and
Parmesan, and poached trout with pesto hummus and rocket.
Roast smoked rabbit is plated with squid-ink risotto and
courgette lyonnaise, while loin of pork is marinated in Cajun
spices and served with a red onion chutney samosa. Desserts
come from nearer home – banoffee pie with Drambuie ice
cream, say, or sticky toffee pudding with butterscotch sauce,
and farmhouse cheeses are British. A white wine from the
Hamble Valley leads the round-the-world section of the list of
around 50 wines, with a further half-dozen or so half-bottles.

Directions: On A334, 1.5 miles from M27 junc 7

SOUTHAMPTON,

De Vere Grand Harbour ❀

*Choose between the set-price menus at Brewsters, or the carte at the
smaller Athertons, at this modern hotel near the site where the
Mayflower sailed. Athertons' more ambitious menu might feature
pigeon and venison cassoulet among the starters, and go on to
parrot-fish steamed with coriander and ginger, and venison collops
with creamed lentils.*

West Quay Road SO15 1AG
Map 4: SU41
Tel: 01703 633033
Fax: 01703 633066
Chef: Michael Walker
Owner: De Vere Hotels
Cost: *Alc* £35, fixed-price L £24/D
£27.50 (4 courses). ☺ H/wine £11.95
Times: Last L 2.15pm/last D 9.45pm

Additional: Bar food; Sunday L; Children welcome; ❸ dishes
Smoking: No-smoking area; Air conditioning
Accommodation: 172 en suite
Credit cards: ▆ ▆ ▆ ▆ ▆ ▆ ▆ JCB

Directions: In 'old town' area, just S of city centre

SOUTHAMPTON, Kuti's Brasserie

Stylish city-centre Indian run by a traditionally attired, friendly team. Extensive menu offers a mix of Bangladeshi and traditional curry house favourites. A recent meal included batak tikka, marinated duck breast, followed by lamb rogan gosht and excellent garlic naan bread. Live Indian music every fortnight.

Additional: Children welcome; ❹ dishes
Smoking: Air conditioning
Credit cards: ▨ ▨ ▨ ▨ ▨ ▨ JCB

Directions: In old part of city near Ocean Village and Docks

37-39 Oxford Street SO14 3DJ
Map 4: SU41
Tel: 01703 221585/333473
Fax: 01703 233025
Chef: Romis Miah
Owners: S S Dhandra, J P Welch, F Benazi, K Miah
Cost: Alc £18; Fixed-price L £8.50/D £15 (Fri & Sat only). ☺ H/wine £7.95
Times: Last L 2pm/last D 11.30pm.
Closed 25-26 Dec

SOUTHAMPTON,
Merchants Restaurant NEW

A modern building with a cathedral ceiling and many modern prints located on the waterfront at Ocean Village. Expect Hong Kong-style scallops and stir-fried vegetables, braised monkfish with crisp shredded vegetables and wild mushroom broth, plus cinnamon apple strudel for dessert.

Ironside House
Ocean Village SO14 3TN
Map 4: SU41
Tel: 01703 333221
Fax: 01703 363604
Please telephone for further details

SOUTHSEA, Queens Hotel

Two menus offer diners a good range of dishes at this stately Edwardian hotel that dominates the Southsea seafront. The restaurant overlooks the garden and pool The sound cooking displays ambition mixed with a strong sense of classicism. Good breakfasts.

Clarence Parade PO5 3LJ
Map 4: SU06
Tel: 01705 822466
Fax: 01705 821901
Please telephone for further details

SWAY, String of Horses

Small hotel set in mature gardens adjoining the New Forest. Low-beamed restaurant, candlelit at night, attracts a loyal local following at weekends. Expect pea and lettuce soup, noisette of lamb with prunes, garlic and rosemary butter, and white chocolate bavarois with dark chocolate sauce.

Smoking: No smoking in dining room
Accommodation: 8 en suite
Credit cards: ▨ ▨ ▨ ▨ ▨ ▨

Directions: From B3055 turn R over station bridge, 2nd L into Mead End Road, 350 yds on L

Mead End Road SO41 6EH
Map 4: SZ29
Tel/Fax: 01590 682631
Chef: Julio Frias Robles
Owners: Chris & Linda Proctor
Cost: Alc £25, fixed price D £21 (4 courses). ☺ H/wine £12.50
Times: D only, last D 9pm.
Closed D Sun & Mon, 1-14 Jan
Additional: Sunday L (last L 1.30pm); ❹ dishes

WICKHAM, Old House Hotel

Pacific Rim, Californian Cool, Modern Med, the fashions come and go, but the Georgian Old House Hotel remains true to its love of French regional cooking. This is the place for snails simmered in shallots, white wine, Pernod, cream and served in a puff pastry case, for fillet steak with a sauce of Madeira, brandy and meat glaze finished with cream and pink, green,

The Square PO17 5JG
Map 4: SU51
Tel: 01329 833049
Fax: 01329 833672
Chef: Nicholas Harman
Owners: Richard & Annie Skipwith
Cost: Alc £31.50. Fixed-price L £10 (2 courses)/D £31.50. H/wine £12.75

white and black peppercorns, or veal kidneys and sweetbreads in a creamy Champagne sauce with wild mushrooms and baby spinach. A selection of fresh fish may be served lightly grilled in virgin olive oil, with a red wine vinegar butter sauce flavoured with thyme and veal jus. One almost has a *crise de foie* just thinking about it – and that's before we get to the bitter chocolate truffle with creamy vanilla and candied ginger custard, and the home-made petits fours. All we can say is – bon appétit.

Directions: In the centre of Wickham, 3 miles N of Fareham at junction of A32/B2177

Times: 12.30pm-last L 1.45pm/7.30pm-last D 9.30pm. Closed L Sat & Mon, Sun, 2 wks Xmas, 1 wk Easter, 2 wks Aug
Additional: Children welcome; ◑ dishes
Seats: 35. Private dining room 12
Smoking: No pipes and cigars in dining room
Accommodation: 9 en suite
Credit cards: ▪ ☲ ☴ ▦ ◖ ⬛

WINCHESTER, Harvey's ❀❀

Fight your way through the crowded, rather raucous, wine bar on the ground floor to this attractive, airy restaurant above. The menu at Harvey's continues the bright, fresh theme. At lunch things are kept relatively simple with dishes along the lines of steamed mussels with thyme and chips, blue cheese and pesto pasta with butternut squash, and dressed crab with green bean salad and new potatoes. Dinner gets a bit more adventurous – our inspector enjoyed smoked chicken risotto with chilli guacamole and rocket, followed by fresh steamed salmon with cucumber tagliatelle, grain mustard and dill. Other modern British dishes could include marinated duck breast with honeyed shallots, fillet of sea bass with crispy polenta, salsa cruda and pesto, and lamb cutlets with tarragon mousse and a ragout of broad beans. Desserts range from summer pudding and clotted cream to poached pear with vanilla ice cream and butterscotch sauce.

Directions: In The Square, which runs parallel to the pedestrianised High Street

31b The Square
SO23 9EX
Map 4: SU42
Tel: 01962 843438
Fax: 01962 850555
Chef: Shane Beaton
Owner: Harvey Simmons
Cost: *Alc* £26, fixed-price L £9.50 (2 courses). ☺ H/wine £9.95
Times: Noon-2.30pm/7-last D 9.30pm. Closed D Mon, all Sun
Additional: Children welcome; ◑ dishes
Seats: 60. Private dining room 30
Smoking: No-smoking area; Air conditioning
Credit cards: ▪ ☲ ☴ ⌐ ◖ ⬛ JCB

WINCHESTER,
Hotel du Vin & Bistro ❀❀

Robin Hutson's and Gerard Basset's early 18th-century town house occupies a splendid central position in Winchester. The interior is charming, a touch of elegance mixed with an easy, relaxed style. This stylish informality is perhaps best marked in the bistro, where bare boards, a pick-and-mix selection of highly polished tables and chairs, with wine memorabilia crowding the walls, form the backdrop for a menu that owes a lot to the Mediterranean and beyond. Endive salad with fresh anchovies and a Caesar dressing, or Thai-spiced crab cakes with chilli jam and tomato dressing, with main courses of escalope of calves' liver with shallot marmalade and sauce diable, or fillet of pork with choucroute, chorizo sausage and a marjoram jam, show the range. However, a series of test meals have left us with the impression that while proprietal eyes were off Winchester, setting up the new Hotel du Vin, Royal Tunbridge Wells (see entry), there has been a slight slip in the quality of the cooking. The wine list, on the other hand, remains a strength, obviously selected by a master hand and offering great choice.

Directions: M3/J11, follow signs for Winchester. Hotel on L just before town centre

14 Southgate Street SO23 9EF
Map 4: SU42
Tel: 01962 841414
Fax: 01962 842458
Chef: Andy Clark
Owners: Robin Hutson, Gerard Basset
Cost: *Alc* £30. H/wine £9.95
Times: Noon-last L 1.45pm/7-last D 9.30pm
Additional: Sunday L; Children welcome; ◑ dishes
Seats: 65. Private dining room 48
Smoking: No pipes or cigars
Accommodation: 23 en suite
Credit cards: ▪ ☲ ☴ ⌐ ▦ ⬛

WINCHESTER, **Hunters**

Hunters has the air of an 80s café bar, with a tiled floor and saucy Victorian prints. Warm salad of scallops, seared chump of lamb, or sesame chicken with an oriental salad, and fig and ricotta cake with natural yogurt, are typical dishes from the short menu.

Additional: Children welcome; 🍴 dishes
Smoking: No-smoking area
Credit cards: ▬ ▥ ▧ ▢ ▤ ▣ ▦

5 Jewry Street SO23 8RZ
Map 4: SU42
Tel/Fax: 01962 860006
Chef: Simon Cox
Owner: David Birmingham
Cost: *Alc* £25, fixed-price D £9.95
(2 courses). ☺ H/wine £9.50
Times: Last L 2pm/last D 10pm.
Closed Sun, 24 Dec-3 Jan

Directions: Towards top of the City just off High Street, 200 yards from Theatre Royal & Library car park

WINCHESTER,
Lainston House Hotel

Sparsholt SO21 2LT
Map 4: SU42
Tel: 01962 863588
Fax: 01962 776672
Chef: Friedrich Litty
Cost: *Alc* £35, fixed-price L £19.50/D £35.50 (6 courses). H/wine £15.
Times: 12.30-last L 2pm/7-last D 10pm
Additional: Bar food L; Sunday L; Children welcome; 🍴 dishes
Seats: 60. Various private dining rooms. Jacket & tie preferred
Smoking: No smoking in dining room
Accommodation: 38 en suite
Credit cards: ▬ ▥ ▧ ▢ ▤ ▣ ▦ JCB

This endearing country house hotel is a popular spot, and the restaurant is a stately panelled room, the carpet ablaze with hundreds of English roses. The Anglo-French *carte* needs time for serious study. First courses might include twice-baked goats' cheese soufflé, or roulade of salmon gravad lax with dill pesto. Fish and meat choices also balance classic and modern ideas with the likes of roulade of Dover sole with diamonds of leek in a tomato and chive sauce, and pigeon in a capriccio-style with lentil velouté and pommes gaufrettes. Red mullet escabeche with deep-fried sardines and Mediterranean vegetables, or a duo of duck with Alsatian spätzle, French bean salad, poached egg and grain mustard sabayon, and Earl Grey parfait with caramel sauce are examples of some lively ideas underpinning the formal *carte*. Heavily endorsed, however, is the chocolate gourmandise, which fully lived up to its name.

Directions: Three miles from the centre of Winchester, off the A272 road to Stockbridge. Signposted.

WINCHESTER, **Nine The Square**

'This was a smashing meal' enthused one inspector of David Bennett's popular wine bar-cum-restaurant. Time spent with Franco Taruschio at the Walnut Tree, Llanddewi Skyrrid (see entry), and at the Carved Angel, Dartmouth (see entry), has paid off – the cooking exudes an assured, no-nonsense style. The Italian influence comes through with carpaccio of beef

The Square SO23 9HA
Map 4: SU42
Tel: 01962 864004
Fax: 01962 879586
Chef: David Bennett
Owners: Mr & Mrs D Bennett
Cost: *Alc* £25, fixed price L £5.95
(2 courses). ☺ H/wine £ 11.25

with Parmesan, home-made pasta accompanied by a classic fennel pesto, and the likes of wild mushroom and gorgonzola risotto, all making an appearance on the short menu. At our autumn lunch, honest polenta flavoured with fresh Parmesan came with simple but good chargrilled vegetables, and was followed by a spot-on 'muttony' yet meltingly tender braised shank of lamb, served with a tomato-based bean stew. Honeycomb ice cream was exceptional. There's a sound selection of wines by the glass, and few bottles, apart from the fizz, breach the £20 barrier.

Directions: Situated in the main square of the city, just outside the grounds of the cathedral and opposite the museum

Times: Noon-last L 2pm, 6-last D 10pm. Closed Sun, 3 days Xmas, some Bhs
Additional: Children welcome; ◑ dishes
Seats: 45. Private room 20
Smoking: No pipes in dining room
Credit cards: ▦ ▦ ▦ ▦ ▦ ▦

WINCHESTER,
Old Chesil Rectory ❀❀

A low front door and low beams are what you would expect of a building dating from Tudor times. A warm, relaxed and informal atmosphere pervades the two-floored restaurant, where the menus are anything but dated. Truffle oil and Parmesan go into asparagus risotto, which an inspector found 'spot on', and sun-dried red pepper salad with tapenade dressing accompanies grilled goats' cheese with roasted pine nuts. Tender and flavoursome shank of lamb is braised with olives and pesto, or there might be a more classic main course of skate wing in black butter. White and plain chocolate mousse layered between Kirsch-soaked chocolate sponge has been well received; bread-and-butter pudding with apricot sauce would make a good alternative, have a glass of pudding wine to go with it. Fine wines from Bordeaux and Burgundy are a feature of the main wine list.

Directions: From King Alfred's statue at the bottom of The Broadway, cross the small bridge and turn R; the restaurant is to the R, just off mini roundabout

1 Chesil Street SO23 8HU
Map 4: SU42
Tel: 01962 851555
Fax: 01962 869704
Chefs: Nicholas A Ruthven-Stuart, Nicola Saunders, Philip Storey
Owners: Nicholas A & Christina M Ruthven-Stuart
Cost: Fixed-price L £20/D £30. ☺ H/wine £12.95
Times: Noon-last L 2pm/7-last D 9.30pm. Closed Sun (except Easter Day & Mothering Sunday), Mon, 2 wks Xmas, 2 wks Aug
Additional: Children welcome; ◑ dishes
Seats: 50. Private dining room 12 &14
Smoking: No-smoking area; No pipes and cigars
Credit cards: ▦ ▦ ▦ ▦ ▦ JCB

WINCHESTER, **Royal Hotel** ❀

Well-established city-centre hotel, popular with both leisure and business guests. Smartly presented, split-level conservatory restaurant has crisp linen, fresh flowers and candle light at dinner giving an intimate feel. Try chicken and vegetable terrine with hazelnut dressing, herb-crusted rack of lamb and port sauce, as well as steamed toffee and date pudding.

Saint Peter Street SO23 8BS
Map 4: SU42
Tel: 01962 840840
Fax: 01962 841582
Please telephone for further details

Directions: Take one-way system through Winchester, turn R off St George's Street into St Peter Street. Hotel on R

WINCHESTER, **The Wessex**

A view across the close to Winchester Cathedral is just one of the plusses at the restaurant of this modern hotel. The Little Gourmet children's menu is among the best we've seen and for grown-ups the soundly executed and interesting carte is supplemented by a separate list of seafood specialities.

Paternoster Row
SO23 9LQ
Map 4: SU42
Tel: 01962 861611
Chef: Stephen Carter
Owners: Forte
Cost: Alc £20, fixed price L £7.95
(2 courses). ☺ H/wine £11.95
Times: Last L 2.15pm/last D 9.45pm
Additional: Bar food; Sunday L;
Children welcome; ✦ dishes
Smoking: No smoking in dining room;
Air conditioning
Accommodation: 94 en suite
Credit cards: ▆ ▆ ▆ ▆ ▆ ▆ ▆

Directions: City centre close to cathedral

WINCHESTER, **Wykeham Arms**

250-year-old inn close to the cathedral in the old part of the city. Place has great buzz and bags of character. Lots of separate eating areas but the same short carte throughout. Expect fish and herb terrine with a light red pepper sauce, roast rack of lamb with a port wine glaze, and bread-and-butter pudding. Very good wine list with a preference for Burgundy.

75 Kingsgate Street SO23 9PE
Map 4: SU42
Tel: 01962 853834
Fax: 01962 854411
Please telephone for further details

Directions: Head S out of city along Southgate Street. Take 3rd turning L into Canon Street, inn on R at end.

HEREFORDSHIRE

HEREFORD, **Ancient Camp Inn**

The location is certainly remote, perched 70 feet above the River Wye on a road that appears to go nowhere; the views are sensational. The unusual name is taken from the Iron Age hill fort that the inn's lawns now cover. The place itself successfully

Nr Eaton Bishop HR2 9QX
Map 3: SO53
Tel: 01981 250449
Fax: 01981 251581
Chef: Ewart McKie
Owners: Pauline & Ewart McKie
Cost: Alc £25. H/wine £8.50
Times: Noon-last L 2pm/7pm-last
D 9pm. Closed D Sun, all Mon (non residents), 2wks Jan
Additional: Bar food L; Sunday L;
No children under 12 at D; ✦ dishes
Seats: 36. Private dining room 8
Smoking: No smoking in dining room;
Air conditioning
Accommodation: 5 en suite
Credit cards: ▆ ▆ ▆ ▆ ▆

blends the rustic – exposed beams, flagstone floors, real fires –
with solid comforts such as pleasant, cheerful bedrooms,
professional service and very good cooking. Booking is
essential. The kitchen changes its menus daily, and the
repertoire is built around fresh produce, much of it regional.
Game is a feature in season, as is Welsh lamb and beef, and
simple terrines and mousses make effective starters. Puddings
are a strength with the Camp sticky toffee pudding and vanilla
ice cream being understandably popular

Directions: Take A465 (Abergavenny road) from Hereford. Turn
R to Ruckhall and Belmont Abbey; inn is 2.5 miles along road

LEDBURY, Feathers Hotel

High Street HR8 1DS
Map 3: SO73
Tel: 01531 635266
Fax: 01531 638955
Chef: John Capaldi
Owner: David Elliston
Cost: *Alc* £22. ☺ H/wine £8.75
Times: Last L 2pm/last D 9.30pm
Additional: Sunday L; Children
welcome; ❹ dishes
Accommodation: 24 en suite
Credit cards: 🔳 🔳 🔳 🔳 🔳 **C** 🔳 JCB

Directions: Ledbury is on
A449/A438/A417, and the hotel is
prominent on the main street

*Stunning timber-framed Elizabethan coaching inn that dominates
the High Street in grand style. Lively menu in Fuggles, ranging from
steaks, own hamburgers with relish, French fries and salad, to a
robust casserole of local wood and field fare, and fresh fish from a
specials 'fish board'. Try chocolate, brandy and ginger cheesecake
for dessert.*

LEOMINSTER,
The Marsh Country Hotel ✿✿

Eyton HR6 0AG
Map 3: SO45
Tel: 01568 613952
Chef: Jacqueline Gilleland
Owners: Jacqueline & Martin
Gilleland
Cost: Fixed price D £24.75.
H/wine £9.50
Times: D only, 7.30-9pm.
Closed 3 wks Jan
Additional: Sunday L (12.30-2pm);
No children under 12; ❹ dishes
Seats: 24
Smoking: No smoking in dining room
Accommodation: 4 en suite
Credit cards: 🔳 🔳 🔳 🔳 **C** 🔳

Painstakingly restored from near-dereliction, this fourteenth-
century timber-framed building has a characterful yet tranquil
interior, including an inglenook fireplace and a splendid great
hall. There's also a large garden from where most of the

vegetables and herbs for the table come. For proprietors Jacqueline and Martin Gilleland are more than simply talented restorers. Martin is responsible for the restaurant's remarkably wide-ranging wine list, while Jacqueline's set-price menu provides plenty of variety, seasonal produce and memorable cooking. An inspection meal began with a mouth-wateringly delicious crab tartlet with mixed peppers, followed by perfectly cooked breast of chicken with tarragon and asparagus on rösti potatoes. Accompanying vegetables were exquisitely fresh and flavourful. No complaints, either, with the mango upside-down pudding, served with a tangy lime mousse. Even the details here are just so: canapés and chocolates are made on the premises, as is the fresh, light olive bread.

Directions: Two miles N/W of Leominster. Follow signs for Eyton and Lucton

ROSS-ON-WYE, Chase Hotel ❀

Gloucester Road HR9 5LH
Map 3: SO52
Tel: 01989 763161
Fax: 01989 768330
Owner: Alan Porter
Cost: *Alc* £25, fixed-price D £25. ☺
H/wine £9.75
Times: Last L 2pm/last D 10pm.
Closed L Sat, Bhs
Additional: Bar food; Sunday L;
❹ dishes
Smoking: No smoking in dining room
Accommodation: 38 en suite
Credit cards: 〓 〓 〓 ⌐ 〓 ▣ ▣

A period hotel set in its own spacious grounds yet within easy reach of the town centre. Dinner (priced for one, two or three courses) might include rack of lamb with honey and mustard crust, cod with tomato fondue and Parmesan wafer, and duck breast with prune and orange compote.

Directions: From town centre follow B4260 towards Gloucester, hotel 200yds on R

ROSS-ON-WYE,

Glewstone Court ❀

Charming Regency house offering a relaxed, informal atmosphere. Fresh local produce influences a menu that shows a strong awareness of modern trends. Enjoy warm crab, leek and lemongrass cheesecake, fillet of Hereford beef with claret mushroom. save room for the dark chocolate truffle torte.

Additional: Bar food; Sunday L; Children welcome; ❹ dishes
Smoking: No pipes and cigars
Accommodation: 7 en suite
Credit cards: 〓 〓 〓 ⌐ 〓 ▣ JCB

Glewstone HR9 6AW
Map 3: SO52
Tel: 01989 770367
Fax: 01989 770282
Chefs: Christine Reeve-Tucker, Philip Meek
Owners: Christine & William Reeve-Tucker
Cost: Fixed-price L £15/D £25 (4 courses). ☺ H/wine £9
Times: Last L 1.45pm/last D 9.30pm.
Closed 25-27 Dec

Directions: From Ross Market Place take A40/A49 (Monmouth/Hereford) over Wilton Bridge. At roundabout L onto A40 (Monmouth/S Wales), after 1 mile R for Glewstone

ROSS-ON-WYE,

Hunsdon Manor Hotel

The local sandstone manor house dates from Elizabethan times, and is now a personally run hotel. Enthusiasm in the kitchen comes through in dishes such as pan-fried scallops with bacon, Welsh leg of lamb with a delciately flavoured ginger sauce, and nice light crêpe flavoured with lemon. Extensive gardens.

Additional: Children welcome; ❹ dishes
Smoking: No-smoking area
Accommodation: 25 en suite
Credit cards: 💳 💳 💳 💳 💳 💳

Directions: On A40 2 miles east of Ross

Weston-under-Penyard HR9 7PE
Map 3: SO52
Tel: 01989 563376.562748
Fax: 01989 768348
Chef: Peter Valleley
Owner: Leila Clarke
Cost: *Alc* £23, fixed price L £16/D £18. ☺ H/wine £12
Times: Last L 2pm/last D 9.30pm. Closed L Sun

ROSS-ON-WYE,

Pengethley Manor ✿✿

There's no doubting Pengethley Manor looks the part: this stately Georgian country house stands proud in 15 acres of grounds, including its own vineyards. Such a venue complements the restaurant's fine cuisine and hospitable service. Both set price menu and *carte* provide a good choice of imaginative dishes. Intense flavours characterise the cooking, as evidenced by a test meal that started with savoury tartlet filled with smoked haddock and white wine, topped with poached egg and Gruyère shavings on a bed of spinach. Apricot lamb continued the theme, the succulent meat marinated in apricot conserve, encrusted in breadcrumbs, oregano and rosemary, and served with onion marmalade. Vegetables, too, are elaborately and expertly prepared. Meringue St Clements – orange sponge, lemon cream crowned with meringue accompanied by a raspberry and mint coulis – also garnered praise. Canapés and petits fours are made in-house, and you can accompany a meal with Pengethley Manor wine (a fruity, dry white).

Directions: Telephone for directions

Pengethley Park HR9 6LL
Map 3: SO52
Tel: 01989 730211
Fax: 01989730238
Chef: Ferdinand van der Knaap
Owners: Patrick & Geraldine Wisker
Cost: *Alc* £30, fixed price L £16/D £25 (4 courses). H/wine £13
Times: Noon-last L 2pm/7-last D 9.30pm
Additional: Bar food L; Sunday L; No children under 10; ❹ dishes
Seats: 50. Private room 25. Jacket & tie preferred
Smoking: No smoking in dining room
Accommodation: 25 en suite
Credit cards: 💳 💳 💳 💳 💳 💳 💳 JCB

ULLINGSWICK, **The Steppes** ✿✿

A delightful old country house, parts of which date back to 1380. With just six tables, the 14th-century dining room has an intimate atmosphere enhanced by heavy oak beams, original tiled floor and a huge inglenook fireplace. Tricia Howland is a talented and award-winning cook, whose imaginative dishes use the best local produce in dishes such as braised leg of pork with brandy, cream and mushrooms, and baked rainbow trout with gooseberry sauce. An early summer meal sampled by our inspector began with coquille à la bretonne, fresh seafood scallops with mushrooms in a tasty white wine sauce with a garnish of crisp salad leaves and whole king prawns. The main dish was braised knuckle of lamb – 'melt-in-the-mouth' tender – served in a rich broth flavoured with bay leaves. Desserts could include warm apple tarte Tatin, pecan nut and toffee cheesecake, and winter berries in port.

Directions: Off the A417 Gloucester to Leominster road

Hereford HR1 3JG
Map 3: SO54
Tel: 01432 820424
Fax: 01432 820042
Chef: Tricia Howland
Owners: Henry & Tricia Howland
Cost: Fixed-price D £26 (4 courses). ☺ H/wine £7.95
Times: D only, 7.30-9pm. Closed Dec-Jan
Additional: No children under 12; ❹ dishes
Seats: 12. Jacket & tie preferred
Smoking: No smoking in dining room
Accommodation: 6 en suite
Credit cards: 💳 💳 💳 💳 JCB

WEOBLEY,
Ye Olde Salutation Inn ❀❀

Market Pitch HR4 8SJ
Map 3: SO45
Tel: 01544 318443
Fax: 01544 318216
Chef: Graham Leavesley
Owners: Mr Christopher Anthony,
Mrs Frances Anthony
Cost: *Alc* £23. Fixed-price L £10.50.
☺ H/wine £8.75.
Times: Noon-last L 2pm/7pm-last
D 9pm. Closed D Sun, Mon, 25 Dec
Additional: Bar food; Sunday L;
❹ dishes
Seats: 38.
Smoking: No smoking in dining room
Accommodation: 4 en suite
Credit cards: ▆ ▆ ▜ ▙ ▆ ▐ ▣ JCB

Combining a former ale and cider house and an adjoining
black-and-white timbered cottage, this delightful little hotel
(which dates back over 500 years) is at the centre of the
medieval village. There's a large inglenook fireplace at the
heart of the restaurant, but the real attraction is the reliably
good cooking. Although favouring tried and tested
combinations of flavours, the menu does not lack interest and
offers dishes such as home-cured gravad lax accompanied by
honey and grain mustard quenelles, barquettes of quails' eggs
with creamed leeks and a chervil flavoured sauce, tenderloin of
pork on a compote of spiced apples and a prune and
Armagnac sauce, and spinach and oyster mushroom-filled
supreme of chicken on a white wine and tarragon sauce. There
is now a separate vegetarian menu. Finish with the likes of
Bramley apple tart with walnut crumble and Calvados ice
cream, or an iced white chocolate cream.

Directions: Down hill into village, take 1st R, then 2nd R

HERTFORDSHIRE

CHESHUNT, **Marriott Hotel** ❀

Halfhide Lane Turnford
EN10 6NG
Map 5: TL30
Tel: 01992 451245
Fax: 01992 440120
Chef: Val O'Kelley
Owners: Marriott International
Cost: *Alc* £19, fixed price D £19.50.
☺ H/wine £10.95
Times: D only, last D 10pm

*There's an international flavour to the extensive modern menu in this
hotel restaurant but the style is informal. Skate comes on a bed of
garden-fresh vegetables flavoured with ginger, spring onions and
chilli. Try the good home-made soups and selection of interesting
salads. Desserts include apple tart, dark chocolate torte and
cheesecake.*

Additional: Bar food; Children welcome; ❹ dishes
Smoking: No smoking in dining room; Air conditioning
Accommodation: 143 en suite
Credit cards: ▆ ▆ ▜ ▙ ▆ ▐ ▣ JCB

Directions: Telephone for directions

ELSTREE, **Edgwarebury Hotel** ❀❀❀

Barnet Lane WD6 3RE
Map 4: TQ19
Tel: 0181 9538227
Fax: 0181 2073668
Chef: Chris Fisher
Owner: Regal Hotel Group plc
Cost: *Alc* £26, fixed-price L & D
£26.95. ☺ H/wine £10.50
Times: 12.30-last L 2.30pm/7-last
D 9.30pm. Closed L Sat
Additional: Sunday L; Children
welcome; ❀ dishes
Seats: 60. Private rooms 18 + 30
Smoking: No smoking in dining room
Accommodation: 47 en suite
Credit cards: 🟦 🟦 💳 💳 💳 💳 💳 JCB

Directions: Access from Ml/J4 & 5,
M25/J19 & 23, Barnet Lane is signed
Elstree & Aldenham

This former millionaire's private mock-Tudor mansion is set in
ten acres of mature grounds within easy reach of the M1 and
M25. The Gothic-style dining room has splendid views over
London. Chris Fisher cooks to a high standard, offering an
enticing, ambitious menu, with lots of fish choices amongst the
starters, as well as a 'plain and simple' menu preferred by
conference guests and the less adventurous (chargrilled sirloin
of beef, grilled whole lemon sole). From the former, our
inspector sampled excellent home-made focaccia, an
immaculately presented tian of scallops layered on spinach and
crisp sharia pastry with a buttery lemongrass sauce, guinea
fowl with lots of morels, nicely pink chicken livers, a
powerfully reduced jus and perfect wilted spinach, and savarin
with 'gorgeous' Agen prunes in a fine syrup with well-made,
creamy crème fraîche ice cream. Other choices could include
tempura of red mullet with saffron and samphire, roast haunch
of venison with pot-roasted beetroot and Belgium mash, and
an intriguing rosewater gratin of blood oranges with rhubarb
ice. Another well-reported meal took in pigeon breast on
wilted spinach with pine nuts, tomato concasse, shallots,
mustard seeds and coriander; pan-fried fillets of John Dory
with caramelised scallops and a saffron sauce; and caramelised
apple tart in the style of a tarte Tatin, served with a cider and
cinnamon sorbet. Service is very attentive. The wine list is not
as long as customary country house offerings. It is well chosen,
however, and keenly priced with a fair number of half-bottles.

HADLEY WOOD,

West Lodge Park Hotel ❀❀

Impressive Regency-style country house that has been run by
the Beale family for half a century. Fillet of red mullet with
saffron risotto, pan-fried chicken, pak choi, smoked bacon and
a red wine sauce, and Paris Brest filled with Baileys cream, are
typical dishes.

Cockfosters Road Barnet
EN4 0PY
Map GtL: C5
Tel: 0181 4408311
Fax: 0181 4493698
Chef: Peter Leggat
Owners: Beale Ltd – West Lodge Park
Cost: Fixed-priced L £21.95/ D
£24.95. ☺ H/wine £12.50.
Times: Last L 2pm/last D 9.30pm

Additional: Bar Food; Sunday L; Children welcome; ❀ dishes
Smoking: No smoking in dining room
Accommodation: 55 en suite
Credit cards: 🟦 🟦 💳 💳 💳 💳

Directions: 1 mile S of M25 exit 24 on the A111; 1 mile from
Cockfosters & Hadley Wood stations

HEMEL HEMPSTEAD,
Watermill Hotel

The Riverside Restaurant offers a good range of dishes based on seasonal produce and prepared with care. Modern flavours came through in a meal that took in Billingsgate fish soup with a light curry flavour, good fresh scallops with a mushroom risotto with a butter sauce, rosemary and white wine, and iced chocolate Amaretto parfait.

Additional: Bar food; Sunday L (Noon-3pm); Children welcome; ❹ dishes
Smoking: No smoking in dining room
Accommodation: 75 en suite
Credit cards: ▆ ▆ ▆ ▆ ▆ ▆ JCB

Directions: From M1/J8 follow signs to and join A41 (Aylesbury), then A4251 to Bourne End

London Road Bourne End HP1 2RJ
Map 4: TL00
Tel: 01442 349955
Fax: 01442 866130
Chef: John Cook
Owner: Saroua Hotels
Cost: Alc £18.50. Fixed-price
D £18.50. ☺ H/wine £12
Times: D only, Last D 9.30pm.

SAWBRIDGEWORTH, The Shoes ❀❀

52 Bell Street CM21 9AN
Map 4: TL41
Tel: 01279 722544
Fax: 01279 832494
Chef: Mark Green
Owners: Lyndon Wootton,
Peter & Doreen Gowan
Times: Noon-1.30pm/7-9.30pm.
Closed L Sat, Sun, L Mon, 2 wks Aug,
2 wks after Xmas
Additional: Children welcome;
❹ dishes
Seats: 60. Private room 25
Smoking: No-smoking area;
Air conditioning
Credit cards: ▆ ▆ ▆ ▆ ▆ ▆

Housed in a tea-shop-like building that was once a coaching inn, The Shoes is nevertheless a bright, modern-looking restaurant found at one end of the high street of this bustling little town. Food, served by friendly, eager staff, is in a modern, international vein, with classical touches. An inspection meal kicked off with terrine of duck confit and foie gras – soft and appealing rillettes served with diced peppers, green leaves, and a nice mulled plum chutney. The main course, moist pan-fried breast of guinea fowl, came with a firm confit leg, root vegetables and a gutsy sweet cider sauce. To finish, warm apricot clafoutis, a pancake/custard cross encasing poached apricots and a rich syrupy coulis, served with creamy Amaretto and amaretti biscuit ice cream. This was followed by simple, chocolaty petits fours. A useful wine list contains some good negociant labels and a few classics.

Directions: From M11/J7 take A414 (Harlow); continue as road becomes A1186 (Bishop's Stortford). Sawbridgeworth is midway between Harlow and Bishop's Stortford

ST ALBANS, The Manor St Michael's Village

Stunning building steeped in history, and set in five acres of grounds, complete with a lake and river. There's talent in the kitchen with Arbroath smokie mousse with strips of smoked salmon and halibut, duck breast on a bubble-and-squeak cake with a cranberry and orange relish, and apple and blackberry ice cream with toffee sauce, setting the pace.

Additional: Sunday L; Bar meals L; No children under 5 in restaurant; ❸ dishes
Smoking: No smoking in dining room
Accommodation: 23 en suite
Credit cards: ▬ ▬ ⌐ ▬

Directions: From the High Street turn into George Street and follow the road past the Abbey (on your L); road continues into Fishpool Street

Fishpool Street AL3 4RY
Map 4: TL10
Tel: 01727 864444
Fax: 01727 848909
Chef: Steve Juett
Owners: Newling-Ward family
Cost: Fixed-price L £19.95/D £29.50. H/wine £12.95
Times: Last L 2pm/last D 9.30pm (10pm Sat/9pm Sun)

ST ALBANS, Noke Thistle

Bertie's, the hotel restaurant, is gaining a local reputation for the quality of its food. Care is taken over bread and canapés, for example, and sound cooking is evident in dishes such as salmon and prawn terrine, tender venison, and tarte Tatin. The wine list reflects the serious approach.

Watford Road AL2 3DS
Map 4: TL10
Tel: 01727 854252
Fax: 01727 841906
Chef: Andrew Stickings
Owner: Thistle Hotels plc
Cost: Alc £33, fixed-price L £16 (2 courses)/D £24. ☺ H/wine £11.75
Times: Last L 1.45pm/last D 9.45pm. Closed L Sat, 27-30 Dec
Additional: Sunday L; Children welcome; ❸ dishes
Smoking: No pipes & cigars; Air conditioning
Accommodation: 111 en suite
Credit cards: ▬ ▬ ◤ ⌐ ▬ ▣ ▣

Directions: On A405, Watford road; from M25/J21A, 1st roundabout, turn L

ST ALBANS, Sopwell House Hotel ❀❀

The Magnolia Conservatory is built onto the house, and has the original magnolia growing through it. The cooking is technically polished, confident and imaginative; the weekly changing 'Concept of the Kitchen' menu might feature terrine of rabbit confit with pear and apple chutney and raisin bread, and seared fillet of grey mullet with dill and sweetcorn blini and tagliatelle of leeks. From the *carte* you can choose roasted red snapper on herb pommes purée with French beans and red wine sauce, and roasted rack of lamb with an aubergine and tomato crust and salsify fritters. A large, nicely chewy, macaroon topped with mixed berries, served with an orange and ginger sorbet, balanced flavours expertly. Filter coffee was an unexpected weak note.

Cottonmill Lane Sopwell AL1 2HQ
Map 4: TL10
Tel: 01727 864477
Fax: 01727 844741
Chef: Warren Jones
Owner: Abraham Bejerano
Cost: Alc £35, fixed-price L £14.95 (2 courses)/D £23.50. H/wine £12.50
Times: 12.30-last L 2.30pm/7-last D 10pm. Closed L Sat, D Sun
Additional: Bar food; Sunday L; Children welcome; ❸ dishes
Seats: 120. Private dining rooms. Jacket & tie preferred
Smoking: No smoking in dining room

Sopwell House Hotel

Accommodation: 92 en suite
Credit cards: ▨ ▨ ▨ ▨ ▨ ▨ ▨

Directions: On London road from St Albans follow signs to Sopwell, over mini-roundabout, hotel is on L

TRING, **Rose and Crown Hotel** ❀

An attractive restaurant in this characterful hotel in the heart of Tring. At the time of our inspection the long-established chef was leaving and the new menu has yet to be tried. It is hoped that those old favourites making good use of fresh ingredients can be continued, especially fillet of cod on a base of champ with a leek jus and a rich chocolate terrine with caramelised oranges.

Directions: Just off A41 between Aylesbury and Hemel Hempstead, 1.5 miles from Tring station

High Street HP23 5AH
Map 4: SP91
Tel: 01442 824071
Fax: 01442 890735
Please telephone for further details

WARE,
Marriott Hanbury Manor ❀❀❀

Marriott's UK flagship hotel provides all the facilities one might expect – impressive Jacobean-style mansion, 200 acres of grounds and wonderful gardens, health and leisure club, and a golf course. The cooking, in the magnificent Zodiac Restaurant (all intricate carved walls and ceiling, white linen and gleaming silver) is suitably polished, skilful and refined. Robert Gleeson certainly has some imaginative ideas – a clever tarte Tatin of red shallots and roasted breast of quail was immaculately constructed, and the rich, sweetish sauce helped disguise the doughy pastry, and pavé of the freshest turbot was served with

Thundridge SG12 0SD
Map 5: TL31
Tel: 01920 487722
Fax: 01920 487692
Chef: Robert Gleeson
Cost: *Alc* £50, fixed-price L £25/D £33. H/wine £19.50
Times: 12.30pm-last L 1.45pm/7.30pm-last D 9.30pm
Additional: Bar food; Sunday L; No children under 8 at D; 🌢 dishes
Seats: 45. Private dining room 20. Jacket & tie preferred
Smoking: No smoking in dining room
Accommodation: 96 en suite
Credit cards: ▨ ▨ ▨ ▨ ▨ ▨ ▨ JCB

Directions: On A10, 12 miles N of M25/J25

truffle mash, vibrant-green broad bean purée and spring
vegetables. Dessert was a good passion fruit brûlée made
unnecessarily complicated by the addition of raspberry sorbet
and hard, honey madeleines. There is no stinting on luxuries:
confit of Scottish salmon with glazed cucumber, caviar and
champagne sauce; cream of lobster soup with Armagnac; roast
squab pigeon with seared foie gras, potato fondant and
redcurrant port sauce. Obligatory East-meets-West dishes
include crispy tempura parcel of Cornish crab, pimento, ginger
and oriental vegetables, and escalope of sea bass with shiitake
mushrooms, Chinese greens and rich port wine sauce. In
season, there may be game such as teal, roasted with braised
red cabbage, sweet potato rösti and garlic confit. Carefully
assembled canapés, and good bread rolls, have also been
endorsed.

KENT

ASHFORD, Eastwell Manor

Eastwell Park Boughton Lees
TN25 4HR
Map 5: TR04
Tel: 01233 219955
Fax: 01233 635530
Chef: Ian Mansfield
Owner: Mr Turrloo F Parrett
Cost: *Alc* £37.50, fixed-price L
£16.50/D £28.50. H/wine £15.50
Times: Noon-last L 2.15pm/7-last
D 9.30pm
Additional: Bar food; Sunday L;
Children welcome; 🍴 dishes
Seats: 65. Private room 75
Smoking: No smoking in dining room
Accommodation: 23 en suite
Credit cards: 💳 💳 💳 💳 💳 💳 💳 JCB

Approached via a long driveway that cuts through sheep-
studded pastures, the Jacobean pile encased in Virginia creeper
really looks the business; it is in fact a 20th-century pastiche, a
rebuilding of an earlier house. The dining room is very much in
keeping with the style of the building, dark, wood-panelled and
rather medieval-looking. Ian Mansfield leads a young,
enthusiastic team, and current reports have been full of praise
for the superb cooking. Note a fresh, clean tasting *amuse-
bouche* that set the tone for the 'richer stuff to come' – a
lightly ceviched brill with a butter-mounted light vegetable
nage and some tiny baby leeks, carrots and turnip. A starter of
sweet, tender, off-the-bone quail with a salad de mache gently
dressed with some fruity oil, and seared foie gras, sauté ceps
and a drizzle of aged balsamic vinegar which added a zingy
edge. The main course was one of the more traditional in Ian
Mansfield's repertoire: a great piece of roast turbot, crusty
without and stunningly white flakes of fish just cooked within,
accompanied by a wild mushroom risotto that provided an
earthy contrast, truffle jus that was well-made and well defined,
and extra vegetables that included a spiral crunchy Japanese
artichoke and some salsify, both great choices that worked well
with the dish as a whole. Milk chocolate and pear torte was
well-constructed. Bread, coffee and petits fours matched the
standards of the meal.

Directions: M20/J9 follow A251
Faversham, hotel on L after
Kennington. From Canterbury, A28
to Ashford L turn to Boughton Lees.

BRANDS HATCH,
Brandshatch Place ❀❀

A Georgian manor set in 12 acres of gardens, a haven of tranquillity considering its proximity to the racing circuit and the M20. Labour-intensive could be an apt description for some of the kitchen's output. A terrine of pheasant, foie gras and pencil leeks, for instance, is served with poached fig, kumquat confit and splashes of balsamic vinegar and basil oil, and even cream of pumpkin soup is topped with deep-fried sorrel. Smoked chicken and orange salad on watercress and lambs' tongue lettuce makes a simpler starter, perhaps followed by roast saddle of lamb in port sauce with dauphinoise potatoes and braised celery, or pot-roast duck breast with pears and mango. Well-flavoured crème brûlée with 'yummy' Ovaltine ice cream in a tuile basket has come in for some praise, and rhubarb and cardamom tart could be among the other dessert choices. The excellent wine list has been compiled by a Master of Wine.

Directions: Off A20, M25/J3, follow signs for Circuit then Fawkham; 2nd turn R after motorway bridge

Fawkham DA3 8NQ
Map 5: TQ56
Tel: 01474 872239
Fax: 01474 879652
Chef: Aimé Zbinden
Owners: Arcadian Hotels
Cost: Alc £30, fixed-price L £14.95/D £22. ☺ H/wine £12.75
Times: 12.30-last L 2pm/7-last D 9.30pm
Additional: Bar food; Sunday L; Children welcome; ⏧ dishes
Seats: 50. Private dining room
Smoking: No smoking in dining room
Accommodation: 41 en suite
Credit cards:
■ ▨ ➷ ⏧ ▨ ⏥ ▨ JCB

BROMLEY, # Chapter One ❀❀❀

see London

CANTERBURY, # Canterbury Hotel ❀❀

Decorated in vibrant shades of gold, terracotta and turquoise, with chandeliers and Impressionist prints, La Bonne Cuisine restaurant cuts a Gallic swathe through this popular, family-run hotel. The French food, served by French staff, is an experience 'gastronomique' – grand openers include duck foie gras with Sauternes jelly, and local lobster gratin in brandy, white wine and mushroom sauce. Fillets of John Dory are roasted temptingly with ginger and samphire and served with a sea urchin sauce, morels form the stuffing for a supreme of guinea fowl. Sauces are suitably accomplished – grand veneur with medaillons of venison, for example. Desserts include the correctly named 'tarte des Demoiselles Tatin', and iced Montelimar nougat with almonds and fruits of the forest coulis.

Directions: On A2, Dover road

71 New Dover Road
CT1 3DZ
Map 5: TR15
Tel: 01227 450551
Fax: 01227 780145
Chef: Jean-Luc Jouvente
Owners: Mr & Mrs F Bevan
Cost: Alc £20, fixed-price L £12.50 (2 courses)/D £16. ☺ H/wine £8.90
Times: Noon-last L 1.45pm/7-last D 9.45pm
Additional: Children welcome; ⏧ dishes
Seats: 55. Private dining room 25. Jacket & tie preferred
Smoking: No-smoking area; No pipes and cigars
Accommodation: 25 en suite
Credit cards: ■ ▨ ➷ ⏧ ▨ ⏥ ▨ JCB

CANTERBURY, Ebury Hotel

Victorian building with fine period features such as carved marble fireplaces, set in two acres of gardens. The carte features skilfully prepared European and chargrill dishes; typical starters include avocado and oak-smoked chicken salad, and hot smoked escalope of salmon with a tomato and coriander coulis.

Smoking: No smoking in dining room
Accommodation: 15 en suite
Credit cards: ▬ ▭ ⊀ ⨌ ▦ ☐ JCB

Directions: Follow ring road around Canterbury. Turn into New Dover Road (signed for Dover), past Safeway, over traffic lights. Hotel on R.

65-67 New Dover Road
CT1 3DX
Map 5: TR15
Tel: 01227 768433
Fax: 01227 459187
Chef: Henry Leach
Owners: Mr A P Mason,
Mr H A F Mason
Cost: *Alc* £16.50
Times: D only, last D 8.30pm.
Closed D Sun, Xmas
Additional: No children under 3;
🌀 dishes

CANTERBURY, Falstaff Hotel

Built in 1403, the Falstaff is steeped in tradition. Cosy public rooms and an attractive restaurant, characterise the interior. The menus span the trendy and the traditional: saffron risotto with roasted octopus, or chicken liver parfait with Cumberland sauce to start, then turbot topped with foie gras, chicken and salmon, or steak and kidney pudding.

Smoking: No smoking in dining room
Accommodation: 28 en suite
Credit cards: ▬ ▭ ⊀ ⨌ ▦ ☐ ▱

Directions: Turn into St Peters Place off the A2, pass Westgate Towers into St Dunstans St, hotel on R

St Dunstans Street Westgate
CT2 8AF
Map 5: TR15
Tel: 01227 462138
Fax: 01227 463525
Chef: Paul Rutter
Owner: Regal Hotel Group plc
Cost: *Alc* £28, fixed-price L & D
£14.95. ☺ H/wine £9.95
Times: Last L 2.30pm/last D 9.45pm
Additional: Bar food; Sunday L;
Children welcome; 🌀 dishes

CANTERBURY,
Ristorante Tuo e Mio

A traditional trattoria. Carpaccio with Parmesan and rocket, sea bream with basil and tomato, or veal chop with sage and rosemary, and zabaglione are the types of stalwarts to expect.

Additional: Children welcome; 🌀 dishes
Smoking: No-smoking area; No pipes & cigars
Credit cards: ▬ ▭ ⊀ ⨌ ▦ ☐ ▱ JCB

Directions: Opposite King's School

16 The Borough CT1 2DR
Map 5: TR15
Tel: 01227 761471
Chefs: Y Mula
Owner: R P M Greggio
Cost: *Alc* £20. ☺ H/wine £8.50
Times: Last L 2.30pm/last D 10.45pm.
Closed Mon, L Tue, last 2 wks Feb,
last 2 wks Aug

CHATHAM,
Bridgewood Manor Hotel

Although relatively modern in style, there is a 'Gothic' edge to the decor in this well-equipped hotel, close to the motorway network. The *carte* varies by the season, even down to the cheese (including a cheese of the week). In spring we sampled duck and foie gras ravioli in a woodland mushroom broth, and boneless spring chicken with blue cheese, celery and sultanas with a port sauce, both sensitively made and deftly constructed. The best bit of a meal from the 'Gourmet Menu' was hot caramelised banana tart with rum and sultana ice cream, although the poached fillet of turbot on an orange

Bridgewood Roundabout
Walderslade Woods
ME5 9AX
Map 5: TQ76
Tel: 01634 201333
Fax: 01634 201330
Chef: Jean-Claude MacFarlane
Owner: Marston Hotels
Cost: *Alc* £28, fixed-price L £17.50/D
£25
Times: 12.30-last L 1.45pm/7-last
D 9.45pm. Closed L Sat

cream sauce with mushrooms, and ricotta and red onion confit parcel scented with sage, were close runner-ups.

Accommodation: 100 en suite
Credit cards:

Directions: Adjacent to roundabout on A229

Additional: Bar food; Sunday L; Children welcome; 🍴 dishes
Seats: 80. Private dining room 40
Smoking: No smoking in dining room; Air conditioning

CRANBROOK, **Kennel Holt Hotel** ❀❀

Goudhurst Road TN17 2PT
Map 5: TQ73
Tel: 01580 712032
Fax: 01580 715495
Chef: Valentine Rodriguez
Owners: Neil & Sally Chalmers
Cost: Fixed-price L & D £25. H/wine £12.50
Times: Last L 1.30pm/last D 9pm. Closed L Sat, L Sun (May-Oct), D Sun (non-residents), all Mon, 2 wks Jan
Additional: Sunday L (Oct-Apr); 🍴 dishes
Smoking: No smoking in dining room
Accommodation: 10 en suite
Credit cards: JCB

Directions: On A262 1 mile from A229 crossroad, 3 miles from Goudhurst towards Cranbrook

Five acres of gardens with pond and topiary is the setting for this peaceful Elizabethan building. The elegantly rustic restaurant, with its collection of Victorian tinsel prints, has a welcoming, homely country-house service from friendly staff. New blood in the kitchen has certainly made an impact – the cooking is confident, assured, with bold flavours. Heavily endorsed have been timbale of Basmati rice and lobster with a well-made beurre blanc and cordon of curry oil, turbot with griddled new potatoes and fennel with ratatouille-style peppers, and tarte Tatin with home-made vanilla ice cream. Wine list is a useful, well-chosen selection offering good value for money.

CRANBROOK, **Soho South** ❀❀

23 Stone Street TN17 3HF
Map 5: TQ73
Tel: 01580 714666
Fax: 01580 715653
Chef: Nigel Tarr
Owners: Nigel & Linnea Tarr
Cost: Alc £21. ☺ H/wine £8.90

With bare floorboards, wooden tables, bunches of dried herbs and Kilner jars of preserved goodies about the place, Soho South is more country-pine chic than Soho. But there is a lot to like about this warm, friendly establishment. A free-form menu

of lighter dishes, supplemented by a blackboard of more substantial offerings, makes it as conducive to casual snacking as a full meal. Typical offerings might include half a dozen snails in garlic and parsley butter with lots of warm crispy baguette, and fillet of sea bream in soft breadcrumbs served with plump home-made chips and a classic sauce gribiche – both much enjoyed at a recent meal. Finish with a faultless chocolate pot.

Directions: In town centre, opposite Barclays Bank, 50 metres from tourist info centre & church

Times: 11am – 2.30pm, 6.30pm-9pm. Closed Sun, Mon, Tues
Additional: Children welcome; 🌢 dishes
Seats: 33
Smoking: No pipes & cigars
Credit cards: ▇▇ ▇▇ ▇▇ ▇

DEAL, **Dunkerley's of Deal** ❀❀

19 Beach Street
CT14 7AH
Map 5: TR35
Tel: 01304 375016
Fax: 01304 380187
Chef: Stephen Harvey
Owner: Ian Dunkerley
Cost: *Alc* £25, fixed-price L £9. ☺ H/wine £8.95
Times: Noon-last L 2.30pm/6-last D 10pm. Closed L Mon
Additional: Bar food; Sunday L; Children welcome; 🌢 dishes
Seats: 35. Private dining room 25
Smoking: No-smoking area; Air conditioning
Accommodation: 16 en suite
Credit cards: ▇▇ ▇▇ ▇▇ ▇ ▇▇ ▇ ▇ JCB

The time-warp restaurant decor and menu presentation do not do justice to the quality of the food at this seafront restaurant. Back-stage effort pays off in dishes such as sea bass with oyster mushrooms, beurre blanc sauce, tomato and herbs. Filleted skate wing is given a shot in the arm when pan-fried with capers, cucumber and pesto sauce, and cod fillet gets a new look when baked with spring onions and leeks and served with a spiced honey sauce. Chillies, garlic and ginger add zest to roasted pork fillet, and a first course of caramelised scallops is thoughtfully balanced with a warm salad of avocado, fine beans and bacon. Cinnamon brûlée glazed with crushed nougatine was described by one inspector as 'the best for a long time'.

Directions: Turn off A2 onto A258 to Deal – 100 yds before Deal Pier

DOVER, **Wallett's Court** ❀❀❀

The Oakleys are rightly proud of their restoration of this fine Jacobean manor house set in gentle countryside only a few miles from Dover. It is a rustically elegant place with bags of historic charm and pleasant touches. Chris Oakley cooks with gusto from a repertoire that has its foundations in a classic training with the Roux Brothers, and its heart in the best local produce he can lay his hands on: Romney Marsh lamb, Wadhurst Park wild boar, locally caught Dover sole and codling. The style is traditional, in many ways reminiscent of a French provincial restaurant. Note, for example, the simple quail terrine served with a zesty Cumberland sauce, and a coarse duck liver parfait that came with an excellent, light orchard jelly and home-made brioche, tested at inspection. That April dinner also produced a fresh, simply roasted turbot

West Cliffe St Margarets-at-Cliffe
CT15 6EW
Map 5: TR34
Tel: 01304 852424
Chefs: Christopher Oakley, Nick Holt
Owners: The Oakley Family
Cost: *Alc* D £30, fixed price L £19/D £24. ☺ H/wine £14
Times: Noon-last L 2pm/7-last D 9pm. Closed L Sat, L Sun, 24-28 Dec
Additional: Bar food L; Children welcome; 🌢 dishes
Seats: 60. Private dining room 40
Smoking: No smoking in dining room
Accommodation: 16 en suite
Credit cards: ▇▇ ▇▇ ▇▇ ▇ ▇▇ ▇ ▇ JCB

with thin asparagus and a light champagne butter sauce, and chicken stuffed with black pudding and smoked bacon on a light sage jus. The 'grand selection of desserts' proved to be an assiette of lemon tart, shortbread of apple and pear, chocolate torte, and bread-and-butter pudding. Bread is home-made and organic, canapés and petits fours have a homely, satisfying taste. The wine list has some well-chosen wines, perhaps more useful than mind blowing, but well suited to the conservative cuisine. Dessert wines are highlighted as a speciality on the dessert menu.

Signature dishes: Mad March hare; delice of monkfish with bacon; Wadhurst Park wild boar; Chartreuse de perdrix

Directions: From A2 take A258 (Dover/Deal) 1st R to St Margarets, hotel on R

EDENBRIDGE, **Honours Mill**

87 High Street TN8 5AU
Map 5: TQ44
Tel: 01732 866757
Chef: Martin Radmall
Owners: Neville, Giles, and Duncan Goodhew
Cost: Fixed-price L (Tue-Fri only) £15.50/D £32.75. ☺ H/wine £10.15.
Times: Last L 2pm/last D 10pm. Closed L Sat, D Sun, all Mon, 2 wks Xmas, Good Friday

This is a pretty, heavily beamed, converted flour mill, set back from the old High Street. At the rear are views over weeping willows and the river. Fixed-price menus are well-balanced, and enhanced by daily specials which may include mussel and saffron soup, poussin stuffed with chicken mousse, and Sussex pond pudding.

Additional: Sunday L; Children welcome; ❹ dishes
Credit cards: ▆▆ ▩ ☜◣ ▢

Directions: Town centre, southern end of High Street, just N of the bridge

FAVERSHAM, **Read's** ✤✤✤

Mummery Court Painters Forstal ME13 0EE
Map 5: TR06
Tel: 01795 535344
Fax: 01795 591200
Chef: David Pitchford
Owners: Rona & David Pitchford
Cost: *Alc* £37, fixed-price L £17.50/D £21. ☺ H/wine £14
Times: Noon-last L 2pm/7-last D 9.30pm. Closed Sun, Mon
Additional: Children welcome; ❹ dishes
Seats: 40. Private room 18
Smoking: No pipes & cigars
Credit cards: ▆▆ ▩ ▢ ▩ ▣ ▣ JCB

David and Rona Pitchford have been in residence at their spacious restaurant for 21 years. The dining room is still mildly shop-like (it was built as a supermarket), but seats are comfortable, tables are elegantly dressed, and there is a back bar whose windows give stunning views over the Belmont Valley, as well as a walled garden with a terrace for summer dining. The food is remarkable, dominated by the seasons, by the best local produce and by a desire on David Pitchford's part not to go overboard for fashion-for-fashion's sake; there is no loss of impact of dishes by over-multiplication of elements. Recommendations extend to a classic smoked haddock mousseline with a poached quail's egg and a chive and butter sauce, locally farmed and rich coq au vin with Kentish herbs, and sirloin of Aberdeen Angus beef with black pudding, melted onions, sweet-cured and a cracked peppercorn sauce. Sweet things run from a mousse of new season rhubarb sandwiched between brandy snap biscuits on a ginger-flavoured sauce, and a hot caramel soufflé with a home-made prune and Armagnac ice cream. Lunch is very good value and offers such idiosyncratic dishes as fresh crabmeat and salmon fishcakes with a home-made tomato 'ketchup', and escalope of veal topped with a fried egg, anchovies and caper butter. For those with little time to work their way through the sound, wide-ranging 250 bin wine list, the thoughtfully condensed list of some of the more reasonably priced wines is recommended. Good selection of half-bottles.

Directions: M2/J6, turn L onto A2, then L into Brogdale Road, signposted Painters Forstal 1.5 miles S of Faversham

FOLKESTONE, **Paul's Restaurant**

Paul's Restaurant specialises in sound bistro cooking with a European twist. Dishes from the hand-written menu are along the lines of poached fillet of trout in a creamy red pepper and white wine sauce. The restaurant is housed in an early 1900s coach house, and has a secluded garden. The wine list is extensive and well-priced.

Additional: Sunday L; Children welcome; ❹ dishes
Credit cards: ▆ ▆ ▆ ▆ ▆ ▆

Directions: Opposite Sainsburys, 50 yds from bus station

2a Bouverie Road West
CT20 2RX
Map 5: TR23
Tel: 01303 259697
Fax: 01303 226647
Chef: Darren Byer
Owners: Paul & Penny Hagger
Cost: *Alc* £18.95, fixed-price D £9.95 (not Sat). ☺ H/wine £8.65
Times: Last L 2.30pm/last D 9.30pm. Closed 1 wk Xmas

FOLKESTONE,

Sandgate Hotel, La Terrasse

The place draws special praise and its attractions are many; it feels more like a French hotel than an English seaside one. Indeed, France is visible on a clear day – the Channel laps on the pebbled beach opposite, and the dedication and commitment of Frenchman Samuel Gicqueau and his English wife, Zara, is evident at every turn. He cooks with an instinctive flair and imagination, while she runs front of house with great style. In the kitchen balance and refinement are keynotes, the dishes flourish through their sheer quality and technique. Set menus are daily changing and very good value considering the foie gras, sea bass and other luxuries on which they are based, and the *carte* reflects the seasons. Note a superlative-strewn May dinner: foie gras ballotine, smooth as butter, served with a 'palate grabbing' Sauternes jelly; sea bass, simply lightly seared, with fat English asparagus spears and an intense light glaze of red wine reduction giving a sweet-and-sour backdrop; perfectly seared scallops accompanied by velvety pomme purée and truffle butter sauce; duck with a honey and sesame seed glaze that came with simple braised red cabbage and roasted salsify; turbot with asparagus spears, spring onions, pommes grenailles, and complemented by a light meat jus; and roast pineapple with a pineapple purée finished with vanilla and an elegant vanilla ice cream. The approach here is remarkably expressive, course after course barely misses a beat, with various flavoured breads, canapés, appetisers and petits fours all marching in unison with the meal.

Signature dishes: Coquilles St Jacques lardées de poitrine fumée sur un coussin d'epinards au beurre d'orange; ecrevisses glacées de sauce Nantua gratinée; raviolis de homard de la baie de Hythe et beurre à l'estragon.

The Esplanade CT20 3DY
Map 5: TR23
Tel: 01303 220444
Fax: 01303 220496
Chef: Samuel Gicqueau
Owners: Zara & Samuel Gicqueau
Cost: *Alc* £40, fixed-price L & D £20.50. ☺ H/wine £13.50
Times: 12.15-last L 1.30pm/7.15-last D 9.30pm. Closed D Sun, all Mon, 4 wks Jan
Additional: Sunday L; Children welcome
Seats: 24
Smoking: No smoking in dining room
Accommodation: 15 en suite
Credit cards: ▆ ▆ ▆ ▆ ▆ ▆ ▆

Directions: On the A259 coastal road in Sandgate, between Hythe and Folkestone

HYTHE, **Imperial Hotel** ✿

A magnificent building on the Hythe seafront, set in a fifty-acre estate with a nine-hole golf course and well-maintained gardens. Modern British cooking is served in the restaurant, where our inspector enjoyed a spring meal of lobster, asparagus and quails' eggs salad, followed by roast saddle of lamb with leek purée.

Accommodation: 100 en suite
Credit cards: ■ ■ ■ ■ ■ ■ ■

Directions: M20/J11/A261 to Hythe; follow signs to Folkestone, turn R into Twiss Rd opposite Bell Inn towards seafront

Princes Parade CT21 6AE
Map 5: TR13
Tel: 01303 267441
Fax: 01303 264610
Chef: Michael Rieder
Cost: *Alc* £28, fixed-price L £16.50/D £23. H/wine £12.50
Times: Last L 2pm/last D 9.30pm. Closed L Sat
Additional: Bar food L; Sunday L; Children welcome; ✇ dishes
Smoking: No smoking in dining room

HYTHE, **Stade Court Hotel** ✿

Stade Court is just a few steps away from the beach, a position the accomplished team in the kitchen may take advantage of in dishes such as local scallops served with thyme and lemon butter. There may also be perfectly cooked rack of English lamb, preceded by ravioli of rabbit with mushrooms, and followed by apricot soufflé.

Smoking: No smoking in dining room
Accommodation: 42 en suite
Credit cards: ■ ■ ■ ■ ■

Directions: M20, J11 on A261

West Parade CT21 6DT
Map 5: TR13
Tel: 01303 268263
Fax: 01303 261803
Chef: Kevin Lea
Owner: Marston Hotels
Cost: *Alc* £23, fixed price D £18. ☺ H/wine £10
Times: D only, last D 9pm
Additional: Bar food; Sunday L (12.30-2pm); Children welcome; ✇ dishes

LENHAM, **Chilston Park** ✿✿

An air of gentle eccentricity is carefully cultivated: the staff wear period dress, the dining room is lit by hundreds of candles and the house is an Aladdin's cave of antiques, knick-knacks and paintings. Our inspector's tower of beef fillet, fondant potato and spinach with foie gras and truffle was succulent but tricky to get to grips with; a first course of seared grey mullet and fresh white crabmeat with an olive and citrus dressing was equally contemporary in concept. A good vegetarian menu offers wider than usual choices. Leave room for the fig tart with cinnamon ice cream and vanilla pod sauce.

Smoking: No smoking in dining room
Accommodation: 53 en suite
Credit cards: ■ ■ ■ ■ ■ ■

Directions: Telephone for directions

Sandiway ME17 2BE
Map 5: TQ85
Tel: 01622 859803
Fax: 01622 858588
Chef: Simon Hagen
Owner: Arcadian International
Cost: *Alc* £34.50, fixed-price L £17.50/D £29.50. H/wine £14.75
Times: Noon-last L 2.30pm/7-last D 9.30pm
Additional: Sunday L; Children welcome; ✇ dishes
Seats: 40. Private dining room 15. Jacket & tie preferred

LENHAM, **The Lime Tree** ✿

Set in the main square, The Lime Tree is a 14th-century beamed restaurant with plenty of country cottage character. The menu features a good selection of modern French dishes such as pan-fried monkfish with a ragout of mussels in a saffron sauce, and deep-fried scallops served with a ginger and spring onion cream sauce.

Smoking: No smoking in dining room
Accommodation: 10 en suite
Credit cards: ■ ■ ■ ■ ■ ■ ■ JCB

Directions: Off the A20. 5 miles from M20

8-10 The Limes The Square ME17 2PL
Map 5: TQ85
Tel: 01622 859509
Fax: 01622 850096
Chef: Alan Sinkinson
Owners: Musa Kivrak
Cost: *Alc* £35, fixed-price L £17.50/D £21.95. ☺ H/wine £11.50
Times: Last L 1.45pm/last D 9.45pm. Closed D Sun, L Mon & Sat
Additional: Sunday L; Children welcome; ✇ dishes

LITTLEBOURNE,
Bow Window Inn ✿

50 High Street CT3 1ST
Map 5: TR25
Tel: 01227 721264
Fax: 01227 721250
Chef: R W Steinmetz
Owners: Mr and Mrs R W Steinmetz
Cost: Alc £16.50. ☺ H/wine £8.50
Times: Last L 2pm/last D 9pm.
Closed L Sat, L Sun
Additional: Bar food; No children
under 2; ◐ dishes
Smoking: No smoking in dining room
Accommodation: 8 en suite
Credit cards: 💳 💳 💳 💳 💳

300-year-old cottage hotel, complete with oak beams and a
traditional Kentish fireplace. A typical summer meal might start with
devilled chicken livers sautéed in paprika, sherry and a hint of
cayenne pepper, followed by roast rack of lamb with redcurrant and
rosemary sauce. A great little place in a pretty village setting.

Directions: Take A257 from Canterbury towards Sandwich:
Littlebourne is approximately 3.5 miles E of the city

LITTLEBOURNE, King William IV ✿

4 High Street CT3 1ST
Map 5: TR25
Tel/Fax: 01227 721244
Chefs: Jim Shale, Phil Macey
Owners: Mr P Thurgate, Mrs L
Thurgate
Cost: Alc £15. ☺ H/wine £7
Times: Last L 2pm/last D 9.30pm
Additional: Bar food L; Sunday L; No
children under 10; ◐ dishes
Accommodation: 7 en suite
Credit cards: 💳 💳 💳 💳 💳

Simple, unassuming but cosy village pub that seems to hit the
balance between drinkers and diners well. Strong commitment to
fresh produce, especially local fish. Broccoli and lemongrass soup,
roasted cod with crab and dill sauce, and peppered pineapple tarte
Tatin with rum ice cream, made up one satisfying test meal.

Directions: On A257 3 miles E of Canterbury

MAIDSTONE, Russell Hotel ✿

Effusive and attentive service ensure that a visit to this Victorian
hotel will be enjoyed. The restaurant menu features modern English
and classical French dishes; typical starters include pan-fried
mushrooms and Stilton in a cream sauce, home-made chicken liver
and pork pâté, and salad of pan-fried tiger prawns wrapped in
bacon.

136 Boxley Road ME14 2AE
Map 5: TQ75
Tel: 01622 692221
Fax: 01622 762084
Chef: Brian Mulrooney
Owner: Mr A Costa
Cost: Alc £20, fixed-price D £15.95.
☺ H/wine £9.75

Directions: Telephone for directions

Russell Hotel

Times: Last L 2pm/last D 9.30pm.
Closed L Sun
Additional: Bar food; Children
welcome; dishes
Smoking: No-smoking area,
No pipes & cigars
Accommodation: 42 en suite
Credit cards: ▨ ▨ ▨ ▨ ▨ ▨ ▨

MAIDSTONE, **Tanyard Hotel** ❀❀

Wierton Hill Boughton Monchelsea
ME17 4JT
Map 5: TQ75
Tel: 01622 744705
Fax: 01622 741998
Chef/Owner: Jan Davies
Cost: Fixed-price L £25/D £29
(4 courses). H/wine £10.50
Times: D only, 7-9pm. Closed 26 Dec
for 4/5 wks
Additional: Sunday L (12.30-1.45pm);
 dishes
Seats: 28
Smoking: No smoking in dining room
Accommodation: 6 en suite
Credit cards: ▨ ▨ ▨ ▨ ▨ ▨

English classics such as fresh local asparagus with hollandaise
sauce, roast rack of lamb with redcurrant and mint sauce,
summer pudding and British cheese are at one with the
surrounds – a gorgeous small medieval manor dating from
1350, heavily beamed with ragstone walls and flagstone floors.
House specialities include twice-baked cheese soufflé, breast of
duck with a bitter orange sauce, and sticky toffee pudding with
a pecan sauce. Other dishes are more modern English but the
style remains unpretentious: grilled fillet of hake with lime and
coriander; roasted tomato soup with basil; hot chicken and
pistachio mousse with red pepper sauce.

Directions: Turn off B2163 at Cock Pub nr Boughton
Monchelsea

ROCHESTER, **The Limehouse** ❀❀

The short modern menu suits the relaxed atmosphere and easy
style, where wooden floor and tables, bentwood chairs, and
paintings by local artists are the backdrop for dishes such as
crab and cucumber tart with horseradish cream, and lamb
rump with Puy lentils and sweet garlic jus. A starter of crushed
Jersey potato salad served with dill and coriander cured
salmon and a wild mushroom dressing had well-balanced
textures, lovely thick slices of fish and a good sweet/sour edge
to the sauce. Confit of duck, apple and black pudding gâteau

327 High Street
ME1 1DA
Map 5: TQ76
Tel: 01634 813800
Chef: Phil Bedford
Owners: Sandro & Eirlys Vistosi
Cost: A/c £21.75, fixed price L&D
£16.95 (2 courses). ☺ H/wine £9.95
Times: Noon-last L 2pm/6.30-last D
9.30pm (Fri 10pm/Sat 11pm).
Closed Sun, 26 Dec, 1 Jan, some Bhs

The Limehouse

Additional: Children welcome;
 dishes
Seats: 35. Private dining room 40
Smoking: No smoking in dining room
Credit cards: ▨ ▨ ▨ ▨

Directions: From town centre, follow
signs to Chatham; restaurant is on L
past railway station next to North
Foreland pub.

with a port and thyme jus was a generous portion with meat
tender enough to fall off the bone. A delicate damson syllabub
with meringues was a sound finale. The lunchtime brasserie
menu includes mussels with Thai spices, and sausages with
mash, red cabbage and gravy.

ROYAL TUNBRIDGE WELLS,
Hotel du Vin & Bistro ❀❀ **NEW**

Designed very much like the Winchester version (see entry,
Hampshire), with stripped pine floors, larger-than-life
paintings, and a host of things oenological. Young staff are
predominantly French and very helpful, especially Jerome the
sommelier, who welcomes a request for advice or guidance.
The menu is bistro-style and changes (subtly) on a weekly
basis. Artichoke and goats' cheese tart with a wafer thin crust
was good, especially the light Chardonnay dressing with the
accompanying mixed leaves, and a simple, pan-fried red bream,
served with a light herb butter, was good quality fish accurately
cooked. First-class orange tart finished the meal on a high note.

Directions: *Please telephone for directions*

Crescent Road TN1 2LY
Map 5: TQ53
Tel: 01892 526455
Fax: 01892 512044
Chef: Chris Start
Owner: The Alternative Hotel Co
Cost: *Alc* £30. H/wine £12
Times: Noon-last L 1.45pm/7-last
D 9.30pm
Additional: Sunday L; Children
welcome; dishes
Seats: 70. Private dining rooms 12-70
Smoking: No pipes & cigars
Accommodation: 25 en suite
Credit cards: ▨ ▨ ▨ ▨ ▨ ▨ ▨

ROYAL TUNBRIDGE WELLS,
Royal Wells Inn ❀❀

Owing its royal prefix to frequent visits by Queen Victoria
when still a young princess, the Royal Wells Inn has an
elevated position overlooking the common. The view is best
enjoyed from the first floor conservatory restaurant where
chef/patron Robert Sloan offers an equally eye-catching menu
of modish dishes. The well-balanced selection might include
starters of French onion and cider soup with Welsh rarebit,
warm crispy duck salad with aromatic dressing, and pork and
brandy pâté with pickles. Escalopes of Scottish salmon in
vermouth and sorrel, flash-fried calves' liver in balsamic
vinegar with bacon, and slow-roast breast of duck with russet
apples and redcurrants are typical main course offerings. To
finish, try the cappuccino mousse, the steamed pudding of the
day, or Scotch woodcock. A well-chosen wine list offers
something to suit most tastes and pockets. The separate Wells
Brasserie provides a less formal setting for similarly styled
cooking.

Mount Ephraim TN4 8BE
Map 5: TQ53
Tel: 01892 511188
Fax: 01892 511908
Chef: Robert Sloan
Owners: David & Robert Sloan
Cost: *Alc* £27, fixed-price L £ 10.50
(2 courses). ☺ H/wine £9.95
Times: 12.30-2.15pm/7.30-9.30pm.
Closed Sun, D Mon, Bhs
Additional: Bar food (Wells Brasserie);
Children welcome; dishes
Seats: 35. Private dining room 20
Accommodation: 19 en suite
Credit cards: ▨ ▨ ▨ ▨ ▨ ▨ ▨ ▨ JCB

Directions: Situated 75 yards from the
junction of the A21 and A264

ROYAL TUNBRIDGE WELLS,
Signor Franco ✱✱

In the High Street, but with its entrance tucked away between a shoe shop and a chemist Franco de Tommaso's restaurant is one of Tunbridge Wells' best kept secrets. Head up the celebrity picture-lined stairs to find a light, modern-looking room with arched windows reaching from floor to ceiling. The Italian menu holds few surprises but the cooking is sound and consistent. Our last visit began with good, variously flavoured bread rolls before ravioli porcini in a wild mushroom sauce topped with freshly grated Parmesan and spezzatino di manzo al Barolo – a wonderful winter dish of tender beef casseroled in a rich winey sauce with polenta. There are about three dozen wines on an exclusively Italian list.

Directions: Near Tunbridge Wells train station

5a High Street TN1 1UL
Map 5: TQ53
Tel: 01892 549199
Fax: 01892 541378
Chef: Giuseppe Miranda
Owner: Franco de Tommaso
Cost: *Alc* £30. ☺ H/wine £10.80
Times: Noon-last L 2.45pm/6.45-last D 11pm. Closed Sun
Additional: Children welcome; dishes
Seats: 55
Smoking: No pipes or cigars; Air conditioning
Credit cards: ▬ ▭ ▰ ▱ ▯

ROYAL TUNBRIDGE WELLS,
The Spa Hotel ✱

Georgian country mansion with a strong Regency character, set in parkland and gardens. The Grand Chandelier restaurant is just that, with domes and waiters in brocade waistcoats to boot. Expect pork liver pâté with truffles and apple and sultana confit, pan-fried cod and bubble and squeak, and steamed ginger pudding.

Additional: Bar food; Sunday L; Children welcome; dishes
Smoking: No-smoking area; No pipes & cigars; Air conditioning
Accommodation: 74 en suite
Credit cards: ▬ ▭ ▰ ▱ ▱ ▯

Directions: On A264 leaving Tunbridge Wells towards East Grinstead

Mount Ephraim TN4 8XJ
Map 5: TQ53
Tel: 01892 520331
Fax: 01892 510575
Chef: Edward Heasman
Owners: The Goring family
Cost: *Alc* £24. ☺ H/wine £9.50
Times: Last L 2pm/D 9.30pm. Closed L Sat

ROYAL TUNBRIDGE WELLS, **Thackeray's**
House Restaurant ✱✱

The restaurant feels as if it has always occupied the 17th-century house, so at ease does it seem with its surrounds. It is a little worn in places, but charmingly so, with sloping floors, low ceilings, well-spaced tables and comfortable chairs, plus vintage copies of Thackeray's works (he lived here) in an alcove. The restaurant is on the ground floor, the bistro below and there's a pleasant lounge upstairs for drinks. Bruce Wass's classically based cooking sticks to what it knows best – it is solid and reliable, rather than adventurous. Recent meals have included artichoke and mushroom terrine, and brill fricassée with fresh shrimps, both typically well-made, with a very rich apricot, walnut, ginger and toffee pudding deliciously way over the top.

Smoking: No-smoking area; No pipes & cigars
Credit cards: ▬ ▭ ▰ ▱

Directions: At corner of London Road/Mount Ephraim Road overlooking Common, 2 mins from hospital

85 London Road TN1 1EA
Map 5: TQ53
Tel/Fax: 01892 511921
Chef/Owner: Bruce Wass
Cost: *Alc* £32, fixed-price L £13.50 (2 courses). H/wine £12.85
Times: 12.30-last L 2pm/7-last D 10pm. Closed D Sun, all Mon, 5 days Xmas
Additional: Sunday L; Children welcome; dishes
Seats: 50. Private dining rooms 12, 15, 22

SEVENOAKS,
Royal Oak Hotel ✿

*Flint-fronted 17th-century hotel located in the town centre, providing
a wide range of dishes in either the bistro or the more formal
restaurant. In the latter you may choose chargrilled tuna with
coconut and lime dressing, lamb fillet with couscous cake and
rosemary gravy, and strawberry cheesecake.*

Additional: Bar food; Sunday L; Children welcome; ❸ dishes
Smoking: No smoking in dining room; Air conditioning
Accommodation: 37 en suite
Credit cards: ▣ ▥ ◈ ◨ ▤ 🄲

Directions: M25/J5; at far end of High Street, opposite
Sevenoaks school, walking distance from the town centre

Upper High Street TN13 1HY
Map 5: TQ55
Tel: 01732 451109
Fax: 01732 740187
Chef: Andrew Cullen
Owner: Brook Hotels plc
Cost: Alc £20, fixed-price L £9.95. ☺
H/wine £9.95
Times: Last L 2.30pm/last D 10pm

SISSINGHURST, **Rankins** ✿✿

Housed in a typical timber and weatherboard Kent building,
Rankins is a simple, but warm and welcoming husband-and-
wife operation. The decor is lovingly worn, and for such a
small place, the tables quite well spaced. The cooking is
modern but user-friendly – their intensely flavoured roast red
pepper terrine with French bean and frisée salad with capers,
balsamic vinegar and olive oil is particularly good. Amongst
the main courses, pan-fried double lamb chop with robust red
wine sauce, green peppercorns and parsley and garlic pesto has
been appreciated for its straightforward gutsy flavours, and a
smoked haddock chowder with Queenie scallops and prawns
was clearly defined.

Directions: Village centre, on R on A262 (Ashford)

TN17 2JH
Map 5: TQ73
Tel: 01580 713964
Chef: Hugh Rankin
Owners: Hugh & Leonora Rankin
Cost: Fixed-price D £26.
H/wine £9.80
Times: D only, 7-last D 9pm. Closed
D Sun, all Mon, Tue, 25 Dec, Bhs
Additional: Sunday L (noon-2pm);
Children welcome; ❸ dishes
Seats: 20
Credit cards: ▣ ▥ ◈

WELLING, **The Tagore** ✿✿

Cuisine from north-west India and Pakistan finds a home at
this small, bright, busy restaurant. Shikumpuri kebab, lightly
battered mashed sweet potato, and green banana with fresh
herbs, makes a delicious starter. Try also 'dum-cooked' dishes
such as koh-e-avadh: lamb on the bone, steam-cooked with
cardamom and saffron.

Additional: Children welcome; ❸ dishes
Smoking: Air conditioning. **Credit cards:** ▣ ▥ ◈

Directions: *Telephone for directions*

3 Welling High Street DA16 1TR
Map GtL: E2
Tel: 0181 3040433
Chef: Rajendra Balmiki
Owner: Nur Monie
Cost: Alc £18. ☺ H/wine £9
Times: D only, last D 11pm

WESTERHAM,
Kings Arms Hotel ✿

*Georgian hotel where the light, airy Conservatory Restaurant offers
a modish menu of soundly cooked dishes. Warm chicken liver salad
with artichoke hearts and red pepper dressing, breast of duck on
caramelised apple with redcurrant sauce, tarte Tatin of aubergine,
beef-tomato and courgette, and braised rump of lamb with
Parmesan herb mash, show the style.*

Market Square TN16 1AN
Map 5: TQ45
Tel: 01959 562990
Fax: 01959 561240
Chef: James Brown
Owner: Old English Pub Co
Cost: Alc £19.95, fixed-price L & D
£19.95. ☺ H/wine £8.95

Kings Arms Hotel

Times: Last L 2pm/last D 10pm
Additional: Bar food; Sunday L;
Children welcome; 🍴 dishes
Smoking: No-smoking area;
No pipes & cigars
Accommodation: 17 en suite
Credit cards: ▬ ▬ 🐦 🗌 ▦ 🔟

Directions: On A25, in the centre of Westerham

WHITSTABLE,
Whitstable Oyster Fisher Co 🏵

Great location bang on the beach, a basic place, full of atmosphere, odd assortment of tables, chairs, peeling paint, bare boards – very popular. Fish, and nothing but from a daily changing blackboard menu. Keep it simple: cod in beer batter and great chips, mackerel with apple sauce, herring roes and bacon on toast. There's a cinema upstairs and rooms in converted beach huts.

Additional: Children welcome; 🍴 dishes
Smoking: No pipes & cigars
Accommodation: 32 en suite
Credit cards: ▬ ▬ 🐦 🗌 ▦ 🔟

Horsebridge Beach CT5 1BU
Map 5: TR16
Tel: 01227 276856
Fax: 01227 770666
Chef: Chris Williams
Cost: Alc £30. ☺
Times: Last L 2pm/last D 9pm.
Closed D Sun, all Mon

Directions: On High Street, follow one-way then 1st L

WYE, Wife of Bath 🏵

Pretty but substantial village house, with discreet water-colours, some nice old pieces of furniture and retaining an air of quiet simplicity. Fresh, sound cooking produces the likes of terrine of smoked fish with chervil mayonnaise, grilled lamb cutlets with chestnut and aubergine, and poached pear with butterscotch sauce. Lovely, attentive service.

Directions: Just off the A28 Ashford to Canterbury Road

4 Upper Bridge Street
TN25 5AW
Map 5: TR04
Tel: 01233 812540
Fax: 01233 813630
Chef: Robert Hymers
Owner: John Morgan
Cost: Alc £23, fixed-price L £10 (2
courses)/D £23.50. ☺ H/wine
£12.25.
Times: Last L 2.30pm/last D 10.30pm.
Closed Sun, Mon, 2 wks after 25 Dec
Additional: 🍴 dishes
Smoking: No-smoking area;
No pipes or cigars in dining room
Accommodation: 6 rooms
Credit cards: ▬ ▬ 🐦 🗌 ▦ 🅲 🔟 JCB

LANCASHIRE

BLACKBURN, **Foxfields Hotel**

Whalley Road Clitheroe
BB7 9HY
Map 7: SD62
Tel: 01254 822556
Fax: 01254 824613
Chef: Alex Coward
Owners: Lyric Hotels
Cost: Alc £20, fixed-price L £7.50
(2 courses)/ D £18.45. ☺ H/wine
£11.40
Times: Last L 2pm/last D 9.30pm.
Closed L Sat
Additional: Bar Food; Sunday L;
No children under 1; ⚠ menu
Smoking: No smoking in dining room;
Air conditioning
Accommodation: 44 en suite
Credit cards: 💳 💳 💳 💳 💳

A modern hotel in a rural location. Expressions Restaurant offers modern British cooking along the lines of pressed salmon terrine with marinated vegetables, duck and venison with red cabbage and Cointreau syrup, and pineapple and pear brûlée.

Directions: From A59 follow sign for Whalley, hotel is 0.5 mile on R

BLACKBURN, **Millstone Hotel**

Church Lane Mellor
BB2 7JR
Map 7: SD62
Tel: 01254 813333
Fax: 01254 812628
Chef: Miguel Armas
Cost: Alc £25, fixed-price L £11.50/D
£21. ☺ H/wine £10
Times: Last L 1.45pm/last D 9.45pm
Additional: Bar food; Sunday L;
Children welcome; ⚠ dishes
Smoking: No smoking in dining room
Accommodation: 24 en suite
Credit cards:
💳 💳 💳 💳 💳 💳 💳 JCB

A 17th-century coaching inn, in a peaceful village, with a restaurant that only 100 years ago was the cowshed. The menus take in the traditional with, say, Bury black pudding to start, then perhaps beef and oxtail braised in ale, roaming further afield for salmon teriyaki or Moroccan-spiced lamb shank.

Directions: M6/J31, follow A677 (Blackburn) for 2 miles. Turn L (Mellor), follow road to top of hill, hotel is on R.

BLACKPOOL, **September Brasserie**

The small first-floor restaurant, decorated with stencils, has an easy-going air. With the open-plan kitchen in one corner, you can practically chat to the chef/patron as he rustles up your buckwheat blinis with smoked salmon, crab and basil. The

15-17 Queen Street
FY1 1PU
Map 7: SD33
Tel: 01253 623282
Fax: 01253 299455
Chef: M Golowicz

short fixed-price menu, supplemented by the blackboard, offers imaginative fish dishes, such as sesame seed encrusted salmon fillet on ink sauce, and lusty numbers such as braised pork knuckle with mushy peas and mustard sauce. Confit of duck leg, practically falling off the bone, was well flavoured, the skin crisped in the oven, enlivened by some unusual beetroot oil. For dessert, lemon tart on a good pastry base was tangy and nicely glazed, served with fresh orange segments for contrast. Wines are chosen by the month, and there is a longstanding commitment to offering a good choice of organic ones. There is also a £5 BYO corkage charge.

Directions: 200 yards from the promenade, adjacent to the Cenotaph

Owners: Mr M Golowicz, Mrs P Wood
Cost: Alc £19, fixed-price L £10.40 (2 courses)/D £17.80. ☺ H/wine £10.50
Times: Noon-last L 1.45pm/7pm-last D 10pm. Closed 1 wk summer, 1 wk winter
Additional: Children welcome; ⚘ dishes
Seats: 40
Credit cards: ▆ ▆ ▆ ▆ JCB

CHIPPING,
Gibbon Bridge Hotel ❀

Extensive gardens provide the restaurant with vegetables, fruit and herbs at this rural hotel, a farm until 1982. Sauté scallops or warm goats' cheese salad could precede roast duckling stuffed with sage and onion, or rabbit pie, with sherry trifle rounding off a meal.

Additional: Sunday L; ⚘ dishes
Smoking: No smoking in dining room
Accommodation: 30 en suite
Credit cards: ▆ ▆ ▆ ▆ ▆ ▆

Directions: In village turn R at T junction for Clitheroe, hotel at 0.75 mile

Forest of Bowland Preston
PR3 2TQ
Map 7: SD64
Tel: 01995 61456
Fax: 01995 61277
Chef: Benjamin Eastwood
Owner: Janet Simpson
Cost: Alc £25, fixed-price L from £14 (& £16 at weekend)/D £20. ☺ H/wine £10.95
Times: Last L 1.30pm/last D 9pm

LANGHO, Northcote Manor ❀❀❀

Northcote Road nr Blackburn
BB6 8BE
Map 7: SD73
Tel: 01254 240555
Fax: 01254 246568
Chef: Nigel Haworth
Owners: Nigel Haworth, Craig Bancroft
Cost: Alc £35, fixed-price L £16/D £37 (5 courses). H/wine £12.90
Times: Noon-last L 1.30pm/7pm-last D 9.30pm. Closed 25 Dec, 1 Jan
Additional: Sunday L; Children welcome; ⚘ dishes

Whether Northcote Manor is a fine restaurant attached to a comfortable and characterful hotel or vice-versa is a moot point; either way, this is an extremely good spot in which to enjoy a drink beside the fire whilst browsing over tempting menus created by chef/patron Nigel Haworth. The large bay window of the sunny dining room overlooks the organic herb garden, put to good use in dishes such as hot-house smoked salmon, tian of mussels and tomatoes, mussel and tarragon mayonnaise, and garlic chive and potato soup with potato gnocchi. Haworth has researched old Lancashire recipes, 18th-century black pudding and buttered pink trout with mustard

and nettle sauce, is now a signature dish, varying only slightly with the seasons. He is also renowned for his skill at cooking meat, and a confit shoulder of pork, fillet, crisp crackling, black pudding mash, wilted greens, tarragon and apple jus was tender and moist, full of interest. Local produce comes to the fore in dishes such as crisp corn-fed Goosnargh duckling (from just down the road), with spring rolls, plum chutney, ginger and spring onion jus, or the more traditional Pendle lamb shanks with layered potatoes and caramelised onions. Certain fish dishes can be taken as a starter, middle course or main dish, Orkney scallops, perhaps, with deep-fried prawn risotto cakes, cumin oil and mango dressing. The size of a praline and banana cheesecake with hot chocolate truffles defeated our inspector; a plate of Lancashire cheeses or Colston Bassett Stilton with preserved stem ginger make good alternatives. The wine list shows particular breadth and depth and is agreeably affordable.

Signature dishes: Assiette of Pendle lamb; risotto of brown shrimps, prawns and basil; black pudding and buttered pink trout with mustard and watercress sauce; apple crumble soufflé, Lancashire cheese ice cream

Directions: From M6/J31 take A59, follow signs for Clitheroe. At first traffic lights L onto Skipton/Clitheroe Rd for 9 miles. L into Northcote Rd. Hotel on R.

Seats: 60. Private dining room 30; Jacket & tie preferred
Smoking: No smoking in dining room
Accommodation: 14 en suite
Credit cards:

AA Wine Award-see page 16 Shortlisted for

LONGRIDGE, **Paul Heathcotes Restaurant** ❀❀❀

104-106 Higher Road
PR3 3SY
Map 7: SD63
Tel: 01772 784969
Fax: 01772 785713
Chefs: Andrew Barnes, Paul Heathcote
Owner: Paul Heathcote
Cost: *Alc* £40, fixed-price L £22.50 (4 courses)/D £30. H/wine £13
Times: Noon-last L 2pm (Fri, Sun only)/7-last D 9.30pm. Closed Mon
Additional: Sunday L; Children welcome; ❸ dishes
Seats: 60. Private dining room 16
Smoking: No smoking in dining room
Credit cards:

The split-level dining room is minimalist in decor but traditional by design. Long flowing cloths, modern, straight-backed chairs and, on our June visit, a brilliant sunflower placed in the centre of each table. There's also a 'cosy' lounge where guests can choose from the thick, glossy one-foot-square menu card. Paul Heathcote has real regional pride and it comes out in his simple style of cooking. A May lunch saw terrine of ham hock with Lancashire cheese and pickles, and a signature black pudding (with a large piece of sweetbread to add variety) on crushed potatoes surrounded by haricot beans in a delicate bay leaf sauce, as well as Morecambe Bay shrimps en croûte served as a canapé at a later dinner. Goosnargh is only 5 miles down the road and duckling makes a frequent appearance. Freshness, texture, exact seasoning, and overall respect and care come through in the flavoured breads of black pudding, cheese and sage, walnut and date, and plain milk. The

aforementioned lunch highlighted leg of rabbit filled with wild mushrooms and Parma ham with a light sauce of truffle juices complementing the dish well. Dinner opened with marinated red mullet with citrus fruits and soused vegetables, and was followed by a wonderfully vibrant poached lobster with sweet vegetables in a herb stock that had great flavours flooding through it. Roast guinea fowl, with the legs stuffed with herbs and served with a truffle sauce, was 'beautiful', crisp skin, moist meat, awash with fresh herbs (chervil and chive), and served with simple, honest buttered spinach, baby turnips, braised parsnip and glazed baby carrots. Warm chocolate fondant was everything it should be, accompanied by a gingerbread ice cream. The wine list is mixed, with Alsace, Rhône, Australia, and the US grabbing most of the attention; here is the good drinking. The extensive half-bottle selection is also one to note. Prices are firm with some fair value.

AA Shortlisted for Wine Award–see page 16

Signature dishes: Roast cutlet of spring lamb, hot-pot potatoes; chilled clear tomato soup; roast partridge, walnut mashed potatoes, own juices; Heathcote's black pudding, bay leaf sauce

Directions: Follow signs for Golf Club & Jeffrey Hill. Higher Road is beside White Bull Pub in Longridge.

PRESTON,
Heathcote's Brasserie ❀❀

23 Winckley Square
PR1 3JJ
Map 7: SD52
Tel: 01772 252732
Fax: 01772 203433
Chef: Jamie Holland
Owner: Paul Heathcote
Cost: *Alc* £20, fixed-price L £10.95.
☺ H/wine £11
Times: Noon-last L 2.30pm/7pm – last D 10.30pm. Closed 25 Dec, 1 Jan
Additional: Bar food; Sunday L; Children welcome; ❹ dishes
Seats: 90
Smoking: No pipes or cigars; Air conditioning
Credit cards: ▨ ▨ ✈ ▯ ▨ ▉

'Le Patron Mange Ici'. Paul Heathcote himself entertains guests to lunch at his satellite brasserie, proving he puts his mouth where his money is. Now a fixture on the Preston Front, the decor is white, white and more white, or rather off-white. Off-white, surprisingly comfortable, plastic chairs, oil cloths, walls, vertical radiators and frosted windows, with all colour focussed on a huge mural and on the plate. It's probably impossible to visit any Heathcote venue without tasting black pudding (as in rabbit stuffed with black pudding and pork sausage, roasted walnuts and red wine sauce), or bread-and-butter pudding (with sauce anglaise and raspberry coulis). Robust flavours dominate, in tagliatelle of mussels with cider and bacon, tagine of lamb shank with apricots, carrots and braised chick peas, and confit of pork with mashed potatoes, ginger and coriander. The downstairs seafood and rotisserie bar serves Loch Fyne oysters, spit-roast chicken and hot-beef sandwiches.

Directions: Town centre

PRESTON, **Preston Marriott Hotel** ✤

Pleasant hotel set in peaceful grounds complete with modern leisure facilities. Typical starters include terrine of veal and guinea fowl served with apple chutney, and salmon and baby vegetable mousse with potato salad. Main courses could be medallions of beef fillet glazed with Brie, and supreme of chicken filled with smoked bacon and mustard sauce.

Smoking: No smoking in dining room; Air conditioning
Accommodation: 98 en suite
Credit cards: ▆ ▆ ▆ ▆ ▆ ▆ JCB

Directions: M6/J32, follow A6 towards Garstang. Hotel approx. 600 yds

Garstang Road Boughton PR3 5JB
Map 7: SD52
Tel: 01772 864087
Fax: 01772 861728
Chef: Gary Jenkins
Owner: Whitbread Hotel Company
Cost: *Alc* £20, fixed-price L £12/D £18.95. ☺ H/wine £11.95
Times: Noon-2pm/7-9.45pm.
Closed L Sat
Additional: Bar food; Sunday L; Children welcome; ✤ dishes

SLAIDBURN, **Parrock Head** ✤

A long, low, white ex-farmhouse, peacefully located in the Forest of Bowland, with a restaurant in what was once the milking parlour. There's a good choice on the set menus, from starters of cauliflower soup or Thai fishcakes, to main courses of fillet of halibut topped with salmon mousseline, or venison baked in ale.

Smoking: No smoking in dining room
Accommodation: 9 en suite. **Credit cards:** ▆ ▆ ▆ ▆

Directions: Take B6478 to Slaidburn; L by village pub up Woodehouse Lane, hotel drive 1 mile on L

Nr Clitheroe BB7 3AH
Map 7: SD75
Tel: 01200 446614
Fax: 01200 446313
Chef: David Gibbons
Owner: J T & K M Hesketh
Cost: Fixed-price D £20.75. H/wine £9.25
Times: Last L 2pm/last D 9pm.
Closed Jan
Additional: Bar food L; Sunday L; Children welcome; ✤ dishes

THORNTON, **Didier's Bistro** ✤✤

The bistro here proved so popular that it's now expanded into the dining room, decorated in the same light blues and yellows, and a large patio is called into service when the weather permits. French provincial cooking, friendly and informal service and fair prices are what to expect. A starter of flavoursome confit of chicken leg gets the thumbs up, as does pan-fried tuna steak, undercooked as requested, served on provençale vegetables – a typically bright and fresh dish in terms of both colour and flavour. The menu also extends to pork rillettes with grilled ciabatta, and spinach and coconut soup to start, and main courses of wild rabbit sautéed with prunes and white wine, veal kidneys in bourguignonne sauce with bacon and mushrooms, and roast loin of pork stuffed with spinach and chestnuts. The list of puddings runs to things like apple and almond tart, and blueberry cheesecake. Good value is the hallmark of the short wine list.

Directions: M55 Kirkham exit – follow A585 (Fleetwood), then Thornton at roundabout, continue towards Fleetwood, turn R at church

FY5 4HF
Map 7: SD34
Tel: 01253 860619
Fax: 01253 865350
Chef: Didier Guerin
Owners: Didier & Louise Guerin
Cost: *Alc* £17, fixed-price L £8.50. ☺ H/wine £6.95
Times: Noon-2pm/6-10pm.
Additional: No children under 6
Seats: 104
Smoking: No pipes & cigars
Credit cards: ▆ ▆ ▆ ▆ ▆ ▆ JCB

UPHOLLAND, **Holland Hall Hotel** ✤✤

Churchill's Restaurant is popular with locals and hotel guests. It sports a cosy, slightly dark interior, and pictures of Winston Churchill adorn the walls. Breads are a popular feature, arriving on a trolley, you can have whatever you fancy from any of the five or more flavours on offer, paprika, sultana, sun-

6 Lafford Lane Skelmersdale
WN8 0QZ
Map 7: SD50
Tel: 01695 624426
Fax: 01695 633433
Please telephone for further details

Holland Hall Hotel

dried tomato, for example. A winter dinner highlighted a good braised lamb shank, honey-glazed with garlic mash and grain mustard, in a meal that also produced soufflé Arnold Bennett with smoked haddock, Gruyère cheese and poached egg, rack of Pendle lamb with minted pesto and a ravioli of sweetbreads, tarte Tatin with Chantilly cream, and steamed syrup and ginger sponge with butterscotch sauce and custard.

Directions: 2 minutes drive from M6/J26. Take A577 (Upholland), turn R into Lafford Lane

WRIGHTINGTON, **High Moor Inn** ❀❀

High Moor Lane WN6 9QA
Map 7: SD51
Tel: 01257 252364
Fax: 01257 255120
Chef: Darren Wynn
Owners: James Sines, John Nelson
Cost: *A/c* £20, fixed-price L & D £10 (2 courses). ☺ H/wine £9.95
Times: Noon-last L 2pm/5.30-last D 10pm. Closed 26 Dec, 1 Jan
Additional: Bar food L; Sunday L; Children welcome; ❀ dishes
Seats: 100
Smoking: Air conditioning
Credit cards: 🔳 🔳 🔳 🔳 🔳 🔳 🔳

It was at the 17th-century Highmoor that George Wright, the last highwayman to be hanged in Britain, was captured. It continues to provide good food for travellers (who, one trusts, are not taken mid salmon fishcake to help with enquiries), although the long menu (19 main courses) smacks of a dated provinciality. The style, however, is modern English, taking in twice-baked Roquefort soufflé with rocket leaves and sun-dried tomato oil, and breast of magret duck with lime, honey, peppercorns and lemon, with just, with the inclusion of a few old favourites such as 'the Highmoor classical prawn cocktail, beef and five kinds of mushroom pudding, and Knickerbocker glory. Fish dishes include salad of spiced skate wing with ginger dressing, and fillet of sea bass with candied spiced tomatoes and basil cream.

Directions: M6/J27, follow sign to Parbold, after hospital turn R into Robin Hood Lane, 1st L into High Moor Lane

WRIGHTINGTON,
Wrightington Hotel 🏵🏵

A modern hotel peacefully situated in the small country village of Wrightington, just off the M6. Excellent modern British cooking is served in the Snape & Nugent Restaurant, where the eponymous chefs make good use of local ingredients in their monthly-changing, market-led menus. Typical starters include braised Welsh mussels, honey-roast parsnip and Guinness soup, and warm salad of calves' liver and oranges. Our inspector enjoyed a winter meal of sautéed chicken livers with herbed polenta, crispy pancetta lardons and a light garlic oil. This was followed by seared medallions of monkfish with a generous portion of deep-fried green lip mussels. Desserts range from poached nectarines layered on hazelnut sponge and mango sauce, to apricot and date sticky toffee pudding coated in butterscotch sauce. The interesting wine list includes two sections, one of bottles priced at £10.50, the other at £12.50. A 'connoisseur selection' is also available.

Moss Lane Standish
WN6 9PB
Map 7: SD51
Tel: 01257 425803
Fax: 01257 425830
Chefs: Ian Snape, Jeff Nugent
Owner: Barry Aspinall
Cost: Alc £18, fixed-price D £19. ☺
H/wine £8.95
Times: D only, last D 9.30pm.
Closed Sun, Bhs
Additional: Children welcome;
🍴 dishes
Smoking: No pipes & cigars
Accommodation: 47 en suite
Credit cards: 🌑 🌑 🌑 🌑 🌑

Directions: From M6/J27, drive 0.25 mile towards Parbold. 200yds past church, fork R. Hotel is 100yds on R.

LEICESTERSHIRE

ASHBY-DE-LA-ZOUCH,
The Fallen Knight 🏵   NEW

A converted public house in the centre of town. Meals in the elegant restaurant are influenced by the Mediterranean, but are essentially modern British. The highlight of a recent meal was the chicken terrine starter, with black pudding and fresh baby asparagus. For dessert try iced hazelnut soufflé with cherry and Kirsch sauce.

Additional: Bar food; Sunday L; Children welcome; 🍴 dishes
Accommodation: 24 en suite
Credit cards: 🌑 🌑 🌑 🌑 🌑 🌑 🌑 JCB

Kilwardby Street LE65 2FQ
Map 8: SK31
Tel: 01530 412230
Fax: 01530 417596
Chefs: Andy Bond, Paul Curran, John Whitehouse
Owners: Mr & Mrs J R Whitehouse
Cost: Alc £25, fixed price L £15/D £19. ☺ H/wine £9.50
Times: Last L 2.30pm/last D 10pm.
Closed D 25-26 Dec

Directions: Cross mini roundabout in town centre, proceed along Kilwardby St, hotel on right next to supermarket car park exit

CASTLE DONINGTON, The Priest
House on the River 🏵

This former working mill has a restaurant overlooking the river Trent. The imaginative menu includes grilled hake topped with tomato tapenade on a vegetable nage, roast peppered duck breast on polenta with a fresh raspberry liquor, and crème brûlée.

Additional: Bar food; Sunday L; Children welcome; 🍴 dishes
Smoking: No smoking in dining room
Accommodation: 45 en suite
Credit cards: 🌑 🌑 🌑 🌑 🌑

Kings Mills DE74 2RR
Map 8: SK42
Tel: 01332 810649
Fax: 01332 811141
Chef: Jeff Cadden
Owner: Arcadian Hotels
Cost: Alc £28, fixed-price L £15.50/D £22.50. ☺ H/wine £11.95
Times: Last L 2pm/last D 9.30pm.
Closed L Sat

Directions: In Castle Donington turn L at 1st traffic lights and follow to river.

EAST MIDLANDS AIRPORT,
The Thistle Donington ✵

Despite the location, this hotel is remarkably peaceful, and the Sherwood Restaurant provides a pleasant setting. Dishes might include 'trio of oriental fish dusted with oils and spices from the East', and game bird casserole, served with cabbage and smoked bacon in a filo basket.

Accommodation: 110 en suite
Credit cards: ▬ ▬ ▬ ▬ ▬ ▬ ▬ JCB

Directions: At East Midlands International Airport, 1 mile from M1/J23A/24 and A42(M) Birmingham link road

Derby DE74 2SH
Map 8: SK42
Tel: 01332 850700
Fax: 01332 850823
Chef: Phil O'Hagen
Owner: The Sherwood Restaurant
Cost: *Alc* £26, fixed-price L £14/D £19.95. ☺ H/wine £11.45
Times: Last L 2pm/last D 10pm.
Closed L Sat
Additional: Bar food; Sunday L; Children welcome; ✦ dishes
Smoking: No smoking in dining room

HINCKLEY, **Sketchley Grange Hotel** ✵

The Willow restaurant offers both a short set menu and a carte. From the latter terrine of duck confit, foie gras and caramelised oranges, roast rump of lamb with roasted vegetables and a thyme jus, or fresh lobster and monkfish flambéed in Tio Pepe and simmered in a cream sauce, show the style.

Sketchley Lane Burbage LE10 3HU
Map 4: SP49
Tel: 01455 251133
Fax: 01455 631384
Chef: John Bacon
Cost: *Alc*: £22, fixed-price L £12.50/ D £19.95. ☺ H/wine £9.75
Times: Last L 2pm/last D 9.30pm.
Closed L Sat, D Sun
Additional: Bar food; Sunday L; Children welcome; ✦ dishes
Smoking: No smoking in dining room; Air conditioning
Accommodation: 55 en suite
Credit cards: ▬ ▬ ▬ ▬ ▬ ▬ ▬ JCB

Directions: From M69/J1 take B4109, at mini roundabout turn L, then 1st R

LEICESTER, **Belmont House** ✵

The conservatory-style Cherry Restaurant overlooks the 200-year-old tree-lined 'New Walk'. Good choice from a menu priced for one to three courses, with typical dishes such as seared king scallops with a hint of ginger, chicken breast with bacon and mushroom, and a creamy glazed lemon tart, showing the range.

De Montfort Street LE1 7GR
Map 4: SK50
Tel: 0116 2544773
Fax: 0116 2470804
Chef: Mark Crockett
Owners: Bowie family
Cost: Fixed-price L £9.95 (2 courses)/D £18.95. ☺ H/wine £9.95.
Times: Last L 2pm/D 10pm.
Closed L Sat, Bhs
Additional: Bar food L; Sunday L; Children welcome; ✦ dishes
Smoking: No-smoking area
Accommodation: 75 en suite
Credit cards: ▬ ▬ ▬ ▬ JCB

Directions: From railway station, first R off A6 southbound

LEICESTER, The Tiffin ✿

1 De Montfort Street LE1 7GE
Map 4: SK50
Tel: 0116 2470420/2553737
Fax: 0116 2625125
Chef: Mohammed Ali
Owners: Mr Hari & Mr Previn-Parmar
Cost: *Alc* £17, fixed-price D £18
(4 courses). ☺ H/wine £12.50
Times: Last L 1.45pm/last D 10.45pm.
Closed L Sat, all Sun, L Bhs
Additional: Children welcome;
🍴 dishes
Seats: 60. Private dining room 35
Smoking: No-smoking area;
Air conditioning
Credit cards: 🖸 🖸 🖸 🖸 🖸 🖸 🖸

A large conservatory runs the length of this popular north Indian restaurant. Short menu of well-cooked favourites, running from prawn puri and tandoori chicken, to lamb biriyani, backed up by specialities such as kadai gosh – lamb in fresh garlic, ginger and mixed spices.

Directions: Near railway station on the corner of De Montfort Street and London Road (A6)

LEICESTER,
Time Out Hotel ✿

Enderby Road Blaby
LE8 4GD
Map 4: SK50
Tel: 0116 2787898
Fax: 0116 2781974
Chef: Carl Swingler
Owner: Regal Hotels Plc
Cost: *Alc* £22, fixed-price L £11.95
(2 courses/ D £17.30. ☺
H/wine £11.25.
Times: Last L 2.30pm/D 9.45pm.
Closed L Sat

A small hotel on the outskirts of the city with a smart Colonial-style restaurant. Oriental mussels and prawns proved a hit with our inspector, as did the chocolate tart. Main courses might include confit of duck with red wine and citrus glaze, and roast monkfish with almond pilau.

Additional: Bar Food; Sunday L; Children welcome; 🍴 dishes
Smoking: No pipes & cigars; Air conditioning
Accommodation: 28 en suite.
Credit cards: 🖸 🖸 🖸 🖸 🖸 🖸 🖸 JCB

Directions: Off the A426, 3 miles S of Leicester

MARKET HARBOROUGH,
Three Swans Hotel ✿

21 High Street LE16 7NJ
Map 4: SP78
Tel: 01858 466644
Fax: 01858 433101
Chef: Richard Payne
Owner: Travelsphere Ltd
Cost: *Alc* £28, fixed-price L £13.95/D
£19.95 (4 courses). ☺ H/wine £10.55
Times: Last L 2pm/last D 10pm.
Closed D Sun

16th-century historic inn much extended with every modern comfort. The formal Swans restaurant mixes the traditional with the Mediterranean in dishes such as black pudding mille-feuille with red onion and plum compote, and baked sea cod with tomato-flavoured hummus and purée of rosemary potatoes.

Additional: Bar food; Sunday L; Children welcome; 🍴 dishes
Smoking: No-smoking area; No pipes and cigars; Air conditioning
Accommodation: 50 en suite
Credit cards: 🖸 🖸 🖸 🖸 🖸 🖸 🖸

Directions: Follow High Street S through town centre; hotel is on R at traffic lights

MELTON MOWBRAY,
Stapleford Park 🏵🏵

Stapleford Park is the epitome of opulent English country living, albeit one manufactured as a nouveau riche idyll. An outpost of the Carnegie Club, there is a sense of camaraderie and informality that is more house party than hotel. The dining room has magnificent Grinling Gibbons carvings and is a fine setting for the short, daily changing selection of dishes – which, in keeping with the whimsical notes found throughout the estate, always features at least one adult nursery dish, such as deep-fried cod in yeast beer batter with home-made ketchup or sausage and mash. A sample dinner might offer gingered shellfish consommé with scallop ravioli, followed by cumin-crusted loin of lamb with couscous, sweet baked onions and thyme pan juices, then orchard fruit tart Tatin with Calvados ice cream and caramel sauce. There is also a separate vegetarian menu. Breakfasts are served in the 16th-century stone-vaulted kitchen on Beatrix Potter china.

Stapleford LE14 2EF
Map 8: SK71
Tel: 01572 787522
Fax: 01572 787651
Chef: Geoff Balharrie
Owner: Stapleford Park plc
Cost: Fixed-price D £39.50. ☺
H/wine £18
Times: 12.30pm-last L
2.30pm/7.30pm-last D 9.45pm
Additional: Bar food ; Sunday L;
No children under 12; 🍴 dishes
Seats: 50 + 24. Private dining rooms
26 +12. Jacket & tie preferred
Smoking: No smoking in dining room
Accommodation: 51 en suite
Credit cards: 💳 💳 💳 💳

Directions: Follow Melton ring road A607 (Grantham) on to B676, 4 miles turn R signed Stapleford

QUORN,
Quorn Country Hotel 🏵🏵

The luxurious small hotel sits in four acres of landscaped gardens, just a pleasant stroll from the River Soar. Of the two restaurants, the Orangery favours a Mediterranean/Californian style of cooking, whereas the Shires takes a more traditional approach. The favourite dish in the latter (it says so on the menu) is roast Gressingham duck, crisp, tender, 'definitely not pink' served with either orange or tangy plum sauce. Another 'signature' dish is a starter of Stilton mushrooms in a creamy sauce on a filo pastry nest. Main course fish dishes include medallion of monkfish with a spicy oriental-style sauce. Our inspector plumped for tender marinated fillet of lamb on a potato and herb cake topped with wild mushrooms, and served with a good red wine and basil sauce. Chocolate marquise was beautifully presented with a mirror image of spicy pear sorbet. There is also a short menu of good quality cheeses, lucidly described.

Charnwood House Leicester Road
LE12 8BB
Map 8: SK51
Tel: 01509 415050
Fax: 01509 415557
Chef: David Wilkinson
Owner: J N Brankin-Frisby
Cost: Alc £25, fixed-price L £ 12
(2 courses)/D £20. ☺ H/wine £9.75
Times: Noon- 2pm/7-9.30pm.
Closed L Sat
Additional: Bar food (not Sat);
Sunday L; Children welcome;
🍴 dishes
Seats: 60. Private room 48
Smoking: Air conditioning
Accommodation: 20 en suite
Credit cards: 💳 💳 💳 💳 💳 💳

Directions: Off A6 in village centre

QUORN, **Quorn Grange**

88 Wood Lane LE12 8DB
Map 8: SK51
Tel: 01509 412167
Fax: 01509 415621
Chef: Shaun Brown
Owner: Jeremy Lord
Cost: *Alc* £30, fixed-price L £9.85 (2 courses)/D £20.50. ☺ H/wine £10.90.
Times: Noon-last L 2pm/7pm-last D 9.30pm. Closed L Sat, 26 Dec, 1 Jan
Additional: Sunday L; ❹ dishes
Seats: 50. Private dining room 120. Jacket & tie preferred (weekends)
Accommodation: 15 en suite
Credit cards: ▤ ▥ ▧ ▨ ▩ ▤ ▨ JCB

Tally-ho! The arrival of a new chef at this peaceful country house hotel has given the kitchen a shot in the arm. A first course of scallops impressed with their super-fresh quality, precise preparation and unusual context – set on a 'cabbage stew', batons of bacon and smoked salmon in a cream and white wine sauce. Home-made pigeon and partridge sausages had good rich flavour, and were served with finely shredded caramelised shallots, creamy Dijon mashed potato and a jus of red wine, game stock and shallots. Orange and Grand Marnier soufflé was well-risen, golden and had a good alcoholic kick. Other interesting dishes include rabbit and venison terrine, mutton broth with pearl barley, and grilled fillet of turbot cooked with lime served with beetroot and watercress pasta. Vegetarians can enjoy parsnip crumble or wild mushroom Stroganoff – and not a bit of Quorn in sight.

Directions: Turn off B591 Quorn High Street into Wood Lane, signed Swithland

REDMILE,
Peacock Farm ⊛

Feathers Restaurant is part of the original 1780's farmhouse. All is prepared on the premises, even the bread. Starters may include artichoke and ricotta ravioli, with a pan-fried trio of marinated pigeon breast, boneless quail and loin of venison among the main courses. For dessert try the rich chocolate brioche pudding.

Additional: Bar food L; Sunday L; Children welcome; ❹ dishes
Smoking: No smoking in dining room
Accommodation: 10 en suite
Credit cards: ▤ ▥ ▧ ▨ ▩ ▤

Directions: From A52 follow signs for Redmile and Belvoir Castle, between Nottingham & Grantham. 0.50 mile before Redmile

Main Street NG13 0GQ
Map 8: SK73
Tel: 01949 842475
Fax: 01949 843127
Chef: Paul Reisenbuchler
Owners: Paul & Jackie Reisenbuchler
Cost: *Alc* £20. ☺ H/wine £6.95
Times: Last L 2.30pm/last D 9.30pm

LINCOLNSHIRE

BELTON, Belton Woods Hotel

Welcoming, attentive service is a strong point at this large hotel set in 475 acres of rolling countryside. The fine-dining Manor restaurant offers such dishes as red mullet and vegetable broth to start, followed by roast saddle of venison or salmon and lobster roulade, then chocolate torte or a trio of lemon desserts.

Accommodation: 136 en suite
Credit cards:

Directions: *Telephone for directions*

Grantham NG32 2LN
Map 8: SK93
Tel: 01476 593200
Fax: 01476 574547
Chef: Mark Hotchkins
Cost: Alc £35, fixed-price D £25. ☺
H/wine £12.95
Times: D only, last D 9.30pm
Additional: Bar food; Sunday L;
Children welcome; 🌢 dishes
Smoking: No smoking in dining room;
Air conditioning

BOURNE, Black Horse Inn NEW

Grimsthorpe PE10 0LY
Map 8: TF02
Tel: 01778 591247
Fax: 01778 591373
Chef: Brian Rey
Owners: Brian & Elaine Rey
Cost: Alc £20, fixed-price L £11.65
(4 courses). ☺ H/wine £8.80
Times: Noon-last L 2pm/7-last
D 9.30pm
Additional: Bar food; Sunday L;
No children under 14; 🌢 dishes
Seats: 48. Private dining room 12
Smoking: No smoking in dining room
Accommodation: 6 en suite
Credit cards: ▆ ▆ ▆ ▆ ▆ ▆ JCB

Pick your way carefully through the blackboard specials in the bar, or study the *carte* in the traditional country restaurant, and you will find some interesting dishes using good quality local produce, including good game and some rare-breed dishes. Warm smoked-duck salad, as well as pan-fried skate wing fillet with wild mushrooms may be listed amongst the starters, and a wide selection of main courses includes pot-roast lamb shanks in a rich mixed bean and vegetable broth and baked guinea fowl breast, glazed with honey and orange on a crisp wild mushroom risotto with rich Madeira sauce. Their lemon tart is particularly good, with a smooth yet zingy filling.

Directions: Follow A151 for 4 miles, west towards Grantham

CLEETHORPES, Kingsway Hotel

Overlooking the Humber estuary, this hotel of long-standing offers traditional service and accommodation. Local fish features regularly on the Anglo/French menu. A spring meal in the wood-panelled restaurant started with chicken and almond soup, followed by fresh fillet of turbot with a rich grain mustard sauce.

Additional: Bar food; Sunday L; No children under 5; 🌢 dishes
Accommodation: 50 en suite. **Credit cards:** ▆ ▆ ▆ ▆ ▆

Directions: At junction of A1098 and sea front

Kingsway DN35 0AE
Map 8: TA30
Tel: 01472 601122
Fax: 01472 601381
Chef: Ivon Trushell
Owners: The Harris Family
Cost: Alc £25, fixed-price L £14.50/D
£17.95. ☺ H/wine £9.95
Times: Last L 1.45pm/last D 9pm
Closed 25, 26 Dec

GRANTHAM, **Harry's Place**

The small room that makes up Harry's Pace is charming –
paintings, personal knick-knacks, beautiful flower displays –
with the three well-sized pine tables that fill the room making
reservations essential. It is basically a double-handed
operation; the eponymous Harry in the kitchen, with Caroline
Hallam in charge of front of house. The hand-written menu
changes daily, just two choices at each course, plus a good
selection of cheese. Harry Hallam is a fine cook, enthusiastic
for strong flavours and robust inventive dishes such as those
eaten one February lunch: provençale fish soup with good,
spicy undertones served with a first-class rouille; Orkney
scallops, sweet, succulent and well timed, accompanied by a
perfectly balanced sorrel hollandaise, plus fine fresh fettucine
tossed in olive oil and Parmesan, a light chutney made with
onions, baby tomato, capers, new asparagus and chives, and
wilted baby spinach leaves; and a delicious, intensely flavoured
rhubarb soufflé, a hint of orange zest just taking off the edge
and giving another dimension. Ancillaries keep up with the
pace: warm granary bread straight from the oven; tiny little hot
savouries of light crisp pastry topped with Ventreche ham and
caviar, concealing a lovely spicy tomato filling with oregano
and chilli; good strong Italian-style coffee. The wine list is
short, well balanced and offers some interesting, well-priced
options.

Signature dishes: Wild River Dee salmon; hot fruit soufflés;
young Yorkshire grouse; Lincolnshire salt-marsh teal.

Directions: On the B1174 2 miles NW of Grantham

17 High Street Great Gonerby
NG31 8JS
Map 8: SK93
Tel: 01476 561780
Chef: Harry Hallam
Owners: Harry & Caroline Hallam
Cost: *Alc* £44. H/wine £16.50
Times: 12.30-last L 2pm/7-last
D 9.30pm. Closed Sun, Mon,
25-26 Dec, Bhs
Additional: No children under 5
Seats: 10
Smoking: No smoking in dining room
Credit cards: ■ ■ ■ ●

HORNCASTLE,

Magpies Restaurant

Appropriately, the *carte* at this low-slung restaurant on the
main road, takes its inspiration from a variety of sources. The
cooking is confident and assured enough to include dishes such
as ragout of lambs' sweetbreads and shiitake mushrooms, and
loin and kidneys of new seasons lamb with pea purée and
marjoram jus. Meat is well sourced – fillet of locally reared
grass-fed Lincoln red beef comes with shallots, mushrooms,
parsley purée and red wine sauce. Grilled fillets of red mullet
with confit of fennel, plum tomatoes and sauce vierge are
amongst the fish dishes. As well as some rich desserts, there is
a board of excellent, ripe cheeses.

Additional: Children welcome
Seats: 35
Smoking: No smoking in dining room
Credit cards: ■ ■

71-75 East Street LN9 6AA
Map 8: TF26
Tel: 01507 527004
Fax: 01507 524064
Chefs: Matthew Lee, Simon Lee,
Chris Duckham
Owners: The Lee Family
Cost: Fixed-price L £15/D £28.
H/wine £10
Times: 12.30-last L 2pm/7.15-last
D 10pm. Closed Sun, Mon, L Tue,
Wed & Sat, 2 wks Aug

Directions: 0.5 mile from Horncastle on A158 towards Skegness

---

LINCOLN, **Wig & Mitre** ✿

No music, no chips and no game machines, but you can expect daily
newspapers and freshly squeezed orange juice at this fine 14th-
century building housing a bar and restaurant. The menu changes
twice a day, with dishes such as leek and cheese soufflé, and chicken
breast in Stilton sauce amongst a good choice.

30 Steep Hill
LN2 1TL
Map 8: SK97
Tel: 01522 535190
Fax: 01522 532402
Chefs: Paul Vidic, Peter Dodd,
Mark Cheseldine

Directions: Close to cathedral, castle and car park at top of Steep Hill

Wig & Mitre

Owners: Michael & Valerie Hope, Paul Vidic
Cost: *Alc* £20. ☺ H/wine £10.25
Times: 8am-last D 11pm
Additional: Bar food; Sunday L; Children welcome; ◑ dishes
Smoking: No pipes & cigars
Credit cards: JCB

LOUTH, Beaumont Hotel ❀

A smartly appointed restaurant with menus which show an Italian influence. Dishes range from pasta all'amatriciana, with its tasty, thick sauce of tomato and smoked bacon, to pink, tender lamb medallions with a red wine and rosemary sauce.

66 Victoria Road LN11 0BX
Map 8: TF38
Tel: 01507 605005
Fax: 01507 607768
Please telephone for further details

LOUTH, Kenwick Park Hotel ❀❀

The Fairway Restaurant, which takes its name from the 18-hole golf course that can be seen from the dining room, is part of this elegant Georgian style hotel. Strong on modern ideas, the kitchen produces an imaginative range of up-to-date English dishes such as baked fillet of sea bream laced with fresh lime, and shallow-fried escalope of salmon with garlic couscous and a Pernod cream. A typical summer meal might start with home-made ravioli filled with mushrooms and shallots and finished with saffron cream and Parmesan, followed by roast chump of lamb topped off with acacia honey and Chablis glaze, and served with warm chilli salsa. The 'Keepers' bar, which also overlooks the golf course, serves a good range or bar meals and real ales in a more relaxed and informal setting.

Directions: Take A631 from Market Rasen

Kenwick Park LN11 8NR
Map 8: TF38
Tel: 01507 608806
Fax: 01507 608027
Chef: Paul Harvey
Owner: S D Flynn
Cost: *Alc* £29.95, fixed-price L & D £18.50. ☺ H/wine £10.75
Times: Noon-last L 1.45pm/7-last D 9.30pm
Additional: Bar food; Sunday L; Children welcome; ◑ dishes
Seats: 44. Private room 22. Jacket & tie preferred
Smoking: No smoking in dining room
Accommodation: 24 en suite
Credit cards:

STALLINGBOROUGH, Stallingborough Grange ❀❀❀

An 18th-century thatched country house, tastefully restored to provide guests with a good standard of service. The oak-panelled restaurant has a relaxed atmosphere in which to enjoy some serious Anglo/French cooking. At a recent meal, our inspector enjoyed a starter of tarte Tatin of salmon with asparagus and fennel butter, but other starters could include parsnip and wild cep velouté with smoked bacon, poached mussels and mustard cream, and seared sea scallops with coriander, pesto and fresh Parmesan. Main courses are well-presented, and range from pot-roasted fillet of pork wrapped

Riby Road DN41 8BU
Map 8: TA11
Tel: 01469 561302
Fax: 01469 561338
Chef: Neal Birtwell
Owners: Mr & Mrs G W Feeney
Cost: *Alc* £23. ☺
Times: D only, 6.30-last D 9.45pm
Additional: Bar food; Sunday L (noon-2pm); Children welcome; ◑ dishes
Seats: 42. Private dining room 8. Jacket & tie preferred

in Parma ham with lemon and herbs, to steamed fillet of turbot with parsley mash, and roasted fennel. Imaginative desserts provide a suitably enjoyable finale to proceedings – our inspector sampled crisp strawberry fritters with lemon and thyme syrup, but other choices include apple and date strudel with hot chocolate pithiviers, and layered terrine of blueberry pancakes with maple syrup and bourbon poached figs.

Directions: On A1173 between Riby crossroads and Stallingborough village

Smoking: No smoking in dining room
Accommodation: 32 en suite
Credit cards: [cards] JCB

STAMFORD, George of Stamford

Splendid 16th-century coaching inn with log fires, a walled monastery garden and cobbled courtyard. Sit down in the oak-panelled restaurant for a feast of traditional English cooking with a continental twist. Expect dishes such as wild mushroom risotto, Woodbridge duck with sage and onion stuffing, and sirloin of beef.

Additional: Bar food; Sunday L; Children welcome; dishes;
Accommodation: 47 en suite
Credit cards: [cards]

Directions: From A1 take B1081 to Stamford. Follow road to traffic lights, hotel on L

St Martins PE9 2LB
Map 8: TF00
Tel: 01780 750750
Fax: 01780 750701
Chef: Chris Pitman
Owner: Lawrence Hoskins
Cost: *Alc* £36, fixed-price L £13.50-£16.50. H/wine £9.75
Times: Noon-11pm

SUTTON-ON-SEA,
Grange & Links Hotel

Both golfers and families with children are welcome at this friendly seaside hotel. An exceptionally wide choice of dishes (we counted 42 main courses) changes daily and might include beef Stroganoff, sirloin steak garni, chicken Kiev and Sandilands baked cod Mornay. Lobsters are served four ways.

Directions: Follow signs to Sandilands from Sutton-on-Sea

Sea Lane Sandilands
Mablethorpe LN12 2RA
Map 9: TF58
Tel: 01507 441334
Fax: 01507 443033
Chef: Tina Harrison
Owners: Eve & Robert McGahon
Cost: *Alc* £22. ☺ H/wine £9.50
Times: D only, last D 9.30pm
Additional: Bar food; Sunday L (noon-2pm); Children welcome; dishes
Accommodation: 24 en suite
Credit cards: [cards]

WINTERINGHAM,
Winteringham Fields

'To have developed such a level of popularity in a relatively isolated location is in itself commendable', commented one inspector on Germain and Annie Schwab's unassuming little

DN15 9PF
Map 8: SE92
Tel: 01724 733096
Fax: 01724 733898
Chef: Germain Schwab

Winteringham Fields

Owners: Germain & Annie Schwab
Cost: *Alc* £60, fixed-price L £20/D
£29. H/wine £13.50
Times: Noon-1.30pm/7-9.30pm.
Closed Sun, Mon, 1st full wk Mar &
Aug, 2 wks from 24 Dec
Additional: Children welcome;
⊕ dishes
Seats: 36. Private dining room 10
Smoking: No smoking in dining room
Accommodation: 7 en suite
Credit cards: ▬ ▬ ▼ ▢▬ ▣

hotel. It's a super place. The house dates from 1540, and sits in
the middle of a rural village a few 100 yards south of the
Humber. Young friendly, professional staff take a cue from
the Schwabs and show a real interest in their guests without
being suffocating; there is a genuine warmth to the place and
eating here is a pleasure. Germain Schwab draws on his Swiss
heritage, the local produce (Lincolnshire lamb, fish, home-
grown salad leaves), keenly honed technical skills, and a great
deal of imaginative flair, to produce outstanding food where
attention to detail is evident in every morsel. A winter
inspection dinner showed something of the tilt. Orders were
taken in either the cosy lounge or the conservatory bar, and
the vast menu was explained, with assistance offered if
needed. The first *amuse bouche* was served at this stage – a
demi-tasse of red pepper soup in which the gentle sweetness
of the peppers was clear and unspoilt by other flavours. After
ordering wine (from a lengthy tome that offers a stunning
range of old vintages, as well as a lot of well-priced treats and
some very good half-bottles), the second *amuse bouche*
appeared – a little filo parcel of duck salé of wonderful intense
flavour. On being seated, a third *amuse bouche*, this time a
crisp tartlet of langoustine with a light bisque-style sauce.
Then a selection of warm, home-made white and brown rolls,
followed by pot-au-feu of sautéed foie gras and scallops in a
light bouillon with baby carrots, broad beans and samphire.
Next, a little swirl of beautifully sharp strawberry sorbet,
piped into physalis fruit and set on a little silver salver filled
with crushed ice, was 'just the right amount and flavour'. The
main course, fillet of venison, came perfectly cooked, tender,
succulent and well flavoured, served with chestnuts and
sprouts and a grand veneur sauce. Then came a superb trolley
of about 35 cheeses, all in tip-top condition, and served with
raisin and walnut rolls, celery, grapes and a tray of dried fruits
and nuts, to be followed by chocolate genoise, a small light
sponge with rich chocolate flavour, with a fine chocolate cup
filled with strong coffee ice and a light chocolate sauce,
alongside a tray of friandises: tuiles, langues de chat, ratafia.
Then back to the lounge for coffee and a further, generous,
tray of 'scrummy chocs'. For those lucky enough to be staying,
breakfast brings a wonderful bakery basket and home-made
lemon curd. Bliss.
   Signature dishes: Rolled rack of Lincolnshire lamb; grilled
baby turbot, mouclade of clams and mussels; hot rabbit and
foie gras tart; Winteringham corn tart with butterscotch

AA Shortlisted for
Wine Award-see page 16

Directions: Village centre, off the A1077, 4 miles S of Humber
bridge.

MERSEYSIDE

BIRKENHEAD, **Beadles** ❀

The Gott's simple restaurant is just a small front room really, no bar or lounge, and decorated in 60s style. A summer dinner took in aubergine brandade with a hot harissa sauce, sorrel flavoured split pea soup, fillet of lamb with finely diced kidneys and field mushrooms, and salsicotto – a meaty, lightly spiced sausage mixed with haricot, red and butter beans.

Smoking: No pipes & cigars
Credit cards: ■ ■ ■ 🗲 🗗 JCB

Directions: Centre of Oxton village

15 Rosemount Oxton L43 5SG
Map 7: SJ38
Tel: 0151 653 9010
Chef: Bea Gott
Owners: Roy & Bea Gott
Cost: Alc £23
Times: D only, last D 9.30pm.
Closed Sun, Mon, 2 wks Aug
Additional: No children under 7;
🍂 dishes

BIRKENHEAD, **Capitol** ❀

A Chinese restaurant, always known as the Capitol, has been on this site for over 30 years. Unusually light walls are covered with original Chinese paintings for sale. All the usual offerings from a mainly Cantonese selection, with set-menu banquets and sizzling hot platters, ribs and dim sum.

Directions: Town centre, at the corner of Hamilton Square

24 Argyle Street Hamilton Square
L41 6AE
Map 7: SJ38
Tel: 0151 6479212
Fax: 0151 6473793
Chef: Yan Tam
Owners: Steve & Annie Tam
Cost: Alc £15, fixed-price L £6.50/D £16. ☺ H/wine £9
Times: Last L 2pm/last D 11.30pm.
Closed L Sat, L Sun, 25-26 Dec
Additional: Children welcome;
🍂 dishes
Smoking: Air conditioning
Credit cards: ■ ■ ■ 🗲 ■ 🗗

LIVERPOOL, **Becher's Brook** ❀❀

The Canadian background of chef/patron David Cooke is reflected in dishes such as pan-roasted goose breast with Saskatchewan wild rice on a woodland berry and rosemary jus, and Nova Scotia-style clam chowder. A former Kikkoman UK Masterchef, he brings credibility to dishes such as roast lobster, orange and coriander salad with sweet-and-sour pickled onions, new potatoes and ginger vinaigrette. The boldly conceived style includes mille-feuille of British veal, aubergine and Gruyère cheese on spiced tomato sauce, steamed Irish sea salmon fillet on smoked haddock brandade with three sauces, and banana in tempura with honey and lime ice cream. Special credit for the Braille menus.

Directions: From M62 follow signs for City Centre and Catholic Cathedral. L into Mount Pleasant Rd, then L again into Hope St. Restaurant is 100yds on L

29a Hope Street L1 9BQ
Map 7: SJ39
Tel: 0151 7070005
Fax: 0151 7087011
Chefs: Gerard Hogan
Owners: David & Donna Cooke
Cost: Alc £28, fixed-price L £17.95. ☺ H/wine £11.50
Times: Noon-last L 2.30pm/5-last D 10pm. Closed L Sat, all Sun, Xmas, Bhs
Additional: No children under 8;
🍂 dishes
Seats: 38
Smoking: No smoking in dining room;
Air conditioning
Credit cards: ■ ■ ■ 🗲 🗗 ■ 💷

SOUTHPORT,

Royal Clifton Hotel ✿

Promenade PR8 1RB
Map 7: SD31
Tel: 01704 533771
Fax: 01704 500657
Chef: Ian Sallery
Owner: Mr R Yoxall
Cost: Alc £25, fixed-price D £16.50
(6 courses). ☺ H/wine £8.95
Times: D only, 6.30pm-9.30pm

Occupying a prime position on the promenade, this is a large hotel with extensive facilities. The Pavilion Restaurant provides a formal setting for a mixed menu of English and French dishes. Game soup, mushroom ravioli, pork Calvados, and steamed halibut with prawn and lobster sauce are typical examples.

Additional: Bar food; Sunday L; Children welcome; 🍴 dishes
Smoking: No-smoking area; no pipes & cigars
Accommodation: 107 en suite
Credit cards: ▆▆ ▆▆ ▆ ▆▆ 🄲

Directions: M6/J26, take M58 (Southport), exit at J3. Follow A570 through Ormskirk – hotel on Southport promenade.

THORNTON HOUGH,

Thornton Hall Hotel ✿✿

Neston Road Wirral L63 1JF
Map 7: SJ38
Tel: 0151 3363938
Fax: 0151 3367864
Chef: Gerard O'Sullivan
Owners: The Thompson Family
Cost: Alc £28, fixed-price L £10/D £21. ☺ H/wine £10.95
Times: 12.30-last L 2.15pm/7-last D 9.30pm. Closed L Sat
Additional: Bar food; Sunday L; Children welcome; 🍴 menu
Seats: 45. Private dining room 24
Smoking: No pipes & cigars
Accommodation: 63 en suite
Credit cards: ▆▆ ▆▆ ▆▆ ▆ ▆▆ 🄲 JCB

Built in the 18th century by a shipping magnate, this country house hotel still reflects the first owner's taste for luxury. The original hall retains its stained glass windows and impressive oak panelling, while in the charming restaurant you'll find the original leather and mother-of-pearl ceiling and a carved fireplace. Luxury is also on the extensive menu with special-occasion starters including risotto of king scallops, chicken and morel sausages, smoked quail and beetroot salad and smoked salmon served with shellfish cappuccino and keta caviar. Main courses also reflect the chef's European influences: try venison with rich Cassis gravy, or duck breast and liver with roast garlic jus. For a simpler meal, choose the grilled steak or fish. Lovers of the cheese course may enjoy Welsh rarebit or a platter with fruit and biscuits, but the desserts, such as hot passion fruit pancake soufflé with apricot sauce, are tempting too.

Directions: M53/J4 onto B5151. Turn R at first crossroads – B5136 (Thornton Hough). Hotel just past village centre on L

NORFOLK

BLAKENEY, **Morston Hall** 🌸🌸🌸

The flint-walled house, dating from the 17th century, stands in delightful, well-tended gardens in a small hamlet close to a tidal quay. Centre of operations is the restaurant, running the width of the house, with garden views, well-spaced tables, white linen and comfortable chairs. Visitors to Morston Hall are fortunate that the appeal of Galton Blackiston's cooking is both for the palate and the eye, and his no-choice dinner is a fine and rewarding experience. Our own visit opened with superb home-made tarragon bread rolls and 'probably the best butter I have ever tasted', and the four-course set-menu began well with warm goats' cheese and lardon salad set on a light and tangy ratatouille fondue. Good as this was, it was excelled by a simple but stunning pan-fried turbot with saffron risotto with a light, refreshing fennel cream. The centrepiece of the meal, juicy duck breast with cocotte potatoes and parsnips was pronounced 'delicious'. To finish, a warm pear tart with light, crisp pastry was served with vanilla cream and a chocolate sauce. As an alternative to dessert, there are fine European cheeses direct from Rungis. Also, 'terrific' coffee and petits fours. Wines of the month are always worth trying and are available by both bottle and glass.

Signature dishes: Lamb with mustard herb crust; locally caught mackerel pan-fried on braised fennel with tarragon nage; saffron risotto, whole grain mustard sauce and sautéed wild mushrooms; warm chicken and Roquefort mousse on sautéed spinach and tomato fondue.

Morston NR25 7AA
Map 9: TG04
Tel: 01263 741041
Fax: 01263 740419
Chefs: Galton Blackiston, Daniel Smith
Owner: Galton & Tracy Blackiston, Justin Fraser
Costs: D £28 (4 courses). ☺ H/wine £9.90
Times: 7.30pm-8pm. Closed 1 Jan-Feb
Additional: Sunday L (12.30pm-1pm); Children welcome; 🌑 dishes
Seats: 40
Smoking: No smoking in dining room
Accommodation: 6 en suite
Credit cards: 💳 💳 💳 💳 💳 💳 JCB

Directions: On A149 (King's Lynn/Cromer) 2 miles W of Blakeney in the village of Morston.

BURNHAM MARKET,
Hoste Arms Hotel 🌸🌸

The Green PE31 8HD
Map 9: TF84
Tel: 01328 738777
Fax: 01328 730103
Chef: Stephen David
Cost: H/wine £9.25. ☺
Times: Noon-last L 2pm/7pm-last D 9pm
Additional: Sunday L; 🌑 dishes
Seats: 144. Private dining room 16
Smoking: No-smoking area; no pipes & cigars
Accommodation: 20 en suite
Credit cards: 💳 💳 💳 💳 💳

Directions: In the centre of the village

Lord Nelson, once a frequent visitor to this 16th-century former coaching inn, would be impressed by the changes wrought by dedicated owner Paul Whittome. It's now a successful combination of village pub, hotel and restaurant, ready to serve locals with a pint and a bite just as happily as city folk seeking a relaxing getaway weekend. The menu ranges from local oysters (the menu warns against mixing them with spirits), and green pea soup, to pan-fried foie gras (with excellent caramelised black pudding and a classic Madeira reduction) and collops of monkfish with rösti potatoes and tomato vinaigrette. There are oriental touches too such as Szechuan dressing with spicy salmon and chilli fishcakes, or the zingy ginger and lemongrass noodles that came with our chargrilled belly of pork marinated in five spice with a hot-and-sour sauce. Desserts are equally varied. Eager polo-shirted service from an international team.

CAWSTON, Grey Gables Hotel ❀

Norwich Road NR10 4EY
Map 9: TG12
Tel/Fax: 01603 871259
Chef: Rosalind Snaith
Owners: James & Rosalind Snaith
Cost: Fixed-price D £17. ☺
H/wine £8
Times: D only, last D 8.30pm.
Closed Xmas
Additional: Bar food; Sunday L;
No children under 5; ✇ dishes
Smoking: No smoking in dining room
Accommodation: 8 en suite
Credit cards: ▬ ▭

Directions: 1 mile S of Cawston
village, near Eastgate

Charming, small country hotel offering sound, traditional cooking built around fresh local produce. Dinner runs from 2 to 5 courses. Expect the likes of Norfolk ham with pease pudding and redcurrant jelly, pheasant cooked with celery, apple, wine and cream, or local plaice cooked in butter.

DISS, Salisbury House ❀❀

84 Victoria Road IP22 3JG
Map 5: TM18
Tel/Fax: 01379 644738
Chef: Barry Davies
Owners: Mr & Mrs Davies
Cost: *Alc* (bistro) £18, fixed-price
D £24.95. ☺ H/wine £8.95.
Times: 12.15-last L 1.45pm/7.15-last
D 9.15pm. Closed Sat L, Sun, Mon,
2 wks summer
Additional: Children welcome;
✇ dishes
Seats: 36. Private dining room 18
Smoking: No smoking in dining room
Accommodation: 3 en suite
Credit cards: ▬ ▭

Directions: On A1066
(Thetford/Scole) 0.25 mile E of Diss
town centre

This solid-looking Victorian house conceals a 16th-century timber-framed building, originally a grain store that became a miller's dwelling. In an acre of mature gardens on the outskirts of town, the decor inside varies from room to room: William Morris and Laura Ashley to bright Mediterranean colours. Choose The Bistro for an eclectic menu with some interesting twists and turns. Game is popular in season – pheasant casseroled with glazed apples in cider and Calvados, say – alongside grilled mackerel with a chilli and tomato chutney, preceded by starters that also come as a main portion of prawns Thermidor, or mousseline of salmon with spinach and fennel sauce. The Restaurant offers more traditional dinners, perhaps lambs' sweetbreads and kidneys in Madeira sauce, through poached fillet of brill with lobster butter and pasta, and then meringue filled with pink champagne sorbet. The wine list is strong in France but the rest of the world gets a decent look in too.

ERPINGHAM, Ark Restaurant

On the edge of a small Norfolk hamlet six miles from the sea, the Ark is a delightful country restaurant with a friendly, informal atmosphere. The owners are dedicated to good food and are often out picking elderflowers for cordial or blackcurrants for Cassis. Most of the vegetables are home-grown, and even the bread – granary and white – is home-made. A summer meal sampled by our inspector started with chicken liver parfait with pickled damsons, the latter providing a piquant contrast to the excellent fresh livers. This was followed by a main course of loin of lamb with mustard and parsley crust. Other dishes from the hand-written menu could include fillet of locally-caught sea bass with fennel, loin of venison with damson and juniper sauce, and mixed mushroom and walnut Stroganoff. For dessert try peach and cherry almond meringue, or fresh apricot frangipane tart with vanilla ice cream.

Directions: Off the A140m 4 miles N of Aylsham

Norwich NR11 7QB
Map 5: TG13
Tel: 01263 761535
Chef: Sheila Kidd
Owners: Sheila & Mike Kidd
Cost: Alc £25, fixed-price D £19.75 (2 courses). H/wine £10
Times: D only, 7-last D 9.30pm. Closed D Sun, all Mon, 2 wks early Oct, Tue mid winter
Additional: Sunday L (12.30-2pm); Children welcome; ♠ dishes
Seats: 30. Private rooms 8/16
Smoking: No smoking in dining room
Accommodation: 3 rooms (2 en suite)
Credit cards: None

GREAT YARMOUTH, Imperial Hotel

Traditional, family-run resort hotel located on the quieter North Beach, a short stroll from the bustling promenade. Choose from a wide range of classical English and French inspired dishes. Expect pea and pear soup, lambs' liver with bacon and onions, Suffolk treacle tart, and a decent list of well chosen wines.

North Drive NR30 1EQ
Map 5: TG50
Tel: 01493 851113
Fax: 01493 852229
Chef: Stephen Duffield
Owner: R S Mobbs
Cost: Alc £24, fixed-price L £12.50 (2 courses)/D £19.50. ☺ H/wine £11.
Times: Last L 2.30pm/last D 10pm. Closed L Sat
Additional: Bar food; Sunday L; Children welcome; ♠ dishes
Smoking: No-smoking area; Air conditioning
Accommodation: 39 en suite
Credit cards: 🔳 🔳 🔳 🔳 🔳 🔳 🔳

Directions: On the seafront 100 yards N of Britannia Pier

GRIMSTON, Congham Hall Hotel

Lynn Road King's Lynn PE32 1AH
Map 9: TF72
Tel: 01485 600250
Fax: 01485 601191
Chef: Stephanie Moon
Owners: Christine & Trevor Forecast
Cost: Fixed-price L £13.50/D £32. H/wine £12.75
Times: 12.30-2pm/7.30-9.30pm
Additional: Bar food L; Sunday L; No children under 12; ♠ dishes
Seats: 50. Private dining room 18.
Jacket & tie preferred at D
Smoking: No smoking in dining room
Accommodation: 14 en suite
Credit cards: 🔳 🔳 🔳 🔳 🔳 🔳 🔳 JCB

Secluded tree-lined gardens ensure privacy and tranquillity in this quintessentially English Georgian country retreat. Herbs and produce from the garden are used in the cooking. The menu, reflecting the chef's travels, covers a lot of ground. Vegetable tempura was served with a courgette cream sauce heightened with Indian spices, and langoustine tortellinis came with red mullet fillet, fennel purée and lemongrass beurre blanc. Excellent roast sea bream was simply served on a King's Lynn shrimp risotto. Roast breast of Norfolk duck with chicory, apple and green peppercorns was a tad over-garnished but had crispy skin and tender flesh. Best pudding sampled has been a pear and almond tart with velvety lavender ice cream.

Directions: 6 miles N/E of King's Lynn on A14, turn R toward Grimston. Hotel is 2.5 miles on L; don't go to Longham.

HETHERSETT, Park Farm Hotel

NR9 3DL
Map 5: TG10
Tel: 01603 810264
Fax: 01603 812104
Chef: Adam Hodge
Owners: Peter & David Gowing
Cost: *Alc* £25, fixed-price L £12.75/ D £18.50. ☺ H/wine £9.50
Times: Last L 2pm/last D 9.30pm
Additional: Bar food; Sunday L; Children welcome; 🍴 dishes
Smoking: No smoking in dining room
Accommodation: 38 en suite
Credit cards: 🌑 🌑 🌑 🌑 🌑 🌑 🌑

Modern hotel that has evolved from a Georgian farmhouse offering straightforward cooking. Expect chicken and pistachio terrine with spicy apple confit, duck breast with green peppercorn sauce, and desserts from the trolley.

Directions: 5 miles S of Norwich on B1172 (the old A11)

HOLT, Yetman's ✿✿

Alison and Peter Yetman have clocked up 10 years at their small, elegant restaurant with its airy, vibrant decor of yellow-washed walls with dashes of white. They succeed in their aim to provide quality food and wine without pretension, using generally simple treatments to bring out the best of their produce, and erring towards restraint rather than exuberance. A red pepper mayonnaise is the dressing for Louisiana crab cakes, and equally well-balanced is another starter of roasted ratatouille-type vegetables with creamed goats' cheese, given extra pizzazz with lots of basil. Tender loin of local lamb stuffed with fresh apricots makes a clean, fresh-tasting early-summer main course. Pork, perhaps chargrilled with balsamic vinegar and red onions, is organic, fish are Norfolk-landed and cheeses are from Neal's Yard. Local hothouse raspberries and Amaretto trifle, cream-laden and gently alcoholic, has been well reported. The layout of the wine list is as exciting as the wines it describes, the New World a particular strength.

37 Norwich Road
NR25 6SA
Map 9: TG03
Tel: 01263 713320
Chef: Alison Yetman
Owners: Peter & Alison Yetman
Times: D only, 7.30-9.30pm. Closed D Mon (in winter),Tue, 3 wks Oct
Additional: Sunday L (12.30-1.30pm); Children welcome; 🍴 dishes
Seats: 32. Private dining room 10
Smoking: No smoking in dining room
Credit cards: 🌑 🌑 🌑 🌑 🌑 🌑

Directions: Village centre

KING'S LYNN, **Rococo**

Cosmopolitan and lively restaurant, decked out in vibrant colours and sporting big abstracts on the walls. The pacy decor carries a set of expectations which do not fall into the mould of country restaurants, but ones which are fulfilled by the kitchen's modern view. Ambition is evident in dishes which demand keen timing, as in tempura of monkfish served with a sweet chilli dressing and set on a fresh bean salad, or a tart of leek and shallots, smoked blue Wensleydale cheese and roasted almonds. Rococo fishcakes, a mix of bass, salmon, monkfish and local shrimp, with a touch of five spice and coriander and balanced by spicy tomato compote, chump of lamb on a light, velvety garlic mash and a successful rosemary and Madeira sauce, and a well-made bread-and-butter pudding, orange zest lifting the dish, cool anglaise saucing adding more depth of flavour, made up one heavily endorsed meal. Bread is home-made, frequently cooked off in batches throughout the meal, and petits fours ensure the finish is on a high note. The wine list offers an excellent selection to suit most palates and pockets – good-value prices.

Directions: Follow signs to The Old Town, next to Tourist Information

11 Saturday Market Place
PE30 5DQ
Map 9: TF62
Tel/Fax: 01553 771483
Chef: Nick Anderson
Owners: Nick & Anne Anderson
Cost: Alc £30, fixed-price L £13.50/D £27.50. H/wine £11.95
Times: Noon-2pm/7-10pm.
Closed L Mon, all Sun, 24-31 Dec
Additional: Bar food L; Children welcome; dishes
Seats: 40
Smoking: No-smoking area;
No pipes & cigars
Credit cards: 💳 JCB

NORTH WALSHAM,
Beechwood Hotel

NEW

Elegant almost country house dining room despite quiet residential surroundings, very friendly and eager service, well chosen useful wine list offers good value for money. Expect very fresh monkfish with wholegrain mustard sauce, good simple vegetables, and summer pudding. Very committed owners.

NR28 0HD
Tel: 01692 403231
Fax: 01692 407284
Please telephone for further details

NORWICH,
Adlard's Restaurant

An air of genuine informality and warmth pervades this striking shop-front restaurant. The vibrant green decor boasts abstracts and more classical artwork, the floor is stripped wood, and the quality cooking is built around the best ingredients. This is good food, with the *carte* kept deliberately short in order to let Aiden Byrne's imagination, technique and mastery of combinations and flavours shine through. Note a dinner that opened with excellent olive oil and rosemary ciabatta, and malty, sweet onion-confit wholemeal bread, and a delicate appetiser of cappuccino of morel and asparagus. Foie gras came next, served on a simple onion and balsamic reduction, its counterpart, a fine dish of langoustines in a light 'unfishy' cappuccino-style frothy soup with apple and ginger purée at the bottom. Turbot en crepinette with cep mousseline and cep and artichoke casserole, proved to be a robust, satisfying dish, and breast of duck with a melting confit leg, and good fondant potatoes had a light, well-made sauce. Both lemon tart brûlée and orange and Grand Marnier soufflé – with liqueur soaked brioche cubes in the bottom -finished the meal on a strong note. Another meal produced truffle risotto, roast sea bass with fennel confit and mizuna salad, and banana Tatin with an elegant vanilla ice cream. The wine list is a

79 Upper St Giles Street
NR2 1AB
Map 5: TG20
Tel: 01603 633522
Fax: 01603 617733
Chefs: Aiden Byrne, Roger Hickman
Owner: David Adlard
Cost: Alc £36, fixed-price L £19/D £27.50. H/wine £11.75
Times: 12.30-last L 2pm/7.30-last D 11pm. Closed L Mon, all Sun
Additional: Children welcome; dishes
Seats: 40
Smoking: No pipes & cigars;
Air conditioning
Credit cards: 💳 JCB

passion, with an impressive selection of prestige names – well worth a detour.

Signature dishes: Steamed snails with asparagus and morels; terrine of peppers, courgettes and fennel; roast turbot, pomme purée and cep casserole; apple crème brûlée, brandy-snap biscuit and vanilla jus.

Directions: City centre, 200 yards behind City Hall

NORWICH, **Brasted's**

A side-street restaurant filled with inviting clutter, worn rugs and fresh flowers. A rabbit warren of narrow passageways lead to the upstairs kitchen where chef Adrian Clarke toils away, producing accurate dishes influenced by modern trends. Starters could include fillet of red mullet with braised fennel and a hint of lemon, sautéed pigeon breasts with wild mushroom and port sauce, and basted cheese parcels with home-made apple and thyme jelly. Main courses range from tenderloin of pork stuffed with prunes to spinach, ricotta and sun-dried tomato tart with a lime and walnut dressing. The house special is a great beef Stroganoff, and there's also steak and kidney pudding, lamb cutlets with shredded chicory and rosemary, and roast pheasant with game chips and bread sauce. The wine list has all the hallmarks of an enthusiast, with many fine vintages for anyone with something to celebrate.

Directions: City centre, close to the Castle & Cathedral, between London Street and St Andrews Street

8-10 St Andrews Hill
NR2 1AD
Map 5: TG20
Tel: 01603 625949
Fax: 01603 766445
Chef: Adrian Clarke
Owner: John Brasted
Cost: *Alc* £25. ☺
Times: Noon-last L 2pm/7-last D 10pm. Closed L Sat, all Sun, Bhs
Additional: No children under 5; dishes
Seats: 20
Credit cards: 🔲🔲🔲🔲🔲🔲🔲 JCB

NORWICH, **By Appointment**

Five small dining rooms, all with antique furniture and silver plated cutlery, make this sumptuous Regency restaurant the perfect place for romantic meals and business meetings alike. Main courses range from roast suckling pig with puréed apple and Calvados sauce, to fillet of beef wrapped in bacon and topped with Dijon mustard.

Additional: No children under 12; dishes
Smoking: No smoking in dining room
Accommodation: 4 en suite
Credit cards: 🔲🔲🔲🔲🔲

Directions: City centre, from St Andrews Hall, down St George's Street, into Colegate then 1st R into courtyard

27-29 St George's Street NR3 1AB
Map 5: TG20
Tel/Fax: 01603 630730
Chef: Timothy Brown
Owners: Timothy Brown, Robert Culyer
Cost: *Alc* £25.85. ☺
Times: D only, 7.30pm-9.30pm. Closed Sun, Mon, 25-26 Dec

NORWICH, **Cumberland Hotel**

Don't be put off by the Cumberland's drab exterior: helpful, enthusiastic service awaits within. Fish, delivered six days a week, is the kitchen's forte, from fish soup to baked monkfish wrapped in Parma ham, although smoked pigeon and bacon salad, and roast rack of lamb may be among the meat options.

Smoking: No smoking in dining room
Accommodation: 25 en suite
Credit cards: 🔲🔲🔲🔲🔲🔲🔲 JCB

Directions: 1 mile E of city centre on A47 to Yarmouth. Nr rail station & football ground

212-216 Thorpe Road NR1 1TJ
Map 5: TG20
Tel: 01603 434550/434560
Fax: 01603 433355
Chef: Craig Robinson
Owner: Michael A Price
Cost: *Alc* £23.50, fixed-price L £12.50/D £17.95. ☺ H/wine £11
Times: Last L 1.15pm/last D 9.15pm. Closed L Sat, L Sun, 26 Dec-2 Jan
Additional: Bar food; No children under 12; dishes

NORWICH, **Femi's** ❀

Light, airy, wood-floored restaurant with simple decor and marble-topped tables. Dishes range from starters of Caesar salad and Norfolk black pudding to mains such as Femi's fish ragout, bacon-wrapped loin of pork with cider brandy sauce, and a fresh pasta dish of the day.

Smoking: No-smoking area; Air conditioning
Credit cards: ▆ ▆ ▆ ▆ ▆ ▆ ▆

Directions: City centre. 200 yds from Castle and Cathedral. Behind Anglia Television.

42 King Street NR1 1PD
Map 5: TG20
Tel: 01603 766010
Chef/Owner: Mr Femi Abodunde
Cost: Alc £18, fixed-price L £7.50. ☺
H/wine £7.25
Times: Last L 2pm/D 10.30pm.
Closed Sun, Mon
Additional: Children welcome;
🍴 dishes

NORWICH,
Greens Seafood Restaurant ❀

Fresh seafood is the speciality of this stylish restaurant, offered from a short lunchtime menu and an evening carte supported by imaginative daily specials. A good fishcake came with watercress and a sweet mustard sauce, followed by pan-fried plaice with crispy bacon and spring onions.

82 Upper St Giles Street NR2 1LT
Map 5: TG20
Tel: 01603 623733
Fax: 01603 615268
Please telephone for further details.

Directions: Near St John's RC Cathedral

NORWICH, **Marco's Restaurant** ❀❀

A Georgian building in an English cathedral city, the dining-room yellow-walled, with full-length drapes, black and gold-backed chairs and smart table settings, seems a rather unlikely setting for some authentic Italian cooking by turns gutsy and refined. A starter of spaghettini with chilli, lemon and garlic impressed an inspector for its simplicity, execution and good powerful flavours. Other pasta starters might involve Norfolk crab, prawns wrapped in Parma ham, or pancetta with Pecorino, while main courses could run to fillet of Loch Fyne salmon roasted with pancetta in sun-dried tomato sauce, pan-fried medallions of venison with Marsala, and sautéed fillet of monkfish. Zabaglione is up there on the list of puddings, but monte nero – meringue covered with halved strawberries, then rich vanilla ice cream, all coated with lashings of thick, velvety rum-based chocolate sauce – stole the show. Virtually every region of Italy is represented on the wine list, with some distinguished producers showing up. House wines are from Sicily.

17 Pottergate NR2 1DS
Map 5: TG20
Tel: 01603 624044
Chef/Owner: Marco Vessalio
Cost: Alc £28, fixed-price L £14.70.
☺ H/wine £12
Times: Noon-last L 2pm/7pm-last
D 10pm. Closed Sun, Mon
Additional: Children welcome;
🍴 dishes
Seats: 22
Smoking: No smoking in dining room
Credit cards: ▆ ▆ ▆ ▆

Directions: City centre: from market place facing Guildhall, turn R then L into Pottergate

NORWICH, **The Old Rectory** ❀ NEW

Enjoy an aperitif in the lounge or bright conservatory of the Entwistle's delightful small hotel while choosing from the daily changing, short menu. Cauliflower soup, carbonnade of beef flamande, and chocolate pot are examples of the homely cooking. Simple, interesting wine list complements the food well.

Accommodation: 8 en suite
Credit cards: ▆ ▆ ▆ ▆ ▆ ▆

Directions: From A147 ring road take A1242 to Thorpe. Hotel on L after the church

103 Yarmouth Road
Thorpe St Andrew NR7 0HF
Map 5: TG20
Tel: 01603 700772
Fax: 01603 300772
Chefs/Owners: Chris & Sally Entwistle
Cost: Fixed price D £15.95 (4 courses). ☺ H/wine £8.50
Times: D only, last D 8.45pm.
Closed D Sun, 23 Dec-12 Jan
Additional: Children welcome;
🍴 dishes
Smoking: No smoking in dining room

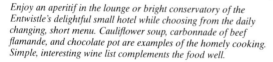

Pinocchio's Restaurant ✿

Twice-weekly jazz and a warm, lively atmosphere attract a young crowd to this informal Italian-style brasserie. You don't have to be young to appreciate good cooking though. Expect seafood bruschetta, crispy potato skins with chicken livers and herbs, lamb steak with Etruscan potatoes, sea bream with chargrilled Mediterranean vegetables, plus pasta dishes.

Additional: Children welcome; 🍴 dishes
Smoking: No-smoking area
Credit cards: 🔳 🔳 🔳 🔳 🔳 🔳

Directions: From City centre follow Castle Meadow to traffic lights, 1st L into Bank Plain, leads to St Benedict's Street

11 St Benedicts Street NR2 4PE
Map 5: TG20
Tel: 01603 613318
Fax: 01603 765377
Chef: Gary Kemp
Owners: Nigel & Jayne Raffles
Cost: *Alc* £16, fixed-price L £5
(2 courses). ☺ H/wine £7.95
Times: Last L 2pm/last D 11.30pm.
Closed Sun, 25-26 Dec

St Benedicts Restaurant ✿

Sister establishment to Pinocchio's next door (see entry above), St Benedicts is an inviting 'church pew' bistro with blackboard menus and sound cooking. Moroccan chickpea and cucumber soup with mint, double-baked cheese soufflé, seared halibut with saffron mash and rosemary oil, and slow-cooked crispy duck with spiced oranges show the style. Well-chosen wines.

Additional: Sunday L (except May-Oct); Children welcome; 🍴 dishes
Smoking: No-smoking area; No pipes & cigars
Credit cards: 🔳 🔳 🔳 🔳 🔳 🔳 🔳

Directions: At city end of St Benedicts. Nearest car park Duke Street (day), on street (evening).

9 St Benedicts NR2 4PE
Map 5: TG20
Tel/Fax: 01603 765377
Chef: Nigel Raffles
Owners: Nigel & Jayne Raffles
Cost: *Alc* £16.50. ☺ H/wine £7.95
Times: Last L 2pm/last D 10.30pm.
Closed D Sun, all Mon, 25 Dec-1 Jan

Sprowston Manor ✿✿

The hotel restaurant is an elegant, pleasant conservatory-style room with pretty views over the grounds and professional, formal-style service. A feature of the dining room is the bread trolley, with eight or more varieties available. Breast of wood pigeon accompanied by a fruit compote opened our most recent meal. This was followed by duck breast with honey and pepper, duck confit and tender artichoke, with pears in filo with a toffee and banana sauce, for dessert. The wine list is very informative and aims to educate with a number of well-chosen wines amongst the commercial names.

Directions: Take A1151 (Wroxham), follow signs to Sprowston Park

Sprowston Park Wroxham Road
NR7 8RP
Map 5: TG20
Tel: 01603 410871
Fax: 01603 423911
Please telephone for further details

The Wildebeest Arms ✿✿

There's a good buzz at this upbeat foodie pub, where simple Norfolk Inn meets *Flame Trees of Thika*. African motifs in the long, single ochre-walled bar include authentic musical

Norwich Road Stoke Holy Cross
NR14 8QJ
Map 5: TG20
Tel: 01508 492497
Chef: Eden Derrick

instruments and wood carvings, but the food from the open kitchen is more Provence than Pretoria. The menu packs a punch: chargrilled tuna with French beans and candied hazelnuts; pressed confit duck and leek terrine with aubergine chutney and granary toast; breast of chicken with pesto crust with wild mushroom and Parmesan risotto; charred salmon with grilled vegetables, rocket leaves and yellow pepper and basil dressing. Desserts might include an enjoyable, creamy banana, bourbon and honeycomb parfait with vanilla bean sauce, and sweet apple and Calvados pastry cream tart with apple strudel ice cream. There are hand-cut chips with their skins on, real ales on tap and no bread plates – it's that kind of place.

Directions: A140 (Ipswich), under southern by-pass. Turn L into last exit before Dunston Hall and follow road into Stoke Holy Cross

Owners: Mr HD Watt, Mr AH Wilkins
Cost: *Alc* £20, fixed-price L £12. ☺
H/wine £8.95.
Times: Noon-last L 2pm/7pm-last
D 10pm (7.30-9.30pm Sun). Closed
25 Dec
Additional: Sunday L (Noon-2.30pm);
Children welcome; ♨ dishes
Seats: 55
Smoking: No-smoking area
Credit cards:

SWAFFHAM, **Romford House** ✿

400-year-old atmospheric, beamed brickwork house with two separate eating areas. There's a good range of light lunches, a long carte, as well as blackboard specials. Fillet of grilled turbot, capers, walnuts and chilli, breast of chicken stuffed with sun-dried tomatoes and Stilton, or Chateaubriand with a choice of sauces show fair cooking.

Additional: No children under 8; ♨ dishes
Smoking: No-smoking area
Credit cards:

Directions: 16 miles from Kings Lynn, on the main Market Place

5 London Street PE37 7DD
Map 9: TF80
Tel: 01760 722552
Chef/Owner: Jane Mitchell
Cost: *Alc* £20. ☺
Times: Last L 2pm/last D 10pm.
Closed L Mon, all Sun

THORPE MARKET,
Elderton Lodge ✿

The former shooting lodge to Gunton Hall maintains its sporting links through paintings and prints and arranged pursuits, and by seasonal game on the menu. Braised Gunton Park venison with Burgundy and herbs under a suet crust, for instance, but local John Dory with butter sauce, and whole local plaice with lemon butter get a look in too.

Directions: Off A149 Cromer/North Walsham rd, 1 mile S of village

Gunton Park nr Cromer NR11 8TZ
Map 9: TG23
Tel: 01263 833547
Fax: 01263 834673
Chefs: Paul Mitchell, Murray Cuthbert
Rudon
Owners: Christine & Martin Worby
Cost: *Alc* (L) £14, fixed-price D £21
(4 courses). ☺ H/wine £8.95
Times: Last L 2pm/last D 9pm.
Additional: Bar food L; Sunday L;
No children under 6 ; ♨ dishes
Smoking: No smoking in dining room
Accommodation: 12 en suite
Credit cards:

TITCHWELL,

Titchwell Manor

Titchwell Manor sits in an unspoiled coastal location overlooking salt marshes and sea. Naturally, fish plays a prominent role on the menu (there's a separate seafood bar too), from poached Brancaster mussels to grilled Dover sole or halibut. Meat-eaters could opt for calves' liver, and crème brûlée should appeal to sweet-lovers.

Additional: Bar food; Sunday L; Children welcome; 🍴 dishes
Smoking: No smoking in dining room
Accommodation: 16 en suite
Credit cards: ▬ ▬ 🐦 ⌂ ▦ ▶ ▣ JCB

Brancaster PE31 8BB
Map 9: TF74
Tel: 01485 210221
Fax: 01485 210104
Chefs: Adam Wright, Ben Handley
Owners: Margaret & Ian Snaith
Cost: Alc £24, fixed-price L £15/D £24. ☺ H/wine £12.50
Times: Last L 2.30pm/last D 9.30pm.
Closed last 2 wks Jan

Directions: on the A149 coast road between Brancaster and Thornham

WYMONDHAM,

Number Twenty Four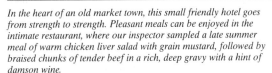

Pleasant market-town restaurant carved out of a series of cottages. Interesting menu with eclectic and challenging combinations from chef/proprietor Richard Hughes. Risotto of smoked haddock with a poached free-range egg, supreme of garlic-baked chicken with a Tuscan bean stew, and warm lemon and yogurt cake with mascarpone cream, are typical examples. Wine list offers cheap, cheerful drinking.

Additional: Children welcome; 🍴 dishes
Smoking: No cigars and pipes
Credit cards: ▬ ▬ 🐦 ⌂ ▶

24 Middleton Street NR18 0BH
Map 5: TG10
Tel/Fax: 01953 607750
Chef: Richard Hughes
Owners: Richard & Sue Hughes
Cost: Alc £18, fixed-price L £7.50 (2 courses)/ D £14 (2 courses). ☺ H/wine £8.50
Times: Last L 2.30pm/last D 9.30pm.
Closed Sun, Mon, Tue, 24-31 Dec

Directions: Town centre opposite war memorial

WYMONDHAM,

Wymondham Consort Hotel ✿

In the heart of an old market town, this small friendly hotel goes from strength to strength. Pleasant meals can be enjoyed in the intimate restaurant, where our inspector sampled a late summer meal of warm chicken liver salad with grain mustard, followed by braised chunks of tender beef in a rich, deep gravy with a hint of damson wine.

Additional: Bar food; No children under 8; 🍴 dishes
Smoking: No smoking in dining room
Accommodation: 20 en suite
Credit cards: ▬ ▬ 🐦 ⌂ ▦ ▶ ▣ JCB

24 Market Street NR18 0BB
Map 5: TG10
Tel: 01953 606721
Fax: 01953 601361
Chef: Gregory Maillet
Owners: Chris & Grace Fiddaman
Cost: Alc £25, fixed-price L £10.95/D £16.95. ☺ H/wine £8.50
Times: Last L 1.45pm/last D 9.30pm.
Closed Xmas

Directions: Town centre opposite War Memorial

NORTHAMPTONSHIRE

CASTLE ASHBY, **Falcon Hotel**

A fine little hotel with charming proprietors and staff, set in lovely gardens, including a beautifully designed herb garden. The restaurant makes a feature of local produce, and if you time your visit for the asparagus season you're in for a real treat.

Directions: From A428 (Northampton-Bedford) turn off at Castle Ashby sign, hotel 1.5 miles ahead

NN7 1LF
Map 4: SP85
Tel: 01604 696200
Fax: 01604 696673
Please telephone for further details.

HELLIDON, **Hellidon Lakes Hotel**

Hotel in a rural setting with extensive grounds including a 27-hole golf course and 12 lakes. The restaurant serves eclectic modern food, with dishes ranging from home-made vegetable and barley broth to a complete Indian main course comprising chicken tikka, pork masala, okra in cream sauce and pilau rice.

Directions: 1.5 miles off A361 at Charwelton, follow signs for Golf Club

Daventry NN11 6LN
Map 4: SP55
Tel: 01327 262550
Fax: 01327 262559
Please telephone for further details.

HORTON, **The French Partridge Restaurant**

Ex-coaching inn on the outside, Victorian gentleman's dining club within, decorated in dark green with lacy shades over each table. The set menu is very good value, and the service friendly and well-tuned. Brandade of salt cod with toast had really smooth texture, and pan-fried tuna with ginger and chilli dressing on mixed leaves delivered big Thai flavours. A succulent breast of chicken was served with a creamy leek and mushroom sauce and a Parmesan risotto. Side dishes of crisp, sautéed potato wedges and brussels sprout tops tossed in butter and garlic were both very good, as was banana Tatin with excellent home-made vanilla ice cream. The menu changes every two months; in season, look out for chicken liver parfait with Muscat jelly, steamed lamb and kidney pudding, curried parsnip soup, and grilled panettone with fruit compote. There is always a savoury – usually Welsh rarebit.

Additional: dishes
Seats: 50
Smoking: No smoking in dining room
Credit cards: None

Directions: On B526, village centre, 6 miles from Northampton

NN7 2AP
Map 4: SP85
Tel: 01604 870033
Fax: 01604 870032
Chef: David Partridge
Owners: David & Mary Partridge
Cost: Fixed-price D £27 (4 courses). H/wine £11
Times: D only, 7.30pm-9pm. Closed Sun, Mon, 2wks Xmas, 2 wks Easter, 3wks summer

AA Wine Award–see page 16
Shortlisted for

KETTERING,

Kettering Park Hotel

Smart purpose-built hotel with a Jacobean-style restaurant – Langberrys – with high backed tapestry chairs and effective lighting. Options might include tiger shrimp tempura with a hot dipping

Kettering Parkway NN15 6XT
Map 4: SP87
Tel: 01536 416666
Fax: 01536 416171
Chef: Darren Winder

sauce, and herb-crusted loin of lamb with grilled Mediterranean
vegetables. A separate vegetarian menu is available.

Smoking: No smoking in dining room
Accommodation: 119 en suite
Credit cards: ■ ■ ■ ■ ■ ■ ■

Directions: A14/J9 – hotel on that roundabout

Owner: Shire Inns
Cost: *Alc* £24, fixed-price L £14.95.
☺ H/wine £11.45
Times: Last L 1.45pm/last D 9.30pm.
Closed L Sat
Additional: Bar food L; Sunday L;
Children welcome; ❹ dishes

MARSTON TRUSSELL, **The Sun Inn** ❀❀

Comfortable 17th-century inn, with a small but busy
restaurant, set in a tiny Midlands' village. A new chef had just
taken over when we called, he was having to see out the
previous chef's more traditional menus, but a more modern
concept had been introduced in blackboard specials, especially
fish dishes such as sea bass and vanilla. The aim is to introduce
contemporary ideas throughout the set menus and the *carte.*
However, we enjoyed ballotine of chicken and duck with
orange and pistachio studded between meats, Dover sole
wrapped around scallops and prawn mousse and topped with
a lightly cooked scallop, and a well-risen chocolate and orange
soufflé.

Directions: 0.5 mile off A4304, 3 miles W of Market
Harborough

Main Street LE16 9TY
Map 4: SP68
Tel: 01858 465531
Fax: 01858 433155
Chef: Simon Johnson
Owners: Mr Furber, Mr Raven
Cost: *Alc* £20, fixed price L £9.95
(2 courses)/D £19.95 (4 courses). ☺
H/wine £9.95
Times: Last L 2pm/last D 9.30pm
Additional: Bar food; Sunday L;
Children welcome; ❹ dishes
Accommodation: 19 en suite
Credit cards: ■ ■ ■ ■ ■ ■

NORTHAMPTON, **Swallow Hotel** ❀

A low rise, modern red-brick hotel providing excellent facilities for
both leisure and business guests. Featuring fine glass engravings of
Northampton church, the elegant Spires Restaurant offers an
interesting carte and friendly service. Typical choices may include
shellfish soup, duck with black cherry sauce, and crème caramel.

Additional: Bar food L; Sunday L; Children welcome; ❹ dishes
Smoking: No-smoking area; Air conditioning
Accommodation: 120 en suite
Credit cards: ■ ■ ■ ■ ■ ■ ■

Directions: M1/J15, follow A508 then A45 (Wellingborough). L
at roundabout signposted Delapre Golf Complex. Hotel on R

Eagle Drive NN4 7HW
Map 4: SP76
Tel: 01604 768700
Fax: 01604 769011
Chef: David Bishop
Cost: *Alc* £23, fixed-price L £14/D
£21 (4 courses). ☺ H/wine £11
Times: Last L 2pm/last D 9.45pm.
Closed L Sat, Bhs

ROADE, **Roadhouse Restaurant** ❀

Smart, very well-run restaurant-cum-small hotel with a kitchen that
shows keen ambition. A test lunch produced pan-fried fillet of
mackerel with pickled red cabbage and anchovy dressing, pan-fried
calves' liver with good spinach and a light balsamic sauce, and very
good panettone bread-and-butter pudding. More sophisticated menu
in the evenings.

Additional: Sunday L; Children welcome
Smoking: No smoking in dining room; air conditioning
Accommodation: 6 en suite
Credit cards: ■ ■ ■ ■ ■

Directions: M1/J15 (A508 Milton Keynes) to Roade, L at mini-
roundabout, 500yds on L

16 High Street NN7 2NW
Map 4: SP75
Tel: 01604 863372
Fax: 01604 862421
Chef: Christopher Kewley
Owners: Christopher & Susan Kewley
Cost: *Alc* £26. Fixed-price L £15.50.
☺ H/wine £10.
Times: Last L 2pm/last D 9.30pm.
Closed L Sat, D Sun, L Mon

TOWCESTER,

Vine House Restaurant

Fax ahead for a menu, and your lunch will be ready on arrival at this pretty stone cottage – a useful option for local businesses. Otherwise, consider the menu in front of the log fire in the small bar where home-made lemonade and ginger beer are offered to those driving. The menu changes daily, and there is a choice of four dishes at each course. Fresh seasonal produce is used wherever possible, and the cooking, in dishes such as pâté of rabbit confit and smoked bacon with green peppercorn dressing, and fillet of sweet-cured pork fillet with mushroom and leek risotto and rosemary sauce, is balanced and considered. Try the excellent apple and blackberry crumble with vanilla ice cream or floating islands with strawberries for dessert. The menu also sensibly requests that anyone with allergies check first with the staff.

Directions: 2 miles S of Towcester, just off A5

100 High Street Paulersbury
NN12 7NA

Map 4: SP64
Tel: 01327 811267
Fax: 01327 811309
Chef: Marcus Springett
Owners: Julie & Marcus Springett
Cost: *Alc* £24.95, fixed-price
L £16.95. H/wine £4.50 ☺
Times: Closed L Sat-Wed, Sun
Additional: Children welcome
Seats: 45. Private dining room 10
Smoking: No smoking in dining room
Accommodation: 6 en suite
Credit cards: ▬ ▬

NORTHUMBERLAND

BELLINGHAM,

Riverdale Hall Hotel ❀   NEW

The cosy restaurant of this family-run hotel offers a five-course dinner with straightforward, well-constructed dishes that get the best out of fresh ingredients. Try roast tenderloin of local venison with a reduced game stock, red wine and cranberry sauce, or perhaps griddled pepper-marinated darne of salmon with coriander and tomato salsa. The wine list is worthy of study.

NE48 2JT
Map 12: NY88
Tel: 01434 220254
Fax: 01434 220457
Please telephone for further details

BERWICK-UPON-TWEED,

Marshall Meadows Hotel ❀

An elegant Georgian mansion set in wooded grounds. The hotel boasts three restaurants, and some tables enjoy sea views. Good modern cooking is served throughout. Our inspector enjoyed a courgette, Brie and sparkling wine soup, followed by an 'excellent' sea bass, served with a champagne vinegar and butter sauce.

Additional: Bar food; Sunday L; Children welcome; ❀ dishes
Smoking: No smoking in dining room
Accommodation: 19 en suite
Credit cards: ▬ ▬ ▬ ▢ JCB

Directions: Just off the A1 N of Berwick

TD15 1UT
Map 12: NT95
Tel: 01289 331133
Fax: 01289 331438

Chef: Ian Frost
Cost: *Alc* £30, fixed-price L £7/D £18. ☺ H/wine £8.
Times: Last L 2pm/D 9.30pm

BLANCHLAND,
Lord Crewe Arms Hotel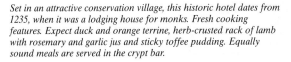

Set in an attractive conservation village, this historic hotel dates from 1235, when it was a lodging house for monks. Fresh cooking features. Expect duck and orange terrine, herb-crusted rack of lamb with rosemary and garlic jus and sticky toffee pudding. Equally sound meals are served in the crypt bar.

Accommodation: 20 en suite
Credit cards: ▬▬ ▬▬ ▢ ▤▤ ▣ JCB

Directions: 10 miles S of Hexham on B6306

Nr Consett DH8 9SP
Map 12: NY95
Tel: 01434 675251
Fax: 01434 675337
Chef: Ian Press
Owners: Ian Press, Alec Todd, Peter Gingell, Lindsey Sands
Cost: Alc £27. ☺ H/wine £9
Times: D only, 7- 9.15pm
Additional: Bar food; Sunday L (Noon-2.30pm); Children welcome; 🍴 dishes

---

CHOLLERFORD, ## George Hotel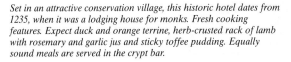

Built right on the North Tyne, its gardens running down to the river, the George isn't far from Hadrian's Wall and Chesters Roman Fort. The restaurant takes in the view of both gardens and river. A main course from the *carte* of smoked fillet of beef with basil mash and roasted vegetables, or roasted monkfish marinated in Barolo served with shellfish risotto show the same Italian influence as a starter of olive bread with paupiette of salmon. Cassoulet of rabbit and woodpigeon on the set-price menu shows an altogether different provenance, although salmon roasted under a herb crust comes with oyster linguine. Finish with perhaps a trio of desserts – chocolate and strawberry soufflé, chocolate parfait and lemon tart or Stilton with pears and celery. A Gourmet Menu offers the likes of beignets of foie gras and wild mushrooms, roast guinea fowl, and sachertorte with banana and lemon ravioli.

Directions: From A6079 take B6318. 400 yds on opposite side of river

Hexham NE46 4EW
Map 12: NY96
Tel: 01434 681611
Fax: 01434 681727
Chef: Martin Strangward
Owner: Swallow Hotels
Cost: Alc £32.50, fixed-price L £15/D £24. 95 (5 courses). ☺ H/wine £12.50
Times: Noon-last L 2pm/6.30-last D 9.30pm
Additional: Lounge menu all day; Sunday L; Children welcome; 🍴 dishes
Seats: 85. Private dining room 50. Jacket & tie preferred
Smoking: No smoking in dining room
Accommodation: 47 en suite
Credit cards: ▬▬ ▬▬ ▚▚ ▢ ▤▤ ▣ ▣ JCB

CORNHILL-ON-TWEED,
Tillmouth Park Hotel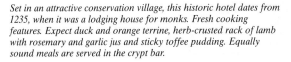

A magnificent country mansion, built in 1882, retaining all its period charm. The kitchen makes much use of produce from north of the border – Berwick crab salad, Aberdeen Angus beef Rossini and noisettes of Borders' lamb — although there's always a choice for vegetarians. Cheeses are local and home-made chocolates are served with coffee.

TD12 4UU
Map 12: NT83
Tel: 01890 882255
Fax: 01890 882540
Chef: David Jeffrey
Owner: Stever Investments
Cost: Fixed-price L £8.50/D £25. ☺ H/wine £9
Times: Last L 1.45pm/last D 9pm. Closed 26 Dec
Additional: Bar food; Sunday L; Children welcome; 🍴 dishes
Accommodation: 14 en suite
Credit cards: ▬▬ ▬▬ ▚▚ ▢ ▤▤ ▣ ▣

Directions: On A698 3 miles E of roundabout at Cornhill-on-Tweed

MORPETH, **Longhirst Hall** ✿

Longhirst NE61 3LL
Map 12: NZ18
Tel: 01670 791348
Fax: 01670 791385
Chef: Colin Bowden
Owner: Longhirst Hall Ltd
Cost: *Alc* £17.50, fixed-price L
£11.95/D £16.50. ☺ H/wine £10.95.
Times: Last L 2pm/D 9.30pm.
Closed L Sat, L Bhs
Additional: Sunday L; No children
under 8; ♨ dishes
Smoking: No smoking in dining room;
Air conditioning
Accommodation: 75 en suite
Credit cards: ▆ ▆ ▆ ▆ ▆ ▆ ▆

Originally a 19th-century stately home, now a much extended hotel with a bright, modern restaurant. Expect chicken broth with mini herb dumplings, fillet of beef en croûte with mushroom duxelle and a Madeira sauce, and banana and walnut mousse served with a rum and raisin sauce.

Directions: 2 miles NE of Morpeth on the B1337 Widdrington road

NOTTINGHAMSHIRE

LANGAR, **Langar Hall** ✿

NG13 9HG
Map 8: SK73
Tel: 01949 860559
Fax: 01949 861045
Chef: Toby Garratt
Owner: Imogen Skirving
Cost: *Alc* £25, fixed-price L £10 (2
courses)/D £15. ☺ H/wine £10.15
Times: Last L 2pm/last D 9.30pm
Additional: Sunday L; Children
welcome; ♨ dishes
Smoking: No-smoking area;
No pipes and cigars
Accommodation: 10 en suite
Credit cards: ▆ ▆ ▆ ▆

30 acres of parkland surround this personally run hotel, just 12 miles from Nottingham. Sound cooking of the likes of hot-pot of mussels, clams, oysters and scallops, braised saddle of rabbit and grain mustard sauce, and poached rhubarb with ginger ice cream.

Directions: Off A46 and A52, in village centre (behind church)

NOTTINGHAM, **Ginza** ✿

Suburban setting for a Japanese restaurant designed cleanly on black and white lines. Large number of tables given over to teppan-yaki (where the chef cooks the meal in front of you). Also various

593-595 Mansfield Road NG5 2FW
Map 8: SK53
Tel: 0115 9691660/9691716
Fax: 0115 9245724
Chef: Ricardo Rebanno

sashimi and sushi, as well as deep-fried vegetables in tempura batter, grilled chicken with yakitori sauce, and sukiyaki.

Additional: Sunday L; Children welcome; dishes
Credit cards: ▬ ▭ ◪ ⬚ ▦ ▣ ▣

Directions: From Nottingham's Victoria Centre follow A60 (Mansfield road) just past Sports Ground and Moat House

Owner: Derek Hung
Cost: *Alc* £18, fixed-price D £15 (2 courses). ☺ H/wine £8.95
Times: Last L 1.30pm/last D 10.30pm. Closed 24-26 Dec, L Bhs

NOTTINGHAM,
Harts Restaurant ❀❀❀

The whole area in which Harts is located is being transformed: smart offices, expensive pied-à-terre and fat-cat cars. Tim Hart is a savvy operator and has hit upon a successful formula. His kitchen team comes with a pedigree, and they certainly know their onions. Indeed, they have taken the ethics of the local heroes to heart: steal and borrow ideas from the rich and make them available (affordable) to a wider market; it is food that would make the Merry Men drool. What we have is the precision and dedication to flavours for which Hambleton Hall (see entry, Oakham, Rutland) is known, without the flamboyance. Many suppliers have extended their London run from Oakham to Nottingham – and it shows. There are lovely soft rolls with a firming crust; chicken and leek (baby) terrine subtly crafted with each flavour combining to produce an excellent spring starter, even a hint of white truffle oil in the dressing of the accompanying salad; firm, fresh pan-fried monkfish served on a bed of heightened tomato-flavour risotto with spinach for colour; iced strawberry soufflé in a delicious balance of fruit, cream, sugar and air. A top-of-the-range brasserie and great fun.

Directions: Follow signs for Castle and from Maid Marian Way take last L after Casino into Park Row. At top turn L into site of old General Hospital.

1 Standard Court, Park Row
NG1 6GN
Map 8: SK53
Tel: 0115 9110666
Fax: 0115 9110611
Chef: Mark Gough
Owner: Tim Hart
Cost: *Alc* £23, fixed-price L £13. H/wine £9.50
Times: Noon-last L 2pm/7-last D 10.30pm
Additional: Sunday L; Children welcome; dishes
Seats: 90. Private dining room 12
Smoking: No-smoking area; Air conditioning
Credit cards: ▬ ▭ ◪ ⬚ ▦ ▣ JCB

NOTTINGHAM, **Hotel Des Clos** ❀❀

The focus of this small riverside hotel is the restaurant, where chef-patron, John Abbey, indulges his passion for all things French. The dining room is well appointed with cushioned cane seating, white napery, fine glassware and Limoges china. In addition to a sensibly short *carte* there are daily and gourmand menus to tempt diners with the likes of ballotine of foie gras with Madeira jus, nage of poached seafood in a mussel and saffron cream, fillet of sea bass with a basil and tomato beurre blanc, and medallions of beef with a Pinot Noir sauce. The highlight of an inspection meal, however, was a delightful starter of a tender pigeon breast on a juniper jus with baby winter vegetables. Finish with desserts such as lemon tart, chocolate marquise (with rosemary scented crème anglaise), or a selection of fine French cheeses. Tasty canapé tartlets are served in the lounge, and friendly staff are attentive and knowledgeable.

Directions: M1/J24, follow A453 (Nottingham) 10 miles. Cross River Trent, follow signs to Old Lenton Lane Industrial Estate. At roundabout L, immediate L again. Follow lane down to river

Old Lenton Lane NG7 2SA
Map 8: SK53
Tel: 0115 9866566
Fax: 0115 9860343
Chef/Owner: John Abbey
Cost: *Alc* £30, fixed-price L £17.50/ D £26 (4 courses). ☺ H/wine £9.95
Times: Noon-2pm/7-9pm. Closed L Sat, D Sun, 2 wks Xmas/New Year
Additional: Sunday L; Children welcome; dishes
Seats: 32
Smoking: No pipes & cigars
Accommodation: 10 en suite
Credit cards: ▬ ▭ ◪ ⬚ ▦ ▣ ▣ JCB

NOTTINGHAM, **Sonny's** ✿✿

Minimalist decor, the open kitchen adding a bit of spice, in a Grade II listed building on a pedestrianised street. Graeme Watson's cooking continues to please the punters with robustly flavoured dishes of pan-fried new potatoes with black pudding and a poached egg, grilled chicken breast with sage-infused mascarpone and onion marmalade, or seared tuna with capers, anchovies and a shallot dressing. Otherwise his monthly-changing menus could offer Bayonne ham with grilled figs and rocket, twice-baked Parmesan soufflé, and then chargrilled spicy salmon with avocado butter, or fillet of pork with Puy lentils and wild mushrooms. Ten wines, plus champagne and pudding wine, are sold by the glass from an interesting list rounded off by a page of fine bottles.

Smoking: No pipes & cigars; Air conditioning
Credit cards: ▅ ▅ ▅ ▅ ▅

Directions: City centre, close to Market Square and Victoria Centre

3 Carlton Street Hockley NG1 1NL
Map 8: SK54
Tel: 0115 9473041
Fax: 0115 9507776
Chef: Graeme Watson
Owner: Ms R Mascarenhas
Cost: Alc £22, fixed-price L £11.50.
☺ H/wine £8.95.
Times: Noon-last L 3pm/7-last D 10.30pm (11pm Fri, Sat). Closed Bhs
Additional: Sunday L; Children welcome; ◑ dishes
Seats: 75

SOUTHWELL,
Vineyard Café & Bistro ✿

High Street location for a café/bistro with a simple interior – plank floor, beamed ceiling and plain white walls with a display of wine memorabilia. Popular during the day with shoppers choosing from a range light meals, which together with the full menu offer fresh food prepared by a committed and enthusiastic chef.

Directions: In the main street

12 King Street NG25 0EN
Map 8: SK75
Tel: 01636 816573
Please telephone for further details

OXFORDSHIRE

BANBURY, **Wroxton House** ✿

Originally one of three 17th-century cottages, the restaurant at Wroxton House is a pretty room with original beams and fireplace. Good use is made of local produce in dishes such as breast of chicken filled with fresh asparagus, lightly grilled salmon escalopes with a chervil cream sauce, and pan-fried red snapper with sautéed cabbage.

Additional: Bar food, Sunday L; Children welcome; ◑ dishes
Smoking: No smoking in dining room
Accommodation: 32 en suite
Credit cards: ▅ ▅ ▅ ▅ ▅ ▅ JCB

Directions: On A422 to Stratford, 3 miles from M40/J11

Wroxton St Mary
OX15 6QB
Map 4: SP44
Tel: 01295 730777
Fax: 01295 730800
Chef: Hylton Bradley
Owner: Lester Hotels Ltd
Cost: Alc £24.50, fixed-price
L £15.50/D £24.50 (5 courses).
☺ H/wine £9.95
Times: Last L 1.45pm/last D 9.30pm

BURFORD,
The Angel at Burford ❀

There's a more formal air at dinner in this charming little Cotswold inn. In the intimate back restaurant you might be offered dishes like leek and potato soup with garlic croûtons, pan-fried salmon fillet with balsamic vinegar, and apple tart with cinnamon anglaise.

14 Witney Street
OX18 4SN
Map 4: SP21
Tel: 01993 822438
Fax: 01993 822714
Please telephone for further details

Directions: Turn R (signposted Widford) off A40 just before Burford. Inn is on L a few yds before High St

BURFORD,
The Bay Tree ❀

12-14 Sheep Street
OX18 4LW
Map 4: SP21
Tel: 01993 822791
Fax: 01993 823008
Please telephone for further directions

A historic Cotswold stone inn with a very traditional restaurant complete with flagstone floors, tapestry-decorated white walls and candle-lit tables. The cooking is more up-to-date however, with pan-fried cod in sesame seeds and coriander noodles preceding the likes of coffee bread-and-butter pudding.

Directions: Off main street in centre of Burford

BURFORD,
Cotswold Gateway Hotel ❀

A 17th-century coaching inn with wood-panelled dining room, this relaxed and friendly venue offers a short menu using seasonal produce. Typical dishes include crab salads, rack of lamb with herb crust and tender pork fillet with mustard sauce. The home-made desserts, such as steamed chocolate pudding, are a must.

Cheltenham Road
OX18 4HX
Map 4: SP21
Tel: 01993 822695
Fax: 01993 823600
Chef: Andrew Lawrence
Owner: Mrs J Ford, Dennis Evans
Cost: *Alc* £18. ☺ H/wine £8.70
Times: D only, last D 9.30pm

Additional: Bar food; Sunday L (12-2.30pm); Children welcome; ❹ dishes
Smoking: No smoking in dining room; Air conditioning
Accommodation: 20 en suite
Credit cards: ▮ ▮ ▮ ▮ ▮ ▮ ▮

Directions: On A40 roundabout at Burford

BURFORD, **Inn For All Seasons** ✿

The Barringtons
OX18 4TN
Map 4: SP21
Tel: 01451 844324
Fax: 01451 844375
Chef: Matthew Sharp
Cost: *Alc* £16.50. ☺ H/wine £9.95
Times: Last L 2.30pm/last D 9.30pm.
Closed 25-26 Dec
Additional: Bar food; Sunday L;
Children welcome; ✿ dishes
Smoking: No-smoking area;
No pipes & cigars
Accommodation: 10 en suite
Credit cards: ▆ ▆ ▆ ▆ ▆ ▆

Attractive roadside inn formed from 16th-century cottages. Cotswold stone walls and floors set the scene. Fish specials supplement an eclectic menu offering four choices for each course. Depth of flavour distinguished roast tomato and basil soup, and roast tarragon chicken came with light, herb-flavoured jus. Sticky toffee pudding completed an enjoyable meal.

Directions: On the A40 at The Barringtons, 3 miles from Burford & 17 miles from Cheltenham

BURFORD, **Lamb Inn** ✿✿

Little wonder visitors return time and time again to this wonderful old inn full of antique furniture, log fires and gleaming copper and brass. Meals, in the pretty pillared rear dining room, are served by well-drilled waitresses in *Upstairs Downstairs* pinnies. The *carte* explores modern trends without frightening off those with more conservative tastes, and the standard of cooking is consistently high. A bright, fresh tian of home-smoked trout layered with roasted red peppers was served with generous dollops of crème fraîche spiked with slivers of preserved ginger. This was followed by excellent roast partridge with caramelised shallots and a richly flavoured sauce and, for dessert, an extremely fine pecan, apple and sour cream tart. Sunday lunch kicks off with Bucks Fizz and takes in marinated tiger prawns with Cornish crab and dill fromage frais, or lambs' kidneys braised in port with minted potato rösti.

Sheep Street OX18 4LR
Map 4: SP21
Tel: 01993 823155
Fax: 01993 822228
Chef: Pascal Clavaud
Owners: Richard & Caroline de Wolfe
Cost: Fixed-price D £24. H/wine £10.
Times: Noon-last L 2pm/7pm-9pm.
Closed 25-26 Dec
Additional: Bar meals L; Sunday L;
Children welcome; ✿ dishes
Seats: 50
Smoking: No smoking in dining room
Accommodation: 15 en suite
Credit cards: ▆ ▆ ▆ ▆ ▆ JCB

Directions: 1st L as you descend the High Street

CHARLBURY, **The Bell Hotel** ✿

Charming old inn with a flagstone-floored bar; it attracts a loyal local clientele. New owners have refurbished throughout, including the cosy dining room. There is an interesting choice of dishes, such as chicken liver parfait with toasted fig brioche, and grilled cod with a white wine and cheese sauce.

Smoking: No smoking in dining room
Accommodation: 13 en suite
Credit cards: ▆ ▆ ▆ ▆ ▆ ▆

Directions: Town centre

Church Street OX7 3PP
Map 4: SP31
Tel: 01608 810278
Fax: 01608 811447
Chef: Peter Southey
Owner: Mr K Vickers
Cost: *Alc* £30. ☺ H/wine £10.45
Times: Last L 2.30pm/last D 9.30pm
Additional: Bar food L; Sunday L;
Children welcome; ✿ dishes

CHINNOR,

Sir Charles Napier ❀❀

Surrounded by beech woods and fields, this casual country inn is a pretty red brick building with a great garden. In the summer months meals can be enjoyed out on the patio while red kites circle over head. Serious cooking is prepared by Sardinian chef Batiste Tolu, with eight to ten choices offered for both starter and main course. Our inspector enjoyed a late spring meal of plump griddled scallops served with a minted pea risotto. Crispy Gressingham duck followed and proved to be 'first class', served with a spicy papaya salsa with soy and ginger. Other dishes could include chargrilled tuna with braised fennel and sauce vierge, baked monkfish with creamed white beans and red wine sauce, and braised shoulder of lamb with cumin, coriander and mashed potato. The wine list is wide-ranging with hundreds of top vintages from around the world, and over twenty dessert wines and thirty half-bottles.

Directions: M40/J6 follow Chinnor; there turn R at roundabout. Carry on straight up hill to Spriggs Alley

Spriggs Alley OX9 4BX
Map 4: SP70
Tel: 01494 483011
Fax: 01494 485311
Chefs: Batiste Tolu & David Jones
Owner: Julie Griffiths
Cost: *Alc* £25, fixed-price L & D £15.50 (both 2 courses). ☺
H/wine £11.75
Times: 12.30-2.30pm (3.30pm Sun)/7.30-10pm. Closed D Sun, all Mon
Additional: Bar food; Sunday L; No children under 7 at D; ✤ dishes
Seats: 75. Private room 45
Smoking: No-smoking area; Air conditioning
Credit cards: ▬ ▬ ▬ ▬ ▬ ▬

CHIPPING NORTON,

Chavignol ❀❀❀

Lovells at Windrush Farm has moved from Minster Lovell to the traditional market town of Chipping Norton, changing its name on the way. In amongst a row of antique shops at the Banbury end of the High Street, Chavignol is a pretty, shop-fronted, Grade II listed cottage restaurant decked out with yellow walls, blue linen, rush matting, wrought-iron wall candelabra, and simple bud vases with striking flowers. Inspectors' reports indicate that the winning formula devised by owner Mark Maguire and chef Marcus Ashenford is off to a flying start. The cooking has not changed its spots. Small, light cheese beignets started one test meal on a high note, strongly aided and abetted by an *amuse-bouche* of a demi-tasse of carrot and orange soup with a ginger glaze that worked very well. A small wooden bread board came with white/brown twin loaf. A super, well-timed dish opened the meal proper: lobster glazed with basil hollandaise, served in the shell on fine, fresh pasta, vegetable ribbons and finished with a lobster bisque. Tender, perfectly cooked medallions of local venison had a good gamey flavour that is rare these days, with 'really good' gratin dauphinoise, sprouts, shallots and roasted apples, and a rich sauce flavoured with framboise. Pudding was a deliciously light but richly flavoured chocolate tart, of fine pastry and good biscuit crumble, accompanied by a tuile basket of flapjack ice cream, with a passion fruit coulis offering a good foil. Wine list presentation was similarly innovative in a small, ring-bound file, with short, witty explanations and peppered with vinous quotations, and with some good vintages and well-priced regional and younger wines.

Directions: On Banbury side of main Chipping Norton road

7 Horsefair OX7 5AL
Map 4: SP32
Tel/Fax: 01608 644490
Chef: Marcus F Ashenford
Owner: Mark P Maguire
Cost: *Alc* £35, fixed price L £25/D £42.50 (7 courses). H/wine £14
Times: 12.30-Last L 1.30pm/7-last D 9.30pm. Closed Sun, Mon, Jan
Additional: Children welcome; ✤ dishes
Seats: 28. Private room 10
Smoking: No smoking in dining room
Credit cards: ▬ ▬ ▬ ▬ ▬ ▬ ▬ JCB

CHIPPING NORTON, Morel's ❀

Fabrice Morel and his wife Rachel run this pretty little restaurant in the hub of the town. Dishes, naturally, have a very French flavour, and may include pig's trotter, breast of pigeon with foie gras, and seasonal fish. Pastry is superb in any of its guises, and there is always a good cheese board.

Additional: Sunday L only (noon-2pm); Children welcome Sun only; ❸ dishes
Smoking: No-smoking area; Air conditioning
Credit cards: ▬ ▭ ▅ ▢ ▐ JCB

2 Horsefair OX7 5AQ
Map 4: SP32
Tel/Fax: 01608 641075
Chef: Fabrice Morel
Owners: Fabrice & Rachel Morel
Cost: Fixed-price D £22. ☺ H/wine £10.50
Times: 7pm- last D 9.30pm. Closed D Sun, Mon, 1 Jan for 3 wks, 1 wk Sept, L Sun May-Sep

Directions: Immediately before town centre entering on A44 Oxford/Banbury road, on rd to Evesham.

CLANFIELD, Plough at Clanfield ❀❀

Peacefully set in its own grounds at the edge of the village amid the Cotswolds, the Plough is everything you would expect of a manor-house built in 1560: stone-built, with mullioned windows and, inside, log fires burning away. The traditional-style dining-room, its well-spaced tables set with white and pink linen and good glassware and silver, is the background for set three-course dinners with a fair choice at each course. Start with rice crackers and olives in the bar before sitting down to start with, say, a chickpea pattie on goats' cheese with ratatouille dressing, or roast pigeon breast with Puy lentils, and go on to a main course of accurately cooked sea bass on a bed of roasted peppers with lobster sauce, or pan-fried loin of pork with orange and cranberry sauce. Currants are marinated in brandy before going in to bread-and-butter pudding, or there may be apple and almond tart. Coffee comes with good petits fours, while eight reasonably priced house wines head a list of French and Australian bottles.

Bourton Road OX18 2RB
Map 4: SP20
Tel: 01367 810222
Fax: 01367 810596
Chef: Alan Robinson
Owners: Mr & Mrs J C Hodges
Cost: Fixed-price L £16.50/D £32.50 (4 courses). H/wine £12.50
Times: Noon-last L 1.45pm/7-last D 9pm. Closed L Sat & Mon, 26-30 Dec
Additional: Bar food L; Sunday L; ❸ dishes
Seats: 32. Private dining room 10
Smoking: No smoking in dining room
Accommodation: 6 en suite
Credit cards: ▬ ▭ ▅ ▢ ▨ ▐ ▣ JCB

Directions: Village centre, on A4095 between Faringdon & Witney, easy reach of A40 and A420

DEDDINGTON,
Dexters Restaurant ❀❀

A popular restaurant in a quiet Cotswold village. The dining room is light and airy, and paintings by local artists add a splash of colour to the primrose yellow walls. The style is modern European, with Med influences coming through in starters such as English asparagus with olive oil balsamico and Parmesan, warm pigeon on crostini of spinach with pimento coulis, and oak-smoked salmon with capers, shallots and black pepper. A set dinner could start with baked goats' cheese on tapenade with basil and roast peppers, followed by confit of duck on herb mash with olives rosemary and a redcurrant jus. Dexters desserts include bread-and-butter pudding, poached pear tart with caramel sauce, and Irish farmhouse cheeses with Russet apples and oat cakes. The wine list is modest, but has a very good selection by the glass, and a number of interesting half-bottles. Reservations are recommended for Sunday lunch.

Market Place OX15 0SE
Map 4: SP43
Tel/Fax: 01869 338813
Chefs: Jamie Dexter-Harrison, Bradley Morris, Stuart Cox
Owners: Jamie Dexter-Harrison, Roger Blackburn
Cost: *Alc* £26, fixed-price L £14.50/D £19.95. ☺ H/wine £10
Times: Noon-last L 2.15pm/7-last D 9.15pm. Closed D Sun, all Mon, Xmas-New Year
Additional: Sunday L; No children under 3; ❸ dishes
Seats: 36
Smoking: No pipes & cigars
Credit cards: ▬ ▭ ▅ ▢ ▨ ▐ JCB

Directions: Village centre, A4260 from Banbury; L at lights

DEDDINGTON, **Holcombe Hotel**

Much olde-worlde charm is to be found in the restaurant of this hospitable 17th-century Cotswold stone hotel. The nicely varied menu ranges from gravlax and Holcombe pâté to game pudding and lamb kleftiko. There's also a substantial snack menu in the bar. Wine list has a strong Bordeaux section.

High Street OX15 0SL
Map 4: SP43
Tel: 01869 338274
Fax: 01869 337167
Chef: Alan Marshal
Owners: Mr & Mrs C Mahfoudh
Cost: *Alc* £25, fixed-price L £13.95/D £22.95. ☺ H/wine £11.95.
Times: Last L 2pm/last D 9.45pm
Additional: Bar meals; Sunday L; Children welcome; ❹ dishes
Smoking: No-smoking area; No pipes & cigars in dining room
Accommodation: 17 en suite
Credit cards: ▓ ▓ ▓ ▢ ▓ ▐

Directions: On A4260 between Banbury & Oxford. M40/J11 – follow A4260 (Adderbury) 7 miles, hotel is on R at traffic light

DORCHESTER-ON-THAMES,
George Hotel ☺

This 15th-century former coaching inn boasts a characterful, beamed restaurant with vaulted ceiling, however, the menu is bang up to date. Typical dishes include confit of guinea fowl on a warm bean salad with truffle dressing, and peppered skate wing with roast cherry tomatoes, warm new potato salad and basil and balsamic dressing.

Smoking: No pipes and cigars
Accommodation: 18 en suite
Credit cards: ▓ ▓ ▓ ▢ ▓ ▐

Directions: In town centre

High Street OX10 7HH
Map 4: SU59
Tel: 01865 340404
Fax: 01865 341620
Chef: Simon Quarrie
Owner: Brian Griffin
Cost: *Alc* £21, fixed-price L £12 (2 courses)/D £20. ☺ H/wine £8.40
Times: Last L 2.15pm/last D 9.30pm
Additional: Bar food; Sunday L; Children welcome; ❹ dishes

DORCHESTER-ON-THAMES,
White Hart Hotel ☺☺

A timbered old coaching house with some parts dating back to 1691, the White Hart is unmissable in this trendy Thameside village much favoured for its winding lanes and fashionable shops. Cheerful, casual staff keep things ticking over as guests choose from a good selection of modern English and French dishes. Starters are along the lines of sautéed lambs' kidneys with wild rice and Dubonnet sauce, pressed chicken and leek terrine with Cumberland sauce, and warm 'morille', baby spinach and kale salad. Follow any of these with mouth-watering main dishes such as seared duck breast with mixed baby greens and spiced spätzle, roasted beef fillet with pancetta ham and thyme, and pan-fried fillet of lemon sole with crème fraîche and watercress purée. Desserts are indulgent without being overly so – try warm apricot and caramel flan with vanilla ice cream. The wine list is commendable for its realistic prices.

Directions: In village centre

High Street OX10 7HN
Map 4: SU59
Tel: 01865 340074
Fax: 01865 341082
Chef: Robert Kerr
Owner: Dorchester Holdings Ltd
Cost: *Alc* £20, fixed-price D £16.50. ☺ H/wine £7.50
Times: Noon-last L 2pm/7-last D 9.30pm (Sun till 9)
Additional: Bar food; Sunday L; Children welcome; ❹ dishes
Seats: 20. Private room 50
Smoking: No-smoking area
Accommodation: 19 en suite
Credit cards: ▓ ▓ ▓ ▢ ▓ ▐

FARINGDON,

The Lamb at Buckland NEW

Buckland SN7 8QN
Map 4: SU29
Tel: 01367 870484
Fax: 01367 870675
Chef: Paul Barnard
Owners: Paul & Peta Barnard
Cost: *Alc* £22, fixed-price L £7.50
(2 courses). ☺ H/wine £8.95
Times: Last L 2pm/last D 9.30pm.
Closed 25-26 Dec

Set in a village on the edge of the Cotswolds, The Lamb is an attractive stone-built building dating from the 18th-century serving good country cooking. We enjoyed rabbit and guinea fowl terrine, pan-fried duck with sliced apples and Calvados cream, and a fine syrup sponge.

Additional: Bar food; Sunday L; Children welcome; ◑ dishes
Smoking: No smoking in dining room
Accommodation: 4 en suite
Credit cards: 🔲 🔲 🔲 🔲 🔲 🔲 JCB

Directions: Midway between Oxford & Swindon on the A420,
4 miles E of Faringdon

GORING,

The Leatherne Bottel ❀❀

RG8 0HS
Map 4: SU68
Tel: 01491 872667
Fax: 01491 875308
Chefs: Keith Read, Julia Storey
Owner: Keith Read
Cost: *Alc* £35, fixed price D £19.50
(Mon/Thu). ☺ H/wine £14.50
Times: 12.15-2.15pm(Sun till
3.30)/7.15-9.15pm. Closed D Sun,
25 Dec
Additional: ◑ dishes
Seats: 50 (75 river terrace). Private
dining room 12
Smoking: No pipes; Air conditioning
Credit cards: 🔲 🔲 🔲

Idyllically set right on the edge of the River Thames, with its splendid riverside terrace, the Leatherne Bottel is the perfect summer venue. On inclement days, the cosy dining room, adorned with modern works of art and colourful photographs, is equally convivial. With herbs and flowers from the garden used in preparing the imaginative range of dishes, and the excellent home-made breads, flavours are fresh and the dishes exciting. Lemongrass-flavoured potatoes accompany guinea fowl roasted with lemons and lemon thyme, and smoked halibut is served with iced creamed horseradish, blanched dandelion leaves and keta caviar dressing. After sweet ginger and coriander bread, served with spicy Oriental soup, came an enjoyable chargrilled marinated halibut with water chestnuts, spring onion and a tomato ragout which contrasted well with the fish. To finish sample one of the freshly made desserts or a selection of British farmhouse cheeses. Lighter, simpler dishes are served weekday lunchtimes.

Directions: M4/J12 or M40/J6, signed off B4009 Goring-
Wallingford

GREAT MILTON, **Le Manoir Aux Quat' Saisons** ✿✿✿✿✿

After all the wrangling over planning permission, the much needed expansion of Raymond Blanc's 15th-century Oxfordshire manor house was still (discreetly) in progress when we visited. But we were able to enjoy some of the new facilities. For example, the pressure has been taken off pre and post dining with the addition of extra lounges, and this has added to the comfortable, plush, cosseting atmosphere. The decor in the new conservatory dining area seems to reflect the continuing expansion of the Oriental theme here, from a Japanese garden right through to the food. And there was, we noted, a surprising lack of formality to the service. Two of the gourmande menus gave a pair of inspectors a full range of dishes, of which good balance, variety, interest and small portions – given the number of courses – made them sum it all up as a ' bargain at £72'. The style is not complicated, methods are quite direct, as could be seen in escabeche of scallops with coriander cream, and a courgette flower stuffed with crab mousse and set on a bed of trompette de mort. Counterpoint of the elements was the essential thinking behind a trio of little dishes consisting of lamb sweetbreads, morels in a Gewürztraminer sauce, and asparagus with lemon sabayon, and in a quail's egg, spinach, Parmesan and truffle ravioli in a rosemary and poultry jus, as well as a watercress salad with pan-fried duck foie gras, apples, black pudding and roasted hazelnut dressing. But a main courses of roast best end of Highgrove lamb in its own juices with garlic purée was just simplicity at its best. A dessert of red fruit soup in Sauternes and Cabernet Sauvignon wine with fresh mint and basil was light and novel, but the highlight was a perfectly executed sugar biscuit 'cassolette' filled with candied apricots and topped with poached meringue and crème anglaise.

Signature dishes: Morels filled with a light chicken mousse, asparagus spears in a Jura wine sauce; essence of tomato, goat's cheese and herb ravioli, tomato sorbet; wild strawberry feuilleté, chibouste cream, rhubarb coulis.

Church Road OX44 7PD
Map 4: SP60
Tel: 01844 278881
Fax: 01844 278847
Chef: Raymond Blanc
Owner: Raymond Blanc
Cost: *Alc* £80, fixed-price L £32/D £72 (8 courses). H/wine £20
Times: 12.15-2.30pm/7.15-10pm
Additional: Children welcome; ✤ dishes
Seats: 99. Private dining room 50
Smoking: No smoking in dining room; Air-conditioning
Accommodation: 19 en suite
Credit cards: 💳 💳 💳 💳 💳 💳 JCB

Directions: From M40/J7 follow A329 towards Wallingford. At 1 mile turn R, signposted Great Milton Manor

HENLEY-ON-THAMES, **Red Lion Hotel** ✿✿

Situated beside the Thames, overlooking the famous Royal Regatta Course, the front rooms and restaurant of this 16th-century, ivy-clad coaching inn offer stunning views of the river. Diners can choose from a short *carte* that offers a well-balanced choice of interesting modern dishes. Everything is kept simple but, as a recent inspection meal revealed, cooking is clear and concise and the results rewarding. Commencing with a full flavoured and perfectly risen warm cheddar soufflé, served with a creamy garlic sauce, the meal progressed to an extremely tender breast of duck with celeriac mash, pancetta and red wine jus, accompanied by colourful, well-cooked mange-tout and sweet green beans. Dessert consisted of a creatively presented iced chocolate parfait, studded with boozy cherries, drizzled with cherry juice and served with fresh vanilla ice cream.

Hart Street RG9 2AR
Map 4: SU78
Tel: 01491 572161
Fax: 01491 410039
Chef: Sarah Payton
Owners: The Miller family
Cost: *Alc* £25. ☺
Times: Noon-last L 2.30pm/6-last D 10pm
Additional: Bar food; Sunday L; Children welcome; ✤ dishes
Seats: 40. Private dining room 6-80
Smoking: No pipes & cigars
Accommodation: 26 en suite
Credit cards: 💳 💳 💳 💳 💳

Directions: On the right when entering Henley by the bridge

HORTON-CUM-STUDLEY,

Studley Priory ❀❀

Oxford OX33 1AZ
Map 4: SP51
Tel: 01865 351203
Fax: 01865 351613
Chef: Peter Hewitt
Cost: *Alc* £27.50. H/wine £19.50
Times: 12.30-last L 1.45pm/7.30-last D 9.15pm
Additional: Bar food L; Sunday L; Children welcome; ❧ dishes
Seats: 40. Private dining room 30
Smoking: No smoking in dining room
Accommodation: 18 en suite
Credit cards: ▆▆ ▆▆ ▆▆ ▆ ▆▆ ▆ ▆

Visitors cannot fail to be impressed by Studley Priory, a former Benedictine nunnery founded in the 12th century, but extended in the 16th century when it was dissolved. It belongs to another, less hectic age. The kitchen displays confidence and skill, both noted in a spring dinner that opened with wood pigeon breasts wrapped in Savoy cabbage with a little truffle and diced trompette de mort in the inner farce, and served on an excellent truffle risotto. A lovely piece of turbot fillet followed, accompanied by nicely wilted spinach and a powerful, but not over-powering, wholegrain mustard cream sauce. Pot-au-feu of Cornish hen was beautifully cooked with good root vegetables, a bold tarragon jus and a perfect chive tagliatelle. A duo of chocolate puddings proved to be a milky mousse with griottine cherries and a mille-feuille of bitter and white chocolate sorbets; a banana tarte Tatin with run and raisin ice cream was everything it should be.

Directions: At top of hill in the village

KINGHAM, **The Mill House Hotel** ❀

Chipping Norton OX7 6UH
Map 4: SP22
Tel: 01608 658188
Fax: 01608 658492
Chef: Patrice Roger
Owners: J P & S A Parslow
Cost: *Alc* £30, fixed-price L £13.95/D £22.75. ☺ H/wine £10.70
Times: Last L 1.45pm/D 9.15pm
Additional: Bar food L; Sunday L
Smoking: No smoking in dining room
Accommodation: 23 en suite
Credit cards: ▆▆ ▆▆ ▆▆ ▆ ▆▆ ▆ ▆ JCB

Directions: On B4450, on southern outskirts of Kingham village

Quaint Cotswold hotel with trout stream in its grounds. A meal, chosen from the carte in the popular Marionette Room restaurant, might start with wild mushroom risotto with quails' eggs, and continue with loin of venison with crispy curry noodles. Bread and petits fours are made in-house. Staff create a homely atmosphere.

KINGSTON BAGPUIZE,
Fallowfields Country House ❀

Charming, personally run small hotel that is making a laudable attempt to promote serious food. Caramelised Red Barron onions and English goats' cheese tartlets with oven-dried tomatoes and black olives, medallions of tenderloin of pork baked in their own sloe gin, and dark chocolate pudding with chocolate sauce, show the ambition at work here. Small wine list, strong on half-bottles.

Accommodation: 10 en suite
Credit cards: ▬ ▭ ⚞ ▢ ▤ ⓒ

Directions: From A34 at Abingdon take A415 (Witney). At mini-roundabout in Kingston Bagpuize turn L. Fallowfields is one mile on L

Faringdon Road OX13 5BH
Map 4: SU49
Tel: 01865 820416
Fax: 01865 821275
Chef: Peta Lloyd
Owners: Peta & Anthony Lloyd
Cost: Fixed-price D £30.50
(4 courses). H/wine £13.50
Times: D only, last D 8.30pm.
Closed D Sun
Additional: No children under 10;
☙ dishes
Smoking: No smoking in dining room

MIDDLETON STONEY,
Jersey Arms Hotel ❀

A charming Cotswold-stone coaching inn with a great village atmosphere. Dinner is served in the oak-panelled dining room where dishes range from pan-fried fillet of cod topped with herbs, to fillet of pork with braised red cabbage. Desserts could include rich chocolate sponge with hot chocolate sauce, and traditional crème brûlée.

Bicester OX6 8SE
Map 4: SP52
Tel: 01869 343234
Fax: 01869 343565
Chef: Douglas Parrott
Owners: Donald & Helen Livingston
Cost: Alc £20. ☺ H/wine £9.55
Times: Last L 2pm/last D 9.30pm
Additional: Bar food; Children welcome; ☙ dishes
Smoking: No smoking in dining room
Accommodation: 16 en suite
Credit cards: ▬ ▭ ⚞ ▢ ▤ ⓒ ▨ JCB

Directions: On B430, 3 miles from Bicester, 10 miles N of Oxford

MILTON COMMON,
The Oxford Belfry ❀

Elegance and comfort are the keynotes at the restaurant behind the ivy-covered façade of the Oxford Belfry. The ambitious carte and set-price menus might offer smoked trout and leek mousse, followed by lambs' sweetbreads or panaché of shellfish in filo, then banana toffee tart. Coffee comes with petits fours.

Accommodation: 86 en suite
Credit cards: ▬ ▭ ⚞ ▢ ▤ ▨

Directions: From S: M40/J7. A329 towards Thame. Cross motorway, turn L (A40) for 300yds, hotel on R. From N: M40/J8. Follow A418 (Aylesbury). Turn R on to A40 (A329). Hotel 1.5 miles on L

Nr Thame OX9 2JW
Map 4: SP60
Tel: 01844 279381
Fax: 01844 279624
Chef: Robert Hubbard
Owner: Marston Hotels Ltd
Cost: Alc £30, fixed price L £16.50/D £25. ☺ H/wine £12.50
Times: Last L 2pm/last D 9.30pm.
Closed L Sat
Additional: Bar food; Sunday L; Children welcome; ☙ dishes
Smoking: No smoking in dining room

MOULSFORD, **Beetle & Wedge**

With connections to *The Wind in the Willows* and *Three Men in a Boat*, this is a Mecca for literary foodies. Each table in the formal dining room has a wonderful view of the Thames and in summer, the floor to ceiling doors open, giving the impression of eating outside. The sophisticated yet understated style of cooking of chef/patron Richard Smith remains unchanged. The set-price dinner menu is short and simply described, and on our visit, strong on fish with seafood and avocado salad with Dijon mayonnaise, mussel and lobster salad, and scallops in the shell with ginger butter sauce, amongst the starters, and lobster sauce flavouring a main course casserole of brill and sole . Mushrooms were also much in evidence with a first course of artichoke heart with wild mushrooms and hollandaise sauce, and two main courses of supreme of Aylesbury duck with sautéed fresh morels, and escalope of sea bass with risotto and mushroom sauce. Desserts sound tempting, with mostly fruity presentations such as hot raspberry soufflé with red fruit coulis, and roast apples with vanilla ice cream and caramel sauce. The wine list is worth exploring, particularly the special recommendations; since diners are not obliged to drink a whole bottle, a dipstick system operates. The same high standard of cuisine characterises the food in the more informal Boathouse, although the style varies and the cooking is centred around a wonderful open charcoal fired grill.

Ferry Lane Wallingford OX10 9JF
Map 4: SU58
Tel: 01491 651381
Fax: 01491 651376
Chef: Richard Smith
Owners: Richard & Kate Smith
Cost: *Alc* £30, fixed-price L £27.50/D £35. H/wine £12.95
Times: 12.30-last L 1.45pm/7.30-last D 10pm. Closed D Sun, Mon (Dining room only), 25 Dec
Additional: Bar food (Boathouse); Sunday L; Children welcome; ❸ dishes
Seats: 30 (Dining Room) 65 (Boathouse). Private dining room 64
Smoking: No smoking in Dining Room
Accommodation: 10 en suite
Credit cards:
■ ▨ ▧ ▨ ▨ ▣ ▣ JCB

Directions: In the village, turn towards the river via Ferry Lane.

OXFORD, **Bath Place Hotel**

Tucked away between two of Oxford's ancient colleges, Bath Place is formed out of several 17th-century cottages that incorporate a small part of the, now all but disappeared, medieval city wall. Full of atmosphere (ask about the numerous historical associations), the restaurant is candlelit in the evening. Cooking is French based but informed by the chef's sojourns in more exotic climes, as evidenced by the vegetable couscous flavoured with Chinese five spice served with a lightly curried fricassée of Dover sole, or the Mexican lime salsa accompanying a crab and king prawn 'aumonière'. A very generous portion of foie gras lightly poached in St Emilion and served with grapefruit segments in honey, and home-made raisin bread, began a successful test meal that continued with a perfectly cooked red snapper surrounded by a variety of garnishes, all hot and lovingly prepared, and ended with a cooked-to-order fresh raspberry clafoutis. The

4/5 Bath Place
Holywell Street OX1 3SU
Map 4: SP50
Tel: 01865 791812
Fax: 01865 791834
Chef: Guillaume Foussier
Owners: Kathleen & Yolanda Fawsitt
Cost: *Alc* £35, fixed-price L £19.50. H/wine £11.95
Times: Noon-last L 2pm/7pm-last D 10pm. Closed D Sun, Mon, L Tues, 3 wks mid Aug, 1 wk end Dec
Additional: Sunday L; Children welcome; ❸ menu
Seats: 32
Smoking: No smoking in dining room; Air conditioning
Accommodation: 13 en suite

interesting wine list is helpfully organised by style and comes with useful tasting notes.

Directions: City centre, opposite Holywell Music Room, between Hertford & New College

OXFORD, **Cotswold Lodge Hotel** ✿

This Victorian building has been extended around a pretty patio area and is now a charming family-run hotel within walking distance of the city centre. The restaurant serves well-prepared, imaginative food that has a classic French base but a contemporary slant.

66a Banbury Road OX2 6JP
Map 4: SP50
Tel: 01865 512121
Fax: 01865 512490
Chef: Garin Chapman
Owner: Mr O Peros
Cost: Alc £30.65, fixed-price L £16.70/D £18.10 (both 4 courses). ☺
H/wine £11.50
Times: Last L 2.30pm/last D 10pm
Additional: Bar food; Sunday L; Children welcome; ♨ dishes
Smoking: No smoking in dining room
Accommodation: 50 en suite
Credit cards: ▇ ▇ ▇ ▣

Directions: Take A4165 (Banbury Road) off A40 ring road, hotel 1.5m on left.

OXFORD, **Liaison** ✿

Smart, friendly Chinese offering an extensive menu. Lunchtime dim sum is enjoyed by students and the local Chinese community who appreciate the quality and style of food. More serious evening fare offers such delicacies as duck web and fishlips claypot, or the classic steamed fish with ginger and spring onion.

Smoking: Air conditioning. **Credit cards:** ▇ ▇ ▇

Directions: Behind main shopping centre

29 Castle Street OX1 1LJ
Map 4: SP50
Tel: 01865 242944/251481
Owner: Yau Tim (Timmy) Tsang
Cost: Alc £16, fixed-price D £14.95.
☺ H/wine £7.50
Times: Last L 2.45pm/last D 11.15pm.
Closed 2 days Xmas
Additional: Sunday L; Children welcome; ♨ dishes

OXFORD, **Munchy Munchy** ✿✿

Marvellous double act, with Tony Ow running front of house and Ethel in charge of the woks in the open-view kitchen. They are both absolutely charming and it is always a delight to eat here. The cooking is Padang-style, a genre indigenous to Malaysia, Singapore and Indonesia. The short daily changing menu lists around six or seven dishes – basically a list of spices and main ingredient, but the sum of the parts is much greater than the breakdown. King prawn with cardamom, star anise, juniper, coconut milk and screw-pine leaves was deliciously mouth-watering enough to whet the appetite for more heavyweight dishes such as lamb curry with allspice, nutmeg, chervil, dill and kumquats in sour cream, or chicken with almonds, cumin, fenugreek, cardamom, cloves, cinnamon and curry leaves. Eat them all with plain, boiled rice. Refresh the palate with passion fruit or mango sorbet.

Directions: W of city centre, between Nuffield College & the station

6 Park End Street OX1 1HH
Map 4: SP50
Tel: 01865 245710
Fax: 01865 730683
Chef: Ethel Ow
Owners: Mr Tony Ow & Mrs Ethel Ow
Cost: Alc £14. ☺ H/wine £7.45
Additional: No children under 6 Fri-Sat D. ♨ dishes
Seats: 60
Smoking: No-smoking area; No pipes & cigars
Credit cards: ▇ ▇ ▇ ▇

Credit cards: ▇ ▇ ▇ ▇ ▇ ▣

OXFORD, **Le Petit Blanc** ❀❀

71-72 Walton Street
OX2 6AG
Map 4: SP50
Tel: 01865 510999
Fax: 01865 510700
Chef: Stuart Lyall
Owner: Raymond Blanc
Cost: *Alc* £25. Fixed-price L £14. ☺
H/wine £9.95.
Times: Noon-last L 3.15pm/6.30pm-
last D 10.45pm. Closed 25 Dec
Additional: Children welcome;
🍴 dishes
Seats: 130. Private dining room 20
Smoking: No-smoking area; air-
conditioning
Credit cards: ▨ ▨ ▨ ▨ ▨ ▨ ▨ JCB

Coloured pot plants in zinc-type holders are the only splash of colour in this open-plan, famous-name eating house. Terracotta seating and walls blend in with the wooden floors and beige table tops, and friendly blue-shirted staff bustle round, their computerised order pads slung around their waists like holsters in a Western movie. Changes in the kitchen since last year's edition of the *Guide,* but the transition appears seamless. Excellent cod brandade arrived with a poached egg on top and an exciting dressing of balsamic, walnuts, capers, shallots and fennel, coq au vin with home-made noodles had great depth of flavour from the use of chicken on the bone, and was bursting with mushrooms, lardons, confit garlic and button onions. A chocolate tarte was classic pâtisserie at its best. The special children's menu includes spit-roasted chicken and fries, and Oxford sausage with mashed potato and onion sauce.

Directions: From centre of Oxford, N up St Giles, L down Little Clarendon St and R at end into Walton Street

OXFORD, **The Randolph** ❀

The grand Victorian splendour of this city-centre hotel is continued in Spires restaurant where the coats-of-arms of the Oxford colleges reach round the walls. At the time of going to press Marco Pierre White was about to take over the restaurant and impose his own inimitable style on the cooking, in the process no doubt transforming its standing.

Beaumont Street OX1 2LN
Map 4: SP50
Tel: 01865 247481
Fax: 01865 791678
Please telephone for further details

Directions: At corner of Beaumont St and Magdalen St, opposite Ashmolean Museum

SHIPTON-UNDER-WYCHWOOD,
Lamb Inn ❀

Very popular 18th-century Cotswold inn with a lovely atmosphere and super looking lunchtime buffet – the whole baked ham looks wonderful. In the evening the kitchen offers the likes of coarse country terrine with Cumberland sauce and red onion marmalade, and breast of chicken stuffed with black pudding and onions with a purée of creamed leeks.

Directions: In village centre

High Street OX7 6DQ
Map 4: SP21
Tel: 01993 830465
Chef: John McGarrigle
Cost: *Alc* £25. ☺ H/wine £9.95
Times: Last L 2pm/last D 9.45pm
Additional: Bar food; Sunday L;
Children welcome; 🍴 dishes
Smoking: No smoking in dining room
Accommodation: 5 en suite
Credit cards: ▨ ▨ ▨ ▨ ▨ ▨

SHIPTON-UNDER-WYCHWOOD,

Shaven Crown Hotel ⊛

14th-century building with low oak beams. Aperitifs and coffee are taken in the Great Hall, a fine medieval room with a 600-year-old double collar braced roof. Salmon fishcakes and chips were appreciated at inspection, served with a spicy tomato sauce, and followed by rich chocolate mousse.

Accommodation: 9 en suite. **Credit cards:** ▆ ▆ ▆ ▆ ▆

Directions: On A361, village centre, 4 miles N of Burford

OX7 6BA
Map 4: SP21
Tel: 01993 830330
Fax: 01993 832136
Chef: Gary Smith
Owners: Robert & Jane Burpitt
Cost: Fixed-price D £20. ☺
H/wine £12
Times: Last L 2pm/last D 9.30pm
Additional: Bar food; Sunday L;
Children welcome; ❹ dishes

STADHAMPTON,

The Crazy Bear ⊛⊛

A seven-foot stuffed bear is just one of the weird and wonderful curios that pepper this cosmopolitan establishment where the bar boasts draught champagne and chilled Mars Bar vodka. There's nothing weird about the good modern cooking however. A dish of pithiviers of oxtail confit with mash and ruby claret sauce was described by our inspector as 'a wonderful dish that simply brought together flavours and textures that have been friends for centuries'. Another hit was seared scallops served in the shell and glazed with soy sauce, lemon juice and balsamic vinegar to lift the caramelised flavour of the shellfish. Our dessert was a play on banoffee pie, in the form of a tian with a Baileys sauce anglaise. Other dishes on a recent menu included parfait of foie gras and chicken livers with a fig compote, fillet of corn-fed Devon beef with wild mushrooms, and lobster mousse-stuffed sea bass with tagliolini and a fricassée of provençale vegetables in a saffron sauce.

Directions: from London leave M40/J 7, turn L onto A329, continue for 5 miles, L after petrol station and L again into Bear Lane

Bear Lane OX44 7UR
Map 4: SU69
Tel: 01865 890714
Fax: 01865 400481
Chef: Pete Ansell
Owner: Jason Hunt
Cost: Alc £23, fixed price L £12.95/D £16.95. ☺ H/wine £ 11.95
Times: Noon-last L 3pm/7-last D 10pm
Additional: Bar food; Sunday L; Children welcome; ❹ dishes
Seats: 50. Private room 35
Smoking: No-smoking area; No pipes & cigars; Air conditioning
Accommodation: 5 en suite (plus 2 cottages)
Credit cards: ▆ ▆ ▆ ▆ ▆ ▆

STEEPLE ASTON, **Hopcrofts Holt** ⊛

An attractive, stone-built hotel, covered in Virginia creeper, dating from 1475. The restaurant is the venue for some well-judged cooking. Cod meunière and beef fillet with sauce béarnaise are classical main courses, smoked duck breast with avocado might be among the starters, and marbled chocolate mousse among the desserts.

OX6 3QQ
Map 4: SP42
Tel: 01869 340259
Fax: 01869 340865
Chef: Pascal Parize
Owner: Westback Ltd
Cost: Alc £26, fixed-price L £11 (2 courses)/D £22. ☺ H/wine £10.45
Times: Last L 2.30pm/last D 9.45pm
Additional: Bar food; Sunday L; Children welcome; ❹ dishes
Smoking: No smoking in dining room
Accommodation: 86 en suite
Credit cards: ▆ ▆ ▆ ▆ ▆ ▆

Directions: Follow A426 through Kidlington towards Deddington. Hotel on R at traffic lights.

STONOR, **Stonor Arms** 🏵🏵

Nr Henley-on-Thames
RG9 6HE
Map 4: SU78
Tel: 01491 638866
Fax: 01491 638863
Chef: Steven Morris
Owner: Peter Fowler
Cost: Alc £30, fixed-price L £21.
H/wine £10.50
Times: Noon-last L 2pm/7-last
D 9.30pm
Additional: Bar food; Sunday L;
Children welcome; 🐾 dishes
Seats: 50. Private dining room 14
Smoking: No pipes & cigars
Accommodation: 10 en suite
Credit cards: 🔲 🔲 🔲 🔲 🔲 🔲

Attractive scenery and a pretty village set the scene for this
small, welcoming hotel, built as a coaching inn in the 18th
century. Enjoy a drink in the bar, with its boating theme, or in
the cosy lounge – both with log fires in winter – before eating in
the dining-room or the conservatory overlooking the lovely
walled garden. The kitchen weaves some interesting variations
around French provincial cooking in cream of onion soup with
truffle and foie gras ravioli, confit of chicken and rabbit, and a
main-course breast of duck on a bean casserole with Toulouse
sausage and smoked bacon sauce. Otherwise, tender langoustine
tails come with fresh-flavoured tomato jelly as a starter, and
could be followed by rump of lamb on olive mash, or grilled sea
bass with squid cannelloni, saffron mash and red pepper sauce.
Star of the pudding menu must be the assiette of desserts – a
chocolate shell filled with light grapefruit sorbet, rich chocolate
sponge, lime crème brûlée, and strawberry and almond gâteau
— double-billed with an excellent choice of cheeses. Vin de Pays
d'Oc heads up the short, sharp list of wines.

Directions: In centre of village

THAME, **Spread Eagle Hotel** 🏵

*Four hundred-year-old former coaching inn, made famous in the
1920s by its then owner, John Fothergill, in his book An Inn Keepers
Diary. It has been run for the last 30 years by the Barringtons with
more than a touch of olde-worlde courtesy. A varied menu continues
to please with its Anglo/French dishes spiced up with more exotic
options. Also, a regularly changing regional menu – Burgundy on
our last visit. Extensive wine list with lots of half-bottles.*

Smoking: No pipes & cigars
Accommodation: 33 en suite
Credit cards: 🔲 🔲 🔲 🔲 JCB

Directions: M40/J6 from S, J8 from N. Town centre on A418
Oxford to Aylesbury road

Cornmarket OX9 2BW
Map 4: SP70
Tel: 01844 213661
Fax: 01844 261380
Chef: Michael Thomas
Owners: David & Sarah Barrington
Cost: Alc £26, fixed-price L £17.95/D
£21.95. ☺ H/wine £9.95
Times: Last L 2pm/last D 10pm.
Closed 28-30 Dec
Additional: Bar food; Sunday L;
Children welcome; 🐾 dishes

WALLINGFORD,
Shillingford Bridge 🏵

*Popular inn on the banks of the Thames with berthing available for
boats. The kitchen mixes the traditional with more modish ideas to
produce dishes such as salmon gravad lax and Arbroath smokie*

Shillingford OX10 8LZ
Map 4: SU68
Tel: 01865 858567
Fax: 01865 858636
Chef: Michel Escalie

roulade, roast pheasant with creamy whisky, juniper sauce and spätzle, and Pina Colada mousse.

Additional: Bar food; Sunday L; Children welcome; ❹ dishes
Accommodation: 42 en suite
Credit cards: ▨ ▨ ▨ ▨ ▨ ▨ ▨

Owners: Forestdale Hotels Ltd
Cost: Fixed price L & D £17.95. ☺
H/wine £8.85
Times: Last L 2pm/last D 10pm.
Closed L Sat

WALLINGFORD, **Springs Hotel** ❀❀

The Springs is a fine example of a mock-Tudor Victorian building, with the restaurant housed in what was a winter garden overlooking the spring-fed lake. The broad-ranging menu takes in starters of rillettes of duck on a dressing of truffle and potato, pan-fried king scallops with chorizo on lemon and basil couscous in a curry sauce, and a roasted chicken sausage, while traditional grilled meat and fish – fillet of salmon with béarnaise sauce and asparagus, for instance – rub shoulders with other main courses of braised breast of guinea fowl on buttery Savoy cabbage with a wild mushroom sauce, or loin of tuna grilled with garlic on a bed of crushed potatoes with a tomato and onion compote. Crêpes Suzette, finished at the table, end things on a high note. France dominates the wine list, although there are some decent bottles from elsewhere, too, particularly the New World.

Directions: From A4130 to Wallingford take A4074 (Reading); over first roundabout, turn R on B4009 (Goring). Hotel 1 mile on R

Wallingford Road
North Stoke OX10 6BE
Map 4: SU68
Tel: 01491 836687
Fax: 01491 836877
Chef: Phil Wilkins
Owner: Springs Hotel (Thames Valley) Ltd
Cost: Fixed-price l £15.50/D £25.50 (4 courses). H/wine £12
Times: 12.30-last L 2pm/7-last D 9.30pm
Additional: Bar food; Sunday L; Children welcome; ❹ dishes
Seats: 80. Private dining room 24
Smoking: No pipes & cigars
Accommodation: 30 en suite
Credit cards: ▨ ▨ ▨ ▨ ▨ ▨ ▨ JCB

WANTAGE, **Foxes** ❀

Central location, cottagey atmosphere for this low-beamed restaurant offering good-value set menus at dinner. Repertoire built around seasonal produce. Expect seafood tart with saffron and dill sauce, partridge marinated with cream, tarragon and port and served with red cabbage, and caramel blood oranges with caramel parfait.

Smoking: No smoking in dining room
Credit cards: ▨ ▨ ▨

Directions: 50 yds from Market Square on A338 Newbury/Reading rd

8 Newbury Street OX12 8BS
Map 4: SU38
Tel/Fax: 01235 760568
Chef: Karen Sweeney
Owners: Karen Sweeney, Nicholas Offen
Cost: Alc £27, fixed-price L £15.95
Times: Last L 1.30pm/last D 9.30pm.
Closed L Sat, Mon, all Sun
Additional: L by arrangement; Children welcome; ❹ dishes

WESTON-ON-THE-GREEN,
Weston Manor Hotel ❀

Baronial surroundings – minstrels' gallery, linen-fold panelling, vaulted ceiling – contrast with a distinctly modish menu at this 15th-century manor house. Tea-smoked pigeon breast on potato and chive salad, halibut with sun-dried tomato risotto and basil nage, and pot-roasted poussin with morels and young vegetables show the style.

Accommodation: 36 en suite
Credit cards: ▨ ▨ ▨ ▨ ▨ JCB

Directions: 2 mins from M40/J9 via A34 (Oxford) to Weston-on-the-Green; hotel in village centre

Oxford OX6 8QL
Map 4: SP51
Tel: 01869 350621
Fax: 01869 350901
Chef: Michael Keenleyside
Cost: Fixed price D £32.50. H/wine £15
Times: Last L 2.15pm/last D 9.45pm
Additional: Bar food; Sunday L; Children welcome; ❹ dishes
Smoking: No smoking in dining room

WOODSTOCK, **The Bear Hotel**

Park Street OX20 1SZ
Map 4: SP41
Tel: 01993 811511
Fax: 01993 813380
Chef: James Arbourne
Owner: Forte Heritage
Cost: Alc £25, fixed-price L £21.50.
☺ H/wine £12
Times: Last L 2pm/last D 10pm
Additional: Bar food L; Sunday L;
Children welcome; ❹ dishes
Smoking: No smoking in dining room
Accommodation: 44 en suite
Credit cards: ▆ ▆ ▆ ▆ ▆ ▆ ▆ JCB

Dating from 1232, The Bear has always been a coaching inn
and retains much of its original character with exposed stone
walls and heavily beamed ceilings. The restaurant delivers
sound cooking based on fresh local produce. The menu reads
well, and buttered duck parfait, peppered venison, and lemon
and rosemary tart may give something of the tilt. Our most
recent meal delivered some spot-on dishes, notably a chicken
breast wrapped in Parma ham and served on a bed of soft
polenta and accompanied by wild mushrooms. That meal was
topped and tailed by spring rolls of spiced confit of pork and
prawns, and a honey and lavender Bakewell tart. There are a
number of fun dishes to try, how about Horlicks soufflé with
Malteser ice cream?

Directions: Town centre, facing the market square

WOODSTOCK, **Chef Imperial** ✿

Unassuming Chinese just round the corner from Blenheim Palace.
Reasonably priced special set lunches and a popular Sunday buffet,
as well as good hot-and-sour soup, crispy duck with paper-thin
pancakes and plum sauce, and crab stir-fried with chilli and black
bean sauce. Excellent standard of cooking, but beware indifferent
service.

Additional: Sunday L; Children welcome; ❹ dishes
Smoking: Air conditioning
Credit cards: ▆ ▆ ▆ ▆ ▆ ▆

Directions: In main street of Woodstock

22 High Street OX20 1TF
Map 4: SP41
Tel: 01993 813593
Fax: 01993 813591
Chef: Mr P C Wong
Owner: Alan Shek
Cost: Alc £15, fixed-price L £5.95/D
£15. ☺ H/wine £8.50
Times: Last L 2.30pm/last D midnight.
Closed 25-26 Dec

WOODSTOCK,
Feathers Hotel ✿✿✿

The Feathers, a 17th-century gem of a building, has class:
there's an understated elegance to much of the decoration
given focus by original wood panelling, low beamed ceilings,
antiques, and the general patina of age. Class, too, in the
kitchen, where Mark Treasure (ex Michael's Nook, Grasmere,
Cumbria, see entry) has taken over command. A meal in June
showed something of the style that's emerging. It opened with
excellent breads, a great variety of olive, sun-dried tomato,

Market Street OX20 1SX
Map 4: SP41
Tel: 01993 812291
Fax: 01993 813158
Chef: Mark Treasure
Owners: Andrew Leeman, Simon
Lowe, Howard Malin
Cost: Alc £37, fixed-price L £21/D
£44 (7-course tasting menu).
H/wine £11.75

Feathers Hotel

Times: 12.30-last L 2.15pm/7.30-last
D 9.15pm. Closed D 25 Dec
Additional: Bar food L (D Mon-Fri
only); Sunday L; Children welcome;
❹ dishes
Seats: 60. Private dining room 20
Smoking: No smoking in dining room;
Air conditioning
Accommodation: 22 en suite
Credit cards: ▆▆ ▆▆ ▆▆ ⬙ ▆▆ ▆ ▆ JCB

focaccia, and good crusty white and brown, then went on to
one of Mark's signature dishes, impressive looking deep-fried
langoustine beignets with watercress purée, tomato fondue and
hollandaise. This was a great dish, well-conceived, with all
elements working well together. Next was a simple warm
gazpacho flavoured with lemon and chives and served with
scallops. The centrepiece of the meal was a splendid pot-
roasted squab pigeon with ceps, caramelised shallots, fondant
potato and spinach in a great jus. Pudding was 'great too' – a
pavé of white chocolate sponge and white chocolate ganache in
a dark chocolate surrounded by fresh raspberries. Other
choices could include an intriguing sounding foie gras, split pea
and parsnip casserole with truffle, poached fillets of brill,
fettucine, braised lettuce, asparagus and tarragon juices, and
hot plum fritters with honey ice cream.

Directions: Town centre

WOODSTOCK,
Kings Head Inn ❀

Chapel Hill Wootton OX20 1DX
Map 4: SP41
Tel/Fax: 01993 811340
Chef: Tony Fay
Owners: Mr & Mrs Tony Fay
Cost: Alc £25. ☺ H/wine £9.95
Times: Noon-last L 2pm/7-last D
9.30pm
Additional: Bar food; Sunday L;
No children under 10; ❹ dishes
Smoking: No smoking in dining room
Accommodation: 3 en suite
Credit cards: ▆▆ ▆▆ ▆▆ ⬙

*A super, little village pub that's all bare brick and beams, with diners
having the choice of eating in a quiet area to the rear or more
informally at the front. Blackboard menus include one with daily
changing fish dishes such as a trio of salmon, zander and sea bass in
a chive sauce. Finish perhaps with iced lemon soufflé.*

Directions: On A44 2 miles N of Woodstock turn R to Wootton.
The Inn is located near church on Chapel Hill

RUTLAND

NORMANTON,
Normanton Park Hotel

The hotel is built around a magnificently restored Georgian stable block, and diners in the Orangery restaurant can watch the sun set over Rutland Water. The sound cooking is predominantly modern in outlook with terrine of foie gras, duck with blackcurrant and cassis sauce, and chocolate parfait, setting the pace at inspection.

Additional: Bar food; Sunday L; Children welcome; ❸ dishes
Smoking: No pipes or cigars
Accommodation: 23 en suite.
Credit cards: 📧

Directions: South shore of Rutland Water near Edith Weston

Oakham LE15 8RP
Map 4: SK90
Tel: 01780 720315
Fax: 01780 721086
Chef: Daren Bale
Owners: Old English Inns & Hotels
Cost: Alc £30 ☺
Times: Last L 2.15pm/D 9.45pm.
Closed D Sat

OAKHAM,
Barnsdale Lodge ✿

The Avenue
Rutland Water LE15 8AH
Map 8: SK80
Tel: 01572 724678
Fax: 01572 724961
Chef: Robert Knowles
Owner: Mr R P H Reid
Cost: Alc £25. H/wine £9.50
Times: Last L 2.15pm/last D 9.30pm
Additional: Bar food; Sunday L;
Children welcome; ❸ dishes
Smoking: No-smoking area
Accommodation: 45 en suite
Credit cards: 📧 📧 🔫 ⬜ 📧 📧 📧

Popular hotel with good conference and function facilities. Its heart is a farmhouse, with sympathetic bedroom and public area extensions. Expect warm seafood quiche, breast of chicken with lardons of bacon and a wild mushroom sauce, and individual pear bavarois with Poire William anglaise and redcurrant coulis.

Directions: Telephone for directions

OAKHAM,
The Boultons Hotel ✿ NEW

The menus in the hotel's Le Jardin restaurant are modern British in style with dinner being an enjoyable affair including tender, pink duck with a compote of apples and mango, and a boozy, hot apple and Calvados soufflé. The hotel stands next to the Rutland Museum.

4 Catmose Street LE15 6HW
Map 8: SK80
Tel: 01572 722844
Fax: 01572 724473

OAKHAM, **Hambleton Hall** ❀❀❀❀

Hambleton LE15 8TH
Map 8: SK80
Tel: 01572 756991
Fax: 01572 724721
Chef: Aaron Patterson
Owners: Tim & Stefa Hart
Cost: Alc £55, fixed-price L £15.50/D
£35. H/wine £16
Times: Noon-2.30pm/7pm-9.30pm
Additional: Sunday L; Children
welcome; ◑ dishes
Smoking: No smoking in dining room
Seats: 60. Private dining room 20;
Jacket & tie preferred
Accommodation: 15 en suite
Credit cards: 💳 💳 💳 💳 💳 💳

Directions: From A1 – A606
Oakham. After 8.4 miles take turning
signed Hambleton/Egleton only. Hotel
on R in main street of Hambleton
village

AA Wine Award-see page 16
Shortlisted for

The setting for Hambleton Hall is truly idyllic, surrounded by
wonderful landscaped grounds and set against the backdrop of
Rutland Water. Inspectors continue to agree that the course set
by Aaron Patterson's cooking has not faltered in six years: 'a
sheer performance, staged to a tee with due place for each
element', aided by the strong style of service (both
knowledgeable and hospitable), presented by the staff. Menus
are seasonal, and one inspector, dining in early autumn, was
disappointed not to try the poulet noir en vessie he had been
told so much about. But he was not disappointed with a dinner
that opened with canapés of such lightness and delicacy, so as
not to 'distract from the main focus to come', then an excellent
appetiser of fresh tasting, frothy-style crab and ginger bisque.
This was followed by foie gras terrine topped with sea salt and
cracked black pepper and served with a tower of intensely
green, tangy chopped green beans and shallot 'salad', baby
artichoke hearts, a Madeira version of the more usual Sauternes
jelly, splashes of vinaigrette, and crusty, rustic-style toast on the
side. Accurately executed pot-au-feu terrine came as a mosaic:
different meats, baby vegetables, and sausages, in their own
jellied stock with a cabbage wrapper surrounded by a creamed
salsa verde-style sauce. Whole roasted grouse, partially carved,
well hung and properly cooked (tender and bloody) came with
traditional accompaniments of delicate bread sauce, crumbs,
and salty game chips, whilst crème de mûre and red wine sauce
was a perfect consistency, and wonderfully complementary.
Rabbit came as a tender, pale loin with a contrasting leg pie,
melting pastry lined with Parma ham and containing braised leg
meat with a touch of sherry vinegar to give an edge. Little
rabbit cutlets were an unexpected touch, scattered on top, with
a properly squeaky, unctuous pear barley risotto and a lightly
spiced grain mustard sauce finishing the dish. The cheese trolley
'was calling to be enjoyed', properly matured cheeses in
excellent condition from the British Isles, Ireland and France.
Assiette of desserts came as perfect, zingy, melt-in-the-mouth
classic lemon tart, a masterpiece pavé of white and dark
chocolate with perfect raspberry sorbet, prune and Armagnac
soufflé and a passion fruit sorbet on praline parfait and a bed
of rhubarb compote. Simple yet effective petits fours did not
impinge on the memories of the meal. The wine list is
magnificent, but take the advice of the sommelier -'charming
and informative, never patronising with such a wonderful list he
still managed to encourage us to have two wines not even
listed, perfect with our dishes. Wines by the glass are ad hoc –
tell him what you fancy and he will oblige'.

Signature dishes: Fricassée of morels with chicken mousse and spears of asparagus; essence of tomato with langoustine tails; caramelised apple tart with blackberries and vanilla ice cream; roasted loin of local fallow venison with roast vegetables and a juniper flavoured sauce.

OAKHAM, **Whipper-In Hotel**

Well-established 17th-century coaching inn overlooking the market square. Beyond the low-beamed lounge bar is the appealing, candlelit restaurant with its choice of modern British dishes. Dishes may include chicken terrine, lamb with couscous and tomato and basil sauce, and chocolate and pear brûlée.

Accommodation: 24 en suite
Credit cards: ▬ ▬ ▬ ▬ ▬ ▬

Directions: In the market place, town centre

The Market Place LE15 6DT
Map 8: SK80
Tel: 01572 756971
Fax: 01572 757759
Chef: James Butterfield
Owner: Brook Hotels
Cost: Alc £26.50, fixed-price L £11.95/D £16.50. ☺ H/wine £9.95
Times: Last L 2pm/last D 9.30pm
Additional: Bar food; Sunday L; Children welcome; ❹ dishes
Smoking: No smoking in dining room

STRETTON, **Ram Jam Inn** ✿

The roadside eaterie has become one of the most famous landmarks along the A1, a destination as well as a transit stop. The style is laid-back, open-plan café/bar with rooms. Good choice includes home-made duck terrine, Rutland sausage and mash, pork normande, and jam sponge pudding with vanilla custard. For kids, there is baby burger and chips, or chicken and chips.

Accommodation: 7 en suite
Credit cards: ▬ ▬ ▬ ▬ ▬ ▬

Directions: On N/bound carriageway of A1, 8 miles N of Stamford; S/bound exit Oakham B668, follow signs under bridge to inn.

Great North Road LE15 7QX
Map 8: SK91
Tel: 01780 410776
Fax: 01780 410361
Chef: Chris Coldwell
Owners: Mr M Littlemore, Mrs M Cox
Cost: Alc £18. ☺ H/wine £9.50
Times: Noon-last D 10pm.
Additional: Bar Food; Sunday L; Children welcome; ❹ dishes
Smoking: No smoking in dining room

UPPINGHAM, **Lake Isle Hotel** ✿✿

High Street East LE15 9PZ
Map 4: SP89
Tel/Fax: 01572 822951
Chefs: David Whitfield, Stuart Mead
Owners: David & Claire Whitfield
Cost: Fixed-price L £10.50 (2 courses)/D £22.50. ☺ H/wine £9.50.
Times: 12.30pm-last L 1.45pm/7.30pm-last D 9.30pm
Closed L Mon

The entrance to the Lake Isle is hidden in the middle of floral displays within the rear courtyard. Once inside, drinks can be taken around an open log fire before moving into the easy-going, rustic-style Anglo-French restaurant. Individual loaves are brought hot to the table, soups include mixed wild mushroom, or celery and Stilton, then there may be quails eggs wrapped in bacon with redcurrant and lime jelly, or brochette of mussels and queen scallops on a bed of wild rice with citrus butter. Main courses include chargrilled marinated gigot of lamb with a rosemary, honey and mustard sauce, and filo pastry parcel of salmon and red sea bream with a leek and sorrel sauce. English farmhouse cheese is served with a malt loaf, and there is a choice of home-made puddings (coconut, lime and banana tart, for example), ice cream or sorbet. The extensive cellar holds some 300 wines, of which around 100 are half-bottles.

Directions: Town centre, on foot via Reeves Yard; via Queen Street by car

Additional: Sunday L; Children welcome; 🍴 dishes
Seats: 40. Private dining room 10
Smoking: No pipes & cigars; Air conditioning
Accommodation: 12 en suite
Credit cards: 🔲 🔲 🔲 🔲 🔲 🔲

SHROPSHIRE

BRIDGNORTH, **Haywain**

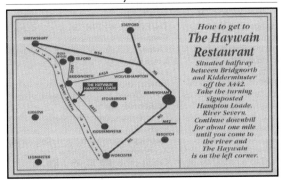

How to get to
The Haywain Restaurant
Situated halfway between Bridgnorth and Kidderminster off the A442. Take the turning signposted Hampton Loade, River Severn. Continue downhill for about one mile until you come to the river and The Haywain is on the left corner.

Hampton Loade WV15 6HD
Map 7: SO79
Tel/Fax: 01746 780404
Chef: Paul Lacey
Owner: David Browning
Cost: *Alc* £14.25, fixed-price D £14.25, Sat D £25.95 (8 courses). ☺
H/wine £7.65
Times: D only from 7.30pm.
Closed D Sun, Mon
Additional: Bar food D; Sunday L (12.30-2.30pm); Children welcome; 🍴 dishes
Seats: 50. Jacket & tie preferred
Smoking: No smoking in the dining room; Air conditioning
Credit cards: 🔲 🔲 🔲 🔲 🔲

Sundays are family days at this popular repro *Olde Englande* spot overlooking the River Severn and the last cable ferry still in current use. The formula, however, is much the same as on other days: cheese dip on arrival followed by home-made soup of the day, a help-yourself cold table, a choice of main course, dessert and lashings of coffee of petits fours. Main courses include a daily fish dish, magret of duck with kumquats, escalope de porc, medallions of wild boar, and roast meats for Sunday lunch. Extra courses take in spare ribs, sorbets and cheese. It's all great fun, excellent quality and terrific value for money.

Directions: Off the A442, halfway between Bridgnorth and Kidderminster, in the village by the river

CHURCH STRETTON, **Mynd House**

Welcoming hotel in the sleepy hamlet of Little Stretton. The daily changing menu shows an enthusiasm for local ingredients, coupled with Mediterranean influences. Our most recent meal included mozzarella and herb-filled field mushrooms, tomato soup, and roasted wood pigeon.

Smoking: No smoking in dining room; Air conditioning
Accommodation: 6 en suite
Credit cards: 🔲 🔲 🔲 🔲 🔲 🔲

Directions: Village centre, 0.5 mile off A49 on B4370 (Little Stretton)

Little Stretton SY6 6RB
Map 7: SO49
Tel: 01694 722212
Fax: 01694 724180
Chef: Janet Hill
Owners: Robert & Janet Hill
Cost: Fixed-price D £27. ☺
H/wine £10
Times: Last L 2pm/last D 8.45pm.
Closed L Sun, Jan, 2 wks summer
Additional: Bar food L; Children welcome; 🍴 dishes

CLEOBURY MORTIMER,
Redfern Hotel ✿

Small family-run hotel noted for its warm, friendly hospitality, well-equipped accommodation and competently cooked food. Both the fixed-price menu and carte offer good choice and variety. Expect classic French fish soup, followed by loin of lamb stuffed with black pudding, and Danish raspberry basket for pudding.

Accommodation: 11 en suite
Credit cards: 🏦 🏧 💳 📇 🖥 🅾 🔲

Directions: Midway on A4117 between Kidderminster and Ludlow. For Kidderminster leave at M5/J3

DY14 8AA
Map 7: SO67
Tel: 01299 270395
Fax: 01299 271011
Chef: Jamie Bailie
Owners: Jon & Lis Redfern
Cost: *Alc* £20, fixed-price L £5.55/D £17.95 (5 courses). ☺ H/wine £7.50
Times: Last L 2pm/D 9.30pm
Additional: Bar food L; Sunday L; No children under 5; 🌢 dishes
Smoking: No smoking in dining room

DORRINGTON, Country Friends
Restaurant ✿✿

Consistency is the watchword here, as it has been for the last 14 or so years, and the set-price menu continues to offer a choice of good, uncomplicated cooking. Twice-baked soufflés are popular, or else try confit of duck on a warm salad of French beans, and orange or spinach fettucine with smoked salmon. Fish of the day, on our visit, was fillet of halibut baked with an olive crust, served with a white wine sauce; alternatives might be Trelough duck breast on an oriental sauce or fillet steak with shallot purée and a red wine sauce. Bread-and-butter pudding was all it should be – light and creamy – accompanied here by good vanilla ice cream. Well-chosen cafetière coffee is freshly brewed and served with home-made petits fours. If staying the night, look forward to a breakfast of scrambled eggs, smoked salmon and bucks fizz.

Directions: On A49 in centre of village, 6 miles S of Shrewsbury

Shrewsbury SY5 7JD
Map 7: SJ40
Tel/Fax: 01743 718707
Chef: Charles Whittaker
Owners: Charles & Pauline Whittaker
Cost: Fixed-price L £24/D £27. H/wine £10.95
Times: Noon-last L 2pm/7pm-last D 9pm. Closed Sun, Mon, 2 wks July
Additional: Bar food L; Children welcome; 🌢 dishes
Seats: 40
Smoking: No smoking in dining room
Accommodation: 3 rooms
Credit cards: 🏦 🏧 💳 📇 🅾 JCB

LUDLOW, The Cookhouse ✿✿

Perhaps it is a little too much to hope that we are witnessing a new trend in roadside inns but, judging by the trade on a spring lunchtime, The Cookhouse has struck the right chord with travellers on the A49. Not that all the trade is of a passing nature. Indeed, most bases are covered in an operation that stretches from breakfast to dinner with a bar, café, bistro and more formal restaurant all part of the enterprising equation. Once evening comes, the sauce bottles disappear from the tables of the functionally chic café and the brown paper cloths signal that the bistro menu is on offer. Here a punchy set menu is offered at realistic prices – more sophisticated fare is served up next door in the sunbright surroundings of the main restaurant. A selection of brasserie favourites define the menu. A welcome lightness of touch accompanies deftly arranged flavours in dishes that include an airy chicken liver parfait with toasted brioche and a 'beautifully cooked' peppered fillet of monkfish with a fruity salsa. Many familiar offerings on the dessert menu too, with, for instance, a worthy lemon tart pepped up by a satisfyingly chewy lime sorbet.

Directions: 1 mile north of Ludlow on A49 to Shrewsbury

Bromfield SY7 8LR
Map 7: SO57
Tel: 01584 856565
Fax: 01584 856661
Chef: Peter Gartell
Owner: Norman Swallow
Cost: *Alc* £20, fixed price L & D £14.75. ☺ H/wine £8.75
Times: Noon-Last L 2.30pm/7-last D 10pm
Additional: Bar food; Sunday L; Children welcome; 🌢 dishes
Seats: 40. Private room 40
Smoking: No-smoking area; No pipes & cigars
Credit cards: 🏦 🏧 💳 📇 🖥 🅾 🔲 JCB

LUDLOW,

Dinham Hall ❀❀

By The Castle SY8 1EJ
Map 7: SO57
Tel: 01584 876464
Fax: 01584 876019
Chef: Richard Quinney
Owner: Mr J P Mifsud
Cost: *Alc* £45, fixed-price L £12.50/D £20.50. ☺ H/wine £10.50
Times: 12.30-last L 2pm/7-last D 9 pm
Additional: Sunday L; Children welcome; ❀ dishes.
Seats: 22. Private dining room 24
Smoking: No smoking in dining room
Accommodation: 13 en suite
Credit cards: 🔲 🔲 🔲 🔲 🔲 🔲 🔲 JCB

The hall is a three-storied building, in its own walled garden opposite the castle, typical of the symmetrical style of Georgian architecture (it went up in 1792). You'll find tasteful appointments and warm hospitality inside, with open fires in the lounges in winter. A large bow window in the restaurant, intimate and candlelit, looks over the garden. Resolutely French menus, with English translations, are the order of the day. The soupe du jour could be well-judged asparagus, or there might be a brioche of lambs' kidneys and wild mushrooms, or shellfish ravioli. Winter could see a main course of cassoulet of meltingly tender lamb and beans, with duck confit with nectarines and blackcurrant sauce in summer. Fillet of salmon is served on a bed of ratatouille, and among puddings could be rich and creamy blueberry crème brûlée, nougat ice cream or almond tart with poached pear. The wine list isn't confined to France, with one of the house wines coming from Herefordshire.

Directions: Town centre, off Market Place

LUDLOW,

The Feathers at Ludlow ❀

Bull Ring SY8 1AA
Map 7: SO57
Tel: 01584 875261
Fax: 01584 876030
Owner: Regal Hotels plc
Cost: Fixed-price L £13.50/D £19.95. ☺ H/wine £11.25
Times: Last L 2pm/last D 9pm

Ornate plaster ceilings and oak panelling abound at this comfortable timber-framed hotel. Vegetarian options always feature on the set-price menus, which may also take in a starter of pork and herb sausage with banana chutney, and main courses of game ragout or baked cod with marinated octopus.

Additional: Bar food; Sunday L; Children welcome; ❀ dishes
Smoking: No smoking in restaurant
Accommodation: 40 en suite
Credit cards: 🔲 🔲 🔲 🔲 🔲 🔲 🔲 JCB

Directions: In centre of Ludlow, which is signposted off A49

LUDLOW,
The Merchant House ❀❀❀

62 Lower Corve Street SY8 1DU
Map 7: SO57
Tel: 01584 875438
Fax: 01584 876927
Chef: Shaun Hill
Owners: Shaun & Anja Hill
Cost: Fixed-price L & D £27.50.
H/wine £12.50
Times: 12.30- 2pm (Fri-Sat only)/7-
9.30pm. Closed Sun, Mon
Seats: 22
Smoking: No smoking in dining room
Credit cards: 🔲 🔲 🔲 🔲 JCB

Exposed oak beams and timbers showing the building's
Jacobean origins, a log-burning fireplace, well-polished tables
and good-quality crockery and cutlery provide the simple
setting in which Shaun Hill presents his fixed-price, three-
course lunch and dinner with around four choices at each
course. 'It's almost as if his ingredients are best friends that
jump through hoops again and again to great effect,' writes an
inspector, and indeed Shaun Hill cooks whatever he's happiest
with, the lack of any fashionable mores attributable to his
being a market leader rather than market-led. A
complimentary *amuse-bouche* arrives first, perhaps creamy
chicken liver parfait in puff pastry, followed by a starter of
simply presented but 'stunning' poached sea bass with Chinese
spices, its liquor of 'magical flavours' of five-spice, lemon, garlic
and an 'itsy-bitsy hint' of oyster sauce. Rack of lamb is a
favoured main course, of superb flavour, perfectly timed,
served with perhaps sweetbreads and potato and olive cakes.
Vegetables julienne of mange-tout, salsify and lozenges of
carrot are well reported too. Terrine of foie gras with quince
may also appear among starters, and hare with braised lentils
and celeriac, or grilled turbot with shallots and watercress
among main courses. 'Great, thick, rich and regretfully waist-
enhancing' chocolate fudge cake with hazelnut ice cream, or
well-kept cheeses — Gorgonzola, Époisses and Wigmore, say –
round things off. Anja Hill leads the friendly front of house,
and house wines from Italy and France head up a mixed bag of
around 50 bottles.

Directions: Town centre, next to Unicorn pub

LUDLOW, Oaks Restaurant ❀❀❀

17 Corve Street SY8 1DA
Map 7: SO57
Tel: 01584 872325
Fax: 01568 780546
Chef/Owner: Kenneth Adams
Cost: Fixed-price D £22.50. ☺
H/wine £10.
Times: D only, 7pm-last D 9.30pm.
Closed Sun, Mon, 1 wk spring,
1 wk autumn
Additional: D Sun on Bhs only;
No children under 8; ❹ dishes

Open only four years, this restaurant housed in a 17th-century
coaching inn nevertheless has the atmosphere of an old dining
club. The dark, reclaimed oak panelling and the kitchen's use
of traditional English ingredients only enhance the formal air,
but there are some contemporary twists to the menu, such as
the parsnip crisps and olives included with the cheese biscuits
in the canapé selection. An excellent choice of starter is the
quenelle of chicken liver and foie gras parfait served with a
terrine of beetroot, carrots and swede set in balsamic
vinaigrette jelly. Nicely dressed leaves and good home-made

Oaks Restaurant

Seats: 30. Private dining room 16
Smoking: No smoking in dining room;
Air conditioning
Credit cards: ▬ ▭ ▰ ▱

brioche are served alongside. For hungry customers, a separate fish course is offered, which may be a smoked haddock boudin on marsh samphire, or a salad of tuna, crab, avocado and pink grapefruit. Fish also features on the main course selection in dishes such as pan-fried John Dory with tomato-saffron sauce, and roast fillet of Cornish hake. Meat-lovers will enjoy the cannon of Welsh lamb in rosemary butter with minced lamb pudding and minted port sauce, or veal loin with shallot confit, bay leaf sauce and a mushroom crumble. Our inspector enjoyed a nicely pink and tender fillet of hare with port and redcurrant-scented jus, caramelised shallots and plenty of trompettes, followed by a rich chocolate fondant for dessert, the liquid centre spilling from the sponge case to combine pleasingly with home-made vanilla-flecked ice cream. The comprehensive wine list includes six house wines available by the bottle or glass.

Signature dishes: Cornish Scallops on onion pastry with foie gras and apple sauce; lobster boudin with marsh samphire and chive beurre blanc; mulberry charlotte with honey ice cream; saddle of hare with mushroom crumble and redcurrant sauce.

Directions: Town centre, bottom of hill below Feathers Hotel

LUDLOW,

Overton Grange ❀❀❀

Hereford Road SY8 4AD
Map 7: SO57
Tel: 01584 873500
Fax: 01584 873524
Chef: Claude Bosi
Owner: Grange Hotels Ltd
Cost: *Alc* £25, ficed-price L&D £20.
☺ H/wine £10
Times: 12.30-last L 2.30pm/7.15-last
D 9.30pm
Additional: Bar food L; Sunday L;
Children welcome; 🍲 dishes
Seats: 35. Private dining room 6-20
Smoking: No smoking in the dining
room
Accommodation: 15 en suite
Credit cards: ▬ ▭ ▰ ▱ ▣ JCB

Perched high above a racecourse town that is rapidly becoming something of a culinary hot-spot, this country house hotel shows no sign of being left behind in the gastronomic stakes. The new kitchen team have brought a classic French style to a menu built on the solid foundation of top quality ingredients. With an approach that is admirably direct, dishes such as a Cornish lobster in a white bean sauce are noted for their delicate balancing of flavour. Simple delights include the superb breads and have included an excellent plate of super-fresh squid with a caramelised balsamic dressing and mint. Top billing on a July inspection was occupied by a 'wonderfully moist' guinea fowl served in two parts: the breast with a flurry of garden vegetables, and the leg was served with a delicate summer salad. Desserts are variations on well-known themes such as a chocolate soufflé intelligently paired with a star anise ice. The good value wine list is carefully compiled and is particularly strong on Spain.

Directions: On B4361 off A49

MARKET DRAYTON,
Goldstone Hall ❀❀

Goldstone TF9 2NA
Map 7: SJ63
Tel: 01630 661202
Fax: 01630 661585
Chef: Carl Fitzgerald Bloomer
Owners: J Cushing, H Ward
Cost: Alc £25, fixed-price L £14.50.
☺ H/wine £9.95
Times: Noon-last L 2pm/7.30-last
D 10pm. Closed D Sun
Additional: Sunday L; Children
welcome; ❹ dishes
Seats: 50. Private dining room 20
Smoking: No-smoking area;
No cigars and pipes
Accommodation: 8 en suite
Credit cards: ▬ ▬ ▬ ⌐ ▤ █ ▣ JCB

Much of Goldstone Hall is Georgian, though its ancestry has been traced back to 1390. Now a friendly, family-run hotel, this country house sits in five acres of grounds. The wood-panelled dining room, like the rest of the house, is furnished with fine antiques. Here, the menu lists traditional dishes such as poached salmon with new potatoes and parsley sauce, alongside food that brings the spice of the new – leek and Parmesan ravioli with star anise and tomato nage, for instance. A meal could begin with a generous portion of mussels and three whole langoustines served in well-seasoned butter sauce, and follow with roast fillet of tender beef with a piquant brandy and green peppercorn sauce. At inspection, crème brûlée, rich with a good brittle crust, preceded freshly made coffee and decent petits fours. Attentive, caring service and a wine list containing several half-bottles also merit praise.

Directions: From A529, 4 miles S of Market Drayton, follow signs for Goldstone Hall Gardens

MUCH WENLOCK, Raven Hotel ❀❀

Barrow Street TF13 6EN
Map 7: SO69
Tel: 01952 727251
Fax: 01952 728416
Chef: E Van Haldren
Owner: Raven Hotel (Wenlock) Ltd
Cost: Alc £23.
Times: Last L 2pm/last D 9.15pm.
Closed 25 Dec
Additional: Bar Food L; Sunday L;
❹ dishes
Smoking: No smoking in dining room
Accommodation: 15 en suite
Credit cards: ▬ ▬ ▬ ⌐ ▤ ▣

Directions: Town centre

Over the years this personally run hotel has grown out of its original 17th-century coaching inn and spread into adjacent, often older buildings. Lounges, one in a conservatory, are comfortable and attractive, and the dining room boasts a wood-burning stove and beams. The kitchen grows its own herbs and uses only fresh produce, most of it bought from Birmingham market. An inspector enjoyed a 'beautifully presented and enjoyable' starter of white crabmeat with ginger, avocado and pink grapefruit in a mustard dressing, and went on to 'lean and tender' cannon of lamb niçoise with a delicately flavoured thyme and red wine jus. The sharpness of blueberry and redcurrant provided a good counterpoint to the creaminess of crème brûlée, and a pot of cafetière coffee with decent petits fours made an upbeat end to the meal.

NORTON,
Hundred House Hotel ❀❀

Bridgnorth Road Shifnal TF11 9EE
Map 7: SJ70
Tel: 01952 730353
Fax: 01952 730355
Chef: Stuart Phillips
Cost: Alc £25. H/wine £10
Times: Noon-last L 2.30pm/6-last D 9.30pm
Additional: Bar food; Sunday L; Children welcome; ❀ dishes
Seats: 80. Private room 35
Smoking: No pipes and cigars; Air conditioning
Accommodation: 10 en suite
Credit cards: ▬ ▬ ▬ ▬ ▬

A true family-run enterprise, this red-brick Georgian inn has four members of the Phillips clan in control. Sylvia Phillips is responsible for the herb and flower garden, as well as interior decor in the warren of bars and two dining areas. Features include patchwork carpets, wood panelling, old tiled flooring and dried herbs hanging from exposed beams. Her husband, Henry, takes care of admin, while son Stuart is the chef, producing brasserie-style cooking and bar meals. Warm tartlet of shallots and nicely sautéed chicken livers started an inspection meal, which continued with supremely tender and full-flavoured breast of organic Hereford duck, sliced over rösti potatoes, spinach and green peppercorn sauce. To finish, apple tart accompanied by smooth raisin and cinnamon ice cream and a sauce anglaise with praline, was a well-balanced dessert. The chef's brother, David, is in charge of the relaxed, but prompt, service.

Directions: Midway between Bridgnorth/Telford on A442, 15 mins from M54/J4

OSWESTRY, The Old Mill Inn ❀

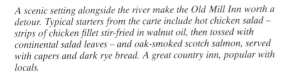

A scenic setting alongside the river make the Old Mill Inn worth a detour. Typical starters from the carte include hot chicken salad – strips of chicken fillet stir-fried in walnut oil, then tossed with continental salad leaves – and oak-smoked scotch salmon, served with capers and dark rye bread. A great country inn, popular with locals.

Accommodation: 5 bedrooms
Credit cards: ▬ ▬ ▬ ▬ JCB

Candy SY10 9AZ
Map 7: SJ22
Tel/Fax: 01691 657058
Chef: David Atkinson
Owners: David & Sharon Atkinson
Cost: Alc £15. ☺ H/wine £8.95
Times: Last L 2.30pm/D 9.30pm. Closed 25 Dec D
Additional: Bar meals; Sun L; Children welcome; ❀ dishes
Smoking: No-smoking area

Directions: From A5 follow B4579 signed Trefonen; after Ashfield take 1st R towards Llansillin then 1st R again.

OSWESTRY,
Pen-y-Dyffryn Hotel ❀ NEW

Built as a rectory in 1845, the hotel has a spacious restaurant looking south over the gardens and hills. The dinner menu offers four options, one vegetarian, with imagination and forethought evident in dishes such as spicy mackerel salad, pot-roasted oxtail with glazed shallots, and raspery crème brûlée.

Additional: Children welcome; ❸ dishes
Smoking: No smoking in dining room
Accommodation: 10 en suite
Credit cards: ▰ ▰ ▰ ▰ ▰ ▰

Directions: Leave A5 at Oswestry, follow signs to Llansilin through town. Hotel is 3 miles W of Oswestry on B4580 Llansilin Road.

Rhydcroesau SY10 7JD
Map 7: SJ22
Tel/Fax: 01691 653700
Chef: Paul Thomasson
Owners: Miles & Audrey Hunter
Cost: Fixed-price D £18.50. ☺
H/wine £8.50
Times: D only, 7pm-last D 8.30pm

OSWESTRY, **Wynnstay Hotel** ❀❀

Designed to reflect the Georgian coaching inn origins of the Wynnstay, the dining room is elegant and comfortable; the air conditioning providing a more modern comfort. By contrast, and rather unexpectedly, the menu is pure Italian. Starters might include a Tuscan pasta and bean soup, carpaccio with Parmesan flakes, and grilled polenta with a sauté of mixed mushrooms. There's a pasta section and a range of mains such as herb-filled fillet of sea bass with saffron sauce, medallions of veal in a sage and rosemary cream sauce served with a sun-dried tomato-topped ciabatta, and lamb shank roasted in a mustard crust with red onion sauce. Look to the trolley for popular desserts. 'Italians' make up about a third of the wine list.

Accommodation: 27 en suite
Credit cards: ▰ ▰ ▰ ▰ ▰ ▰ ▰ JCB

Directions: In centre of town, opposite church

Church Street SY11 2SZ
Map 7: SJ22
Tel: 01691 655261
Fax: 01691 670606
Chef: Martin Harrop
Owner: Earlymulti plc
Cost: Alc £20, fixed-price L £10.50 (2 courses)/D £16.95. ☺
H/wine £8.45
Times: 12.30pm-last L 2pm/7pm-last D 9.30pm. Closed L Sat, D Sun
Additional: Bar food; Sunday L; Children welcome; ❸ dishes
Seats: 46. Private dining room 200
Smoking: No pipes & cigars; Air conditioning

SHIFNAL,
Park House Hotel ❀❀

Peacefully set on the edge of the historic market town of Shifnal, Park House, originally two separate 17th-century houses, offers comfortable, elegant surroundings. The Silvermere Restaurant is a smart, high-ceilinged room whose tall windows look over the gardens. Choosing from the set-price menu might bring you duck liver parfait with caramelised oranges, then pan-fried salmon with tarragon sauce, and rich and creamy rice-pudding brûlée. The slightly longer choice on the carte could have terrine of foie gras and ham knuckle, or seafood sausage among the starters, and main courses of loin of rabbit braised in smoked bacon with mustard sauce, or fillet of turbot with ginger and chive sauce; a separate page lists traditional dishes like baked Dover sole and steaks. Grand Marnier soufflé might star among the puddings. About half of the long wine list is devoted to France.

Directions: From M54/J4 take A464 through Shifnal; hotel is 200 yards after railway bridge

Park Street TF11 9BA
Map 7: SJ70
Tel: 01952 460128
Fax: 01952 461658
Chef: Graeme Shaw
Owner: MacDonald Hotels (UK) Ltd
Cost: Alc £30, fixed-price L £13.50/D £23.50 (4 courses). H/wine £12.50
Times: 12.30-last L 2pm/7-last D 9.30pm. Closed L Sat
Additional: Bar food; Sunday L; Children welcome; ❸ dishes
Seats: 50. Private dining room
Smoking: No smoking in dining room
Accommodation: 54 en suite
Credit cards: ▰ ▰ ▰ ▰ ▰ ▰ ▰

SHREWSBURY,
Albright Hussey Hotel ❀❀

Ellesmere Road SY4 3AF
Map 7: SJ41
Tel: 01939 290571/290523
Fax: 01939 291143
Chefs: Robert Green, Martin Galley
Owner: Franco, Vera & Paul Subbiani
Cost: Alc £26, fixed-price L £12.50/D
£19.50 (4 courses). ☺ H/wine £9.75.
Times: Noon-last L 2.15pm/7-last
D 10pm
Additional: Bar food L; Sunday L;
No children under 3; ❹ dishes
Seats: 90. Private dining room 50.
Jacket & tie preferred
Smoking: No smoking in dining room
Accommodation: 14 en suite
Credit cards: ▆ ▆ ▆ ▆ ▆ ▆ ▆ JCB

This moated, timbered manor, dating from the 16th century,
was a farm until just 20-odd years ago. It still stands in four
acres of open countryside, the building itself looking
archetypically English. Main courses are in the modern idiom
of braised shank of lamb with garlic mash and sweet glazed
shallots, and fillets of sea bass wrapped in Parma ham served
with rocket and Parmesan. These could be preceded by tomato
and coriander soup, or chargrilled tuna with potatoes and
capers, and followed by cappuccino cake with Tia Maria sauce,
crème brûlée, or chargrilled fruits with raspberry coulis. An
uncommon Muscat from Samos is one of four pudding wines
sold by the glass, and there's a long list of other bottles to
choose from.

Directions: On A528, 2 miles from centre of Shrewsbury

SHREWSBURY,
Sol Restaurant ❀❀❀ NEW

82 Wyle Cop SY1 1UT
Map 7: SJ41
Tel: 01743 340560
Fax: 01743 340552
Chef: John Williams
Owners: John & Debbie Williams,
Simon Cousins, Clare Cadwallader
Cost: Alc £15 (L only), fixed-price
D £25. H/wine £8.95

As evening falls, all that can be glimpsed through the heavy
drapes that cover the former shop front is the gleam of candlelight. Inside, the unusual decor is striking: bright colours,
traditional elegance streaked with a futuristic look. The
restaurant itself is split-level, separated by a smooth, 'groovy-
looking' bar. Upstairs there are two further rooms – one for

small parties and another that allows a view of the chefs at work. Lunch offers a fast-paced, cheaper and lighter selection than the dinner menu (also available), and it is on the latter that the brigade displays its real talent in depth. At our test meal an *amuse-bouche* of an unusual shredded veal on a light sauce gribiche laced with chervil immediately set the right tone and, for the rest of the meal, each course barely missed a beat. Fresh, clean flavours and a 'delectable' texture marked out a ballotine of Shetland salmon with herbs, horseradish cream and rocket, and a main course of pan-fried Shropshire rabbit wrapped in smoked bacon with tarragon mousse with a jus of rabbit juices was perfectly timed and balanced. The trio of chocolate desserts was a stunning presentation of milk chocolate mousse, a boat-shaped tuile filled with white chocolate sorbet, and a warm chocolate fondant with a light anglaise – all very accomplished. Petits fours are worth saving space for: Florentines (making a comeback these days), fudge that dissolves on the tongue, raspberry sorbet in mini chocolates, glazed lemon tart, fork butter biscuits. The wine list is averagely priced and provides for most tastes. This is one to watch.

Times: 11am-last L 2.30pm/6.30-last D 9.30pm. Closed Sun, Mon
Additional: Children welcome; ⑤ dishes
Seats: 50. Private dining room 24
Smoking: No-smoking area
Credit cards: ▆ ▆ ▆ ▆

Directions: From A5 by-pass follow town centre signs, cross English Bridge & restaurant is at top of hill on L after Lion Hotel. Best to park at bottom and walk up.

TELFORD, **Holiday Inn**

Modern hotel conveniently located next to the Racquet and Exhibition Centre. Indeed, tennis memorabilia is a decorative feature of Courts restaurant. Here the kitchen is aware of current trends, offering a healthy eating menu as well as a carte. From the latter expect scallops with Thai spicy cabbage salad, and beef tournedos with polenta and salsa verde.

Accommodation: 100 en suite
Credit cards: ▆ ▆ ▆ ▆ ▆ ▆

Directions: M54/J4 (Telford East), follow signs for town centre; then 2nd exit off St Quentin roundabout

St Quentin Gate TF3 4EH
Map 7: SJ60
Tel: 01952 292500
Fax: 01952 291949
Chef: Paul Goring
Owner: Mr Brian Gray
Cost: *Alc* £18, fixed-price L £10.95/D £15.95. ☺ H/wine £10.95
Times: Last L 2.15pm/last D 9.45pm. Closed L Sat
Additional: Bar food; Sunday L; Children welcome; ⑤ dishes
Smoking: No-smoking area; Air conditioning

TELFORD, **Valley Hotel**   NEW

A bright, attractively-decorated restaurant offering sound cooking. Typical dishes include chicken liver pâté, ratatouille ravioli, trout fillets with herb and Parmesan crust, pork fillet with mustard sauce, and a particularly light lemon cheesecake.

Ironbridge TF8 7DW
Map 7: SJ60
Tel: 01952 432247
Fax: 01952 432308
Please telephone for further details

WORFIELD, **Old Vicarage Hotel**

The Old Vicarage has something of a holding entry in the 1998 edition of *Best Restaurants*. This is because of a chef change. Richard Arnold is now in charge as executive chef, with Blaine Reed as head chef, and reports suggest that the changeover has been seamless. The Edwardian parsonage is a stylish place, of polished wood floors and tables, fresh flowers, and a bright conservatory giving splendid views of the rolling Shropshire countryside. The food complements the setting. Sophisticated food, yet with its foundation based on what the region can produce, from a peppered loin of Shropshire lamb with confit shallot and sauce of wild mushrooms and tarragon, to a splendid Shropshire Blue from the selection of traditional, hand-made British farmhouse cheeses. Appetisers give the first hint of the style, with crab and chive fritter with saffron mousse taking pride of place. Breads come in several varieties

Bridgnorth WV15 5JZ
Map 7: SO79
Tel: 01746 716497
Fax: 01746 716552
Chefs: Richard Arnold, Blaine Reed
Owners: Mr & Mrs P Iles
Cost: Fixed-price D from £25. H/wine £14
Times: D only, 7-last D 8.45pm
Additional: Sunday L (noon-last L 1.45pm); Children welcome; ⑤ dishes
Seats: 40. Private room 14
Smoking: No smoking in dining room
Accommodation: 14 en suite
Credit cards: ▆ ▆ ▆

Old Vicarage Hotel

including a good cheese and onion loaf. A splendid chicken mousse is filled with melting goats' cheese with tapenade and roasted red peppers, and black bream served with good carrot polenta and an excellent red wine jus. Top-notch puddings include a stunning crème brûlée, served with lovely buttery shortbread and a really tangy, creamy mango curd ice cream.

Signature dishes: Rump of new seasons Shropshire lamb on parsnip and chive mash, balsamic vinegar sauce; chargrilled Brixham sea bass on mango salsa with ginger and sweet pepper dressing; roasted red legged partridge with basil, dauphinoise and mustard cream; Ludlow venison on confit of garlic and shallots with Puy lentils and star anise jus.

Directions: From Wolverhampton take A454 Bridgnorth Road; from M54/J4 take A442 towards Kidderminster.

SOMERSET

BATH, Bath Priory ✿✿

Weston Road BA1 2XT
Map 3: ST76
Tel: 01225 331922
Fax: 01225 448276
Chef: Robert Clayton
Owner: Andrew Brownsword
Cost: *Alc* £37.50, fixed-price L £15/D £37.50. H/wine £15
Times: Noon-last L 1.45pm/7-last D 9.30pm
Additional: Bar food L; Sunday L; Children welcome; ✦ dishes
Seats: 60. Private dining room 12

A delightful Georgian building on the west side of the city, Bath Priory markets itself as a thoroughly English experience; a stay here successfully combines the beauty of the surrounding countryside with the sophistication of this classical city. However, it is the standard of cooking served in the small, luxurious dining room that grabbed our inspector's attention. Overlooking the hotel's stunning gardens, a summer meal might start with warm salad of sautéed monk fish, or perhaps mille-feuille of pan-fried calves' liver with apricot chutney. Our inspector enjoyed a starter of first-rate scallops, pan-fried and served with asparagus, tagliatelle and a robust lobster sauce. This was followed by top-quality loin of veal, served with Savoy cabbage, speck and morel sauce. Dessert was a classical apple tart with honey ice cream and lime and vanilla syrup. The meal was finished off with loose-leaf tea, brandy snaps and dark chocolate truffles.

Directions: At the top of Park Lane, on W side of Victoria Park, turn L into Weston Rd; 300 yds on L

BATH, Bath Spa ❀❀

Sydney Road BA2 6JF
Map 3: ST76
Tel: 01225 444424
Fax: 01225 444006
Chef: Jonathan Fraser
Cost: *Alc* £35, fixed-price D £35. H/wine £18.50
Times: Noon-last L 2pm/6.30-last D 10pm
Additional: Sunday L; Children welcome; ❹ dishes
Seats: 70. Private dining room 100
Smoking: No smoking in dining room; Air conditioning
Accommodation: 98 en suite
Credit cards: ▆ ▆ ▆ ▆ ▆ ▆ ▆

An imposing Georgian building set in immaculately maintained gardens overlooking the city. Guests have a choice of where to eat. In the Vellore Restaurant, a former ballroom, gutsy, elaborate dishes are served by a well-drilled team of smiling staff. Our inspector sampled a risotto of spinach, field mushrooms, goats' cheese and pesto, followed by a simple fillet of lamb with rich thyme sauce. In 'Alfresco', the more informal of the hotel's restaurants, the cooking is more eclectic, with influences from the Far East and the Med spicing up traditional British dishes. Look out for main courses such as grilled polenta with ricotta, yogurt and coriander, and Thai green chicken with haricot vert, rice and crispy noodles. There are also a number of 'hot summer salads': try sesame-battered chicken breast with lemon, ginger and coriander. Desserts include baked caramel custard laced with Grand Marnier; and brandy snaps filled with fresh strawberry Chantilly.

Directions: From A4 turn L onto A36 Warminster, R at mini roundabout and pass fire station, turn L into Sydney Place

BATH, Cliffe Hotel ❀

An elegant Regency country house hotel with a stylish dining room overlooking the Avon valley. Typical dishes are giant mussels poached in white wine and served in saffron sauce, and lamb en croûte with leek and mustard crumble. The vegetarian menu might include stuffed roast peppers, and mushroom tagliatelle.

Accommodation: 11 en suite
Credit cards: ▆ ▆ ▆ ▆ ▆ ▆ JCB

Directions: From A36 take B3108 (Bradford-on-Avon), turn R before rail bridge, to Limpley Stoke. Hotel on brow of hill

Crowe Hill Limpley Stoke BA3 6HY
Map 3: ST76
Tel: 01225 723226
Fax: 01225 723871
Chef: Trevor Faithfull
Owners: John Hawken, Carol Nottage
Cost: *Alc* £24, fixed-price L £12.75.
☺ H/wine £9.95
Times: Last L 2pm/last D 9.30pm
Additional: Bar food; Sunday L; Children welcome; ❹ dishes
Smoking: No smoking in dining room

BATH, **Clos du Roy** ❀❀

Bang in the middle of town and handy for pre or post-theatre dining, Clos du Roy is appropriately decorated in a musical theme including a white baby grand in the middle of the room. French staff bring French food from the French chef and you can choose from the short but good-value set menu, or the more extensive *carte*. Starters include onion tarte Tatin with pan-fried foie gras and a honey and red wine sauce, or tomato and basil consommé with pesto ravioli. Main-course saddle of rabbit features two legs, plenty of chanterelles and a good sauce; there are also daily-changing fish main courses based on what's good at market. The assiette of desserts shows good flavour but could do with a better variety of textures. The interesting wine list is helpfully set out by wine style – light and dry, full and fruity etc. – and this consideration extends to the choice of house red, an excellent Bordeaux for just £2.95 per glass.

1 Seven Dials Saw Close
BA1 2EN
Map 3: ST76
Tel: 01225 444450
Fax: 01225 404044
Chef: François Gardilloux
Owner: Phillipe Roy
Cost: *Alc* £24, fixed-price L £12.85/D £19.50. ☺ H/wine £9.85
Times: Noon-last L 2.15pm/6-last D 10.30pm
Additional: Sunday L; No children under 8; ❀ dishes
Seats: 90. Jacket & tie preferred
Smoking: No-smoking area; No pipes & cigars
Credit cards: ▨ ▨ ▨ ▨ ▨ ▨ JCB

Directions: Next to Theatre Royal

BATH, **Combe Grove Manor** ❀

Elegant 18th-century manor house-cum-leisure hotel enjoying stunning views over beautiful countryside. Stylishly furnished, it offers a choice of two restaurants, the informal Manor Vaults Bistro and the Georgian Restaurant. Menus in the latter may feature wild mushroom soup, and medallions of beef with garlic confit and a red wine and shallot sauce.

Brassknocker Hill
Monkton Combe BA2 7HS
Map 3: ST76
Tel: 01225 834644
Fax: 01255 834961
Chef: Martin Horsley
Owner: Jack Chia MPH Ltd
Cost: *Alc* £40, fixed-price L £18.50/D £25. H/wine £14
Times: Last L 2.30pm/last D 9.30pm
Additional: Bar food; Sunday L; No children under 7; ❀ dishes
Smoking: No smoking in dining room
Accommodation: 40 en suite
Credit cards: ▨ ▨ ▨ ▨ ▨ ▨ ▨ JCB

Directions: A4 from Bristol to roundabout (Newton St Loe), 2nd exit for Combe Down (5 miles). At Combe Down continue for 1.5 miles, hotel entrance on R

BATH, The Hole in the Wall Restaurant ❀❀

16 George Street BA1 2EH
Map 3: ST76
Tel/Fax: 01225 425242
Chef: Eric Lepine
Owners: Chris & Gunna Chown
Cost: *Alc* £26, fixed-price L £11.50/D £16.50. ☺ H/wine £11
Times: Noon-last L 2pm/6-last D 11pm. Closed Sun
Additional: Children welcome; ❸ dishes
Seats: 70
Smoking: No-smoking area; Air conditioning
Credit cards: ▆ ▆ ▆ ▆ ▆

Although both dining rooms are hung with original artwork, each creates a different mood – one with wooden tables and plaid upholstery, the other more upbeat. The restaurant still holds a revered place in the history of 20th-century British cooking; these days it is less a pioneer, more a follower of fashion. Raviolo of prawns and sweet potato in a chilli and coriander broth, and roast chump of lamb with mild spices and aubergine couscous are in tune with current ideas, though there's a nod to the past with roast breast of duck a l'orange and crêpes Suzette. More innovative dishes include potted pig's tongue and wild rabbit with piccalilli, and seared fillet of sturgeon with caviar and vodka sauce.

Directions: Town centre. George Street is at top end of Milsom Street

BATH, The Moody Goose ❀❀❀

7A Kingsmead Square BA1 2AB
Map 3: ST76
Tel/Fax: 01225 466688
Chefs: Stephen Shore, Andy Blackburn
Owners: Stephen & Victoria Shore
Cost: *Alc* £27, fixed-price L £10 (2 courses)/D £20. ☺ H/wine £10.50
Times: Noon-2pm/6pm-9.30pm (10pm Sat). Closed Sun, 2 wks Feb, Bhs (except 25 Dec)
Additional: No children under 7; ❸ dishes
Seats: 30. Private dining room 8
Smoking: No smoking in dining room
Credit cards: ▆ ▆ ▆ ▆ ▆ ▆

The namesake pottery goose keeps broody guard, like a querulous Parisian concierge, between the two loos. The decor has been done with bags of style, if not much money, but the effect is remarkable. Once through the unprepossessing basement entrance, there's a spacious bar with understated, modern seating and up-to-date glossy mags; the dining-room proper has cool, whitewashed walls and a low vaulted ceiling, white china, crisp linen and fresh flowers. The food is in that modern English style that can sometimes be called confusion cooking, but here reflects inquiring minds, a light touch and good local ingredients. The two chefs, Stephen Shore and Andy Blackburn, clearly work in harmony to offer dishes such as baked goats' cheese with caramelised beetroot and watercress, or feuilleté of pan-fried lambs' kidneys, chicken livers and tomato with sherry and grain mustard, and honey-roasted supreme of Deben duck with ginger, shallots and redcurrant sauce. Presentation is refined; note a pressed terrine of duck confit, roasted pear and Parma ham with balsamic vinegar that tasted as simple and elegant as it looked. A main course of black bream with ratatouille (with every ingredient separate, rather than a deep melding of flavours) and rösti, proved to be spanking fresh fish. Those looking for goose on the menu are most likely to find it in metaphorical form, as the Moody Goose Gâteau, a house speciality of layers of sponge, meringue and chocolate ganache studded with griottine cherries and served with a violet cream. A square of shortbread is served with coffee – an off-note which our inspector thought made it feel like teatime.

Signature dishes: Boudin of saddle of rabbit, confit leg, sundried tomatoes and wild mushrooms; ragout of lobster, baby onions and veal jus; roasted partridge with a compote of blueberries and raspberry vinegar; parfait of foie gras and Sauternes jelly

Directions: *Telephone for directions*

BATH, No 5 Bistro ❀❀

No 5 Bistro continues to excel. Ideal for lunch or dinner, it offers an intimate charm and warm welcome. The daily and regular menus proclaim that all food is cooked to order and our inspector's chicken breast with mushrooms, tarragon and garlic was found to be perfectly done. Good, too, were the gamey venison rissoles, and a Far-East inspired combination of duck, fresh pineapple, lemon grass, coconut milk, coriander and chilli. The puddings will not disappoint; try the rhubarb brûlée with rice pudding, the bite of the fruit complementing the sweet, buttery rice. With your meal, ask for the local Batheaston white wine, admired for its big nose and fruity flavour, or one of the interesting bottled beers. Afterwards, there's good espresso. On Monday and Tuesday evenings you are invited to bring your own wine – no corkage charged. Wednesday nights are dedicated to a 'Fish Feast' featuring all manner of seafood.

5 Argyle Street BA2 4BA
Map 3: ST76
Tel: 01225 444499
Fax: 01225 318668
Chefs: Stephen Smith, Paul Hearne
Owners: Stephen Smith, Charles Home
Cost: *Alc* £22. ☺ H/wine £8.95.
Times: Noon-last L 2.30pm/6.30pm-last D 10pm (11pm Sat). Closed Sun, L Mon, 1 wk Xmas
Additional: Children welcome, 🍴 dishes
Seats: 35
Smoking: No smoking in dining room
Credit cards: ▬ ▬ ▬ ▢ ▬ ◖ ▣

Directions: 30 yds from Pulteney Bridge towards Laura Place

BATH, The Olive Tree at The Queensberry Hotel ❀❀

Lovingly restored, the Bath-stone townhouse is only a few minutes walk from the city centre. The Olive Tree Restaurant, up-market Tuscan rather than Georgian in style, has a strong local following and hotel residents need to book in advance, especially at weekends. The cooking is modern English with strong Med overtones, and the menu, with its pretty wash illustrations, reads temptingly: chargrilled monkfish, pepperonata and basil dressing; grilled fillet of John Dory, fried leeks, saffron

Russel Street BA1 2QF
Map 3: ST76
Tel: 01225 447928
Fax: 01225 446065
Chef: Mathew Prowse
Owners: Stephen & Penny Ross
Cost: *Alc* £30, fixed-price L £14.50/D £21. ☺ H/wine £11.50.
Times: Noon-last L 2pm/7pm-last D 10pm. Closed Sun L, 1wk Xmas

The Olive Tree at
The Queensberry Hotel

risotto; Poulet Noir grilled with asparagus and tarragon cream. Salmon and avocado bruschetta opened our inspection meal, went on to an interesting dish of hake with chorizo and rocket, and finished with chocolate and pistachio parfait. Other dessert choices might be warm coconut and mango tarte, or terrine of white chocolate with orange and strawberries.

Additional: Children welcome; ☺ dishes
Seats: 50. Private dining room 40
Smoking: No smoking in dining room; Air conditioning
Accommodation: 29 en suite
Credit cards: ▬ ▩ ▼ ⌐ ▣

Directions: 100 yds north of Assembly Rooms in Lower Lansdown

AA Shortlisted for *Wine Award*-see page 16

BATH, **Restaurant Lettonie** ❀❀❀❀

'At last we have found a suitable setting for our family and guests – a lovely Georgian house with lovely views', writes Siân Blunos. It's all very different to the cramped Bristol restaurant. The Blunos' have moved lock, stock and barrel to the outskirts of Bath. The new premises have substantial grounds, five splendid bedrooms, and a spacious restaurant. Service is overseen by Siân with a bevy of French staff. Martin Blunos' food is a curious combination of simple concepts, extravagant twists but frugal attitudes, Eastern European rusticity, and the occasional lightness of touch; in other words, his cooking style is really quite unique. Appetisers here are almost always little pies, either fish or meat, a neat idea, and when we inspected proved to be a good salmon and sole pie with a light dill sauce. Next came a gleaming bowl of sherried rabbit consommé, filled with dice of rabbit and green cabbage leaves and accompanied by croque-en-bouche of foie gras – a delightful parody of the French wedding cake in that the little cone parfait of foie gras was covered in the tiniest choux dripping with a little veal jus – the combination of the two was masterful. Assiette of duck came with the breast pink and sliced in two, the leg stuffed and presented as a sausage, and confit. Each component was served on a purée of compatible veg: carrot, celeriac, parsnip. The pre-dessert was a real cracker – it looked exactly like a boiled egg with toasted soldiers, but was in fact an egg shell filled with vanilla cream and mango purée, with biscuit soldiers. Dessert proper was a light, hot toffee pudding with a really good, bitter caramel sauce with small spoonfuls of mascarpone of the side.

35 Kelston Road BA1 3QH
Map 3: ST76
Tel: 01225 446676
Fax: 01225 447541
Chef: Martin Blunos
Owners: Siân & Martin Blunos
Cost: Fixed-price L £25/D £44. ☺
H/wine £14
Times: Closed Sun, Mon
Additional: Children welcome
Smoking: No smoking in dining room
Accommodation: 5 en suite
Credit cards: ▬ ▩ ▼ ⌐ ▩ ▣ ▣

Directions: 2 miles from Bath on A431 Bilton Road

BATH, **Royal Crescent Hotel**

16 Royal Crescent BA1 2LS
Map 3: ST76
Tel: 01225 823333
Fax: 01225 339401
Chef: Steven Blake
Cost: Fixed-price D £42.
H/wine £19.50
Times: Brasserie: L 12.30-2pm/D 7-
10pm (10.30pm Fri, Sat). Pimpernels
D only Tue-Sat, 7-9.30pm.
Closed beginning of Jan
Smoking: No smoking in dining room;
Air conditioning
Accommodation: 45 en suite
Credit cards: ▇ ▇ ▇ ▇ ▇ ▇ ▇

Directions: In city centre follow signs
to Royal Crescent

Discreetly placed in the centre of John Wood's masterpiece of
Georgian architecture, the Royal Crescent is an exemplary
hotel. There are two separate restaurants. Pimpernels, a small,
intimate room in the main house, is the showcase for some
individualistic cooking from Steven Blake, based on
imaginative blends of quality produce and East-meets-West
herbs and spices. He also overseas the Brasserie and Bar which
occupies the pretty Dower House in the garden, where Mark
Bradbury leads a team in offering a short set-menu, plus a
carte ,with a strong Mediterranean slant. Dinner in Pimpernels
got off to an upbeat start with *amuse-bouche* of spicy cabbage,
pork satay and crab ravioli, and the kitchen kept up the pace
throughout. First course was a light langoustine tempura,
followed by a simple but effective dish of lobster with shellfish
sauce, a hint of vanilla, and brown rice wrapped in cabbage,
then an unusual, perfectly done pre-dessert of a vivid green
crème brûlée of mint and sweet basil topped with tomato
concasse, followed by a banana soufflé of 'really good flavour'
with caramel ice cream. Timing and technique are spot-on, this
is cooking that is really moving forward. In The Brasserie
dishes such as red mullet escabeche on a cod brandade dressed
with orange, chilli, ginger and coriander oil, pigeon breast set
on truffled risotto and spinach leaves with a slice of foie gras
and accompanied by a pungent reduction of juices, and a
tartlet of crisp rhubarb pastry offset by a smooth ginger ice
cream are equally memorable – this is strong cooking.

BATH, **Tilleys Bistro**   ＮＥＷ

3 North Parade Passage
BA1 1NX
Map 3: ST76
Tel: 01225 484200
Chef: Dave Mott
Owners: Dave & Dawn Mott
Cost: *Alc* £17. Fixed-price L £6.90/D
£16.50. ☺ H/wine £8.90
Times: Last L 2.30pm/last D 11pm.
Closed Sun L, 5 days over Xmas
Additional: Children welcome;
❹ dishes
Smoking: No-smoking area
Credit cards: ▇ ▇ ▇ ▇ JCB

*Restaurant on two floors – the basement is the largest, with
flagstones, a stone staircase and two inglenook fireplaces. There's a
choice of menus, one exclusively vegetarian, with choices taking in
coquilles Saint-Jacques, spaghetti with chicken livers, smoked bacon,
chilli and garlic, and an avocado and Roquefort gratin.*

Directions: In the centre of Bath, 200 metres S of Bath Abbey in
a pedestrian passageway

BATH, **Woods Restaurant**

9-13 Alfred Street BA1 2QX
Map 3: ST76
Tel: 01225 314812
Fax: 01225 443146
Please telephone for further details

Three inter-connecting rooms with an informal café-style bar
at one end, wooden floors, high ceilings, smallish tables and
wicker-backed chairs make up Woods Restaurant. The menu,
now in print rather than on a blackboard, is short and to the

point, with a well-balanced selection. Lunch is a bargain ('and they are not skimpy portions, either'). Chicken liver parfait with home-made chutney, red sea bream with a Pernod, herb and cream sauce, and duck in a soy and sherry-based sauce, with apple and blueberry tart, and hot chocolate pudding with a mint crème anglaise show something of the style.

Directions: Opposite the Assembly Rooms

BECKINGTON, **Woolpack Inn**

Bath BA3 6SP
Map 3: ST85
Tel: 01373 831244
Fax: 01373 831223
Chefs: Jason Schroeder, Ashley James
Owner: Old English Pub Co plc
Cost: Alc £25. H/wine £9.95
Times: Noon-last L 2.30pm/7-last D 9.30pm
Additional: Bar food; Sunday L; Children welcome; ✿ dishes
Seats: 40. Private dining room 18
Smoking: No-smoking area; No pipes & cigars
Accommodation: 12 en suite
Credit cards: 💳 💳 💳 💳 💳 💳

Beckington was mentioned in the Doomsday Book, but the Woolpack's history is a little shorter: it dates from the 16th century, with beams and flagstones to prove it. Yet the conservatory-style dining room brings a touch of the Med to the traditional old England look, with simple terracotta walls and lively, up-to-date cooking. Menus are built around fresh produce, much of it local. Pâtés, fresh fish, and vegetables have all been praised, and puddings are memorable. Breakfasts, too, are worth dreaming about.

Directions: Village centre. Beckington recently by-passed. On A36 (Bath – Southampton) near junction with A361.

BRENT KNOLL,
Woodlands Hotel ✿✿

Hill Lane TA9 4DF
Map 3: ST35
Tel/Fax: 01278 760232
Please telephone for further details

This is a great little hotel that is fast gaining a reputation as the place to stay in the area. Bernadette Gibson is a natural running front of house. Her husband, Keith, has a down-to-earth approach, cooks with flair and imagination but has not lost sight of the importance of quality ingredients. This honest style translates as spiced chicken satay served on Italian bread with a creamy sauce; herb-crusted rack of lamb with a well-judged sauce flavoured with sun-dried tomatoes; good vegetables cooked to perfection; and spiced pear with cinnamon ice cream showing great pastry work in an accompanying tuile biscuit. Daily specials supplement the carte, and canapés, petits fours, and the good locally baked bread, show laudable attention to minor details.

Directions: From A38 take 1st turn L into village, then 5th turn R into Church Lane, 1st L into Hill Lane; hotel on R at 250yds

BRUTON, **Truffles Restaurant**

We wouldn't be surprised if many a romantic question were popped over Truffles own gâteau – layers of sponge, chocolate mousse and meringue, served with bitter chocolate sauce. The atmosphere of this little candle-lit, restaurant is tailor-made for intimate moments, assuming parties concerned still have the strength after an excellent dinner of, say, hot game mousse with chestnuts, cranberries and Madeira sauce, and fillet of pork with pancetta jacket, roasted with porcini mushroom stuffing and served with Calvados sauce. The menu changes monthly – March included fillets of whiting with a scampi centre wrapped in nori seaweed and deep-fried in a tempura batter with an oriental sauce, and a tranche of calves' liver on a bed of polenta mash with a lime and sage jus. A midweek supper menu (which needs to be pre-booked) is good value at £12.95. Look out for various themed evenings.

95 High Street BA10 0AR
Map 3: ST63
Tel/Fax: 01749 812255
Chef: Martin Bottrill
Owners: Denise & Martin Bottrill
Cost: Fixed-price L £13.95/D £22.50.
☺ H/wine £9.95.
Times: D only, 7pm-last D 9pm.
Closed D Sun, Mon, 2wks Feb
Additional: Sunday L (Noon-2pm);
No children under 5; dishes
Seats: 22
Smoking: No pipes & cigars
Credit cards: ▬ ▬ ▧

Directions: Bruton centre, at start of one-way system, on L

CASTLE CARY, **The George Hotel**

Market Place BA7 7AH
Map 3: ST63
Tel: 01963 350761
Fax: 01963 350035
Chef: Martin J Barrett
Owners: Sue & Greg Sparkes
Cost: Alc £23, fixed price L £ 11.95.
☺ H/wine £9
Times: Last L 2pm/last D 9pm.
Closed 27 Dec
Additional: Bar food; Sunday L;
Children welcome; dishes
Smoking: No smoking in dining room
Accommodation: 14 en suite
Credit cards: ▬ ▬ ▧ ▱ ▬

Food is honest home-cooking, making much of fresh local ingredients, at this 15th-century inn with a distinctive thatched roof. Cheddar cheese filo with red onion chutney plus a sweet basil and tomato sauce, Somerset lamb loin, and local honey and saffron crème brûlée and home-made shortbread whirls, are typical dishes from the dinner menu.

Directions: From A303 take A371 at Wincanton to Castle Cary. Centre of town

DULVERTON, **Ashwick House**

Prepare to be pampered at Richard Sherwood's small Edwardian hotel on the edge of Exmoor. The daily changing set menu, with choice at starter and pudding only, offers the likes of Roquefort cheese mousse, boned local quail in a filo pastry basket, fillet of lemon sole Veronique, leek bake, and a rich rum and chocolate torte for dessert.

Accommodation: 6 en suite
Credit cards: None

TA22 9QD
Map 3: SS92
Tel/Fax: 01398 323868
Chef/Owner: R Sherwood
Cost: Fixed-price D £21.50
(4 courses). ☺ H/wine £10.25
Times: D only, 7.15-8.30pm
Additional: Sunday L (12.30-1.45pm);
No children under 8; dishes
Smoking: No smoking in dining room

Directions: From M5/J27 follow signs to Dulverton, then take B3223 Lynton road and turn L after second cattle grid

DUNSTER, **Exmoor House Hotel**

Antiques and fine pictures are a feature of this tranquil restaurant overlooking the Lion Courtyard. The Garden Room is candlelit at night, elegantly complementing the early Georgian building. Imaginative, freshly prepared dishes are offered at dinner, with a choice of starter and pudding and a set fish and main course.

Accommodation: 6 en suite. **Credit cards:** ▬ ▬ ▬ ▬ ▬ JCB

Directions: To Dunster on A396, off High Street, 75yds from church

12 West Street TA24 6SN
Map 3: SS94
Tel: 01643 821268
Fax: 01643 821267
Chef: Karan Howell
Owners: David & Karan Howell
Cost: Fixed-price D £24.50
(4 courses). ☺ H/wine £7.95
Times: D only, last D 8pm
Additional: Bar food L;
No children under 12; ✪ dishes
Smoking: No smoking in dining room

EXEBRIDGE, **Anchor Inn Hotel**

Charming inn featured in Blackmore's Lorna Doone, set beside the River Exe and close to Exmoor National Park. The Riverside Restaurant offers freshly prepared dishes from both set and carte menus, which make extensive use of local fish and game.

Directions: M5/J27, through Tiverton to Exebridge

Dulverton TA22 9AZ
Map 3: SS92
Tel: 01398 323433
Fax: 01398 323808
Please telephone for further details.

EXFORD, **Crown Hotel**

Park Street TA24 7PP
Map 3: SS83
Tel: 01643 831554
Fax: 01643 831665
Chef: Eric Bouchet
Owners: Michael Bradley, John Atkin
Cost: Alc £30, fixed price D £27.50.
H/wine £10.50
Times: Noon-last L 2pm/7-last
D 9.30pm
Additional: Bar food; Sunday L;
Children welcome; ✪ dishes
Seats: 34. Private room 16
Smoking: No-smoking area;
No pipes & cigars
Accommodation: 17 en suite
Credit cards: ▬ ▬ ▬ ▬ ▬ ▬ JCB

Set by a picturesque village green in Exmoor, this 17th-century coaching inn combines the functions of smart country hotel, well-appointed restaurant, and convivial village pub. A new chef has taken charge, but the menu still boasts carefully sourced ingredients and modern eclectic cooking. Bar meals are excellent and include several light starter-or-main-course meals, such as twice-baked cheese soufflé with salad, plus more substantial dishes of braised shoulder of Exmoor lamb with pearl barley, for instance, and fillet of cod with bubble-and-squeak. Several meals taken in the restaurant this year have singled out for praise fresh skate tempura atop crushed garlic mash, with squid tentacles and olive oil; ravioli with langoustine and sole filling with mussels and basil liquor; a 'quite delicious' roasted partridge served off the bone with a robust jus, roasted root vegetables and a light celeriac mousse; Gressingham duck breast with minted tagliatelli and strawberry sauce. Lavish praise, too, for the choice of West Country cheeses. Banana parfait with a crisp tuile and chocolate ice cream, or chocolate pavé with candied carrots precedes coffee and sweetbreads. The wine list is serious but not pricy; house champagne at £3.50 a glass is light years away from London pricing.

Directions: Village centre facing the green

FARRINGTON GURNEY,

Country Ways Hotel ✿

The dining room of Janet and Gareth Richards' small country hotel is quiet and romantic with a homely atmosphere. The half-dozen choices at each stage of Janet's dinner menu might include carrot and coriander soup with herb dumpling, salmon hollandaise, Gressingham duck with orange and redcurrant sauce, and apple dumpling. Good house wine.

Accommodation: 6 en suite. **Credit cards:** 🟥 ▦

Directions: From village take A362 to Midsomer Norton, then 1st R into Marsh Lane. Hotel next to Farrington Golf Club

Marsh Lane BS18 5TT
Map 3: ST65
Tel: 01761 452449
Fax: 01761 452709
Chef: Janet Richards
Owners: Janet & Gareth Richards
Cost: *Alc* £24. ☺ H/wine £8.50
Times: L by prior arrangement/D 7pm-8.45pm. Closed Sun, 1 wk Xmas
Additional: ⓪ dishes
Smoking: No smoking in dining room

FROME, **Talbot Inn Restaurant** ✿

Coaching inn dating from the 15th century. The popular, hop-strewn, oak beamed restaurant offers soundly cooked dishes that range from fresh shellfish bisque with spicy chilli rouille, roasted rack of local lamb with garlic sauce, and pot-roasted local rabbit with grain mustard sauce, to steaks and pies.

Mells BA11 3PN
Map 3: ST74
Tel: 01373 812254
Fax: 01373 813599
Chef: Mark Jones
Owner: Roger Elliot
Cost: *Alc* £16. ☺ H/wine £7.50
Times: Last L 2pm/last D 9.30pm. Closed 25-26 Dec
Additional: Bar food L; Sunday L; Children welcome; ⓪ dishes
Smoking: No-smoking area
Accommodation: 7 en suite
Credit cards: 🟥 ▦ 🟥 🟥 🟥

Directions: From M5/J23, follow Wells & Shepton Mallet towards Frome. Before Frome turn L to Mells.

HINTON CHARTERHOUSE,

Homewood Park

Bath BA3 6BB
Map 3: ST75
Tel: 01225 723731
Fax: 01225 723820
Chef: Andrew Harmer

Shortly before we went to press we learned that four AA Rosetted chef Gary Jones had left Homewood Park for Cliveden

(see entry, Buckinghamshire), and has been replaced by his sous chef of two years, Andrew Hamer. No rosettes this year, as we felt it was early days to assess Andrew's cooking fairly. But all indications are that standards will be maintained, and to give an idea, this is what we found at our last meal under the previous regime:

Patrolled by nothing more threatening than a flock of Jacob sheep, this pretty but unassuming Georgian house gives little hint of the bounty to be found within. Interiors are bright and stylish, service is cheerfully precise, but the real flashes of brilliance emanate from the kitchen. The cooking is out of the top drawer, and it is worth taking the eight-course tasting menu in order to sample the full range of masterly talents in a variety of dishes based on classical foundations but fizzing with inspiration. Even our most seasoned inspectors have been taken aback by a magic twist to a seemingly straightforward dish. Not that this is exhibitionist cooking; technique, flair and enterprise are judiciously deployed, there is little meaningless embellishment and the effort is directed at pleasing the palate rather than impressing with fripperies. The skill, though, is apparent enough – pig's trotter with sweetbreads and black pudding is closer to the peasantish style of Pierre Koffman's original than Marco Pierre White's lighter version, but the flawless execution is worthy of either. There are numerous signs that the kitchen recognises the value of paring down a dish to the essentials and the dessert menu offers a number of examples. Tiramisu may be seriously over-played on the nation's menus by now, but like a correctly used cliché, this version is a reminder of why the thing came into being. Peripheries are taken seriously; both canapés and petits fours are well-manicured and to the point (a miniature tarte au citron being a classic example), and breads are inspired. The wine list offers some reliable growers in France and some good claret vintages, particularly in half-bottles.

Owners: Fentum-Gueuning Families
Cost: *Alc* £45, fixed-price L £21/D £52 (7 courses). H/wine £15
Times: Noon-1.30pm/7-9.30pm
Additional: Bar food; Sunday L; Children welcome; ⅃ dishes
Seats: 60. Private dining room
Smoking: No smoking in dining room
Accommodation: 19 en suite
Credit cards: JCB

Directions: 5 miles south-east of Bath off A36, turning marked Sharpstone

HOLFORD, **Combe House Hotel** ❀

Enjoying a peaceful location, deep in the heart of the Quantocks, this charming 17th-century house, formerly a tannery, offers a friendly, relaxed atmosphere and a short, fixed-price menu focusing on fresh produce. Dinner could include hearty mushroom soup, Victorian chicken pie, and hazelnut meringue, all rounded off by an imaginative cheeseboard.

Accommodation: 16 en suite
Credit cards:

Directions: M5/J24 (A39 Bridgwater) towards Minehead. Turn L up lane between Holford Garage and Plough Inn

Nr Bridgwater TA5 1RZ
Map 3: ST14
Tel: 01278 741382
Fax: 01278 741322
Chef: Lynn Gardner
Owners: Mr J N & Mrs S D Page
Cost: *Alc* £18.75. ☺ H/wine £7.95
Times: Last L 2pm/last D 8.30pm
Additional: Bar food L; Children welcome; ⅃ dishes
Smoking: No smoking in dining room

HUNSTRETE,
Hunstrete House Hotel ❀❀❀

The 18th-century house stands in a 92-acre estate of park and woodland that can only be described as a haven of peace and tranquillity. Stewart Eddy comes with impeccable credentials: junior sous chef at Lucknam Park, sous chef at Le Manoir aux Quat'Saisons, and at Gidleigh Park under Michael Caines. Suffice to say that he has been classically trained and is able to mobilise all the necessary techniques. The freshness and

Pensford
BS39 4NS
Map 3: ST66
Tel: 01761 490490
Fax: 01761 490732
Chef: Stewart Eddy
Owners: Mr & Mrs M Fentum
Cost: *Alc* £45, fixed price L £19.50/D £55 (8 courses). H/wine £14.95

Hunstrete House Hotel

Times: Noon-last L 2pm/7-last D 9.30pm
Additional: Sunday L; Children welcome; 🍴 dishes
Seats: 60. Private room 25
Smoking: No smoking in dining room
Accommodation: 23 en suite
Credit cards: 💳 💳 💳 💳 💳 💳 💳

quality of ingredients is of prime importance and an April dinner reported enthusiastically on sensitive and accurate cooking. A complimentary starter set the tone: smooth spinach and watercress soup with a truffle-flavoured poached quail's egg. Next came foie gras, fried perfectly with a light crust and creamy within, layered with red cabbage and potato cakes. The main course was two new season's lamb cutlets accompanied by some shredded cabbage, broad beans, fine beans and a light lamb jus lifted by thinly sliced lamb's kidney. Pudding was an Arabic espresso coffee ice cream served with a light mocha cream. Breads are made on the premises, canapés are superb: deep-fried turbot with tartare sauce, salmon tartare en croûte, smooth chicken parfait and crisply fried vegetables on our visit, and petits fours keep up the high note.

Directions: On A368 – 8 miles from Bath

Signature dishes: Best end of Wiltshire lamb, a sauté of its kidney and sweetbreads provençale with a simple lamb jus; Trelough duck with pak choi, tomato confit and a ginger-scented sauce; potage of oysters, mussels and cockles with fine herbs and sevruga caviar; fillet of beef with a red wine sauce and a tarragon sabayon.

MINEHEAD, Periton Park Hotel ✿✿

Middlecombe TA24 8SW
Map 3: SS94
Tel/Fax: 01643 706885
Chef: Angela Hunt
Owners: Richard & Angela Hunt
Cost: Fixed-price D £22.50 (4 courses). ☺ H/wine £8.50
Times: D only, 7-last D 9pm.
Closed Jan
Additional: No children under 12; 🍴 dishes
Seats: 24. Private dining room 14
Smoking: No smoking in dining room
Accommodation: 8 en suite
Credit cards: 💳 💳 💳 💳 💳 JCB

Periton Park's dining room, part-panelled and done out in autumnal shades, has a double aspect with views over the grounds. This was the billiard room when the house was built in Victorian times. Have an aperitif in front of the log fire in the comfortable drawing room before dinner of three courses, with a well-balanced choice of around half-a-dozen starters and slightly more main courses. Blinis and vodka sauce are an interesting spin on traditional smoked salmon, while a sauce of ginger, garlic and tomatoes with red mullet has hints of influences from even further east, as does an Indian-style spicy mango sauce that comes with a main course of pan-cooked halibut. There could also be loin of Somerset lamb on an onion soubise, pan-fried Exmoor venison with a bramble glaze, and medallions of monkfish in a herby sauce of white wine and tomatoes. The two house white wines are from a Somerset vineyard; the third, a red, is a vin de pays.

Directions: Off A39 signposted Porlock & Lynmouth. Hotel about 1 mile on left

MONTACUTE,
Kings Arms Inn Hotel ❀❀

The 16th-century inn built of local Hamstone, in one of Somerset's most picturesque and unspoilt villages, has a strong local following. The menu is short modern and well-balanced. Poached quails' eggs with a warm red wine jus and continental salad, and pithiviers of fish mousse on a pool of tomato and leek butter, might precede pan-fried venison steak with baby vegetables and juniper sauce or chargrilled sea bass on a tower of ratatouille. There is always a special fish of the day choice, and a good selection of fresh vegetables. The richness of a good, bitter chocolate-flavoured torte was nicely undercut by the sharpness of a cherry coulis. Cona coffee, however, could be improved upon.

Directions: Take A3088 roundabout off A303; inn is in village centre, next to church

Bishopstow TA15 6UU
Map 3: ST41
Tel: 01935 822513
Fax: 01935 826549
Chef: Michael Stone
Owner: Old English Inns & Hotels
Cost: *Alc* £21, fixed-price L £12.50 (2 courses)/D £15.50 (2 courses). ☺
Times: Noon-last L 2pm/7pm-last D 9pm. Closed D Sun
Additional: Bar food; Sunday L; Children welcome; ❀ dishes
Seats: 45. Private dining room 19
Smoking: No smoking in dining room
Accommodation: 15 en suite
Credit cards:

NAILSEA,
Sweet Bartley's Bistro ❀

2 King's Hill BS19 2AU
Map 3: ST47
Tel: 01275 858348
Chef: Philippe Descailleux
Owner: Gillian Howard
Cost: H/wine £7.25. ☺
Times: D only, 6.30-last D 10.30pm. Closed D Sun, Mon, seasonal & Bhs
Additional: Sunday L; Children welcome; ❀ dishes
Smoking: No-smoking area
Credit cards: ▒ ▒ ▒ ▒ ▒ ▒

Casual, bistro-style neighbourhood restaurant, with blackboard menus, whitewashed walls, and good-value food. Strong Med influences of pesto and garlic, but otherwise leek and potato soup, crab and avocado mousse, duck breast with Madeira sauce, guinea fowl saltimbocca with artichokes, apples, juniper and spices, and classic crème brûlée.

Directions: In old village near West End shopping precinct

NUNNEY,
The George at Nunney ✤

An 18th-century hotel, inn and restaurant in the centre of the village, with its own dining club offering set meals at a very low price to members. Carte options include fresh Brixham scallops with salmon sauce, and Exmoor venison with cranberries, truffles and port wine sauce.

Additional: Bar food; Sunday L; Children welcome; ❹ dishes
Smoking: No-smoking area; No pipes and cigars
Accommodation: 9 en suite
Credit cards: ▬ ▦ ▰ ⊑ JCB

11 Church Street BA11 4LW
Map 3: ST74
Tel: 01373 836458
Fax: 01373 836565
Chef: Caroline Filder
Owners: D R & M I Page
Cost: *Alc* £20, fixed-price L & D £11.
☺ H/wine £8
Times: Last L 2pm/last D 9pm

Directions: Take A361 Frome to Shepton Mallet road and turn off in village centre, opposite medieval castle

PORLOCK,
The Oaks Hotel ✤✤

From its elevated position this charming Edwardian country house offers distant views of Porlock Bay. Both Tim and Anne Riley cook, in a style described by *Telegraph* reviewer Paddy Burt as 'Delia rather than Rick', which we thought spot-on – it is hugely enjoyable cooking, packed with fresh flavours. Home-made cheese and onion rolls opened a spring dinner on a high note that never faltered. Cream of mushroom soup, tiny haddock mousse served hot, breast of chicken 'which really tasted as it should', served with a lemony hollandaise and garnished with fresh asparagus, and custard tart with nutmeg ice cream, and strawberry and banana hazelnut meringue (we tried both), all elicited praise. There's a sound wine list with a good choice of half-bottles.

Doverhaye TA24 8ES
Map 3: SS84
Tel/Fax: 01643 862265
Chef: Anne Riley
Owners: Tim & Anne Riley
Cost: Fixed-price D £25 (4 courses).
☺ H/wine £10
Times: D only, 7-8.30pm.
Closed Nov-mid Mar
Additional: No children under 8
Seats: 20
Smoking: No smoking in dining room
Accommodation: 9 en suite
Credit cards: ▬ ▦ ▰ ⊑

Directions: At bottom of Dunstersteepe Road, on L, on entering Porlock from Minehead

SHEPTON MALLET,
Bowlish House ✤✤

Housed in a striking 18th-century property on the outskirts of town, the Bowlish House restaurant occupies an equally dramatic room, decorated in pale yellow with crisply clothed, well-appointed tables and proper napkins. It's a busy, yet relaxing place with very friendly service. The fixed-price menu has five or six choices for each course offering well-executed dishes such as garlic mushroom soufflé, double-baked, moist, and finished with cream and Cheddar. Main courses also provide genuine flavours, saddle of lamb, for example, nicely pink, came with good jus and a wealth of vegetables. Pudding, too, was a treat – rich chocolate mousse with stem ginger, garnished with strawberries. It's the details that make a visit here so enjoyable: lovely black olives to start, great smoked salmon appetisers, a fine choice of real cheeses (many local), simple petits fours and a well-annotated, international wine list.

Bowlish BA4 5JD
Map 3: ST64
Tel/Fax: 01749 342022
Chef: Linda Morley
Owners: Bob & Linda Morley
Cost: *Alc* £24.45, fixed-price
D £22.50. ☺ H/wine £9.95
Times: D only, 7-9.30pm.
Closed 1 wk autumn, 1 wk spring
Additional: Sunday L (1st Sun of month); Children welcome; ❹ dishes
Seats: 24
Smoking: No smoking in dining room
Accommodation: 3 en suite
Credit cards: ▬ ▦ ▦

Directions: 0.25 mile from town centre on A371 Wells road

SHEPTON MALLET, **Brottens Lodge** ❀

A 200-year-old gamekeeper's lodge is the setting for this restaurant, sunny by day, candlelit at night. Monthly-changing set-price menus are the vehicles for such dishes as king prawns in tempura with crispy seaweed, followed by rack of lamb with rosemary and redcurrant sauce, then lemon sponge pudding with vanilla sauce.

Additional: Sunday L (once a month); Children welcome; ♨ dishes
Smoking: No smoking in dining room
Accommodation: 4 en suite
Credit cards: ▄▄ ▄▄ ✈ £ ▶

Directions: From Frome take A361 (Shepton Mallet). Turn L after Abby Narn pub – hotel signposted

Doulting BA4 4RB
Map 3: ST64
Tel: 01749 880352
Fax: 01749 880601
Chef: Santa Checkley
Owners: Roger & Santa Checkley
Cost: Alc £22.95, fixed-price L £8.50 (2 courses)/D £17.50. ☺
H/wine £8.95
Times: Last L 2.30pm/last D 9.30pm. Closed L Tue, Fri & Sat, all Sun & Mon

SHEPTON MALLET,
Charlton House Hotel ❀❀❀

As shop windows go, Charlton House has few peers. Owned by the founders of the Mulberry Design Company, the 17th-century house is lavishly decked out with fabrics, furnishings, china and glass from the company's own collection in a rich mix with antiques, paintings and a quirky collection of curios. The theatrical feel is at its height in the drama of the elaborately stencilled dining room which is now the province of new chef Adam Fellows, and early indications are that he and his team will have few problems living up to the surroundings. The menu, like the cooking, is neatly understated, with simple descriptions that are an accurate reflection of a cuisine that concentrates on the main ingredient with sauces and garnishing delicately handled. Many of the raw materials are local – beef from Drewton, ducks from the Quantocks – and there is a welcome philosophy that "second best will not do" in terms of quality. Less than surprising then to find a simple salad of scallops and wild mushrooms utilising the sweetest of shellfish and half-a-dozen carefully chosen fungi on a well-dressed bed of rocket, or rack of lamb offering generously flavoured meat stuffed with a spinach and chicken mousse with roast garlic and a "wonderfully aromatic" basil jus. Also standing out at an early summer visit was a "beautifully constructed" terrine of seafood appetiser, layered and textured with precision and suffering only slightly from being a tad too cold.
Signature Dishes: Sea bream with a light saffron nage, aubergine caviar and fennel confit; mosaic of guinea fowl and duck foie gras, hazelnut oil and aged balsamic vinegar; roast squab pigeon in a cage of puff pastry, juniper berry scented jus.

Charlton Road BA4 4PR
Map 3: ST64
Tel: 01749 342008
Fax: 01749 346362
Chef: Adam Fellows
Owners: Mr & Mrs Roger Saul
Cost: Alc £22, fixed-price L £17/D £30. H/wine £14
Times: 12.30pm-last L 2pm/7.30pm-last D 9.30pm
Additional: Bar meals L; Sunday L; Children welcome; ♨ dishes
Seats: 56. Private dining room 80
Smoking: No smoking in dining room
Accommodation: 17 en suite
Credit cards: ▄▄ ▄▄ ✈ £ ▄▄ ▶ ▣

Directions: M4/J 17, follow A350 S. At Trowbridge join A361. Hotel is located 1 mile before Shepton Mallet on L

SHEPTON MALLET,
Shrubbery Hotel ❀

Formerly a wool merchant's house dated 1770, this intimate dining room with sparkling crystal and period furniture is reminiscent of a gentleman's club. The menu unexpectedly combines Spanish dishes such as sopa de pescado and Catalan mussels with traditional rack of lamb, pan-fried skate with black pepper butter and French apple tart.

Commercial Road
BA4 5BU
Map 3: ST64
Tel: 01749 346671
Fax: 01749 346581
Chefs: Christopher West, Rachel Harris
Owner: Christopher West

Directions: Situated on main A361 through town, near police station

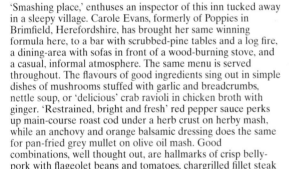

SHEPTON MALLET,

The Three Horseshoes ❀❀ NEW

'Smashing place,' enthuses an inspector of this inn tucked away in a sleepy village. Carole Evans, formerly of Poppies in Brimfield, Herefordshire, has brought her same winning formula here, to a bar with scrubbed-pine tables and a log fire, a dining-area with sofas in front of a wood-burning stove, and a casual, informal atmosphere. The same menu is served throughout. The flavours of good ingredients sing out in simple dishes of mushrooms stuffed with garlic and breadcrumbs, nettle soup, or 'delicious' crab ravioli in chicken broth with ginger. 'Restrained, bright and fresh' red pepper sauce perks up main-course roast cod under a herb crust on herby mash, while an anchovy and orange balsamic dressing does the same for pan-fried grey mullet on olive oil mash. Good combinations, well thought out, are hallmarks of crisp belly-pork with flageolet beans and tomatoes, chargrilled fillet steak on rösti with green pea sauce, and turkey and cranberry crumble. Vegetables are 'fresh and appealing', breads, tomato and olive among them, are moreish, and puddings bring accolades: go for intensely orange burnt cream, as smooth as silk. Sunday lunch sees traditional fare of roast leg of Welsh lamb with mint sauce, weekdays the likes of black pudding with celeriac and apple mash, or steak and kidney pie. Six house wines, all sold by the glass, head up an excellent list.

SHIPHAM,

Daneswood House Hotel ❀❀

Once an Edwardian health hydro, Daneswood House is set amid woods and well-tended gardens, with spectacular views overlooking the Bristol Channel. Food is served in three intimate rooms where the walls are wood-panelled and the china is delicate. There's plenty of choice on the fixed-price menu, which is accompanied by a serious wine list (good house wines and many pricier options). Potted terrine of goose leg confit and foie gras, served with gooseberry compote, might follow canapés. An inspection meal continued with marinated chicken breast on crisp polenta croûte, topped with salsa verde and rich Madeira sauce. The highlight, however, was the

---

Shrubbery Hotel

Cost: Alc £23, fixed-price L £13.95/D £15.95. ☺ H/wine £8.95
Times: Last L 2pm/last D 9pm. Closed D Sun
Additional: Bar food; Sunday L; Children welcome; ❀ dishes
Smoking: No smoking in dining room
Accommodation: 7 en suite
Credit cards: ▆ ▆ ▆ ▆ ▆ ▆ ▆

Shepton Mallet BA4 6HE
Map 3: ST64
Tel: 01749 850359
Fax: 01749 850615
Chef: Carole Evans
Owner: West Country Village Inns Ltd
Cost: Alc £18. ☺ H/wine £9.95
Times: Noon-last L 1.45pm/7-last D 9pm
Additional: Sunday L; Children welcome; ❀ dishes
Seats: 36
Smoking: No smoking in dining room
Credit cards: ▆ ▆ ▆ ▆ ▆ JCB

Directions: 6 miles from Frome off A359

Cuck Hill Winscombe BS25 1RD
Map 3: ST45
Tel: 01934 843145
Fax: 01934 843824
Chefs: Julian Prosser, Heather Matthews
Owners: David & Elise Hodges
Cost: Alc £29.90, fixed-price L £ 12.95/D £27.95. H/wine £9.95
Times: Noon-2pm/7-9.30pm. Closed L Sat, 26 Dec-4 Jan
Additional: Sunday L; Children welcome; ❀ dishes

Daneswood House Hotel

Seats: 50. Private dining room 8-30
Smoking: No smoking in dining room
Accommodation: 12 en suite
Credit cards: ▆ ▆ ▆ ▆ ▆ ▆ ▆

Directions: On A38 Bristol/
Bridgwater, just outside the village

complimentary dish, a wild mushroom and bacon salad, nicely presented. Dessert featured top-notch white and dark chocolate mousse, with a champagne and raspberry coulis, and the cheeseboard contains several local specimens. Canapés, bread, and petits fours are all made here and add to the well-balanced meals. Most enjoyable.

SIMONSBATH,

Simonsbath House Hotel ❀

Good, honest cooking using the freshest of local ingredients can be savoured at this delightful 17th-century house, nestling in the Barle Valley and surrounded by beautiful Exmoor scenery. An enjoyable inspection meal yielded salmon and bacon fishcakes, and a succulent fillet of beef with a grain mustard based jus, and delicious vegetables.

Smoking: No smoking in dining room
Accommodation: 7 en suite
Credit cards: ▆ ▆ ▆ ▆ ▆ ▆ ▆ JCB

Directions: Situated on B3223 in the village

Minehead TA24 7SH
Map 3: SS73
Tel: 01643 831259
Fax: 01643 831557
Chef: Sue Burns
Owners: Mike & Sue Burns
Cost: Fixed-price D £20. ☺
H/wine £8.25.
Times: Last L 3pm/last D 8pm.
Closed Dec-Jan
Additional: Bar food L;
No children under 10

STON EASTON, **Ston Easton Park** ❀❀

Bath
BA3 4DF
Map 3: ST65
Tel: 01761 241631
Fax: 01761 241377
Chef: Mark Harrington
Owners: Mr & Mrs P Smedley

As 18th-century mansions go, Ston Easton is surely one for the purists. Inside and out, the architecture and decorations are a monument to the Palladian tradition. Buildings as fine as this do take a lot of looking after, and this great house (like so many others) now earns its keep as a renowned country house hotel. The style may be old fashioned but service is far from stiff, and there is a relaxed openness about proceedings that extend to a fairly cosmopolitan menu. It is the more traditional elements that provide the highlights: a simply roasted squab pigeon being a particularly tender example, served with Puy lentils and a moist slither of sautéed foie gras. The relatively straightforward approach can sometimes result in worthy but unremarkable dishes such as a rather ordinary tian of provençale vegetables and mozzarella. Desserts are skilfully arranged and always include one hot choice, perhaps a sharp, flaky apple and blackberry croustade.

Cost: Alc £45, fixed-price L £16/D £39.50. H/wine £14.50
Times: 12.30-last L 2pm/7-last D 9.30pm
Additional: Bar food L; Sunday L; No children under 7; ◑ dishes
Seats: 45. Private dining room 24. Jacket & tie preferred
Smoking: No smoking in dining room
Accommodation: 20 en suite
Credit cards: ▆▆ ▆▆ ▆▆ ▆ ▆▆ ▆ ▆ JCB

Directions: On A37 from Bristol to Shepton Mallet, about 6 miles from Wells.

TAUNTON,

Castle Hotel ❀❀❀❀

Castle Green TA1 1NF
Map 3: ST22
Tel: 01823 272671
Fax: 01823 336066
Chef: Phil Vickery
Owners: The Chapman Family
Cost: Fixed-price D £23. H/wine £11.50
Times: 12.30-2pm/7.30-9pm
Additional: Bar food; Sunday L; Children welcome; ◑ dishes
Seats: 60. Private dining room 80
Smoking: No smoking in dining room
Accommodation: 44 en suite
Credit cards: ▆▆ ▆▆ ▆ ▆▆ ▆ ▆

The setting of the Castle Hotel is remarkable: the wisteria-clad building is just a step from the town centre yet is tranquillity itself, sheltered from the reality of late 20th-century existence by mature gardens. The interior impresses without seeming awesome and is in keeping with the nine centuries of history the place boasts; it is old England at its best. The restaurant is a lovely room, calm and serene with eau-de-nil walls with big modern prints, and decently spaced tables. Phil Vickery manages a balance between clever ideas and straightforwardness by the use of exact yet rounded flavours that he brings out. This was noted in a summer dinner that kicked off with an exquisitely flavoured lobster and crab sausage accompanied by a light saffron couscous and a slightly creamy seafood dressing and some simple green leaves. A real fusion dish, spiced duck, matched Chinese spicing with classic European elements – crisp, thin rösti on top of spinach leaves, surrounded by braised carrots and brought together with a fine jus that was not too deeply reduced and equally matched by the spices. Custard tart was a slice of the finest pâté sucré with a soft, golden creamy custard with a dash of raspberry purée and a shallow tuile filled with a nutmeg-flavoured ice cream. The short menu is simply described: potted duck with spiced pears; steamed sea bass with saffron mashed potatoes, roast garlic and sorrel cream; steamed hazelnut sponge with apple compote and butterscotch sauce. Sourcing is all important and Phil Vickery's suppliers are listed at the front of the menu;

Directions: Town centre follow directions for Castle & Museum

most hail from the West Country. The wine list is extensive, but continues to offer an edited selection of some 30 wines under £25, half are under £15, and there is a good selection of half-bottles. The main body of the list is still remarkable for price and it is worth taking the time to study. As we went to press a new brasserie opened, to complement the restaurant. Early reports have been very positive.

TAUNTON, **Farthings Hotel** ❀

Utterly charming small country house hotel offering sound cooking including excellent home-made rolls and simply cooked, locally grown vegetables. Delicious carrot soup is thick enough to stand a spoon in, and chicken with lemon and black pepper and garlic sauce is 'rather well done'. Puddings are irresistible – leave room.

Smoking: No smoking in dining room
Accommodation: 9 en suite
Credit cards: ▬ ▬ ▬ ⌐ ▬ ▣ JCB

Directions: Village centre, just off A358 between Taunton (M5/J25) & Ilminster

Hatch Beauchamp TA3 6SG
Map 3: ST22
Tel: 01823 480664
Fax: 01823 481118
Chefs: Jill Sparkes, Kerry Tindall
Owners: Messrs Sparkes & Tindall
Cost: Alc £18.95. Fixed-price D £18.95. ☺ H/wine £9.95.
Times: D only, 7pm-last D 9pm. Closed Sun
Additional: No children under 14; 🍴 dishes

TAUNTON, **Meryan House Hotel** ❀

Meryan House dates back nearly 400 years and boasts lots of old beams, a well, and more than one inglenook fireplace. Mrs Clark sensibly limits her menu to four or five dishes at each stage. Typical offerings include smoked haddock soufflé, salmon trout with dill butter sauce, and griddled lamb with ratatouille, potato galette and tapenade.

Accommodation: 12 en suite. **Credit cards:** ▬ ▬ ▬ ⌐ ▣ JCB

Directions: From Taunton/A38 direction Wellington. After 1 mile take 1st R (past crematorium) signed Bishops Hull Rd. Hotel is 600 yds.

Bishops Hull TA1 5EG
Map 3: ST22
Tel: 01823 337445
Fax: 01823 322355
Chef: Mrs C Clark
Owners: Mr & Mrs N P Clark
Cost: Alc £18, fixed-price D £18. ☺ H/wine £9
Times: D only, last D 8.30pm. Closed Sun, Bhs
Additional: Children welcome; 🍴 dishes
Smoking: No smoking in dining room

TAUNTON, **Mount Somerset Hotel** ❀

Splendid Georgian country house set in sweeping grounds that give distant views Expect toasted goats' cheese with ripe plum tomatoes and celery, pan-fried loin of Somerset pork with spiced apple purée and deep-fried celeriac, and chocolate and tea terrine with bergamot sauce.

Henlade TA3 5NB
Map 3: ST22
Tel: 01823 442500
Fax: 01823 442900
Chef: Simon Thyer
Cost: Alc £25, fixed-price L £16.95/D £25. ☺ H/wine £11
Times: Last L 2pm/last D 9.30pm
Additional: Sunday L; No children under 12; 🍴 dishes
Accommodation: 11 en suite
Credit cards: ▬ ▬ ▬ ⌐ ▬ ▣ ▣ JCB

Directions: 3 miles SE of Taunton. From M5/J25 take A358 (Chard), turn R in Henlade (Stoke St Mary), then L at T-junction, hotel entrance 400yds R

WELLINGTON, **Bindon House**

Langford Budville TA21 0RU
Map 3: ST12
Tel: 01823 400070
Fax: 01823 400071
Chef: Patrick Robert
Owners: Mark & Lynn Jaffa
Cost: Alc £39, fixed-price L £15/D
£29 (5 courses). H/wine £12.50
Times: Noon-last L 2pm/7.30-last
D 9.30pm
Additional: Sunday L;
No children under 14; ❹ dishes
Seats: 35. Private room 25. Jacket &
tie preferred
Smoking: No smoking in dining room
Accommodation: 12 en suite
Credit cards:

Nestling in seven acres of formal and woodland gardens, this
baroque country house lies in deepest rural Somerset yet is just
10 minutes from the motorway. The building has been restored
by Mark and Lynn Jaffa who, with a well-trained team, run
things with a happy combination of professionalism and
friendliness. Dinner is a short fixed-price affair with an
additional list of dishes priced as supplements to the main
menu. We began our most recent meal with mosaic of foie
gras, wild mushroom and duck confit on a crisp brioche with
orange Muscat jelly before sea bass and scallops on a chive
sauce. The dessert, chocolate tart with a banana and chocolate
parfait with tuile, was rather eclipsed by the excellent petits
fours that included a mini lemon tart, chocolate éclair, rum
baba and chocolate truffle. The wine list, which majors on
France, has some really informative notes on the different
areas covered.

Directions: *Telephone for directions*

WELLS,
Ancient Gate House Hotel

*An enchanting 500-year-old building opposite Wells Cathedral.
Tourists and locals appreciate the old-fashioned Italian hospitality at
the Rugantino restaurant, where squid, mussels and prawn salad
could be followed by fettucine with smoked salmon, cream and
Parmesan, then a large main course of tender veal escalope with
tomato sauce and cheese.*

20 Sadler Street BA5 2RR
Map 3: ST54
Tel: 01749 672029
Fax: 01749 670319
Chef: Luigi Abis
Owners: Mr F & Mrs H L Rossi
Cost: Alc £19.50, fixed-price L
£7.90/D £13.75. ☺ H/wine £7.90
Times: Last L 2pm/D 10pm.
Closed over Xmas
Additional: Bar food L; Sunday L;
Children welcome
Smoking: No pipes and cigars
Accommodation: 9 rooms
Credit cards:

Directions: The corner of Cathedral
Green and Sadler Street

WELLS,
The Fountain Inn

1 St Thomas Street BA5 2UU
Map 3: ST54
Tel: 01749 672317
Fax: 01749 670825
Chef: Julie Pearce
Owners: Adrian & Sarah Lawrence
Cost: *Alc* £16, fixed-price L £7.50. ☺
H/wine £8
Times: Last L 2pm/last D 10pm.
Closed 25-26 Dec
Additional: Bar food; Sunday L;
Children welcome; ♨ dishes
Smoking: No pipes & cigars
Credit cards:

Built to house the labourers working on nearby Wells Cathedral.
The Fountain offers a bar and a first-floor restaurant with pine and
Laura Ashley fabrics. The menu ranges far and wide, from Orkney
smoked salmon to Caesar salad, and stir-fried king prawns with soy,
honey and ginger to Somerset pork flambé in apple brandy.

Directions: At junction of A371 & B3139 in city centre, 50 yds
from cathedral

WELLS,
The Market Place Hotel

Although this 400-year-old hotel and restaurant has undergone
extensive refurbishment, the dining room retains its original
beams and, combined with flagstones and peasant-style
furnishings, the atmosphere is modern and characterful. The
lovely restaurant looks out over a courtyard which is a popular
choice for alfresco dining in summer. Contemporary British
dinner menus include starters such as pork and bacon terrine
with Cumberland jelly, and celery and mushroom soup. Our
inspector described as stunning the main course of lamb with
Madeira jus and a medley of al dente vegetables. Vegetarians
will enjoy sweet red pepper mousse or the three-bean pattie
with goats' cheese and warm ratatouille dressing. Typical
desserts are sticky toffee pudding with butterscotch sauce and
poached pear, caramelised rice pud and home-made ice
creams. Local cheeses with crackers and grapes are also
available. Conclude with good espresso served with light
Italian biscuits and you will be promising to return.

One Market Place BA5 2RW
Map 3: ST54
Tel: 01749 672616
Fax: 01749 679670
Chef: Tony Smith
Owner: Christopher Chapman
Cost: *Alc* £24.50. ☺ H/wine £9.95
Times: 12.30-last L 2pm/7.30-last
D 9.30pm
Additional: Sunday L; Children
welcome; ♨ dishes
Seats: 50
Accommodation: 34 en suite
Credit cards:

Directions: A39 – A371. In centre of town, down one way
system. Directly in front of Conduit in Market Square

WILLITON, Curdon Mill ✿

Former water mill, now a delightful hotel, with the first-floor
restaurant featuring the original mill shaft and water wheel. Great
views too of the Quantock Hills and surrounding countryside.
Expect terrine of ham hock and capers, seared scallops with spring
onion beurre blanc, or rabbit and juniper casserole, and nougatine
parfait.

Yellow TA4 4LS
Map 3: ST04
Tel: 01984 656522
Fax: 01984 656197
Chef: Tim Sandy
Owners: Richard & Daphne Criddle
Cost: *Alc* £23, fixed-price L £9
(2 courses)/D £23. ☺ H/wine £8.10

Directions: From A358 take Yellow/Stogumber road. Hotel 1 mile on L

Curdon Mill

Times: Last L 2pm/last D 9pm.
Closed D Sun, L Mon
Additional: Sunday L;
No children under 8; ☘ dishes
Smoking: No smoking in dining room
Accommodation: 6 en suite
Credit cards: ▬ ▬ ▬ ▬ ☲ ▬

WILLITON, **White House Hotel** ❀❀❀

Long Street TA4 4QW
Map 3: ST04
Tel: 01984 632306
Chefs/Owners: Dick & Kay Smith
Cost: Fixed-price D £31.50.
Times: D only, 7.30-8.30pm.
Closed early Nov-mid May
Additional: Children welcome
Seats: 22
Smoking: No smoking in dining room
Accommodation: 12 rooms
Credit cards: None

Directions: On the A39 in the centre of village

Shortlisted for
AA Wine Award-see page 16

A pleasant easy-going atmosphere runs through Kay and Dick Smith's small Georgian hotel not far from Cleeve Abbey and the Brendon Hills. Inside, a mixture of antique and modern furnishings, paintings and ceramics all add to its sense of style. Exposed-stone walls and hessian wall coverings and a variety of tables and chairs all combine to give a rather peasant-like feeling in the dining-room, a perfect backdrop for the unfussy, unpretentious style of cooking. A soup is the first thing to appear during the four-course dinners; provençale fish soup, or lobster bisque say, and light, buttery tarts often crop up among the choices of the second course: a herby filling of olives, anchovies, tomatoes and onions, or Brixham crab and prawns; soufflé suissesse and air-dried Dorset ham with melon could also be on offer. Fish, again from Brixham, and seasonal game are used to good effect for main courses: superbly fresh John Dory with seared scallops and a Noilly Prat-based sauce adding piquancy, or marinated woodpigeon, chargrilled to pinkness and thinly sliced on hot beetroot. Grilled sea bass with tomato coulis, and pan-fried duck breast with Cassis sauce may turn up too. The kitchen uses seasonal fruits in puddings of strawberries, grapes and oranges with strawberry sorbet, or loganberries with crème brûlée, and there could be something richly chocolatey too. Dick Smith will offer guidance through the compelling wine list.

Signature dishes: roasted loin of local lamb with sauce paloise; escalope of wild salmon baked in pastry with ginger and lime.

WINSFORD, **Royal Oak Inn**

Ancient, impressive thatched inn set in the heart of an Exmoor village. Good country cooking is based on fresh ingredients, and takes in coarse liver, bacon and chicken terrine with home-made chutney, pot-roasted pheasant with caramelised apples and a rich cider jus, and a selection of West Country cheeses. Breakfast is recommended too.

Directions: From M5/J27 take A396 (Minehead) 20 miles turn L to Winsford, then L in village

Exmoor National Park TA24 7JE
Map 3: SS93
Tel: 01643 851455
Fax: 01643 851009
Owner: C R Steven
Cost: Fixed-price D £25
Times: Last L 1.15pm/last D 9.15pm
Additional: Bar food; Sunday L; Children welcome; ❹ dishes
Accommodation: 14 en suite
Credit cards: 💳 💳 💳 💳 💳 💳 💳 JCB

WINSFORD,
Savery's at Karslake House ❀❀

A 15th-century malthouse provides the setting for this small, comfortable, warmly decorated hotel on a hillside. Locally sourced produce is a strength of the kitchen, so seasonality is brought to the fore. Guinea fowl and pheasant may make an appearance on the set three-course menus, the former as a main-course breast with black pudding, smoked bacon and roast shallots in a herby red wine sauce, the latter as a terrine dressed with port and redcurrants. Otherwise, there could be spicy grilled belly-pork on Chinese greens, followed by 'beautifully tender' roast rack of lamb on spring onion mash with a mint and caper sauce, or confit of duckling with parsnip purée, and, among fish dishes, deep-fried prawns and courgettes with a mango salsa, and a catch of the day. Pastry desserts are a strong point among the puddings, and good hand-made chocolates are served with coffee. Four house wines are sold by the glass from the short list, which has a further page of 'Something Special', mainly noble clarets.

Directions: From A396 follow signs to Winsford and Exford. Enter Winsford and turn L at garage. On the R past the Royal Oak Inn

Halse Lane TA24 7JE
Map 3: SS93
Tel/Fax: 01643 851242
Chefs: John Savery, Nikki Plumb
Owners: Patricia Carpenter, John Savery
Cost: *Alc* £24.95. H/wine £10.50
Times: D only, 7-9.15pm. Closed Sun, Feb
Additional: Bar food D (only Sun & Mon, for residents); No children under 15; ❹ dishes
Seats: 30
Smoking: No smoking in dining room
Accommodation: 7 en suite
Credit cards: 💳 💳 💳 💳 💳 JCB

WITHYPOOL, **Royal Oak Inn** ❀

Right in the centre of Exmoor National Park, this charming village inn has character in spades, plus an old-fashioned dining room with silver service. A test meal produced watercress soup, supreme of chicken with mushrooms and sherry sauce, and banoffee pie.

Directions: On B3224 towards Raleigh Cross and Exford – Exford to Withypool signposted

TA24 7QP
Map 3: SS83
Tel: 01643 831506
Fax: 01643 831659
Chef: Jill Tapp
Owner: Richard Howard
Cost: *Alc* £24, fixed-price D £18.50. ☺ H/wine £9.60
Times: Last L 2pm/last D 9.30pm
Additional: Bar food; Sunday L; No children under 2; ❹ dishes
Smoking: No cigars or pipes
Accommodation: 8 en suite
Credit cards: 💳 💳 💳 💳 💳 💳 JCB

WIVELISCOMBE, **Langley House**

Peter and Anne Wilson continue to please guests at their Grade II-listed hotel. The age of the building – it dates from the 16th century, with 18th-century additions – its setting in a dip in the Brendon Hills, the elegance and charm of the interior and the polished service all contribute to its appeal. Everyone eats at the same time in the intimate, candlelit restaurant, with its beams and inglenook. Dinner is a set four courses, with no choice until pudding. The well-balanced menus make the most of seasonal local produce, with fish from Brixham and vegetables and herbs from the four acres of gardens. Dinner might start with a fruity first course or something like roasted cod, perfectly cooked, under a pine nut crust served with buttery lemon sauce. Somerset lamb is a typical main course, perhaps with a pungent tartlet of onion and Cassis and flavoursome vegetables, followed by local cheeses. Bread-and-butter pudding, or a timbale of plain and white chocolate with orange sauce could round off the meal. Wine-lovers will find much of interest on the long list, particularly those who can afford to push the boat out and go for one of the mature clarets.

Accommodation: 8 en suite
Credit cards: ▬ ▬ ▬

Directions: Off B3277 0.5 miles from Wiveliscombe on Langley Marsh Rd

Langley Marsh TA4 2UF
Map 3: ST02
Tel: 01984 623318
Fax: 01984 624573
Chef: Peter Wilson
Owners: Peter & Anne Wilson
Cost: Fixed-price D £31.50 (4 courses). H/wine £12.50
Times: D only, 7.30-last D 8.30pm
Additional: No children under 7; ✪ dishes
Seats: 18. Private dining room 18
Smoking: No smoking in dining room

AA Shortlisted for *Wine Award-see page 16*

WOOKEY HOLE, **Glencot House**

Jenny Attia has done a marvellous job filling this successful hotel to the beams with antiques, along with bric-a-brac from the Middle East – it all works very well, the customers love it. The food is good too. Poached fillet of smoked haddock glazed with Welsh rarebit, breast of chicken stuffed with oysters, smoked bacon and mushrooms, and white chocolate mousse, show the style.

Glencot Lane BA5 1BH
Map 3: ST54
Tel: 01749 677160
Fax: 01749 670210
Chef: Andrew Palmer
Owner: M J Attia
Cost: Fixed-price D £22.50. H/wine £8.95
Times: D only, last D 8.30pm. Closed 1 wk Xmas
Smoking: No smoking in dining room
Accommodation: 13 en suite
Credit cards: ▬ ▬ ▬ ▬ ▬ ▬

Directions: In village, turn L at sign for hotel after pink cottage on hill brow

WOOLVERTON,
Woolverton House Hotel

A 19th-century former rectory. The restaurant serves rustic French-style cuisine, complemented by a keenly priced and interesting list of French wines. The set dinner menu offers three choices at each course. Sweet-and-sour pork, tender and full of flavour, proved very enjoyable, as were the well-kept cheeses.

Bath BA3 6QS
Map 3: ST75
Tel: 01373 830415
Please telephone for further details.

Directions: On the A36 7 miles south-east of Bath

YEOVIL, **Little Barwick House** ✿✿

Barwick Village BA22 9TD
Map 3: ST51
Tel: 01935 423902
Fax: 01935 420908
Chef: Veronica Colley
Owners: Veronica & Christopher Colley
Cost: Fixed-price D £25.90 (4 courses). H/wine £10.90
Times: D only, 7-last D 9pm. Sun residents only. Closed Xmas & New Year
Additional: Children welcome; ✿ dishes
Seats: 40. Private dining room 14.
Smoking: No smoking in dining room; Air conditioning
Accommodation: 6 en suite
Credit cards: ▆▆ ▆▆ ▆ ▆▆ ▆

There are some original ideas on the menu at this charming Georgian dower house: freshly roasted chicken tikka, with avocado, lime and dill sauce; chargrilled brochettes of pork tenderloin, fresh coriander and cream cheese stuffing with a spicy sauce; cream catalan with a hint of fennel. More straightforward tastes are catered for with rack of local lamb, and fillets of sole à la meunière. There's nothing like the thought of an old-fashioned pie to make the mouth water, and Sussex pie with tender steak, Guinness, port and mushrooms sounded too good to miss, and a roast confit of duck leg in honey glaze with sautéed strips of duck breast marinated in ginger and noodles had the balance between sweet and spicy spot-on. Desserts are good – we can recommend the lemon and lime meringue, and rice pudding with prunes and Armagnac.

Directions: Turn off A371 Yeovil/Dorchester opposite Red House pub, 0.25 mile on L

YEOVIL, **Yeovil Court Hotel** ✿

West Coker Road
BA20 2NE
Map 3: ST51
Tel: 01935 863746
Fax: 01935 863990
Chef: Howard Mosley
Owners: Brian & Carol Devonport
Cost: A/c £20. ☺ H/wine £8.90
Times: Last L 1.45pm/last D 9.45pm Closed L Sat, D Sun
Additional: Bar food L; Sunday L; Children welcome; ✿ dishes
Smoking: No smoking in dining room
Accommodation: 26 en suite
Credit cards: ▆▆ ▆▆ ▆ ▆ ▆▆ ▆ ▆ JCB

Comfortable, family-run hotel, not at all hotel-like in feel, and a good option for a meal out. At a winter dinner we tried duck spring roll with plum sauce, chicken with cabbage and smoked bacon and a mustard sauce plus a huge selection of vegetables that included sautéed potatoes with black pudding. Dessert was chocolate marquise with caramel sauce.

Directions: On A30 2.5 miles W of town centre

STAFFORDSHIRE

ACTON TRUSSELL, **Moat House**

This 17th-century timbered building enjoys a peaceful canalside setting. Diners can opt for star anise-flavoured seared scallops with watercress and rocket, fillet of lamb with ratatouille timbale and glazed turnips, and chocolate and mint terrine from the imaginatively written menu.

Accommodation: 21 en suite
Credit cards: 💳 ▨ ▨ ▨ ▨ **C**

Directions: M6/J13 head towards Stafford, 1st R to Acton Trussell; Moat House by church.

ST17 0RJ
Map 7: SJ91
Tel: 01785 712217
Fax: 01785 715344
Chef: Matthew Davies
Owners: John, Mary & Chris Lewis
Cost: *Alc* £27.50, fixed-price L £14.95/D £18.95 (4 courses). ☺
H/wine £11.50
Times: Last L 2pm/last D 9.45pm
Additional: Bar food; Sunday L; Children welcome; ❹ dishes
Smoking: No smoking in dining room

BURTON UPON TRENT,
Riverside Hotel

Grab a window table and enjoy the views over the garden to the river and the bird sanctuary on the bank opposite. Thai crab-cakes, followed by duck leg stuffed with wild mushroom and juniper risotto show that the style is up to the minute; order a pudding – perhaps banoffee pie – from the traditional choice on the trolley.

Smoking: No pipes and cigars
Accommodation: 22 en suite
Credit cards: ▨ ▨ ▨ ▨ ▨

Directions: Off A5121 to Burton

Riverside Drive Branston DE14 3EP
Map 8: SK22
Tel: 01283 511234
Fax: 01283 511441
Chef: Philip Wright
Owner: Roger Kerry
Cost: *Alc* £22, fixed-price D £17.95 (4 courses). ☺ H/wine £9.95
Times: Last L 2pm/last D 10pm.
Closed L Good Fri
Additional: Bar food; Sunday L; Children welcome; ❹ dishes

NEWCASTLE-UNDER-LYME,
Deansfield Hotel ✿

98 Lancaster Road ST5 1DS
Map 7: SJ84
Tel/Fax: 01782 619040
Chef: David Evans
Owners: David & Susan Evans
Cost: *Alc* £30, fixed-price L £15.50/D £25 (6 courses). ☺ H/wine £10.25.
Times: Last L 2pm/last D 9.30pm.
Closed Sun, Mon, 25-31 Dec
Additional: Children welcome; ❹ dishes
Accommodation: 11 en suite.
Credit cards: ▨ ▨ ▨ **C**

Set in a residential district, this large, semi-detached Victorian house retains many original features. Mussel casserole, cheese and watercress soufflé, roast cod with crayfish sauce, fillet of beef with red wine sauce, and pastry puff of wild mushrooms and chicken livers, give a flavour of the menu.

Directions: M6 J15 follow A34 to town centre, turn R into The Avenue (City General Hospital), Lancaster Road third on L.

SUFFOLK

ALDEBURGH, **Regatta Restaurant**

Cheerful restaurant with an informal feel – blue and white checks and stripes, white wood and wicker chairs as well as seaside murals. Fish sets the tone, perhaps smoked fillet of local cod with butter bean cassoulet and aïoli, but there's also Peking-style duck, and grilled breast of chicken with a light curry and pineapple sauce. Concise but wide ranging wine list.

Smoking: No-smoking area
Credit cards: ▆▆ ▆▆ ▆▆ ▆ ▆▆ ▆ JCB

Directions: Town centre

171 High Street IP15 5AN
Map 5: TM45
Tel/Fax: 01728 452011
Chefs: R E Mabey,
N Ramsbottom
Owners: Mr & Mrs R E Mabey
Cost: Alc £18. ☺ H/wine £9
Times: Last L 2.30pm/last D 10pm
Additional: Bar food; Sunday L;
Children welcome; 🍴 dishes

BILDESTON, **The Bow Window**

A beamed village restaurant in the market square, ideal for intimate dining. The carte is supported by an evening blackboard menu and a good wine list with a wide range of prices. Dishes to sample include tiger prawns with lime, garlic and coriander, and fillet of lamb in a puff pastry case.

Directions: In main street on B1115 between Stowmarket and Hadleigh

116 High Street IP7 7EB
Map 5: TL94
Tel/Fax: 01449 740748
Please telephone for further details.

BROME, **Cornwallis Arms**

Delightful 16th-century dower house located at the end of a long avenue of lofty elms. The elegant Victorian Oaksmere restaurant adjoins the intimate, vine-laden conservatory, and offers a wide choice. Dishes may include salmon parfait, grilled Dover sole, and venison with red wine, cranberry and apple sauce.

Directions: Just off A140 at Brome, midway between Norwich & Ipswich

Eye IP23 8AJ
Map 5: TM17
Tel: 01379 870326
Fax: 01379 870051
Chef: Tim Turner
Owner: St Peter's Brewery Co Ltd
Cost: Alc £28. ☺
Times: Last L 2pm/last D 10pm.
Additional: Bar food; Sunday L;
Children welcome; 🍴 dishes
Accommodation: 11 en suite
Credit cards: ▆▆ ▆▆ ▆ ▆▆ ▆

BURY ST EDMUNDS, **Angel Hotel**

Dating from the 15th century and retaining much of its period charm, the Angel is at the heart of this market town. The elegant, high-ceilinged Regency restaurant offers the likes of goats' cheese

Angel Hill IP33 1LT
Map 5: TL86
Tel: 01284 753926
Fax: 01284 750092
Chef: Didier Piot

Angel Hotel

Owner: Mrs Mary Gough
Cost: *Alc* £28. ☺ H/wine £9.95
Times: Last L 2pm/last D 9.45pm

ravioli, grilled Dover sole or duck breast with beetroot mousse, and bread-and-butter pudding. Coffee is served with home-made petits fours, including white-chocolate physalis.

Additional: Bar food; Sunday L; Children welcome; ✿ dishes
Smoking: No smoking in dining room
Accommodation: 42 en suite
Credit cards:

Directions: Town centre, close to Tourist Information

BURY ST EDMUNDS,
The Priory Hotel ✿

Fine Georgian house on the site of a 13th-century priory, popular with both business and leisure guests. Strong local following in the restaurant for such dishes as timbale of shredded duck with shallot and Cassis marmalade, and sautéed medallions of monkfish, chive potato purée and red wine and coriander sauce.

Additional: Children welcome; ✿ dishes
Smoking: No-smoking area
Accommodation: 27 en suite
Credit cards: ▄▄ ▄▄ ▄▄ ▄▄ ▄▄

Directions: Leave A14 at exit for Bury St Edmunds West. Turn L and after 1 mile turn R at 1st mini roundabout, hotel entrance on R

NEW

Tollgate IP32 6EH
Map 5: TL86
Tel: 01284 766181
Fax: 01284 767604
Chef: Kevin Wood
Cost: *Alc* £27, fixed price L & D £21.
☺ H/wine £10.95
Times: Last L 1.45pm,/last D 9.45pm.
Closed L Sat & Sun, 26 Dec

BURY ST EDMUNDS,
Ravenwood Hall ✿

Squirrels and Muntjac deer come to dine in the grounds of this charming country house, as do guests from far and wide who appreciate the secluded woodland setting and the eclectic mix of vibrant and traditional dishes served in the restaurant. Expect the likes of wood-smoked fillet of beef with wild mushroom and truffle jus.

Accommodation: 14 en suite
Credit cards: ▄▄ ▄▄ ▄▄ ▄▄ ▄▄ ▄▄ ▄▄ JCB

Directions: 3 miles E of Bury on A14, signposted to Rougham

Rougham IP30 9JA
Map 5: TL86
Tel: 01359 270345
Fax: 01359 270788
Chef: Annette Sherman
Owner: Craig Jarvis
Cost: *Alc* £26.95, fixed-price L
£18.95/D £26.95. ☺ H/wine £9.95
Times: Last L 2pm/D 9.30pm
Additional: Bar food; Sunday L;
Children welcome; ✿ dishes
Smoking: No smoking in dining room

FRESSINGFIELD, Fox and Goose

Nr Diss IP21 5PB
Map 5: TM27
Tel: 01379 586247
Fax: 01379 586688
Chef: Maxwell Dougal
Owners: Tim and Pauline O'Leary
Cost: *Alc* £26.50, fixed-price L £9.50
(2 courses)/D £17.50. ☺ H/wine
£13.50
Times: Noon-last L 2pm, 7-last
D 9.30pm. Closed 25-26 Dec
Additional: Bar food; Sunday L;
Children welcome: ◑ dishes
Seats: 40. Private dining room 20
Smoking: No smoking in dining room
Credit cards:

One of those curious quirks of history means that the building, which dates from 1500, is still owned by the church, visible across the graveyard. Mortal pleasures however are still to be freely enjoyed at the unspoilt, old English inn with its welcoming open fires, atmospheric bar and bright, pretty dining room. Ingredients are carefully sourced, from Morecambe Bay potted brown shrimps, to Barbary duck cooked with a cassoulet of butter beans and spicy meat balls, and the roast sirloin of Orkney Island beef for Sunday lunch. Quite what 'seized local cod', with a garlicky and saffron mash and gremolata, implies about local fishing techniques, we can only hazard. Puddings may include treacle tart, or caramelised banana with rum and raisin ice cream. There are some excellent British and Irish cheeses, and occasionally a fruit 'cheese' such as quince – enjoy, along with a 'glass of unassuming port'.

Directions: A140 & B1118 (Stradbroke) L after 6 miles – in village centre by church

HINTLESHAM, Hintlesham Hall

IP8 3NS
Map 5: TM04
Tel: 01473 652268
Fax: 01473 652463
Chef: Alan Ford
Owner: David Allan
Cost: *Alc* £32, fixed-price L £19.50/D
£26. H/wine £12.90
Times: Noon-last L 2pm/7-last
D 9.45pm. Closed L Sat
Additional: Sunday L; No children
under 10 at D; ◑ dishes
Seats: 120. Private rooms 16-80.
Jacket and tie preferred
Smoking: No smoking in dining room

Hintlesham is a fine example of a country house hotel although its magnificent Georgian façade belies the Tudor origins of the house, parts of which date from 1570. Alan Ford's technique and timing are spot-on, and he mobilises flavour through careful choice of the best ingredients; one inspector was moved to report that the most memorable aspect of a spring dinner was its sheer simplicity. This came through in a canapé of courgette quiche, a turbot and ham tower, essentially a sausage created from the 'lovely' fish and ham and presented on a risotto and red wine sauce, and some first-class vegetables, among them bright green asparagus, and plump sweet cherry tomatoes that accompanied a main course of straightforward, beautifully cooked guinea fowl with well-truffled tagliatelle and jus. Puddings are ambitious, none more so than the chocolate assiette: two mousses, a white chocolate tart, two chocolate ice creams, and a lovely chocolate gâteau (though it was more of a fondant), a really squidgy, collapsing soufflé. An extensive wine list with nice range by the glass of some nine quality wines and a couple of pages of 'House Selections', most under £20. A splendid halves list, some inexpensive drinking in the Country Wine section, and some great wines showing a good hand at the other end of the scale.

Signature dishes: Roast loin of new season's lamb with chargrilled vegetables and lemon oil dressing; carpaccio of east coast scallops with pickled young fennel and a salad of rocket leaves; pears poached in mulled wine, set on chocolate risotto, served with cinnamon ice cream; pot-au-feu of local pheasant with pancetta, caramelised onions and ceps.

Accommodation: 33 en suite. **Credit cards:**

Directions: 5 miles west of Ipswich on the A1071 Hadleigh road.

AA Wine Award-see page 16 Shortlisted for

IPSWICH, **Cock Inn** ❀   NEW

Rural pub at the top of the village green – a local watering hole as well as a good provincial restaurant. The cooking is eclectic, covering a lot of ground. Note king scallops topped with lemon zest and served with thick chargrilled gammon slices, and egg custard with nutmeg ice cream.

The Green Polstead CO6 5AL
Map 5: TM14
Tel: 01206 263150
Fax: 01206 263950
Please telephone for further details

IPSWICH,
Marlborough Hotel ❀❀

Henley Road IP1 3SP
Map 5: TM14
Tel: 01473 257677
Fax: 01473 226927
Chef: Simon Barker
Owners: Robert & Karen Gough
Cost: *Alc* £28.50, fixed-price L £16/D £19.85. ☺ H/wine £9.85
Times: 12.30-last L 2pm/7.30-last D 9.30pm. Closed L Sat
Additional: Bar food; Sunday L; Children welcome; ♦ dishes
Seats: 48. Private dining rooms 14, 60
Smoking: No smoking in dining room
Accommodation: 22 en suite
Credit cards:

Quiet residential surroundings and the red-brick exterior belie the country-house atmosphere within this hotel to the north of town. Have a drink in the contemporary surroundings of the bar before moving on to the restaurant: done out in deep pastels, it's an elegant room with swags and candlelight. A seasonally changing menu is offered alongside the daily one. Game soup laced with alcohol makes a fine starter, with perhaps Cromer crab tart, or goujons of salmon also making an appearance. Tender loin of venison in a sauce of a reduction of its juices with black pepper and Cognac has impressed for its accurate timing; roast rack of lamb in a pesto crust with provençale sauce may be among other meat offerings and baked skate wing with cider and sage sauce among the fish. Home-made breads like pine nut and herb rolls have been singled out, and bread-and-butter pudding has been approved for its lightness and good custard flavour. A 'quick list' of wines will guide you to something appropriate if you don't want to read the whole thing.

Directions: Take A12/14 (Felixstowe & Yarmouth), R at lights at brow of hill, hotel is 500 yds on R

IPSWICH, **The Old Boot House**

Enjoying a peaceful rural setting on the edge of Shotley village, the Old Boot House offers unpretentious modern British cooking and enthusiastic and friendly service in its rustic, beamed dining room. With quality ingredients sourced locally, chef/proprietor Ian Chamberlain carefully prepares the interesting choice of dishes listed on the short *carte*. Our inspector recently sampled delicious home-made granary bread, a well-constructed and seasoned chicken, Stilton and bacon terrine, and an excellent fish pie – chunks of white and smoked fish, mussels and asparagus tips in a light buttery velouté finished with chives. Pudding was a good iced lemon and Pastis parfait on a robust blackcurrant coulis. Other dishes offered could include lamb with tarragon and mustard seed sauce, pigeon pie, and steamed whisky and marmalade sponge pudding. Because of the remote location, booking is recommended. Well chosen list of wines from Adnams.

Directions: 7 miles SE of Ipswich on the B1456, through Chelmondiston and 0.25 mile beyond Shotley. Sign on R

Shotley IP9 1EY
Map 5: TM14
Tel: 01473 787755
Chef: Ian Chamberlain
Owners: Ian & Pamela Chamberlain
Cost: *Alc* £20. ☺ H/wine £8.50
Times: Noon-1.30pm/D from 7pm.
Closed Sun D, all Mon
Additional: Sunday L;
Children welcome
Seats: 45
Smoking: No smoking in dining room
Credit cards: 💳 💳 💳 💳

IPSWICH, **Scott's Brasserie**

Brasserie in a delightful old building, run with individual style, serving snacks and a full restaurant menu. Menu shows lots of cosmopolitan influences with jazzy flavours. Look out for black linguine with three cheese cream sauce and Caesar salad, grilled skate wing with lime and honey dressing, and blackberry and mascarpone crème brûlée.

Smoking: No-smoking area; No pipes & cigars
Credit cards: 💳 💳 💳 💳 💳 💳

Directions: Near Buttermarket shopping centre, close to Cox Lane and Foundation Street car parks

4a Orwell Place IP4 1BB
Map 5: TM14
Tel: 01473 230254
Fax: 01473 218851
Chef: Scott Davidson
Owners: Charles Lewis, Scott Davidson
Cost: *Alc* £25, fixed-price L & D £25.
☺ H/wine £9.95
Times: Last L 2.45pm/last D 10pm.
Closed L Sat, all Sun, Bhs
Additional: Bar food;
No children under 14; 🍴 dishes

IPSWICH,
Swallow Belstead Brook Hotel

An elegant and quietly intimate wood-panelled restaurant which retains its original Jacobean character. Sound cooking from a varied and interesting menu of up-beat contemporary food.

Additional: Bar food; Sunday L; Children welcome; 🍴 dishes
Smoking: No smoking in dining room
Accommodation: 88 en suite
Credit cards: 💳 💳 💳 💳 💳 💳 💳

Directions: Take A1214 exit at main A12/A14 interchange then 3rd exit at 1st roundabout; after bridge take 1st L

Belstead Brook Park
Belstead Road IP2 9HB
Map 5: TM14
Tel: 01473 684241
Fax: 01473 681249
Chef: Alex Honeywell
Owner: Swallow Hotels
Cost: *Alc* £25, fixed-price L £12.50/D
£19.50 (5 courses). ☺ H/wine £10.25
Times: Last L 1.50pm/last D 9.50pm.
Closed L Sat

IXWORTH,
Theobalds Restaurant

Visitors to Theobalds, a town-centre restaurant housed in a 16th-century building, can expect a hearty meal of Anglo/French dishes with some Oriental influences. The short

68 High Street
IP31 2HJ
Map 5: TL97
Tel/Fax: 01359 231707
Chef: Simon Theobald

carte offers a mix of indulgent traditional dishes such as pan-fried fillet steak with bacon and wild mushrooms, and roast breast of duckling with a port and redcurrant sauce, together with a number of lighter, more contemporary ideas along the lines of roast baby guinea fowl with ginger and lime. Our inspector chose potted crab with avocado, cucumber and chive mayonnaise, followed by breast of corn-fed chicken sautéed with bacon and tarragon and served with a rich Madeira sauce. The dining room is smart with lots of exposed beams and an inglenook fireplace, while in summer months guests can dine alfresco in the patio garden. The excellent wine list includes top-rate dessert wines by the glass.

Directions: 7 miles from Bury St Edmunds on A143 Bury/Diss road

Theobalds Restaurant

Owners: Simon & Geraldine Theobald
Cost: *Alc* £28, fixed-price L £11 (2 courses). H/wine £14.60
Times: 12.15-1.30pm/7.15-9.30pm. Closed L Sat, D Sun, all Mon, 2 wks Aug
Additional: Sunday L; No children under 8 at D; ❹ dishes
Seats: 36
Smoking: No smoking in dining room
Credit cards: 🔲 🔲 🔲 🔲 🔲

LAVENHAM,

Angel Hotel ✿

The building was first licensed as an inn in 1420 and remains a focal point, at the heart of one of England's finest market towns. The daily changing restaurant menu is built around local ingredients such as duck and game in season, interpreted by the kitchen in a sound rustic style. Look out for game terrine, roast loin of lamb, and warm winter pudding.

Directions: Take A143 from Bury St Edmunds and turn onto A1141 after 4 miles; hotel is on Market Place, off High Street

Market Place CO10 9QZ
Map 5: TL94
Tel: 01787 247388
Fax: 01787 248344
Chefs: Michael Pursell, Chris Boyle
Owners: Roy & Anne Whitworth, John Barry
Cost: *Alc* £15. ☺ H/wine £7.95
Times: Last L 2.15pm/last D 9.15pm. Closed 25-26 Dec
Additional: Bar food; Sunday L; Children welcome; ❹ dishes
Smoking: No-smoking area
Accommodation: 8 en suite
Credit cards: 🔲 🔲 🔲 🔲 🔲 🔲

LAVENHAM, **The Great House**

Market Place CO10 9QZ
Map 5: TL94
Tel: 01787 247431
Fax: 01787 248007
Chef: Régis Crépy
Owners: Régis & Martine Crépy
Cost: Alc £28, fixed price L £9.95 (2 courses)/D £17.95. ☺ H/wine £10.20
Times: Last L 2.30pm/last D 9.30pm. Closed D Sun, all Mon (to non-residents), 3 wks Jan
Additional: Bar food L; Sunday L; Children welcome
Smoking: No smoking in dining room
Accommodation: 5 en suite
Credit cards: 🟦 🟦 🟦 🟦 🟦 🟦 JCB

Historic house on the town square. Restaurant boasts great inglenook, smell of logs, big old furniture, large flower arrangements, white linen, assortment of chairs and tables. Very French feel that extends to the classic cooking: fresh scallops and 'tricolor' peppers served marinated in olive oil and fresh herbs; prime fillet of beef with béarnaise sauce. Predominantly French wine list with good selection by glass and half-bottle.

Directions: In Market Place (turn into Market Lane from High Street).

LAVENHAM, **The Swan**

High Street CO10 9QA
Map 5: TL94
Tel: 01787 247477
Fax: 01787 248286
Chef: Martin Horsley
Owner: Forte UK Ltd
Cost: Alc £30, fixed-price L £9.95 (2 courses)/D £24.95. ☺ H/wine £8.95
Times: Noon-last L 2pm/6.30-last D 9.30pm
Additional: Bar food; Sunday L; Children welcome; 🍴 dishes
Seats: 80. Private room 40
Smoking: No smoking in dining room
Accommodation: 46 en suite
Credit cards: 🟦 🟦 🟦 🟦 🟦 🟦 🟦 JCB

A delightful timber-framed hotel dating back to the 15th century. With open fires, a minstrels' gallery and lovely courtyard gardens all creating a traditional atmosphere, the Swan is a great place to relax and unwind. Dinner in the beamed restaurant takes on a modern English feel, with plenty of European influences. Try, for example, warm goats' cheese with pesto and orange salad, or terrine of pressed chicken and roasted pine nuts for starters. Follow this with a main course of roast forerib of beef with smoked shallot sauce, or chargrilled tuna steak with oyster sauce vinaigrette. A high summer meal sampled by our inspector started with accurately-cooked scallops on a bed of mixed leaves, followed by thinly sliced rosettes of lamb lightly roasted shallots and sweet peppers. Desserts are along the lines of Grand Marnier soufflé, surrounded by an ocean of raspberry and mango coulis.

Directions: In the centre of the village on the A1141

LONG MELFORD,
Chimneys Restaurant ❀❀

Hall Street CO10 9JR
Map 5: TL84
Tel: 01787 379806
Fax: 01787 312294
Chef: David Clarkson
Owners: Sam & Zena Chalmers
Cost: Alc £20. H/wine £10.95
Times: Noon-2pm/7-9.30pm.
Closed D Sun
Additional: Sunday L;
Children welcome; ❀ dishes
Seats: 45
Credit cards: ▨▨ ▨▨

The bustling village of Long Melford is cluttered with antique shops and *olde worlde* pubs, and this 16th-century timbered house looks every inch the part with its blackened beams, brick fireplaces and leaded windows. The restaurant is fairly large and offers a reasonable *carte* of English and French dishes. A meal in May began with baked filo parcels stuffed with feta cheese and shrimps. Other starters might include salad of quails' eggs with fresh asparagus, and terrine of sea trout and halibut with a watercress and dill sauce. The main course – breast of chicken with basil mousseline – had a 'lovely flavour', and was served with Jersey Royals and mange-tout. Choosing dessert could prove tricky, with the likes of apple and cinnamon strudel and baked vanilla and sultana cheesecake on the menu, but our inspector wasn't deterred, boldly opting for fresh baked profiteroles filled with Chantilly cream and covered in rich chocolate sauce.

Directions: On main street of Long Melford village

LONG MELFORD, # The Countrymen ❀

The Green CO10 9DN
Map 5: TL84
Tel: 01787 312356
Fax: 01787 374557
Chef: Stephen Errington
Owners: Stephen & Janet Errington
Cost: Alc £15, fixed-price L £9.95/D £20.75 (4 courses). ☺ H/wine £10
Times: Last L 1.45pm/D 9.30pm.
Closed D Sun, all Mon, Jan
Additional: Bar food; Sunday L;
Children welcome; ❀ dishes
Smoking: No smoking in dining room
Accommodation: 9 en suite
Credit cards: ▨▨ ▨▨ ▨▨ ▨ ▨▨ ▣ JCB

There's a loyal following of local diners at this hotel on the village green. The main restaurant offers a choice of menus, and dishes sampled at a test meal included scallops stir-fried with ginger on home-made spinach noodles, followed by calves' liver with mushrooms and mild mustard sauce.

Directions: On the village green in Long Melford

LONG MELFORD,

Scutchers Restaurant 🏵🏵

A bright, lively bistro, with light wood beams, pine tables and lots of pictures and prints of flowers. The *carte* has a continental feel, although there are one or two oriental dishes thrown in. Typical starters include carpaccio of beef with Med vegetables in balsamic and olive oil, seared scallops with a tomato and shallot salsa topped with crispy bacon, and toasted goats' cheese and potato terrine with a green tomato chutney. At a meal in May, our inspector tried a tasty starter of crispy duck with spring onion, cucumber and hoisin sauce. This was followed by an amazing dish of seared tuna on spicy melting tomato. Other main courses include roasted halibut with asparagus and lemon hollandaise, and sautéed lamb fillets with mushrooms and rosemary gravy. Puddings are indulgent: check out white and dark chocolate truffle with caramel sauce, or clotted crème brûlée with a compote of fresh raspberries.

Westgate Street CO10 9DP
Map 5: TL84
Tel: 01787 310200
Fax: 01787 785443
Chef: Nicholas Barrett
Owners: Nicholas & Diane Barrett
Cost: *Alc* £20
Times: Noon-last L 2pm/7-last D 9.30pm. Closed Sun, Mon, 24-26 Dec, 1st wk Jan
Additional: Children welcome; 🍴 dishes
Seats: 75
Smoking: No pipes & cigars
Credit cards: 💳 💳 💳 💳 💳 💳

Directions: About a mile from Long Melford on the road to Clare

---

LOWESTOFT, **Ivy House Farm** 🏵

Just outside Lowestoft, this delightful 18th-century hotel nestles on the edge of Oulton Broad in tranquil countryside. Cooking in the Crooked Barn Restaurant is modern European with a bit of adventure thrown in – try grilled fillet of sea bass with creamy arborio rice risotto, or home-made tagliatelle tossed with oyster mushrooms and spinach.

Ivy Lane Oulton Broad NR33 8HY
Map 5: TM59
Tel: 01502 501353
Fax: 01502 501539
Chef: Richard Pye
Owners: Caroline Sterry, Paul Coe
Cost: *Alc* £30, fixed-price L £17.95/D £20.95. ☺ H/wine £9.95
Times: Last L 1.45pm/last D 9.30pm
Additional: Sunday L; 🍴 dishes
Smoking: No smoking in dining room
Accommodation: 12 en suite
Credit cards: 💳 💳 💳 💳 💳 💳 💳

Directions: From Lowestoft – follow A146 (Norwich). Hotel approx 0.25 mile after junction to A1117 (Ipswich), over small railway bridge.

MILDENHALL, **Riverside Hotel** 🏵

Personally run, popular hotel, with a cheerful, informal atmosphere. The restaurant is a bright modern room with full-length windows opening on to gardens and the river. Slivers of freshly grilled tuna fish with niçoise salad, and medallions of venison with a cherry and red wine glaze, are typical dishes. House recommended wines are good value.

Accommodation: 21 en suite
Credit cards: 💳 💳 💳 💳 💳 💳 💳 JCB

Directions: Leave M11/J9, then take A1101 from A11. L at mini roundabout along High St. Hotel is last building on L before bridge

Mill Street IP28 7DP
Map 5: TL77
Tel: 01638 717274
Fax: 01638 715997
Chef: Scott Pammenter
Owners: Carolyn & John Child, Alison & Keith Lardner
Cost: *Alc* £22, fixed-price L & D £17. ☺ H/wine £9.95
Times: Last L 2pm/last D 9pm (9.30pm Sat & Sun)
Additional: Bar food; Sunday L; Children welcome; 🍴 dishes
Smoking: No-smoking area

NAYLAND, White Hart Inn

A bare board floor, scrubbed pine tables and a large fireplace – nothing extraordinary for a village pub over 500 years old, even if it does have a ghost. It's the quality of the cooking that's the attraction here, the appeal enhanced during the summer by a lovely terrace surrounded by flowers where barbecues are often held. 'Farmhouse cooking with European influences' is how the White Hart describes its style. Ploughman's and sandwiches at lunch times ('huge' writes an inspector) accompany flexible fixed-price offerings of between one and three courses: white-bean soup, braised shoulder of lamb, and vanilla crème brûlée might all be on the menu. A broader selection is offered in the evening, ranging from flavoursome fish soup with Gruyère, croûtons and rouille, to breast of guinea fowl with tagliatelle and lemon butter, or grilled brill with girolles and asparagus. English farmhouse cheeses, or something like light and alcoholic rum baba with summer berries round things off nicely. A wine list of around 30 wines, with something for everyone, is supplemented by a page of more expensive fine wines.

High Street CO6 4JF
Map 5: TL93
Tel: 01206 263382
Fax: 01206 263638
Chef: Mark Prescott
Owners: Mark Prescott, Michel Roux
Cost: Alc £22, fixed-price L £16. ☺
H/wine £9.80
Times: Noon-last L 2pm/6.30-last D 9pm. Closed 26 Dec-1 Jan
Additional: Bar food L; Sunday L; No children under 10 after 8pm; ③ dishes
Seats: 70. Private room 40
Accommodation: 7 en suite
Credit cards:

Directions: In the centre of village

NEWMARKET, Bedford Lodge Hotel

Race days see the hotel's Godolphin Restaurant packed out. Punters come for a menu that covers much ground, and packs ambitious flair in dishes such as duck foie gras, fallow venison and baked pear, and crème caramel with ginger cream. Wine list offers a useful selection.

Accommodation: 56 en suite
Credit cards: JCB

Directions: From town centre follow A1303 towards Bury St Edmunds for half a mile

Bury Road CB8 7BX
Map 5: TL66
Tel: 01638 663175
Fax: 01638 667391
Chef: Tony Smith
Owner: Barnham Broom Golf Club Ltd
Cost: Alc £25, fixed price L & D £16.95. ☺ H/wine £9.95
Times: Last L 2pm/last D 9.30pm
Additional: Bar food L; Sunday L; Children welcome; ③ dishes
Smoking: No-smoking area

NEWMARKET, The Chifney Restaurant at Tattersalls

Park Paddocks The Avenue CB8 9AU
Map 5: TL66
Tel: 01638 666166
Fax: 01638 666099
Chef: Paul Murfitt
Owner: David Allan

They live, sleep and breathe horses round here; luckily they don't eat them, though other four-legged beasts aren't spared so easily. Still, it's all in a good cause when it comes to dishes

such as fillet of beef with a filo pithiviers of snails and pancetta with sauce béarnaise, or chump of lamb on rosemary scented pearl barley and an etuvée of girolles. The *carte* has all the style befitting patrons of the sport of kings: duck consommé is served with candied beetroot and foie gras raviolo; saddle of monkfish is braised with baby fennel and saffron in its own nage. There is some pretension in the menu language, but even if you're not sure what you ordered, it's a racing cert you'll come away well-fed and watered.

Directions: Centre of Newmarket. Enter Park Paddocks from The Avenue, which is a turning off High St near Jockey Club

Cost: *Alc* £25, fixed-price L £15.75. ☺ H/wine £9.60
Times: Noon-last L 2.30pm/7-last D 10pm. Closed D Sun, all Mon
Additional: Bar food L; Sunday L; Children welcome; ♨ dishes
Seats: 70. Private dining room 30-100
Smoking: No-smoking area; Air conditioning
Credit cards: ▨ ▨ ▨ ▨ ▨ ▨

NEWMARKET, **Heath Court Hotel** ❀

Just a few minutes' walk from the high street and overlooking one of the main racehorse-training grounds, this modern hotel's restaurant offers a brasserie-style menu. Expect salad of smoked pork and mackerel with grapefruit, breaded lemon sole with lemongrass and coriander sauce, and tarte Tatin.

Accommodation: 41 en suite
Credit cards: ▨ ▨ ▨ ▨ ▨ ▨ ▨

Directions: Off town centre – turn R at clock tower into Moulton Road

Moulton Road CB8 8DY
Map 5: TL66
Tel: 01638 667171
Fax: 01638 666533
Chef: Darren Worthington
Owner: Heath Court Investments Ltd
Cost: *Alc* £18.50. ☺ H/wine £10.25
Times: Last L 1.45pm/last D 9.45pm. Closed L Sat
Additional: Bar food; Sunday lunch; Children welcome; ♨ dishes
Smoking: No-smoking area

SOUTHWOLD,
Crown at Southwold ❀

The wine list is a magnet here, as you would expect since the Crown is owned by Adnams, wine merchant and brewer. But the imaginative menus have their attractions too. Eat in bar or restaurant – in the latter you might have chicken and pigeon terrine with plum chutney, baked sea bass with wild mushrooms, and mango and lime parfait.

Smoking: No smoking in dining room; Air conditioning
Accommodation: 12 (not all en suite)
Credit cards: ▨ ▨ ▨ ▨ ▨ ▨ ▨

Directions: Take A1095 from A12; hotel at top of High Street, just before Market Place

90 High Street IP18 6DP
Map 5: TM57
Tel: 01502 722275
Fax: 01502 727263
Chef: Craig Dunn
Owner: Adnams
Cost: *Alc* £23, fixed-price L £17. ☺ H/wine £7
Times: Last L 2.30pm/last D 9.30pm. Closed 4-12 Jan
Additional: Bar food; Sunday L; Children welcome; ♨ dishes

SOUTHWOLD, **Swan Hotel** ❀

Esteemed local brewery Adnams owns this smartly attired ex-coaching inn, so wines and beers are top-notch. The three set menus exhibit variety and imagination, with pressed terrine of foie gras, liver and pigeon, hot-peppered pineapple (served as an improvement on the ubiquitous sorbet), simply roasted monkfish with a light ginger and lemongrass sauce, and a passion fruit cheesecake showing the style.

Accommodation: 45 rooms (42 en suite)
Credit cards: ▨ ▨ ▨ ▨ ▨ ▨

Directions: Take A1095 off A12; follow High Street into Market Place, hotel on left

Market Place IP18 6EG
Map 5: TM57
Tel: 01502 722186
Fax: 01502 724800
Chef: David Smith
Owner: Adnams & Co
Cost: Fixed price L £16/D £22. ☺ H/wine £9.95
Times: Last L 1.45pm/last D 9.30pm. Closed L Jan-Apr
Additional: Bar food L; Sunday L; No children under 5; ♨ dishes
Smoking: No smoking in dining room

SUDBURY,
Brasserie Four Seven

A bistro-style restaurant in the town square, popular for speedy lunchtime snacks as well as leisurely dinners. The open-plan galley allows guests to view the preparation of up-to-date dishes such as roast fillet of cod with pesto mash, ricotta and spinach tortellini with mange-tout, and chargrilled sirloin steak with a creamy tarragon sauce.

Credit cards: ▬ ▬ ▢ ▬ ▣

Directions: 150 yards from Market Hill, next to Gainsborough House Museum

47 Gainsborough Street
CO10 6ET
Map 5: TL84
Tel/Fax: 01787 374298
Chefs: Guy Alabaster, Fraser Green
Owners: Fiona & Fraser Green
Cost: Alc £18. ☺ H/wine £7.95
Times: Last L 1.50pm/last D 9.50pm. Closed Sun, D Mon, Bh Mon
Additional: Children welcome; ◑ dishes
Smoking: No-smoking area; Air conditioning

SUDBURY, Red Onion Bistro

Lively, vibrant bistro serving fresh, simple food. Great concept of jug house wines, and a cellar room of over 80 wines where visitors can choose their own bottles. Melting-pot menu of deep-fried squid tempura with tomato and fresh coriander salsa, griddled fillet of turbot with fennel dressing, and vanilla pannacotta with rhubarb compote.

Additional: Children welcome; ◑ dishes
Smoking: No pipes & cigars. **Credit cards:** ▬ ▬ ▰ ▢ ◪

Directions: On A131 Chelmsford road out of Sudbury

57 Ballingdon Street
CO10 6DA
Map 5: TL84
Tel: 01787 376777
Fax: 01787 883156
Chef: Darren Boyles
Owners: Gerry & Jane Ford
Cost: Alc £17.50, fixed-price L £7.75/D £9.75. ☺ H/wine £7.25
Times: Last L 2pm/last D 10pm. Closed Sun, Bh Mon, 25-26 Dec, 1 Jan

WESTLETON, The Crown

Busy village inn, well established and popular, featuring home-made dishes such as spinach tagliatelle and grilled Barbary duckling with a Cassis and blackcurrant sauce, plus good bread and ice cream. Rustic yet elegant dining room adjoining the log-fired bar. Recommended wines are highlighted, and a big selling point is nearly 90 malt whiskies.

IP17 3AD
Map 5: TM46
Tel: 01728 648777
Fax: 01728 648239
Please telephone for further details

WOODBRIDGE,
Captain's Table

Pascal Pommier and Jo Moussa will be well known to fans of the Normandie, Bury (see entry, Greater Manchester). They plan a simpler operation here. The historic beamed cottage (in a busy street of this Suffolk town) has been turned into something special: there's vibrance in colourful plates, cushions and modern simple cutlery, combined with plain, traditional wooden tables and a light yellow decor. Dishes are based on fresh local produce, say, pressed mackerel and potato with 'tartare' dressing, sea bass, potato rösti and basil sauce, and Pavlova with red fruits and cream. An early report was enthusiastic about ham hock terrine with a spiced fruit chutney, smoked haddock and salmon fishcake with a lemon and chive butter sauce, and chocolate and raspberry parfait with a crème fraîche ice cream. The well-chosen, good-value wine list has some nice names along with more budget choices, to suit the varied needs of the clientele.

3 Quay Street IP12 1BX
Map 5: TM24
Tel: 01394 383145
Chef: Pascal Pommier
Owners: Jo Moussa, Pascal Pommier
Cost: Alc £17, fixed-price L £5 (1 course). ☺ H/wine £8.95
Times: Noon-last L 2pm (3pm Sun)/6.30pm-last D 9.30pm (10pm Fri, Sat) Closed D Sun, Mon
Additional: Sunday L; Children welcome; ◑ dishes
Seats: 50
Smoking: No-smoking area
Credit cards: ▬ ▬ ▰ ▢ ◪

Directions: From A12, pass garden centre on L. Quay St is opposite station & theatre; restaurant 100 yds on L

WOODBRIDGE,
Seckford Hall Hotel ❀

Magnificent creeper-clad Tudor mansion in sweeping parkland complete with willow-fringed lake. Plenty of interest on a menu that offers game terrine, two soup of red pepper and watercress, monkfish tail, pancetta and wild mushroom risotto, and lobster in its own vinaigrette. Wine list offers lots of smaller high quality producers, plus a Verre de Vin for about ten wines by the glass.

Additional: Bar food (Bistro); Sunday L; Children welcome; ❹ dishes
Smoking: No smoking in dining room; Air conditioning
Accommodation: 32 en suite
Credit cards: ▨ ▨ ▨ ▢ ▨ ▢ ▨ JCB

Directions: Telephone for directions

IP13 6NU
Map 5: TM24
Tel: 01394 385678
Fax: 01394 380610
Chef: Mark Archer
Owners: Mr & Mrs Bunn
Cost: *Alc* £26, fixed price L £13.50.
H/wine £10.25
Times: Last L 1.45pm/last D 9.30pm.
Closed 25 Dec

YAXLEY, # The Bull Auberge ❀

The eclectic menu of this historic hostelry juxtaposes the familiar with the imaginative. Expect sautéed medallions of beef with a green peppercorn and cognac sauce, and loin of lamb seasoned with Eastern spices and accompanied by a star anise jus and orange-glazed sweet potatoes.

Additional: Bar food; Children welcome; ❹ dishes
Credit cards: ▨ ▨ ▨ ▢ ▨ ▢ ▨

Directions: Adjacent to A140 (Norwich to Ipswich) on junction B1117 to Eye

Ipswich Road IP23 8BZ
Map 5: TM17
Tel/Fax: 01379 783604
Chef: John Stenhouse
Owners: John & Dee Stenhouse
Cost: *Alc* £25, fixed-price L£9.50 (2 courses)/D £14.95. ☺ H/wine £8.95
Times: Last L 2pm/last D 9pm. Closed Sun

YOXFORD, # Satis House Hotel ❀

East meets West at this country house hotel, where exotic Malaysian cooking is served in the elegant dining room. Look out for braised duck with lemongrass, chilli and ginger, and spicy chicken and noodle soup with coconut and king prawns. If the choice is too much, opt for the 'Kenduri Banquet', with dishes selected by the chef.

Additional: No children under 7; ❹ dishes
Smoking: No-smoking area
Accommodation: 7 en suite
Credit cards: ▨ ▨ ▨ ▢ ▨ ▢ ▨

Directions: On A12 just north of village

IP17 3EX
Map 5: TM36
Tel: 01728 668418
Fax: 01728 668640
Chefs: Debbie Forrance & Chim Blackmore
Owners: Mr & Mrs C R Blackmore
Cost: *Alc* £18.95, fixed price D £22.50 (5 courses). ☺ H/wine £9.50
Times: D only, last D 9.30pm. Closed Sun, 26 Dec

SURREY

BAGSHOT, **Pennyhill Park** 🏵🏵🏵

London Road GU19 5ET
Map 4: SU96
Tel: 01276 471774
Fax: 01276 473217
Chef: Karl Edmunds
Owners: Exclusive Hotels
Cost: A/c £55, fixed-price L £26.50.
H/wine £14.50
Times: Noon-last L 2pm/7-last
D 10pm. Closed L Sat
Additional: Bar food; Sunday L;
Children welcome; 🍴 dishes
Seats: 32. Private dining room 25.
Jacket & tie preferred
Smoking: No smoking in dining room
Accommodation: 106 en suite
Credit cards: 🟦 🟦 ✈️ 💳 🟦 🅲 💳 JCB

The original, creeper-clad Victorian house may have been significantly extended, but it makes a fine hotel with a lot to offer: magnificent formal gardens; 120 acres of grounds; stables; golf course. Within, the Tudor-style Latymer bar complements the ornate, heavily beamed restaurant which, in summer, extends onto a lovely flagged terrace with a covered eating area. Attentive, friendly service, professional enough to take Prince Edward, who was dining at the next table, in its stride – 'happily not a flap or fawn in sight'. A classic French style permeates Karl Edmunds' cooking, but that is not to say he is unaware of modern trends. Note roasted langoustine with avocado, red onion and corn salsa, and roasted squab pigeon with celeriac dauphinoise and Marc de Bourgogne sauce. Our meal took in toasted scallops on a tomato brunoise with coriander, mille-feuille layered with spinach and thin slices of quail, seafood spaghetti – a panaché of various bream, red mullet, lobster, scallop – with snappy saffron pasta, and a dessert of assiette of raspberries that included a light soufflé, a sorbet covered with purée and a tuile layered with milky chocolate ganache. The wine list shows depth in France but it does not ignore other wine growing regions. However, half-bottles are exclusively French.

Directions: On A30 between Bagshot and Camberley

CLAYGATE,
Le Petit Pierrot Restaurant 🏵🏵

4 The Parade
KT10 0NU
Map 4: TQ16
Tel: 01372 465105
Fax: 01372 467642
Chef: Jean-Pierre Brichot
Owners: Jean-Pierre & Annie Brichot
Cost: Fixed-price L from £10.75 (2
courses)/D £21.75. ☺ H/wine £9.95
Times: 12.15-2.15pm/7.15-9.30pm.
Closed L Sat, all Sun, 2 wks end Aug
Additional: No children under 8;
🍴 dishes
Seats: 32
Smoking: No pipes & cigars
Credit cards: 🟦 🟦 🟦 🅲 💳

Any restaurant off the beaten track that is always busy at lunchtime is a good sign. The small, intimate (i.e. you can hear the conversation on adjacent tables) interior could do with a bit of a face-lift, but the French cooking is the strength of the place. Medallions of monkfish on potato blinis with verjus sauce was a tasty, good-looking starter, and excellent quality meat was done full justice in a main course of pan-fried calves' liver with limes, accompanied by a selection of vegetables, served on a side dish. Crème caramel and warm plum and almond tart with vanilla sauce are amongst the desserts. The set lunch at £10.75 (croustade of scrambled eggs and coq au vin, for example) is very good value.

Directions: Village centre, 1 mile from Esher

DORKING, **The Burford Bridge**

This pleasant hotel nestles in the lee of Box Hill. The Emlyn Room restaurant offers a modern menu with ample choice, and dishes based on fresh produce where care and skill are evident in presentation.

Box Hill RH5 6BX
Map 4: TQ14
Tel: 01306 884561
Fax: 01306 880386
Please telephone for further details

DORKING, **Partners & Sons**

Oak beams testify to the medieval origins of this building, decorated in warm, rustic colours, with fresh flowers and plants adding to the appeal. Cappuccino of haricots blancs with morels makes a fashionable starter, and others, of langoustine soufflé with shellfish bisque for example, or spicy belly-pork with crisped pak choi and a relish of pear and pepper highlight the kitchen's eclecticism. Pan-fried best end of lamb 'tender, good flavour,' noted an inspector, on Puy lentils with Parmesan polenta and mint jus, smoked wild boar with sauerkraut, bread dumplings and caramelised apples, and roulade of scallops and Scottish salmon in chervil sauce have all appeared as main-course offerings. Puddings could run from simple rhubarb and custard to rum-flamed bananas served with coconut ice cream. Themed evenings, Italian, say, or American, take place every month. The wine list is well chosen and well priced.

Directions: Town Centre – Guildford end of High Street

2,3 & 4 West Street
RH4 1BL
Map 4: TQ14
Tel: 01306 882826
Fax: 01306 885741
Chef: James Tea
Owner: Irmgard Bland
Cost: *Alc* £27, fixed-price L £16/D £29. H/wine £11
Times: Noon-last L 2.30pm/7-last D 10pm. Closed Sun, Jan
Additional: Children welcome; dishes
Seats: 70. Private dining room 20/30
Smoking: No-smoking area; Air conditioning
Credit cards: 💳 💳 💳 💳 💳 💳 💳 JCB

EGHAM, **Runnymede Hotel**

Handy for the M25, but set on the Thames, this popular modern business hotel has recently spawned a smart restaurant, Leftbank. Two Olympic-style torches mark the entrance, while the bright interior has a nautical theme and an open-view kitchen. In summer, tables can be moved forward for alfresco riverside eating. The modern menu has Mediterranean and southern hemisphere influences, with a good balance of flavours. Fish is their forte, as evidenced by a main course of seared tuna on lettuce with a julienne of ginger, spring onions and chilli in spicy soya sauce. Praise too for a raspberry tartlet, light crisp coconut brioche topped with fresh raspberries and bitter chocolate sauce. Knowledgeable staff are happy to explain the concise wine list, which offers well-priced options as well as several vintage châteaux.

Windsor Road TW20 0AG
Map 4: TQ07
Tel: 01784 436171
(Freephone: 0800 121515)
Fax: 01784 436340
Chef: Laurence Curtis
Owner: Ralph Trustees Ltd
Cost: *Alc* £26.75, fixed price D £17.95. H/wine £12.95
Times: Noon-last L 2.15pm/D 7-last D 10.15pm. Closed L Sat, D Sun
Additional: Bar food; Sunday L; Children welcome; dishes
Seats: 150. Private rooms 10-350
Smoking: No-smoking area; Air conditioning
Accommodation: 180 en suite
Credit cards: 💳 💳 💳 💳 💳

Directions: On A308 Windsor road from M25/J3

EPSOM, **Le Raj** ✹

A kitchen run by keen owners who rely on a Bengali culinary background but temper the seasoning and spices to suit western palates. Usual array of choice – onion bhajia, lamb Madras, king prawn vindaloo – with a special selection that draws on marinated meat dishes.

Additional: Sunday L; Children welcome; ❹ dishes
Smoking: No smoking in restaurant; Air conditioning
Credit cards: ▆ ▆ ▆ ▆ ▆ ▆ ▆

Directions: Off the A217, near the racecourse

211 Firtree Road KT17 3LB
Map 4: TQ26
Tel: 01737 371371
Fax: 01737 211903
Chef/Owner: Enam A Ali
Cost: Alc £30. ☺ H/wine £9.95
Times: Last L 2.15pm/last D 11pm.
Closed 25-26 Dec

ESHER,
Good Earth Restaurant ✹

A warm welcome at this smart Chinese next to Sandown Park racecourse. Enjoyable dishes from the set menu include sizzling seafood platter of scallops, monkfish, prawns and squid, tamarind chicken with ginger and spring onions, and fried rice with shrimps and chopped vegetables.

Additional: Children welcome; ❹ dishes
Smoking: No-smoking area; No pipes & cigars;
Air conditioning
Credit cards: ▆ ▆ ▆ ▆ ▆ ▆ JCB

Directions: Sandown Park end of High Street

14-18 High Street KT10 9RT
Map 4: TQ16
Tel: 01372 462489
Fax: 01372 465588
Chef: Diep Sing
Owner: Holland Kwok
Cost: Alc £25, fixed-price L £12
(2 courses)/D £21.80 (2 courses).
☺ H/wine £10
Times: Last L 2.30pm/last D 11pm.
Closed 23-26 Dec

EWELL, **C'est la Vie** ✹

French restaurant in a listed 16th-century building. Expect classic dishes such as moules à la provençale, creamed langoustine and crab soup, magret de canard with honey and mixed peppercorn sauce, and grilled tournedos of beef served with red wine, mushroom, shallot and smoked bacon sauce.

Directions: Village 1 mile from Epsom towards Kingston.
Restaurant is opp. Lloyds Bank

17 High Street KT17 1SB
Map 4: TQ26
Tel: 0181 3942933
Fax: 0181 7867123
Chef: Lionel Jouanet
Owner: Clive Lane
Cost: Alc £22.50, fixed-price L
£8.95/D £15.95 (4 courses). ☺
H/wine £9.25
Times: Last L 2.15pm/last D 9.45pm
Additional: Children welcome;
❹ dishes
Smoking: No-smoking area;
Air conditioning
Credit cards: ▆ ▆ ▆ ▆ ▆ ▆ ▆

FARNHAM, Bishop's Table Hotel ❀❀

27 West Street GU9 7DR
Map 4: SU84
Tel: 01252 710222
Fax: 01252 733494
Chef: Douglas Hull
Owner: Mr K Verjee
Cost: Fixed-priced L&D £19. ☺
H/wine £9.95.
Times: 12.30pm-last L 1.45pm/7pm-
last D 9.45pm. Closed L Sat,
26 Dec-3 Jan
Additional: Sunday L;
No children under 14; ❹ menu
Seats: 50. Private dining room 20
Smoking: No -smoking in dining
room
Accommodation: 17 en suite
Credit cards: 💳 💳 💳 💳

Personally run by the Verjee family, this charming Georgian
town-house hotel is located on the west side of town. Attentive
service adds to the enjoyment of dining in a well-appointed
restaurant where three menus, one a particularly strong
vegetarian selection, offer a wide choice of interesting dishes
often utilising exotic ingredients. Roast rump of ostrich with
chestnut and pearl barley stuffing, for example, or the well-
judged combination of pungent chilli and fresh coriander that
dressed our lightly seared king scallops. Interest is maintained
with the likes of mushroom ratatouille wrapped in spinach
among carefully handled vegetables, but leave room for
desserts such as a well-made blackberry soufflé served with a
delicate Bramley apple ice cream. The wine list includes some
useful minor bottlings at realistic prices.

Directions: In the centre of the town

GUILDFORD,
The Angel Posting House ❀❀

91 High Street GU1 3DP
Map 4: SU94
Tel: 01483 564555
Fax: 01483 533770

Chef: Anthony O'Hare
Owner: Gordon Wigginton
Cost: Alc £33, fixed-price L £18.50/D
£21.50. ☺ H/wine £10.75.
Times: Noon-last L 2.30pm/7-last
D 10.30pm
Additional: Sunday L;
Children welcome; ❹ dishes

Ancient town centre hostelry, now a charming small hotel, run
with dedication and professionalism. The hotel's restaurant,
located in a 13th-century vaulted undercroft – which gives it a
church-like setting – has dark wood tables, silver cutlery, high-
backed tapestry chairs and is frequently fully booked, so
reservations are recommended. The kitchen shows an ambition
well matched to its strong creative flair and undoubted
technical skills. An early spring dinner earned praise from our
inspector for a smooth, 'full of flavour' smoked mackerel

mousse with king prawns and pimento vinaigrette, and a calves' liver feuilleté ('pastry a winner') with crème fraîche, grapes and foie gras. Sabayon of forest fruits with coconut sorbet was nicely offset by a tangy raspberry coulis. Other choices from a short, imaginative menu could be lobster tournedos with sautéed morels and fresh asparagus, and pan-fried pigeon with mushroom ravioli and a casserole of beans. Wines are pricy, formally presented and served.

Seats: 35. Private dining rooms 80
Smoking: No-smoking area;
Air conditioning
Accommodation: 21 en suite
Credit cards: JCB

Directions: In town centre (one way street)

GUILDFORD, Gate Restaurant ❀❀

Into its second year, the Gate has already built up a local following. Lemons, oranges and greens transform this small, narrow room down a back-alley into a cheery place; French staff also help produce a continental feel. Cooking is modern and light, with intriguing flavour combinations: grilled cinnamon quail on carrot and ginger with pomegranate, for instance. Dessert of white and dark chocolate mousse ('excellent taste and texture; good presentation') was the highlight of a recent inspection meal, which started with Lebanese meze (chopped peppers and dressed salad), and went on to tender chicken breast in a yogurt and ginger sauce. Drink is the Gate's other attraction, with a good value, extensively annotated list. Wines are ordered both by price and by diners' moods. Order pinot grigio Mezzacorona 1996 if you 'need refreshment now!'

Directions: In a passageway just off the main High Street in central Guildford

3 Milkhouse Gate GU1 3EZ
Map 4: SU94
Tel: 01483 576300
Fax: 01483 455068
Chef: Keith Russell
Owner: Liz Reid
Cost: Alc £25, fixed price L £12.95.
☺ H/wine £10.95
Times: Noon-last L 2.30pm/7-last D 9.45pm. Closed L Sat, D Sun, 25 Dec, Bhs
Additional: Sunday L; Children welcome; ◑ dishes
Seats: 44
Smoking: No-smoking area
Credit cards:

HASLEMERE, Lythe Hill Hotel ❀❀

Part of a hotel that is itself created out of a cluster of historic buildings, the restaurant, Auberge de France, is located in a 14th-century black-and-white timbered building in the grounds. Inside it is all mellow oak panelling and ancient beams and there is a bench set into the wall where, when this was a courthouse in the 18th century, miscreants sat awaiting trial. Today's guests are rather more comfortably seated to enjoy the cooking of long-serving chef Roger Clarke. A French-based menu acknowledges modern trends with the likes of sun-dried tomatoes in the tomato and basil soufflé, soy sauce in the crevettes à l'oriental, and medallions of ostrich garnished with a sauté of Mediterranean vegetables. These appear alongside classics such as Chateaubriand Henry VIII and the spectacle that is crêpes Suzette.

Petworth Road GU27 3BQ
Map 4: SU93
Tel: 01428 651251
Fax: 01428 644131
Chef: Roger Clarke
Owner: Lythe Hill Hotel Ltd
Cost: Alc £37, fixed-price D £24.50.
☺ H/wine £12.25
Times: D only, 7.15pm – last D 9.15pm. Closed Mon
Additional: Bar food L; Sunday L (12.15pm-2.15pm); Children welcome; ◑ dishes
Seats: 60. Private dining room
Smoking: No smoking in dining room
Accommodation: 40 en suite
Credit cards:

Directions: 1 mile E of Haslemere on B2131 off A286

HERSHAM, Dining Room ✿

*A suburban village cottage restaurant with heart and soul Fun-
reading menu, mainly British based, but boosted by other world
influences – Thai, Mexican, Cajun – from a specials board. Garlic-
pungent tomato summer pudding, and lamb and mint pie, are
recommended. A fun, informal place with pride in the kitchen.*

10 & 12 Queens Road KT12 5LS
Map 4: TQ16
Tel: 01932 231686
Cost: *Alc* £17.50, fixed-price L/D
£12.75 (2 courses). ☺ H/wine £9.50
Times: Last L 2.30pm/last D 10.30pm.
Closed L Sat, D Sun, 24 Dec-3 Jan,
Bh Mon
Additional: Sunday L; ❹ dishes
Smoking: No-smoking area; No cigars
& pipes; Air conditioning
Credit cards: ▨ ▨ ▨ ▨ ▨ ▨

Directions: From A3 at Esher take
A244 (Walton-on-Thames); turn L into
Hersham at Barley Mow
pub/roundabout; restaurant just
beyond village green

HORLEY, Langshott Manor ✿

*Elizabethan manor house of enormous charm and appeal plus
award-winning gardens. The Med inspires the menu – grilled sea
bass comes with roasted peppers, crispy prosciutto, olive and caper
dressing – although some fusion appeal with warm salad of chicken
served with kohl rabi, mooli and Japanese dressing.*

Additional: Sunday L; ❹ dishes
Smoking: No smoking in dining room
Accommodation: 15 en suite
Credit cards: ▨ ▨ ▨ ▨ ▨ ▨ ▨ JCB

Directions: From A23 Horley, take Ladbroke Road turning off
Chequers Hotel roundabout, 0.75 mile on R

Ladbroke Road RH6 9LN
Map 4: TQ24
Tel: 01293 786680
Fax: 01293 783905
Chef: Damon Dalmedo
Owners: Peter & Debra Hinchcliff
Cost: *Alc* £35, fixed-price L £24/D
£39 (5 courses). H/wine £16
Times: Last L 2pm/last D 9pm

KINGSTON-UPON-THAMES,
Ayudhya Thai Restaurant ✿✿

see London

OCKLEY,
Bryce's Seafood Restaurant ✿ NEW

*A former school, dating from 1825, with the building split between a
traditional pub and a restaurant. The emphasis is on fish and
seafood, with some meat alternatives. Plaice fillets filled with salmon
mousse and served with champagne sauce and pastry fleurons
proved an enjoyable main course at inspection.*

Additional: Bar food; Children welcome; ❹ dishes
Smoking: No smoking in dining room
Credit cards: ▨ ▨ ▨ ▨ ▨

Directions: 8 miles south of Dorking on A29

RH5 5TH
Map 4: TQ14
Tel: 01306 627430
Fax: 01306 628274
Chefs: Bill Bryce, Neil Taylor
Owner: Bill Bryce
Cost: *Alc* £24.75, fixed price
L £15.50 (2 courses). ☺ H/wine £12
Times: Last L 2.15pm/last D 9.15pm.
Closed 25-26 Dec

NUTFIELD, **Nutfield Priory**

Redhill RH1 4EN
Map 4: TQ35
Tel: 01737 822066
Fax: 01737 823321
Chef: David Rees
Owner: Arcadian Hotels (UK) Ltd
Cost: *Alc* £35, fixed-price L £16/D
£24. ☺ H/wine £13
Times: Noon-last L 2pm/7pm-last
D 9.45pm. Closed L Sat
Additional: Bar food; Sunday L;
Children welcome; ☻ dishes
Seats: 60. Private dining room 6-100
Smoking: No smoking in dining room
Accommodation: 60 en suite
Credit cards: 💳 💳 💳 💳 💳 💳 💳

An extravagant Victorian-gothic creation, the Priory is set high on Nutfield Ridge with far-reaching views over the Surrey and Sussex countryside. The Cloisters restaurant (inspired by the cloisters at the Palace of Westminster) takes full advantage of the view while offering sound cooking from a modern menu. Plump, succulent scallops with herbed polenta and a drizzle of herb oil, made a grand start to a recent meal that continued with nicely caramelised duck breast and sweet pickled cabbage, and ended with a beautifully bitter chocolate tart. Other choices on that day included carpaccio of venison with rocket, figs and a balsamic dressing, double-baked soufflé of goats' cheese and wild salmon, seafood navarin with roast garlic, thyme and red wine jus, and ballotine of pheasant with trompette mushrooms and parsnip purée. Desserts range from lemon tart with liquorice ice cream to spotted dick.

Directions: On A25 1 mile east of Redhill

REIGATE, **Bridge House Hotel**

An old coaching inn with sweeping country views, Lanni's Restaurant at Bridge House is now a friendly Mediterranean-inspired restaurant with an authentic Italian feel. Dinner could start with chicken and duck liver terrine, followed by fillet of salmon with mussels, prawns and a basil cream sauce. On most nights there's live music.

Smoking: No pipes & cigars in dining room
Accommodation: 39 en suite. **Credit cards:** 💳 💳 💳 💳

Directions: M25/J8 (Reigate), A217 under footbridge and then on R

Reigate Hill RH2 9RP
Map 4: TQ25
Tel: 01737 246801/244821
Fax: 01737 223756
Chef: David Dunn
Owner: Onesto Lanni
Cost: *Alc* £35, fixed-price L £15.50/D
£21. ☺ H/wine £11.75.
Times: Last L 2.15pm/D 10pm.
Closed L Sat, D Sun, Bhs
Additional: Sunday L;
Children welcome; ☻ dishes

REIGATE, **The Dining Room**

There's a lot to like about this very civilised first-floor restaurant in the High Street; its 'dining club' atmosphere, quality appointments and attentive, personable staff combined with a menu in modern eclectic style make this a place full of interest. The likes of roasted sea scallops with sweet-and-sour tomatoes and crispy fried cabbage, chicken and morel sausage roll with baby leeks and water vinaigrette, and tempura salmon with pad Thai and spicy dipping sauce, might be followed by

59a High Street RH2 9AE
Map 4: TQ25
Tel: 01737 226650
Chef: Anthony Tobin
Owner: Elite Restaurants Ltd
Cost: *Alc* £35, fixed-price L £10
(2 courses)/D £14.95 (2 courses).
☺ H/wine £9.50
Times: Noon-last L 2pm/7-last
D 10pm. Closed L Sat, all Sun, Xmas,

seared tuna niçoise with fresh herb dressing and balsamic syrup, perhaps roast fillet of veal with preserved lemon couscous and tomato chilli jam, or peppered beef fillet with lemon and thyme potato waffles and roast tomatoes. The one thing that is always on the menu is the super potato mash with olive oil. The short (two choices at each stage) lunch menu is particularly good value. Bibendum supplies the short list of wines.

Directions: First floor restaurant on Reigate High Street

Easter, 2 wks summer
Additional: Children welcome; ❹ dishes
Seats: 50
Smoking: No smoking in dining room; Air conditioning
Credit cards: 🔳 🔳 🔲 🔳 🅖

RIPLEY, Michels' Restaurant ❀❀❀

An air of tranquillity pervades this serious and expensive French restaurant, two minutes from the M25 on the way to Gatwick. There is very proper service, Wedgwood china and pristine table linen. The *carte* makes entrancing reading: rabbit cooked slowly with bacon and served with mustard cream sauce; freshly salted cod with a purée of garlic, new potatoes cooked in cream and finished with chicken jus; loin of hog marinated in red wine, pan-fried, and served with a terrine of black pudding and slices of pig trotter stuffed with mushrooms. It is a style of well-thought out, considered cooking one rarely finds these days. Tournedos of lobster with ragout of baby artichokes and fava beans with a balsamic vinegar dressing and crisp Serrano ham, was a superb dish. Big flavours with a big sauce came from a main course of hare cooked in Burgundy with garlic, shallots, thyme and bacon, served on an apple Tatin and dauphinoise potatoes. A selection of English farm cheeses, served in the French manner before a dessert of poached meringue in light custard and caramelised almonds, was included in the price of the latter. House wines are noteworthy for their drinkability, but although there is a comprehensive wine list by anyone's standards, the selection of half-bottles could be improved.

13 High Street GU23 6AQ
Map 4: TQ05
Tel: 01483 224777
Fax: 01483 222940
Chef: Erik Michel
Owners: Erik & Karen Michel
Cost: *Alc* £44, fixed-price L £21/D £23 (4 courses). H/wine £9.50
Times: 12.30-last L 1.30pm/7.30-last D 9pm. Closed L Sat, D Sun, Mon, beginning of Jan
Additional: Sunday L; Children welcome; ❹ dishes
Seats: 50. Private dining room 12
Credit cards: 🔳 🔳 🔳 🔲 🔳 🅖 💳

Directions: Take M25/J10 towards Guildford. First exit to Ripley just past lights on R

SHERE, Kinghams ❀❀

Shere seems a perfect English village in every detail, down to the blacksmith's forge, and Kinghams is a picture book house awash with rambling roses, the odd bronze statue and a garden ideal for outside dining. Interesting combinations of flavours are explored but handled with discretion: cold tomato and mango soup; tuna marinated in wasabi and soy dressing with a warm potato and chive pancake; shellfish fricassée with

Gomshall Lane
GU5 9HE
Map 4: TQ04
Tel: 01483 202168
Chef/Owner: Paul Baker
Cost: *Alc* £30, fixed-price L £10.95 (2 courses)/D £12.50 (2 courses). ☺ H/wine £10.50

Kinghams

Times: 12.15-last L 2pm/7-last
D 9.30pm. Closed D Sun, all Mon,
25-30 Dec
Additional: Sunday L;
Children welcome; 🍴 dishes
Seats: 45. Private dining room 24
Smoking: No smoking in dining room
Credit cards: 🔳 🔳 🔳 🔳 🔳 🔳

Directions: From Dorking follow A25;
from Guildford follow A246 then A25

coriander, spring onions and chilli. Main courses are more
conventional, roasted fillet of lamb perhaps, served with
tarragon mousseline on a potato galette, or tenderloin of pork
with apricot relish on Calvados apple sauce, plus there are
three prime quality fish dishes daily. If our inspector's lemon
and lime mousse with candied lemons and raspberry compote
is anything to go by, there's an expert pudding maker hard at
work in the kitchen.

SOUTH GODSTONE,
Tu Tu L'Auberge Restaurant   ❀❀

Tilburstow Hill RH9 8JY
Map 5: TQ35
Tel: 01342 892318
Fax: 01342 893435
Chef: Paul Hutchins
Owner: Antoine LS Jalley
Cost: *Alc* £28, fixed price L & D £15.
☺ H/wine £12.50
Times: Noon-last L 1.45pm/7-last
D 9.45pm. Closed D Sun, all Mon,
25-26 Dec
Additional: Sunday L; Children
welcome; 🍴 dishes
Seats: 70. Private room 30
Smoking: No-smoking area; No pipes
and cigars
Credit cards: 🔳 🔳 🔳 🔳 🔳 🔳 🔳 JCB

A name change (from La Bonne Auberge) and a new chef has
not altered the mien of this singular restaurant. The setting is
entirely English – a country house surrounded by extensive
grounds including a lake – yet service is very French, and
cooking is in the rustic French/Mediterranean idiom. High-tech
steel chairs furnish the bar, while the side lounge has a 1930s
aura. Food is served in the more traditional lounge and
conservatory. At inspection, slow-roasted tomato and goats'
cheese tart with walnut pesto offered well-balanced flavours.
Careful cooking was also evident in the main course of pan-
fried calves' liver with caramelised shallots and fried sage.
Steamed wild mushroom pudding with wilted spinach is an
interesting vegetarian alternative. Chocolate and pecan tart
with chocolate sauce and vanilla ice cream made a rich finale
to a pleasing meal. The long, serious wine list also merits
inspection; look out for bargains among the *premier cru*
Bordeaux.

Directions: M25/J6 – A22 (Godstone)
turn right after Bell pub

STOKE D'ABERNON,

Woodlands Park ®®

Woodlands Lane KT11 3QB
Map 4: TQ15
Tel: 01372 843933
Fax: 01372 842704
Chef: James Chapman
Cost: Alc £29, fixed-price L £17/D
£24. ☺ H/wine £11.95
Times: 12.30-last L 2pm/7-last
D 9.30pm. Closed L Sat, D Sun
Additional: Bar food; Sunday L;
Children welcome; ⍟ dishes
Seats: 28. Private dining room 8-140
Smoking: No smoking in dining room
Accommodation: 59 en suite
Credit cards: ▤ ▤ ▧ ▱ ▦ ▣ ▨

Victorian country house hotel with top marks for enthusiasm
and effort in the kitchen. The emphasis is on understatement,
backed up by accurate technique and sound buying of produce.
An interesting reading menu offers the likes of roast guinea
fowl with Savoy cabbage, smoked bacon, garlic and onion
creamed potatoes. A dinner in May produced boudin of
chicken on creamed leeks with Madeira jus, very fresh sea bass,
perfectly cooked, served with bok choi, good miniature root
vegetables, saffron potato round, and a red pepper and
balsamic dressing, and an excellent baked lemon torte with
whisky and orange sauce. Attention to detail comes through in
excellent bread, and a fun appetiser of a perfect single scallop
topped with a dummy shell made of thin filo.

Directions: On the A245 between Leatherhead and Cobham,
close to M25/J10

TADWORTH, **Gemini** ®

Suburban Surrey restaurant offering good-value lunches and a more
involved dinner menu of classically prepared dishes. Inspection
began with a wonderfully timed seafood tagliatelle, followed by
breast of guinea fowl with a five-spice cream sauce, and finished with
pineapple and apple charlotte served with mascarpone.

28 Station Approach KT20 5AH
Map 4: TQ25
Tel: 01737 812179
Chef/Owner: Robert Foster
Cost: Fixed-price L & D £24.50
Times: Last L 2pm/D 9.30pm.
Closed D Sun, Mon, L Sat,
2 wks Xmas & summer

Additional: Sunday L; Children welcome for L; ⍟ dishes
Smoking: No cigars or pipes
Credit cards: ▤ ▤ ▧ ▱ ▦ ▣

Directions: M25/J8, on roundabout turn R to Sutton, on 3rd
roundabout take 2nd exit to Tadworth, At traffic lights turn R,
restaurant is on L.

THAMES DITTON,

Avant Garde ®®

Typical French-style bistro 'except the decor's blue and white
instead of red and white', in the village centre. There's a
selection of works of art for sale on the walls, and the kitchen
delivers classic French cooking with a modern twist from a

75 High Street KT7 0SF
Map GtL: B1
Tel/Fax: 0181 398 5540
Chef/Owner: Frederick Dervin
Cost: Alc £20, fixed-price L £9.50/D
£15.95 (4 courses). ☺ H/wine £8.95.

range of menus – the set being especially good value – and daily blackboard specials. Fish soup with all the trimmings including a wonderful rouille loaded with saffron and garlic, medley of fruits de mer in which the fish quality was surprising – fresh, sweet tasting queen scallops, lobster and sole being the main players – and served with a champagne sauce, monkfish in red pepper sauce with a leek garnish, and magret of duck with a lemon and pink peppercorn sauce, show something of the style. Desserts include a nougat glace with chocolate sauce.

Times: Last L 2.30pm/D 10pm (10.30pm Fri & Sat).
Additional: Children welcome; 🌢 dishes
Credit cards: ▦ ▦ 𝍖 ℂ ▦ ▐ 🄯 JCB

Directions: 5 mins from Hampton Court Palace

WEYBRIDGE,
Oatlands Park Hotel ✿

146 Oatlands Drive KT13 9HB
Map 4: TQ06
Tel: 01932 847242
Fax: 01932 821413
Please telephone for further details

There are fine views from the picture windows of the Broadwater Room and diners can look forward to elements of classical cooking. Dishes to look out for include steamed turbot with champagne sauce, and chocolate gâteau, one of a tempting selection from the dessert trolley.

Directions: Through town, up Monument Hill, L into Oatlands Drive. Hotel on L.

WEYBRIDGE, The Thistle Ship ✿

Monument Green KT13 8BQ
Map 4: TQ06
Tel: 01932 848364
Fax: 01932 857153
Chef: Andrew Smith
Owner: Thistle Hotels
Cost: Alc £27, fixed-price L £13.75/D £19.75. ☺ H/wine £10.95
Times: Last L 1.45pm/last D 9.45pm. Closed L Sat
Additional: Bar food; Sunday L; Children welcome; 🌢 dishes
Smoking: No smoking in dining room
Accommodation: 39 en suite
Credit cards: ▦ ▦ 𝍖 ℂ ▦ ▐ 🄯 JCB

Town centre hotel with service that shows an extra degree of dedication. In the kitchen a young brigade try hard, producing well-timed, honest tasting food. Expect chicken liver terrine with Cumberland sauce, chicken supreme with glazed shallots and a mushroom sauce, and apple crumble with sauce anglaise.

Directions: Town centre – M25/J11, or A3/J10

SUSSEX EAST

ALFRISTON,
Moonraker's Restaurant

A 16th-century cottage provides a homely setting, an open log fire adds to the atmosphere on less cheerful days, and in the intimate setting a gentle mellow mood usually prevails by the end of a meal. Certainly the value, particularly lunch, merits smiles. The cooking is English with a French accent and features pâtés, roasted meats and fish with simple sauces, and desserts along the lines of crème brûlée.

Additional: Sunday L; No children under 8; ♨ dishes
Seats: 45. Private dining room 16
Smoking: No-smoking area; No pipes and cigars
Credit cards: ▬ ▬ ▰ ▱ ▬ JCB

Directions: Alfriston signposted from A27 between Brighton and Eastbourne

High Street BN26 5TD
Map 5: TQ50
Tel: 01323 870472
Chef: Mark Goodwin
Owners: Norman & Angela Gillies
Cost: *Alc* £19, fixed-price D from £12.95. ☺ H/wine £8.95
Times: D only, 7-10pm.
Closed D Sun, 1-14 Jan

BATTLE,
Netherfield Place

Netherfield TN33 9PP
Map 5: TQ71
Tel: 01424 774455
Fax: 01424 774024
Chef: Clinton Webb
Owners: Helen & Michael Collier
Cost: *Alc* £35, fixed-price L £16.95/D £26. ☺ H/wine £10.95.
Times: Noon-last L 2pm/7pm-last D 9.30pm (9pm Sun).
Closed 2wks Xmas/New Year
Additional: Bar food; Sunday L; Children welcome; ♨ dishes
Seats: 50. Private dining room 40
Smoking: No pipes or cigars in dining room
Accommodation: 14 en suite
Credit cards: ▬ ▬ ▰ ▱ ▬ ▬ ▬ JCB

Much of the fresh produce served in the fine panelled dining room, comes from the hotel's own vegetable garden – red cabbage, beetroot, broccoli and new potatoes on the night we were there – and bread is home-made. The kitchen works hard and has high aspirations. Mille-feuille of goats' cheese and duck livers sounded grim on the face of it, but confounded our inspector's cynicism by being hugely successful. Roast sea bass with sun-dried tomato and black-olive crust was well timed. Tempting ideas include pot-roasted wild rabbit with root vegetables and house-smoked saddle of Ashburnham venison with a rich Cassis sauce. A tarte Tatin was a little lacking in the caramel flavour department, but cafetière coffee came with dinky mini-sachertorte, flapjacks and Turkish Delight.

Directions: M25/J5 – A21 (Hastings) to A2100 for Netherfield; hotel is on L after 1.5 miles

BATTLE,
PowderMills Hotel ❀❀

Powdermill Lane TN33 0SP
Map 5: TQ71
Tel: 01424 775511
Fax: 01424 774540
Chef: Daniel Ayton
Owners: DC & J Cowpland
Cost: *Alc* £27.50, fixed-price L
£14.95/D £19.95. ☺ H/wine £10.50
Times: Noon-last L 2pm/7pm-last
D 9.30pm
Additional: Bar food L; Sunday L;
No children under 10; ❹ dishes
Seats: 100. Private dining room
18-20.
Smoking: No-smoking area;
No pipes or cigars
Accommodation: 35 en suite
Credit cards: ▆ ▆ ▆ ▆ ▆ ▆ ▆ JCB

Bonfire night has to be celebrated cautiously here – the original house, at the centre of a gunpowder works, was destroyed by an explosion in 1796; the present wisteria-clad mansion was built the same year. Back to the present – The Orangery Restaurant has colonial-style wicker seating and a black and white marble floor. In summer, meals can be taken on the terrace. The lengthy *carte* is best described as modern restrained, beef carpaccio with tapenade, and pickled pear and Parma ham salad, are amongst a choice of mostly cold first courses, followed perhaps by seared calves' liver with red onion confit and Puy lentils, or breast of partridge with creamed Savoy and roasted chestnut. Desserts might include caramelised lemon tart with tea-scented syrup and honey ice cream.

Directions: Past Battle Abbey toward Hastings, 1st turn R into Powdermill Lane just before Battle train station; hotel is on R after 1 mile.

BRIGHTON,
Black Chapati ❀❀

Oblivious to the vagaries of London fashion, the Black Chapati continues to plough its own furrow. Woefully under appreciated, even by the supposedly cosmopolitan citizens of Brighton, this place was doing fusion food long before the term was coined. Pan-Asian ingredients and concepts are given an intelligent twist. Hot-and-sour seafood soup is a great amalgam of flavours and textures, whilst crispy fried haddock with toe-tingling ginger and tamarind sauce is a revelation. French classics also get the treatment: duck rillettes re-emerge perked up with Chinese spices and garnished with a Japanese-style salad and toasted sourdough bread. Desserts are simpler, a lemon tart, or banana ice cream and butterscotch sauce. Decor is an exercise in minimalism – black tables and chairs, white walls and rather stark halogen lighting. Raw Breton cider and Czech Budweiser are both good quaffing companions.

12 Circus Parade
New England Road BN1 4GW
Map 4: TQ30
Tel: 01273 699011
Chef: Stephen Funnell
Owners: Stephen Funnell,
Lauren Alker
Cost: *Alc* £20, fixed price £10. ☺
H/wine £9.95.
Additional: Children welcome;
❹ dishes
Times: D only 7-10.30.pm (Sat from
6.30). Closed Sun, Mon, 2 wks Xmas,
2 wks July
Seats: 32
Smoking: No pipes or cigars in dining
room
Credit cards: ▆ ▆ ▆ ▆ ▆ ▆

Directions: Directions are complex. Readers are advised to use a local map

BRIGHTON, **La Marinade**

Intimate restaurant with friendly, helpful service. A test meal included a salad of smoked haddock and squid with tomato vinaigrette, and was followed by a matelote of John Dory, pan-fried with a wine and mushroom sauce. Dessert was an assiette including crème brûlée, chocolate delice and rhubarb tart.

Smoking: No-smoking area; Air conditioning
Credit cards: ▆▆ ▆▆ ▆▆ ▆▆ ▆▆ **C** ▆ JCB

Directions: From Palace Pier take direction of Marina, turn L at Royal Sussex Hospital sign, then first L

77 St George Road
Kemp Town BN2 1EF
Map 4: TQ30
Tel/Fax: 01273 600992
Chef/Owner: Vincent Lhuillery
Cost: Fixed-price L £13/D £18.50. ☺
H/wine £9.80
Times: Last L 1.30pm/last D 10pm.
Closed D Sun, all Mon
Additional: Sunday L; Children welcome; 🍴 dishes

BRIGHTON, **One Paston Place**

Clean, well-defined flavours are the hallmark of Mark Emmerson's style of cooking. He uses flavour to great effect in modern European dishes such as stuffed squab pigeon with boudin blanc and wild mushrooms, and roasted lemon sole with rosemary and asparagus. A meal in May started with a good pan-fried fillet of crispy red mullet with chargrilled asparagus, artichoke and a nice tomato coulis. Cannon of lamb was the centrepiece of a main course that burst with flavour: the meat came topped with a piquant mint and rocket pesto, and was served with tabouleh and oven-dried tomatoes. Dessert was a sound caramel and chocolate parfait topped with an orange and cardamom sorbet. A handful of New World wines and fine vintages bolster the mainly Gallic list. The restaurant is light and airy with yellow walls and stripped floorboards and a trompe l'oeil mural of an idyllic garden scene.

Directions: Just off the seafront about halfway between the Palace Pier and the Marina

1 Paston Place BN2 1HA
Map 4: TQ30
Tel: 01273 606933
Fax: 01273 675686
Chef: Mark Emmerson
Owners: Mark & Nicole Emmerson
Cost: *Alc* £30, fixed-price L £16.50.
H/wine £11
Times: 12.30-last L 2pm/7.30-last D 10pm. Closed Sun, Mon, 1st 2 wks Jan & Aug
Additional: No children under 5 at D; 🍴 dishes
Seats: 45
Smoking: No pipes and cigars; Air conditioning
Credit cards: ▆▆ ▆▆ ▆▆ ▆▆ ▆▆ **C** ▆ JCB

BRIGHTON, **Terre à Terre**

Great modern vegetarian, new location. But the menu remains global, the style bold. Chips are chunky with home-made ketchup or aïoli, bread is Italian – focaccia or ciabatta – and there's Thai green curry, sushi, even split-pea pikelet. Leave room for the parkin pudding with whisky butterscotch sauce, but the kids will want 'bum' until they find out it's Italian sheeps' cheesecake.

Directions: Town centre near Cannon cinema, close to Palace Pier

71 East Street BN1 1HQ
Map 4: TQ30
Tel: 01273 729051
Fax: 01273 327561
Chefs: Paul Morgan, Lawrence Glass, Ricky Hodgson
Owners: Philip Taylor, Amanda Powley
Cost: *Alc* £17.50. ☺ H/wine £9.20
Times: Last L 5.30pm/last D 10.30pm.
Closed L Mon, 25-26 Dec
Additional: Children welcome; 🍴 dishes
Smoking: No-smoking area
Credit cards: ▆▆ ▆▆ ▆▆ ▆▆ ▆▆ **C** ▆ JCB

BRIGHTON, **The Thistle Brighton**

Bang on the seafront, this modern hotel has two restaurants, one buffet-style. In La Noblesse you can expect seasonal cooking with puddings a strength: goats' cheese and wild mushroom ravioli, roast pheasant with redcurrant jus, and a trio of desserts (crème brûlée, chocolate parfait and apple tart) are typical.

King's Road BN1 2GS
Map 4: TQ30
Tel: 01273 206700
Fax: 01273 820692
Chef: James Williams
Owner: Thistle Hotels
Cost: *Alc* £23, fixed-price L £16.50/D £28.50. ☺ H/wine £12.50
Times: Last L 2pm/last D 10pm
Additional: Bar food L ; Sunday L; Children welcome; ⚫ dishes
Smoking: No-smoking area; Air conditioning
Accommodation: 204 en suite
Credit cards: ▬ ▬ ▬ ▬ ▬ JCB

Directions: On the seafront

BRIGHTON, **Whytes** ❀❀

A Grade II listed ex-fisherman's cottage (just where Brighton meets Hove) houses this unassuming restaurant with red banquette seating around the walls and cream-painted brick above. Pickled walnuts add a new dimension to a starter of poached pear with Parma ham, while balsamic and tomato dressing finishes off smoked haddock topped with Welsh rarebit. East meets West in main-course best end of English lamb roasted pink and plated on wilted pak choi with an 'Asian' sauce, and of equally contemporary mode is boned breast and leg of guinea fowl, stuffed with spinach and pine nuts and dressed with tapenade. Fresh fish may pop up in a first course of Thai-spiced cod with prosciutto, and there's always a fresh fish of the day. Staff announce the puddings, vegetables are said to be accurately and simply cooked, and those who order coffee get chocolate truffles. Three white and two red house wines start off the wine list and a choice for connoisseurs rounds it off.

33 Western Street BN1 2PG
Map 4: TQ30
Tel: 01273 776618
Chef: Ian Whyte
Owners: Ian & Jane Whyte
Cost: Fixed-price D £20.50. ☺ H/wine £9.40
Times: D only, 7-last D 9.30pm. Closed Sun, Mon, last wk Feb, 1st wk Mar
Additional: ⚫ dishes
Seats: 36. Private dining room 12
Smoking: No pipes & cigars
Credit cards: ▬ ▬ ▬

Directions: On the Brighton-Hove border, Western St is off the seafront, 1st R after the Norfolk Resort Hotel

CROWBOROUGH,
Winston Manor Hotel ❀❀ NEW

Things are getting better all the time at this pleasant hotel, and although the dining room looks a little dated, it is compensated for by enthusiastic, charming staff. The two head chefs have taken part in many competitions and their certificates are proudly displayed around the room. Our inspection meal started with a very pleasing dish of pan-fried scallops topped with intense tomato fondue and a raw salsa of courgettes, peppers and tomatoes, followed by (if you don't count the lemon sorbet) confit and breast of duck with sweet garlic mash, braised Puy lentils and a clear, rich, claret-based jus. An excellent dessert comprised three superbly executed chocolate puddings.

Beacon Road TN6 1AD
Map 5: TQ53
Tel: 01892 652772
Fax: 01892 665537
Chefs: Andrew Owen, Jason Kilby
Owner: Chasley Lifestyle plc
Cost: *Alc* £32.50, fixed-price D £21.50. ☺ H/wine £10.50
Times: D only, 7-9.30pm
Additional: Bar food; Sunday L (noon-2); Children welcome; ⚫ dishes
Seats: 50. Private dining room 30-180
Smoking: No smoking in dining room
Accommodation: 51 en suite
Credit cards: None

Directions: Midway between Tunbridge Wells and Uckfield on A26

EASTBOURNE,
The Downland Hotel

*Convenient for the town centre and seafront, this small, personally
run hotel provides warm hospitality and a pretty restaurant offering
an inventive carte as well as a set menu. Dishes are prepared with
quality ingredients and may include lobster and Armagnac soup,
venison with shallots, Calvados and foie gras, and dark chocolate
parfait.*

Additional: No children under 10; ⬥ dishes
Smoking: No cigars and pipes in dining room
Accommodation: 14 en suite
Credit cards: ▬ ▬ ▬ ⬛ JCB

Directions: On A2021 about 0.5 mile from the town centre

37 Lewes Road BN21 2BU
Map 5: TV69
Tel: 01323 732689
Fax: 01323 720321
Chef: Patrick Faulkner
Owners: Patrick & Stephanie Faulkner
Cost: Alc £27, fixed-price D £17.50.
☺ H/wine £10.50
Times: D only, 6.30-9pm.
Closed Sun, Mon

EASTBOURNE,
Grand Hotel, Mirabelle ❀❀

King Edward's Parade BN21 4EQ
Map 5: TV69
Tel: 01323 410771
Fax: 01323 412233
Chefs: Keith Mitchell, Simon Hulstone
Owner: Elite Hotels
Cost: Alc £35, fixed-price L £18.50/D
£30 (6 courses). H/wine £15.50
Times: 12.30-last L 2pm/7-last
D 10pm. Closed Sun, Mon, 2 wks
Jan, 2 wks Aug
Additional: ⬥ dishes
Seats: 40
Smoking: Air conditioning
Accommodation: 164 en suite
Credit cards: ▬ ▬ ▬ ▬ ⬛

The Mirabelle restaurant has its own access from the street, as
well as via the hotel, and is a bright, light room, in pink and
peach. There's a good set menu with interesting choices from
three starters and four main courses, but it is the *carte* that
reads particularly well, offering a variety of influences, with a
few oriental twists and some imaginative highlights. Crab
cannelloni, for instance, served on a fennel ceviche with
lemongrass and ginger butter sauce, was a cleverly conceived
and constructed dish. Cassis marinated venison was accurately
cooked, served with mushroom risotto with a good, sharp
cranberry jus counteracting the slight sweetness of the sauce.
Its counterpart, a very colourful and 'timed to perfection'
medley of seafish in a light shellfish nage, proved to be
immaculately presented on a squid ink pasta square 'table
cloth'. Tian of chocolate was filled with a delicate nectarine
mousse and accompanied by a peach schnapps ice cream in a
tiny brandy snap basket. Good cafetière coffee and petits
fours.

Directions: On the seafront at the western end of town

FOREST ROW,
Ashdown Park Hotel ✿✿

Wych Cross RH18 5JR
Map 5: TQ43
Tel: 01342 824988
Fax: 01342 826206
Chef: John McManus
Cost: *Alc* £40, fixed-price L £21/D £33. H/wine £14
Times: 12.30-last L 2pm/7.30-last D 9.30.pm

At various times a private home, convent and management training centre, this splendid Victorian country mansion, set in many acres of wood and parkland, is now a fine hotel. In the restaurant (which has an enviable outlook across a lake towards the forest), the attraction is the cooking of John McManus, and his team; it seems to get better every time we visit. Things begin with moreish canapés – on our last visit it was nice to be offered 'seconds' while a very successful cheese and smoked haddock soufflé starter was being prepared – and other details like the four different types of bread roll get equal attention. Mains from the *carte* might include goujons of John Dory with noodles and wild mushroom cream, lightly caramelised duck breast with crisp confit and spiced peaches, and saddle of rabbit stuffed with sweetbreads and pistachios and finished with quince jelly. Knowledgeable service is matched by a sound, working wine list, at its best in France.

Additional: Bar food L; Sunday L; Children welcome; ✿ dishes.
Seats: 120. Private dining room up to 150. Jacket & tie preferred
Smoking: No pipes and cigars
Accommodation: 95 en suite
Credit cards: 💳 💳 💳 💳 💳 💳 💳

Shortlisted for *AA Wine Award-see page 16*

Directions: From A22 at Wych Cross take Hartfield turning, hotel is 0.75 mile on R

FRANT, **Restaurant 37** ✿

35 High Street TN3 9DT
Map 5: TQ53
Tel: 01892 750635
Chef: Chris Billingsley
Owners: Mr P Allen, Mr K Sinclair
Cost: *Alc* £35, fixed-price L £15/D £22. ✿ H/wine £15
Times: Last L 1.30pm/last D 9pm.
Closed L Sat, D Sun, all Mon

Atmospheric building, dating in part from the 16th century, with Victorian additions. A modern menu offers the likes of terrine of cassoulet with olive oil and chive dressing, roast monkfish fillet wrapped in Parma ham with a red wine sauce, and rhubarb soufflé with fresh ginger ice cream.

Additional: Sunday L; ✿ dishes
Smoking: No smoking in dining room
Credit cards: 💳 💳 💳 💳 💳 💳 JCB

Directions: Opposite the village church

HAILSHAM, **Boship Farm Hotel** ✿

Former farmhouse, now a congenial hotel, serving honestly cooked food. Expect smoked salmon timbale filled with prawns and horseradish cream, pan-fried escalopes of pork with apple and redcurrant compote and Calvados and cinnamon sauce, with burnt orange cream for dessert.

Additional: Bar food; Sunday L (12.30-2.15pm); Children welcome; 🌢 dishes
Smoking: No smoking in dining room
Accommodation: 46 en suite
Credit cards: 🔳 ▨ ▧ ▨ ▨ ▨ ▨

Directions: On A22 at Boship; junction of A22/A267/A271

Lower Dicker BN27 4AT
Map 5: TQ50
Tel: 01323 844826
Fax: 01323 843945
Chef: Simon Dene
Owners: Forestdale Hotels Ltd
Cost: Fixed-price D £18.
H/wine £8.85
Times: D only, last D 9.45pm.

HASTINGS & ST LEONARD'S,
Beauport Park ✿

A fine Georgian mansion, surrounded by formal gardens. In the comfortable dining room waitresses in Victorian costume serve dishes ranging from grilled tuna with shiitake mushrooms and soy sauce, and Chateaubriand béarnaise, to steamed ginger pudding.

Additional: Bar food; Sunday L; Children welcome; 🌢 dishes
Smoking: No smoking in dining room; Air conditioning
Accommodation: 23 en suite
Credit cards: 🔳 ▨ ▧ ▨ ▨ ▨ ▨ JCB

Directions: On main A2100, 3 miles from both Hastings and Battle

Battle Road TN38 8EA
Map 5: TQ80
Tel: 01424 851222
Fax: 01424 852465
Chef: Duncan Biggs
Cost: Alc £30, fixed-price L £16/D £22. ☺ H/wine £10
Times: Last L 2pm/last D 9.30pm

HASTINGS & ST LEONARD'S,
Röser's Restaurant ✿✿✿

64 Eversfield Place
TN37 6DB
Map 5: TQ80
Tel/Fax: 01424 712218
Chef: Gerald Röser
Owners: Gerald & Jenny Röser
Cost: Alc £35, fixed-price L £18.95/D £21.95. ☺ H/wine £10.95
Times: Noon-2pm/7-10pm. Closed L Sat, all Sun, Mon, 1st 2 wks Jan, 2nd 2 wks Jun

Röser's is on the seafront road near the pier, and is distinguishable by its bow window 'although it does seem to merge into the other buildings and I drove past it three times'. Within, it's lots of banquette seating, frilly lamp shades, lots of wood. Quality and skill define Gerald Röser's style, with local produce frequently forming the backbone of his short menus. A signature dish of loin of Romney Marsh lamb, for example, marinated in olive oil, ginger, coriander and rosemary, or roast

Rye Bay scallops with a light lobster sauce. There's industry in the kitchen too. Wild boar sausages are home-made, and the salmon served with a potato pancake with crème fraîche and chives is home-smoked. Our own test meal produced some very satisfying food. Crostini of wood pigeon was full of flavour, and a simply prepared, well-timed chargrilled sea bass was served with a Med-style ravigote of black olives, capers, tomatoes and parsley. Dessert was an apple mille-feuille with Calvados flavoured crème pâtissière and a butterscotch sauce, all good flavours. Good bread rolls – saffron, white, rye – and excellent petits fours show the eye is never off the ball. Booking is essential.

Signature dishes: Roast seafood with langoustine stock; wild mushroom salad with truffle dressing; roast mallard with nine-spice sauce and pickled plums.

Additional: Children welcome; dishes
Seats: 30. Private dining room 30
Smoking: No pipes & cigars
Credit cards: ▨ ▨ ▨ ▨ ▨ ▨

Directions: On the seafront, opposite Hastings pier

HERSTMONCEUX,

Sundial Restaurant ❀❀

Thirtysomething years on and Guiseppe and Laure Bertoli remain as enthusiastic and as serious as ever about quality food at their auberge-style restaurant, dominated by a central display of cheese, fruit and vegetables. There are those who think the Franco-Italian *carte* a tad dated; others welcome the chance to enjoy feuilleté aux fruits de mer, mignon de boeuf au Stilton, and chocolate profiteroles done with brio and immense professionalism. The entire *carte* changes every fortnight and everything is cooked freshly to order and served in hugely generous quantities, along with excellent home-made breads. So, gird your loins, loosen your belt and feast on bouillabaisse, marinated fillet of venison with chive and garlic sauce, tender lambs' kidneys in mustard sauce, Spring lamb fillet en croûte, gâteaux and home-made desserts. And do bring the children, they will be made particularly welcome.

Hailsham BN27 4LA
Map 5: TQ61
Tel: 01323 832217
Chef: Giuseppe Bertoli
Owners: Mr G & Mrs L Bertoli
Cost: *Alc* £35, fixed-price L £19.50/D £27.50. H/wine £12.25
Times: Noon-last L 2pm/7pm-last D 9.30pm. Closed D Sun, Mon, Xmas-20 Jan, 15 Aug – 1st wk Sep
Additional: Sunday L; Children welcome; dishes
Seats: 50. Private dining room 22
Smoking: No smoking in dining room
Credit cards: ▨ ▨ ▨ ▨ ▨ ▨ ▨ JCB

Directions: In centre of village, on A271

HOVE, **Quentin's** ❀❀

This popular little restaurant has a strong local following who return time and again to enjoy French-style dishes with oriental twists. Quentin and Candy Fitch run the show, with Quentin cooking and Candy serving. The menu changes monthly and features locally caught seafood with additional lunchtime specials chosen from the blackboard. A typical February meal might start with a salad of pigeon and quails' eggs, dressed with walnut oil and mixed with croûtons and bacon lardons. This might be followed by pan-fried venison steak with juniper and port sauce, or perhaps breast of French duck served with a Madeira sauce and orange mashed potato. Desserts from the hand-written menu include apple pie with lavender ice cream, mixed fruit compote crème brûlée, and passion fruit mousse with spiced butter biscuits. All dishes are cooked to order, and the results are well worth the wait.

42 Western Road BN3 1JD
Map 4: TQ20
Tel: 01273 822734
Chef: Quentin Fitch
Owners: Quentin & Candy Fitch
Cost: *Alc* £20, D £18.95. ☺
H/wine £9.95
Times: Noon-last L 2pm/7-last D 10pm. Closed L Sat, all Sun, Mon, Bhs (not 25 Dec)
Additional: Children welcome; dishes
Seats: 28. Private dining room 20
Smoking: No pipes and cigars; Air conditioning
Credit cards: ▨ ▨ ▨ ▨ ▨ ▨ ▨

Directions: On the south side of Western Road between Brunswick Square and Palmeira Square

JEVINGTON, Hungry Monk ❀❀

Polegate nr Eastbourne BN26 5QF
Map 4: TQ50
Tel/Fax: 01323 482178
Chefs: Claire Burgess, Sharron Poulton, Gary Fisher
Owners: Nigel & Sue Mackenzie
Cost: Fixed-price D £24.95. H/wine £11
Times: D only, 7-last D 10pm. Closed Bhs (not Good Friday), 24 Dec
Additional: Sunday L (noon-2.30pm); No children under 4; ❧ dishes
Seats: 40. Private dining rooms 6-16
Smoking: No smoking in dining room; Air conditioning
Credit cards: ▨

This 15th-century flint house was once a monastic retreat, and original oak beams and log fires continue to set the tone in the candlelit dining room. French country cooking is the order of the day and guests are confronted with a difficult choice between classic dishes such as fresh Scotch salmon with red wine and shallot sauce, perhaps breast of Normandy chicken stuffed with leeks and cream cheese, and fillet of beef filled with foie gras and served with a caramelised onion sauce. Puddings include banoffee pie, as well as delights such as apple charlotte with vanilla ice cream, passion fruit custard tart, and mille-feuille of marron with cherries soaked in Kirsch. The wine list makes interesting reading, and includes a couple of bottles from nearby Barkham Manor vineyard, as well as a number of classic French wines to suit all pockets.

Directions: Follow the A22 towards Eastbourne. Turn R on to the B2105. The restaurant is between Polegate and Friston

LEWES,
The Thistle Shelleys ❀❀

High Street BN7 1XS
Map 5: TQ41
Tel: 01273 472361
Fax: 01273 483152
Chef: Allen Sperring
Owner: Thistle Hotels
Cost: A/c £30, fixed-price L £14.50 (2 courses)/D £25. H/wine £12.50
Times: Noon-last L 2.15pm/7-last D 9.15pm
Additional: Bar food L; Sunday L; Children welcome; ❧ dishes
Seats: 30. Private dining room 10. Jacket & tie preferred
Smoking: No smoking in dining room
Accommodation: 19 en suite
Credit cards: ▨ ▨ ▨ ▨ ▨ ▨ ▨ JCB

Once the home of the poet's aunt, the Georgian hotel stands in the main street of town yet retains a period dignity thanks to its fine furnishings and civilised atmosphere. The dining room overlooks a peaceful private garden with a terrace where meals can be taken in summer. The cooking is serious and considered, but keeps within charted waters. Dinner might start with red mullet and baby prawn terrine, or three-colour salmon ravioli in a saffron sauce, then continue with roast pheasant with foie gras stuffing and glazed kumquats or pan-fried fish medley with wilted spinach, oyster and champagne sauce. Seasonal specialities, such as morel and cep risotto with spring onions and Parmesan shavings, are offered at a supplement.

Directions: Town centre

NEWICK, **Newick Park** ❀❀

The Georgian house has been lovingly restored, and the panelled dining room, hung with splendid oil paintings, is light and airy from the floor to ceiling windows. Star turn of our inspection meal was the croustillant au chocolat, a richly flavoured but light chocolate mousse, served with pistachio ice cream, pistachio cream and vanilla sauce. We tell you this now, so you can leave room in advance for the superb puds. There were top marks also for the starter of tender, grilled lobster on leaf spinach with pea ragout, and the main course veal cutlet (top quality) served with a panaché of root vegetables, gratin dauphinoise and a rich veal jus.

Seats: 40. Private dining room 40. Jacket and tie preferred
Smoking: No smoking in dining room
Accommodation: 13 en suite
Credit cards: ▆ ▆ ▆ ▆ ▆ ▆

Directions: From Newick on A272 between Haywards Heath/ Uckfield, turn S on Church Road, at end of road turn L. Hotel 0.25 mile on R

BN8 4SB
Map 5: TQ42
Tel: 01825 723633
Fax: 01825 723969

Chef: Timothy Neal

Owners: Michael & Virginia Childs
Cost: Alc £32.50, fixed-price L £17.50/D £25. H/wine £9.75
Times: Noon-last L 2.15pm/7.30-last D 10.15pm
Additional: Bar food; Sunday L; Children welcome; ❀ dishes

PEASMARSH,
Flackley Ash Hotel ❀

Local seafood and fresh seasonal vegetables are the specialities in the spacious restaurant of this extended Georgian house, located a short distance from historic Rye. Traditional dishes such as chicken and brandy terrine and roast lamb with apple and mint jelly are carefully prepared and well executed.

Directions: M25/J5, take A21 (Flimwell), turn L on to A268 (Peasmarsh)

Rye TN31 6YH
Map 5: TQ82
Tel: 01797 230651
Fax: 01797 230510
Chef: Dale Skinner
Owners: Clive & Jeanie Bennett
Cost: Fixed-price D £22.50. ☺ H/wine £9.95
Times: Last L 1.45pm/last D 9.30pm
Additional: Bar food; Sunday L; Children welcome; ❀ dishes
Smoking: No smoking in dining room
Accommodation: 42 en suite
Credit cards: ▆ ▆ ▆ ▆ ▆ ▆ ▆ JCB

RYE, **Landgate Bistro** ❀

Friendly, informal bistro, open for dinner only. Good following for honest cooking that shows an awareness of modern trends. Fish is a strength. Note local squid braised with white wine, tomatoes and garlic, a very fishy stew based on the local catch and served with aïoli, as well as lambs' sweetbreads with ginger and coriander, and free-range chicken with tarragon sauce.

Smoking: No pipes & cigars
Credit cards: ▬ ▬ ▬ ▬ ▬ ▬ ▬ JCB

Directions: From the High Street head towards the Landgate. The bistro is in a row of shops on L

5-6 Landgate TN31 7LH
Map 5: TQ92
Tel: 01797 222829
Chef: Toni Ferguson-Lees
Owners: Nick Parkin, Toni Ferguson-Lees
Cost: *Alc* £20, fixed-price D £14.90.
☺ H/wine £8.40
Times: D only, last D 9.30pm.
Closed Sun, Mon

RYE, **The Mermaid Inn** ❀

Inn of some antiquity that's strong on beamed ceilings, leaded windows, ancient fireplaces, and linen-fold panelling. The cooking has a strong English character. Dinner in the atmospheric restaurant could be cream of celariac and Stilton soup, roast loin of English lamb, or meats from the cold table, and lemon tart.

Additional: Bar food L&D; Sunday L; Children welcome;
❸ dishes
Accommodation: 31 en suite
Credit cards: ▬ ▬ ▬ ▬ ▬ ▬ ▬ JCB

Directions: Town centre. Car park through archway

Mermaid Street TN31 7EU
Map 5: TQ92
Tel: 01797 223065
Fax: 01797 225069
Chef: Neal Sadler
Owners: Mr RI Pinwill, Mrs J Blincow
Cost: *Alc* £26, fixed-price L £14.95/D £25 (4 courses). ☺ H/wine £9.50.
Times: Last L 2.15pm/ last D 9.15pm

SEAFORD, **Quincy's** ❀❀

An attractive family-run restaurant housed in an old cobbler's shop on the High Street. Warm colour schemes, illuminated pictures and bookcases add to the atmosphere. The highlight of the seasonal, fixed-price menu is the range of freshly-caught fish from Newhaven: perhaps grilled sea bass on a bed of spinach with butter and chive sauce, or baked turbot with hollandaise. But there are many more treats to be found – look out for loin of venison with apples, chestnuts and sherry sauce, or guinea fowl braised with Puy lentils, basil and balsamic vinegar; and grilled fillet of lamb with aubergines and fennel. Starters could include devilled crab baked in puff pastry and fusilli with Gorgonzola and sage, while desserts range from warm almond and polenta cake with raspberries, to lemon and muscovado granita with brandied fruits. The wine list plunders the globe in search of quality, and features a range of bottles from the English vineyard Breaky Bottom.

Directions: From the A259 turn into Broad Street (opposite Caffyns Garage) then L into old High Street. Restaurant is 50 metres up on R

42 High Street BN25 1PL
Map 5: TV49
Tel: 01323 895490
Chef: Ian Dowding
Owners: Ian & Dawn Dowding
Cost: Fixed-price D £23.50.
H/wine £9.25
Times: D only, 7-10pm.
Closed D Sun, Mon, 1st wk Jan
Additional: Sunday L (noon-2pm); Children welcome; ❸ dishes
Seats: 28
Smoking: No-smoking area;
No pipes & cigars
Credit cards: ▬ ▬ ▬ JCB

UCKFIELD, **Buxted Park** ❀❀

Rattan chairs, climbing plants, unusual wrought iron chandeliers and lovely views over gardens and parkland, make the Orangery Restaurant a stylishly agreeable place in which to dine. The best dish sampled at inspection was a first course of tuna tataki served with a sweet soy and sesame dressing.

Buxted TN22 4AX
Map 5: TQ42
Tel: 01825 732711
Fax: 01825 732770
Owner: Virgin Hotels Ltd
Cost: *Alc* £38, fixed-price L £14.50/D £28 (4 courses). H/wine £11.50

Concepts are interesting: saddle of Sussex rabbit filled with a leek and morel mousseline with sloe gin sauce; baked fillet of halibut topped with a foie gras and tarragon mousseline with Vermouth cream.

Accommodation: 44 en suite
Credit cards: ▆ ▆ ▆ ▆ ▆ ▆ ▆

Directions: Turn off A22 Uckfield By-pass (London-Eastbourne road), then take A272 to Buxted. Cross set of traffic lights, entrance to hotel is 1 mile on R

Times: 12.30-last L 2.30pm/7-last D 9.30pm. Closed L Sat
Additional: Bar food; Sunday L; Children welcome; 🌢 dishes
Seats: 60. Private dining room 12-120. Jacket & tie preferred at weekends
Smoking: No smoking in dining room

UCKFIELD,

Hooke Hall, La Scaletta 🏵🏵

250 High Street TN22 1EN
Map 5: TQ42
Tel: 01825 766844
Fax: 01825 768025
Chef: Michele Pavanello
Owners: Juliet & Alistice L £9.75
(2 courses). ☺ H/wine £11
Times: 12.15pm – last L 2pm/7.15pm – last D 9pm. Closed L Sat, Sun, 2 wks Feb/May
Additional: No children under 8; 🌢 dishes
Seats: 30. Private dining room 26
Smoking: No smoking in dining room; Air conditioning
Accommodation: 9 en suite
Credit cards: ▆ ▆ ▆ ▆

Within a classic Queen Anne town house, La Scaletta is an elegant restaurant with something of the feel of a well-to-do family dining room. Table linen is crisp and white, table settings correct and service a combination of formality and friendliness. In contrast to the very English surroundings, the cooking is strictly Italian with the emphasis on the northern Veneto and Liguria regions: warm leek and bacon quiche with tomato and basil coulis; gnocchi with artichokes and smoked scamorza cheese; salmon mille-feuille with a courgette and broad bean purée; chicken with balsamic vinegar and braised lettuce; osso buco milanese. Desserts might include pannacotta with yogurt sauce, Venetian-style meringue and cream parfait, and dark chocolate, banana and rum soufflé. A few French wines supplement an otherwise Italian list.

Directions: Northern end of High Street.

UCKFIELD, **Horsted Place** 🏵🏵🏵

This is one of the country's finest examples of the Gothic-revivalist style of architecture. The magnificent pile is surrounded by its own 100-acre estate which includes the East Sussex National Golf Club. Within, there's a splendid Pugin staircase and smart public rooms. Allan Garth cooks in an assured manner, his menus are short, and offer a meeting point between traditional and contemporary ideas. Thus 'confit' of rabbit terrine is served with Savoy cabbage, baby onions and foie gras, and pan-fried fillet of beef with horseradish sabayon, braised shallots and asparagus. A well-reported test meal opened with ragout of red mullet and lobster set on a mound of spinach, went on to chump of spring lamb served with a

Little Horsted TN22 5TS
Map 5: TQ42
Tel: 01825 750581
Fax: 01825 750459
Chef: Allan Garth
Owner: Granfel Holdings Ltd
Cost: Alc £32, fixed-price L £17.95/D £30. H/wine £13.50
Times: 12.30-last L 2pm/7.30-last D 9.15pm. Closed 3-8 Jan
Additional: Bar food; Sunday L; No children under 5; 🌢 dishes
Seats: 40. Private dining room 22
Smoking: No smoking in dining room

crisp rösti, a parcel of onion compote wrapped in spinach, some broccoli and a mixture of tomato concasse, fine beans and runner beans. Pudding was an egg custard tart with prunes and crème anglaise with a blackcurrant coulis, and the meal was rounded off by excellent espresso and good petits fours.

Signature dishes: Roasted spiced tuna with spring onion, coriander and tomato; medallions of veal with squash gnocchi, globe artichoke and Marsala sauce; escalope of salmon filled with scallops and dill, served on a purée of Jerusalem artichoke and ratatouille; kougloff.

Accommodation: 17 en suite
Credit cards: JCB

Directions: Two miles South of Uckfield on the A26

WILMINGTON, Crossways Hotel ❀❀

A small Georgian hotel surrounded by good walking country in the heart of the Cuckmere valley. The restaurant has a relaxed feel to it, and is filled with oblong tables set on the diagonal. The fixed-price monthly-changing menu includes four courses and coffee, with typical starters taking in smoked duck and citrus salad, mushroom and bacon noodles, and ginger salmon with avocado. Our inspector enjoyed a meal that began with a light seafood pancake filled with smoked haddock, salmon and prawns with a white sauce. This was followed by a simple vegetable soup, and then a substantial main course of tender calves' liver and bacon with onion gravy. Next came dessert, and the choice so overwhelmed our inspector that she tried two! First was an iced white chocolate mousse with raspberry coulis which proved to be 'an excellent combination'. Second choice was chocolate and Cointreau mousse with Cape gooseberry garnish.

Directions: A27, 2 miles W of Polegate

Nr Polegate BN26 5SG
Map 4: TQ50
Tel: 01323 482455
Fax: 01323 487811
Chefs: David Stott & Juliet Anderson
Owners: David Stott & Clive James
Cost: Fixed-price D £26.95.
H/wine £10.50
Times: D only, 7.30-8.45pm.
Closed Sun, Mon, Jan
Additional: No children under 12;
 dishes
Seats: 24
Smoking: No smoking in dining room
Accommodation: 7 en suite
Credit cards: JCB

SUSSEX WEST

AMBERLEY, Amberley Castle ❀❀

Arundel BN18 9ND
Map 4: TQ01
Tel: 01798 831992
Fax: 01798 831998
Chef: Sam Mahoney
Owners: Mr & Mrs M G Cummings

An 11th-century castle complete with medieval gate house and working portcullis: the high curtain walls conceal delightful gardens in which white peacocks roam. Under Joy and Martin

Cummings the castle has been transformed into a luxury hotel, with individually-decorated bedrooms of great charm. Guests dine in the Queen's Room, centuries-old with a barrel-vaulted ceiling dating back to 1103. The colour scheme is an impressive turquoise and a 16th-century mural, commemorating the visit of Catherine of Braganza, adorns one of the walls. Chef Sam Mahoney runs the kitchen, producing sophisticated English dishes along the lines of juniper roast monkfish with smoked haddock ravioli and lemon broth, and grilled grey mullet with creamed potatoes, artichokes and a lobster shellfish sauce. Other dishes could include supreme of chicken with ragout of potatoes and pumpkin with warm parsley salad, and wild mushroom polenta with confit of fennel, spring vegetables and chive butter.

Cost: Fixed-price L £12.50 (2 courses)/D £35 (6 courses). ☺
H/wine £13.95
Times: Noon-2pm/7-last D 9.30pm
Additional: Sunday L;
No children under 10; ❹ dishes
Seats: 35. Private dining room 12, 48. Jacket & tie preferred
Smoking: No smoking in dining room
Accommodation: 15 en suite
Credit cards: 〓 〓 ▧ 〓 〓 〓

Directions: Off the B2139 between Amberley and Houghton villages.

ARUNDEL, **Burpham Hotel** ✿

At one time this country hotel was a shooting lodge used by the Duke of Norfolk. Now its peaceful location and relaxing walks are enjoyed by guests year round. The restaurant offers a Swiss take on European cooking with dishes such as 'butterleberli' – strips of calves' liver, pan-fried in butter with onion and chives.

Old Down Burpham BN18 9RJ
Map 4: TQ00
Tel: 01903 882160
Fax: 01903 884627
Chef: Stephen Piggott
Owners: George & Marianne Walker
Cost: Fixed-price D £23. ☺
H/wine £9.50
Times: D only, last D 9pm.
Closed Mon, 2 wks early Jan
Additional: No children under 10;
❹ dishes
Smoking: No smoking in dining room
Accommodation: 10 en suite
Credit cards: 〓 〓 ▧ 〓 〓

Directions: 3 miles NE of Arundel, off A27

ARUNDEL, **George & Dragon** ✿✿

Heavily beamed with a large inglenook fireplace, the old smuggling inn has a separate bar with its own extensive menu, as well as a more formal restaurant with linen napkins and cloths. The mainstream Anglo-French menu offers a good choice of dishes such as rack of Southdown lamb with a rosemary crust on an apricot and brandy sauce, and steamed brill fillet served on a bed of braised leeks with a Noilly Prat and lime sauce. Smoked quail salad with quails' eggs and a walnut dressing on a bed of French leaves is a lovely first course. Desserts are freshly prepared.

Burpham BN18 9RR
Map 4: TQ00
Tel: 01903 883131
Chefs: Gary Scutt, Kate Holle
Owners: James Rose, Kate Holle
Cost: Fixed-price D £19.75. ☺
H/wine £10
Times: D only, 7.15-last D 9.30pm.
Closed 25 Dec, Bh Mon
Additional: Bar food; Sunday L (12.15-2pm); No children under 6; ❹ dishes
Seats: 36.

Smoking: No pipes & cigars
Credit cards: 〓 〓 ▧ 〓 〓 〓 JCB

Directions: 2.5 miles up no-through road signposted Burpham off A27, 1 mile E of Arundel

ARUNDEL, Norfolk Arms Hotel ✤

Characterful old hotel, popular with local businesses. The kitchen makes a genuine effort to served soundly cooked, attractively presented food. Smooth chicken and leek terrine with a tangy tomato relish, pan-fried pork fillet served with a brandy Meaux mustard sauce, and bread-and-butter fruit pudding, show the range.

Smoking: No smoking in dining room
Accommodation: 35 en suite
Credit cards: 🖩 🌐 🌐 🗐 🌐 🌐 🌐

Directions: In Arundel High St

High Street BN18 9AD
Map 4: TQ00
Tel: 01903 882101
Fax: 01903 884275
Chef: Neil Jack
Times: Last L 2pm/last D 10pm (Sun till 9.30)
Additional: Bar food L; Sunday L; ⌘ dishes

ARUNDEL, The Swan Hotel ✤

This popular hotel in the heart of town has a lively bar as well as a tastefully appointed restaurant. The long, interesting menu may run from a starter of marinated sole fillets, through main courses of bacon-wrapped pork fillet or grilled salmon with prawn butter, to chocolate marquise or lemon and mascarpone tart.

Smoking: No smoking in dining room; Air conditioning
Credit cards: 🖩 🌐 🌐 🗐 🌐 🌐 🌐

Directions: Town centre

27-29 High Street BN18 9AG
Map 4: TQ00
Tel: 01903 882314
Fax: 01903 883759
Chef: Michael Collis
Owners: John Ryan, Steve Lowson
Cost: Alc £25, fixed-price D £14. ☺ H/wine £8
Times: Last L 2.30pm/last D 9.30pm
Additional: Bar food; Sunday L; Children welcome; ⌘ dishes

BOSHAM, Millstream Hotel ✤

Attractive, privately owned hotel, just four miles from Chichester; it's a popular venue locally for special occasions. Food is good. Expect smoked salmon and goats' cheese tart, leek and potato soup, cannon of lamb with thyme coulis, chocolate terrine with whole hazelnuts, and praline, and mango and passion fruit parfait.

Directions: Take A259 exit from Chichester roundabout and in village follow signs for quay

Bosham Lane PO18 8HL
Map 4: SU80
Tel: 01243 573234
Fax: 01243 573459
Chef: Bev Boakes
Owner: John Wild
Cost: Fixed-price L £13.50/D £19.95. ☺ H/wine £9.75
Times: Last L 2pm/D 9.30pm
Additional: Bar food L; Sunday L; Children welcome; ⌘ dishes
Smoking: No smoking in dining room; Air conditioning
Accommodation: 33 en suite
Credit cards: 🖩 🌐 🌐 🗐 🌐 🌐 🌐

BRACKLESHAM,
Cliffords Cottage Restaurant ✤✤

Classic French food is served at this intimate cottage restaurant with an *olde worlde* atmosphere. From the *carte,* you can order evergreen favourites such as chilled vichyssoise,

Bracklesham Lane PO20 8JA
Map 4: SZ89
Tel: 01243 670250
Chef: Tony Shanahan
Owners: Tony & Brenda Shanahan

escargots bourguignonne, scampi frite, Lobster Thermidor and magret de canard. The prix-fixe menu spreads its wings with dishes such as cream of fennel and red pepper soup, venison steak with peppered pineapple on red wine sauce, and fried chicken filled with mango on curry and coconut sauce. But don't forget the garlic bread.

Directions: On B2179 Birdham/Bracklesham road

Cost: *Alc* £24, fixed-price L £11.50/D £18.50. ☺ H/wine £9.25
Additional: Sunday L; No children under 5; ❹ dishes
Seats: 28
Smoking: No-smoking area; No pipes and cigars; Air conditioning
Credit cards: 🔲 🔲 🔲 🔲 🔲 🔲 🔲

CHICHESTER, Comme Ça ❀❀

Near the Festival Theatre (there are special pre- and post-theatre menus), Michel Navet's restaurant provides authentic French cooking in a charming setting. The main room – old brick fireplace, stencil decoration, dried hops hanging from a beamed ceiling – opens on to a delightful garden room with a terrace and verdant garden patio beyond, where tables are set under a creeper-covered portico. Starters might include mussels cooked in cider, onions and cream in the style of Michel's native Normandy, spicy beef salad with coriander, pecan nuts and sesame oil, and dressed Selsey crab with a mango glaze. Principal dishes range from roast guinea fowl with grilled fennel and orange butter sauce, and foie de veau à la sauge, to roast cod provençale. A tartelette de fruits à la violette made a splendid finale to our last meal here. Youngsters have their own menu that avoids the usual clichéd offerings. Good, carefully composed wine list with lots of choice under £20.

Directions: On the A286 near Festival Theatre

67 Broyle Road PO19 4BD
Map 4: SU80

Tel: 01243 788724/536307
Fax: 01243 530052
Chefs: Michel Navet, Olivier Vennetier
Cost: *Alc* £24, fixed-price L £17.75. ☺ H/wine £9.95.
Times: Noon-last L 2pm/6pm-last D 10.30pm. Closed D Sun, Mon, Bhs
Additional: Bar food L; Sunday L; Children welcome; ❹ dishes
Seats: 70. Private dining room 46
Smoking: No smoking in dining room
Credit cards: 🔲 🔲 🔲 🔲 🔲

CHILGROVE, White Horse Inn ❀❀

The setting is glorious – on the village green, at the foot of the Downs – the wine list outstanding, and the food of a consistently high standard. There are daily specials, perhaps oysters, scallops or foie gras, to supplement an already strong choice, plus daily fish dishes. The style varies – straightforward dishes include fresh hot asparagus served with a mousseline sauce and grilled calves' liver on a galette of bubble-and-squeak; others are more complex, such as supreme of local pigeon on a bed of spring vegetables topped with a roasted quail filled with pigeon mousse and drizzled with a port wine sauce.

Smoking: No smoking in dining room; Air conditioning
Credit cards: 🔲 🔲 🔲 🔲 🔲 🔲 JCB

Directions: On the B2141 between Chichester and Petersfield

Chichester PO18 9HX
Map 4: SU81
Tel: 01243 535219
Fax: 01243 535301
Chef: Neil Rusbridger
Owners: Barry & Dorothea Phillips, Neil Rusbridger
Cost: Fixed-price L £16 (2 courses)/D £23 (4 courses). ☺ H/wine £15
Times: Noon-last L 2pm/6-last D 9.30pm. Closed D Sun, all Mon
Additional: Bar food; Sunday L; ❹ dishes
Seats: 65. Private dining room 12, 20

CLIMPING, Bailiffscourt Hotel ❀❀

The setting might be 'repro', but the effect is highly convincing. The 'medieval' house was created in the 1930s from original 13th-century materials and antique architectural salvage. The restaurant has leaded windows and vaulted ceilings, and the formal service is by friendly young French staff. The *carte* is a mix of classical and modern styles – marinated woodpigeon with a salad of celeriac and beetroot with a mustard marinade, or warm confit of duck leg on seasonal salad leaves with truffle oil dressing, might be followed by oven-baked guinea fowl with

Littlehampton
BN17 5RW
Map 4: SU90
Tel: 01903 723511
Fax: 01903 723107
Chef: Frank Eckermann
Owners: Mr & Mrs Goodman
Cost: *Alc* £45, fixed-price L £19.50/D £35. H/wine £13.95
Times: 12.30pm-last L 1.45pm/7pm-last D 9.30pm.

Bailiffscourt Hotel

Additional: Bar food L; Sunday L;
No children under 8
Seats: 45. Private dining room 30
Smoking: No smoking in dining room
Accommodation: 32 en suite
Credit cards:  JCB

peppered swedes and Madeira jus, or fillet of sea bass on a creamed sauce of basil with house-made noodles. On our visit, dessert of tarte fine of plums – light crisp pastry topped with caramelised fruit, on a lovely tart sauce with a plum sorbet – was outstanding.

Directions: W of Littlehampton off the A259, signposted Bailiffscourt

COPTHORNE,
Copthorne London Gatwick

Copthorne Way RH10 3PG
Map 5: TQ33
Tel: 01342 714971
Fax: 01342 717375
Chef: Richard Duckworth
Owner: Millenium & Copthorne Hotels
Cost: *Alc* £25, fixed-price L £18.50/D £22.50. ☺ H/wine £11.75
Times: Noon-2.30pm/7-10pm. Closed L Sat, all Sun
Additional: Bar food; Sunday L (Brasserie); Children welcome; dishes
Seats: 50. Private dining room 10. Jacket & tie preferred
Smoking: No smoking in dining room; Air conditioning

The Lion d'Or restaurant has exposed beams and cosy corners and serves a sophisticated menu of modern French and English cuisine. Rabbit, lobster, crayfish, and oysters all feature – rabbit saddle, for example, is served roast with the thyme-braised leg in a grain mustard gravy, and lobster steamed with a balsamic beurre blanc. Rhubarb chutney and home-made soda bread make a fine accompaniment to wild boar pâté with pistachio nuts, and saffron mash with braised chicory and a Marsala jus underscore a main course of pan-fried calves' liver with veal sweetbread and kidney. Chocolate truffle tart is served slightly warm with whipped cream.

Accommodation: 227 en suite
Credit cards:  JCB

Directions: From M23/J10 follow A264 signed East Grinstead; take 3rd exit off 1st roundabout

CRAWLEY,
Holiday Inn London – Gatwick

A choice of eating here with the all-day La Brasserie and slightly more formal Colonnade Restaurant. As befits an airport hotel, the latter's menu takes inspiration from more than one destination: tabouleh salad with pan-fried red mullet; pesto mash and 'minestrone' jus with braised English lamb shank; Thai inspired roast cod.

Additional: Sunday L (12.30-2pm); Children welcome; ⏺ dishes
Smoking: No-smoking area; Air conditioning
Accommodation: 221 en suite
Credit cards: ▆▆ ▆▆ ▆▆ ⬛ ▆▆ ▆ ▆

Directions: M23/J10, take A2011 (Horsham & Crawley). Hotel at junction of A23 & A264

Langley Drive RH11 7SX
Map 4: TQ23

Tel: 01293 529991
Fax: 01293 515913
Chef: David J Woods
Owner: Holiday Inn
Cost: *Alc* £24, fixed-price D £18.50.
☺ H/wine £10.95
Times: D only, last D 10pm.
Closed D Sun

CUCKFIELD,
Ockenden Manor ❀❀

During summer, take drinks in the fine garden of this 16th-century manor house; in winter, warm yourself at one of the open fires. The oak-panelled restaurant provides a delightful ambience in which to enjoy the contemporary yet unintimidating food on the *carte* or daily changing menu. There's much emphasis on fish and seafood with typical starters including a robust shellfish casserole, cream-enriched bisque of Cornish crab and mussel, or home-cured salmon. The locally-farmed duck is another favourite, served pink and sliced in a honey and ginger sauce, or as a pistachio-studded terrine. Desserts may be bitter chocolate fondant with pistachio ice cream and black cherry sauce, or a spiced poached pear filled with mascarpone and wrapped in pastry. Alternatively, try the English farmhouse cheeses, some of which may also be local. The wine list, though predominantly French, shows care, imagination and offers a decent selection of halves.

Directions: Village Centre, off main street

Ockenden Lane RH17 5LD
Map 4: TQ32
Tel: 01444 416111
Fax: 01444 415549
Chef: Geoff Welch
Owners: Mr & Mrs Sandy Goodman
Cost: *Alc* £43.35, fixed-price L
£18.50/D £32.50. H/wine £14.50
Times: 12.30pm-last L 2pm/7.15pm-last D 9.30pm
Additional: Sunday L;
Children welcome; ⏺ dishes
Seats: 45. Private dining room 75.
Jacket & tie preferred
Smoking: No smoking in dining room
Accommodation: 22 en suite
Credit cards: ▆▆ ▆▆ ▆▆ ⬛ ▆▆ ▆

EAST GRINSTEAD,
Gravetye Manor Hotel ❀❀❀

East Grinstead RH19 4LJ
Map 5: TQ33
Tel: 01342 810567
Fax: 01342 810080
Chef: Mark Raffan
Owner: Peter Herbert
Cost: *Alc* £50, fixed-price L £25/D
£32. H/wine £16.50
Times: 12.30pm-last L
1.45pm/7.30pm-last D 9.30pm.
Closed 25 Dec D (non-residents)
Additional: Sunday L;
No children under 7; ❸ dishes
Seats: 55. Private dining room 16.
Jacket & tie preferred
Smoking: No smoking in dining room
Accommodation: 18 en suite
Credit cards: ▆ ▆ ▆ ▆ ▆

Gravetye was one of the first of the grand post-war country house hotels, and it remains an exemplar of all that such a hotel should be. Of course, it helps to start with a splendid Elizabethan stone manor house set in 1,000 acres that includes William Robinson's famous English garden, now restored to its former glory. The walled kitchen garden is also the source of much fresh produce, used by Mark Raffan to produce an imaginative range of dishes. Expectations here are high, along with the prices. An inspection meal included chicken terrine with aubergine mousse, oranges, walnuts and chilli dressing, followed by fillets of sea bass with caramelised cabbage and a sweetish sauce but a tempura soft-shell crab that had a clumsy batter more akin to that found in a chip shop. A caramelised lemon tart with raspberry coulis was well made with thin, crisp pastry. Details show that the kitchen can perform well with smaller details – super bread and petits fours, for example. Raffan was formerly chef to the King of Jordan, and some of the *carte* dishes display a distinct Middle Eastern influence, an interesting departure from the norm. The extensive wine list covers France in depth; note the range of champagnes. However, few choices by the glass and much that is pricy, but the Australia/New Zealand section rewards careful study.

Signature dishes: Pillow of salmon filled with crab, with lobster sauce; roast saddle of lamb with minted lamb pudding, with vegetables; ravioli of wild mushrooms; assiette of game; venison, teal, pheasant and partridge

AA Wine Shortlisted for *Award-see* page 16

Directions: Take B2110 from East Grinstead towards Turners Hill. After 2 miles watch for Gravetye Manor sign, forking L off main road

FINDON, **Findon Manor Hotel** ❀❀

High Street BN14 0TA
Map 4: TQ10
Tel: 01903 872733
Fax: 01903 877473
Chef: Stanley Ball
Owners: Mike & Jan Parker-Hare
Cost: Fixed-price D £19.95. ☺
H/wine £10
Times: Noon-last L 2pm/7-last D 9pm
Additional: Bar food; Sunday L;
No children under 12; ❸ dishes

The cooking here is gratifyingly better than both the pleasant but unexceptional setting and the mental alarm bells set off by the elaborate menu – honey roast cod, mâche and pickled onion salad, lime and star anise fumet, for example. But a complimentary starter of flavour-packed boudin of quail set the tone, followed by beautifully prepared ravioli of lobster on a potato and chive galette with tempura vegetables and a well-judged lime and ginger infusion. Then traditional cassoulet Languedoc, with a mango tartlet baked to order served with a

Findon Manor Hotel

Seats: 45. Private dining room 28
Smoking: No smoking in dining room
Accommodation: 15 en suite
Credit cards: ▆▆ ▆▆ ▆▆ ▆ ▆▆ ▆

little sauce anglaise and Benedictine and coconut ice cream that was spot on.

Directions: 500 metres off the A24 in Findon village, 3 miles N of Worthing.

GATWICK AIRPORT, London Gatwick Airport Hilton ❀

A large hotel directly connected to the airport's South Terminal by covered walkway. In the Garden Restaurant the menu never stands still. Recent offerings included hot-and-sour coriander bouillon, seared sea bass with pancetta, rocket and focaccia, soy-marinated beef fillet in black sesame seed crust, and cinnamon quince bread pudding.

RH6 0LL
Map 4: TQ23
Tel: 01293 518080
Fax: 01293 610894
Chef: Ken Paterson
Owner: Hilton
Cost: Alc £27.95, fixed-price L & D £25.95. H/wine £13.75
Times: Last L 2.15pm/last D 10.15pm. Closed L Sat
Additional: Bar food; Sunday L; Children welcome; ◕ dishes
Smoking: No-smoking area; Air conditioning
Accommodation: 548 en suite
Credit cards: ▆▆ ▆▆ ▆▆ ▆ ▆▆ ▆ ▆

Directions: Within Gatwick Airport complex at South Terminal

GOODWOOD, Marriott Goodwood Park Hotel ❀❀

Dating from 1786, this former coaching inn is set within the 12,000 acre Goodwood Estate, ancestral home of the Dukes of Richmond. The restaurant provides a smart, comfortable, and very English setting, for cooking from a kitchen brigade that has a strong foundation of skills and technique. The menu is a fusion of traditional and modern ideas as evidenced by dishes such as terrine of chicken and Parma ham with a tomato and red onion salsa, pan-fried foie gras with Calvados, apples and watercress salad, osso buco of monkfish on squid-ink noodles with a saffron and vegetable broth, and fillet steak on

Chichester PO18 0QB
Map 4: SU80
Tel: 01243 775537
Fax: 01243 520120
Chef: Mark Morris
Cost: Fixed-price L/D £22.50. ☺ H/wine £13.
Times: 12.30pm-last L 2pm/6.30pm-last D 10.30pm. Closed L Sat
Additional: Sunday L; Children welcome; ◕ dishes
Seats: 100. Private dining room 120

Marriott Goodwood Park Hotel

Smoking: No smoking in dining room
Accommodation: 94 en suite
Credit cards: ▨ ▨ ▨ ▨

horseradish and thyme polenta with salsa verde and red wine sauce. A saddle of hare with sage and bacon on plum sauce with spinach was particularly commended at inspection. Among the desserts a summer-like compote of berries was also praised as being tangy and full of sunshine.

Directions: 3 miles NE of Chichester. From Portsmouth head E along A27, staying S of Chichester. Signposted within area

HORSHAM, **Random Hall Hotel** ✿

A beautifully restored 16th-century farmhouse boasting old beams and flagstones, a relaxing atmosphere and enjoyable modern British cooking. Simple yet imaginative dishes may include chicken liver parfait with three peppercorn pickle, a rich lamb ragout with herb dumplings, and a well balanced chocolate and walnut mousse. Wines are well chosen and good value.

Credit cards: ▨ ▨ ▨ ▨ ▨ ▨

Directions: 4 miles W of Horsham, 15 miles SW of Gatwick Airport

Stane Street Slinfold RH13 7QX
Map 4: TQ13
Tel: 01403 790558
Chef: Jonathan Gettings
Owners: Nigel & Cathy Evans
Cost: Fixed price D £22. H/wine £11
Times: Last L 2pm/last D 10pm. Closed 27 Dec-5 Jan
Additional: Bar food; Sunday L; No children under 8; ✿ dishes
Smoking: No smoking in dining room
Accommodation: 15 en suite

HURSTPIERPOINT, **Boles** ✿

Situated on the high street in the heart of the village, Boles offers a monthly changing menu featuring seasonal local produce. Start with pear and Gorgonzola tartlet followed, perhaps, by roast cod with garlic and nut crust and a beurre blanc. There are regular jazz dinner nights.

117 High Street BN6 9PU
Map 4: TQ21
Tel: 01273 833452
Chef/Owner: Michele Bole
Cost: Alc £25, fixed price D £17.95. ☺ H/wine £8.25
Times: Weekday L by arrangement/D only, last D 9.30pm. Closed D Sun, Mon, 1 wk Feb, 2 wks Aug-Sep
Additional: Sunday L; Children welcome; ✿ dishes
Smoking: No-smoking area; No pipes and cigars
Credit cards: ▨ ▨ ▨ ▨

Directions: In town centre, half way along High Street

LANCING,
Sussex Pad Hotel ❀❀

Old Shoreham Road
BN15 0RH
Map 4: TQ10
Tel: 01273 454647
Fax: 01273 453010
Chef: Paul Hornsby
Owner: Mr WJ Pack
Cost: *Alc* £22.25. ☺ H/wine £10.50
Times: Noon-last L 2pm/7pm-last
D 10pm.
Additional: Bar food; Sunday L;
Children welcome; ❹ dishes
Seats: 40.
Smoking: No smoking in dining room
Accommodation: 20 en suite
Credit cards: 🟦 🟦 📶 🟦 🟦 🟦 🟦

The hotel is a popular local haunt, and the spacious, multi-purpose conservatory/lounge/bar/breakfast room is busy throughout the day. Ladywells Restaurant offers a fixed-price menu and specialises in fish such as sea bass with courgettes, aubergines and red onions in a pepper and orange sauce, or fillet of sole poached in white wine with Scottish mussels and prawns with parsley scented cream sauce and pilau rice. The cooking can be very successful, but there are moments when the advertised flavours do not stand up as they should – a pot of devilled crab gratinated with cheese lacked spiciness, and a grainy chocolate marquise came with a poorly flavoured coffee-bean sauce (not improved by the use of aerosol cream). Rack of Southdown lamb coated in Dijon mustard and herby breadcrumbs, with a sauce of lamb jus, capers and olives, however, was spot-on. Service remains attentive and efficient.

Directions: On the A27 between Shoreham & Lancing, opposite Shoreham Municipal Airport & by Lancing College

LOWER BEEDING,
Jeremy's at the Crabtree ❀❀

Contemporary British cooking with global influences is the order of the day at this roadside pub/restaurant. The style is a modern mix of Mediterranean with eastern touches showing through in dishes such as roast spiced lamb on pilaff rice with pickled aubergine and cucumber raita, and deep-fried squid with a chilli batter on crispy vegetables. A spring lunch might start with sautéed pigeon breast with lentils, bacon and a red wine and shallot dressing, followed by chargrilled veal kidneys on buttered noodles with tarragon in a light Dijon mustard sauce. The non-smoking dining room has a more formal atmosphere than the smoking room, but both enjoy roaring open fires in winter months. The wine list is well-presented and covers the favourites from both new and old worlds. Two dessert wines are available to accompany puddings such as orange polenta cake, hazelnut tart, and creamed rice with strawberry compote.

Brighton Road RH13 6PT
Map 4: TQ22
Tel: 01403 891257
Fax: 01403 891606
Chefs: Fredi Djuric, Jeremy Ashpool
Owner: Jeremy's Restaurant Ltd
Cost: *Alc* £18.50, fixed-price L
£10.50 (2 courses)/D £25. ☺
H/wine £10
Times: 12.30-last L 2.30pm/7.30-last
D 9.45pm. Closed D Sun
Additional: Bar food L; Sunday L;
Children welcome; ❹ dishes
Seats: 45. Private dining room 25
Smoking: No-smoking area
Credit cards: 🟦 🟦 📶 🟦 🟦

Directions: 4 miles SE of Horsham on A281 Brighton road

LOWER BEEDING,
South Lodge Hotel ❀❀❀

Brighton Road Horsham RH13 6PS
Map 4: TQ22
Tel: 01403 891711
Fax: 01403 891766
Chef: Lewis Hamblet
Owner: Mr G Pecorelli
Cost: *Alc* £45, fixed-price D £35
(5 courses). H/wine £18.50
Times: Noon-last L 2.30pm/7-last
D 10pm
Additional: Bar food; Sunday L;
No children under 9 at D; ❂ dishes
Seats: 40. Private room 80. Jacket &
tie preferred at D
Smoking: No smoking in dining room
Accommodation: 39 en suite
Credit cards: ▆ ▆ ▆ ▆ ▆ ▆ JCB

This beautifully restored Victorian mansion is the perfect place for a quiet break away from it all. Escorted walks over the 90 acres of well-tended gardens containing over 260 varieties of camellia and rhododendron are popular with guests, and a good way to work up an appetite for Lewis Hamblet's skilled, attentive cooking, backed up by industrious enterprise: good use is made of produce grown in the hotel's walled garden, for example. He picks and chooses ideas with dexterity, pulling in influences from far and wide. An April dinner produced pan-fried foie gras with apple and raisin chutney, scallops with pine butter sauce set on a bed of puréed parsnips and served with yam chips, confit of duck with pumpkin risotto, John Dory with Anna potatoes and a foie gras butter, warm oranges in a clove syrup with pistachio ice cream, and Belgian chocolate mousse with rhubarb and fig sorbet. Canapés, home-made bread rolls, and petits fours, are all prepared with equal dedication. An excellent, short-choice set lunch could bring fried polenta with peppers and olive oil, loin of Marsh lamb with sweet-and-sour tomatoes and dauphinoise potatoes, and warmed red fruits with clotted cream. The wine list is comprehensive, but best of all (within reason) they will open any bottle for serving by the glass.

Directions: At junction of A279 (Horsham) and A281, turn onto the Cowfold/Brighton road. Hotel is 0.5 mile on R

MIDHURST, Angel Hotel ❀❀

North Street
GU29 9DN
Map 4: SU82
Tel: 01730 812421
Fax: 01730 815928

A fine old building, Tudor with Georgian additions, which was used as a courthouse until the late 19th century. In the kitchen, Leo Manin'Tveld thoughtfully incorporates interesting ingredients into classic dishes – steamed Devon brill with samphire, crayfish and shellfish sauce, cold poached salmon with pickled fennel and lemon mayonnaise, and salt cod fishcakes with niçoise salad, for example, or uses familiar items in unfamiliar ways, such as chargrilled Scotch rib of beef with horseradish beignets and herb butter, or honey roast duck with damsons. Confidence in the quality of ingredients is witnessed by the inclusion in the *carte* of dishes such as antipasta of Italian cured meats with mustard fruits and gremolata, and lobster, avocado and mango salad. A first course of chicken liver and pork pâté with fig chutney was

Chef: Leo Manin'Tveld

Owners: Peter Crawford-Rolt,
Nicholas Davies
Cost: *Alc* £24.95, fixed price L
£15.50/D £21. ☺ H/wine £11.75
Times: Noon-last L 2.30pm/7.-last D
9.30pm

Angel Hotel

Additional: Bar food; Sunday L;
Children welcome; ❸ dishes
Seats: Private dining rooms 35 & 60
Smoking: No pipes and cigars
Accommodation: 28 en suite
Credit cards: 🔲 🔲 🔲 🔲 🔲 🔲

well made but somewhat closely textured. A clear thumbs-up,
however, on a main course of excellent roast rack of lamb
coated with mustard and herbed breadcrumbs, with a fine
lamb and rosemary jus, some excellent gratin dauphinoise
and a selection of precisely-timed baby vegetables. The
standards remains consistently high through to dessert with
Eton mess, summer pudding with clotted cream, and hot
banana tart, featuring among the spot-on desserts. As well as
the elegant, airy Cowdray Room, you can eat in The
Brasserie, where a menu of warm salad of duck confit, spring
onions and plum juice, or local free-range chicken breast
chargrilled with ratatouille and basil oil, and braised
marinated oxtail with orange and port wine; poached pear in
mulled wine with red wine ice cream, also requires serious
judicial consideration.

 Signature dishes: Lobster, avocado and mango salad; roast
best end of Southdown lamb, ragout of kidneys and
redcurrants; honey roast duck breast with damsons in a port
wine sauce; roast stuffed breast of turkey with spinach, pine
nuts and lemon

Directions: Town centre, junction of A286 and A2721

MIDHURST,
Southdowns Hotel ❀❀

Trotton GU31 5JN
Map 4: SU82
Tel: 01730 821521
Fax: 01730 821790
Chef: Toni Bale
Owner: Dominic Vedovato
Cost: *Alc* £10, fixed-price D £19.95.
☺ H/wine £10.95
Times: Noon-last L 2pm/7-last
D 9.30pm
Additional: Bar food; Sunday L;
No children under 12; ❸ dishes
Seats: 60. Private dining room 20
Smoking: No-smoking area; No pipes
and cigars; Air conditioning
Accommodation: 20 en suite
Credit cards: 🔲 🔲 🔲 🔲 🔲 🔲 🔲

Expect informal lunches and candlelit dinners at this
welcoming country hotel in the heart of rural West Sussex. The
room's centrepiece of flowers, liqueurs and cheeses appears

fairly conventional when contrasted with a 'fusion' menu that combines Mediterranean flavours with Pacific Rim influences. Dishes such as sushi of king prawn with wasabi and pickled samphire, prosciutto and honey-roasted fig, for example, or charred sea bass with saffron risotto and scallop roe essence, perhaps sea-salted skate wing with green onion and soy refreshments, and a five pepper and herb-seared venison with cherry tomato fondue and boudin noir sauce. There are some interesting vegetarian options too. For the less adventurous there are steaks with tomatoes, field mushrooms and béarnaise sauce. Caramelised lemon tart with clotted cream, and traditional bread-and-butter pudding are among desserts that might also include pannacotta with tamarind sauce.

Directions: 1 mile off A272 Petersfield Road

MIDHURST, **Spread Eagle Hotel**

South Street GU29 9NH
Map 4: SU82
Tel: 01730 816911
Fax: 01730 815668
Chef: Ken Jelf
Owners: Mr & Mrs Goodman
Cost: Fixed-price D £28.50.
H/wine £9.95
Times: 12.30-2pm/7.30- 9.30pm
Additional: Sunday L; Children welcome; 🍴 dishes
Seats: 70. Private dining room 6-22
Smoking: No smoking in dining room
Accommodation: 40 en suite
Credit cards: ▨ ▨ ▨ ▨ ▨

Overlooking the market square, this medieval coaching inn is full of character with its sloping floors, ancient beams and inglenook fireplaces. Today's guests can, however, expect considerably more comfort than their predecessors. They can also look forward to some splendid meals, with the restaurant offering a modern take on traditional dishes such as sautéed calves' liver with tomato, basil and spinach, breast of maize-fed chicken with morel mushroom risotto, and Loch Fyne salmon with roasted provençale vegetables and a light pistou sauce. A summer meal sampled by our inspector started with parsnip soup and home-made breads, followed by Orkney scallops with spinach sauce and salad leaves. The main course of breast of guinea fowl with lentils and root vegetables was correctly cooked, while for dessert, orange terrine with citrus compote was nice and zingy. The wine list provides substantial choice, but stick to the house selection to get the best value.

Directions: Town centre, corner of South and West Streets.

PULBOROUGH, **Chequers Hotel**

Dating back to the 16th-century, Chequers is a small, intimate hotel overlooking the Arun Valley. For three decades John Searancke has ensured that the service and hospitality here are of the highest standard. New ideas and enthusiasm in the kitchen have recently boosted the fixed-price lunch and dinner menus, so that visitors can now expect modern English dishes

Church Place RH20 1AD
Map 4: TQ01
Tel: 01798 872486
Fax: 01798 872715
Chef: Kevin Chatfield
Owner: John Searancke
Cost: Fixed-price L 12.50/D £20.95
(4 courses). ☺ H/wine £10.25

Times: Noon-last L 1.45pm/7.15-last
D 8.45pm
Additional: Bar food; Sunday L;
Children welcome; ❸ dishes
Seats: 24. Private dining room 19
Smoking: No smoking in dining room
Accommodation: 11 rooms (10 en
suite)
Credit cards: ▬ ▬ ▬ ▬ ▬ ▬ ▬

along the lines of sauté of pigeon breasts on savoury mash with
rich game jus, and casserole of saffron-scented seafood with
fresh herb pasta. A winter dinner by candlelight might start
with soup of root vegetables topped with sour cream, followed
by roast tenderloin of pork with glazed apricots and a
peppercorn sauce. Dessert could be sticky toffee pudding, or
perhaps bread-and-butter pudding filled with bananas and
rum. On sunny summer days guests are encouraged to take
their aperitif on the patio or in the secluded garden.

Directions: On A29 just N of Pulborough, turn R opposite the
church

PULBOROUGH, Stane Street Hollow Restaurant ❀❀

René and Ann Kaiser have built up a loyal following at their
long-established restaurant. The stone building dates back
nearly 500 years. It is a charming place with several cosy
dining rooms, and cow bells, flags and emblems proclaiming
René's Swiss origins. Ann looks after front of house in a
relaxed and caring way; the newspaper provided for our lone
inspector being a typically thoughtful touch. The French
country menu changes monthly to reflect the availability of
seasonal produce and takes in home-grown herbs and
vegetables, as well as home-smoked salmon and ham. A well-
reported meal began with a slither of duck parfait with star-
shaped croûton and pickled chanterelles before the starter
proper, a coriander-flavoured crab galette. A moist supreme
of guinea fowl stuffed with smoked ham and sage and served
on a bed of lentils with red wine sauce, proved a successful
main dish. An intensely rich chocolate tart came with a tangy
orange sauce, which proved to be a good foil. The sound wine
list is fairly priced.

Directions: N of Pulborough on A29 at Codmore Hill

Codmore Hill RH20 1BG
Map 4: TQ01
Tel: 01798 872819
Chef: René Kaiser
Owners: René & Ann Kaiser
Cost: *Alc* £25.50, fixed-price L
£15.50. H/wine £12
Times: 12.30-1.15pm/7.30-9.30pm.
Closed D Sun, Mon, Tue, 24 Dec-6
Jan, 2 wks May, 2 wks Oct
Additional: Sunday L; Children
welcome; ❸ dishes
Seats: 34. Private dining room 14/20
Smoking: No smoking in dining room
Credit cards: ▬ ▬ ▬ ▬ ▬ JCB

STORRINGTON,
Manleys Restaurant ❀❀❀

Manley's is real country restaurant, something of an institution
nowadays. There's a cottagey feel to the decor, but that is
tempered by a degree of elegance in the table settings, with the

Manleys Hill RH20 4BT
Map 4: TQ01
Tel: 01903 742331
Fax: 01903 740649
Chef/Owner: Karl Löderer

M logo prominent on plates, silverware and cutlery. Karl Löderer continues to plough the same classical furrow, built into what one inspector describes as the full country-house Monty: canapés to petits fours with *amuse-bouche* and three full courses thrown in, chosen from menus written in French with concise English translations. Canapés were a bouchée of cream cheese and smoked salmon, melted Stilton on crisp toast, and paprika-coated cheese straws. An *amuse-bouche* was an assembly of smoked chicken and grated Gruyère with some well-dressed leaves and tomato concasse. Crab and langoustine gratin flavoured with a quite intense ginger jus opened the meal proper, to be followed by a main course that also had ginger notes – a good breast of duck in an oriental marinade, grilled and served with ginger-flavoured cabbage. Pudding was a meringue hollowed out and filled with butterscotch ice cream with Chantilly and a good butterscotch sauce, the kind of confection Karl does well. Margaret Löderer runs front of house with great style.

Signature dishes: Scallops and king prawns in puff pastry with aubergine purée; pancake – mixed fresh fruit and raspberry sauce.

Directions: On the main A283, off the A24, just E of Storrington.

Cost: *Alc* £42.80, fixed-price L £19.60/D £33.50. H/wine £14.80
Times: 12.15-last L 1.45pm/7.15-last D 8.45pm. Closed D Sun, all Mon, D Tue, 2 wks Jan
Additional: Sunday L; Children welcome; ◑ dishes
Seats: 48. Private room 22
Smoking: No pipes & cigars
Accommodation: 1 en suite
Credit cards: ▒▒ ▒▒ ▒▒ ▒ ▒▒ ▒ JCB

STORRINGTON, Old Forge ❀❀

6 Church Street RH20 4LA
Map 4: TQ01
Tel: 01903 743402
Fax: 01903 742540
Chef: Clive Roberts
Owners: Cathy & Clive Roberts
Cost: *Alc* £27.50, fixed-price L £16/D £22.50. ☺ H/wine £11
Times: 12.30-last L 1.30pm/7.15-last D 9pm. Closed L Sat, D Sun, all Mon, Tue, 2 wks spring, 2 wks autumn
Additional: Sunday L; Children welcome; ◑ dishes
Seats: 36. Private room 14
Smoking: No smoking in dining rom
Credit cards: ▒▒ ▒▒ ▒▒ ▒ ▒▒ ▒

Set just off the main street, the Old Forge enjoys a cosy atmosphere with its low beams, rough white walls and three separate dining rooms. Cathy Roberts welcomes guests while Clive cooks. His monthly menus bring touches of invention to reliable dishes such as roast calves' liver with raspberry vinegar, bacon and sage apples, and chargrilled corn-fed chicken on artichoke and black olive pappardelle. An early summer meal might start with chicken and ham terrine with a mixed leaf salad, followed by grilled fillet of sea bass served with an orange and toasted almond sauce. For dessert, a caramelised orange tart with Campari sorbet or perhaps apple and champagne shortbread. An attractive wine list goes for the New World in a big way, although there is a fair representation from across the globe. All bottles are keenly priced and come with personal tasting notes.

Directions: On a side street in the village centre

TURNERS HILL, **Alexander House**

Alexander House is a particularly fine 17th-century country mansion set in over one hundred acres of well-tended gardens. The public rooms feature luxurious furnishings and splendid works of art: the sunny south drawing room and the oak-panelled library – warmed by a log fire in winter months – are both great places to relax before dinner. Tail-coated waiters provide an impressively polished service in the dining room, where guests enjoy a range of modern British cooking prepared by chef Neil Wiggins. Typical starters include white bean soup flavoured with truffle oil, seared scallops with lobster and mussel jus, and pan-fried terrine of goats' cheese with sun-dried tomato and black olive tapenade. An inspection meal in February started with mille-feuille of duck confit between layers of lacy potato. The main course, a nicely-cooked fresh fillet of brill, was steamed just so and served with saffron potatoes and baby leeks.

East Street RH10 4QD
Map 4: TQ33
Tel: 01342 714914
Fax: 01342 717328
Chef: Neil Wiggins
Owner: International Hotels Ltd
Cost: Alc £45, fixed-price L £22/D £28. H/wine £15.25
Times: 12.30-last L 2.30pm/7-last D 9.30pm
Additional: Bar food; Sunday L; ◑ dishes
Seats: 60. Private dining room 10, 30
Smoking: No smoking in dining room
Accommodation: 15 en suite
Credit cards: ▆ ▆ ▆ ▆ ▆ JCB

Directions: 1.5 mile east of Turners Hill on the B2110

WASHINGTON, **The Chardonnay**

Large, cottage-style restaurant with conservatory extension that offers a lengthy menu. It enthusiastically takes in devilled crab, Caesar salad, roast cod with butter beans, fennel and garlic mayonnaise, as well as crisp roast Norfolk duck with sage and onion stuffing and orange sauce, and medallions of pork with tomato, basil and garlic jus.

Smoking: No-smoking area in dining room
Credit cards: ▆ ▆ ▆ ▆ ▆

Old London Road RH20 3BN
Map 4: TQ11
Tel: 01903 892271/892575
Chef: Carl Illes
Owners: Carl & Julie Illes
Cost: Fixed-price L £24.75/D £25.75. H/wine £10.50
Times: Last L 2pm/last D 9pm. Closed Sun, Mon
Additional: Children welcome; ◑ dishes

Directions: Telephone for directions

WEST CHILTINGTON,
Roundabout Hotel

Monkmead Lane Nr Pulborough RH20 2PF
Map 4: TQ01
Tel: 01798 813838
Fax: 01798 812962
Chef: David Isles
Owner: Richard David Begley
Cost: Alc £27.75, fixed-price L £13.75/D £19.15. ☺ H/wine £10.50
Times: Last L 1.45pm/last D 9pm
Additional: Bar food; Sunday L; No children under 3; ◑ dishes
Smoking: No smoking in dining room
Accommodation: 23 en suite
Credit cards: ▆ ▆ ▆ ▆ ▆ JCB

Mock-Tudor hotel dating from the 1930s, which enjoys a peaceful setting deep in the Sussex countryside. Pleasant dining room with a set menu and a carte. Goats' cheese fritters, jalapeño peppers and red pepper sauce, half a roast duck with a rich orange sauce, and Amaretti chocolate tart, show the range.

Directions: 1.75 miles S of West Chiltington via A293

WORTHING, Ardington Hotel

A bright, airy hotel restaurant notable for its eclectic menus. The set menu features a number of interesting dishes, perhaps Japanese glazed mackerel with soy, ginger and steamed rice, while the carte offers more traditional choices. Starters include steamed dim sum with plum sauce, and roasted pepper and goats' cheese tart.

Accommodation: 45 en suite
Credit cards: ▆ ▆ ▆ ▆ ▆ ▆ ▆ JCB

Directions: Central Worthing

Steyne Gardens BN11 3DZ
Map 4: TQ10
Tel: 01903 230451
Fax: 01903 526526
Chef: Richard Catling
Owner: Mr & Mrs BA Margaroli
Cost: Fixed-price D £18.75. ☺
H/wine £10.25.
Times: Last L 2pm/last D 8.30pm.
Additional: Bar meals L;
Children welcome; ◑ dishes

TYNE & WEAR

BOLDON,
Forsters Restaurant

Barry Forster's mostly contemporary cooking, in which the main ingredients do the talking, balances voguish dishes against more predictable traditional ones, a reflection of the diverse customer base in this suburban village. Thus, first courses might feature a choice between king prawns 'Thai Style' with soy, ginger, chilli and beansprouts, and eggs Benedict, with main courses ranging between roast duck breast, French black pudding and red wine sauce (an inspirational combination), and chargrilled fillet steak au poivre. Everything comes without spurious garnishes. Fish dishes are selected on a daily basis. Although there is a good vegetarian choice – blue Stilton and walnut soufflé, for example – dishes must be ordered 48 hours in advance when selecting from the *carte*, rather than the good-value set dinner. Desserts are wickedly enticing – bitter chocolate parfait with Amaretto sauce was two slabs of deep delight.

Directions: In village of East Boldon, off A184 Newcastle/ Sunderland rd

2 St Bedes Station Road NE36 0LE
Map 12: NZ36
Tel: 0191 5190929
Chef: Barry Forster
Owners: Barry & Sue Forster
Cost: *Alc* £24, fixed-price D £17.50.
☺ H/wine £8.50.
Times: D only, 7pm-9.30pm.
Closed Sun, Mon, 2 wks May & Aug,
Xmas, New Year, Bhs
Additional: No children under 8;
◑ dishes
Seats: 28
Smoking: No pipes and cigars
Credit cards: ▆ ▆ ▆ ▆

GATESHEAD,
Eslington Villa Hotel

Easy access to the A1, combined with a peaceful situation overlooking the Teme Valley, make this relaxed hotel a popular place. The restaurant certainly attracts a local following, offering dishes such as pan-fried calves' liver on herb risotto, medallions of venison with fresh pasta, griotte cherries in a creamy game sauce, and passion fruit delice for dessert.

Additional: Sunday L; Children welcome; ◑ dishes
Smoking: No smoking in dining room
Accommodation: 12 en suite
Credit cards: ▆ ▆ ▆ ▆ ▆ ▆

Directions: Off A1(M) along Teme Valley, turn R at Eastern Avenue, then L into Station Road

8 Station Road Low Fell
NE9 6DR
Map 12: NZ26
Tel: 0191 4876017
Fax: 0191 4200667
Chef: Ian Lowery
Owners: Nick & Melanie Tulip
Cost: *Alc* £28, fixed-price L £9.95 (2 courses)/D £22.95. ☺ H/wine £10.50
Times: Last L 2pm/last D 10pm.
Closed L Sat, D Sun, 25 Dec, Bhs

NEWCASTLE-UPON-TYNE,
Blackgate Restaurant ❀

Period building in the centre of the city housing a spacious restaurant . Both the short set menu and carte offer good choice, perhaps dry-roasted chicken breast in aromatic spices with cucumber and mint yogurt, or tenderloin of lamb with a tartlet of creamed onion and rosemary scented meat juices.

Credit cards: 💳 💳 💳 💳 💳 💳 💳 JCB

Directions: 2 mins walk from Newcastle Central Station. Situated behind St Nicholas Cathedral, opposite Castle Keep

The Side NE1 3JE
Map 12: NZ26
Tel: 0191 2617356
Chef: Douglas Jordan
Owners: Douglas & Susan Jordan
Cost: Alc £24, fixed-price L & D £11.95 (2 courses). ☺ H/wine £11.95
Times: Last L 2pm/last D 10pm.
Closed L Sat, D Mon, all Sun, Bhs
Additional: Children welcome;
🍴 dishes
Smoking: No-smoking area

NEWCASTLE-UPON-TYNE, Café 21 ❀

Younger sibling of Terence Laybourne's 21 Queen Street restaurant (see below), this informal, café-style eatery offers minimalist decor and a varied menu. Penne à la provençale, dressed crab, steak with chips and salad, salmon with choucroute and Gewürztraminer sauce, raspberry sablé and apple crumble tart demonstrate the range.

35 The Broadway Darras Hall
Ponteland NE20 9PW
Map 12: NZ26
Tel/Fax: 01661 820357
Chef: Andrew Waugh
Owners: Terence & Susan Laybourne
Cost: Alc £20, fixed price L £14.50/ D £12.50. ☺ H/wine £9.50
Times: Last L 2pm/last D 10.30pm.
Closed Sun, Mon, Bhs
Additional: Children welcome;
🍴 dishes
Smoking: No-smoking area;
No pipes and cigars
Credit cards: 💳 💳 💳 💳 💳 💳

Directions: From the A696, follow signs for Darras Hall and turn L at the mini-roundabout, 200yds to restaurant

NEWCASTLE-UPON-TYNE,
The Copthorne ❀

Le Rivage is hidden away at the side of the modern hotel, right on the riverside. It provides an intimate setting in navy and gold for a wide choice of carefully presented dishes. Examples are lobster ravioli on a bed of beetroot 'spaghetti', and quail stuffed with a mushroom farce.

The Close Quayside
NE1 3RT
Map 12: NZ26
Tel: 0191 2220333
Fax: 0191 2301111
Chef: J Haliday
Cost: Alc £31.85. ☺ H/wine £11.50
Times: D only, last D 10.30pm.
Closed Sun
Additional: Children welcome;
🍴 dishes
Smoking: No-smoking area;
Air conditioning
Accommodation: 156 en suite
Credit cards: 💳 💳 💳 💳 💳 💳 💳 JCB

Directions: From S cross Redheugh Bridge, turn L at B1600 for Quayside, hotel on R

NEWCASTLE-UPON-TYNE,
Courtneys ❀❀

This small and cosy, split-level restaurant, on Newcastle's quayside, was refurbished early in 1998 to a decadent Edwardian atmosphere, with a colour scheme of light crimson and dark green. Ordering off the short set-lunch menu might bring you smoked salmon and wild garlic chowder, followed by venison and red wine sausages with herby mash. Vegetarians do well by the *carte:* blue cheese soufflé, then pepper stuffed with ratatouille with polenta croûtons and sun-dried tomato oil are among the options. Meat-eaters could opt for a parfait of Northumbrian pheasant complemented by tart blueberry relish, then pork fillet roasted with honey and mustard on caramelised apples with a rosemary jus, or loin of lamb au poivre. The high point of an inspector's meal was a lightly textured champagne and vanilla mousse enhanced by raspberry coulis. House wines are from Australia, or be tempted by the wine list's annotation of 'aromas of cherries, prunes and figs' for a Sicilian red.

Directions: Bottom of Dean St on R before roundabout at Quayside.

5-7 The Side NE1 3JE
Map 12: NZ26
Tel: 0191 2325537
Fax: 0191 2211745
Chefs: D H Field, I Hunter
Owners: Miss D Miller, D W Buckle, D H Field
Cost: *Alc* £30, fixed-price L £15. H/wine £11.95
Times: Noon-last L 2pm/6-last D 10.30pm. Closed L Sat, all Sun, 2 wks May, 1wk Xmas
Additional: Children welcome; ❸ dishes
Seats: 32
Smoking: No-smoking area; No pipes and cigars; Air conditioning
Credit cards: ▀▀ ▀▀ ▀▀ ▀▀ ▀▀ ▀▀ JCB

NEWCASTLE-UPON-TYNE,
Fisherman's Lodge ❀❀

Fish is what they do best here – not the activity but the cooking, in which they have specialised for twenty years. This does not imply any lack of adventure in the repertoire; on the contrary, daily specials might include tempura of shellfish and fish with Chinese soy sauce, or grilled sea scallops with saffron couscous, spring onions, ginger and sukiyaki sauce. Seared peppered salmon with spicy cucumber pickle was perfectly prepared, with duck confit and a Thai dressing contributing to a whole sea bass on fresh pasta. Meat-eaters are catered for with Northumbrian lamb or roast partridge, and for those who play both ways, surf-and-turf remains a fixture. The setting of the formal, sophisticated restaurant is, as always, a pleasure – alongside a stream in a wooded valley, yet only five minutes from the city centre.

Directions: 2.5 miles from City centre, off A1058 (Tynemouth) road at Benton Bank, middle of Jesmond Dene Park

Jesmond Dene Jesmond NE7 7BQ
Map 12: NZ26
Tel: 0191 2813281
Fax: 0191 2816801
Chefs: Steven Jobson, Paul Amer
Owners: Franco & Pamela Cetoloni
Cost: *Alc* £35, fixed-price L £17.80/D £29.50. H/wine £12
Times: Noon-last L 2pm/7pm-last D 11pm. Closed L Sat, Sun, Bhs
Additional: No children under 9 at D; ❸ dishes
Seats: 65. Private dining rooms 8-43
Smoking: No smoking in dining room
Credit cards: ▀▀ ▀▀ ▀▀ ▀▀ ▀▀ ▀▀ ▀▀ JCB

NEWCASTLE-UPON-TYNE,
Fishermans Wharf

Civilised and stylish (at one time a bank) Fishermans Wharf is a traditional and classical seafood restaurant (although carnivores have a handful of choices). Melt-in-the-mouth scallops with cheese sauce come as a starter, then there might be baked brill with cabbage and bacon, or salmon creole, with rice pudding to finish.

Additional: Children welcome; ◕ dishes
Credit cards: ▬ ▭ ▭ ▭ ▭ ▭ ▭

Directions: From N side of Tyne bridge, turn L into Mosley Street, L into Dean Street and L again into The Side

15 The Side NE1 3JE
Map 12: NZ26
Tel: 0191 2321057
Fax: 0191 2320496
Chef: Simon Tennet
Owner: Alan E Taylor
Cost: *Alc* £35, fixed-price L £15.
H/wine £13
Times: Last L 2pm/D 10.30pm.
Closed L Sat, all Sun

NEWCASTLE-UPON-TYNE,
Hospitality Inn

NEW

Considerable improvements have been made at this hotel, particularly to the public areas, which now include the attractively appointed Hospitality Restaurant. Dishes sampled include poached quenelles of salmon mousse with a clam risotto, and seared tuna steak with marinated tomatoes, coriander and lime.

Smoking: No-smoking area; no pipes & cigars
Accommodation: 89 en suite
Credit cards: ▬ ▭ ▭ ▭ ▭ ▭ ▭

Directions: Telephone for directions

64 Osborne Road Jesmond
NE2 2AT
Map 12: NZ26
Tel: 0191 2817881
Fax: 0191 2816241
Chef: Phil Mason
Owner: Thistle Hotels
Cost: *Alc* £24. Fixed-price L £8.50 (2 courses)/D £18.95. ☺ H/wine £9.95
Times: Last L 2pm/last D 9.45pm
Additional: Bar food L; Sunday L; Children welcome; ◕ dishes

NEWCASTLE-UPON-TYNE, The Magpie
Room Restaurant ◈◈

St James Park NE1 4ST
Map 12: NZ26
Tel: 0191 2018439
Fax: 0191 2018611
Chef: John Blackmore
Owners: Newcastle United F C
Cost: *Alc* £25, fixed-price D £16.50.
☺ H/wine £10.95
Times: Noon-last L 2.30pm/7-last D 10pm. Closed L Sat, D Sun
Additional: Sunday L; Children welcome; ◕ dishes

There's literally a birds-eye view from the spacious roof-top restaurant over the city and the pitch. You can't, however, watch a match whilst enjoying the the baked hake with deep-fried green beans, sauté potatoes and garlic anchovy cream, because the restaurant is closed during fixtures. Perhaps it's as well to concentrate on serious dishes such as sausage of maize-fed chicken and wild mushrooms on spicy couscous, and ragout of root vegetables with rump of pork marinated in sage and garlic with prune and red wine sauce – then, just when you think it's all over; along comes the maple syrup sponge with rich vanilla custard. That's what we call a match.

Directions: From the South, follow Gateshead A1 signs, then A692 over Redheugh Bridge, Blenheim St & then L on Bath Lane

Seats: 80. Private dining room 10.
Jacket & tie preferred
Credit cards: ▓▓ ▒▒ ▓▓ ▒ ▓▓ ▣ JCB

NEWCASTLE-UPON-TYNE,
Malmaison Hotel ❀

NEW

Quayside NE1 3DX
Map 12: NZ26
Tel: 0191 2455000
Fax: 0191 2450566
Chef: Gavin Elon
Cost: Alc £25, fixed-price L & D £25
Times: Last L 2.30pm/last D 11pm
Additional: Bar food L; Sunday L;
Children welcome; ❸ dishes
Smoking: Air conditioning
Accommodation: 116 en suite
Credit cards: ▓▓ ▒▒ ▒ ▓▓ ▣ ▣

Directions: Telephone for directions

Upbeat newcomer to Newcastle's Quayside – Malmaison has finally crossed the border. Book a riverside table at the all-day Brasserie for no-nonsense, contemporary cooking. Relatively short, straightforward menu of creamy wild mushroom risotto, or salmon and cod fishcakes with parsley sauce, accompanied by heaps of fresh baguette. The adjoining bar is seductively styled. Enjoy.

NEWCASTLE-UPON-TYNE, Swallow
Gosforth Park Hotel ❀❀

A new entry in last year's *Guide*, and gaining a second rosette this year, the sound cooking of the kitchen brigade is matched by excellent service in the Brandling Restaurant, where old fashioned courtesies abound and dinner is accompanied by a pianist. The French inspired menu has a classical feel with the likes of wild mushroom consommé en croûte, and chicken velouté with spinach and goose liver ravioli among the starters, and mains such as roast and confit of duck with a cinnamon and black cherry flavoured sauce, steak Diane and seared supreme of turbot 'Rossini'. There's a good sprinkling of half-bottles on a wine list that majors on France and the classic wine-growing regions. Handy for the airport and the racecourse, the hotel is just off the A1 to the north of the city.

Directions: 2 mins from A1

High Gosforth Park NE3 5HN
Map 12: NZ26
Tel: 0191 2364111
Fax: 0191 2368192
Chef: Simon Devine
Owners: Swallow Hotels
Cost: Alc £35. Fixed-price L £20/D £25. ☺ H/wine £13.
Times: Noon-last L 2.30pm/7pm-last D 10.30pm
Additional: Bar food; Sunday L; Children welcome; ❸ dishes
Seats: 120. Private dining room 40. Jacket & tie preferred
Smoking: No smoking in one dining room; Air conditioning
Accommodation: 178 en suite
Credit cards: ▓▓ ▒▒ ▓▓ ▒ ▓▓ ▣ ▣

NEWCASTLE-UPON-TYNE,
21 Queen Street ❀❀❀

One unusual aspect of chic 21 Queen Street is that while other major restaurants outside London look to the capital's top chefs to keep them up to date, Terry Laybourne stays ahead of the game his way, providing some of the most daring and

21 Queen Street Quayside
NE1 3UG
Map 12: NZ26
Tel: 0191 2220755
Fax: 0191 2210761
Chef: Terence Laybourne

21 Queen Street

Owners: Terence & Susan Laybourne
Cost: *Alc* £34.30, fixed-price L
£17.50. H/wine £12
Times: Noon-last L 1.45pm/7-last
D 10.45pm. Closed L Sat, all Sun,
Xmas, Bhs
Additional: Children welcome;
🕭 dishes
Seats: 70
Smoking: No pipes
Credit cards: ▬ ▬ ▬ ◥ ℂ ▦ ▶ ▣

Directions: Queen Street runs parallel
to and just behind Newcastle Quay –
almost under the Tyne Bridge on N
side of the river

simple concepts you'll find anywhere in the country. Less is
definitely more here, and Terry realises that combining just a
few accurate flavours is so much more manageable than
working with complex combinations; thus the accuracy of the
dishes he creates is stunning. Note a late spring lunch that
opened with a lobster and vegetable spring roll whose low-key
description only heightened the surprise of the dish: great,
clear flavours with a bisque-based sauce, and vegetables that
took in fresh morels, fresh corn and a fine paysanne of root
vegetables. Roast breast of corn-fed chicken with foie gras jus,
was a another great combination, with the pithiviers of the leg
laced with truffle – glorious. Warm chocolate sponge with
runny centre came completely balanced by a coconut sorbet in
a chocolate tuile. Breads are top-quality home-baked French
sticks. The wine list is predominantly French with an almost
cheeky list of New World wines for those who like something a
little different.

Signature dishes: Terrine of Tweed salmon, new potatoes and
spring vegetables with dill crème fraîche; thin tomato tart,
warm pistou and a friture of herbs; roasted partridge with
braised cabbage and bacon.

NEWCASTLE-UPON-TYNE,

Vermont Hotel ❀❀❀

Castle Garth NE1 1RQ
Map 12: NZ26
Tel: 0191 2331010
Fax: 0191 2331234
Chef: John Connell
Owner: Taz Group Ltd
Cost: *Alc* £33

In what is becoming a familiar scenario in several major cities,
Newcastle's former, and very imposing County Hall has been
turned into an hotel. The Vermont occupies the grand old
building with considerable style. A brasserie provides meals all

day, but it is the Blue Room where the real culinary action can be found. New Zealander John Connell heads an ambitious team and he offers a punchy version of fusion food, tempered by some old fashioned European classicism. Thus a spiced foie gras is pan-fried with polenta and served with a fruit tea sauce, but is balanced by a more sober warm pressed terrine of free-range chicken, foie gras and shallots with Madeira jus. Nor does fusion mean confusion here, with a clearly well thought out loin of lamb with an individual moussaka, merguez sausage and lamb jus. Results on the plate are good. Note an inspection meal that took in crab risotto with orange oil, dry-roasted monkfish with Indian spices and a tiger prawn bhaji, and mascarpone iced white chocolate cream with a raspberry coulis. There's a good wine list with some depth and breadth, but with especially strong emphasis on Burgundy and Bordeaux.

Signature dishes: Lobster salad, curry oil and Asian herbs; wild apricots with thyme ice cream; pasta with caviar; truffle dishes.

Directions: City centre, by the Castle and swing bridge

Times: D only, 6.30-last D 10.15pm. Closed D Sun, 2 wks summer, 2 wks Dec/Jan
Additional: Bar food; Sunday L (brasserie); Children welcome; 𝄞 dishes
Seats: 80. Jacket & tie preferred.
Accommodation: 101 en suite.
Credit cards: ▉ ▩ ◪ ▣ ▤ ▣ ▣ JCB

SUNDERLAND, **Swallow Hotel**

The hotel has a traditional feel with a marble entrance hall, wood panelling and paintings. The Promenade restaurant has panoramic views over Whitby Sands and features a unique Victorian bandstand where a pianist plays at dinner. Ricotta and spinach gnocchi, and trio of lamb fillet tournedos with smoked venison and beetroot noodles show the range.

Additional: Bar food L; Sunday L; Children welcome; 𝄞 dishes
Smoking: No-smoking area; Air conditioning
Accommodation: 65 en suite
Credit cards: ▉ ▩ ◪ ▣ ▤ ▣

Queen's Parade, Seaburn
SR6 8DB
Map 12: NZ35
Tel: 0191 5292041
Fax: 0191 5294227
Chef: Andrew Forrest
Owners: Swallow Hotels
Cost: *Alc* £35, fixed-price D £24 (4 courses). ☺ H/wine £12
Times: Last L 2pm/last D 9.45pm

Directions: On A184 (Boldon): at roundabout after Boldon turn L, then 1st R to Seaburn. L at next roundabout, follow road to coast. Turn R; hotel is 100m on R

WARWICKSHIRE

ABBOT'S SALFORD,
Salford Hall Hotel ❀❀

Built around 1470 as a guest house for the monks of nearby Evesham Abbey, the atmospheric oak-panelled dining room is part of the 'new' extension added a mere century and a half later. The *carte* may include two terrines – corn-fed chicken, and Brixham turbot and crab meat with langoustine oil – as well as quenelles of smoked trout mousse with a citrus flavoured crème fraîche dressing. At inspection, a supreme of chicken was filled with chorizo 'pata negra' and mozzarella cheese, surrounded by a plum tomato and red pepper coulis. There is a good cheese menu, and the likes of passion fruit soufflé with raspberry ice-cream for dessert.

Directions: On the A439 8 miles W of Stratford-upon-Avon

Evesham WR11 5UT
Map 4: SP05
Tel: 01386 871300
Fax: 01386 871301
Chef: Robert Bean
Cost: Fixed-price D £25. H/wine £11.75
Times: 12.30-last L 2pm/7.30-last D 9.30pm. Closed L Sat, Xmas
Additional: Bar food L; Sunday L; Children welcome; 𝄞 dishes
Seats: 50. Private dining room 50
Smoking: No smoking in dining room
Accommodation: 33 en suite
Credit cards: ▉ ▩ ◪ ▣ ▤ ▣ ▣ JCB

ALDERMINSTER,

Ettington Park Hotel ✸✸

Away from the tourist bustle of Stratford-upon-Avon (just five miles down the road), Ettington Park is a marvellous Victorian-Gothic manor. There are many original features, not least in the Oak Room Restaurant with its eponymous panelling, Rococo ceiling and view across the Victorian garden to the family chapel (now a conference room). In contrast to the setting the cooking is very much in the modern British style with its Mediterranean influences, as in our seared scallops on a bed of tagliolini with a light herb sauce, and fillet of lamb (pink and tender) served with couscous spiked with thyme and olive jus. Other dishes that caught our eye included wild mushroom soup flavoured with Armagnac, steamed fillet of brill with smoked salmon and a tomato velouté, and lemon posset topped with raspberries. The wine list offers useful tasting notes and each of the seven house wines is available by the glass.

Directions: 5 miles S of Stratford

Stratford-upon-Avon CV37 8BU
Map 4: SP24
Tel: 01789 450123
Fax: 01789 450472
Chef: Chris Hudson
Cost: *Alc* £40, fixed-price L £15/D £30.50. H/wine £15.75
Times: Noon-last L 1.45pm/7-9.30pm (Fri & Sat till 10)
Additional: Bar food; Sunday L; Children welcome; ✤ dishes
Seats: 40. Private dining room. Jacket & tie preferred
Smoking: No smoking in dining room.
Accommodation: 48 en suite
Credit cards: 🔲 🔲 🔲 🔲 🔲 🔲 🔲

ATHERSTONE,

Chapel House Hotel ✸✸

Friar's Gate CV9 1EY
Map 4: SP39
Tel: 01827 718949
Fax: 01827 717702
Chefs: Gary Thompson, Adam Bennett
Owner: David Arnold
Cost: *Alc* £23. H/wine £9.85. ☺
Times: D only, 7pm-last D 9.30pm. Closed D Sun, Xmas, Bhs
Additional: Sunday L (noon-2.30pm); No children under 10; ✤ dishes
Seats: 50. Private dining room 26
Smoking: No smoking in dining room
Accommodation: 13 en suite
Credit cards: 🔲 🔲 🔲 🔲 🔲 🔲 🔲 JCB

Nestling beside a church, this charming hotel-restaurant has appropriately attentive, caring and professional service. The kitchen's monthly-changing menu offers a vibrant array of flavours yet the chef is happy to prepare simpler dishes on request. There are occasional themed events, such as a 'Befores and Afters', where guests choose their meal from a tempting selection of starters and desserts. These may include a lovely salmon and monkfish terrine wrapped in spinach, or smoky chicken ravioli. There's an intriguingly-titled dessert called 'Wait and See!', a delightful chocolate and nut sponge with butterscotch sauce, plus favourites such as flavoured crème brûlées, iced parfaits and hot soufflés with ice cream. Separate fish courses are available if desired and the chef has daily specials for vegetarians and meat-lovers alike. Good coffee comes with a selection of home-made petits fours. A pleasing well-priced wine list with several half bottles available.

Directions: Town centre

KENILWORTH,
Restaurant Bosquet ❀❀

The cooking at this elegant French restaurant is classically based and the unreconstructed style will be welcomed by those whose gastronomic tastes were formed by dishes such as boneless quail stuffed with veal sweetbreads served with a sweet wine sauce, duck and goose foie gras with a mousse of duck liver garnished with a compote of figs and port aspic, and loin of veal with truffle juice and Madeira sauce. Younger diners should eat here to fill a gap in their education – but there are also more modern touches in dishes such as saddle of Welsh lamb with black olives and sun-dried tomato, wrapped in a fresh herb pastry.

97a Warwick Road CV8 1HP
Map 4: SP27
Tel: 01926 852463
Chef: Bernard Lignier
Owners: B J & J Lignier
Cost: Alc £30, fixed-price D £23.
H/wine £11.50
Times: L by arrangement/7-9.15pm.
Closed Sun, Mon, 3 wks Aug,
1 wk Xmas

Additional: Children welcome
Seats: 26
Smoking: No pipes and cigars
Credit cards: 💳 💳 💳 💳 💳 💳 JCB

Directions: In main street of Kenilworth.

KENILWORTH,
Simpson's ❀❀

This popular restaurant cultivates a light, informal look with a stripped-wood floor, green and white basketwork chairs, and fresh white linen cloths. Earthy intelligent cooking with spot-on Mediterranean flavours defines Andreas Antona's style. An open foie gras ravioli, for example, served with caramelised orange segments, or pigeon breast, again accompanied by a ravioli filled with herbs and wild mushroom mousse, with crisp potato rösti, creamed leeks of an intense, almost sweet flavour and a dark truffle sauce of good sheen and flavour interspersed with raisins. Puddings are a strength, and a nicely risen Amaretto soufflé with a whipped praline cream served alongside was all it should be.

101-103 Warwick Road CV8 1HL
Map 4: SP27
Tel: 01926 864567
Fax: 01926 864510
Please telephone for further details

Directions: In main street of Kenilworth

ROYAL LEAMINGTON SPA,
Lansdowne Hotel ❀

Close to the city centre, an intimate, vinously-themed dining room within a charming creeper-clad Regency hotel. Careful cooking of quality ingredients is a hallmark of the daily-changing, fixed-price menu, from which we chose a densely flavoured wild mushroom risotto and concluded with a traditional plum Brown Betsy. Melt-in-the-mouth home-made shortbread accompanied the coffee.

87 Clarendon Street CV32 4PF
Map 4: SP36
Tel: 01926 450505
Fax: 01926 421313
Chefs: Lucinda Robinson, Sebastian Spencer
Owners: David & Gillian Allen
Cost: Fixed-price D £18.95. ☺
H/wine £8.95.
Times: D only, 7.30-9.30pm.
Closed D Sun, Xmas

Additional: No children under 5; 🍴 dishes
Smoking: No smoking in dining room
Accommodation: 14 en suite
Credit cards: 💳 💳 💳 💳

Directions: Town centre, crossroads of Warwick Street and Clarendon Street

ROYAL LEAMINGTON SPA,

Leamington Hotel ✦

Smart Victorian town house. The Bistro happily mixes modish trends with some traditional French cooking. Expect smoked haddock fishcakes with red onion and pineapple salsa, and fresh roasted sea bass on a bed of garlic and basil mash.

Credit cards: 🟦 🔲 ▨ ▯ ▨ ▶ ▣

Directions: Along Newbold Terrace, turn L at lights. Hotel on right-hand corner of Willes Road & Upper Holly Walk

64 Upper Holly Walk CV32 4JL
Map 4: SP36
Tel: 01926 883777
Fax: 01926 330467
Chef: Robert Rouse
Owner: Frank Nixey
Cost: *Alc* £16. ☺ H/wine £8.25
Times: Last L 1.45pm/last D 9.30pm
Additional: Bar food L; Sunday L;
Children welcome; ✦ dishes
Accommodation: 20 en suite

ROYAL LEAMINGTON SPA,

Mallory Court Hotel ✦✦✦

Harbury Lane
Bishop's Tachbrook CV33 9QB
Map 4: SP36
Tel: 01926 330214
Fax: 01926 451714
Chef: Allan Holland
Owners: Allan Holland, Jeremy Mort
Cost: *Alc* £50, fixed-price L £22.50/D £35. H/wine £18
Times: Noon-last L 2pm/7pm-last D 10pm
Additional: Sunday L;
No children under 9; ✦ dishes
Seats: 50. Private dining room 20
Smoking: No smoking in dining room
Accommodation: 18 en suite
Credit cards: 🟦 ▨

Allan Holland heads a highly skilled team at this beautifully restored, chintzy English country house with gorgeous gardens. Study the *carte* over canapés in the comfortable lounge, perhaps Waldorf salad in a vol-au-vent, chicken liver parfait on toast, and smoked salmon mousse tartlet, before moving into the panelled dining-room or, in summer, the terrace. Descriptions are nicely understated, with terrine of foie gras with Madeira jelly, mille-feuille of red mullet with tiger prawns and aubergine caviar, poached fillet of salmon with pickled cucumber and hollandaise sauce, and roast pigeon with braised cabbage and roasting juices, saying all that needs to be said. Classic dishes include salad of Parma ham and fresh figs, Caesar salad, grilled Dover sole with herb butter, and Chateaubriand with béarnaise sauce. Sauternes custard with Armagnac prunes and pavé of chocolate with griottine cherries and crème anglaise both stand out on the dessert menu. A good set menu might include old-fashioned pork terrine, pot-roasted rabbit with grain mustard sauce, and pears poached in red wine with brown-bread ice cream. Warm oysters on fine tagliatelle was superbly simple, moistened with just the liquor and a touch of white wine. Pan-fried calves' liver with lime on a bed of wilted baby spinach was of equally impeccable quality, cooked perfectly pink, served with a fine, thyme-flavoured mash. Caramel soufflé with tangerine sorbet needed cooking more in the centre, and whatever you think about the practice of pairing cold sorbets with hot soufflés, the flavours undoubtedly worked well together. Service throughout is charming, friendly and attentive.

Directions: 2 miles S of Leamington off the B4087 towards Harbury

ROYAL LEAMINGTON SPA,
Regent Hotel ❀

When it opened in 1819 with 100 bedrooms this was the world's largest hotel. There is still a very traditional air to the place including the restaurant menus which, for dinner, could feature lobster quenelles with a brandy and shrimp sauce, followed by pink, tender lamb with a red wine and blackberry jus and walnut biscuit-based coffee torte.

77 The Parade CV32 4AX
Map 4: SP36
Tel: 01926 427231
Fax: 01926 450728
Please telephone for further details

Directions: In the town centre near Royal Priors Shopping Centre

STRATFORD-UPON-AVON,
Alveston Manor ❀

Clopton Bridge CV37 7HP
Map 4: SP25
Tel: 01789 204581
Fax: 01789 414095
Please telephone for further details

Directions: Take A46 towards Stratford, then A439 to town centre; hotel is on S side of river

A striking red brick, half-timbered façade with well-tended grounds that feature a magnificent cedar of Lebanon create favourable first impressions at this long-established hotel. The interior retains some original 16th-century decor. In the restaurant, the menu offers simple food which at the time of inspection was centred around a traditional theme.

STRATFORD-UPON-AVON,
The Arden Thistle ❀

Waterside CV37 6BA
Map 4: SP25
Tel: 01789 294949
Fax: 01789 415874
Chef: Richard Jones
Cost: *Alc* £34. Fixed-price D £24.95 (4 courses). ☺ H/wine £10.80.
Times: Last L 2pm/5.45pm-last D 9.30pm
Additional: Bar food; Sunday L; Children welcome; ❸ dishes
Smoking: No smoking in dining room
Accommodation: 62 en suite
Credit cards: ▬ ▬ ⇥ ◻ ▦ ◉

Directions: On Waterside, opposite Royal Shakespeare and Swan Theatres

In the heart of Stratford, at the water's edge opposite the Royal Shakespeare and Swan theatres – the most enviable hotel position in town. New blood in the kitchen is ensuring that the cooking lives up to the setting with dishes such as lattice of foie gras and artichoke, spring lamb with lentil mousse, ratatouille and a port wine jus.

STRATFORD-UPON-AVON,
Billesley Manor Hotel

Away from the tourist bustle of Stratford, the Manor
is set in 11 acres of grounds that include some splendid topiary.
Green leather chairs are interspersed with some upholstered
in tapestry-style fabric in a restaurant that boasts oak-panelled
walls and stone-mullioned windows. Tomato and shellfish
bisque with lobster ravioli, terrine of pheasant and asparagus,
rosemary scented noisettes of lamb with cranberry marmalade,
seared scallop and sea bass gâteau, and breast of duck with a
confit of the leg and a blackberry and lentil cassoulet shows the
style of the shortish *carte.*

Additional: Bar food L; Sunday L; Children welcome; ♨ dishes
Seats: 70. Private dining room 18
Smoking: No smoking in dining
Accommodation: 41 en suite
Credit cards: ▬ ▭ ➹ ▯ ▦ ▐ ▨

Directions: On the A46, 3 miles west of Stratford-upon-
Avon

Alcester B49 6NF
Map 4: SP25
Tel: 01789 279955
Fax: 01789 764145
Chef: Chris Short
Owners: Moat House
Cost: Fixed-price D £30 (4 courses).
H/wine £12.50
Times: 12.30pm-last L 2pm/7.30pm-
last D 9.30pm. Closed L Sat
room

STRATFORD-UPON-AVON,
The Boathouse

Swan's Nest Lane CV37 7LS
Map 4: SP25
Tel/Fax: 01789 297733
Chef: Patrick Robiquet
Owner: William Meredith-Owen
Cost: *Alc* £24.50, fixed-price L £9.90
(2 courses)/D £24.50 (Sat only). ☺
H/wine £9.80
Times: Noon-last L 1.50pm/6-last D
9.50pm. Closed L Sat, all Sun, L Mon
Additional: Children welcome;
♨ dishes
Seats: 90
Smoking: No-smoking area
Credit cards: ▬ ▭ ▯

Unusually located above a working boathouse on the river, the
restaurant is only a short walk from Stratford's theatres. Inside,
a mix of exposed beams, polished wooden floors, and modern
wrought iron make an informal context for serious modern
French cooking. Technical skills are to the fore in dishes such
as guinea fowl and wild mushroom sausage, and exuberant
ideas light up a fricassée of squid and roasted pepper in a pesto
sauce with black linguine. An interest in spicing is shown in a
roasted parsnip mousse in a spring onion, lemongrass and star
anise nage. Simple roast free-range chicken with red wine and
rosemary risotto, though, is hard to beat.

Directions: From town centre, cross river by Clopton Bridge
toward Oxford and Banbury, then double back around
roundabout 50 yards on, then 1st L.

STRATFORD-UPON-AVON,

Desports 🌼🌼

You climb the stairs of the old 16th-century building and enter a vibrant atmosphere of yellow and electric blue decor, stripped wood and rustic wrought iron. Many dishes can be taken as starters or main courses, and more than a few have a pronounced Asian/Thai twist: fragrant duck with five spice, grapefruit and spring onion noodles; crab and coconut milk risotto; peppered tuna fish with candied plum tomatoes, caperberries and mustard oil. A delicate hand with monkfish and scallops on sesame shrimp toast with wok-fired pak choi, yellow pepper and coriander juice ensured the excellent, fresh ingredients were used to best advantage. Great flavour distinguished a torte of lamb with tomato, basil and black olive pesto, and a terrific chocolate and honeycomb soufflé was accompanied by superb home-made nutmeg ice cream. With its friendly and relaxed atmosphere, this newcomer could well become Stratford's best.

NEW

13-14 Meer Street CV37 6QB
Map 4: SP25
Tel/Fax: 01789 269304
Chef: Paul Desport
Owners: Julie & Paul Desport
Cost: *Alc* £24, fixed-price L £13. ☺
H/wine £9.95
Times: Noon-last L 2pm/6-last
D 11pm. Closed D Sun, all Mon,
25-26 Dec, 2 wks Jan
Additional: Sunday L (noon-4pm);
Children welcome; 🌰 dishes

Seats: 50
Smoking: No-smoking area; No pipes & cigars
Credit cards: ■ ▒ ◥ 〔 ▦ ◖ JCB

Directions: In town centre between Market Place and Shakespeare Centre

STRATFORD-UPON-AVON,

Grosvenor Hotel 🌼

The Garden Room features hand-painted murals and a choice of modern dishes. At a well-reported inspection meal we tried smoked haddock ravioli, lamb fillet wrapped in spinach and filo pastry and moist chocolate-chip sponge.

Warwick Road CU37 6YT
Map 4: SP25
Tel: 01789 269213
Fax: 01789 266087
Please telephone for further details

STRATFORD-UPON-AVON,

Lambs of Sheep Street 🌼

A heavily timbered building on two floors. It is popular with theatregoers, and busy both before and after performances. You can order a plate of pasta or the full three courses from the flexible modern menu – roast salmon fillet with sauce vierge and basil oil was a highlight.

12 Sheep Street CV37 6EF
Map 4: SP25
Tel/Fax: 01789 292554
Please telephone for further details.

Directions: From Stratford town centre, head towards 'Waterside' and 'Royal Shakespeare Theatre'. Sheep Street is 1st R on Waterside

STRATFORD-UPON-AVON,

The Shakespeare 🌼

Landmark hotel with gabled timber façade and central location. Othello's restaurant offers an assiette of smoked fish with a lemon vinaigrette, collops of pork and caramelised apple with a sweet-and-sour sauce, and chilled chocolate soufflé with a hot chocolate sauce. There's a bistro for lighter meals and snacks.

Chapel Street
CV37 6ER
Map 4: SP25
Tel: 01789 294771
Fax: 01789 415411
Chef: Gordon Inglis
Owners: Forte Hotels

The Shakespeare

Cost: Fixed price D £21. ☺ H/wine
£12
Times: D only, last D 9.30pm
Additional: Bar food; Sunday L; No
children under 5; 🍴 dishes
Smoking: No smoking in dining room
Accommodation: 74 en suite
Credit cards: ▆ ▆ ▆ ▆ ▆ **C** ▆ JCB

Directions: Follow signs to town centre. Go round one-way
system up Bridge Street. At roundabout turn L. Hotel is 200yds
on L-hand side

STRATFORD-UPON-AVON,

Welcombe Hotel 🏵🏵

Warwick Road CV37 0NR
Map 4: SP25

Tel: 01789 295252
Fax: 01789 414666
Chef: Mark Naylor
Owner: Yamada UK
Cost: Alc £40, fixed-price L £19.50/D
£35 (4 courses). H/wine £15
Times: Noon-last L 2pm/7-last
D 9.30pm
Additional: Sunday L;
Children welcome; 🍴 dishes
Seats: 60. Private room 18-120.
Jacket & tie preferred
Smoking: No smoking in dining room
Accommodation: 67 en suite
Credit cards: ▆ ▆ ▆ ▆ ▆ **C** ▆ JCB

The Jacobean-style Victorian manor and golf course are set in
hundreds of acres just a mile from the centre of town. The
public rooms are particularly attractive, the lounge magnificent
with wooden panelling and a large, ornate black-marble
fireplace. The elegant, comfortable dining-room, with
chandeliers and drapes at the windows, is the appropriate
setting for some ambitious dishes based in the classical
repertoire overlaid with the fashions of the day. Thus, a starter
of mille-feuille of duck is served on parsnip purée and
scattered with fried pancetta, and a timbale of prawns and
crayfish comes with basil and cumin couscous. Duck may crop
up again as a main course, as roast breast – 'excellent' noted an
inspector – with confit of the leg, caramelised pear crumble
and Armagnac sauce, or there might be fillet of red snapper
with a basil ratatouille ravioli. Gâteau Opéra is a perfect
textbook dessert. Bread is first-class, canapés are decent and
service is professional but friendly. The wine list has much of
interest, but prices are high.

Directions: On A439 1 mile from town centre

WISHAW, **The Belfry** ❀❀

Sutton Coldfield B76 9PR
Map 7: SP19
Tel: 01675 470301
Fax: 01675 470178
Chef: Eric Bruce
Owner: De Vere Hotels
Cost: *Alc* £35, fixed-price L £16.50/D £30 (4 courses). H/wine £14.95
Times: 12.30-last L 2pm/7.30-last D 10pm. Closed L Sat, D Sun, some Bhs
Additional: Bar food; Sunday L; ❹ dishes
Seats: 70. Private dining room 12. Jacket & tie preferred
Smoking: No-smoking area; No pipes and cigars
Accommodation: 324 en suite
Credit cards: ▭ ▭ ▭ ▭ ▭ ▭

The busy hotel complex is geared up for top-level golfing, leisure and international conference needs, and the French Restaurant scores with a team of enthusiastic staff who, as our inspector put it 'could sell coal to Newcastle'. The dining-room is old-fashioned looking, but everyone gets fussed over enough to ensure they become regulars. The cooking is consistently even and of a good standard: leg of duckling braised with red wine and haricot beans; Dublin Bay prawns fried in crispy saffron batter with sweet-and-sour sauce; red mullet and fennel broth with noodles; double baked French cheese soufflé with nut salad and walnut oil dressing; lamb cutlets with home-made faggot and Anna potato. A bread-and-butter pudding was light, fluffy and creamy, but cheeses were not in peak condition.

Directions: At junction of A446 & A4091, 1 mile NW of M42/J9

WEST MIDLANDS

BALSALL COMMON, **Haigs Hotel** ❀❀

Kenilworth Road CV7 7EL
Map 7: SP27
Tel: 01676 533004
Fax: 01676 535132
Chef: Paul Hartup
Owners: Alan & Hester Harris
Cost: *Alc* £29, fixed-price D £19.95. ☺ H/wine £9.95

A small hotel run in friendly fashion by Hester and Alan Harris with the help of a caring and attentive team. In Poppys restaurant the head chef of 10 years, Paul Hartup, continues to please with an interesting and varied choice of dishes on the *carte* and daily menus. Our most recent meal began with a rich terrine of chicken, pork and ceps served with a sweet red onion marmalade, before a dish of tender lamb fillet on a bed of young spinach leaves with a well-balanced tomato and basil jus. A freshly caramelised banana crème brûlée made a good ending. Everything from bread rolls to the chocolates that accompany the good cafetière coffee is home-made.

Credit cards: ▆ ▆ ▆ ▆ ▆ ◖

Directions: On A452, 4 miles N of NEC/Airport, on L before village centre

Times: D only, 7.30–last D 9.30pm.
Closed D Sun, 25 Dec-4 Jan
Additional: Bar food; Sunday L
(12.30-2pm); Children welcome;
◑ dishes
Seats: 60. Private dining room 28
Smoking: No smoking in dining room
Accommodation: 23 en suite

BALSALL COMMON, Nailcote Hall ❀ ❀

Nailcote Lane Berkswell CV7 7DE
Map 7: SP27
Tel: 01203 466174
Fax: 01203 470720
Chef: Andrew Clayton
Owner: Rick Cressman
Cost: Fixed-price L £21.50/D £29.50
Additional: Bar food L; Sunday L;
Children welcome; ◑ dishes
Seats: 45. Private dining room 27-45
Jacket and tie preferred
Accommodation: 38 en suite
Credit cards: ▆ ▆ ▆ ▆ ▆ ◖ ▣ JCB

Diners heading for the suave, Tudor-style Oak Room Restaurant are advised not to take the wrong turning and end up below the leisure and conference centre complex in Rick's Ibiza-style restaurant/night-club where partying goes on till 2am. Still, each to their own, and dancing the hours away might be just the thing to work off the chargrilled sirloin steak glazed with Stilton and horseradish glaze or the panaché of Cornish seafood served in a soupier with champagne and chervil sauce, followed by the crisp dark chocolate shell filled with iced Baileys parfait and warm chocolate sauce, before you stagger up the stairs to the luxurious bedrooms in the Elizabethan mansion.

Directions: On B4101 (Balsall/Coventry), 10 mins from NEC/Birmingham Airport

BIRMINGHAM, Burlington Hotel ❀

Within walking distance of New Street station, this Victorian hotel has been refurbished to meet the needs of today's more demanding visitor. Dinner in the Berlioz restaurant could include a starter of strips of lambs' liver and bacon served on a toasted brioche, followed by coffee-roasted duck with kumquats, berries and baby squash.

Additional: Bar food; Sunday L; Children welcome; ◑ dishes
Smoking: No-smoking area; Air conditioning
Accommodation: 112 en suite
Credit cards: ▆ ▆ ▆ ▆ ▆ ◖ ▣

Directions: Adjacent to New Street Railway Station.

Burlington Arcade
126 New Street B2 4JQ
Map 7: SP08
Tel: 0121 6439191
Fax: 0121 6435075
Chef: Charles Anderson
Owner: Hortellux Ltd
Cost: *Alc* £22.50; fixed-price L
£11.95/D £18.95. ☺ H/wine £10
Times: Last L 2.30pm/last D 10pm

BIRMINGHAM,
Chung Ying Garden ❀

Spacious, popular Chinese, noted for lunchtime dim sum. Barbecue dishes take in crispy belly pork and roast piglet, as well as the usual standard Cantonese fare, but for the adventurous there is some interesting offal such as ox tripe with black bean sauce, crispy fried pork intestine, as well as stewed eel with belly pork, and stewed brisket with spices.

Additional: Sunday L; Children welcome; 🍴 dishes
Smoking: Air conditioning
Credit cards: 🟦 🟧 🟥 💳 📷 📄

Directions: City centre, off Hurst Street, nr Hippodrome Theatre

17 Thorp Street B5 4AT
Map 7: SP08
Tel: 0121 6666622
Fax: 0121 6225860
Chef/Owner: S C Wong
Cost: Alc £17, fixed price L & D £13 (2 courses). ☺ H/wine £8.50
Times: Open all day, last D midnight. Closed 25 Dec

BIRMINGHAM,
Copthorne Birmingham ❀

Smart, modern, centrally located hotel. Eat informally in Goldie's Brasserie or choose Goldsmiths Restaurant where the emphasis is on classic cooking – confit of duck with caramelised apricots, perhaps, or pan-fried turbot with basil and potato purée, seared jumbo scallops and warm lobster dressing.

Additional: Bar food; Children welcome; 🍴 dishes
Smoking: Air conditioning
Accommodation: 212 en suite
Credit cards: 🟦 🟧 🟥 💳 📷 💳 📄 JCB

Directions: City centre

Paradise Circus B3 3HJ
Map 7: SP08
Tel: 0121 2002727
Fax: 0121 2001197
Chef: Neil Southgate
Owners: Copthorne Hotels
Cost: Alc £24.95, fixed-price D £24.95. ☺ H/wine £9.25
Times: D only, last D 9.45pm. Closed Sun, Bhs

BIRMINGHAM,
Lombard Room Restaurant ❀❀

180 Lifford Lane
Kings Norton B30 3NT
Map 7: SP08
Tel: 0121 4595800
Fax: 0121 4598553
Chef: Anthony Morgan
Owners: Anthony Morgan, Antony Davis
Cost: Fixed-price L £16.85/D £23.50.
☺ H/wine £13.85

Although there is a monthly changing set menu, several of the dishes at this elegant former paper mill carry supplementary charges – so be prepared to shell out a little more should you fancy terrine of Welsh venison and black pudding with grilled white pudding and apple chutney, or Staffordshire Barbary duck with polenta, roasted tomatoes and pesto sauce. That still leaves plenty of choice from a repertoire that is fresh and uses

herbs and spices in imaginative ways: leek and ginger broth
with couscous and garlic dumplings; boneless shin of Cornish
lamb with creamed celeriac and marjoram; confit belly of pork
with a wild mushroom and juniper faggot, English mustard and
tarragon cream sauce. Desserts that contain nuts, such as
toasted banana sandwich with mango custard and double
cream, are helpfully identified on the menu.

Additional: Bar food L; Sunday L; Children welcome; ☺ dishes
Seats: 64. Private dining room 12
Smoking: No smoking in dining room; Air conditioning
Accommodation: 9 en suite
Credit cards: ▬ ▬ 🗗 🗗 ▬ 🗗 🗗

Directions: From city centre take A441 (Pershore road) until
Stirchley. Turn L at Breadon Bar, hotel is 1 mile on R

Times: 12.30pm-last L 2pm/7.30pm-
last D 9.30pm. Closed L Sat, D Sun,
L Mon, 1st 2 wks Jan

*AA Wine Shortlisted for
Award-see page 16*

BIRMINGHAM, Shimla Pinks ❀

*The strikingly minimalist decor is a far cry from the flock wallpapers
of less enterprising Indian restaurants, though the menu is familiar
enough with bhajis, samosas, tandooris and tikkas all making an
appearance.*

Additional: Children welcome; ☺ dishes
Smoking: No-smoking area
Credit cards: ▬ ▬ 🗗 🗗 ▬ 🗗

Directions: In city centre, opposite Novotel and near the ICC

214 Broad Street B15 1AY
Map 7: SP08
Tel: 0121 6330366
Fax: 0121 6436383
Chef: Ganesh Shrestha
Cost: *Alc* £18, fixed-price L £6.95 (2
courses)/D £12.95. ☺ H/wine £9.50
Times: Last L 2.15pm/last D 10.45pm.
Closed L Sat & Sun, 25-26 Dec, 1 Jan

BIRMINGHAM, Swallow Hotel ❀❀❀

12 Hagley Road Five Ways B16 8SJ
Map 7: SP08
Tel: 0121 4521144
Fax: 0121 4563442
Chef: Jonathan Harrison
Cost: *Alc* £35, fixed-price L £21.50/D
£32 (4 courses). H/wine £15.50
Times: 12.30-last L 2.30pm/7.30-last
D10.30pm (Sun till 10). Closed L Sat
Additional: Sunday L; Children
welcome; ☺ dishes
Seats: 60. Private rooms 20
Smoking: No-smoking area;
Air conditioning
Accommodation: 98 en suite
Credit cards: ▬ ▬ 🗗 🗗 ▬ 🗗 🗗

Smart, landmark hotel that has played host to US President
Clinton in the last 12 months. The Sir Edward Elgar is the
hotel's premier restaurant (Langtry's is more traditionally
English). Jonathan Harrison heads the brigade, cooking with
style and punchy self-confidence. A spring test dinner had one
inspector singing the praises of canapés of falafel, grilled
vegetable kebab, and tomato and red purée croûton, and the
choice of breads off the trolley – five in all. A great start to a
meal that never missed a beat. Lobster and leek ravioli was
excellent, keenly presented in a fine pasta with a sound bisque
sauce. Tender lamb fillet, its flavour gently boosted by thyme
and garlic, was found to be simple but exact, accompanied by
grilled Mediterranean vegetables that were controlled and

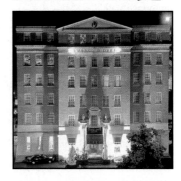

exact. Star anise parfait with blackberry compote was also excellent, well-crafted with complementary flavours. Stark espresso with a fun array of freshly made petits fours rounded off the whole meal. The serious wine list is backed up by a knowledgeable sommelier.

Signature dishes: Roasted monkfish with spring vegetable; langoustine salad crisp; dessert 'Louis XV'.

Directions: City end of the A546, at the Five Ways roundabout.

COVENTRY,
Brooklands Grange Hotel ❀❀

The rural origins of the converted 17th-century farmhouse have been absorbed into a smart modern business hotel on the outskirts of Coventry. The dining room, with conservatory extension, has richly coloured decor. Grilled tuna steak with tomato and lime salsa, and asparagus risotto with roasted Mediterranean vegetables and basil dressing, sit alongside 80s favourites such as deep-fried Camembert with spiced plum purée and crispy roast duck with sweet red pepper sauce. As well as retro cooking – pork schnitzels with paprika sauce and noodles, prawn cocktail and baked salmon with English parsley sauce and crepes Suzette- there are evergreens such as pan-fried breast of chicken with garlic and lemon and summer pudding. In other words, something for everyone.

Directions: On A4144; on right at Allesley roundabout

Holyhead Road CV5 8HX
Map 4: SP37
Tel: 01203 601601
Fax: 01203 601277
Chef: Neil Oates
Cost: *Alc* £23.68. ☺ H/wine £10.95
Times: Noon-last L 2pm/7-last D 10pm. Closed L Sat, 26 Dec, 1 Jan
Additional: Bar food; Sunday L; Children welcome; ✍ dishes
Seats: 60. Private dining room 18
Smoking: No smoking in dining room
Accommodation: 30 en suite
Credit cards:

COVENTRY, Hyland's Hotel ❀❀ NEW

Strong blues, primary yellow, polished beech flooring, metal Starke chairs, add up to an ultra-modern restaurant within Hyland's Hotel. The menu is equally up-to-date, mixing fashionable classics such as grilled fillet steak with Café de Paris butter with the more globally inspired oven-roasted cod fillet marinated in curry spices with a purée of spicy beans and coriander sauce. The trend for pick-and-mix ingredients shows up in a breast of duck with braised leek and pearl barley, roasted sweet potato and Madeira cream jus, and supreme of corn-fed chicken with shallots, black pudding and smoked pork, herb mash and Burgundy wine sauce. Desserts include glazed lemon tart with warm plum sauce and crème fraîche, and white chocolate chip mousse with a bitter chocolate sauce. Informal service by casually uniformed staff.

Directions: *Telephone for directions*

Warwick Road CV3 6AU
Map 4: SP37
Tel: 01203 502501
Fax: 01203 501027

Chef: Darion Smethurst

Owner: Allied Tri-Star Hotels
Cost: Fixed price D £14.50. ☺ H/wine £10.95
Times: Last L 2.30pm/last D 10.30pm. Closed L Sat
Additional: Sunday L; Children welcome; ✍ dishes
Seats: 80. Private room 40
Smoking: No-smoking area; Air conditioning
Accommodation: 54 en suite
Credit cards:

HOCKLEY HEATH,
Nuthurst Grange Hotel ❀❀❀

Flashes of real brilliance inform the cooking of chef/proprietor David Randolph at his red-brick country house hotel, at once secluded and remarkably convenient for the NEC and the motorway network. Deceptive simplicity and old-fashioned values are indicative of his standing as a Master Chef of Great Britain – all the classic cuts of meat are on show, as well as the

Nuthurst Grange Lane
Solihull B94 5NL
Map 7: SP17
Tel: 01564 783972
Fax: 01564 783919
Chef/Owner: David L Randolph
Cost: *Alc* L £20, fixed-price D from £29.50. H/wine £12.90

Nuthurst Grange Hotel

Times: Noon-last L 2pm/7pm-last
D 9.30pm. Closed L Sat, Xmas
Additional: Sunday L; Children
welcome; 🌢 dishes
Seats: 50. Private dining room 10-20
or 90
Smoking: No smoking in dining room
Accommodation: 15 en suite
Credit cards: ▬ ▬ ▼ ⏁ ▬ ⦿ ⊉

best seasonal ingredients. Dinner starts with a collection of
tasty morsels – chicken satay with yogurt and red shallot dip,
smoked salmon and tomato on pumpernickel, savoury egg
salpicon and toast, plus an *amuse-gueule* such as pavé of cod,
with salmon mousseline on a rustic cassoulet of vegetables
flavoured with saffron and champagne. Randolph is not afraid
to turn his hand to boning out animal extremities – a first
course of oxtail stuffed with chicken and vegetable mousse
studded with pistachio was succulent and fondant; monkfish
wrapped in pancetta on sauerkraut with a light beurre blanc
also demonstrated considerable technical skill. Desserts can be
outstanding, of note is a superb brandy snap basket brimming
with luscious milk chocolate mousse, chocolate ice cream and
compote of summer fruits – enough to make the most reserved
palate drool.

Signature dishes: Fillet of Welsh spring lamb in a brioche and
herb crust with scorched root vegetables and rosemary;
summer fruits marinated in brandy, gratinéed with peach
schnapps sabayon; fillet of Scotch beef with lemon, garlic,
parsley and thyme, shallot purée; loin of venison with bubble-
and-squeak, gin and juniper sauce.

Directions: Off A 34000, half mile S of Hockley Heath, turning
at notice board into Nuthurst Grange Lane.

MERIDEN, **Manor Hotel** ❀❀

Main Road CV7 7NH
Map 4: SP28
Tel: 01676 522735
Fax: 01676 522186
Chef: Peter Griffiths
Cost: *Alc* £25, fixed-price L £17.95/D
£18.95. ☺ H/wine £11.95.
Times: Noon-last L 1.45pm/7pm-last
D 9.45pm. Closed L Sat
Additional: Bar meals; Sunday L;
Children welcome; 🌢 dishes
Seats: 160. Private dining room 200.
Smoking: No smoking in dining room;
Air conditioning
Accommodation: 114 en suite.
Credit cards: ▬ ▬ ▼ ⏁ ▬ ⊉

The open-plan Regency Restaurant of this much-extended
Georgian hotel offers a menu that creates a nice balance
between the imaginative and the more familiar dishes. The fish

section might include roast cod with mushy peas, spiced tomato and pulses, alongside brill with ginger stir-fried vegetables and plum sauce, while among the meat dishes, beef fillet with horseradish mousse and baby Yorkshire puddings can be found next to breast of duck with star anise sauce, chive mash and exotic fruit gâteau. There's also a good vegetarian section. Afters range from bread-and-butter pudding with apricot compote and crème fraîche, and Black Forest trifle, to a marbled dark chocolate mousse. A shortish wine list comes with helpful tasting notes. The Triumph Buttery provides less formal all-day eating. The hotel is located in a quiet village within easy reach of the NEC.

Directions: In centre of village

MERIDEN,
Marriott Forest of Arden Hotel

Extensive sporting and leisure facilities are features of this impressive, modern hotel in a rural location convenient for the motorways and NEC. Diners can expect attentive service in the restaurant and an evening carte which offers an imaginative choice of competently cooked dishes.

Maxstoke Lane CV7 7HR
Map 4: SP28
Tel: 01676 522335
Fax: 01676 523711
Please telephone for further details

Directions: From M42/J6, take A45 (Coventry) after Stonebridge island, then L (Shepherds Lane), 1.5 miles on L

OLDBURY,
Jonathans' Hotel &

16-24 Wolverhampton Road
Oldbury B68 0LH
Map 7: SP08
Tel: 0121 4293757
Fax: 0121 4343107
Chef: Jonathan Bedford
Owners: Jonathan Bedford,
Jonathan Baker
Cost: *Alc* £25, fixed-price D £16. ☺
H/wine £11
Times: Last L 2pm/last D 10pm.
Closed D Sun
Additional: Sunday L;
No children under 11; ❸ dishes
Smoking: No-smoking area;
No pipes and cigars; Air conditioning
Accommodation: 44 en suite
Credit cards: ▆ ▆ ▆ ▨

Jam-packed with Victorian memorabilia, the modern British restaurant is staggered not only across several intimate rooms but several floors of this charismatic hotel. Sat at charmingly mismatched antique chairs and tables, you will enjoy the super home-made bread, mussels in garlic and parsley broth and meltingly delicious pot-roast lamb knuckles.

Directions: From M5/J2 take A4123 (Birmingham), 1.5 miles on L

SOLIHULL,

Solihull Moat House

Modern hotel handy for NEC and Cadbury World. The restaurant – modern, light and Mediterranean in concept – is upbeat, stylish. Menu reads well. Expect flakes of white crab meat, cucumber and lemon balm base and ginger dressing, grilled breast of duck with a timbale of wild rice and chestnuts in a rich orange sauce, and profiteroles with chocolate sauce.

Additional: Sunday L; Children welcome; ❹ dishes
Smoking: No-smoking area; No pipes; Air conditioning
Accommodation: 115 en suite
Credit cards: ▬ ▦ ▅ ▆ ▆ ▐ ▐ JCB

Directions: Follow signs to Town Centre and Conference Centre, 3rd turn at roundabout (Homer Road)

61 Homer Road B91 3QD
Map 7: SP17
Tel: 0121 6239988
Fax: 0121 7112696
Chef: Eddie Stephens
Owner: Queens Moat Houses
Cost: *Alc* £20-£30, fixed-price L
£10.80/D £18. ☺ H/wine £11.75
Times: Last L 2pm/last D 10pm.
Closed L Sat

SUTTON COLDFIELD,

The Thistle New Hall 

The beautifully restored New Hall is reputedly the oldest moated manor house in England. Grounds include a walled rose garden, a yew-tree walk and an ornamental pool, as well as leisure facilities such as a 9-hole golf course, tennis court, putting green and golf-driving range. Within, there are all the ingredients for a serious country house setting, with cosseting bar, wood-panelled dining room with stained glass, formal and knowledgeable service and care and dedication by the magnum full. The menu, which includes daily specials, reads with interest and shows imagination. Our May test meal rose to the occasion and delivered what it promised in the shape of excellent canapés and fresh rolls, duck leg confit with foie gras and sultana/jasmine sauce, a delicate roasted sole and langoustine with a light crab ravioli and saffron nage, plus tiramisu for dessert, followed by 'decadent' petits fours. Other choices could include veal and bacon terrine with home-made piccalilli, or timbale of rabbit with tarragon and shallot sauce, then perhaps, pan-fried sea bream with ginger, garlic and choi cum finished with a soy dressing, or roasted pigeon with beetroot, artichoke and cocotte potatoes with port wine sauce. The New Hall assiette of bananas looks intriguing.

Walmley Road B76 1QX
Map 7: SP19
Tel: 0121 3782442
Fax: 0121 3784637
Chef: David Lake
Owner: Thistle Hotels
Cost: *Alc* £38.75, fixed-price L
£20.50. H/wine £14.95
Times: Noon-last L 2pm/7-last D
10pm. Closed L Sat
Additional: Bar food L; Sunday L;
No children under 8; ❹ dishes
Seats: 50. Private dining room 8-50.
Jacket & tie preferred
Smoking: No smoking in dining room
Accommodation: 60 en suite
Credit cards: ▬ ▦ ▅ ▆ ▐ ▐ JCB

Directions: On B4148 E of Sutton Coldfield, close to M6/M42

WALSALL,

The Fairlawns at Aldridge ❀

An attractive red-brick hotel with lots of charm. Varied menus offer modern English cooking along the lines of scallop and Parma ham brochette, and breast of corn-fed chicken stuffed with award-winning black pudding. For dessert, our inspector enjoyed a freshly baked apple turnover served on a pool of sweet toffee sauce.

178 Little Aston Road
Aldridge WS9 0NU
Map 7: SP09
Tel: 01922 455122
Fax: 01922 743210
Chef: Todd Hubble
Owners: John and Tammy Pette
Cost: *Alc* £28, fixed-price L £14.50
(2 courses)/D £22.95 (5 courses). ☺
H/wine £10.95.
Times: Last L 2pm/last D 10pm.
Closed L Sat, D Sun, Bhs
Additional: Bar Food; Sunday L;
Children welcome; ❹ dishes
Accommodation: 46 en suite
Credit cards: ▨ ▨ ▨ ▨ ▨ ▨ ▨

Directions: Outskirts of Aldridge,
400 yards from crossroads of A452
(Chester Road) & A454 (Little Aston
Road)

WIGHT, ISLE OF

GODSHILL, Cask & Taverners ❀

In a pretty village, this cosy restaurant forms part of a popular inn. Interesting menus include dishes of fresh black pasta with tomatoes and mussels, roast calves' liver with red wine and oyster mushrooms, and prune and Armagnac tart. A separate vegetarian menu is available.

Smoking: No smoking in dining room
Credit cards: ▨ ▨ ▨ ▨

Directions: From Shanklin take A3020 3 miles into Godshill

High Street PO38 3HZ
Map 4: SZ58
Tel: 01983 840707
Fax: 01983 840861
Chef: Stephen Chiverton
Owner: Burts Brewery Ltd
Cost: *Alc* £20, fixed-price L £9.75/D
£15.75 (4 courses). ☺ H/wine £7.50
Times: Last L 2.30pm/D 9.30pm
Additional: Bar food; Sunday L;
Children welcome; ❹ dishes

SEAVIEW, Seaview Hotel & Restaurant ❀❀

High Street PO34 5EX
Map 4: SZ69
Tel: 01983 612711
Fax: 01983 613729
Chef: Charles Bartlett
Owners: Nicholas & Nicola Hayward
Cost: *Alc* £21.25. ☺ H/wine £8.95
Times: 12.30-last L 2pm/7.30-last
D 9.30pm. Closed D Sun (not Bhs)
Additional: Bar food; Sunday L;
No children under 5 at D; ❹ dishes
Seats: 80. Private dining rooms 12, 16
Smoking: One no-smoking dining
room; No pipes; Air conditioning
Accommodation: 16 en suite
Credit cards: ▨ ▨ ▨ ▨ ▨ ▨ ▨

A popular seaside hotel set with great views across the water. The Seaview is run with friendly professionalism by Nick and Nicola Hayward and their well-motivated team. There are two restaurants, one of which has been decked out like a modern ocean liner with ropes, model ships and blue decor, the other more formal and traditional. Both offer an exciting range of modern English dishes such as marinated breast of chicken with lemon pesto, and steamed smoked haddock on spinach mash with mustard sauce. At a meal in June, our inspector started with the house speciality – a ramekin of white and brown crab meat with potato and cheese. This was followed by a scallop and cream ragout with bacon, mange -out and walnuts. For dessert, delights such as passion fruit and apricot meringue, steamed treacle pudding and hot chocolate sponge were spurned in favour of a tasty red berry 'tipsy' trifle.

Seaview Hotel & Restaurant

Directions: In High Street, near seafront, 3 miles E of Ryde

VENTNOR, **The Royal** ❀❀

Tinkling piano keys and crystal chandeliers, swagged curtains, candles and silver cruets add to the stately, old-fashioned atmosphere of this hotel, located in the Victorian spa town of Ventnor. The set dinner menu, however, does not hark back to the days when Queen Victoria used the Royal as an annexe to Osborne House, but looks firmly to the present for inspiration for dishes such as chargrilled salmon with grilled aubergine and cherry tomatoes dressed with pesto and olive tapenade. A heavy hand with the garlic unfortunately overpowered a first course of pan-fried tiger prawns with coriander and lime, but our main course, a breast of chicken with a wild mushroom and onion compote, was accurately cooked with a well-tempered Stilton cream sauce. Mango and passion fruit crème brûlée, and baked lemon and sultana croissant pudding with English custard, are among the dessert choices.

Belgrave Road PO38 1JJ
Map 4: SZ57
Tel: 01983 852186
Fax: 01983 855395
Chef: Alan Staley
Owner: William Bailey
Cost: Fixed-price D £20.
H/wine £9.50. ☺
Times: D only, 7pm-last D 9pm.
Additional: Bar food L; Sunday L; Children welcome; ♨ dishes
Seats: 120. Private dining room 40
Smoking: No smoking in dining room
Accommodation: 55 en suite
Credit cards: ▬ ▬ ▬ ▬ ▬ ▬ JCB

Directions: On main A3055 coastal road

YARMOUTH, **George Hotel** ❀❀❀

Historic, colour-washed hotel that looks out between the pier and the castle as you approach by ferry from the mainland. Jeremy and Amy Willcock have transformed this former town house with great panache, and public rooms capture most moods: a bright, sunny brasserie overlooking the sea with an up-beat Mediterranean slanted menu; an attractive garden terrace; a comfortable lounge that is candlelit in the evening; a panelled bar; an elegant restaurant. In the latter, Kevin Mangeolles offers a short dinner menu of inspired cooking that shows a keen awareness of current trends. A test dinner in April started on a high note with a stellar ravioli of tongue with foie gras and garlic beignets, and a superbly presented red mullet, couscous and a tomato dressing with wafer-thin triangles of a savoury biscuit. The centrepiece was a rich, very successful loin of rabbit with its liver, kidney, and wild mushrooms, its counterpart, pan-fried loin of lamb with a black olive and lamb sausage on a lamb jus. Prune parfait, and a mini rhubarb tart with some sorbet and a mini mousse were all pronounced 'delicious'. Only one red and one white on offer by the glass from a wine list that lists by price rather than type.

Quay Street PO41 0PE
Map 4: SZ38
Tel: 01983 760331
Fax: 01983 760425
Chef: Kevin Mangeolles
Owners: Jeremy & Amy Willcock, John Illsley
Cost: Fixed-price L £24.50 (brasserie)/D £36.75. H/wine £12.50
Times: D only (restaurant) 7-last D 10pm. Closed D Sun, all Mon
Additional: Sunday L (noon-3pm); No children under 8; ♨ dishes
Seats: 20. Private dining room 15
Smoking: No smoking in dining room; Air conditioning
Accommodation: 16 en suite
Credit cards: ▬ ▬ ▬ ▬ ▬ ▬ JCB

Directions: Ferry from Lymington. Hotel visible from ferry between castle and pier

WILTSHIRE

ALDBOURNE, **Raffles Restaurant**

'Country dining, cottage-style – Mrs Hannan presides over the dining room, she is obviously well-liked...diners filing in tasty bits of gossip to entertain her', reports one inspector on this friendly, well-supported restaurant just off the village green. Aldbourne is something of a time-warp and the setting for the TV series based on the AA – *The Last Post*, yet the menu successfully blends the old and the new. Traditional favourites include fillet steak with brandy, cream and mushroom sauce, but more modern interpretations are along the lines of Thai fishcakes with oriental dip. A test dinner highlighted a classic duck à l'orange served with perfectly cooked fresh vegetables, and a brilliant crisp meringue packed with hazelnut pieces and cream, tasty and fresh. Wines are by the bottle or glass, priced fairly they represent a fair cross section from around the world.

Directions: On B4192 between M4/J14 & 15

The Green SN8 2BW
Map 4: SU27
Tel: 01672 540700
Fax: 01672 540038
Chef: James Hannan
Owners: James & Mary Hannan
Cost: *Alc* £17. ☺ H/wine £10.10
Times: 12.30-2pm/7-last D 10 pm.
Closed L Sat, D Sun, all Mon, 25-31 Dec, 2 wks Sep
Additional: Sunday L;
Children welcome; ♨ dishes
Seats: 36. Private room 40
Smoking: No-smoking area;
No pipes & cigars; Air conditioning
Credit cards: 💳 💳 💳 💳

AMESBURY,
Antrobus Arms Hotel

A Georgian hotel with a traditional, formal restaurant whose French windows open out onto a terrace and large walled garden. An element of innovation features in the largely classical menu, as in mackerel in a cucumber cream sauce, roast duck with a raspberry and blackberry sauce and medallions of venison with a rosemary and juniper jus.

Additional: Bar food; Sunday L; Children welcome; ♨ dishes
Smoking: No smoking in dining room
Accommodation: 19 (16 en suite)
Credit cards: 💳 💳 💳 💳 💳 💳 💳

Directions: In town centre

15 Church Street SP4 7EU
Map 4: SU14
Tel: 01980 623163
Fax: 01980 622112
Chef: Simon Rees
Owner: John M Halliday
Cost: *Alc* £20, fixed-price L £12.95/D £14.95. ☺
Times: Last L 2pm/last D 9pm

BRADFORD-ON-AVON,
Georgian Lodge

Bradford-on-Avon is a cross between York and Bath but on a much smaller scale; Georgian stone buildings abound and there is a street called the Shambles, just like its counterpart in York. Georgian Lodge is set beside the River Avon – within it boasts a bright modern look. An imaginative, varied menu offers starters such as wild mushroom risotto with shaved Parmesan and truffle oil, and main courses along the lines of seared salmon with spiced Puy lentils and coriander, and roast lamb with caponata chutney and rosemary oil. Breads are home-made, and delicious. Our test meal produced feta, tomato and olive salad with falafel, smoked haddock rarebit, and orange and almond cake with fresh oranges and crème fraîche. The wine list offers an above average selection by the glass

Directions: Town centre, off Silver Street, S of River Avon

25 Bridge Street BA15 1BY
Map 3: ST86
Tel: 01225 862268
Fax: 01225 862218
Chef: Peter Stott
Owner: Peter & Elizabeth Stott
Cost: *Alc* £22, fixed-price L £8 (2 courses). ☺ H/wine £9.25
Times: Last L 2.30pm/last D 9.45pm.
Closed L Mon
Additional: Sunday L; Children welcome; ♨ dishes
Accommodation: 10 en suite
Credit cards: 💳 💳 💳 💳 💳 💳

BRADFORD-ON-AVON,
Woolley Grange

Woolley Green BA15 1TX
Map 3: ST86
Tel: 01225 864705
Fax: 01225 864059
Chef: Phil Rimmer
Owners: Nigel & Heather Chapman
Cost: Fixed-price L £18/D £34.50.
H/wine £11.75
Times: 12.30-last L 2pm/7.30-9.30pm
Additional: Sunday L; Children
welcome; ❹ dishes
Seats: 60. Private dining room 22
Smoking: No smoking in dining room
Accommodation: 23 en suite
Credit cards: ▬ ▭

As befits such a splendid family hotel, Woolley Grange offers a range of 'eating options', from a formal dinner, to a lighter meal in the Victorian conservatory to an 'alfresco' delight on the terrace or round the pool. Grown-up meals are in an upbeat style that enlivens the usual country-house mode and the Victorian walled garden supplies, much of the fruit, vegetables and herbs. Local suppliers provide exceptional cheese, butter, lamb, and free-range pork. 'Special treat' dishes include seared sea scallops with wild rice, garlic fritters and balsamic sauce, and roasted wood pigeon with crushed potatoes, tomatoes, olives and rosemary. Children have their own lunch and tea.

Directions: On B105 at Woolley Green, 1 mile NE of Bradford, 20 mins from M4/J17

CALNE, Hayle Farm Hotel

Quemerford Calne Wiltshire
SN11 8UJ
Map 3: ST97
Tel/Fax: 01249 813275
Please telephone for further details

An old, former farmhouse, now a small hotel, located at the foot of the Marlborough Downs within sight of the White Horse at Chervil. In the restaurant there's a regularly changing menu of carefully cooked, mostly familiar classics.

Directions: Restaurant at junction of A4 and Compton Bassett roads three miles E of Calne.

CASTLE COMBE, Castle Inn

Chippenham SN14 7HN
Map 3: ST87
Tel: 01249 783030
Fax: 01249 782315
Chef: Jamie Gemmell
Owner: Hatton Hotels Group
Services Ltd
Cost: ☺ H/wine £11.50
Times: Last L 2pm/last D 9.15pm
Additional: Bar food L; Sunday L;
❹ dishes
Smoking: No smoking in dining room
Accommodation: 11 en suite
Credit cards: ▬ ▭ ◥ ▯ ▭ ▯

An ancient hostelry tracing its origins back to the 12th century. Olivers Restaurant (Oliver Cromwell sought refuge from the Royalists here) shares its menu with a popular bar. Dishes range from goats' cheese salad, cod with an almond, ginger and herb crust, grilled gammon in green peppercorn sauce, to warm treacle tart with clotted cream.

Castle Inn

Directions: In village centre, M4/J17

CASTLE COMBE,
Manor House Hotel ❀❀❀

Chippenham SN14 7HR
Map 3: ST87
Tel: 01249 782206
Fax: 01249 782159
Chef: Mark Taylor
Cost: *Alc* £45, fixed-price L £18.95/D £35 (4 courses). H/wine £16.50
Times: Noon-last L 2pm/7-last D 10pm
Additional: Bar food; Sunday L; Children welcome; ❀ dishes
Seats: 95. Private rooms up to 30. Jacket & tie preferred
Smoking: No smoking in dining room
Accommodation: 45 en suite
Credit cards: ▆ ▆ ▆ ▆ ▆

A romantic Italian garden, 26 peaceful acres that incorporates an 18-hole golf course, natural stone textures, log fires: this sympathetically extended 14th-century country house has much going for it. 'I can certainly understand why so many guests choose to stay here in order to relax,' observed one inspector. Mark Taylor's natural style of cooking puts the emphasis on the materials themselves, and enlivens them with imaginative combinations, a watercress soup, for example served with oysters and pears, or fillet of Scottish beef, smoked and served with tomato, rosemary and foie gras, pea purée and dauphinoise potatoes, and fillet of lemon sole with a Swiss cheese crust and sauce of smoked shrimps. Bacon, shallot and morel soufflé certainly impressed with its accurate timing and marvellous aromas when broken open, and a sea bass came with an unusual crab and coconut risotto, plus pepper and tomato salsa in chilli and coriander oil. Diced and spiced apple in filo came with cinnamon ice cream and a pool of caramel. Simpler, more straightforward dishes are available on request. The comprehensive wine list contains a reasonable selection of halves, but little by the glass.
   Signature dishes: Terrine of new potatoes, Glenarm salmon, young leeks, lemon oil; strawberry puff, strawberry daiquiri sorbet, lemon caramel; roulade of guinea fowl, foie gras, rhubarb, peppered caramel; breast of duck roasted with vanilla, red wine, sour cherries.

Directions: Off B4039 near centre of village, R immediately after the bridge

COLERNE, Lucknam Park ❀❀❀

This magnificent Palladian mansion has a lot going for it: a mile-long, tree-lined drive, 500 acres of parkland, elegant public rooms, extensive leisure facilities including a notable equestrian centre. Paul Collins, formerly sous chef, has been promoted to head up the kitchen brigade. He continues the imaginative, seasonal emphasis of his predecessor, in a style that includes the traditional, Dover sole with chips, pea purée

Chippenham SN14 8AZ
Map 3: ST87
Tel: 01225 742777
Fax: 01225 743536
Chef: Paul Collins
Cost: *Alc* £61, fixed-price D £40. H/wine £16
Times: D only 7.30-last D 9.30pm (7-10 Fri & Sat)

and parsley sauce, for example, and the more complex roasted squab, mushroom tortellini and thyme jus. Dishes endorsed at a late winter dinner included ravioli of chicken and truffle with morel sauce, asparagus tart with roast scallops and herb oil, roast duck, beetroot sauce and braised red cabbage, the five spice ice cream accompanying an apricot soufflé, and chocolate and Amaretto gâteau. The restaurant is elegant, spacious, and oozes quality, and has an abundance of staff to carry out exemplary service, and to advise on the high-class wine list.

Signature dishes: Cannon of spring lamb, noodles and garlic cream; cannelloni of lobster with tomato and basil; tart of asparagus, roast lobster with a herb oil; apple charlotte, mulled wine sorbet.

Smoking: No smoking in dining room
Accommodation: 41 en suite
Credit cards: ▆ ▆ ▅ ▆ ▆ ▆ ▆ JCB

Directions: Turn off A4 2 miles from Bath for Batheaston and L for Colerne, L again at crossroad, entrance 0.25 mile on L

Lucknam Park

Additional: Bar food L; Sunday L (12.30-2pm); No children under 12 in dining room; ❸ dishes
Seats: 80. Private room 36. Jacket & tie preferred

AA Shortlisted for Wine Award–see page 16

FORD, **White Hart Inn** ❁

A dream of a country pub, hard by a trout stream in a small hamlet, with log fires, good food and a great selection of wines. The cooking emphasises pronounced flavours, with dishes such as spicy lamb meatballs with couscous, and pan-fried loin of pork with grain mustard mash.

Directions: M4/J17 or 18, 10 minutes drive on A420 Colerne road

Chippenham SN14 8RP
Map 3: ST87
Tel: 01249 782213
Fax: 01249 783075
Chef: Tony Farmer
Owners: Mr C J & Mrs JM Phillips
Cost: Alc £20. ☺ H/wine £10.95
Times: Last L 2pm/last D 9.30pm
Additional: Bar food L; Sunday L; No children under 12 at D; ❸ dishes
Smoking: No pipes or cigars
Accommodation: 11 en suite
Credit cards: ▆ ▆ ▅ ▆ ▆ ▆

AA Shortlisted for Wine Award–see page 16

HINDON, Grosvenor Arms ❀❀

Originally dating from the 1700's this village-centre former coaching inn has recently undergone restoration, enhancing its Georgian character. There are more modern elements, too, one being a new glass-fronted, open-plan kitchen which adds to the attraction of the dining room. The menu keeps to the modern idiom, beginning with a selection of starters, the majority of which are also available in main course portions. Typical of the choices are salmon and prawn rillette with a lemon and herb dressing, pan-fried wood pigeon, the breast cooked pink and served on a well-executed apple and parsnip risotto, roast rack of Welsh lamb with a garlic and herb crust, and roast saddle of locally-farmed rabbit stuffed with field mushrooms and thyme then wrapped in Parma ham and accompanied by a mustard sauce. The rabbit's flavour greatly impressed our inspector, as did the accurate saucing. He finished with a simple, but very enjoyable chocolate and honey brûlée.

Salisbury SP3 6DJ
Map 3: ST93
Tel: 01747 820696
Fax: 01747 820869
Chef: Paul Suter
Owner: West Country Village Inns
Cost: *Alc* £20. H/wine £9.95
Times: Last L 2pm/last D 9.30pm
Additional: Bar food; Sunday L;
No children under 5; ❹ dishes
Smoking: No smoking in dining room
Accommodation: 7 en suite
Credit cards: 🔳 🔤 🔀 💲 🅒 JCB

Directions: 1 mile from both the A350 & A303

HINDON, Lamb at Hindon ❀

Salisbury SP3 6DP
Map 3: ST93
Tel: 01747 820573
Fax: 01747 820605
Owner: John Croft, Cora Scott
Times: Last L 2pm/last D 9.30pm
Additional: Bar food; Sunday L;
Children welcome; ❹ dishes
Smoking: No smoking in dining room
Accommodation: 14 en suite
Credit cards: 🔳 🔤 🔀 💲 🔳 🅒

A stone-built freehouse with an interesting choice of contemporary dishes on the fixed-price menu including grilled salmon oriental, marinated duck with a coriander and citrus sauce, and pan-fried beef fillet with a wild mushroom sauce.

Directions: In village centre, 1 mile off A303 & A350

INGLESHAM, Inglesham Forge ❀❀

A 300-year-old metalworks is the unusual setting for this popular restaurant. The chef-patron has a particular enthusiasm and talent for sauce making and at times it can seem as though everything comes with its own unctuous accompaniment – hollandaise for the broccoli, cheese sauce for the cauliflower, french beans with béchamel. Our inspector's starter of seafood Breton was a pleasing mixture including smoked salmon and various fruits of the sea in a traditional white wine sauce, sprinkled with Parmesan cheese, and grilled. The house speciality of tournedos Forge has tender, lightly pan-fried medallions of fillet steak topped with melted Stilton cheese and finished with port sauce. Supreme of chicken Forge comes with a rich napping of Madeira and mushrooms. For vegetarians, there's 'tortollini' stuffed with cheese and served

Lechlade Swindon SN6 7QY
Map 4: SU29
Tel: 01367 252298
Chef/Owner: Manuel Gomez
Cost: *Alc* £24. H/wine £9.95. ☺
Times: Noon-last L 1.45pm/7pm-last D 9.45pm. Closed L Sat, Sun, L Mon, Bhs
Additional: Children welcome;
❹ dishes
Seats: 30
Smoking: No pipes or cigars in dining room
Credit cards: 🔳 🔤 🔀 🅒

with cream sauce. Desserts change daily and may include orange and passion fruit cheesecake. Stay for the very good cafetière coffee and chocolate mints.

Directions: In hamlet just off A361 midway between Highworth and Lechlade

MALMESBURY,

The Horse and Groom

Charming, well-run 16th-century village pub, built in Cotswold stone. Here you will find an eclectic selection of dishes ranging from fresh tuna steaks grilled with lemon and parsley, to breast of duck with oriental stir-fried vegetables. Desserts are a favourite of the kitchen with Aunt Molly's steamed pudding and Bakewell tart both regular features.

Accommodation: 3 en suite.
Credit cards: 💳 💳 💳 💳 💳

Directions: M4/J17, take 2nd roundabout exit, B4040 (Cricklade). 2 miles to Charlton, pub on L

The Street Charlton SN16 9DL
Map 4: ST98
Tel: 01666 823904
Fax: 01666 823390
Chefs: Neil Lowthian, Robert Bieniasz
Owners: Nichola King & Philip Gilder
Cost: Alc £16. ☺ H/wine £7.15
Times: Last L 2pm/D 10pm
Additional: Bar food; Sunday L; Children welcome; 🌢 dishes

MALMESBURY,

Knoll House Hotel ❀❀

The dining room which overlooks the patio and gardens is discreetly decorated in shades of pink and apricot. The cooking is careful and committed with all dishes freshly cooked to order. Amongst more familiar ideas, beef carpaccio on roquette leaves with Parmesan shavings, for example, or calves' liver with bubble-and-squeak and shallot red wine jus, others stand out just for originality of concept and instant appeal: butternut and prawn broth with seafood ravioli; pan-fried salmon burger on vegetable spaghetti and tomato butter sauce; braised spiced shank of lamb with preserved lemon and chickpeas. Warm apricot tart with white chocolate ice cream was as satisfying as it sounded.

Directions: From M4/J17 take A429 (Cirencester); turn onto B4042 (Swindon); hotel is 500 yards on L

Swindon Road SN16 9LU
Map 3: ST98
Tel: 01666 823114
Fax: 01666 823897
Chef: Alan Johnson
Cost: Alc £25, fixed-price D £20. ☺ H/wine £9.50
Times: Noon-last L 1.45pm/7-last D 9.30pm
Additional: Bar food; Sunday L; Children welcome; 🌢 dishes
Seats: 40. Private dining room 25
Smoking: No smoking in dining room
Accommodation: 22 en suite
Credit cards: 💳 💳 💳 💳 💳 💳

MALMESBURY,

Mayfield House Hotel ❀

Guests return year after year to this pleasant hotel. A simple cooking style runs through the menu, epitomised by steak and ale casserole with a puff pastry case, and sticky toffee pudding served with locally made vanilla ice cream. A more imaginative streak is apparent in the likes of chicken and smoked bacon ravioli with a fresh tarragon cream sauce. Sound wine list.

Accommodation: 23 en suite
Credit cards: 💳 💳 💳 💳 💳 💳 💳 JCB

Directions: 10 minutes from M4/J17. On A429 in village centre between Malmesbury and Cirencester

Malmesbury SN16 9EW
Map 3: ST98
Tel: 01666 577409
Fax: 01666 577977
Chef: Mark Bullows
Owners: Max Strelling, Chris Marston
Cost: Fixed-price D £15.95. ☺ H/wine £8.25
Times: Last L 1.45pm/last D 8.45pm
Additional: Bar food; Sunday L; Children welcome; 🌢 dishes
Smoking: No smoking in dining room

MALMESBURY, **Old Bell Hotel** ✿✿

Abbey Row SN16 0AG
Map 3: ST98
Tel: 01666 822344
Fax: 01666 825145
Chef: Simon Holling
Owners: Nicholas Dickinson,
Nigel Chapman
Cost: Alc £26, fixed-price L £15/D
£19.95. ☺ H/wine £15
Times: Noon-last L 2pm/7-last
D 9.30pm.
Additional: Bar food; Sunday L;
Children welcome; ❸ dishes
Seats: 60. Private dining rooms 16 &
24
Smoking: No pipes & cigars
Accommodation: 32 en suite
Credit cards: ▤ ▤ ▧ ▣ ▤ ▐ ▣ JCB

Bedrooms here are named after people associated with this
ancient building: Loring, the abbot who built the guest-house
to the abbey in around 1220, Joe Moore, who added the
extension in 1908, Robins, a widow of the 17th century who
lived in next-door Castle House, now incorporated into the
Old Bell, and so on. Sample a slice of history before moving on
to eat in the grand surroundings of the Edwardian dining-
room. Start with confit of duck leg hinting of garlic and ginger
with red onion chutney, and continue with delicately grilled
scallops and turbot with pepper risotto and crab bisque-type
sauce. Alternatively, go for Cornish crab cake with mango
chutney, then honey-glazed breast of duck on parsnip purée
with thyme jus. Egg-custard tart is a traditional way to finish,
even if it does come with passion fruit sorbet and raspberry
coulis. Cheeses are British and served with home-made bread.
Quality house wines start off the wine list, notable for some
reputable producers.

Directions: In centre of town

MALMESBURY,
Whatley Manor ✿

*Impressive Cotswold stone-built manor house set in fine grounds
overlooking the Avon valley. Making the most of the view, the
warmly decorated restaurant offers diners an interesting fixed-price
menu. Expect carrot and coriander soup, poussin with a honey,
lemon and Armagnac sauce, and chocolate cheesecake with berry
compote.*

Easton Grey SN16 0RB
Map 3: ST98
Tel: 01666 822888
Fax: 01666 826120
Chef: Peter Haliday
Cost: Fixed-price L £15.50/D £29.
H/wine £13.50
Times: Last L 1.45pm/last D 9pm.

Additional: Bar food; Sunday lunch; Children welcome;
❸ dishes
Accommodation: 29 en suite
Credit cards: ▤ ▤ ▤ ▣

Directions: 3 miles W of Malmesbury on B4040. 15 mins from
M4/J17 or J18.

MARLBOROUGH, **Ivy House Hotel** ✿

*Ivy-clad Georgian building with regal decor in a classic style. Plain
dishes – baked ratatouille-stuffed field mushroom, homely apple*

High Street SN8 1HJ
Map 4: SU16
Tel: 01672 515333
Fax: 01672 515338

Ivy House Hotel

Chef: Richard Mellor
Owners: David Ball, Josephine Scott
Cost: *Alc* £24, fixed-price L 12.50. ☺
H/wine £8.50
Times: Last L 2pm/last D 9.15pm
Additional: Bar food L; Sunday L;
Children welcome; 🌢 dishes
Smoking: No smoking in dining room
Accommodation: 30 en suite
Credit cards: 🔳 🔳 🔳 🔳 🔳 🔳

meringue pie and English custard – sit alongside modern ideas such
as duck breast with hoisin and stir-fried vegetables.

Directions: Town centre in main street

MELKSHAM, Shaw Country Hotel ❀

Bath Road Shaw SN12 8EF
Map 3: ST96
Tel: 01225 702836/790321
Fax: 01225 790275
Chefs: Nicholas & Paul Lewis
Owners: Mr & Mrs Lewis
Cost: *Alc* £17.95, fixed-price L
£12.95/£13.95. ☺ H/wine £7.50
Times: Last L 1.30pm/D 8.45pm.
Closed D Sun, 26-28 Dec
Additional: Bar Food; Sunday L;
Children welcome; 🌢 dishes

*Friendly, creeper-clad hotel well placed for Bath and the M4. In the
homely Mulberry Restaurant, visitors have a choice of menus, each
featuring a range of interesting dishes. At a recent inspection meal
pan-fried duck livers with cherry vinaigrette was followed by lamb
with sautéed spinach and an excellent jus.*

Smoking: No smoking in dining room
Accommodation: 13 en suite
Credit cards: 🔳 🔳 🔳 🔳 🔳 🔳 🔳 JCB

Directions: 1 mile NW of Melksham on A365, from M4/J17 or J18

MELKSHAM, Toxique ❀❀

187 Woodrow Road SN12 7AY
Map 3: ST96
Tel: 01225 702129
Fax: 01225 742773
Chef: Helen Bartlett
Owners: Helen Bartlett, Peter Jewkes
Cost: Fixed-price L £18.50 (2
courses)/D £31. H/wine £12.50
Times: D only, 7.30-10pm.
Closed D Sun, Mon & Tue
Additional: Sunday L (12.30-2pm);
Children welcome; 🌢 dishes
Seats: 40. Private dining rooms 16, 24
Smoking: No smoking in dining room
Accommodation: 5 en suite
Credit cards: 🔳 🔳 🔳 🔳 🔳 🔳 JCB

Directions: Take Calne road from
Melksham centre, 0.3 mile turn into
Forest Road. Restaurant is on L after
0.75 mile

A cottage-style stone farmhouse hidden down a country lane,
its outside walls covered with roses. Inside, however, expect
the unexpected. The dining room is exotically coloured in
aubergine and midnight blue, and is filled with original
artwork, chunky candles in flowerpots and huge fur cones
lining the tops of the walls. Cooking is modern English, and a
typical meal chosen from the *carte* might start with deep-fried
fishcakes with lemongrass salsa, followed by pan-fried salmon
with juniper, glazed onions and mustard mash. An early

summer meal enjoyed by our inspector started with a fragrant soup with coconut milk, lemongrass and ginger dumplings. Marinated lamb brochette followed – tender pieces of lamb loin skewered between grilled sweet peppers and aubergines, and served on a bed of Parmesan polenta. The dessert list includes the likes of dark and white chocolate mousse, and prune and almond tart with crème fraîche.

NOMANSLAND, Les Mirabelles

An improbably named village on the Wiltshire-Hampshire border is the setting for this French restaurant divided in two by hop-covered archways: 'just like relaxing in France,' say the proprietors. 'Modern French' might be the appellation of *le menu*, written en français with subtitles, combining the classic, grand-mére's and the fashions of the day. Wild boar pâté – chunks of tasty meat mixed with mushrooms – has a mould of lentils on the side, while another pâté, this time quail, comes with prunes and Armagnac. Ginger and lime enhance a parcel of white crabmeat, truffle juice doing the same for carpaccio with Parmesan. Le confit de canard – a crisply skinned whole leg, moist and well-flavoured – is an exemplar of its kind, while beef dishes figure prominently, although veal sweetbreads stewed with morels, or poached turbot with Sauternes sauce could also make an appearance. Granité de caramel au chocolat rather let the side down on one occasion. *La cave* spreads its net surprisingly widely, though its heart is in *la patrie*.

Directions: A36 (Salisbury-Southampton); turn R into New Road (signposted Nomansland); straight ahead at crossroads and over cattle grid. Within a mile restaurant on R by church

Forest Edge Road
SP5 2BN
Map 4: SU22
Tel/Fax: 01794 390205
Chef: Eric Nicolas
Owners: Eric Nicolas & Claude Laage
Cost: *Alc* £23. ☺ H/wine £9.50
Times: Noon-last L 2pm/7-last D 9.30pm. Closed D Sun, all Mon
Additional: Children welcome; ❹ dishes
Seats: 50
Smoking: No-smoking area; No pipes and cigars
Credit cards: ▬ ▭ ⚞ ▯ 🄫

PEWSEY,
London House Restaurant

Market Place
SN9 5AB
Map 4: SU16
Tel: 01672 564775
Fax: 01672 564785
Chef: Peter Quinion
Owner: Mr D J Gerhardt
Cost: *Alc* £33, fixed price L £21. ☺ H/wine £12
Times: Noon-last L 2pm/7-last D 10pm. Closed L Mon, all Sun, 25-29 Dec

'This is serious dining territory', notes an inspector of this smart restaurant housed in a listed Queen Anne building. The various past experiences of the staff reads like a who's who of cuisine. A bloody Mary, for example, was as carefully made as any dish in the kitchen 'the sommelier obviously learned a few skills in cocktail making at Le Manoir Aux Quat'Saisons, where he worked last'. Chef Peter Quinion hails from Cliveden, and his cooking exudes a confidence in flavours and textures. A basket of exquisite breads, light as a feather, smelled glorious and did

not need butter, or anything to embellish them. Salmon with a
light salsa of coriander and tomato arrived next, tasty and
colourful. Roasted plum tomato, pancetta and basil soup with
sun-dried tomato tortellini was a revelation: the consistency of
consommé, but with the flavour of a more pungent, rustic dish;
tortellini were postage stamp-size, texture and taste was spot-
on. Chargrilled brill on baby leeks with seared scallops and a
truffle cream sauce was perfect – well balanced, everything in
harmony. Desserts really showed the skills associated with a
dedicated pastry team – hazelnut tuiles were paper-thin, cut
with architectural precision, between each layer were the
thinnest slices of poached peach kept in place by small blobs of
lime-flavoured cream. An accompanying ice cream was a
smooth creamy ball infused with kaffir lime leaf. The front-of-
house team fall over themselves to accommodate ones wishes,
as does the wine list. There are wines from Argentina and
Switzerland, and all destinations between. All the big names
are there, and the back four or five pages are dedicated to those
who have the occasion to push the boat out financially, yet
prices are not over the top. Do ask advice. The sommelier's
interest in telling us about a glass of house wine was just as
intense as if it were a £200 bottle of claret.

Additional: No children under 7;
dishes
Seats: 30. Private rooms 12, 30
Smoking: No smoking in dining room
Credit cards:

Directions: *Telephone for directions*

PURTON,

The Pear Tree at Purton ❁❁

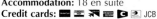

Church End SN5 9ED
Map 4: SU08
Tel: 01793 772100
Fax: 01793 772369
Chef: Alan Postill
Owners: Francis & Anne Young
Cost: Fixed-price L £17.50/D £29.50
(4 courses). H/wine £11.50
Times: Noon-last L 2pm/7pm-last
D 9.30pm. Closed L Sat, 26-30 Dec
Additional: Sunday L; Children
welcome; dishes
Seats: 50. Private dining room 50
Smoking: No pipes or cigars in dining
room
Accommodation: 18 en suite
Credit cards: JCB

A transformation has been wrought upon this former vicarage,
built of Cotswold stone. The conservatory restaurant is pretty
in pink, and elegantly equipped with monogrammed china,
fresh flowers and candles. Staff are smart and well-dressed.
The kitchen is equally well-drilled and even on a busy night
can ensure a cracking flow of high standard dishes. Marinated
scallops in a tomato and walnut vinaigrette, and crisp filo hat
of braised quail, chorizo and apricot might be amongst the
starters, with slow-roasted tomato and mozzarella tartlet as an
entrée on the four-course set dinner. Best end of lamb is
scented with tarragon and wrapped in streaky bacon, poached
breast of maize-fed chicken flavoured with dried mousseron
mushrooms, and pork fillet wrapped in bacon with a stunningly
good sauce of creamed goose livers. From the dessert list,
warm toffeed pears with butterscotch and fudge ice cream
sounds both appropriate and quite irresistible.

Directions: From M4/J16 follow signs to Purton. Turn right at
Spa shop, hotel 0.25 mile on right

REDLYNCH,
Langley Wood Restaurant ❀

Salisbury SP5 2PB
Map 4: SU22
Tel: 01794 390348
Chef: Sylvia Rosen
Owners: David & Sylvia Rosen
Cost: *Alc* £24. ☺ H/wine £12.50.
Times: Last L 2pm/D 10pm.
Closed D Sun, Mon, Tue, L Sat
Additional: Sunday L;
Children welcome; ❂ dishes
Smoking: No smoking in dining room
Accommodation: 3 rooms
Credit cards: 🖃 🖃 🖃 🖃 🖃 🖃 🖃 JCB

Children are welcome, as long as they can 'stay the course'; there's no children's menu but small portions are provided. Homely and friendly, a typical dinner might comprise smoked salmon and cream tart, fillet of brill with roasted peppers and shallot sauce, and rose-petal mousse cake with red fruit compote.

Directions: In village, between Downton (on A338 Salisbury to Bournemouth) & Landford (A36 Salisbury)

ROWDE, **George & Dragon** ❀❀

The 17th-century pub manages to be at once unfussy and full of character. Old school tables, wooden floors, an impressive fireplace adorned with dried flower garlands and a display of pickled goodies for sale leaves the food to take rightful centre stage. Fish predominates – this is the AA/Seafish Authority Seafood Pub of the Year – and the excellent choice fresh from Cornwall might include roast hake with aïoli and peppers, turbot with oyster and champagne sauce, and monkfish with borlotti beans. Start with wild rabbit risotto or terrine of John Dory with green mayonnaise. There's rhubarb crumble and custard, and chocolate and orange liqueur mousse for afters.

High Street SN10 2PN
Map 3: ST96
Tel: 01380 723053
Fax: 01380 724738
Chefs: Tim Withers, Hannah Seal, Kate Phillips
Owners: Tim & Helen Withers
Cost: *Alc* £20, fixed-price L £10. ☺ H/wine £9
Times: Noon-last L 2pm/7-last D 10pm. Closed Sun, Mon, 25-26 Dec
Additional: Bar food;
Children welcome
Seats: 35

Smoking: No smoking in dining room
Credit cards: 🖃 🖃 🖃 🖃

Directions: On A342 Devizes-Chippenham road

SALISBURY,
The Coach & Horses ❀

Natural slate floors are a feature of the bars at this, Salisbury's oldest inn. Dinner is served in the intimate, carpeted dining room. The menu is imaginative with the simpler dishes to be preferred.

Additional: Bar food; Children welcome; ❂ dishes
Smoking: No-smoking area
Accommodation: 2 en suite
Credit cards: 🖃 🖃 🖃 🖃 🖃 🖃 🖃 JCB

39 Winchester Street
SP1 1HG
Map 4: SU12
Tel: 01722 336254
Fax: 01722 414319
Chef: Martin Cooper
Owners: Martin & Angie Cooper
Cost: *Alc* £20. ☺ H/wine £7
Times: 10am-last D 10pm.
Closed Sun, 25 Dec

Directions: Past Guildhall Square on L

SALISBURY,
Howard's House Hotel ❀❀❀

Teffont Evias SP3 5RJ
Map 4: SU12
Tel: 01722 716392
Fax: 01722 716820
Chef: Paul Firmin
Owner: Paul Firmin, Jonathan Ford
Cost: Fixed-price L £18.50/D £25.
H/wine £9.95
Times: D only, 7.30-last D 9.30pm.
Closed 25-27 Dec
Additional: Sunday L (12.30-2pm);
Children welcome
Seats: 30
Smoking: No smoking in dining room
Accommodation: 9 en suite
Credit cards: 🔳 🔳 🔳 🔳 🔳 🔳

The 17th-century dower house is set in one of the prettiest villages in Wiltshire, surrounded by attractive gardens that seem to stretch in to the pale-green dining room with its plants and flower arrangements. Paul Firmin likes the flavour of his ingredients to speak for themselves, and simplicity is a watchword, with dishes such as crab mousseline with a spaghetti of vegetable and a dill sauce, wild mushroom risotto with rocket salad and Parma ham, and sautéed calves' liver, creamed parsnips and aubergine confiture, giving an idea of the style. Our June inspection dinner was a cracker. Boudin blanc with truffle served on a ragout of peeled broad beans and spring onions in a beurre blanc, was followed by a perfect, dramatically presented baked cod set atop a good onion marmalade and surrounded by a deep, glossy red wine sauce. A light as a feather, strongly flavoured, well-risen chocolate soufflé came with chocolate sauce and a well-balanced white chocolate and mint ice cream. It was a winner, although Calvados bread-and-butter pudding and cream was a strong contender. Finish the meal with good, strong cafetière coffee and petits fours. For those staying the night, breakfasts are worth looking forward too.

Directions: A36/A30 from Salisbury, turn onto B3089, 5 miles W of Wilton, 9 miles W of Salisbury

SALISBURY, Milford Hall Hotel ❀❀

206 Castle Street SP1 3TE
Map 4: SU12
Tel: 01722 417411
Fax: 01722 419444
Chef: Peter Roberts
Owners: Mr G Fitch, Mrs P Bruford
Cost: Alc £22.50, fixed-price L
£9.95/D £15.50. ☺ H/wine £9.95
Times: Noon-last L 2pm/7-last
D 9.30pm
Additional: Bar food; Sunday L;
Children welcome; ❹ dishes
Seats: 80. Private room 24
Smoking: No smoking in dining room
Accommodation: 35 en suite
Credit cards: 🔳 🔳 🔳 🔳 🔳 JCB

Just a short walk from the city centre, this extended Georgian mansion boasts a garden-style restaurant. The menu is French based but inventive, with many modern touches. Starters might include pheasant Tatin with a wild berry vinaigrette, a classic terrine de campagne with walnut oil and balsamic dressing, and marinated salmon with orange salad. Mains range from pepper-crusted tuna on marinated aubergine with tomato coulis, fricassée of rabbit with tarragon and courgette gratin, and chargrilled sirloin with a lie-du-vin sauce. Finish with the likes of warm coconut tart with chocolate sauce and clotted cream or star anise-flavoured crème brûlée.

Directions: At junction of Castle Street, A30 ring rd & A345 (Amesbury), less than 0.5 mile from Market Square

SALISBURY, **The Old Mill**

Dating from the 13th century, the Old Mill straddles the River Nadder as it wends its way through water meadows to Salisbury. The mill-race cascades through the beamed restaurant to create a delightful setting. Dishes to look out for include pot-roasted shank of lamb, and salmon coulibiac.

Additional: Bar meals; Sunday L; Children welcome; ❹ dishes
Smoking: No pipes & cigars.
Accommodation: 10 en suite
Credit cards: ■ ☰ ☵ ▦ ◖

Town Path West Harnham
SP2 8EU
Map 4: SU12
Tel: 01722 327517
Fax: 01722 333367
Chef: Roy Thwaites
Owners: Roy & Lois Thwaites
Cost: *Alc* £20, fixed-price D £18 (4 courses). ☺ H/wine £9.95.
Times: Last L 2pm/last D 10pm

Directions: On the A3094 S of Salisbury, head towards Wilton. Turn L into Lower St

SWINDON,
Blunsdon House Hotel

A hotel and leisure club run by the Clifford family for over 30 years. In the opulent restaurant our most recent meal, from a varied menu, centred on a well-executed dish of various charcoal-grilled fish with hollandaise sauce. Carrie's provides a less formal eating option.

Additional: Bar food; Sunday L; Children welcome; ❹ dishes
Smoking: No-smoking area; Air conditioning
Accommodation: 135 en suite
Credit cards: ■ ☰ ☵ ▢ ▦ ◖ ▣ JCB

Blunsdon SN2 4AD
Map 4: SU18
Tel: 01793 721701
Fax: 01793 721056
Chef: Elisley Haines
Owners: The Clifford Family
Cost: *Alc* £23.50, fixed-price L £17.50/D £23.50. ☺ H/wine £11
Times: Last L 2pm/last D 10pm. Closed L Sat

Directions: 3 miles N of town centre. From A419 take turning signposted Broad Blunsdon, then first L

SWINDON,
Chiseldon House Hotel

A former manor house surrounded by lawned gardens and equally convenient for both the town centre and the M4. The Orangery Restaurant is light, airy and home to some skilled cooking from the kitchen brigade. With a modern English slant, the sensible-length menu is full of interest, with dishes such as chilli-marinated roast fillet of pork served on a liquorice jus, and whole salt-baked John Dory flavoured with olive oil and lemon served with a salad of red pepper and leek, catching the eye. Presentation is a strength, as is flavour to judge by our chicken mousse and spinach terrine, and the perfectly executed mille-feuille of salmon, cabbage and leek.

New Road Chiseldon
SN4 0NE
Map 4: SU18
Tel: 01793 741010
Fax: 01793 741059
Chef: Kai Taylor
Owner: Marlene Ltd
Cost: Fixed-price L £14.95/D £24.95 (4 courses). H/wine £10.25. ☺
Times: Noon-last L 2.30pm/7pm-last D 9.30pm. Closed L Sat
Additional: Bar food D; Sunday L; Children welcome; ❹ dishes

The highlight of an already good meal was a delicious lemon torte well matched by raspberry sauce and a caramel flavoured custard. Wines from around the world on an informative list.

Directions: Easily accessible from M4/J15 & 16, on B4006. Short distance from Swindon town centre

Seats: 65. Private dining room 30
Smoking: No-smoking area
Accommodation: 21 en suite
Credit cards: ■ ☰ ⊼ ▦ ▣

WARMINSTER,
Bishopstrow House ❀❀

Classic Georgian house with everything going for it: 27 acres of lovely Wiltshire countryside, furnished with English antiques, 19th-century paintings, log fires – no wonder it was full of Americans when our inspector called one June day. The restaurant is very attractive and offers a classy environment, plus lovely Spode china and good table linen. The menu reads well with the kitchen working with the seasons, and keeping up with current trends. At our last visit toasted goats' cheese came with Mediterranean vegetables, chicken with wild mushrooms and grilled asparagus, and chocolate dice with griottines proved a super ides and was well-presented in a box shape with dice dots iced on. Coffee was served with good chocolate truffles and a mini lemon tart.

Accommodation: 31 en suite
Credit cards: ■ ☰ ⊼ ⬚ ▦ ▣ ▣ JCB

Directions: From Warminster take B3414 (Salisbury). Hotel is signposted

BA12 9HH
Map 3: ST84
Tel: 01985 212312
Fax: 01985 216769
Chef: Chris Suter
Owners: Simon Lowe, Andrew Leeman, Howard Malin
Cost: Alc £31.50, fixed-price D £31.50. H/wine £13.50
Times: Noon-last L 2.15pm/7.30-last D 9.30pm
Additional: Bar food; Sunday L; Children welcome; ❧ dishes
Seats: 65. Private room 25
Smoking: No smoking in dining room

WARMINSTER,
Les Parisiens ❀❀

A stylish Parisian-style bistro, decorated in burgundy and cream with French prints and jolly Gallic music. Sam Snook makes desserts and tends front of house, while husband Nigel is hands-on in the kitchen. All dishes are freshly made to order, and the menus feature everything from simple crêpes and croque monsieur, to more sophisticated dishes such as magret of duck with raspberry vinegar and bitter chocolate sauce, and couscous with roasted shallots and peppers, ratatouille and spiced lemon. A recent lunch enjoyed by our inspector started with a piping hot French onion soup, and deep-fried spiced goats' cheese with sweet pear and tarragon salad. The main dish was a light smoked haddock and Emmental crêpe, and for dessert, a bitter chocolate terrine with delicious caramel sauce. The restaurant organises annual trips to France, and monthly gourmet dinners, which are very popular and great value.

Directions: In town centre

28 High Street BA12 9AF
Map 3: ST84
Tel: 01985 217373
Chef: Nigel Snook
Owners: Nigel & Samantha Snook
Cost: Alc £25, fixed-price L £8.75/D £15.75. ☺ H/wine £9.75
Times: 10am-last L 2pm/7-last D 9.30pm. Closed Sun, Mon, 2 wks Feb, 2 wks Aug
Additional: Snack menu L; Children welcome; ❧ dishes
Seats: 40
Smoking: No-smoking area; No pipes and cigars
Credit cards: ■ ☰ ⊼ ⬚ ▣

WORCESTERSHIRE

ABBERLEY, **The Elms** 🐾🐾

Those who like to at least contemplate some light exercise over dinner ought to request a window table in the restaurant of this 18th-century mansion. On a summer evening a sedate game of croquet is likely to be taking place on the lawn outside and there is a fine view of the baise-like surface and the mature grounds beyond. Service is of a similar easy pace with the genial Frichots much involved front of house. A June inspection found the kitchen in the midst of change with the new team yet to be fully assembled. Scallops with a spiky salsa and a pungent goats' cheese ravioli are indications of a slightly bolder approach than in the past, although fillet of beef with a ratatouille of roasted shallots and aubergine (featuring excellent meat) would have benefited from an extra element of bite. Wines are well sourced and mark-ups are fair.

Directions: 15 minutes from M5/J5. 10 miles from Worcester

WR6 6AT
Map 3: SO76
Tel: 01299 896666
Fax: 01299 896804
Chef: Stuart Robbins
Owners: Mr & Mrs Marcel Frichot
Cost: *Alc* £32, fixed-price L £12.50
(2 courses)/D £29.50. H/wine £12
Times: 12.30-2pm/7.30-9.30pm
Additional: Bar food L; Sunday L;
Children welcome; 🍴 dishes
Seats: 80. Private dining room 100.
Jacket & tie preferred
Smoking: No smoking in dining room
Accommodation: 16 en suite
Credit cards: 🔲 🔳 🔳 🔳 🔳 🔳

BROADWAY,
Dormy House Hotel 🐾🐾

Willersley Hill WR12 7LF
Map 4: SP03
Tel: 01386 852711
Fax: 01386 858636
Chef: Alan Cutler
Owner: J Philip-Sorensen
Cost: *Alc* £40, fixed-price D £30.50.
H/wine £12.50
Times: 12.30-2pm/7pm-9.30pm.
Closed L Sat, 24-27 Dec
Additional: Bar food; Sunday L;
Children welcome; 🍴 dishes
Seats: 70. Private dining room 40
Smoking: No-smoking area
Accommodation: 49 en suite
Credit cards: 🔲 🔳 🔳 🔳 🔳 🔳 🔳

Surrounded by extensive grounds high above Broadway, the Dormy House is now a large complex developed from a 17th-century farmhouse. Tapestries, its attractive restaurant, is located partly in the old farmhouse (in a series of small alcoves with stone walls, oak beams and tapestry upholstery) and partly in an adjoining conservatory. The extensive menu changes daily, keeping abreast of modern trends and offering such intricate constructions as roast supreme and ballotine of chicken filled with chanterelle mousse on a cucumber and lime sauce. Vegetarians have a choice of enticements, like tortellini filled with wild mushrooms and sun-dried tomatoes with watercress and lemon sauce. Apple and rhubarb crisp was a high point of an inspection meal, served in a filo basket with good, own-made ice cream that was 'really refreshing'. Wine buffs should give the impressive list lengthy consideration, though a selection of suggested wines by the glass is helpful.

Directions: Take Saintbury turn off A44, after 1 mile bear L at staggered crossroads

BROADWAY, **Lygon Arms** ✿✿✿

The Lygon Arms has come a long way since it first welcomed travellers in the 16th century. It still retains the appearance of the coaching inn it once was, but sympathetic conversion has upgraded the place to that of a distinctive hotel owned by the Savoy Group. Graham Nesbitt (ex sous chef at Hanbury Manor, see entry) had only just taken up his position of head chef when our inspector called, but early reports of the new regime are promising. Meals are served in the Great Hall, a splendid, almost medieval looking place with a brightly painted arched ceiling, heraldic banners, large feature fireplace, heavy drapes and minstrels gallery. Menus are a combination of complex dishes (though not over complicated) balanced by straightforward chargrilled items. Our meal opened with Deben duck confit with foie gras, which was well balanced by a red plum compote. Spanking fresh Cornish sea bass followed, filled with a light lobster mousseline and topped with pieces of lobster meat; this was accompanied by oyster mushrooms, red pepper and braised fennel. An individual pear Tatin came with a crowdie cream laced with a good amount of alcohol and toasted oatmeal. Service is proficient and efficient. The wine list is fairly comprehensive but majors on France.

Directions: In the centre of the High Street

WR12 7DU
Map 4: SP03
Tel: 01386 852255
Fax: 01386 858611
Chef: Graham Nesbitt
Owner: The Savoy Group
Cost: Alc £45, fixed-price L £24.50/D £38. H/wine £14
Times: 12.30-2pm/7.30-9.15.pm
Additional: Bar food L; Sunday L; No children under 8 at D; ✿ dishes
Seats: 80. Private room 80
Smoking: No smoking in dining room
Accommodation: 65 en suite
Credit cards: 🔲 🔲 🔲 🔲 🔲 🔲 🔲 JCB

BROMSGROVE, **Grafton Manor** ✿✿

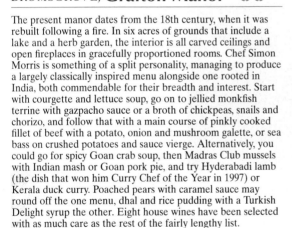

The present manor dates from the 18th century, when it was rebuilt following a fire. In six acres of grounds that include a lake and a herb garden, the interior is all carved ceilings and open fireplaces in gracefully proportioned rooms. Chef Simon Morris is something of a split personality, managing to produce a largely classically inspired menu alongside one rooted in India, both commendable for their breadth and interest. Start with courgette and lettuce soup, go on to jellied monkfish terrine with gazpacho sauce or a broth of chickpeas, snails and chorizo, and follow that with a main course of pinkly cooked fillet of beef with a potato, onion and mushroom galette, or sea bass on crushed potatoes and sauce vierge. Alternatively, you could go for spicy Goan crab soup, then Madras Club mussels with Indian mash or Goan pork pie, and try Hyderabadi lamb (the dish that won him Curry Chef of the Year in 1997) or Kerala duck curry. Poached pears with caramel sauce may round off the one menu, dhal and rice pudding with a Turkish Delight syrup the other. Eight house wines have been selected with as much care as the rest of the fairly lengthy list.

Directions: Off the B4091, 1.5 miles S of Bromsgrove

Grafton Lane B61 7HA
Map 7: SO97
Tel: 01527 579007
Fax: 01527 575221
Chef: Simon Morris
Owners: The Morris Family
Cost: Fixed-price L £20.50/D £27.85. H/wine £11.95
Times: 12.30-last L 1.30pm/7-last D 9.30pm. Closed L Sat
Additional: Sunday L; Children welcome; ✿ dishes
Seats: 60. Private dining room 50
Smoking: No smoking in dining room
Accommodation: 9 en suite
Credit cards: 🔲 🔲 🔲 🔲 🔲 🔲

BROMSGROVE, **Pine Lodge Hotel** ✿✿

Under its beamed ceiling the Parador restaurant is light, airy and comfortable with, as the name suggests, a Spanish flavour to the decor. The menu offers generously-sized dishes that are full of interest without straying too far from recognised combinations of flavours: terrine of duck with warm onion marmalade and vine-leaf-wrapped cranberries; medallions of beef on tossed watercress with a Roquefort and white wine sauce; steamed lamb and rosemary boudin on a leek soubise; papaya and green figs with pineapple fromage frais and a

Kidderminster Road B61 9AB
Map 7: SO97
Tel: 01527 576600
Fax: 01527 878981
Chef: Mark Higgins
Owner: Andrew Weir Hotels Group
Cost: Alc £30, fixed-price L £15.50/D £17.25 (4 courses). ☺ H/wine £9.95.
Times: Noon-last L-1.45pm/7pm-last D-9.45pm. Closed L Sat

Pine Lodge Hotel

Additional: Sunday L; Children
welcome; ❹ dishes
Seats: 100
Smoking: No smoking in dining room;
Air conditioning
Accommodation: 114 en suite
Credit cards: 🔳 ▨ ▢ ▨ 🅿

honey and ginger punch. There is also a range of flambé dishes
prepared at the table. The wine list includes a good choice of
half bottles.

Directions: On A448 Kidderminster road 1 mile W of
Bromsgrove centre

CHADDESLEY CORBETT,

Brockencote Hall ❀❀❀

There is something of the French style in the simple lines of
this understated Victorian mansion. Appropriately so, for these
days the owners Joseph and Alison Petitjean bring a distinctly
Gallic influence to bear on what is in many ways a
quintessentially English country house hotel. In the kitchen its
no surprise to find a Frenchman at the stove with Didier
Phillipot continuing to steadily hone his craft to increasingly
good effect. This is the cooking of an enthusiast, with a style
that acknowledges rather than reproduces the works of the
culinary giants and is uncompromising in the use of top quality
produce. Dual set menus offer a choice of prices and a
complex system of adjustments allows for mixing and matching
between the two. Descriptions are French, but annotation is in
English, and either way it is immediately apparent that
demanding targets are being set. Roast quail for instance
comes stuffed with foie gras and is further accompanied by
veal sweetbreads, wild mushrooms and a crisp parsnip rösti, all
of which were found to be suitably precise at one inspection
meal. Combinations are intelligent with main ingredients

Kidderminster DY10 4PY
Map 7: SO87
Tel: 01562 777876
Fax: 01562 777872
Chef: Didier Philipot
Owners: Alison & Joseph Petitjean
Cost: Fixed-price L £19.50/D £42.50.
☺ H/wine £12.80
Times: Noon-last L 1.30pm/7-last
D 9.30pm. Closed L Sat
Additional: Sunday L; Children
welcome; ❹ dishes
Seats: 75. Private room 28
Smoking: No smoking in dining room
Accommodation: 17 en suite
Credit cards: 🔳 ▨ ▢ ▨ 🅿

Directions: On A448, just outside
village, btw Kidderminster &
Bromsgrove (M5/J5, M42/J1)

allowed to dominate and cute balancing of flavours apparent in offerings like a hugely successful fried fillet of hickory-smoked salmon with crispy bacon and lime-butter sauce. Nowhere is the studious approach more apparent than in the *symphonie gourmande* of desserts with tiny but perfectly formed rum baba, bitter chocolate torte and crème brûlée all amongst the selection. Predictably, the wine list majors on France but like the rest of the operation, is none the worse for that.

CLIFTON UPON TEME, The Lion Inn

This very popular hostelry has parts dating back to the 13th and 17th centuries. The dining room is an extension of the characterful lounge bar, with blackboard menus listing both familiar and more imaginative dishes whose flavours are sound.

1 The Village WR6 6DH
Map 3: SO76
Tel: 01886 812617
Please telephone for further details

CORSE LAWN,
Corse Lawn House Hotel

The pond outside this elegant Grade II listed building was built as the eighteenth-century equivalent to a carwash: it's big enough for a coach-and-four to be driven into, washed, and turned round to emerge grimeless. Inside, the hotel is as stylishly and soothingly decorated and furnished as you could wish for. The restaurant remains the centre of operations. The French and British schools may be the basis of the style of cooking, but influences from further afield make their presence felt too. Nettle soup, Thai fishcakes, roast asparagus with balsamic dressing and Parmesan, and feuilleté of wild mushrooms with soy and Madeira could all share first-course billing, while Chinese-spiced pork with lime leaves, ginger and honey, roast fillet of beef with bourguignonne sauce and parsnip mash, and grilled shellfish – lobster, crab, langoustine, scallops, mussels and cockles – could crop up among main courses. Fruit can be a strong suit at pudding, rhubarb compote with a sorbet and fool of the same fruit, say. An impressive wine cellar has been built up over the years.

GL19 4LZ
Map 3: SO83
Tel: 01452 780771
Fax: 01452 780840
Chefs: Baba Hine, Andrew Poole
Owners: The Hine Family
Cost: Alc £35, fixed-price L £14.95 (2 courses)/D £25. H/wine £9.50
Times: Noon-2pm/7-last D 9.30pm. Closed 2 days Xmas
Additional: Bar food; Sunday L; Children welcome; dishes
Seats: 50. Private dining room 25

AA Shortlisted for Wine Award-see page 16

Smoking: No smoking in dining room
Accommodation: 19 en suite
Credit cards:

Directions: Village centre, on B4211 5 miles south-west of Tewkesbury

EVESHAM, The Evesham Hotel

Georgian in appearance, this grand old hotel actually dates back to 1540. Six mulberry trees reputed to be 500 years old are dotted about the gardens, where guests can take an evening stroll before dinner. Typical starters include avocado and artichoke salad, and sautéed chicken livers with grapes on a potato pancake.

Coopers Lane WR11 6DA
Map 4: SP04
Tel: 01386 765566
Fax: 01386 765443
Chef: Ian Mann
Owners: John Jenkinson
Cost: Alc £21. H/wine £10.50
Times: Last L 2pm/last D 9.30pm
Closed 25-26 Dec

Additional: Children welcome; dishes
Smoking: No smoking in the dining room
Accommodation: 40 en suite
Credit cards:

Directions: Coopers Lane is off road alongside River Avon

EVESHAM,
The Mill at Harvington ❀❀

Anchor Lane Harvington WR11 5NR
Map 4: SP04
Tel/Fax: 01386 870688
Chefs: Jane Greenhalgh, Bill
Downing, John Hunter
Owners: Simon & Jane Greenhalgh
Cost: *Alc* £24, fixed-price L £14.95/D
£ 22. ☺ H/wine £10.75.
Times: Noon-last L 1.45pm/7pm-last
D 8.45pm. Closed Xmas
Additional: Bar food L; Sunday L;
No children under 10; ❹ dishes
Seats: 40. Private dining room 14
Smoking: No smoking in dining room
Accommodation: 21 en suite
Credit cards: ▆▆ ▆▆ ▆▆ ▆ ▆▆ ▆ ▆ JCB

Directions: Turn S off B439, opposite
Harvington village, down Anchor
Lane

With lawns running down to the edge of the River Avon, this
Georgian house and former malting mill enjoys a delightfully
tranquil rural setting to the east of the village. The kitchen
prides itself on making good use of local Evesham produce,
according to the season – fruit and vegetables, of course, but
also game, meat, and herbs from the garden. Stilton beignets
with fresh tomato coulis, warm duck salad, smoked salmon and
avocado mousses with herb mayonnaise, blanquette of veal,
walnut-coated rack of lamb, and salmon in pastry show the
style. A terrace makes the ideal spot for a light summer lunch,
in winter head for a place by the fire in the lounge. Lots of
half-bottles on an interesting wine list, and there are always a
couple of fine wines available by the glass.

EVESHAM, **Riverside Hotel** ❀❀

The Parks Offenham Road WR11 5JP
Map 4: SP04
Tel: 01386 446200
Fax: 01386 40021
Chef: Rosemary Willmott
Owners: Vincent & Rosemary
Willmott
Cost: *Alc* £14.80, fixed-price
L £16.95/D £26.95 (4 courses).
H/wine £11.50
Times: 12.30pm-last L 1.45pm/7.30pm-
last D 9pm. Closed D Sun, Mon,
25 Dec, 1st 2 wks Jan (excl wkends)

Bay windows overlook three acres of gardens sloping down to
the River Avon. The family-owned hotel has a relaxed
atmosphere and dedicated, keen staff. The cooking is a
strength and the daily changing *carte* is modern without being
modish. First courses might include home-made fresh crab
ravioli with tomato and crab fumet, linguine with Parma ham
and Parmesan sauce, or a warm salad with pink pigeon breast
and pancetta. Fillet of chargrilled sea bass is served with
'scallions', ginger and stir-fry vegetables, but most main courses
play a straight wicket, for example, crisp roast duck with fresh

sage and onion stuffing and apple sauce, or tender haunch of
venison cooked pink with mushroom, port and shallot jus. The
short dessert menu nonetheless offers a difficult choice
between the likes of rich warm chocolate Armagnac cake with
chocolate fudge sauce, or fresh pineapple and mango with
walnut ice cream.

Directions: 2 miles from town centre on B4510 (Offenham).
At end of narrow lane marked 'The Parks'

Additional: Sunday L; Bar Meals L;
Children welcome
Seats: 48
Smoking: No smoking in dining room
Accommodation: 7 en suite
Credit cards: ■ ▦ ▨ ▨

EVESHAM,

Wood Norton Hall ❀❀

Wood Norton WR11 4YB
Map 4: SP04
Tel: 01386 420007
Fax: 01386 420190
Chef: Steve Waites
Owners: BBC
Cost: *Alc* £32.50, fixed-price L
£19.50/D £32.50. H/wine £13.95
Times: 12.30-2.30pm/7.30-last
D 9.30pm. Closed L Sat, Xmas
Additional: Bar food; Sunday L;
Children welcome; ❸ dishes
Seats: 70. Private dining room 32
Accommodation: 45 en suite
Credit cards: ▦ ▧ ▨ ▨ ▣ ▨

Built in the last century, the hall was bought by the BBC at the
start of the last war and became a broadcasting centre. The
corporation still owns the hotel today, serving as both a
training centre and commercial operation. Oak panelling,
draped windows, comfortable upholstered chairs and formal
table-settings provide the backdrop for dining. A terrine of
foie gras with Madeira and morel jus, smooth kipper parfait
with a poached egg, and duck confit with soy, honey, star anise
and orange salad illustrate the inspiration behind starters. Pan-
fried pork cutlet with tarte Tatin, crackling and mustard jus,
saddle of rabbit with mash and a casserole of root vegetables,
and fillet of brill steamed with oysters and cucumber served
with an emulsion of herbs and tomatoes show the range of the
kitchen's main-course output. Strawberry soufflé with vanilla
ice cream and hot chocolate sauce is there for those who can
afford to wait 15 minutes – the more impatient could try a
salad of berries with iced vanilla parfait and raspberry sorbet.
Perusing the wine list takes time too – it runs to 15 pages –
although the house selection is helpful.

Directions: 2 miles NW of Evesham on the A4538. Hotel is 0.5
mile on R

MALVERN,

Colwall Park Hotel ❀❀

The hotel was built in 1903 as part of Colwall racecourse; the
course itself closed after the Second World War, so the hotel
now stands alone in its own grounds. The restaurant has been
refurbished in shades of burgundy and pinks to create a warm

Colwall WR13 6QG
Map 3: SO74
Tel: 01684 540206
Fax: 01684 540847
Chef: Peter Botterill
Owners: Clive & Heather Sturman

Colwall Park Hotel

Cost: Alc £35, fixed-price L £15/D £25. H/wine £13
Times: 12.30-last L 2pm/7.30-last D 9pm
Additional: Bar food; Sunday L; Children welcome; 🍴 dishes
Seats: 40. Private dining room 10
Smoking: No smoking in dining room
Accommodation: 23 en suite
Credit cards: ▆▆ ▆▆ ▅▆ ▆ ▆▆ ▆ ▆ JCB

atmosphere, with fabric designs reflecting its Edwardian origins. Verbs figure prominently on the menu: a starter of a terrine of chicken and morels is 'presented' with orange and pear compote, another, of smoked haddock in puff pastry, is 'enhanced' by a quails' egg and chive cream. Medallions of venison with port and green peppercorn jus, steamed halibut with spinach and saffron cream, and roast breast of corn-fed chicken in a breadcrumb and mustard crust encompass the style of main courses. Coconut parfait may have more exotic appeal than sticky toffee pudding among the desserts. A bottle from across the border in Herefordshire figures on the wine list, which has a decent choice of half-bottles.

Directions: On B4218 btw Ledbury and Malvern

MALVERN,

The Cottage in the Wood ❀❀

Holywell Road
Malvern Wells WR14 4LG
Map 3: SO74
Tel: 01684 575859
Fax: 01684 560662
Chef: Dominic Pattin
Owners: John & Sue Pattin
Cost: Alc £28, fixed-price L £14. H/wine £13.50
Times: 12.30-last L 2pm/7-last D 9pm
Additional: Sunday L; Children welcome; 🍴 dishes
Seats: 50. Jacket & tie preferred

The cottage is actually a cluster of three white-painted buildings in seven acres of thickly wooded grounds on the side of the Malvern Hills. Views are magnificent – across 30 miles of the Severn Valley to the Cotswolds in the distance – and in summer the doors of the lounge are flung open so that guests can enjoy a drink on the terrace and gaze over the countryside. The kitchen's industry is exemplified by main courses of home-made pork faggot, on pea purée with onion gravy, and white pudding with foie gras on a risotto of swede and pearl barley. Otherwise, there could be game in season – breast of pheasant with apple and chestnuts, say, and an imaginative approach to fish shows up in baked halibut with crispy Parma ham and red wine sauce, or dorado in pesto with crushed potato and diced scallops. Fish could also crop up among starters of smoked eel and apple tartlets, with seasonal wild mushrooms going into a risotto with crispy black pudding. Nutmeg ice cream makes a fine complement to baked egg custard, and treacle tart could be another traditional dessert. Even Uruguay is represented on the thoughtfully compiled, extensive wine list.

Smoking: No smoking in dining room; Air conditioning
Accommodation: 20 en suite
Credit cards: ▬ ▬ ▬ ▬ ▬ JCB

Directions: Signed turning 3 miles S of Great Malvern off A449

AA Shortlisted for Wine Award-see page 16

MALVERN,

Croque-en-Bouche ❀❀❀

221 Wells Road WR14 4HF
Map 3: SO74
Tel: 01684 565612
Chef: Marion Jones
Owners: Marion & Robin Jones
Cost: D £25-£38. H/wine £10
Times: D only, 7pm-last D 9.30pm.
Closed Sun-Wed &
1 wk Xmas-New Year
Additional: Children welcome
Seats: 22. Private dining room 6
Smoking: No smoking in dining room
Credit cards: ▬ ▬ ▬ ▬ ▬

This is a small-scale operation, with Marion Jones cooking and husband Robin running the front of house, so it comes as no surprise to find that it's open on just Thursday to Saturday evenings. Growing their own herbs, vegetables and salad leaves takes time, too, of course. Dinner of up to six courses is well-paced, and reservations are carefully timed to ensure there's no sudden rush. A large white tureen of soup is left on the table for guests to help themselves - perhaps fish and shellfish with herbs and rouille. There's a choice of three dishes at the next two courses: a 'Japanese selection' made up of crab wrapped in a pancake tied with chives into a little parcel atop lovely marinated vegetables, tiger prawns with soba noodles and squid rolls with asparagus and sweetcorn, all as impressive as an alternative of 'delicious, well-balanced' Cornish skate with shoots of young sea kale (from the garden) and salsa verde. Next might come a 'very enjoyable' home-smoked leg of Orkney lamb marinated in parsley pesto and roasted with a stuffing of aubergine, spinach and herbs, or oriental-style roast Trelough duck, then a salad with maybe grilled vegetables. Cheeses in peak condition don't disappoint either. Among desserts could be chocolate mocha pie, or light, wafer-thin apple tart with lemon pelargonium ice cream and blackcurrant and redcurrant sorbet. The wine cellar must be one of the most coveted in the country indeed, this is a wine merchant with the full list running to hundreds of bottles. An abbreviated version can be sent to people in advance, and Mr Jones has chosen around a dozen to partner the food.

Directions: 2 miles S of Gt Malvern on A449

MALVERN,

Holdfast Cottage ❀❀

Little Malvern
WR13 6NA
Map 3: SO74
Tel: 01684 310288
Fax: 01684 311117
Chef: Jane Knowles
Owners: Stephen & Jane Knowles
Cost: Fixed-price D £20 (4 courses).
☺ H/wine £9.95

Imaginative cooking is to be found in this pretty dining room looking out over the hotel's two acres of gardens and a wisteria-clad terrace. The 17th-century oak-beamed building, enlarged during Victorian times, boasts a cosy bar and a dining room outfitted with antique silver, candlelight and fresh flowers. The reasonably priced wine list takes an international approach with bottles from England, South Africa and Chile

Holdfast Cottage

Times: D only, 7.30-8.45pm.
Closed D Sun, Xmas
Additional: Children welcome;
◑ dishes
Seats: 24. Private dining room 14
Smoking: No smoking in dining room
Accommodation: 8 en suite
Credit cards: ▇ ▇ ⫧ ⊂ ▇

alongside favourites from continental Europe including house
Burgundies available by the bottle, half or glass. The tempting
menu may include home-made soups such as potato and
lovage, and home-smoked trout with lime mayonnaise. Typical
main courses are roast guinea fowl with green peppercorn and
brandy sauce and beef braised in ale. Vegetarians are well
catered for with dishes such as lemony garlic mushrooms on
potato pancake, and leek and stilton clafoutis. To finish, spiced
chocolate brioche pudding or pears poached in honey with
lavender cream reflect the hotel's well-deserved reputation.

Directions: On A4104 midway between Welland and Little
Malvern

WORCESTER,

Brown's Restaurant ❀❀

The cooking at this cleverly converted corn mill, on the banks
of the River Severn, remains as reliable and well-judged as
ever, hence its continuing popularity for both smart dinners
and business lunches. The set-price menu is slightly larger at
night, otherwise there is no difference. Dishes are described
with pleasing simplicity: warm salad of chicken livers, smoked
bacon and croûtons; roast guinea fowl with a cassoulet of
beans; roast pheasant with apple and Calvados. There is also a
daily fish dish. Our inspector's crab cakes with red Thai salsa
were good and tasty, followed by beautifully tender lamb
shank, braised with tomato and rosemary that simply fell off
the bone. Vegetables included beetroot with cream sauce,
swede purée and good dauphinoise potatoes. Soufflé of creamy
rice pudding flavoured with coconut was a delicious cold sweet,
surrounded by a thick and rich caramel sauce.

Smoking: No-smoking area; no cigars & pipes in dining room
Credit cards: ▇ ▇ ⫧ ⊂ ▇ ▇

Directions: City centre, along river bank, car park opposite

The Old Cornmill
South Quay WR1 2JJ
Map 3: SO85
Tel: 01905 26263
Fax: 01905 25768
Chef: WR Tansley
Owners: WR & PM Tansley
Cost: Fixed-price L £18.50/D £34.50.
H/wine £11.50
Times: 12.30pm-last L
2.45pm/7.30pm-last D 9.45pm.
Closed Mon, L Sat, D Sun,
1 week Xmas
Additional: Sunday L;
No children under 8; ◑ dishes
Seats: 80

YORKSHIRE
EAST RIDING

BEVERLEY,

The Manor House

Northlands Walkington HU17 8RT
Map 8: TA03
Tel: 01482 881645
Fax: 01482 866501
Chef: Derek Baugh
Owners: Derek & Lee Baugh
Cost: *Alc* £30, fixed-price D £18.50.
☺ H/wine £11.95.
Times: D only, 7.30pm-last D
9.15pm. Closed Sun, 25-26 Dec
Additional: No children under 12;
🌢 dishes
Seats: 55
Smoking: No pipes and cigars in
dining room
Accommodation: 7 en suite
Credit cards: ▆ ▆ ▆ ▆ ▆ JCB

Set in carefully tended gardens, this tranquil hotel-restaurant
boasts an elegant conservatory dining room filled with lush-
green plants and parasols. Quality local ingredients take pride
of place on the interesting *carte* and simpler set menus. Crispy
prawn tart is a posh prawn cocktail in pastry with fresh-from-
the-sea prawns and lashings of Marie Rose sauce. The rack of
lamb has plentiful meat and a well-made sauce with vegetables
incorporated in the dish and potatoes served on the side. Other
typical main courses are fillet of beef tournedo with Beaujolais
jus, a panaché of plaice, monkfish and halibut with tarragon
velouté, and roast quail with seared fresh foie gras, Puy lentils
and sloe gin sauce. Our inspector's coconut crème brûlée was
nicely done but lacking in coconut flavour. Journey to the
comfortable lounge for the good quality coffee and petits
fours; the open fires on colder days make it most inviting.

Directions: 4 miles SW off the B1230

BEVERLEY,

Tickton Grange Hotel ❀

*Likeable hotel that retains much of its original Georgian character.
Choose between refined dishes such as mousseline of Scottish
salmon on cucumber sauce, and baked roulade of lamb loin and
courgette in delicate rosemary pastry, or go for the simply cooked
steaks and fish. Good cheese. Save room for the luscious Tickton
truffles.*

Additional: Bar food L; Sunday L; Children welcome; 🌢 dishes
Smoking: No smoking in dining room
Accommodation: 17 en suite
Credit cards: ▆ ▆ ▆ ▆ ▆ ▆ ▆

Tickton HU17 9SH
Map 8: TA03
Tel: 01964 543666
Fax: 01964 542556
Chef: David Nowell
Owners: The Whymant family
Cost: Fixed-price L £14.95/D £25
(4 courses). ☺ H/wine £9
Times: Last L 2pm/D 9.30pm

Directions: From Beverley take A1035 towards Bridlington.
Hotel on L, after 3 miles, just past village of Tickton

MARKET WEIGHTON,
Londesborough Arms Hotel

NEW

A newcomer to the Yorkshire scene, this carefully restored Georgian hotel bang in the centre of town is all set to go places. Andrew Dixon (ex Crown at Exford, see entry Somerset) had only been in place a couple of months when we inspected, but early reports are full of praise. The cooking is cosmopolitan, imaginative and focus's on modern techniques to replicate classical themes. It works well, but then light textures and subtle flavours are Andrew's trademarks. His menu is simply structured to avoid over stuffiness. A sparely described pan-fried guinea fowl sausage with mashed potatoes turned out to be a delicate boudin blanc studded with the fillet, the mash a delectable herb affair of great freshness, the accompanying sauce was of brown butter flecked with chervil. Roasted tail of monkfish with noodles was again a low-key description for a stunning dish that worked well with a deep, rich, very 'shallotty' beurre blanc. Iced banana parfait was a knock-out, outstanding in presentation and execution. The wine list was being updated as we went to press.

44 High Street YO4 3AH
Map 8: SE84
Tel: 01430 872214
Please telephone for further details

WILLERBY, **Willerby Manor Hotel** ❀

Elegant Victorian house, which stands in three acres of landscaped gardens. The Lafite Restaurant offers interesting menus and commendable cooking. Tagliatelle of smoked chicken and pancetta, followed by calves' liver with Dubonnet jus, and chocolate sponge with sauce anglaise, are typical choices. Friendly, professional service.

Additional: Bar food; Sunday L; Children welcome; ❁ dishes
Accommodation: 51 en suite
Credit cards: 💳 💳 💳 💳 💳

Directions: Off the A1105 W of Hull, just off main street of Willerby

Well Lane HU10 6ER
Map 8: TA03
Tel: 01482 652616
Fax: 01482 653901
Chefs: David Roberts, David Leaf
Cost: Alc £24, fixed-price L £14.50/D £16.50. ☺
Times: Last L 2pm/last D 9.30pm. Closed L Sat, D Sun, 25 Dec- 2 Jan

YORKSHIRE NORTH

APPLETON-LE-MOORS,
Appleton Hall Hotel ❀

Victorian country house set in delightful gardens in an unspoilt village. Dinner brings a set, four-course meal built around fresh produce. Expect Wensleydale mushrooms, roast breast of duck with an orange and brandy sauce, or rack of lamb with port, rosemary and redcurrant.

Accommodation: 9 en suite
Credit cards: 💳 💳 💳 💳 💳

Directions: 1.5 miles off A170, 2 miles E of Kirkbymoorside

York YO6 6TF
Map 8: SE78
Tel: 01751 417227
Chef: Norma Davies
Owners: Graham & Norma Davies
Cost: Fixed-price D £19.50 (4 courses). ☺
Times: D only, last D 8pm
Additional: No children under 12; ❁ dishes
Smoking: No smoking in dining room

ARNCLIFFE,
Amerdale House Hotel ❀❀

Arncliffe, population less than 100, is at the heart of the
Yorkshire Dales National Park in the valley of the River
Skirfare, which runs through behind the church. Amerdale
House, a former manor, has a country setting at the edge of the
village. Vegetables from the garden, chargrilled in this case, go
with a main-course roast fillet of sea bass in pesto, and apples
may be made into a pie and served with cinnamon ice cream
for dessert, and poached plums could accompany rice pudding.
Minted Yorkshire pudding, with roast loin of Dales lamb, gives
a novel twist to an old favourite. Starters on the four-course
dinner menus could include seared scallops with lardons, and
deep-fried sweetbreads with a piquant dip, while Thai fishcakes,
wild mushroom consommé, or plain asparagus with hollandaise
could constitute the second course. Breads are testimony to the
kitchen's dedication and skill, and oatcakes, with an impressive
selection of Dales cheeses, are home made, as are petits fours.
The wine list is notable for a broad span and reasonable prices.

Littondale Skipton BD23 5QE
Map 7: SD97
Tel/Fax: 01756 770250
Chef: Nigel Crapper
Owners: Paula & Nigel Crapper
Cost: Fixed-price D £29 (4 courses).
H/wine £12.50
Times: D only, 7.30-8.30pm.
Closed mid Nov-mid Mar
Additional: No children under 8;
❹ dishes
Seats: 24
Smoking: No smoking in dining room
Accommodation: 11 en suite
Credit cards: ▆▆ ▆▆ ▆▆ ▆

Directions: On edge of village

ASENBY, Crab & Lobster ❀❀

'It's like Steptoe's Yard, but boy does it work', comments our
inspector, completely taken by the 'any old items' that are
slung from walls, ceilings, and crowd shelves. The 17th-century
thatched cottage with hanging lobster pots and crabs on the
roof would not be out of place in Cornwall. A late spring lunch
elicited high praise for excellent cold asparagus simply served
with a very light smoked salmon mousse, fresh and sweet
halibut well-matched by langoustine noodles, and a classic
crème brûlée with raspberries. Otherwise there's posh fish,
chips and peas, cod chunk with saffron mash and parsley sauce,
as well as meatier offering s such as crisp duck confit, black
pudding and pineapple pickle. The reasonably priced wine list
offers a fair representation of wines from around the world.

Directions: Leave A1 for A19 at Dishforth, 3 miles turn L for
Asenby

Dishforth Road YO7 3QL
Map 8: SE37
Tel: 01845 577286
Fax: 01845 577109
Chef: Michael Pickard
Owners: David & Jackie Barnard
Cost: Alc £25, fixed price L £14.50.
☺ H/wine £10
Times: 11.30am-Last L 2.30pm/6.30-
last D 9.30pm. Closed 25 Dec
Additional: Bar food; Sunday L;
Children welcome; ❹ dishes
Seats: 60. Private room 12, 20
Smoking: No smoking in dining room;
Air conditioning
Accommodation: 9 en suite
Credit cards: ▆▆ ▆▆ ▆▆ ▆ ▆▆ ▆

ASKRIGG, King's Arms Hotel ❀❀

With Silks Grill and the Drover's Bars for steak and ale pie,
and gammon steak and eggs, and the panelled Georgian
Clubroom for more formal dining, the famous 200 year-old
former coaching inn, manor house, racehorse stables, and TV
location (*All Creatures Great and Small*) just about covers all
needs. The set five-course dinner is fairly elaborate – typical
dishes include cannon of Barnsley best end, stuffed with cloves
and sautéed garlic and flavoured by a rich Madeira espagnol.
The range is further enlivened by the use of diverse ingredients
in such dishes as gâteau of Scottish salmon with monkfish tail
mousseline that's laced with black pepper on a turmeric,
Grand Marnier cream reduction, and the saucing of Cassis and
orange liquor in a Charolais beef fillet, constructed as a mille-
feuille with spinach and shallot farcie. A hot cappuccino soufflé
was fluffy, golden and delicate – a clear winner.

Directions: 0.5 mile off A684 from A1 (Leeming Bar); in centre
of village.

Market Place Leyburn
DL8 3HQ
Map 7: SD99
Tel: 01969 650258
Fax: 01969 650635
Chef: John Barber
Owners: Elizabeth & Raymond
Hopwood
Cost: Fixed-price L £12.50/D £25
(5 courses). ☺ H/wine £8.50
Times: Noon-last L 2pm/7pm-last
D 9pm
Additional: Bar food; Sunday L;
No children under 10 in restaurant;
❹ dishes
Seats: 30. Private dining room 10
Smoking: No smoking in dining room
Accommodation: 11 en suite
Credit cards: ▆▆ ▆▆ ▆▆ ▆ ▆▆ ▆ JCB

BOROUGHBRIDGE, The Crown Inn

*A typical English country pub with a pleasant restaurant attached.
The menu includes simple but enjoyable dishes such as salmon fish
cakes with a well-made hollandaise sauce, and pan-fried pheasant
breast wrapped in bacon with a good port-wine sauce.
Accompanying vegetables are fresh and flavoursome.*

Roecliffe YO5 9LY
Map 8: SE36
Tel: 01423 322578
Fax: 01423 324060
Please telephone for further details

BUCKDEN, Buck Inn

In olden days it was local wool auctions that brought folk to
this atmospheric village inn, today the attraction is the good
food served in both bar and restaurant. Local produce is used
whenever possible for a menu with a modern slant and dishes
that are full of interest: confit of duck breast terrine wrapped
in pancetta with soy and honey; black pudding parfait with
home-baked brioche; seared tuna with coriander and salsa
dressing; salmon on a bed of egg noodles with a chive beurre
blanc; baked breast of chicken on black pudding risotto with
dijonnaise sauce. Desserts offer more traditional temptations
with the likes of summer pudding (with mascarpone cream),
sticky date pudding with hot toffee and ginger sauce, and
chocolate truffle cheesecake. The globetrotting wine list offers
a good selection by the glass and half-bottle.

Directions: In centre of village

Near Skipton BD23 5JA
Map 7: SD97
Tel: 01756 760228
Fax: 01756 760227
Chef: Jonathan Chapman
Owners: Roy & Marjorie Hayton
Cost: A*lc* £23.95. ☺ H/wine £12.30
Times: Noon-last L 2pm/6.30-last
D 9.30pm
Additional: Bar food; Sunday L;
Children welcome; ❹ dishes
Seats: 40. Private dining room 36
Smoking: No smoking in dining room;
Air conditioning
Accommodation: 14 en suite
Credit cards: ▆ ▆ ▆ ▆ ▆ JCB

BURNSALL, Red Lion

*400-year-old ferryman's inn with fine views of the River Wharfe and
Burnsall Fell. Modern English cooking that could include fricassée
of fresh seafood with chive mash, supreme of chicken roasted with
olives, sun-dried tomatoes and basil, and roast rack of lamb with
parsnip chips.*

BD23 6BU
Map 7: SE06
Tel: 01756 720204
Fax: 01756 720292
Chef: James Rowley
Owner: Elizabeth Grayshon
Cost: Fixed-price L £14.95/D
£23.50. ☺
Times: Last L 2.30pm/last D 9.30pm
Additional: Bar food; Sunday L;
Children welcome; ❹ dishes
Smoking: No smoking in dining room
Accommodation: 11 en suite
Credit cards: ▆ ▆ ▆ ▆ ▆ ▆ JCB

Directions: On B6160 between
Bolton Abbey (A59) & Grassington

CRATHORNE, Crathorne Hall

A stately Edwardian hotel with a peaceful location in 15 acres
of grounds between the Yorkshire Dales and the North
Yorkshire Moors. Public areas retain many original features
and the formal dining room is adorned with some fine oil
portraits and landscapes. Enjoy some *amuse bouche* in the
clubby bar while choosing from a dinner menu that offers an
interesting choice of classical and contemporary dishes. The
latter might include smoked queen scallops with elderflower

Yarm TS15 0AR
Map 8: NZ40
Tel: 01642 700398
Fax: 01642 700814
Chef: David Spencer
Owner: Virgin Hotels Ltd
Cost: A*lc* £30, fixed-price L £14.95/D
£24.95. ☺ H/wine £11.50
Times: Noon-2pm/7-10pm

vinaigrette, seared black tuna, ginger and honey-glazed Goosnargh duck, and Welsh lamb with apple and lavender jus. The dessert list provided the highlight of a recent meal in the form of a zesty, iced orange and dark chocolate terrine. The wine list leaves few wine making counties unrepresented.

Directions: From A19, take junction signposted Crathorne and follow the signs. Hotel entrance is to the L on way into village.

Additional: Bar food; Sunday L; Children welcome ; ✪ dishes
Seats: 50. Private dining room 30-40
Smoking: No smoking in dining room
Accommodation: 37 en suite
Credit cards:

EASINGTON, Grinkle Park Hotel ✪

Extensive grounds set off this elegant Victorian house. Local produce is used where possible in dishes such as grilled fillet of Whitby cod with a sweet-and-sour sauce, pan-fried Pickering trout with olives and lemon segments, and Baysdale lamb fillet with redcurrant and lime sauce.

Accommodation: 20 en suite
Credit cards:

Directions: Nine miles from Guisborough, signed L off main A171 Guisborough-Whitby road

Saltburn-by-the-Sea
TS13 4UB
Map 8: NZ71
Tel: 01287 640515
Fax: 01287 641278
Chef: Timothey Backhouse
Owner: Bass plc
Cost: Alc £23.05, fixed-price
L £12.75/D £18. ☺ H/wine £9.25.
Times: Last L 2pm/D 9pm
Additional: Bar food; Sunday L;
Children welcome; ✪ dishes
Smoking: No cigars and pipes

ESCRICK, The Parsonage Hotel ✪

A charming country house atmosphere, well-appointed bedrooms and interesting food are the attractions at this early 19th-century parsonage, peacefully situated in its own grounds close to the church. Soundly cooked dishes may include lobster and saffron ravioli, followed by chicken sautéed with fennel and ginger.

Accommodation: 22 en suite.
Credit cards:

Directions: From York head S on A19, Parsonage on R 4 miles out of town in Escrick village

Main Street YO4 6LE
Map 8: SE64
Tel: 01904 728111
Fax: 01904 728151
Chef: Kenny Noble
Owner: Karen Ridley
Cost: Alc £25, fixed-price L £12/D
£18.50. ☺ H/wine £9.95
Times: Last L 2pm/D 9.30pm
Additional: Bar food L; Sunday L;
✪ dishes
Smoking: No smoking in dining room

GOATHLAND, Mallyan Spout Hotel ✪

Attractive stone-built Victorian hotel standing on the edge of a moorland village. Expect traditional accommodation, friendly hospitality, and well prepared food. Our inspector recently enjoyed fresh sea bream served with a good saffron sauce, followed by a deliciously light sticky toffee pudding.

Whitby YO22 5AN
Map 8: NZ80
Tel: 01947 896206
Fax: 01947 896327
Chefs: David Fletcher, Martin Skelton
Owner: Judith Heslop
Cost: Alc £25, fixed-price L £13.50/D
£19.50. H/wine £9
Times: Last L 2pm/last D 8.30pm.
Closed 25 Dec
Additional: Bar food; Sunday L;
No children under 6; ✪ dishes
Accommodation: 26 en suite
Credit cards:

Directions: Off A169 (Pickering-Whitby) in village, opposite church

GRASSINGTON, **Grassington House** ✦

Boasting a prime position in the centre of the town square, this hotel enjoys a popular following for its bar and restaurant meals made from fresh ingredients. There's hearty gourmet sandwiches, plenty for vegetarians, and an exciting selection of desserts as well as simple soup, melon, gravad lax, Scotch fillet and lemon sole.

Accommodation: 10 en suite. **Credit cards:** ▬ ▭ ⫚ ⫇ ⦿

Directions: From Skipton bypass take B6265 to Grassington

5 The Square BD23 5AQ
Map 7: SE06
Tel: 01756 752406
Fax: 01756 752135
Chef: Catherine Rayner
Owner: Gordon Elsworth
Cost: Alc £18. ☺ H/wine £8.25
Times: Last L 2pm/last D 9pm
Additional: Bar food; Sunday L;
Children welcome; ❹ dishes
Smoking: No pipes & cigars

HARROGATE, **La Bergerie** ✦✦

Very typical French restaurant, simply but comfortably decorated, with 'Edith Piaf singing constantly'. A classic menu, in French with English translations, offers sound cooking. Fish provençale with very fresh scallops, mussels and prawns in 'a quite delicious sauce which I mopped up with the lovely French bread', opened an early spring dinner. Best end of lamb with mushroom and port wine sauce followed, pronounced 'really good', and served with fresh, bright vegetables. Crème brûlée was 'very correct' with a slight hint of lemon adding extra interest. Otherwise there could be mille-feuille of salmon and smoked cod with spinach in a caper butter sauce, chicken breast served with a rich tarragon and ginger sauce, and frangipane tart with pears cooked in red wine.

Directions: From one-way system 1st L onto Cheltenham Mount and 1st R into Mount Parade

11/13 Mount Parade HG1 1BX
Map 8: SE35
Tel/Fax: 01423 500089
Chef: Jacques Giron
Owners: Jacques & Juliet Giron
Cost: H/wine £8.50
Times: D only, 7-last D 11pm.
Closed Sun, 25-28 Dec
Additional: L by arrangement;
Children welcome; ❹ dishes
Seats: 35. Private room 25
Smoking: No-smoking area;
Air conditioning
Credit cards: ▭

HARROGATE, **The Bistro** ✦✦

Harrogate this may be, but the Mediterranean atmosphere generated by the cream and blue colour scheme at this small mews restaurant has spread to the menu: walnut pesto with gnocchi, fish soup with rouille and croûtons, roast cod in an olive crust with basil purée and sun-dried tomato risotto, provençale vegetables and olive jus with lamb shank – you can even order a side order of tapenade. A tartlet of smoked haddock with spinach and a poached egg, scallop risotto with herbs, or wild mushroom macaroni may be among other first-course ideas. Wild mushrooms, this time in ravioli, also make an appearance with a main course of roast chicken breast and spinach, while duck breast roasted with honey and soy shows the influence of the orient. Expect the place to be busy with delegates from the nearby conference centre when there's something on, quieter at other times.

1 Montpellier Mews HG1 2TG
Map 8: SE35
Tel: 01423 530708
Fax: 01423 567000
Chef: Marc Papon
Owner: Maurizio Capurro
Cost: Alc £22. ☺
Times: Noon-2.30pm/7-10pm.
Closed Sun, Mon, 10 days Xmas
Additional: Children welcome;
❹ dishes
Seats: 36
Smoking: No pipes & cigars
Credit cards: ▬ ▭ ⫚ ⫇ ⦿

Directions: Town centre, just west of Parliament St, near the Cenotaph

HARROGATE, **Boar's Head Hotel** ✦✦

Ripley Castle is well worth a visit while you're in this delightful village a few miles out of Harrogate. The Boar's Head, on the cobbled market square, is part of the castle estate, with portraits and antiques to prove it. There are two comfortable lounges and an informal bar/bistro as well as the elegant restaurant, where professional and friendly staff, all French, contribute to one's enjoyment. In here, a complimentary cup of perhaps Thai soup with home-made breads start things off. A terrine of chicken, sweetbreads and bacon, well presented and

Ripley Castle Estate
HG3 3AY
Map 8: SE35
Tel: 01423 771888
Fax: 01423 771509
Chef: Steven Chesnutt
Owner: Sir Thomas Ingilby
Cost: Fixed-price L £13.50 (2 courses)/D £27.50. H/wine £11
Times: Noon-last L 2pm/6.30-last D 9.30pm

Boar's Head Hotel

Additional: Bar food; Sunday L;
Children welcome; ❸ dishes
Seats: 40
Smoking: No pipes and cigars
Accommodation: 25 en suite
Credit cards: 💳 💳 💳 💳 💳 💳 💳

full of flavour, makes a good starter, followed by, say, an equally enjoyable main course of roasted sea bream drizzled with lobster oil and accompanied by wild mushrooms and an impressive olive potato cake. The star of an inspector's meal was an inventive crêpes Suzette soufflé. Leave room for the home-made petits fours that come with coffee, and allow time to browse through the long and generally well-priced wine list.

Directions: On A61, 3 miles N of Harrogate

HARROGATE, Dusty Miller ❀❀

Built as a pub in the early 19th century, this square stone building under a Yorkshire slate roof is almost engulfed by Virginia creeper, a blaze of colour in the autumn. Within, the three rooms, one with a wonderful Victorian bar and a welcoming fire blazing away in winter, are furnished with what the proprietors describe as 'humble Yorkshire antiques'. Canapés give a promising foretaste of what is to follow. The item on the menu described as 'A Good Soup' was endorsed by an inspector who started with cream of wild mushroom of 'superb flavour'. Other starters could run from Parma ham with melon to a tartlet of lobster, basil and tomatoes. The fish of the day could be 'superbly fresh' halibut served simply with a light beurre blanc and creamy mash, two scallops added for luxury; rack of Nidderdale lamb, or roast duckling with apples and Calvados may also be on the menu. Crème brûlée is well reported, and peach and almond crumble will appeal to those who want something more substantial.

Low-Laithe Summerbridge
HG3 4BU
Map 8: SE35
Tel: 01423 780837
Chef: Brian Dennison
Owners: Brian & Elizabeth Dennison
Times: D only, 7-11pm.
Closed Sun, Mon, Tue
Credit cards: 💳 💳 💳

Directions: Situated on B6165,
10 miles from Harrogate

HARROGATE,
Harrogate Brasserie Hotel ❀

Lively place, a typical brasserie that offers live jazz and blues on certain evenings. Chicken liver and smoked duck pâté with Cumberland sauce, rack of lamb with boulangère potatoes, and a light pancake filled with 'fruits of the forest' and accompanied by a light zabaglione, set a cracking pace at inspection.

Smoking: No-smoking area; No pipes and cigars
Accommodation: 13 en suite. **Credit cards:** 💳 💳 💳 💳 💳 💳

Directions: In town centre, 500m from railway station, behind theatre

28-30 Cheltenham Parade
HG1 1DB
Map 8: SE35
Tel: 01423 505041
Fax: 01423 530920
Chef: Brian Dale
Owners: Richard & Amanda Finney
Cost: *A/c* £17, fixed-price D £12.50
(2 courses). ☺ H/wine £8.95
Times: Last L 2pm/last D 10pm.
Closed L Sun, 26 Dec
Additional: Bar food L;
Children welcome; ❸ dishes

HARROGATE,

Harrogate Moat House

Adjacent to the International Conference Centre this distinctive, glass-fronted building features the intimate Boulevard Restaurant on the first floor. The menu offers a good choice of imaginative dishes including tomato and courgette soup with crispy croûtons and pesto, and roast shank of lamb with confit of aubergine and red wine jus.

Kings Road HG1 1XX
Map 8: SE35
Tel: 01423 849988
Fax: 01423 524435
Please telephone for further details

HARROGATE, Old Swan Hotel

This long-standing hotel is proud of its famous connections – in 1926 Agatha Christie chose to 'disappear' here, and a world-wide 'manhunt' ensued. Visitors eat in the ornate Wedgwood Room or the intimate Library Restaurant. Try Nidderdale trout with prawns and black noodles with lemon butter sauce.

Accommodation: 136 en suite
Credit cards: ▬ ▬ ▬ ▬ ▬

Directions: Town centre near junction of Swan Road and York Road

Swan Road HG1 2SR
Map 8: SE35
Tel: 01423 500055
Fax: 01423 501154
Chef: Philip Walters
Cost: Alc £25, fixed-price L £12.95/D £19.95. H/wine £14.40
Times: Last L 2pm/last D 9.45pm
Additional: Bar food; Sunday L; Children welcome; ✦ dishes
Smoking: No smoking in dining room

HARROGATE, Rudding Park House

You'll find the light, airy Clocktower Bar & Brasserie in the converted stable block of Rudding Park House, a Regency-style conference venue with extensive grounds. Notably friendly staff serve Mediterranean-influenced food: starters such as wild mushroom tart with red onion marmalade, and main courses typified by lemon and thyme chicken with chargrilled vegetables and pesto mash.

Accommodation: 50 en suite. **Credit cards:** ▬ ▬ ▬ ▬ ▬ ▬

Directions: 3 miles S of Harrogate, just off the A658 linking the A61 from Leeds to the A59 York road

Follifoot HG3 1JH
Map 8: SE35
Tel: 01423 871350
Fax: 01423 872286
Chef: Michael Madeley-Bell
Owner: Simon Mackaness
Cost: Alc £22, fixed-price L £10 (2 courses). ☺
Additional: Bar food; Sunday L; Children welcome; ✦ dishes
Smoking: No pipes and cigars; Air conditioning

HARROGATE, Studley Hotel

Swan Road HG1 2SE
Map 8: SE35
Tel: 01423 560425
Fax: 01423 530967
Chef: Michel Boulineau
Owner: Mr GG Dilasser
Cost: Alc £22, fixed-price D £16.95. ☺ H/wine £10.
Times: Last L 1.45pm/last D 10pm
Additional: Bar food L; Sunday L; Children welcome
Smoking: No pipes & cigars in dining room; Air conditioning
Accommodation: 36 en suite
Credit cards: ▬ ▬ ▬ ▬ ▬ ▬ ▬

Directions: Close to Conference Centre, near the entrance to Valley Gardens

Watch dishes such as entrecôte bordelaise, brochette of monkfish, or sardines dijonnaise, being cooked to order on the authentic charcoal grill – a feature of the restaurant here. Other items on the menu of long-standing chef Michel Boulineau, include scallops and prawns florentine, and magret of duck with a red berry and port sauce.

HARROGATE, **The White House** ❀❀

10 Park Parade HG1 5AH
Map 8: SE35
Tel: 01423 501388
Fax: 01423 527973
Chef/Owner: Jennie Forster
Cost: Alc £26.50, fixed-price L
£15.50/D £12.95 (2 courses). ☺
H/wine £9.25
Times: Noon-last L 1.30pm/7.30-last
D 9pm. Closed Sun except L by
arrangement
Additional: Children welcome;
❧ dishes
Seats: 36. Private dining room 12
Smoking: No smoking in dining room
Accommodation: 10 en suite
Credit cards: ▓▓ ▓▓ ▓▓ ▓ ▓▓ 🅒 JCB

In 1836, Harrogate's mayor built the White House in the style
of a Venetian villa. Today it is an elegant restaurant-with-
rooms set in gardens overlooking the Stray. The hard-working
chef-owner, Jennie Forster, spices her menus with quotations,
so take heed of Oscar Wilde ('the only way to resist temptation
is to yield to it') before perusing the imaginative *carte* and set
menus. The modern European cooking has the occasional nod
to tradition, so ink-fish risotto with prawns might share the
starter list with Yorkshire pudding with raspberry vinegar.
Recent main courses have included salmon with a crust of
couscous and olives with coriander, and tenderloin of pork
with crushed pepper and brandy sauce. Puddings tend to be
staunchly British: Yorkshire parkin with butterscotch, for
instance. The wine list has a choice of moderately priced labels,
several half-bottles, plus a few heavyweights in the 'cellar
collection'.

Directions: Opposite Christchurch, parallel with A59 close to
Wetherby/Skipton junction

HELMSLEY, **The Black Swan** ❀

Old-fashioned courtesies, crisp linen, polished silver and fresh
flowers are the hallmarks of this historic hotel in the town square.
Enjoy a drink in one of the many cosy lounges or the stunning
walled garden, before dining on confit of duck with citrus dressing,
and grilled sea bream with tomato and chives.

Market Place YO6 5BJ
Map 8: SE68
Tel: 01439 770466
Fax: 01439 770174
Chef: Nigel Wright
Owner: Forte
Cost: Alc £15, fixed-price L £15/D
£24.50. ☺ H/wine £14
Times: Last L 2pm/last D 9pm

Additional: Bar food L; Sunday L; Children welcome; ❧ dishes
Smoking: No smoking in dining room
Accommodation: 45 en suite
Credit cards: ▓▓ ▓▓ ▓▓ ▓ ▓▓ 🅒 ▓

Directions: Take A170 from Scarborough or Thirsk; Black Swan
is in centre of village, at top end of Market Place

HELMSLEY,
Feversham Arms Hotel ❀

An old coaching inn covered with roses in the summer. Dishes
served in the restaurant are influenced by English, French and
Spanish cooking. At a meal in May, our inspector started his meal

1 High Street YO6 5AG
Map 8: SE68
Tel: 01439 770766
Fax: 01439 770346
Chefs: David Brown & Linda Barker

with ravioli in a rich brandy cream sauce, followed by 'zarzuela' – a
very enjoyable Spanish casserole of fish and seafood.

Smoking: No smoking in dining room
Accommodation: 18 en suite
Credit cards: ▬ ▭ ▭ 🖪

Directions: 200 yds N of Market Place

Owners: Gonzalo Aragues, Rowan
Bowie
Cost: *Alc* £28, fixed-price L £15
(4 courses)/D £20 (4 courses). ☺
H/wine £10
Times: Last L 2pm/last D 9.30pm
Additional: Bar food; Sunday L;
No children under 6; 🍴 dishes

HELMSLEY, **Star Inn** ❀❀

Harome YO6 5JE
Map 8: SE68
Tel: 01439 770397
Fax: 01439 771833
Chef: Andrew Pern
Owners: Andrew & Jacquie Pern
Cost: *Alc* £20.25. ☺ H/wine £10
Times: Noon-2pm/6.45-9.30pm (Sun
noon-6pm). Closed D Sun, Mon,
25 Dec, 2 wks Jan
Additional: Bar food; Sunday L;
Children welcome; 🍴 dishes
Seats: 35. Private room 10
Smoking: No smoking in dining room
Credit cards: ▬ ▭ ✈ ▭

A thatched roof, low beams and bags of old-pub charm, the
Star Inn's attractions are apparent even before you sit down to
chef/proprietor Andrew Pern's robust, up-to-date cooking. The
inn, sited in a secluded village, dates back to the 14th century,
but its cellars are 500 years older. Monks once used the place
as a stop-off en route to York Minster. Now, food-lovers beat
a track here for such delights as grilled red mullet with black
bean salsa, to be followed by the likes of warm salad of guinea
fowl, morteau sausage, mushrooms and truffle, or steamed
steak and kidney suet pudding (huge amounts of tender meat
and delicious gravy, though the base could have been fluffier).
A tangy lemon tart made for a simple but effective end to an
inspection meal. Charming service and a well-annotated wine
list are yet more Star attractions.

Directions: 3 miles SE of A170, first building in village

HETTON, **Angel Inn** ❀❀

Skipton BD23 6LT
Map 7: SD95
Tel: 01756 730263
Fax: 01756 730363

AA Wine Award—see page 16
Shortlisted for

Plush is the word for the restaurant of the old drover's inn, with its crisp linen and sparkling glass contrasting with the stone walls and heavy beams. The cooking, though, is crisp and up-to-date. Breast of corn-fed chicken is rubbed with garlic and herbs, chargrilled and served on a pearl barley and cep mushroom risotto, and Goosenargh duckling is given a fusion treatment with crispy noodles and a mango, shallot, tomato and red chilli salsa. There is sirloin steak bordelaise for the traditionalist, plus a daily fish dish. Starters include the regional revamp of lightly smoked haddock set on black pudding glazed with Lancashire rarebit. To even the balance, there's Yorkshire curd tart with cinnamon ice cream. A terrific choice of bar food redefines the term. The wine list is magnificent with some two dozen by the glass.

Additional: Bar food; Sunday L (noon-2pm); Children welcome; dishes
Seats: 56
Smoking: No-smoking area; No pipes & cigars
Credit cards:

Directions: In village centre, B6265 (Rylestone) from Skipton bypass

Angel Inn

Chefs: John Topham & Richard Smith
Cost: *Alc* £28.50, fixed-price D £28.50 (4 courses). ☺ H/wine £9.95
Times: D only, 6-last D 9.30pm. Closed D Sun, 26 Dec, 1 Jan

HOVINGHAM,

Worsley Arms Hotel

York YO6 4LA
Map 8: SE67
Tel: 01653 628234
Fax: 01653 628130
Chef: Andrew Jones
Owner: Euan Rodger
Cost: Fixed-price L £16/D £25. ☺ H/wine £11.50
Times: Noon-last L 2pm/7pm-last D 9.30pm
Additional: Bar food; Sunday L; Children welcome; dishes
Seats: 40. Private dining room 30.
Smoking: No smoking in dining room
Accommodation: 18 en suite
Credit cards:

Serious, but different, styles of eating are available in both the formal restaurant and the bar-brasserie. Dinner in the former might comprise terrine of chicken and courgette stuffed with fresh truffle and coriander, wrapped in smoked ham with a salad of rocket and orange, followed by roast escalope of salmon with roast ratatouille, saffron and olive oil, then hot mango tart with pear sorbet. At Cricketer's Bistro, the choice instead might run to steamed Scottish mussels and king scallops with a fresh herb, ginger and garlic butter, braised Yorkshire ham shank with pease pudding and a broth of vegetables or pan-fried calves' liver with herb mash, tomato confit, crispy smoked bacon and red wine sauce. Desserts include sticky toffee pudding and glazed lemon tart with clotted cream. Afterwards, take a restorative turn around the idyllic estate village of Hovingham.

Directions: On B1257 midway between Malton and Helmsley

KIRKBYMOORSIDE,
George & Dragon Hotel ❀

17 Market Place YO62 6AA
Map 8: SE68
Tel/Fax: 01751 433334
Chef: Shari Jahangiri
Owners: Stephen & Frances Colling
Cost: *Alc* £17. ☺ H/wine £9.90
Times: Last L 2.15pm/last D 9.15pm
Additional: Bar food; Sunday L;
Children welcome; ⬧ dishes
Smoking: No smoking in dining room
Accommodation: 18 en suite
Credit cards: ▬ ▬ ❧ ◻ ◖

Directions: *Telephone for directions*

A new chef has reinvigorated the cooking at this 17th-century former coaching inn. Whether you chose bar, bistro or restaurant the same wide-ranging menu is available with dishes as varied as steak ale and mushroom pie, whole trout baked with lemon and herbs, rabbit braised in Dijon mustard with green ginger sauce, and sweet-and-sour vegetable stir-fry on egg noodles.

KNARESBOROUGH, Carriages ❀

Down-to-earth style brasserie-cum-wine bar with central location, rough cast walls, stone flagged floors, old tables, chairs, candles. Blackboard menu offers a cosmopolitan selection: Chinese-style pancake filled with shredded duck and spicy plum sauce; calves' liver and red wine sauce, wild mushrooms with Lexia raisins and lardons; crème brûlée.

Smoking: No pipes and cigars. **Credit cards:** ▬ ▬ ▬ ❧ ◻ ▬

Directions: On the A59 York to Harrogate Road, in the town centre

89 High Street HG5 0HL
Map 8: SE35
Tel: 01423 867041
Chef: Bruce Gray
Owners: Bruce Gray & Jon Holder
Cost: *Alc* £17, fixed price D £17.50.
☺ H/wine £8
Times: Last L 2.30pm/last D 9.30pm.
Closed D Sun, all Mon, 2 wks Jan
Additional: Bar food;
Children welcome; ⬧ dishes

KNARESBOROUGH,
Dower House Hotel ❀

Bond End HG5 9AL
Map 8: SE35
Tel: 01423 863302
Fax: 01423 867665
Chef: Howard Cansfield
Owners: The Davies family
Cost: *Alc* £17. Fixed-price D £19.50
(5 courses). ☺ H/wine £9.25.
Times: D only, 7pm-9.30pm
Additional: Bar meals L; Sunday L;
⬧ dishes
Smoking: No smoking in dining room
Accommodation: 32 en suite
Credit cards: ▬ ▬ ◻ ▬ ▣

Directions: At Harrogate end of
Knaresborough High Street

Overlooking a pretty terrace and garden, the restaurant of this Jacobean hotel offers sound modern English cooking. Start with the likes of local game terrine, or tomato, chive and smoked cheddar

tartlet, before pot-roasted leg of lamb, salmon with a broth of root vegetables, or something from the vegetarian selection. There's a good dessert list too.

KNARESBOROUGH,
General Tarleton Inn

Linked to the equally impressive Angel Inn at Hetton (see entry), the General Tarleton is an 18th-century coaching inn that has been overhauled along similar lines. The philosophy is much the same: one brasserie-style menu served throughout; orders taken at the bar; casual but courteous staff. However, this is not simply a replica – the kitchen here is prepared to go its own way. So look out for starters such as carpaccio of tuna with noodle salad and Thai lemon dressing; roast baby cod with crispy onions and salsa verde; and parfait of chicken livers and foie gras with grape chutney. Main courses mix up the influences too. Try chargrilled haunch of venison with roast butternut squash and rocket salad, or roast loin of lamb on a bed of polenta, spinach and ratatouille. A dozen or so wines by the glass are chalked on a board, and the printed list reads well.

Directions: A1M/Boroughbridge Junction. Follow A6065 (Knaresborough) for 3 miles to Ferrensby

Boroughbridge Road
Ferrensby HG5 0QB
Map 8: SE35
Tel: 01423 340284
Fax: 01423 340288
Chef: John Topham
Owners: Denis Watkins & John Topham
Cost: Alc £26.50, fixed price L £17.50/D £26.50 (4 courses). ☺ H/wine £9.95
Times: Noon-2pm/6-10pm
Additional: Bar food; Sunday L; Children welcome; ✸ dishes
Seats: 70. Private room 30-40
Smoking: No-smoking area; No pipes & cigars
Accommodation: 14 en suite
Credit cards: ▅▅ ▅▅ ▅▅ ▅ ▅▅

LEYBURN, Foresters Arms

The journey to get here is up hill and down dale, but the effort is well worth it, as popularity proves. The inn is seemingly untouched by the passage of time, full of flagstone floors, low creaking beams, open-face stone walls and roaring fires. The bar is a mish-mash of furnishings, contrasting with the surprisingly plush and opulent restaurant. Local game terrine with Sauternes jelly was a wonderfully rustic starter – simple but powerful. Equally understated and unfussy, but with real flavour, was a beautiful ragout of guinea fowl with sautéed wild mushrooms, attacked by our inspector with gusto. A bitter chocolate marquise had just one fault – it was irresistibly rich and waist-enhancing. Good vegetarian choice includes leek and blue cheese strudel with chargrilled vegetables, and amongst the extensive choice of fish specialities is whole roast haddock with capers and lemon butter sauce. There is also a light lunch menu. This place is a gem.

Carlton-in-Coverdale DL8 4BB
Map 7: SE19
Tel/Fax: 01969 640272
Chef/Owner: BK Higginbotham
Cost: Alc £25. ☺ H/wine £9.60
Times: Noon-last L 2pm/7-last D 9pm. Closed D Sun, Mon, Jan
Additional: Bar food; Sunday L; No children under 12 in restaurant; ✸ dishes
Seats: 30. Private dining room 15-20
Smoking: No-smoking area
Accommodation: 3 en suite.
Credit cards: ▅▅ ▅▅ ▅▅ ▅ ▅

Directions: Off the A684, 5 miles S of Leyburn

MALTON,
Burythorpe House Hotel

Believed to date from the 1750s, this imposing building has a comfortable lounge and an oak-panelled, traditionally furnished dining room. Dinner may include loin of local venison with Cumberland sauce, or Whitby haddock with bacon, sweetcorn and mushrooms, preceded by smoked trout pâté and followed by a dessert from the trolley.

Accommodation: 11 en suite. **Credit cards:** ▅▅ ▅▅ ▅▅ ▅

Directions: Edge of Burythorpe village, 4 miles S of Malton

Burythorpe YO17 9LB
Map 8: SE77
Tel: 01653 658200
Fax: 01653 658204
Chefs/Owners: Mr & Mrs T Austin
Cost: Alc £17, fixed price D £17. ☺ H/wine £9.50
Times: D only, last D by arrangement
Additional: Sunday L; Children welcome; ✸ dishes
Smoking: No pipes & cigars; Air conditioning

MARKINGTON, **Hob Green Hotel**

A tranquil country house set in 800 acres of Dales countryside. Both fixed-price menus and the carte encompass traditional, modern and French-influenced dishes. Baked Barnsley chop with redcurrant and rosemary sauce could follow melon and lychee cocktail with ginger and Advocaat cream. Staff are helpful and friendly.

Accommodation: 12 en suite
Credit cards: ▅▅ ▆▆ ▜▜ ⌐ ▆▆ ◖ ▙ JCB

Directions: One mile W of village off A61

Harrogate HG3 3PJ
Map 8: SE26
Tel: 01423 770031
Fax: 01423 771589
Chef: Christopher Taylor
Cost: *Alc* £26, fixed price L £14.50/D £21.50. ☺ H/wine £10.95
Times: Last L 1.30pm/last D 9.30pm
Additional: Bar food L; Sunday L; Children welcome; ◑ dishes
Smoking: No pipes and cigars

MIDDLEHAM,
Millers House Hotel

Close to Middleham Castle and the racehorse training centre, Miller's House is a Georgian building nestled in the heart of Herriot country. Your meal may feature warm salad of pigeon breast, Puy lentils and pancetta, monkfish wrapped in Parma ham with tomato and basil sauce, and a dessert of lemon tart, or banana parfait.

Additional: No children under 10; ◑ dishes
Smoking: No smoking in dining room
Accommodation: 7 en suite
Credit cards: ▅▅ ▆▆ ⌐ ◖

Directions: A1 & A684 (Bedale & Leyburn). At Leyburn turn L to Middleham

DL8 4NR
Map 7: SE18
Tel: 01969 622630
Fax: 01969 623570
Chef: Judith Sunderland
Owners: Crossley & Judith Sunderland
Cost: Fixed-price D £20.50.
☺ H/wine £6.
Times: D only, 7-8.30pm

MIDDLEHAM,
Waterford House

Kirkgate DL8 4PG
Map 7: SE18
Tel: 01969 622090
Fax: 01969 624020
Chef: Everyl M Madell
Owners: Everyl & Brian Madell
Cost: *Alc* £25, fixed-price D £21.50.
☺ H/wine £11.
Times: L by prior arrqangement/7pm-last D 9.30pm
Additional: Sunday L; Children welcome; ◑ dishes
Seats: 20

Delightful, hospitable restaurant-with-rooms just off the village square. The oldest part of the building is thought to have been a bondsman's cottage in the time of Richard III. Within, it's a veritable Aladdin's cave of antiques and objets d'art, including every conceivable device for opening, handling and decanting the wine that is Brian Madell's passion; the cellar boasts nearly 1000 bins. On the food front it is Everyl Madell who, working single-handedly at the Aga, delivers the goods with clear flavours and accurate seasoning in dishes like our perfectly balanced fresh artichoke and Stilton soup and, at the other end of the meal, a superb chocolate tart. Other typical dishes to be found on the short, daily-changing menu might include bouillabaisse, mousseline of chicken livers, roast duck with apricot, kumquat and Grand Marnier sauce, and rack of Yorkshire lamb with herb and garlic crust and Cassis sauce.

Directions: Just off Market Square

Smoking: No smoking in dining room
Accommodation: 5 en suite
Credit cards: ▬ ▤ ▨ ⬜ ◖ JCB

MIDDLEHAM,
White Swan Hotel ✿

Attractive, traditional inn with a kitchen that runs on imagination and ambition. Wonderful home-made smoked fishcakes with a superb, light tomato salsa, and roast pheasant with crisp bacon and a first-class juniper sauce, show a team with their sights set on higher things.

Smoking: No-smoking area. **Accommodation:** 10 en suite
Credit cards: ▬ ▤ ▨ ⬜ ◖

Directions: town centre

Market Place DL8 4PE
Map 7: SE18
Tel: 01969 622093
Fax: 01969 624551
Chef: Andrew Morris
Owners: Christine & Richard Wager
Cost: Alc £18, fixed-price L&D £12.
☺ H/wine £7.95
Times: Last L 2pm/last D 9pm.
Closed 1st 2 wks Jan
Additional: Sunday L; Bar food L&D;
Children welcome; ❹ dishes

MIDDLESBROUGH,
The Purple Onion ✿✿

A fun place to eat, this busy, bustling brasserie occupies a large Victorian building that's full of bric-a-brac, parlour plants, paper-clothed tables and informally dressed staff in long white aprons; live music in a new cellar bar adds to the buzz. Notwithstanding the informal atmosphere, there is a serious attitude to the food which, on a recent visit, included a well-made haddock and spring onion risotto ('not at all stodgy'), strips of the tenderest beef casseroled with wild mushrooms and smoky bacon, excellent chips, and a classic crème brûlée with added raspberries. Ciopino di Mare, a San Franciscan fish stew 'as served at Aliotos Restaurant on North Beach' is a house speciality. In addition to the *carte* there are daily blackboard specials, a children's menu and, for footie fans, a 'Match Day' menu.

Directions: Exit A66 at Hospitality Inn near Riverside Football Stadium. Restaurant centrally located nr Law Courts/Odeon Cinema

80 Corporation Road
TS1 2RF
Map 8: NZ41
Tel: 01642 222250
Fax: 01642 248088
Chefs: Graham Benn, Tony Chapman
Owners: Bruno & John McCoy
Cost: Alc £30. ☺ H/wine £9.95
Times: Noon-2.30pm/5-last D
10.30pm. Closed 25-26 Dec, 1 Jan
Additional: Sunday L;
Children welcome; ❹ dishes
Seats: 90
Smoking: Air conditioning
Credit cards: ▬ ▤ ▨ ⬜ ▣

MOULTON,
Black Bull Inn ✿

A fabulous venue that will suit all tastes. There is considerable choice in where to eat – the traditional bar, colonial conservatory or perhaps the real 1932 Pullman coach from the Brighton Belle. A wide-ranging menu focuses on seafood: fresh langoustine in garlic butter, and moules marinière are firm favourites.

Additional: Bar food L; No children under 7; ❹ dishes
Credit cards: ▬ ▤ ▨ ⬜ ▣ ◖ ▣ JCB

Directions: Off A1M, 1 mile S of Scotch Corner

Richmond DL10 6QJ
Map 8: NZ20
Tel: 01325 377289
Fax: 01325 377422
Chef: Paul Grundy
Owners: GH & AMC Pagendam
Cost: Alc £25, fixed-price L £14.95.
☺ H/wine £8.50
Times: Last L 2pm/last D 10.15pm
Closed L Sat, all Sun, 24-26 Dec

NORTHALLERTON,
Solberge Hall Hotel

A Georgian country house retaining many fine period features.
The Garden Room has a Victorian grandeur and offers views of
the North Yorkshire Moors. Good variety of dishes, including
vegetarian, from the pasta, fish, international, gourmet, and Country
Grill sections of the carte.

Smoking: No smoking in dining room
Accommodation: 24 en suite.
Credit cards: ▬ ▭ ▨ ▢ ▨ ▣

Directions: 2 miles S of Northallerton, turning R off A167

Newby Wiske DL7 9ER
Map 8: SE39
Tel: 01609 779191
Fax: 01609 780472
Chef: Peter Wood
Owner: John Hollins
Cost: Fixed-price L £7.95
(4 courses)/D £21 (5 courses).
☺ H/wine £11.95
Times: Last L 1.30pm/last D 9.30pm
Additional: Bar food L; Sunday L;
Children welcome; 🌢 dishes

PATELEY BRIDGE,
Sportsman's Arms

In the heart of beautiful Nidderdale, the Sportsman's Arms has been
run by the Carters with friendly good humour for more than 20
years. Not least of its attractions is the charming dining room where
prime local produce is used to good effect in English and French
inspired dishes.

Smoking: No smoking in dining room
Accommodation: 13 (11 en suite)
Credit cards: ▬ ▭ ▢

Directions: A1, A59, B6451, B6265. Restaurant is 2 miles N of
Pateley Bridge

Wath-in-Nidderdale
HG3 5PP
Map 7: SE16
Tel: 01423 711306
Fax: 01423 712524
Chef: Ray Carter
Owners: Ray & Jane Carter
Cost: Alc £25, fixed-price L £17.50/D
£21.50 (4 courses). ☺ H/wine £10
Times: Last L 2.15pm/last D 9.30pm.
Closed 25 Dec
Additional: Bar food; Sunday L;
Children welcome; 🌢 dishes

PICKERING, **Fox & Hounds**

Attractive, stone-built inn dating back two centuries. Typical modern
British dishes from the carte could include local pigeon and rabbit
terrine with grape chutney, scallops on a bed of cabbage with
smoked salmon, and fillet of plaice with orange and ginger stuffing.
Service is unassumingly attentive.

Smoking: No smoking in dining room
Accommodation: 10 en suite
Credit cards: ▬ ▭ ▢

Directions: In centre of Sinnington, 300 yards off A170 between
Pickering and Helmsley

Main Street Sinnington
York YO62 6SQ
Map 8: SE78
Tel: 01751 431577
Fax: 01751 432791
Chef: Mark Wilson
Owners: Andrew & Catherine
Stephens
Cost: Alc £17, fixed-price D £17. ☺
H/wine £8.95
Times: Last L 2pm/last D 9pm
Additional: Bar food; Sunday L;
Children welcome; 🌢 dishes

PICKERING, **White Swan** **NEW**

A countrified, family-run coaching inn with a spacious restaurant.
Choose blackboard bar snacks or imaginative, well-executed dishes
on the carte, such as fishcake with lemon cream and crisped leeks.
Roast rump of lamb with aubergine caviar and black olive jus might
follow. A notable wine list majors in St Emilion.

Accommodation: 12 en suite
Credit cards: ▬ ▭ ▨ ▢ ▨ ▣

Directions: *Telephone for directions*

Market Place YO18 7AA
Map 8: SE78
Tel: 01751 472288
Fax: 01751 475554
Chef: Douglas Hamilton
Owners: The Buchanan Family
Cost: Alc £19. H/wine £9.95
Times: Last L 2.30pm/last D 9.30pm
(2pm & 9pm winter)
Additional: Bar food L; Sunday L;
Children welcome; 🌢 dishes
Smoking: No smoking in dining room

RAMSGILL,
Yorke Arms ❀❀

Frances and Gerald Atkins, the current owners of the Yorke Arms, made a name for themselves at Shaw's in Old Brompton Road, London before moving north to take over this converted pub in the wilds of the north Yorkshire Dales. The original building started life as a dairy where cheese was made for Fountains Abbey. It was then rebuilt as a shooting lodge and in the late 19th century became an inn for passing travellers. Nowadays, the beamed restaurant provides a traditional setting for Frances's creative modern English cooking – dishes such as sautéed pork with prunes, Armagnac and black pudding, and fresh river trout with orange sauce jostle for the attention of guests. Our inspector opted for a starter of warm duck salad with rocket and a perfect lemon and grapefruit dressing, followed by tender shank of lamb with pesto mash and fresh leeks. Dessert was a very good home-made cheesecake served with a compote of cherries and plums.

Pateley Bridge HG3 5RL
Map 7: SE17
Tel: 01423 755243
Fax: 01423 755330
Chef: Frances Atkins
Owners: Gerald & Frances Atkins
Cost: *Alc* £23. ☺ H/wine £9.65
Times: Noon-last L 1.45pm/7-last D 8.45pm. Closed D Sun (to non-residents)
Additional: Sunday L; Children welcome; ✦ dishes
Seats: 65
Smoking: No smoking in dining room
Accommodation: 14 en suite
Credit cards: ▨ ▨ ▨ ▨ ▨ ▨

Directions: Take B6265 from Ripon. Turn R in Pateley Bridge for Ramsgill

---

ROSEDALE ABBEY,
Milburn Arms ❀❀

Pickering YO18 8RA
Map 8: SE79
Tel/Fax: 01751 417312
Chef: Alister Passley
Owners: Terry & Joan Bentley
Cost: *Alc* £25, fixed price D £19. ☺ H/wine £8.95
Times: D only, 7-last D 9.30pm. Closed 25 Dec
Additional: Bar food; Sunday L (noon-2.30pm); ✦ dishes
Seats: 50
Smoking: No smoking in dining room; Air conditioning
Accommodation: 11 en suite
Credit cards: ▨ ▨ ▨ ▨

Welcoming small hotel that dates, in parts, to the 16th century, tucked into the centre of a village that is itself in a fold of the North Yorkshire Moors. Changes in the kitchen but, after a settling-in period, inspectors are now reporting positively on sound cooking skills. A dinner in April opened with a super 'taste tickler' – deep-fried mussels with crab – which would make a great starter. That, however, was a crab, queenies and ginger risotto, with the hint of ginger rightly judged. Duck breast on Chinese vegetables was well-matched by a dark citrus sauce, and a classic crème brûlée finished off proceedings. Home-made and 'very good' breads included green olive, walnut and granary.

Directions: In village centre, 3 miles W of A170 at Pickering

SCARBOROUGH, **Wrea Head Hotel**

Scalby YO13 0PB
Map 8: TA08
Tel: 01723 378211
Fax: 01723 355936
Chef: James Chamberlain
Owner: Joan & Barry Turner
Cost: Alc £35, fixed-price L £12.50/D
£25. ☺ H/wine £12.50
Times: Last L 2pm/last D 9.30pm
Additional: Bar food; Sunday L;
Children welcome; ◑ dishes
Smoking: No smoking in dining room
Accommodation: 20 en suite
Credit cards: 💳

*Historic Victorian country house to the north of Scarborough.
Well-presented, nicely cooked food and high marks for flavour.
Try goats' cheese and courgette samosa with Caesar salad, confit of
lamb accompanied by a tian of sauté potato and black pudding
and a compote of local berries.*

Directions: Take A171 N from Scarborough, past Scalby village
until hotel is signposted

SKIPTON, **Devonshire Arms**

Bolton Abbey BD23 6AJ
Map 7: SD95
Tel: 01756 710441
Fax: 01756 710564
Chef: Andrew Nicholson
Owners: The Duke & Duchess of
Devonshire
Cost: Alc £37, fixed-price D £37
(4 courses). ☺ H/wine £14.50
Times: D only, 7-last D 10pm
Additional: Bar food; Sunday L
(noon-2.30pm); Children welcome;
◑ dishes
Seats: 60. Private room 90.
Jacket & tie preferred
Smoking: No smoking in dining room
Accommodation: 41 en suite
Credit cards: 💳

For two hundred years Bolton Abbey, surrounded by the
rolling Yorkshire Dales, has been owned by the Dukes of
Devonshire. First opened in 1873 as a coaching house, the
Devonshire Arms is now run as a stylish country house hotel
by a team of delightful staff. An eclectic range of dishes is
prepared using local produce – some of it grown in the hotel's
own kitchen garden – to great effect. A typical meal in the
opulent Burlington Restaurant could begin with pan-fried
scallops, followed by fillet of red mullet with chargrilled fennel,
buttered noodles and basil oil. Our inspector enjoyed a late
spring meal of asparagus cream soup followed by seared
salmon with foie gras and butter beans. This was polished off
with a superb chocolate and banana sponge. The wine list is
comprehensive and, for wine enthusiasts, a detailed summary
of each wine label is available.

Directions: On the B6160 to Bolton Abbey, 250 yards north of
A59 roundabout junction

SKIPTON,
Hanover International Hotel

The spacious and attractively appointed restaurant at this modern hotel has light and airy views over a canal. The quality of ingredients shines through such starters as escalopes of salmon on marinated tomatoes and a main course of tournedos Rossini with noteworthy vegetables. Bread-and-butter pudding comes with orange sauce and crème anglaise.

Additional: Bar food; Children welcome; dishes
Smoking: No smoking in dining room; Air conditioning
Accommodation: 75 en suite
Credit cards: ▬ ☰ ☜ ▤ ▦ ▣ ▨

Directions: From M62/J26 onto M606, follow signs for A650 (Keighley), then A629 (Skipton). Hotel 1 mile S of town centre

Keighley Road Snaygill
BD23 2TA
Map 7: SD95
Tel: 01756 700100
Fax: 01756 700107
Chef: Gavin Horton
Owner: Hanover International Hotel & Club
Cost: Fixed-price D £15.95. H/wine £9.75
Times: D only, last D 9.30pm

STADDLEBRIDGE,
McCoys (Tontine Inn)

The marvellously idiosyncratic restaurant may only be open for dinner three nights a week, but the same menu is available all week in the downstairs bistro. The food could be described as 'hard-core crossover', with influences from here, there and everywhere, but the cooking is based on a natural understanding of raw materials and the ability to treat them with energy, enthusiasm and respect. Turbot, for example, comes with Chinese leaves and deep-fried ginger, or magret of duck with a salad of chicory, charred celery, fennel and red pepper with spicy hot plum sauce. Pot-roast pigeon, served on a potato and pancetta rösti with swede purée, Puy lentils and foie gras sauce has been heavily endorsed, game in season is worth seeking out, and both choc-o-block Stanley and raspberry charlotte with raspberry purée are pure taste sensations.

Directions: At the junction of the A19 & A172

Northallerton DL6 3JB
Map 8: SE49
Tel: 01609 882671
Fax: 01609 882660
Chef: Tom McCoy
Owners: McCoy Bothers
Times: Noon-last L 2pm/7-last D 10pm (Bistro). Restaurant D Thur, Fri, Sat only. Closed 25-26 Dec, 1 Jan
Additional: Bar food; Sunday L; Children welcome; ✿ dishes
Seats: 60. Private dining room 30
Smoking: Air conditioning
Credit cards: ▬ ☰ ☜ ▤ ▦ ▣

TADCASTER,
Hazlewood Castle   NEW

In the spring of 1998 Hazlewood Castle opened as a hotel. Early reports of this stately looking pile (first mentioned in Domesday Book) have been full of praise, but we have been unable to award rosettes for this edition of the *Guide* as Restaurant 1086, headed by John Benson-Smith (ex Victoria and Albert Hotel, Manchester) and his brother Matthew, had not yet opened as we went to press.

Paradise Lane LS24 9NJ
Map 8: SE44
Tel: 01937 530631
Please telephone for further details

THIRSK, **Sheppard's Hotel**

Front Street YO7 1JF
Map 8: SE48
Tel: 01845 523655
Fax: 01845 524720
Chef: Andrew Noble
Owner: Olga Sheppard
Cost: *Alc* £27.51 (Bistro £20.59). ☺
H/wine £10.25
Times: Last L 1.30pm/last D 10pm.
Closed 1st wk Jan
Additional: Bar food L; Sunday L;
Children welcome; ♨ dishes
Smoking: No pipes and cigars in
restaurant
Accommodation: 8 en suite
Credit cards: ▨ ▨ ▨ ▨ ▨

A converted granary and stable, Sheppard's Hotel has a formal restaurant and lively bistro with open brick walls and flagstone floors. Choose from the blackboard menu, which highlights the fresh fish of the day, or from the carte: try steamed mussels with coconut cream, followed by breast of guinea fowl stuffed with pistachios.

Directions: 0.5 mile S of Thirsk market place, off A61 Thirsk/Ripon road towards Sowerby

WEST WITTON,
Wensleydale Heifer Inn NEW

Log fires blaze when the nights draw in at this rambling Dales guest house, which dates from the 16th century. A mix of rustic country cooking combined with modern ideas make good use of local produce, and there is a clear emphasis on fish. Typical main courses include whole roast partridge with bread sauce, and grilled lemon sole with fennel.

Accommodation: 16 en suite
Credit cards: ▨ ▨ ▨ ▨ ▨ ▨ ▨ JCB

Directions: On A684 Leyburn to Hawes road.

Wensleydale DL8 4LS
Map 8: SE08
Tel: 01969 622322
Fax: 01969 624183
Chef: Adrian Craig
Owners: John & Anne Sharp
Cost: Fixed-price D £23.50. ☺
H/wine £9.25
Times: Last L 2pm/last D 9pm
Additional: Bar food; Sunday L;
Children welcome; ♨ dishes
Smoking: No-smoking area

YARM, **Judges Hotel**

Kirklevington TS15 9LW
Map 8: NZ41
Tel: 01642 789000
Fax: 01642 782878
Chef: Jason Moore
Owner: Michael Downs
Cost: *Alc* £33, fixed-price L £14.95/D
£25 (4 courses). H/wine £10.95.
Times: Last L 2pm/D 10pm.
Closed L Sat
Additional: Bar meals L; Sunday L;
Children welcome; ♨ dishes
Smoking: No smoking in dining room
Accommodation: 21 en suite
Credit cards: ▨ ▨ ▨ ▨ ▨ ▨ ▨

Directions: From A69 take A67
towards Kirklevington, hotel 1.5 miles
on left.

Restored country mansion, once used to accommodate visiting judges (hence the name). The attractive restaurant has a conservatory extension overlooking the gardens. Dishes are inventive and well presented. Particularly enjoyable at inspection were the home-made breads, and a starter of asparagus with caraway and nutmeg porridge.

YORK, **Ambassador**

Close to the city and convenient for the racecourse, this former Georgian town house offers a quiet elegance and relaxed air. Haddock soup with a poached egg, tender saddle of lamb on a bed of spinach with a well-made tomato and basil jus and good fresh vegetables, are typical of the repertoire.

Smoking: No smoking in dining room
Accommodation: 25 en suite. **Credit cards:** ▆▆ ▆▆ ▆▆ ▆ ▆▆ ▆

Directions: 5 minutes walk from city centre, near junction of A1036 and A59

125 The Mount YO2 2DA
Map 8: SE65
Tel: 01904 641316
Fax: 01904 640259
Chef: Alexandra Trenholme
Owners: Sallie Gray, David Miller
Cost: Alc £23, fixed-price L £10.50/D £19.50. ☺ H/wine £10.60
Times: D only, 6.30pm-last D 9.15pm.
Additional: Bar meals L; Sunday L; Children welcome; ☙ dishes

YORK, **Dean Court Hotel**

Recently refurbished Victorian hotel opposite York Minster. Food is beautifully presented and modern. Start, perhaps, with smoked duck and chicken, sweet peppers and cucumber, bound with crème fraîche and follow with seared loin of halibut wrapped in pancetta with aubergine and a herb, olive and tomato dressing. Popular tea room and coffee shop.

Duncombe Place YO1 2EF
Map 8: SE65
Tel: 01904 625082
Fax: 01904 620305
Chef: Peter Brown
Owners: David & Wendy Brooks
Cost: Alc £25, fixed-price L £13.50/D £21. ☺ H/wine £9.95.
Times: Last L 2pm/last D 9.30pm
Additional: Bar food; Sunday L; Children welcome; ☙ dishes
Smoking: No smoking in dining room
Accommodation: 40 en suite
Credit cards: ▆▆ ▆▆ ▆▆ ▆ ▆▆ ▆ ▆ JCB

Directions: City centre, directly opposite York Minster

YORK, **The Grange Hotel**

A short walk from the city centre finds this Regency townhouse hotel with its range of places to eat. In addition to the smart Dom Ruinart seafood bar there's a brasserie/bistro with a menu that encompasses eggs Benedict, Thai roasted chicken breast, corned beef hash, and steak and kidney

1 Clifton YO3 6AA
Map 8: SE65
Tel: 01904 644744
Fax: 01904 612453
Chef: David Bates
Owner: Jeremy Cassel
Cost: Alc £28. Fixed-price L £11.50/D £24. ☺ H/wine £10.50.
Times: 12.30pm-last L 2pm/7pm-last D 10pm. Closed L Sat, L Sun
Additional: Children welcome; ☙ dishes
Seats: 35. Private dining room 60
Smoking: No pipes & cigars in dining room,
Accommodation: 30 en suite
Credit cards: ▆▆ ▆▆ ▆▆ ▆ ▆▆ ▆ ▆ JCB

Directions: 400 yds to N of city walls on A19

pudding. The Ivy Restaurant offers a *carte* that begins with the likes of watercress and Jerusalem artichoke soup with bruschetta, and terrine of guinea fowl, sweetbread and foie gras wrapped in Parma ham, before such mains as a scallop mousse-filled sea bass on a crispy pancake with red pepper sauce, and mint soufflé-topped lamb cutlets with bubble-and-squeak and mint flavoured red wine gravy. Desserts might include warm whisky pudding with heather honey sabayon and tiramisu with Amaretti biscuits. Pleasant sweetmeats and good cafetière round things off.

YORK, Kilima Hotel ❀

Former Victorian rectory, now a comfortable hotel, situated within easy walking distance of the city centre. Friendly service and interesting, sound cooking in the intimate basement restaurant. Expect pan-fried black pudding with tikka masala sauce, chicken breast with peanut sauce, and apple and blackberry pie for dessert.

Smoking: No smoking in dining room
Accommodation: 15 en suite
Credit cards: ▬▬ ▬▬ 🐜 💷 ▦ 🄲 💷

Directions: On the W side on A59 (Harrogate) road

129 Holgate Street
YO24 4AZ
Map 8: SE65
Tel: 01904 625787
Fax: 01904 612083
Chef: Christopher Betteridge
Owner: Richard Stables
Cost: Fixed-price L £15/D £18.95
(4 courses). ☺ H/wine £8.75
Times: Last L 1.30pm/last D 9.30pm
Additional: Children welcome;
🍴 dishes

YORK, Knavesmire Manor Hotel ❀

Overlooking the racecourse, the Edwardian-style restaurant, in a former home of the Rowntree family, serves a range of modern dishes from Thai crab cakes with chilli and soy sauce, to wild boar and apple sausage, and fresh seared tuna with egg noodles and roasted pepper and tomato salsa.

Accommodation: 21 en suite
Credit cards: ▬▬ ▬▬ 🐜 💷 ▦ 🄲 💷 JCB

Directions: A64 to York, then A1036 York-Bishopthorpe leads on to Tadcaster Rd. Hotel on left overlooking racecourse

302 Tadcaster Road YO2 2HE
Map 8: SE65
Tel: 01904 702941
Fax: 01904 709274
Chef: Andrew Hagan
Owners: Ian & Margaret Senior
Cost: *Alc* £18.50. Fixed-price
D £13.50. ☺ H/wine £9
Times: D only 6.30pm-last D 9.15pm.
Additional: Sunday L (noon-2pm);
Children welcome; 🍴 dishes
Smoking: No smoking in dining room

YORK, Melton's Restaurant ❀❀

7 Scarcroft Road YO23 1ND
Map 8: SE65
Tel: 01904 634341
Fax: 01904 635115
Chef: Michael Hjort
Owners: Michael & Lucy Hjort

The blue shop-fronted restaurant is very inviting, prints hang around the walls and a mural incorporating local scenes, diners and chef, is a feature of this family-run place. The cooking is

Anglo-French, and there are some bargains at lunchtime and for 'early birds'. Bread is home-made and, at our last inspection, a choice of three flavours were on offer. That well-reported meal included a fresh tasting polenta with wild mushrooms and white truffle oil, an excellent duck confit, falling off the bone and accompanied by a bitter leaf salad, and a light ginger sponge with a posh sherry custard.

Cost: *Alc* £25, fixed-price L £15/D £19.50. ☺ H/wine £12
Additional: Sunday L; Children welcome; ◑ dishes
Smoking: No-smoking area
Credit cards: ▉ ▓ ▄ ▢ ◖

Directions: From centre head south across Skeldergate Bridge, restaurant opposite Bishopthorpe Road car park

Times: Last L 2pm/5.30-last D 10pm. Closed L Mon, D Sun, 1 wk Aug, 3 wks Xmas

AA Wine Shortlisted for *Award-see page 16*

YORK, **Middlethorpe Hall** ❀❀❀

Magnificent William III country house, close to the city centre yet easily accessible from the ring road. All the fine features of the original building are retained, and the gardens are splendidly maintained. Dinner is served in either the Oak or Marble dining room, with a more informal alternative offered by the Grill Room. Andrew Wood heads the brigade, and his cooking is much approved. His short menus are built on prime seasonal produce and usually include an interesting twist. Steamed courgette flowers, liberally stuffed to bursting with basil paste, opened a late spring dinner. Ham hock, with a combination of bacon lardons, chorizo and a tomato sauce, canellini beans and a herbed mousse holding the ham together crepinette-style, was pronounced very good, simply served with green beans. Perfectly poached apples, spiced with nutmeg and cinnamon and stuffed with sultanas, were surrounded by 'lovely' îles flottantes on a vanilla-flavoured semolina – this was great, just finished off with a light caramel. Small details such as well-textured and flavoured breads, good canapés and petits fours, and unstuffy, relaxed service by formally clad waiters, add to the enjoyment.
Signature dishes: Fillet of turbot with girolles, baby prawns and sauce dugléré; terrine of rabbit and foie gras with baby carrots and balsamic dressing; banana parfait with dark chocolate sorbet, passion fruit sauce and glazed bananas; daube of beef, celeriac purée, braised shallots, smoked bacon.

Directions: 1.5 miles S of York, next to the racecourse

Bishopthorpe Road YO23 2GB
Map 8: SE65
Tel: 01904 641241
Fax: 01904 620176
Chef: Andrew Wood
Owner: Historic House Hotels
Cost: *Alc* £38.95, fixed-price L £12.50 (2 courses)/D £29.95. H/wine £13
Times: 12.30-last L 1.45pm/7-last D 9.45pm. Closed 25 Dec (non-residents)
Additional: Sunday L; No children under 8; ◑ dishes
Seats: 60. Private room 45. Jacket & tie preferred
Smoking: No smoking in dining room
Accommodation: 30 en suite
Credit cards: ▉ ▓ ▢

YORK, Mount Royale Hotel

Proudly family-run, this charming restaurant with separate bar and a cocktail lounge overlooks the period hotel's mature English garden. The interesting daily changing dishes (including a vegetarian menu) are predominately French and British. A typical meal may include baked Brie with bramble sauce or roast salmon with herb brioche topping and citrus butter.

Accommodation: 23 en suite
Credit cards: ▆▆ ▆▆ ▆▆ ▆ ▆▆ ▆ JCB

Directions: On The Mount (A1036) leading SW out of the city

The Mount YO2 2DA
Map 8: SE65
Tel: 01904 628856
Fax: 01904 611171
Chef: Karen Brotherton
Owners: The Oxtoby Family
Cost: Alc £29. ☺ H/wine £10.95
Times: D only, last D 9.30pm
Additional: Bar food;
Children welcome; ✪ dishes
Smoking: No smoking in dining room

YORK, York Pavilion Hotel

This Georgian hotel stands in its own pleasant grounds on the A19 to the south of the city. A newly established brasserie serves modern, inventive dishes; the *carte* changes every six weeks, and there are daily market specials. A bowl of rustic fish soup was almost a meal in itself, full of flavour and pieces of fish; other first courses might be warm chargrilled asparagus with seared home-cured gravad lax and dill dressing, or Caesar salad with smoked chicken. Some dishes, such as spicy Thai fishcakes with coriander and lime noodles can be taken either as starters or main courses. Main courses take in roast rump of lamb with broad bean and asparagus broth and a hotpot of potatoes, or pork and coriander sausages on leek mash with sun-dried tomatoes and caramelised shallots, for example. This being Yorkshire, Sunday lunch reverts to type and stars roast sirloin and Yorkshire pudding.

45 Main Street Fulford YO1 4PJ
Map 8: SE65
Tel: 01904 622099
Fax: 01904 626939
Chef: David Spencer
Owners: Andrew & Irene Cossins
Cost: Alc £25. ☺ H/wine £10.50
Times: Noon-last L 1.45pm/6.30pm-last D 9pm
Additional: Sunday L;
Children welcome; ✪ dishes
Seats: 100. Private dining room 50
Smoking: No smoking in dining room
Accommodation: 44 en suite
Credit cards: ▆▆ ▆▆ ▆▆ ▆ ▆

Directions: From York city centre head S on A19 (Selby), hotel 2 miles on L

YORKSHIRE SOUTH

BARNSLEY, Armstrongs

A lovely Victorian house on the edge of town, originally built for the Mayor of Barnsley and now run as a busy restaurant. Both the dining room and lounge bar are decorated in National Trust pale yellow, with large pictures and ornate indigo drapes with charcoal stripes. The mood is informal and

102 Dodworth Road
S70 6HL
Map 8: SE30
Tel: 01226 240113/244990
Chef: Nick Pound
Owners: Nick Pound & Deborah Swift

the food remains good value, particularly at lunch. The style is modern British: roast breast of duck with kumquats and fennel; Cornish sea bass with pak choi and fresh water chestnuts; breast of chicken with Bombay aloo and burnt onion. An early summer meal got off to a good start with sauté of chicken livers with leeks, oyster mushrooms and bacon strips. Fillet of cod followed, topped with crunchy thin asparagus and served with rocket pesto. To finish, a banana caramel tartlet – slices of banana in soft caramel, crisp sweet pastry and melting ice cream – scrumptious!

Directions: One mile from M1/37. Take A625 towards Barnsley, on right

Cost: *Alc* £28, fixed-price L £14.50/D £16.95. ☺ H/wine £10.95
Times: Noon-last L 1.45pm/7-last D 9.45pm. Closed L Sat, all Sun, Mon, 2 wks summer
Additional: Children welcome; ◑ dishes
Seats: 50
Smoking: No pipes & cigars
Credit cards:

CHAPELTOWN,
Greenhead House Hotel ❀❀

There's a homely feel to this suburban restaurant with pretty walled garden; the house dates back to the 17th century and many original features have been preserved. The menu changes monthly: in March there was parsleyed ham with gribiche sauce, and veal sweetbreads served with both roast red pepper sauce and a mixed fresh herb, shallot and white wine cream sauce. High profile saucing stands out – mousseline sauce with seared salmon steak and salmon quenelles flavoured with wild mushrooms, or the dark Madeira and truffle with foie gras and mushroom puff pastries. Skilfully prepared desserts include sweet pastry tart filled with frangipane and poached pears with apricot coulis. Home-made salmon fishcakes are on the good-value light lunch menu.

Directions: M1/J35 follow signs to Chapeltown, straight across 2 roundabouts onto Buncross Rd. Restaurant is on R, 200m

84 Buncross Road Sheffield S35 1SF
Map 8: SK39
Tel: 0114 2469004
Chef: Neil Allen
Owners: Neil & Anne Allen
Cost: Fixed-price D £29 (4 courses). H/wine £11
Times: Noon-last L 1pm/7-last D 9pm. Closed L Sat, all Sun, Mon, Tue & Wed, 23 Dec-3 Jan, 2 wks Easter, 2 wks Aug
Additional: Bar food L; Children welcome; ◑ dishes
Seats: 32
Smoking: No-smoking area
Credit cards:

ROTHERHAM, Swallow Hotel ❀

Large, modern hotel ideal for both business and leisure purposes. Interesting dinner menu in Capistrano, with a lively something-for-everyone global appeal: gazpacho; seared scallops with squid ink linguine; confit of duck with braised red cabbage and sweet potato; chargrilled steaks. Good selection of wines by the glass.

Credit cards:

Directions: From the M1/J37; the hotel stands on the A630, 2 miles from Rotherham centre

West Bawtry Road S60 4NA
Map 8: SK49
Tel: 01709 830630
Fax: 01709 830549
Chef: Mark Ancill
Cost: *Alc* £25, fixed-price D £17. ☺ H/wine £12
Times: D only, last D 9.30pm
Additional: Bar food L; Sunday L (noon-2pm); Children welcome; ◑ dishes
Accommodation: 100 en suite

SHEFFIELD, Charnwood Hotel ❀

The Charnwood is a Georgian mansion house within walking distance of the city centre. The lively brasserie is authentically French, with green tablecloths, white napkins and tiles on the floor. Our inspector enjoyed a starter of duck liver parfait with red onion and orange marmalade, followed by poached sea bass with baby leeks and scallops.

Directions: M1/J33 & A621. 1.5 miles SW of city centre, off London Road

10 Sharrow Lane S11 8AA
Map 8: SK38
Tel: 0114 2589411
Fax: 0114 2555107
Chef: Paul MacNiel
Owners: Mr & Mrs C J King
Cost: *Alc* £18, fixed-price D £12. ☺ H/wine £8.95
Times: D only, last D 10.30pm. Closed Sun, 24-30 Dec
Additional: Bar food D; Children welcome; ◑ dishes

SHEFFIELD, Harley Hotel ✿

A well-maintained hotel with an elegant dining room where competent, professional standards of service prevail together with fixed-price menus and a carte. A good range of dishes includes fettucine of scallops and roast guinea fowl breast with seared vegetables and tapenade.

Directions: In University and Teaching Hospitals campus, 0.5 miles from centre on junction of West Street (A57) and Hanover Street (Inner City Ring Road)

334 Glossop Road S10 2HW
Map 8: SK38
Tel: 01142 752288
Fax: 01142 722383
Please telephone for further details

SHEFFIELD,
Mosborough Hall Hotel ✿

16th-century manor house with gardens and a village setting. Seasonal menus feature fresh scallops on a tomato and basil croûte with saffron fondant, perhaps followed by tuna steak in a herby crust, with white chocolate and soft fudge torte to finish.

Additional: Bar food; Sunday L; Children welcome; ❸ dishes
Accommodation: 24 en suite
Credit cards: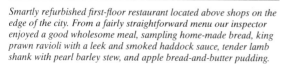

Directions: Hotel on A616, 5 miles from M1/J30

High Street S20 5AE
Map 8: SK38
Tel: 0114 2484353
Chef: Ian Torpey
Cost: Alc £25, fixed-price L £10.95/D £17. H/wine £9.25 (litre)
Times: Last L 1.45pm/last D 9.30pm. Closed L Sat, D Sun, Bhs

SHEFFIELD, Rafters Restaurant ✿ NEW

Smartly refurbished first-floor restaurant located above shops on the edge of the city. From a fairly straightforward menu our inspector enjoyed a good wholesome meal, sampling home-made bread, king prawn ravioli with a leek and smoked haddock sauce, tender lamb shank with pearl barley stew, and apple bread-and-butter pudding.

Additional: No children under 5; ❸ dishes
Smoking: No pipes & cigars
Credit cards:

Directions: Telephone for directions

220 Oakbrook Road
Nethergreen S11 7ED
Map 8: SK38
Tel/Fax: 0114 2304819
Chefs/Owners: Wayne & Jamie Bosworth
Cost: £21.50, fixed-price L & D £21.50. ☺ H/wine £8.90
Times: D only, last D 10pm. Closed 25-26 Dec, 1 Jan, Bhs

SHEFFIELD,
Smith's of Sheffield ✿✿✿

34 Sandygate Road S10 5RY
Map 8: SK38
Tel: 0114 2666096
Chef: Richard William Smith
Owners: Mr & Mrs RW Smith, Mr & Mrs JA Tetchner
Cost: Alc £24.50. ☺ H/wine £8.50
Times: D only. Closed Sun, Mon
Additional: Children welcome; ❸ dishes
Seats: 44. Private dining room 20
Smoking: No smoking in dining room
Credit cards: ▬ ▬ ▬ ▬ ▬

A newly opened upstairs room, logically named 'Upstairs at Smith's', is now used for private dining, cookery demonstrations, wine dinners, and as a weekend restaurant for seven-course gastronomic dinners, conjured by Richard Smith out of his large, open-plan kitchen. Downstairs, in the informal tented dining room, a regular clientele flows in for dishes such as confit of chicken terrine, leeks, morels, piccalilli and toasted brioche, or pan-roasted cod and oak-smoked haddock with spring onion mash and vichyssoise sauce, and roast crispy duck breast with Parma ham, herb polenta, provencale vegetables and salsa verde. The cooking, in other words, romps through the whole catalogue of contemporary trends and ideas. Pairings are imaginative but never gimmicky: Cornish crab cakes come with roasted garlic aïoli, oregano oil and sweet potato crisps, while carpaccio of Asian pear is served with salad rocket, shaved Parmesan, toasted pine nuts, balsamic syrup and white truffle oil. Spring rolls are favourite starters – perhaps classically filled with aromatic vegetables and sweet chilli sauce, or stuffed with Montrachet goats' cheese and slow-roasted tomatoes and pesto – a particularly felicitous combination. A strongly-flavoured tower of tuna, mussel risotto, wilted spinach, Parmesan crackling and basil oil is cooked either rare or medium rare to order, as is rib-eye of Angus beef with béarnaise sauce, fondant potato, buttered French beans and red wine jus. Beautifully presented desserts include a thin Bramley apple tart with vanilla ice cream and caramel sauce, or iced nougat glacé with passion fruit sorbet and passion fruit sauce. Strong cafetière coffee comes with a single chocolate truffle – but, by then, that's all you need. Wines are well-chosen, but you can also bring your own on midweek evenings.

Signature dishes: Rack of lamb, celeriac mash, braised celery, truffle sauce; crispy spring roll of Montrachet goats' cheese, plum tomatoes, basil pesto; pumpkin ice cream, hot blackberries, nutmeg biscuits; crisp paupiette of Whitby cod, shallot purée, Barolo wine sauce.

Smith's of Sheffield

Directions: From Sheffield centre take A57; at Crosspool turn R onto Sandygate Road. 100 yds on R

SHEFFIELD, **Staindrop Lodge** ✤

Delightful house in its own gardens that offers two short menus with interesting choices and the emphasis on flavour. At our most recent meal calves' liver and tender veal came with a rich, well-made sherry sauce, and bread-and-butter pudding with whisky-soaked apricots was delicious. Excellent bread from a local bakery.

Directions: From M1/J35 follow signs to Chapeltown and Huddersfield; go over first roundabout, turn R at second and hotel is 0.5 mile on R

Lane End S30 4UH
Map 8: SK38
Tel: 0114 2846727
Fax: 0114 2846783
Chef: Andrew Turner
Owners: David Johnson & Jeffrey Crockett
Cost: *Alc* £25, fixed-price L £12.50/D £21.50 (4 courses). ☺
H/wine £12.95
Times: Last L 2pm/last D 9.30pm. Closed D Sun, Bhs
Additional: Sunday L; Children welcome; ✿ dishes
Smoking: No smoking in dining room
Accommodation: 13 en suite
Credit cards: 🟦 🟦 🟦 🟦 🟦

YORKSHIRE
WEST

BRADFORD,
Quality Victoria Hotel ✸

A former Victorian railway hotel updated for the 21st-century: rooms are now equipped with CD players and video machines. Dishes served in the Parisian-style brasserie include salmon and plaice wrapped in spinach with a sweet pepper sauce, and duck breast with caramelised onions. A pianist plays traditional melodies in the evenings.

Bridge Street BD1 1JX
Map 7: SE13
Tel: 01274 728706
Chef: Stephen Craig Evans
Cost: *Alc* £18, fixed-price L £11.95/D £14.50. ☺ H/wine £8.75
Times: Last L 2pm/last D 10pm. Closed L Sat & Sun

Additional: Bar food; Children welcome; ◑ dishes
Smoking: No-smoking area; No pipes & cigars
Accommodation: 60 en suite
Credit cards:

Directions: From M606 take 3rd turn at roundabout (A6177). Next roundabout R (A641). End of dual carriageway R at roundabout (Hallings). R at next traffic lights; hotel on L

BRADFORD,
Restaurant Nineteen ✸✸✸

19 North Park Road BD9 4NT
Map 7: SE13
Tel: 01274 492559
Chef: Stephen Smith
Owners: Stephen Smith, Robert Barbour
Cost: *Alc* £25. ☺ H/wine £13
Times: D only, 7-last D 9.30pm. Closed Sun, Mon, 1 wk Jan, 1 wk Aug
Additional: Children welcome; ◑ dishes
Seats: 30
Smoking: No pipes and cigars
Accommodation: 4 en suite
Credit cards:

Stephen Smith and Robert Barbour have run their exceptional restaurant for some fourteen-odd years. The solid late Victorian house in a leafy Bradford suburb offers wonderfully ornate dining rooms decorated in warm oranges, yellows, light green and red, with a comfortable lounge bar and four well-equipped bedrooms. The menu has been simplified, cut down to a choice of four at each course offering such dishes as grilled salmon with a leek and courgette pancake, toasted tuna flakes and soy, roast rack of Welsh lamb with a rosemary and thyme lamb charlotte, and a rhubarb crumble tart with stem ginger cream. Quality is paramount as can be noted in a March dinner of sautéed scallops with a light, smooth Jerusalem artichoke mousse and a jus of star anise, roasted breast of corn-fed chicken with a touch of crispness but no hint of dryness, served with a Savoy cabbage parcel of plain button mushrooms and chicken livers, and a creamy Marsala sauce.

Toasted rice pudding for dessert came with a very good gingery parkin ice cream. The hand-written wine list includes some surprisingly reasonably priced wines, plus a pricier bin-end selection.

Signature dishes: Rack of lamb, aubergine, courgette and red pepper hot-pot; red mullet sausage, pesto noodles; poached pears with Bakewell tart ice cream and raspberry jam sauce; roast saddle of venison with beetroot risotto.

Directions: Take A650 (Manningham Lane) from Bradford. L at Manningham Park gates, then 1st R onto North Park Road

DEWSBURY,
Healds Hall Hotel ✿

Leeds Road WF15 6JA
Map 8: SE22
Tel: 01924 409112
Fax: 01924 401895
Chef: Philip McVeagh
Owners: Mr & Mrs TJ Harrington
Cost: *Alc* £25, fixed-price L £10.75/D £18.50 (4 courses). ☺ H/wine £8.25.
Times: Last L 2pm/D 9pm;
Closed L Sat, D Sun, 26 Dec, 1 Jan
Additional: Bar food L; Sunday L; Children welcome; ♨ dishes
Smoking: No smoking in dining room
Accommodation: 25 en suite
Credit cards: ▄▄ ▄▄ ▄▄ ▟ ▄▄ ▟ ▟ JCB

Conveniently placed for the M62, this large 18th-century house provides comfortable accommodation and friendly service. The interesting fixed-price and well-balanced carte offer a good range of dishes, and selections may include chicken liver terrine with home-made chutney, and beef fillet with bacon, shallot and claret sauce.

Directions: On A62 Leeds/Huddersfield road near M1/J40 and M62/J26-27 (turn right at Swan pub)

HALIFAX,
The Design House ✿✿

The flavours of the food at this converted carpet mill are as crisp, clean and up-to-date as the interior, with its plain white walls hung with modern art, and the Philippe Starck furniture matched by orange curtains. The seductively priced set menu could consist of, among others, rillettes of duck and turkey with piccalilli, roast salmon with bacon, and Swaledale cheese with home-made biscuits. The more extensive *carte* could start with smoked shellfish broth, or peppered fillet of venison with rocket, Parmesan and crisps of sweet potato, and go on to smoked Whitby cod with a bouillon of vegetables, calves' sweetbreads with wild mushroom and Madeira risotto, or chargrilled chicken breast with Italian sausage. Puddings of chocolate and sour cherry terrine, or Mascarpone cheesecake mousse bring up the rear. The beers on offer are as interesting as the wine list.

Dean Clough HX3 5AX
Map 7: SE02
Tel: 01422 383242
Fax: 01422 322732
Chef: David Watson
Owner: John Leach
Cost: *Alc* £22.50, fixed-price L £9.95 (2 courses)/D £12.95. ☺
H/wine £9.95
Times: Noon-2pm/6.30-10pm.
Closed L Sat, all Sun, 25-27 Dec, 1 Jan
Additional: Bar food L; ♨ dishes
Seats: 70
Smoking: No pipes & cigars; Air conditioning
Credit cards: ▄▄ ▄▄ ▄▄ ▟ ▄▄

Directions: From M62 follow signs to Halifax, Dean Clough is signposted (approx 0.5 miles from town centre).

HALIFAX, **Holdsworth House** ❀❀

Holdsworth HX2 9TG
Map 7: SE02
Tel: 01422 240024
Fax: 01422 245174
Chef: Garry Saunders
Owners: Gail Moss, Kim Pearson
Cost: Alc £24, fixed-price L £12. ☺
H/wine £9.75.
Times: Noon-last L 2pm/7pm-last
D 9.30pm. Closed L Sat, L Sun, Xmas
Additional: Children welcome;
❀ dishes
Seats: 70. Private dining rooms 130.
Jacket & tie preferred
Smoking: No-smoking area;
No pipes or cigars
Accommodation: 40 en suite

Only three miles north of Halifax, yet this beautifully
preserved Jacobean manor house enjoys a peaceful rural
setting surrounded by its own grounds. Twin wood-panelled
dining rooms with open fireplaces, antique furniture and fresh
flowers provide an elegant setting for guests who can choose
either a three or four-course meal from the compact menu.
Confit of duck terrine with herb oil, Thai fishcakes with satay
sauce, fillet of salmon with crab risotto, fillet of beef drizzled
with olive oil, and chocolate and orange torte and hot
strawberry soufflé show the range. The wine list is thoughtfully
arranged by grape variety rather than region.

Credit cards: ▆ ▆ ▧ ▆ ▆ ▆ ▆

Directions: From Halifax take A629 (Keighley), 2 miles turn R at
garage to Holmfield, hotel 1.5 miles on R

HALIFAX, **The Imperial Crown** ❀

*An impressive hotel in the centre of town, close to the railway
station. The restaurant is themed around Wallis Simpson and has a
fine collection of royal memorabilia. The menu, however, follows a
more popular route, with breaded fillet of plaice 'Holstein', Indian-
style balti curry, and a roast joint of the day showing the style.*

Smoking: No pipes & cigars
Accommodation: 56 en suite
Credit cards: ▆ ▆ ▧ ▆ ▆ ▆ ▆ JCB

Directions: Hotel is opposite railway station

42-46 Horton Street
HX1 1QE
Map 7: SE02
Tel: 01422 342342
Fax: 01422 349866
Chef: Steven Pim
Owner: Regal Hotel Group plc
Cost: Alc £20, fixed-price D £16.95.
☺ H/wine £11.95
Times: D only, last D 9.45pm
Additional: Children welcome;
❀ dishes

HAWORTH, **Weavers Restaurant** ❀❀

Weavers celebrates its twenty-first birthday in 1999. Cluttered,
comfortable and stylish, it occupies what were three weavers'
cottages at the top of this Brontë pilgrimage village. A short
section on the menu of 'traditionals' – Pennine meat and
potato pie, Cumbrian sausage with mash and onion gravy, and
Whitby fisherman's pie – sits alongside other main courses
showing a contemporary approach: calves' liver with gin and
lime sauce and colcannon; roast monkfish and Dublin Bay
prawns in green Thai sauce; and baked halibut with crushed
new potatoes and a herby sauce. Elsewhere there may be

15 West Lane BD22 8DU
Map 7: SE03
Tel: 01535 643822
Fax: 01535 644832
Chefs/Owners: Jane & Colin
Rushworth
Cost: Alc £20, fixed-price D £13.50.
☺ H/wine £9.50
Times: D only, 6.45-last D 9.15pm.
Closed Sun, Mon, 2 wks after Xmas
Additional: Children welcome;
❀ dishes

chargrilled ribeye, shank of local lamb with root vegetable mash and rosemary gravy, or seared salmon with asparagus and herbed crème fraîche. You could start with hearty smoked haddock soup, or something lighter like Caesar salad, and finish with home-made vanilla ice cream, lemon tart or bread-and-butter pudding with custard. Eight wines are sold by the glass from a wide-ranging list.

Directions: Haworth centre, by Brontë Museum car park

HUDDERSFIELD, **Bagden Hall**

A traditional hotel restaurant in a pleasant rural location. Menus include a full-flavoured pheasant and duck terrine, roast monkfish with a red wine jus and well-made coconut and almond tart with warm vanilla sauce.

Smoking: No-smoking area; Air conditioning
Accommodation: 17 en suite
Credit cards: 🔲 🔲 🔲 🔲 🔲 🔲 🔲

Directions: Leave M1/J39; hotel is on A636 Denby Dale road after 8 miles

Wakefield Road Scissett HD8 9LE
Map 7: SE11
Tel: 01484 865330
Fax: 01484 861001
Chef: Jeramey Hanson
Owners: Robert & Mandie Braithwaite
Cost: Alc £25, fixed-price L £10.75/D £17.95 (4 courses). ☺ H/wine £8.50
Times: Last L 2pm/last D 9.30pm
Additional: Bar food; Sunday L; Children welcome; 🍴 dishes

HUDDERSFIELD, **The Lodge Hotel** ❀

Pleasant, family-run hotel on the edge of town. Seasonal menus offer the likes of smoked lamb sausage with couscous and mixed pea purée, leek and celery soup, halibut with mussel and wild mushroom ragout, and lemon tart with a fruit and berry coulis. Unusual breads such as date and walnut, or cheese and rock salt.

Smoking: No smoking in dining room
Accommodation: 13 en suite.
Credit cards: 🔲 🔲 🔲 🔲

Directions: M62/J24 (Huddersfield), L at 1st lights (Birkby Road), R after Nuffield Hospital (Birkby Lodge Road), 100 yds on L

48 Birkby Lodge Road
Birkby HD2 2BG
Map 7: SE11
Tel: 01484 431001
Fax: 01484 421590
Chefs: DG & KJ Birley, R Hanson
Owners: David Garry & Kevin John Birley
Cost: Fixed-price L £13.95/D £23.95 (4 courses). ☺ H/wine £11.25
Times: Last L 1.45pm/last D 9.30pm. Closed L Sat, D Sun, 25-26 Dec
Additional: Sunday L; Children welcome; 🍴 dishes

HUDDERSFIELD,
Weavers Shed Restaurant ❀❀

Twenty-five years old, The Weavers Shed has a long and enviable history of good food and fine dining behind it. Formerly a woollen mill in the 18th century, it stands in a village on the foothills of the Pennines. The restaurant itself is based in the former mill and has exposed stone walls, quarry tiles and plenty of beams. The lunch menu is short but good value, and in the evenings a *carte* full of modern British dishes is available. Our inspector opted for a creamy wild mushroom risotto with chargrilled asparagus, followed by roasted halibut with a 'delicious' fennel cream sauce. The wine list features a good choice of dessert wines, together with a tempting selection of malt whiskies. Look out for any number of special events staged here, ranging from jazz dinners to guest chef evenings.

Directions: M62/24 & 23 (no exit westbound) take A640, turning L to Golcar, follow rd into village, 3 miles W of Huddersfield

Seats: 65. Private dining room 14
Smoking: No smoking in dining room; Air conditioning
Accommodation: 3 en suite
Credit cards: 🔲 🔲 🔲 🔲 🔲 🔲 🔲 JCB

Acre Mill's Knowl Road
Golcar HD7 4AN
Map 7: SE11
Tel: 01484 654284
Fax: 01484 650980
Chefs: Ian McGunnigle, Robert Jones, Stephen Jackson
Owner: Stephen Jackson
Cost: Alc £35, fixed-price L £12.95. ☺
Times: Noon-2pm/7-10pm. Closed L Sat, all Sun, Mon, Bhs
Additional: Children welcome; 🍴 dishes
Seats: 50. Private room 30
Smoking: No pipes & cigars
Accommodation: 5 en suite
Credit cards: 🔲 🔲 🔲 🔲 🔲

ILKLEY,

The Box Tree ❀❀❀

35-37 Church Street LS29 9DR
Map 7: SE14
Tel: 01943 608484
Fax: 01943 607186
Chef: Thierry Leprêtre Granet
Owner: The Box Tree Restaurant (Ilkley) Ltd
Cost: *Alc* £27
Times: Noon-2.30pm/7-last D 9.30pm. Closed D Sun, all Mon, 26-30 Dec, last 2 wks Jan
Additional: Sunday L; Children welcome; ❸ dishes
Seats: 50. Private dining room 16
Smoking: No smoking in dining room
Credit cards: ▬ ▭ £ ▬

Still going strong after all these years. Although fairly central within Ilkley, this long-standing restaurant is in fact an original stone farmhouse, built around 1720. The place is a collection of small rooms, all richly furnished with objets d'art, fine art and various collections distributed in an almost haphazard way; comfortable furnishings 'showing genteel wear in places' add to the lived-in, comfortable look. Thierry Leprêtre-Granet's menu is short and to the point, based on prime seasonal ingredients. Its heart may lie in classic French cooking but there is an English accent. Note the sautéed Cornish scallops served with a fruit chutney and lemon sauce that appeared on the same *carte* as a more traditional terrine of duck foie gras served with toasted raisin and walnut bread. The more vibrant flavours of the Mediterranean, however, come through in main courses such as ragout of rabbit with fennel, olives and tomatoes, and roasted sea bass with piperade, courgettes and provençale sauce. A summer lunch opened with succulent and tender breast of wood pigeon, which came wrapped in cabbage leaves and sliced on to a juniper berry sauce. Super game flavours complemented the tenderness, with the cabbage leaves giving a contrast in textures, and the fine sauce (with good sheen and balanced flavour) giving a clear, almost earthy flavour of juniper. Braised fillet of turbot was delicate and full flavoured, topped with a crust of wild mushrooms. The accompanying basil sauce was brilliant – not just for its bright green-pea colour, but also the fragrant smell and concentrated flavour. Vegetables were kept to a minimum: simple aubergine, super flavoured asparagus, and plainly boiled, thinly sliced new potatoes. Hot raspberry soufflé was perfectly cooked and presented, with a real fruity punch to the soufflé, which was further supplemented by a pouring sauce of raspberry. The comprehensive wine list includes a choice of wines by the glass and two pages of half-bottles.

Signature dishes: Warm oyster mousseline with poached oysters, white wine butter sauce; wild steamed salmon with piperade; roast rump of veal with spinach and wood mushrooms; fillet of Aberdeen Angus beef with cep purée and port wine sauce.

Directions: On A65, on the Skipton side of Ilkley near the Church

ILKLEY,

Rombalds Hotel ✿

11 West View
Wells Road LS29 9JG
Map 7: SE14
Tel: 01943 603201
Fax: 01943 816586
Chef: Andrew Davey
Owners: Colin & Jo Clarkson
Cost: *Alc* £24, fixed-price L £9.95/D
£12.95. H/wine £9.75. ☺
Times: Last L 2pm/last D 9.30pm.

On the edge of Ilkley Moor, the Wedgwood-blue restaurant of this Georgian terrace hotel makes good use of local produce, with beef pastured in the Vale of Nidd, lamb from the Yorkshire Dales, pork from local farmers. This translates into a modern menu that is full of interest. Good selection of half-bottles on a globetrotting wine list.

Additional: Bar meals; Sunday L; Children welcome; ◑ dishes
Smoking: No smoking in dining room
Accommodation: 15 en suite
Credit cards: ▬ ▭ ⧄ ⬚ ▦ ▶ ▣ JCB

Directions: From A65 lights in town, turn up Brook Street, cross The Grove to Wells Road and hotel is 600 yds on L

LEEDS,

Brasserie Forty Four ✿✿

44 The Calls LS2 7EW
Map 8: SE23
Tel: 0113 2343232
Fax: 0113 2343332
Chef: Jeff Baker
Owner: Michael Gill
Cost: *Alc* £21.50, fixed-price L & D
£12.95. ☺ H/wine £9.90
Times: Noon-last L 2pm/6.30-last D
10.30pm. Closed L Sat, all Sun, Bhs
Additional: Children welcome;
◑ dishes
Seats: 110. Private room 55
Smoking: No pipes and cigars;
Air conditioning
Credit cards: ▬ ▭ ⧄ ⬚ ▦ ▶ ▣

Converted grain store by the river with white-painted brick walls, block wood floors and modern paintings. The style of food reflects the cool, minimalist interior: cosmopolitan dishes such as Moroccan spiced lamb meatballs and home-cured salt beef with green olives are scattered across the menu. Our inspector enjoyed a May meal that kicked off with crisp smoked salmon fishcakes with a light fish sauce. This was followed by sautéed calves' liver with full-flavoured Italian bacon, served on a bed of deep green spinach with a light pan jus. Desserts include prune and Armagnac parfait with a compote of spiced winter fruits, and bitter chocolate and orange marquise with broken ginger biscuits and an apricot coulis. Summer meals can be enjoyed on the veranda overlooking the restored canal. The good-value wine list features around sixty bottles from a zesty modern slate.

Directions: From Crown Point Bridge, L past Church, L into High Court Road. On the riverside

LEEDS, Fourth Floor at Harvey Nichols ❀

NEW

107/111 Briggate LS1 6AZ
Map 8: SE23
Tel: 0113 2048000
Fax: 0113 2048080
Chef: Simon Shaw
Owner: Harvey Nichols Ltd
Cost: *Alc* £21, fixed-price L £15/D £15.95. ☺ H/wine £11.95
Times: Last L 3pm/last D 10.30pm. Closed D Mon-Wed, all Sun, 25-26 Dec
Additional: Children welcome; ✪ dishes
Smoking: No-smoking area; Air conditioning
Credit cards: ▬ ▬ ▬ ▬ ▬ ▬ ▬ JCB

Contemporary design and decor, panoramic views across Leeds, and a bustling atmosphere are among the attractions at this trendy café-restaurant. From an 'open to view' kitchen come substantial portions of fully flavoured dishes, perhaps chargrilled ribeye steak with horseradish ketchup, lemon sole, duck breast with peppercorn sauce, and lime tart.

Directions: In Harvey Nichols department store

LEEDS, Haley's Hotel ❀❀

Shire Oak Road Headingley
LS6 2DE
Map 8: SE23
Tel: 0113 2784446
Fax: 0113 2753342
Chef: Jon Vennell
Owner: John J Appleyard
Cost: *Alc* £25. ☺ H/wine £10.65
Times: D only, 7.15pm-last D 9.45 pm. Closed D Sun (except residents), 26-30 Dec
Additional: Sunday L (12.15pm-2pm); Children welcome; ✪ dishes
Seats: 52. Private dining room 24
Smoking: No smoking in dining room; Air conditioning
Accommodation: 29 en suite
Credit cards: ▬ ▬ ▬ ▬ ▬ ▬ ▬ JCB

That the hotel is so close to the county cricket ground is only one of Haley's attractions. In a quiet, tree-lined cul-de-sac, the solid stone Victorian house is richly furnished without any degree of pretentiousness, and the cooking plays a steady wicket in a field of modern ideas. Considerable technique is demanded in dishes such as poached wing of skate stuffed with salmon mousse, served on a shellfish broth and sautéed samphire, whilst flavour is to the fore in feisty main courses such as confit of belly pork with Puy lentils and sherry vinegar sauce, and beautifully braised lamb shank with root vegetables and chickpeas. Classic combinations also include roasted partridge with bread sauce and pan-fried sea bass with citrus butter sauce. Amongst the choice of simple but effective desserts is a well-made plum tarte Tatin. The menu changes monthly and a first course is included in the price of the main course.

Directions: On A660 (Leeds/Otley) in Headingley between Lloyds and Midland banks

LEEDS, Leeds Marriott

Large, modern hotel right in the heart of the city offering a popular all-day bistro as well as the more formal restaurant, Dysons, themed after a famous clock maker and jeweller. A test meal in the latter, reported well on a starter of pan-fried red mullet that had crisp skin and was served with sweet, intense roasted plum tomatoes flavoured with a little garlic. Calves' liver had a very rustic, hearty appearance and came set on a mound of creamy mashed potato fully flavoured with sage, and accompanied by lightly smoked bacon and onions. A white chocolate mousse was balanced by a blackberry compote with autumn fruits and blackberry coulis. Good cafetière made a strong finish.

Directions: From M1 or M62 follow signs to City Centre, turn into Sovereign St, L at lights, R into NCP car park adjacent to hotel

LS1 6ET
Map 8: SE23
Tel: 0113 2366444
Fax: 0113 2366367
Chef: Peter McMahon
Please telephone for further details

LEEDS, Leodis Brasserie

There's a real buzz to this busy brasserie set in a converted warehouse with its original brick walls and cast-iron pillars still very much in evidence. Classic brasserie dishes – duck rillettes, ham hock and parsley terrine, coq au vin, confit of duck with Puy lentils – share the menu with more British offerings such as steak and Guinness pudding, pork and leek bangers with champ and, at lunchtime, roast lamb from the trolley. A recent meal got off to a good start with a well-executed croustade of mushrooms topped with a perfectly cooked poached egg and hollandaise sauce, and ended with a light rhubarb custard fool. Good home-made bread and an impressive globe-trotting wine list. There is a separate bar.

Directions: Follow the M/way sign from City square, turn L by the Hilton Hotel onto Sovereign Street, 100 yards on L.

Victoria Mill Sovereign Street LS1 4BJ
Map 8: SE23
Tel: 0113 2421010
Fax: 0113 2430432
Chef: Steve Kendall
Owners: Martin Spalding, Steve Kendall, Paul Richardson
Cost: *Alc* £25, fixed-price L & D £13.95. ☺ H/wine £10.95.
Times: Noon-last L 2pm/6pm-last D 10pm. Closed L Sat, Sun, 25-26 Dec, L Bhs
Additional: Children welcome; ❹ dishes
Seats: 180
Credit cards: 🔲 🔲 🔲 🔲 🔲 🔲 🔲

LEEDS, The Thistle Merrion

A smart city-centre hotel with an Art Deco-style first-floor restaurant – Starlets. Its menus offer an interesting and sometimes unusual choice of dishes including a slice of warm brioche with pâté and mushroom sauce to begin, and tender fillet with smoked halibut filling and oyster sauce to follow.

Directions: Town centre

Merrion Centre LS2 8NH
Map 8: SE23
Tel: 0113 243 9191
Fax: 0113 242 3527
Please telephone for further details

LEEDS, Olive Tree Greek Restaurant

A good Greek restaurant is a rare breed in these parts and, as such, very popular, with Tuesdays and Fridays the time for live Greek music and dancing. Satisfying starters include tyropitakia-light filo parcels filled with feta and mint, followed perhaps by succulent chicken Hydra, with baklava to finish in style.

Directions: By Rodley roundabout on Leeds outer ring road (A6120) NW of city

55 Rodley Lane LS13 1NG
Map 8: SE23
Tel: 0113 2569283
Chefs: George Psarias, Andreas Iacovou
Owners: George & Vasoulla Psarias
Please telephone for further details

LEEDS, **Oulton Hall Hotel** ❀

An imposing 19th-century mansion, surrounded by well manicured grounds, a golf course and even a church. An early spring lunch in the oak-panelled Brontë Restaurant began with cream of cauliflower and Stilton soup, was followed by pan-fried breast of chicken with buttered spinach, and rounded off with a dark chocolate marquise.

Rothwell Lane Oulton LS26 8HN
Map 8: SE23
Tel: 0113 2821000
Fax: 0113 2828066
Chef: Stephen Collinson
Owner: Brontë Restaurant
Cost: Alc £35, fixed-price L £15/D £23. ☺ H/wine £12.95.
Times: Last L 1.45pm/D 10pm. Closed L Sat
Additional: Sunday L; Children welcome; 🍴 dishes
Smoking: No smoking in dining room. Air-conditioning
Accommodation: 152 en suite
Credit cards: 🔲 🔲 🔲 🔲 🔲 🔲 JCB

Directions: M62/J30, follow signs to Rothwell

LEEDS, **Pool Court at 42** ❀❀❀

44 The Calls LS2 7EW
Map 8: SE23
Tel: 0113 2444242
Fax: 0113 2343332
Chef: Jeff Baker
Owner: Michael Gill
Cost: Fixed-price L £12.50 (2courses)/D £ 29.50. H/wine £12.95
Times: Noon-last L 2pm/7-last D 10pm. Closed L Sat, all Sun, Bhs
Additional: Children welcome; 🍴 dishes.
Seats: 38
Smoking: No pipes & cigars; Air conditioning
Credit cards: 🔲 🔲 🔲 🔲 🔲 🔲 🔲

Gleaming chrome and pale blond-wood characterise the Milanesque chic of this sophisticated converted mill set down a cobbled lane in a stylish restaurant district near the Liverpool-Leeds canal. Appealing to a clientele of designer-clad northern *riche*, business suits and foodies, the restaurant's careful image construction extends to the design of the menus, of which there are three: set lunch, a *carte*,, and a six-course 'classics' affair for traditionalists. Good breads such as five-grain, ciabatta and brioche are offered to start with delicious French butter. Highlights of the kitchen include a delightfully smooth and creamy terrine of foie gras with spiced winter fruits and toasted walnut loaf, and a boudin blanc of chicken wrapped in Bayonne ham with Savoy cabbage and an intense truffled Madeira sauce. Accurate cooking typifies the main courses – pan-fried veal sweetbreads come well-coloured, and moist, roast Lincolnshire duckling is tender with a nice crispness to the skin. The latter is served with an enjoyable black olive sauce and leg confit salad, making it seem like two dishes in one. The great puddings include an assiette of chocolate comprising chocolate cheesecake, white chocolate and raisin cup and a dark chocolate and sultana pot. Also recommended

Directions: From M1 follow A61 (Harrogate) into city centre, cross River Aire via Crown Point Bridge. 2nd L at roundabout on to Maude St and you arrive at The Calls

is the warm apple and frangipane tart with vanilla ice cream and Calvados anglaise. Strong, good-quality espresso and moreish truffles end the meal on a high note. The building also houses a sister-brasserie at number 44, ideal for more informal occasions. The well-chosen, personalised wine list offers good depth and variety.

Signature dishes: Tarte Tatin of caramelised onions with seared scallops and two dressings; roast Saltburn sea bass with Whitby crabmeat, confit of tomato and lobster oil vinaigrette; pot-roasted veal sweetbreads and cepes with creamed Savoy cabbage and pancetta; terrine of foie gras with spiced winter fruits and walnut loaf.

LEEDS, **Rascasse**

Canal Wharf Water Lane LS11 5BB
Map 8: SE23
Tel: 0113 2446611
Fax: 0113 2440736
Chef: Simon Gueller
Owners: Simon Gueller, Nigel Jolliffe
Cost: *Alc* £28, fixed-price L & D ('till 7.30) £17. ☺ H/wine £11
Times: Noon-last L 2pm/6.30-last D 10pm (10.30pm Fri/Sat). Closed L Sat, Sun, 1 wk after Xmas, Bhs
Additional: Bar food L; Children welcome; ♨ dishes
Seats: 100 + 30 outside
Smoking: No pipes and cigars; Air conditioning
Credit cards: ■ ▩ ⇴ ▯ ▦ ■ ▨ JCB

Atmosphere, service, design and, above all, cooking, make Simon Gueller's canalside restaurant a huge asset to Leeds. Within walking distance of the city centre, Rascasse is housed within a restored 18th-century granary. The stone building retains much of its original character, including a superb timber roof which soars above the reception area, and the first-floor balcony bar. The extensive use of stainless steel, glass and polished wood is softened by shrubs and plants, comfortable banquettes and dining chairs upholstered in warm, bright colours. 'Modern French Mediterranean' is the style: cappuccino of potato and pancetta, with poached hens' eggs; grilled guinea fowl, Vichy carrots, brioche dumplings and Madeira sauce; tranche of sea bass, brandade of fennel and celeriac, beignets of sage, tapenade, olives, and basil oil. Both a pressing of lobster, salmon and pink peppercorn with sauce gazpacho, and a marinière of sea scallops and calamari with coriander infusion, glowed with clear distinct flavours and fine textures. Immense technical flair and superb produce were the underlying components of two main courses, one of calves' liver with buttered spinach, pomme purée and bourguignon garnish, the other roast pigeon de Bresse with Savoy cabbage, pancetta, pomme fondant, and Madeira sauce. Classic sauce making skills – Madeira, diable, red wine, grain mustard – are judiciously, balanced by the use of jus, flavoured oils, butters and dressings. The dessert list makes lively reading – caramelised pear tart with honey ice cream, warm chocolate fondant with coconut sorbet, and chilled rice pudding with fresh fruit poached with spices. Good espresso coffee is served with squares of Valrhona chocolate. Well-chosen wines from known producers are fairly priced. The 'Fastrack' menu, available at lunch and evenings before 7.30pm, is a bargain at the price.

Directions: 0.5 mile from M1/J47 & M621/J3; follow signs to City Centre, turn L Water Lane. then R on Canal Wharf. On Canal Basin

Signature dishes: Mediterranean fish soup, rouille, croûtons and Gruyère; risotto of white truffle oil and button mushrooms; supremes of squab pigeon, papillote of foie gras and wild mushrooms, jus of thyme; warm chocolate fondant, coconut sorbet

LEEDS, Shear's Yard

The Calls LS2 7EY
Map 8: SE23
Tel: 0113 2444144
Fax: 0113 2448102
Chef: Danny Janes
Owner: Rob Noble
Cost: *Alc* £20. ☺ H/wine £9.95
Times: Last L 2.30pm/last D 10.30pm. Closed Sun, Bh Mon, 1 wk Xmas
Additional: Bar food; Children welcome; ⑤ dishes
Smoking: No-smoking area; No pipes & cigars; Air conditioning
Credit cards:

Fun place to eat, a former shearing yard (hence the name), that now has all the hustle and bustle of a popular meeting place. Simple menu, backed up by blackboard specials, with crab and Gruyère tart plus a lime dressing, confit of smoked duck on wilted greens and whisky soy, and glazed lemon tart with blackcurrant sorbet, show a kitchen with an eye firmly on modern trends.

Directions: From M1 follow signs for Crown Point Bridge. Cross bridge and turn L at roundabout on to Kirkgate, restaurant 200yds on R

RIPPONDEN,
Over the Bridge Restaurant

Millfold HX6 4DJ
Map 8: SE23
Tel: 01422 823722
Fax: 01422 824810
Chefs: Sue Tyer & Ian Beaumont
Owner: Ian Beaumont
Cost: *Alc* £25.50. ☺ H/wine £9.50
Times: D only, last D 9.30pm. Closed Sun, Mon, Bhs
Additional: Children welcome; ⑤ dishes
Smoking: No pipes & cigars
Credit cards:

A comfortable but smart restaurant next to a bridge over a stream in the centre of the village. Endorsements continue to be made for light soufflés, one perhaps of oak-roasted salmon with asparagus, while main courses could run to pink, crisp-skinned duckling on mushroom barley pilau, or halibut baked in a potato and lime crust, with perhaps orange and Grand Marnier baba among desserts.

Directions: M62/J22(E)/J24(W), A58 from Halifax, in village centre by church

WENTBRIDGE,
Wentbridge House Hotel

Set in spacious gardens, the Wentbridge House dates from the 1700s. Its Fleur De Lys restaurant (with wood-panelled walls and polished service) features complex, intriguing dishes, perhaps asparagus and salmon parcels with roasted scallops and caviar remoulade to start, followed by venison with roast cauliflower, Roquefort mousse and morel jus. Long, varied wine list.

Additional: Sunday L; Children welcome; 🌢 dishes
Smoking: No pipes in dining room
Accommodation: 19 en suite
Credit cards: ▆ ⬛ ⬛ ⬛ ⬛ ⬛

Directions: 0.5 mile off the A1, 4 miles S of M62/A1 interchange

WF8 3JJ
Map 8: SE41
Tel: 01977 620444
Fax: 01977 620148
Chef: John Lyons
Owner: Mr G Page
Cost: *Alc* £29, fixed-price L £14.50/D £21. ☺ H/wine £10.95
Times: Last L 2pm/last D 9.30pm. Closed D 25 Dec

WETHERBY, Wood Hall Hotel

Grade II listed Georgian Country House with a classical-style restaurant. Good home-made bread (try the black pudding variety) and some adventurous combinations are offered. A highlight at inspection was a robust starter of sun-dried tomato and spring onion risotto, served with a cep cream and poached quails' eggs.

Directions: In town, take turning opposite Windmill pub signed Wood Hall and Linton

Trip Lane Linton LS22 4JA
Map 8: SE44
Tel: 01937 587271
Fax: 01937 584353
Chef: Phillip Pomfret
Owner: Arcadian International Ltd
Cost: *Alc* £29.95, fixed price L £15.95/D £29.95. H/wine £11.95
Times: Last L 2pm/last D 9.30pm. Closed L Sat
Additional: Bar food; Sunday L; Children welcome; 🌢 dishes
Smoking: No smoking in dining room
Accommodation: 43 en suite
Credit cards: ▆ ⬛ ⬛ ⬛ ⬛ ⬛ ⬛

CHANNEL ISLANDS
ALDERNEY

ALDERNEY, Inchalla Hotel

The conservatory restaurant at this small, modern hotel looks on to the garden with views of the sea in the distance; the patio outside makes a pleasant spot for alfresco dining. The sea plays a leading role on the menus, with starters of giant prawns drenched in garlic and parsley butter, whitebait with lemon and dill mayonnaise, and Thai fish soup. Eastern flavourings go into main-course fishcakes, too, or there might be swordfish with lime butter. Taramasalata, hummus and tsatsiki make a nice sunny starter, especially as they come with freshly baked olive and basil bread, and might be followed by roast rack of lamb with garlic, cloves and thyme and a redcurrant reduction, and there's always a selection of steaks. Puddings are a litany recited at the table, while wines on the short, well-chosen list are reasonably priced.

Directions: On the outskirts of St Anne, 3-4 minutes' walk from town centre

St Anne GY9 3UL
Map: 16
Tel: 01481 823220
Fax: 01481 824045
Chef: Anne Marie Burbidge
Owner: Valerie Willis
Cost: *Alc* £20, fixed-price L £11 (4 courses). ☺ H/wine £7.50
Times: Noon-last L 2pm/7pm-last D 8.45pm. Closed D Sun, Xmas, New Year
Additional: Bar food (L only); Sunday L; No children under 2; ❹ dishes
Seats: 30
Smoking: No-smoking area in dining room
Accommodation: 9 en suite
Credit cards: ▆ ▆ ✈ ▆ ▆ ☒ JCB

GUERNSEY

CATEL, Cobo Bay Hotel

Pick the right time of the evening and there are spectacular sunsets across the bay to be enjoyed from the picture windows of the restaurant at this family-run hotel. Foodwise the daily *carte* might include collops of deep-fried chicken breast in a satay and coriander marinade, and country vegetable soup, before the likes of a navarin of fresh seafood on a bed of root vegetables with a champagne, dill and lobster butter sauce, or escalope of veal with grain mustard and mushroom sauce, and rack of Welsh lamb in a mustard and herb crumb with a basil and tomato fondue. Good fresh vegetables are carefully handled. We ended our most recent meal with a well-made, light-textured apricot and sultana steamed pudding. Short, mainly French, list of wines at fair prices.

Directions: First turn L from hotel, approximately 3 miles to St Peter Port

Cobo GY5 7HB
Map: 16
Tel: 01481 57102
Fax: 01481 54542
Chef: John Chapman
Owner: David Nussbaumer
Cost: *Alc* £18. Fixed-price L £12.95/D £17.95 (4 courses). ☺ H/wine £7.95.
Times: D only, 7.00pm-last D 9.30pm. Closed L (except Sun), Jan/Feb
Additional: Sunday L (noon-2pm); Children welcome; ❹ dishes
Seats: 120
Smoking: No pipes & cigars in dining room; Air conditioning
Accommodation: 36 en suite
Credit cards: ▆ ▆ ☒ ▆

CATEL, La Grand Mare

One hundred acres of ground, gardens, with views over the Atlantic Ocean are a magnificent setting for this modern, purpose-built hotel designed in the grand style. The kitchen cooks in a fashion that readily suits the clientele: many classical French dishes, with some flambé dishes at table. This is not to say that they are not aware of modern trends, and tucked away between the pressed game terrine, the fillet steak Café de Paris, and the lobster Thermidor, could be smoked lamb salad with a chilli and tomato dressing, or pan-fried veal

The Coast Road
Vazon Bay GY5 7LL
Map: 16
Tel: 01481 56576
Fax: 01481 56532
Chef: Fergus Mackay
Owners: The Vermeulen Family
Cost: *Alc* £25, fixed-price L £11.95/D £16.50. ☺ H/wine £7.95
Times: Noon-last L 2pm/7-last D 9.30pm

with a tomato confit and a black olive and lime sauce. For a real piece of theatre though, order the crêpes Suzette for dessert.

Smoking: No-smoking area; Air conditioning
Accommodation: 27 en suite
Credit cards: ▆ ▆ ▆ ▆ ▆ ▆ ▆

Directions: *Telephone for directions*

PERELLE, L'Atlantique Hotel ✿✿

The setting is enviable – Perelle Bay is famed for its sandy beaches and spectacular sunsets – and the restaurant of this comfortable, modern hotel makes full use of the view, with large windows overlooking the sea. Locally caught seafood is a highlight of both the regularly changing set menus and the *carte*, though other local, seasonal ingredients are also a feature of the modern cooking. A May meal might begin with glazed Crottin cheese with asparagus spears, red onion jam ice cream and beetroot balsamic vinaigrette. Grilled fillet of Guernsey brill with saffron potatoes and local shellfish minestrone might follow, while pudding could be peach tart with strawberry soup and churned vanilla-bean cream. The choice of wines is extensive, with notes often suggesting pairings with food.

Directions: On west coast road overlooking Perelle Bay

Additional: Bar food L; Sunday L; Children welcome; ❹ dishes
Seats: 180. Private dining room 30

Perelle Bay St Saviours
GY7 9NA
Map: 16
Tel: 01481 64056
Fax: 01481 63800
Chef: John Tonge
Owner: Michael Lindley
Cost: *Alc* £25, fixed price D £16 (5 courses). ☺ H/wine £8.40
Times: D only, last D 9.30pm. Closed Jan, Feb
Additional: Bar food; Sunday L (noon-2pm); Children welcome; ❹ dishes
Seats: 50
Smoking: No-smoking area; No pipes & cigars; Air conditioning
Accommodation: 21 en suite
Credit cards: ▆ ▆ ▆

ST MARTIN, La Barbarie ✿

An extended 16th-century former priory enjoying a peaceful location and retaining all the charm and character of the original building. On the food front expect a good choice of soundly cooked dishes ranging from traditional potted shrimps and lemon sole Colbert, to ham and cheese mille-feuille with tomato and shallot fondue, and the lobster Thermidor enjoyed on our last visit.

Additional: Bar food L; Sunday L; Children welcome; ❹ dishes
Smoking: No-smoking area
Accommodation: 33 en suite
Credit cards: ▆ ▆ ▆

Directions: At traffic lights in St Martin take road to Saints Bay – hotel is on R at end of Saints Road

Saints Road Saints Bay
GY4 6ES
Map: 16
Tel: 01481 35217
Fax: 01481 35208
Chef: Anthony Lawson
Owner: Andrew Coleman
Cost: *Alc* £22.50, fixed-price D £14.75 (5 courses). ☺ H/wine £7.95
Times: Last L 2pm/last D 9.30pm

ST MARTIN, **Hotel Bon Port**

A cliff top location affords wonderful coastal views from this well presented hotel. The restaurant is warmly decorated in royal blue and terracotta, with etchings and watercolours depicting Guernsey landscapes and shorelines. All tables have views of Moulin Huet Bay and the Peastacks. A good choice of bread is offered with Guernsey butter, and a triangular terrine of lobster and salmon came bound in a thin layer of smoked salmon. Beef hotch-potch proved a complex dish, comprising fillet of beef layered between celeriac crisps, oxtail filled with a cabbage and lardon farce and spicy beef dumpling wrapped in crepette. The highlight, however, was the hot chocolate soufflé, with vanilla ice cream in a delicate tuile basket.

Directions: Follow road from airport into St Martin. At last traffic lights turn R and follow signs.

Moulin Huet Bay GY4 6EW
Map: 16
Tel: 01481 39249
Fax: 01481 39596
Chef: Phil Ashman
Owner: Peter Yates
Cost: *Alc* £21.50, fixed-price L £15/D £17.50 (5 courses). ☺ H/wine £8.50
Times: Noon-last L 1.45pm/7pm-last D 8.45pm
Additional: Bar food L; Sunday L; No children under 12
Seats: 45. Private dining room 12
Smoking: No smoking in dining room; Air conditioning
Accommodation: 18 en suite
Credit cards: 〓 〓 〓 〓 〓 〓

ST MARTIN, **Hotel Jerbourg**

Enjoying fine sea views from its clifftop location, this smartly appointed conservatory-style restaurant is enthusiastically run by a dedicated team. A test meal produced a delightful pressed terrine of salmon and roasted pepper, followed by a super fillet of sea bass, served on a crab and coriander cake with a chive beurre blanc, with dark chocolate tart to finish.

Smoking: No-smoking area; No pipes & cigars
Accommodation: 32 en suite. **Credit cards:** 〓 〓 〓 〓 〓

Directions: 5 mins drive from St Peter Port on main road

Jerbourg Point GY4 6BJ
Map: 16
Tel: 01481 38826
Fax: 01481 38238
Chef: Kevin Buckley
Owner: Arthenella Guernsey Ltd
Cost: *Alc* £22.50, fixed-price D £15.95 (5 courses). ☺ H/wine £8.50
Times: Last L 2.30pm/last D 9.30pm
Additional: Bar food; Sunday L; Children welcome; ✦ dishes

ST MARTIN, **Idlerocks Hotel**

Views of the French coast, crashing waves and the call of gulls provide the atmosphere outside this popular hotel. Local produce - especially fish - dictates the menu. Try wok-fried local scallops with oriental cabbage and honey and soy dressing, or pan-fried halibut bonne femme with caramelised onions.

Smoking: No-smoking area; No cigars & pipes
Accommodation: 28 en suite
Credit cards: 〓 〓 〓 〓 〓 〓 〓

Directions: 5 mins drive from St Peter Port on main road

Jerbourg Point GY4 6BJ
Map: 16
Tel: 01481 37711
Fax: 01481 35592
Owners: Paul & Jan Hamill
Cost: *Alc* £15, fixed-price L £10.50/D £14.50 (both 5 courses). ☺ H/wine £9.90
Times: Last L 2pm/D 9pm
Additional: Bar food; Sunday L; Children welcome; ✦ dishes

ST MARTIN, **St Margaret's Lodge**

Convenient for the airport, guests expect good standards of service and hospitality. A varied selection of modern and classical French dishes is served in the well-appointed restaurant, which overlooks the garden. Local seafood is a strong point. Look out for roast sea bass with saffron jus, or seared salmon with rocket and black treacle chutney.

Accommodation: 47 en suite
Credit cards: 〓 〓 〓

Directions: Out of airport, turn L. Follow road for 1.5 miles. Hotel on L

Forest Road GY4 6UE
Map: 16
Tel: 01481 35757
Fax: 01481 37594
Chef: Aidrian Davison
Cost: *Alc* £25, fixed-price L £11/D £15.95 (5 courses). ☺ H/wine £7.60
Times: Last L 1.45pm/last D 9.30pm
Additional: Bar food; Sunday L; Children welcome; ✦ dishes
Smoking: No smoking in dining room

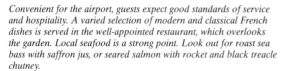

ST PIERRE-DU-BOIS,
Café du Moulin ❀❀

At night, the atmosphere and menu go up a gear in this rustic restaurant, full of knick-knacks, opposite the mill. Follow ravioli of home-smoked chicken in a creamy mushroom sauce, with lattice of fillets of salmon and brill with a gremolata crust and a saffron butter sauce, or a duet of Gressingham duck - the breast pan-fried with kumquat and Grand Marnier sauce, served with a confit of the leg. Vegetarians have a good choice-sweetcorn and spring onion fritters with refried black beans, rice pilaff and a mild jalapeño pepper sauce, for example. Lunchtimes, there may be prawn linguine or home-made chargrilled fillet of beef burger with tomato salsa and 'proper chips', as well as a selection of bar snacks. Home-made desserts include cappuccino ice cream, iced meringue gâteau and Turkish rice cooked in coconut milk, served chilled with a brûlée crust.

Directions: Take the Forest rd from St Peter Port, L in St Peters – signed Torteval, take 3rd R; restaurant 0.25 miles

Rue du Quanteraine GY7 9DP
Map: 16
Tel: 01481 65944
Fax: 01481 65708
Chef: David Mann
Owners: David & Gina Mann
Cost: *Alc* £27.85. ☺ H/wine £9
Times: 12.15pm-last L 1.15pm/7pm-last D 9pm. Closed D Sun, Mon
Additional: Bar food L; Sunday L; ◑ dishes
Seats: 45
Smoking: No smoking in dining room
Credit cards: 🔲 🔲 🔲 🔲 🔲

ST PETER PORT, # The Absolute End ❀

Longstore GY1 2BG
Map: 16
Tel: 01481 723822
Fax: 01481 729129
Chef: Antonio Folmi
Owner: Gastone Toffanello
Cost: *Alc* £22, fixed-price L £11.☺ H/wine £8
Times: Last L 2pm/last D 10pm. Closed Sun, Jan
Additional: ◑ dishes
Smoking: No pipes & cigars
Credit cards: 🔲 🔲 🔲 🔲 🔲 🔲

A seafood restaurant in a converted fisherman's cottage, this is a great little place overlooking the sea. A summer meal might start with deep-fried scampi with sauce tartare or perhaps fried Brie in pepper sauce, followed by fillet of local brill, baked with wine, peppers, mussels and prawns, and served in a lobster sauce.

Directions: Less than 1 mile from town centre, going N on seafront road to St Sampson

---

ST PETER PORT, # La Frégate ❀

Lovely views over the harbour from the traditional old-style restaurant of this fine hotel. A test meal produced home-made leek and potato soup, good quality fresh turbot meunière, and a dessert that pushed up the calorie count with a plum and apple crumble served with vanilla anglaise, coulis, and excellent home-made cinnamon ice cream.

Additional: No children under 10; dishes
Smoking: Air conditioned
Accommodation: 13 en suite
Credit cards: 🔲 🔲 🔲 🔲 🔲 🔲 🔲 JCB

Directions: Town centre, above St Julian's Avenue

Les Cotils GY1 1UT
Map: 16
Tel: 01481 724624
Fax: 01481 720443
Chef: Günter Botzenhardt
Owner: Guernsey Summer Holidays Ltd
Cost: *Alc* £23, fixed-price L £13.50/D £20. ☺ H/wine £9.50.
Times: Last L 1.30pm/D 9.30pm

ST PETER PORT,
Le Nautique Restaurant ❀

French restaurant housed in a 400 year old warehouse overlooking the harbour. Expect duck with orange, and Chateaubriand with béarnaise sauce. Fish, such as Dover sole meunière, or poached turbot with hollandaise is usually a sound bet. Desserts are mostly meringue, fruit and ice cream permutations.

Seats: 68. Private dining room 30
Smoking: No pipes and cigars
Credit cards: 💳 💳 💳 💳 💳 💳

Quay Steps GY1 2LE
Map: 16
Tel: 01481 721714
Fax: 01481 721786
Chef: Vito Garau
Owner: Carlo Graziani
Cost: *Alc* £22.50. ☺ H/wine £8.25.
Times: Noon-last L 2pm/7pm-last
D 10pm. Closed Sun, 24 Dec-10 Jan
Additional: No children under 5;
☻ dishes

Directions: Sea front opposite Harbour and Victoria Marina

ST PETER PORT,
St Pierre Park Hotel ❀❀

Rohais GY1 1FD
Map: 16
Tel: 01481 728282
Fax: 01481 712041
Chef: John Hitchen
Cost: *Alc* £29.95, fixed-price L
£11.95/D £19.95 (4 courses). ☺
H/wine £9.95
Times: Noon-last L 2.30pm/7-last
D 11pm. Closed L Sat, D Sun
Additional: Sunday L; Children
welcome; ☻ dishes
Seats: 70. Private dining rooms 30
Smoking: No-smoking area;
Air conditioning
Accommodation: 135 en suite
Credit cards: 💳 💳 💳 💳 💳 💳

This modern, purpose-built hotel boasts both a lake and a 9-hole golf course in its extensive grounds. One can eat casually in the Café Renoir, but the serious action takes place in the Victor Hugo Restaurant. Here, the cooking is ambitious, pulling ideas from everywhere to create fusion dishes such as gâteau of crab with papaya and chilli chutney, or marinated pineapple and orange with lime and ginger and toasted coconut. Fish is the star, and can be served any which way with any number of classic sauces - lemon butter, white wine and herb, hollandaise - or with more unusual pairings: roast loin of monkfish marinated in ginger with black linguine, stir-fried vegetables and essence of carrot and coriander, for example, or braised lobster cooked with vanilla and cardamom with lemon pilau and pumpkin cream. Meat is not overlooked with roast rack of lamb coming with kidney and herb sausage, whole grain mustard mash, confit of root vegetables, flat-cap mushrooms and a light whisky jus.

Directions: 1 mile from town centre on route to west coast

VALE, **Pembroke Bay Hotel** ❀

The Ristorante Riva at the Pembroke Bay Hotel offers a comprehensive menu of modern Italian dishes. Among the antipasti are bresaola and deep-fried squid, followed by a choice of risotto

Pembroke Bay GY3 5BY
Map: 16
Tel: 01481 41175
Fax: 01481 48838
Chef: Santino Magnu

and pasta dishes. Main courses encompass fillet of brill with fresh asparagus, and roast saddle of lamb with artichokes.

Accommodation: 12 en suite
Credit cards: ▆ ▆ ▞ ▙ ▐

Directions: Northern tip of island, next to Royal Guernsey Golf Club

Owners: Lorenzo & Santino Magnu
Cost: *Alc* £25. ☺ H/wine £8.50
Times: Last L 2pm/last D 10pm.
Closed Mon
Additional: Children welcome;
🌙 dishes
Smoking: No pipes & cigars

JERSEY

GOREY,
Jersey Pottery Restaurant ❀❀

The Jersey Pottery is primarily a commercial business producing ceramics, and visitors can watch every stage of production as well as stroll around the gardens. The Brasserie serves snacks and light lunches, but the main thrust of the catering side of the operation is the spacious, conservatory-style Garden Restaurant, memorable for its foliage and 35-year-old fruiting vine over the roof. First-class seafood dominates the long menu: Jersey oysters, or tiger prawns with coconut and chilli sauce to start, although there could also be carrot soup, say, or asparagus with hollandaise. Scallops, prawns, lobster and crab all figure prominently among main courses, together with other items like baked sea bass and grilled Dover sole and a handful of choices for meat-eaters. Choose a dessert - perhaps plain and white chocolate mousse - from the central buffet. Some reliable producers can be found on the compact wine list.

Directions: In Gorey village, well signposted from main coast road.

Gorey Village JE3 9EP
Map: 16
Tel: 01534 851119
Fax: 01534 856540
Chef: Tony Dorris
Owner: The Jones Family
Cost: *Alc* £20. ☺ H/wine £11.50
Times: L only, noon-last L 4pm.
Closed Sun, 10 days Xmas
Additional: Children welcome;
🌙 dishes
Seats: 250
Smoking: No smoking area;
Air conditioning
Credit cards: ▆ ▆ ▞ ▙ ▆ ▐ ▣ JCB

GOREY, Suma's ❀❀ NEW

Gorey Hill St Martins
JE3 6ET
Map: 16
Tel: 01534 853291
Fax: 01534 851913
Chef: Mark Anderson
Owners: Sue Duffy, Malcom Lewis
Cost: *Alc* £23.50. Fixed-price L £13.75. ☺ H/wine £8.50

This new addition to Jersey's restaurant scene has hit the ground running; as baby sister to Longueville Manor, it comes with an impeccable pedigree. There are splendid views of the harbour from the balcony, and the smart interior is Med-cool, with white walls and colourful paintings. The menu is long and modish, with all the up-to-date stove top practices to the fore:

roasting (monkfish with Parma ham, onion marmalade and sage jus), searing (supreme of brill with oysters, quails' eggs, spring onions and ginger), grilling (Jersey scallops with black pudding, mushy peas and pancetta) braising (belly of pork with noodles, Chinese leaves and shiitake mushrooms). Desserts are less complicated - warm chocolate pudding with Grand Marnier custard, perhaps, or carrot cake with spiced fruit compote. In-house breads come with a little dish of virgin olive oil for dipping purposes, and good espresso coffee is served with yummy chocolate truffles.

Directions: *Telephone for directions*

GOREY, The Village Bistro ❀❀

Times: Noon-last L 2.30pm/6.30pm-last D 10pm. Closed D Sun, Mon, Xmas, Jan
Additional: Sunday L; Children welcome; ❸ dishes
Seats: 45
Smoking: Air conditioning
Credit cards:

Gorey Village JE3
Map: 16
Tel: 01534 853429
Chef: David Cameron
Owners: David & Sandra Cameron
Cost: *Alc* £27, fixed-price L £12.50. H/wine £6.50
Times: Noon-last L 2pm/7-last D 10pm. Closed Mon, 2 wks Feb
Additional: Sunday L; Children welcome; ❸ dishes
Seats: 40
Smoking: No pipes & cigars
Credit cards:

A former chapel, in the centre of Gorey, decorated with suns and moons. The restaurant has a strong local following, supplemented by holiday-makers, so booking is essential. The range of menus offers a wide choice, from the set lunch to the large *carte,* and the two blackboards offering daily specials and vegetarian options. The cooking is modern with some Asian influences. A starter of woodland risotto was a real hit, followed by fillet of cod with pak choi, lardons and a garlic-infused mash. Puddings range from passion fruit crème brûlée to a plate of four chocolate desserts with two chocolate sauces.

Directions: Village centre

ROZEL BAY, Château La Chaire ❀❀

JE3 6AJ
Map: 16
Tel: 01534 863354
Fax: 01534 865137
Chef: Simon Walker
Owners: Hatton Hotels Ltd
Cost: *Alc* £27, fixed-price L £13.95/D £21.50 (both 4 courses). ☺ H/wine £9.95
Times: Noon-last L 2pm/7-last D 10pm

Château La Chaire is stunningly located high up over Rozel Bay, on the side of a wooded valley, surrounded by five acres of terraced gardens. The oak-panelled dining room, with its conservatory extension, is a fine setting for the skilful and consistent cooking. Imaginative menus, including a good-value fixed-price menu, feature the best of local produce and reflect contemporary trends. Roast scallops, fat and sweet, were successfully accompanied by a date and apricot tagine on a bed of couscous. Freshest possible sea bass followed, with spinach, beurre blanc and Jersey royals, and an excellent almond and raspberry tart was served with thick Jersey custard.

Additional: Bar food L; Sunday L; Children welcome; 🅓 dishes
Seats: 60. Private dining room 20
Smoking: No-smoking area; No pipes & cigars
Accommodation: 14 en suite
Credit cards: 🔳 🔳 🔳 🔳 🔳

Directions: From St Helier head N/E towards Five Oaks, Maufant, then St Martin's Church & Rozel; 1st L in village, hotel 100m

Château La Chaire

ST BRELADE,
The Atlantic Hotel ✸✸

Mont de la Pulente JE3 8HE
Map: 16
Tel: 01534 44101
Fax: 01534 44102
Chef: Ken Healy
Owners: Patrick Burke & family
Cost: Alc £32.50, fixed-price L £15/D £23.50 (4 course). ☺ H/wine £9.50.
Times: 12.45pm-last L 2.15pm/7.30pm-last D 9.30pm. Closed Jan-Feb
Additional: Sunday L; Children welcome; 🅓 dishes
Seats: 80. Private dining room 24
Smoking: No pipes or cigars
Accommodation: 50 en suite
Credit cards: 🔳 🔳 🔳 🔳 🔳 🔳 🔳 JCB

Get dressed up to enjoy fully this glamorous restaurant, which has a sense of occasion and lovely views to match. Culinary highlights include the freebie appetizers such as smoked duck and asparagus on biscuit base, and the first course of chicken liver parfait, properly smooth and served with excellent brioche and Cumberland sauce. Cheese, tomato and walnut and raisin are amongst the delicious flavours of home-made breads. For main courses, there's breast of duck with a confit of leg on blackcurrant sauce, a wild mushroom risotto, and roast pork fillet on a bed of puréed shallots with smoked bacon, griddled Parma ham and a port wine sauce. Excellence can be found in the hot banana soufflé, emerging proudly from the kitchen full of fruity flavour. The extensive wine list has a number of premier choices. Don't hesitate to drop in at lunchtime for one of the brilliant club sandwiches served on the terrace overlooking the pool.

Directions: From St Brelade take the road to Petit Port, turn into Rue de Sergente and R again, signed to hotel

ST BRELADE, **Hotel L'Horizon**

St Brelade's Bay JE3 8EF
Map: 16
Tel: 01534 43101
Fax: 01534 46269
Chef: Paul Wells
Owner: Arcadian Group
Cost: Alc £22, fixed-price L £15/D £24 (4 courses). ☺ H/wine £12
Times: 12.30-last L 2pm/7.30-last D 10pm
Additional: Bar food; Sunday L; No children under 12; ❸ dishes
Seats: 50. Jacket & tie preferred
Smoking: Air conditioning
Accommodation: 107 en suite
Credit cards:

For a beach-side position, L'Horizon is hard to beat, and the sea views are spectacular. There is a choice of restaurants, the Terrace, the Crystal Room and, for more serious eating, the Grill, which attains the two-rosette award. The quality of the seafood is very high, and Royal Jersey oysters figure among the starters alongside crab and salmon fishcake with blackened pineapple salsa. From the lunch menu, our inspector sampled chargrilled mackerel fillet with dill and fennel essence, served on tabbouleh. Dinner options include a choice of grills - Scotch fillet steak, locally caught Dover sole, and lamb cutlet - and perhaps an assiette of scallops, lobster and prawns with lime jalapeño pasta, dill and crab sauce.

Directions: Overlooking St Brelade's Bay

ST BRELADE, **Hotel la Place** ❀❀

The 17th-century former farmhouse enjoys a rural location, yet is within easy distance of the airport. Knights Restaurant may sport a medieval look but the cooking is bang up-to-date. An accurate, well-balanced foie gras and artichoke terrine with cherry salad opened our most recent meal, and was followed by a mélange of seafish (red mullet, sea bass, brill, scallops) with saffron linguine and a coriander and lemongrass nage, plus a fine macedoine of mixed peppers giving good colour contrast. Dark chocolate sponge with chocolate sauce and white chocolate ice cream made a fine finish. Canapés, bread and petits fours kept up with the standards set by the rest of the meal. The wine list is extensive, featuring France quite heavily, but with a small representation from other wine-growing regions.

Directions: Before St Aubin turn up La Haule Hill by La Haule Manor Hotel, then L at sign towards red houses, hotel 400yds on R

Route du Coin La Haule JE3 8BT
Map: 16
Tel: 01534 44261
Fax: 01534 45164
Chef: Tommy Illing
Owner: T L S Hotels
Cost: Alc £25. ☺ H/wine £10.75
Times: D only, last D 9.30pm
Additional: Bar food L; Sunday L (noon-2pm); Children welcome; ❸ dishes
Smoking: No-smoking area; No cigars & pipes
Accommodation: 42 en suite
Credit cards:

ST CLEMENT,
Green Island Restaurant ❀ NEW

There is an emphasis on fish and shellfish at this beachside restaurant, which has a distinct Mediterranean influence. Fresh local oysters, crab salad and a garlicky gazpacho were all just right for a

JE2 6LS
Map: 16
Tel: 01534 857787
Fax: 01534 866453
Chef: Sarah Moore

hot summer day. Other options included an aromatic nasi goreng, and squid sautéed with lemon and garlic.

Additional: Sunday L; Children welcome; 🍴 dishes
Credit cards: ■ ▨ ▧ ▨ ▨

Directions: *Telephone for directions*

Owner: Alan Winch
Cost: *Alc* £23, fixed price L £11.75.
☺ H/wine £8.50
Times: Last L 2.30pm/last D 9.30pm.
Closed D Sun, all Mon, 2 wks Nov,
2 wks Mar

ST HELIER,
Bistro Central ❀

Busy town centre restaurant with the feel of a French brasserie. The extensive menu offers 'plats du jours' and a range of traditional carte dishes. Richly flavoured duck confit, followed by a trio of fish - pan-fried brill, salmon and sea bass with a cream sauce, were inspection highlights.

Additional: Children welcome; 🍴 dishes
Smoking: Air conditioning
Credit cards: ■ ▨ ▧ ▨ ▨ ▨ ▨ JCB

Directions: *Just off pedestrian precinct*

7-11 Don Street JE2 4TQ
Map: 16
Tel: 01534 876933
Fax: 01534 80423
Chef: S Murray
Owner: Michel Thebault
Cost: *Alc* £25, fixed-price L £11.50
(2 courses)/D £19.50 (4 courses). ☺
H/wine £7.25
Times: Last L 2.15pm/last D 10.15pm.
Closed Sun, Bhs

ST HELIER,
The Grand Hotel ❀❀

The Esplanade JE4 8WD
Map: 16
Tel: 01534 22301
Fax: 01534 37815
Chef: Calum Watson
Owners: De Vere Hotels Ltd
Cost: *Alc* £25, fixed-price L £15.50/D
£22.75 (4 courses). H/wine £10.50
Times: 12.30-last L 2.15pm/7-last
D 10pm. Closed L Sat, D Sun
Additional: Sunday L;
Children welcome; 🍴 dishes
Seats: 140. Jacket & tie preferred
Smoking: No-smoking area;
Air conditioning
Accommodation: 115 en suite
Credit cards: ■ ▨ ▧ ▨ ▨ ▨

Prominently located on the sea front, this busy hotel overlooks St Aubin's Bay and Elizabeth Castle. Guests are welcomed by a dedicated and smartly turned-out team of staff, who ensure that a stay at The Grand is thoroughly enjoyed. Where better to enjoy the best of local cuisine than Victoria's, the hotel's elegant restaurant? The standard of cuisine continues to improve and, at a recent meal, our inspector enjoyed roulade of guinea fowl stuffed with veal sweetmeats and pistachio. The real highlight of the meal was, however, the starter of succulent langoustine and lobster ravioli, served with wild mushroom and tarragon broth, which made good use of the fresh catch. On Fridays and Saturdays a live band plays swing and jazz: guests who feel the need to burn off a few calories can dance the night away - given sufficient courage - on the small dance floor.

Directions: On outskirts of town, overlooking Victoria Park

ST HELIER, **Pomme d'Or Hotel**

Liberation Square JE2 3NF
Map: 16
Tel: 01534 880110
Fax: 01534 37781
Chef: Steve Le Corre
Owner: Seymour Hotels
Cost: Alc £23, fixed-price L £14.50/D £16.50 (5 courses). ☺ H/wine £6.50.
Times: 12.30pm-last L 2pm/7pm-last D 10pm.
Additional: Sunday L; Children welcome; ◑ dishes
Seats: 45. Private dining rooms 200
Smoking: Air conditioning
Accommodation: 147 en suite
Credit cards: ▨ ▨ ▨ ▨ ▨ ▨ ▨

La Petite Pomme, one of three dining areas in this well-known city centre hotel, aspires to a style of elegant dining befitting the island's financial status, as well as its rather time-warped atmosphere. The cooking is generally of a good standard, if rather conventional, with the *carte* featuring the likes of flambés, supreme de canard, and medaillons de veau. But lapses in the kitchen were evident at our most recent inspection: avocado came with mussels, crab and prawns but not the advertised tomato and fennel dressing, sea bass showed no hint of promised ginger, nor was the salmon with red onion and new potato confit glazed with lemon mousseline sauce as billed. There were no complaints however, about the subsequent dessert of coffee and praline parfait with warm compote of fresh peaches.

Directions: Opposite Harbour and Marina

ST SAVIOUR,
Longueville Manor

JE2 7WF
Map: 16
Tel: 01534 25501
Fax: 01534 31613
Chef: Andrew Baird
Owners: Malcom Lewis & Sue Dufty
Cost: Alc £45, fixed-price L £20/D £35 (4 courses). H/wine £9
Times: 12.30-last L 2pm/7.30-last D 9.30pm

With parts of this prestigious estate dating back to the 13th century, Longueville Manor is not short of character or history. The building is surrounded by fifteen acres of grounds, and a stream trickles down the hillside into the hotel's lake, home to black swans and mandarin ducks. The twin dining rooms (one is reserved for non-smokers) feature ancient, heavily carved oak-panelling and provide an appropriately refined setting for the fine modern English cooking of chef Andrew Baird. At a recent inspection, harmonious combinations of first-class ingredients were apparent in sophisticated dishes such as a smooth mosaic terrine of foie gras parfait and maize-fed poussin, served with glazed apple and toasted brioche, and grilled calves' liver with creamed potatoes, quenelle of onion marmalade and wafer-thin Parma ham. Other dishes from the well-balanced menus could include grilled supreme of sea bass on a ragout of local shellfish, pot-roasted saddle of rabbit with ravioli, leek and ham, and braised shoulder and rump of lamb with tomato, thyme and barley. The extensive wine list leans predominantly towards France, but with very little under £30. Guests with more limited budgets are catered for however, with over forty half-bottles and a number of cheaper vintages from elsewhere in Europe and the New World.

Signature dishes: Pot-au-feu of local shellfish with langoustine tortellini; grilled supreme of turbot on an aromatic herb noodle salad; oven-roast Gressingham duck with glazed pears and cranberries

Directions: From St Helier take A3 to Gorey, hotel 0.75 mile on left

Additional: Bar food; Sunday L; Children welcome; dishes
Seats: 70. Private dining rooms 16, 21
Smoking: No-smoking area; Air conditioning
Accommodation: 32 en suite
Credit cards: ▧ ▨ ▤ ▥ ▦ ▧ ▨

SARK

SARK, **La Sablonnerie** ✿✿

GY9 0SD
Map: 16
Tel: 01481 832061
Fax: 01481 832408
Chef: Colin Day
Owner: Miss Elizabeth Perrée
Cost: *Alc* £19.80, fixed-price L £24.50/D £26.50 (both 5 courses). ☺ H/wine £6.80
Times: Noon-2.30pm/7-9.30pm. Closed mid Oct-Easter
Additional: Bar food; Sunday L; Children welcome;  dishes
Seats: 39. Private room 12
Smoking: No-smoking area; No pipes & cigars
Accommodation: 22 rooms
Credit cards: ▧ ▨ ▤

A charming 16th-century converted farmhouse reached by a narrow isthmus, La Sablonnerie is surrounded by secluded gardens and commands spectacular sea views. Enjoy a pre-dinner drink in the smart bar, where in the winter months a roaring log fire keeps guests warm. Modern dishes with a French base are served in the restaurant, a reasonably sized room with white-washed walls and dark wood tables. The chef, Colin Day, has now been here for over four years, and his consistent cooking continues to impress. Our inspector tried terrine of rabbit and veal with a red onion confit, a well-executed dish with clear flavours. This was followed by escalope of salmon with pickled ginger beurre blanc; other dishes could include pan-fried beef fillet with venison liver parfait; grilled Sark lobster with garlic butter; and breast of maize-fed chicken with blue cheese mousse.

Directions: On southern part of island

SCOTLAND
ABERDEEN CITY

ABERDEEN, Ardoe Hotel

An impressive baronial mansion providing good food in the wood-panelled restaurant. In the evening, there is a choice between the *carte* and a set five-course 'Gourmet Dinner'. Prime Scottish produce is very much a feature in dishes such as roulade of salmon and scallop with a chive risotto, braised shank of Scottish lamb with braised Savoy cabbage, and rack of Highland venison with beetroot mousse. A choice of grills features quality Aberdeen Angus Cross from the finest grass-fed herds. Vegetarian dishes are also listed, including the likes of artichoke and asparagus ravioli in a white wine, saffron and chive sauce. The wine list offers an extensive range of good vintages from all over the world, a fitting complement to a varied menu.

Directions: 3 miles from Aberdeen on B9077, on left-hand side

Blairs South Deeside Road
AB1 5YP
Map 15: NJ90
Tel: 01224 867355
Fax: 01224 861283
Chef: Ivor Clark
Cost: *Alc* £32. H/wine £14.50
Times: 12.30-last L 2pm/6.30-last D 9.45pm. Closed L Sat
Additional: Bar food; Sunday L; Children welcome; ✪ dishes
Seats: 60. Private dining room 200. Jacket & tie preferred
Smoking: No smoking in dining room
Accommodation: 71 en suite
Credit cards: ▬ ▆ ▆ ▆ ▆

ABERDEEN,
Copthorne Aberdeen

Smart, comfortable hotel restaurant serving a light and interesting menu. A test dinner produced an excellent caramelised red onion tart with pesto and tapenade, seared fillet of turbot on a confit of caramelised shallots and dill butter sauce, and baked plum and raspberry tartlet served with a mango coulis.

Additional: Bar food L&D; Children welcome; ✪ dishes
Smoking: No-smoking area
Accommodation: 89 en suite
Credit cards: ▬ ▆ ▆ ▆ ▆

Directions: *Telephone for directions*

122 Huntly Street AB10 1SU
Map 15: NJ90
Tel: 01224 630404
Fax: 01224 640573
Chef: Mark Bannerman
Owner: The Copthorne Aberdeen
Cost: *Alc* £25, fixed-price L £9.95/D £17.95. ☺ H/wine £10.50
Times: Last L 2pm/last D 10pm. Closed L Sat, L Sun

ABERDEEN, Maryculter House ✿

Set on the riverbank of the Dee, part of this charming hotel dates back to the 13th-century when it was a priory for the Knights Templar. These days guests can feast in the stone-walled Priory restaurant where typical dishes might include chargrilled tuna steak with paprika butter, and grilled breast of duckling.

Additional: Bar food; Sunday L; Children welcome; ✪ dishes
Smoking: No smoking in dining room
Accommodation: 23 en suite
Credit cards: ▬ ▆ ▆ ▆ ▆

Directions: 8 miles west of Aberdeen off A93 or B9077

South Deeside Road AB1 6BB
Map 15: NJ90
Tel: 01224 732124
Fax: 01224 733510
Chef: Alfie Murray
Owner: Templar Hotels
Cost: Fixed-price D £29.50 (4 courses)
Times: Last L 2pm/last D 9pm. Closed D Sun

ABERDEEN, Norwood Hall

A Victorian mansion set in wooded grounds and retaining many original features, especially stained glass windows and ornate

Garthdee Road Cults AB15 9FX
Map 15: NJ90
Tel: 01224 868951
Fax: 01224 869868

fireplaces. Traditional Scottish dishes in the elegant Ogston Restaurant, where dishes to look out for include pot roasted halibut and creamy potato mash, and fillet of Aberdeen Angus beef with pepper sauce.

Smoking: No smoking in dining room
Accommodation: 21 en suite
Credit cards: ▬ ▩ ₹ ⌂ ▩ ▣

Directions: *Telephone for directions*

Chef: Craig Park
Cost: Fixed-price D £21.50. ☺
H/wine £11.50
Times: Last L 2pm/last D 9.30pm
Additional: Bar food; Sunday L;
Children welcome; ❹ dishes

ABERDEEN, Patio Hotel ❀

Beach Boulevard AB24 5EF
Map 15: NJ90
Tel: 01224 633339
Fax: 01224 638833
Chef: Ian Green
Cost: *Alc* £30. ☺ H/wine £10.95
Times: D only, last D 10.30pm.
Closed Sun, Mon
Additional: Children welcome;
❹ dishes
Smoking: No-smoking area;
Air conditioning
Accommodation: 124 en suite
Credit cards: ▬ ▩ ₹ ⌂ ▩ ▣ ▣ JCB

Cosy hotel restaurant, contemporary in style, with candles and fresh orchids on each table every night, as well as Italian furnishings and accessories. Seafood is a speciality of the French carte, with dishes such as crevettes géantes a l'Indienne, bouillabaisse, and locally smoked haddock, alongside pork forestière and Chateaubriand.

Directions: From Union St turn onto King St; at 1st traffic lights turn R onto East North St; at next roundabout about 2nd exit. Hotel on L

ABERDEEN, Q Brasserie ❀❀

9 Alford Place
AB1 1YD
Map 15: NJ90
Tel: 01224 595001
Fax: 01224 582245
Chef: David McCallum
Owner: Stuart Clarkson
Cost: *Alc* £25. ☺ H/wine £10.95

That the building was once a Church of Scotland training establishment explains the lofty chapel-like setting (the bar is in the former altar area) of this popular restaurant. The contemporary menu is as appealing as the setting, with starters like flash-roasted sea scallops with tomato and basil

vinaigrette, open ravioli of wild mushrooms and artichokes with watercress sauce, and langoustine bisque with haricot blanc and langoustine tortelloni. Mains range from roast guinea fowl on a shallot soubise with truffled red wine sauce and roast fillet of baby turbot with crisp herb polenta and an orange and tomato fondue, to pot roast belly of pork cooked with soy sauce and citrus fruit served on a bed of bok choi. On our last visit we enjoyed a 'wicked' chocolate tart from a dessert list that also included toasted coconut marshmallow with a pot-pourri of fruit and passion fruit sauce.

Times: Noon-last L 2pm/7-last D 10.45pm. Closed L Sat, all Sun
Additional: Bar food L; Children welcome; ✪ dishes
Seats: 120. Private dining room 15
Credit cards: ▬ ▬ ▢ ▦ ▣

Directions: Top of Union Street at Holborn Junction

ABERDEEN,

Simpson's Hotel ✤

NEW

59 Queens Road AB15 4YP
Map 15: NJ90
Tel: 01224 327777
Fax: 01224 327700
Chef: Paul Whitecross
Owner: Four Pak Ltd
Cost: *Alc* £21.50. ☺ H/wine £9.75
Times: Last L 1.45pm/last D 9.45pm
Additional: Children welcome; ✪ dishes
Smoking: No-smoking area; Air conditioning
Accommodation: 37 en suite
Credit cards: ▬ ▬ ▨ ▢ ▦

A stunning hotel brasserie, where Moroccan columns support a colonnade of arches, and at the foot of the sweeping staircase a fountain tumbles before palms and exotic flowers. Mediterranean-style dishes include seared scallops, black pudding and garlic, and sea bass with sweet potato and bouquet asparagus.

Directions: *Please telephone for directions*

ABERDEENSHIRE

ABOYNE,

White Cottage Restaurant ✤✤

Once two estate workers' cottages, this granite-walled building looks like a gingerbread house from the outside. The restaurant is one long room, pine-floored, panelled walls painted white, with a fire at each end and a central spiral staircase from an old Glasgow tram. Those who eat in the conservatory can watch the ducks on the small pond. Typical of the daily changing hand-written menu is a starter of 'light and enjoyable' crab cake rösti with gazpacho sauce, then steamed halibut on a bed of spinach with a tangy lemon butter sauce, and a pudding of lemon tart, of good texture and flavour, presented with slices of sweet strawberries to provide contrast.

AB34 5BP
Map 15: NO59
Tel/Fax: 013398 86265
Chef: Laurie Mill
Owners: Laurie & Josephine Mill
Cost: *Alc* £19.55, fixed price D £28.50 (4 courses). H/wine £12
Times: 11.30am-last L 2.45pm/7-last D 9pm. Closed Sun, Mon (please phone for holiday closures)
Additional: Bar food; ✪ dishes
Seats: 36. Prtivate dining room 24
Credit cards: ▬ ▬ ▢

Directions: On A93 between Aboyne and Kincardine O'Neil

BALLATER,
Balgonie House Hotel 🏵🏵

There's a friendly and relaxed atmosphere at Balgonie House, built in Edwardian times and set in its own substantial grounds. Canapés, including perhaps gravad lax on toast, are offered in the bar before the set four-course dinner, with three choices at each stage except the second: this is normally something fishy, like pan-fried sea bass on green beans, or salmon and cod fishcake. Before this there might be a soup – pungent tomato, or green pea – or melon with Cumbrian ham. Main courses have included confit of duck, the meat falling off the bone, on garlic potatoes, fillet of halibut under a herb crust with sun-dried tomato risotto and sauce vierge, and medallions of Aberdeen Angus with onion marmalade and a thyme jus. An inspector finished a meal with 'very rich and much enjoyed' crêpes Suzette. Bread is considered excellent and cheeses are Scottish.

Directions: On outskirts of Ballater, signposted off A93 (Ballater-Perth)

Braemar Place AB35 5NQ
Map 15: NO39
Tel/Fax: 013397 55482
Chef: John Finnie
Owners: John & Priscilla Finnie
Cost: Fixed-price L £17/D £29
(4 courses). H/wine £14.50
Times: 12.30-last L 2pm (by
reservation only)/7-last D 9pm.
Closed Jan-mid Feb
Additional: Sunday L;
No children under 5; 🥄 dishes
Seats: 30
Smoking: No smoking in dining room
Accommodation: 9 en suite
Credit cards: ■ ▒ ▄ ▐ ▓ JCB

BALLATER,
Darroch Learg Hotel 🏵🏵🏵

This pink and grey granite mansion overlooking the Dee has been in the capable hands of the Franks family for nearly 40 years. The conservatory dining room, its colour scheme blue and beige, with white napery and silver cutlery, provides the backdrop, with views to the fore, for set dinners that may or may not offer some choice, depending on availability. The kitchen's industry is apparent in the breads – granary with fruit, or five-spice, for instance – and a starter of home-smoked salmon with blinis and a poached egg. Other starters could range from rich and creamy chicken liver parfait with Cumberland sauce to tomato soup. Fillet of Aberdeen Angus with a hat of artichoke and foie gras, plus some fried shallots, on a bed of braised lettuce makes a good main course, the meat of excellent flavour. Breast of Gressingham duck with black pudding and pommes lyonnaise, or chicken supreme with tarragon sauce could also be on offer. A simple, classic lemon tart, its pastry thin and buttery, with raspberry coulis makes an impressive finale, while those of more robust appetites might prefer sticky toffee pudding with rum and raisin ice cream. The wine list is a gem, its annotations giving histories and backgrounds to the wines described as well as tasting notes, and includes some top-notch producers and vintages at decent prices. What's more, eight house wines are sold by the glass.
   Signature dishes: Terrine of home-smoked salmon with a confit of tomatoes and anchovy butter; 'tiare' of salmon with artichokes and truffle; warm chocolate fondant with lemon sorbet and chocolate sauce.

Directions: On A93 at the W end of village

Braemar Road AB35 5UX
Map 15: NO39
Tel: 013397 55443
Fax: 013397 55252
Chef: David Mutter
Owners: The Franks Family
Cost: Fixed-price D £29.50
Times: 12.30-last L 2pm/7-last
D 9pm. Closed Xmas, 3 wks Jan
Additional: Bar food L; Sunday L;
Children welcome
Seats: 48
Smoking: No smoking in dining room
Accommodation: 18 en suite
Credit cards: ■ ▒ ▐ ▓ ▨ JCB

BALLATER, # Glen Lui Hotel 🏵

A small hotel overlooking the golf course towards the mountain of Lochnagar. Formal meals are served at both lunch and dinner in one or two of the dining rooms, and offer modern Scottish cooking.

Invercauld Road AB35 5RP
Map 15: NO39
Tel: 013397 55402
Fax: 013397 55545
Chefs: Jan Tomlin, Cameron Kelly

Dishes sampled include chicken liver parfait, and freshly landed turbot with asparagus and dill sauce.

Smoking: No smoking in dining room
Accommodation: 19 en suite
Credit cards: ▉ ▆ ▆ ▆ ▆

Directions: *Please telephone for directions*

Owners: Serge & Lorraine Geraud
Cost: Alc £18, fixed-price L £8.50
(2 courses)/D £18. ☺ H/wine £9.20
Times: Last L 2pm/last D 9pm.
Closed Feb
Additional: Sunday L;
Children welcome; ✿ dishes

BALLATER, **Green Inn** ✤✤

9 Victoria Road AB35 5QQ
Map 15: NO39
Tel/Fax: 013397 55701
Chef: J J Purves
Owners: Mr & Mrs J J Purves
Cost: Alc £26.75, fixed-price D £25.
H/wine £10.45
Times: D only, 7-last D 9pm.
Closed 2 wks Oct
Additional: Sunday L (12.30-1.45pm);
Children welcome; ✿ dishes
Seats: 32
Smoking: No smoking in dining room;
Air conditioning
Accommodation: 3 en suite.
Credit cards: ▉ ▆ ▆

The Green Inn at Ballater, an unpretentious restaurant-with-rooms by the village green, continues to go from strength to strength. The innovative menu impresses with a great selection of modern Scottish dishes with cosmopolitan flavours. The highlight of a summer meal was the starter – a twice-baked cheese soufflé presented on a thin oatcake with a salad laced with dried apricots. Also excellent was a main course of pan-fried salmon, trout and sea bass atop scallop potatoes and fresh spinach, served with a rich langoustine sauce. Other main courses could include roasted duck breast with Japanese noodles and a rhubarb and ginger sauce, grilled breast of free-range chicken with pesto, and roast rump of Scotch beef with Yorkshire pudding. Sweets include iced Cranachan mousse with local berries and whisky syrup, and chocolate terrine with hot prunes. The wine list is extensive and very carefully chosen with good representation from around the world

Directions: On A93 in centre of Ballater on the Green

BANCHORY,

Raemoir House Hotel ✤

An elegant Georgian dining room in a fine country mansion provides the setting for modern Scottish cooking from a choice of menus. Enjoyable dishes include seafood crêpe filled with lobster, scampi, scallops and prawns, followed by a melt-in-the-mouth Dover sole, and a wicked chocolate and rum mousse.

Accommodation: 25 en suite
Credit cards: ▉ ▆ ▆

Directions: A93 to Banchory then A980, hotel at crossroads in 2.5 miles

AB31 4ED
Map 15: NO69
Tel: 01330 824884
Fax: 01330 822171
Chef: David Kinnes
Owners: Roy & Lesley Bishop-Milnes
Cost: Fixed-price D £27.50 (4 courses). H/wine £12
Times: Last L 2pm/last D 9.30pm
Additional: Bar food; Sunday L;
Children welcome; ✿ dishes
Smoking: No smoking in dining room

BRIDGE OF MARNOCH,
The Old Manse of Marnoch

By Huntly AB54 7RS
Map 15: NJ55
Tel/Fax: 01466 780873
Chef: Keren Carter
Owners: Patrick & Keren Carter
Cost: Fixed-price D £27 (4 courses).
H/wine £9
Times: D only, 7.30-last D 8.30pm.
Closed 2 wks Nov
Additional: No children under 12;
dishes
Seats: 25. Jacket & tie preferred
Smoking: No smoking in dining room
Accommodation: 9 en suite
Credit cards: ▦ ▦ ▦ ▦ JCB

Standing on the bank of a river and set in mature gardens, this
200-year-old granite building has, as the proprietors describe it,
'a distinct churchy history'. Within, a relaxed atmosphere
prevails, with an inviting lounge full of mementoes of the
owners' travels. The dining room, with its vaguely nautical
theme, is the setting for a four-course dinner followed by coffee
with shortbread and mints. A no-choice soup starts things off:
richly flavoured mushroom one day, leek and potato another.
Two options are offered at the next three courses. There could
be asparagus with red pepper mayonnaise or home-cured
gravad lax, with main courses of duckling with a well-matched
sauce of kumquat and vermouth, or spicy chicken breast with
raita. Vegetables are described as 'excellent', and raspberry and
apple pie 'delightful'. Helpful, interesting tasting notes make
the wine list particularly user-friendly. Not surprisingly, there's a
good choice of malt whiskies.

Directions: On B9117 just off A97 Huntly/Banff road

INVERURIE, **Thainstone House**

AB51 5NT
Map 15: NJ72
Tel: 01467 621643
Fax: 01467 625084
Chef: Allan Donald
Owner: Macdonald Hotels
Cost: Alc £32, fixed-price L £16/£30
(4 courses). H/wine £14
Times: Noon-last L 1.45pm/7pm-last
D 9.30pm.
Additional: Bar food; Sunday L;
Children welcome; dishes.
Seats: 60. Private dining room 40
Smoking: No smoking in dining room;
Air conditioning
Accommodation: 48 en suite
Credit cards: ▦ ▦ ▦ ▦ ▦ ▦ ▦ JCB

Set amid 40 acres of parkland, the present Georgian-style
mansion was built in the 19th century to replace an earlier
building that was destroyed by fire. The elegant restaurant is in
keeping with the palatial style of the building. There's a short
fixed-price menu, but it is with the carte that the kitchen really

Directions: 2 miles from Inverurie on
the A96 Aberdeen road

gets into gear with innovative dishes reflecting modern culinary trends. Cappuccino of smoked haddock, terrine of lamb and niçoise vegetables with tomato and basil pesto, confit of duck leg with a ragout of beans, caramelised orange and a balsamic dressing, Scottish salmon and lobster with gingered vegetables and a crayfish and coriander sauce, and guinea fowl with apricots, pistachios, crispy bacon and thyme gravy, show the style. Out last test meal began with a delicious little appetiser of battered black pudding with a sweet fruit chutney and ended with a 'wicked' dark chocolate marquise.

KILDRUMMY, **Kildrummy Castle** ✿

AB33 8RA
Map 15: NJ41
Tel: 019755 71288
Fax: 019755 71345
Chef: Kenneth Whyte
Owners: Thomas and Mary Hanna
Cost: *Alc* £31, fixed price L £16/D £29 (4 courses). ☺ H/wine £12
Times: Last L 1.45pm/last D 9pm. Closed Jan
Additional: Sunday L; Children welcome; 🍴 dishes
Smoking: No smoking in dining room
Accommodation: 16 en suite
Credit cards: 💳 💳 💳 💳 💳 💳 JCB

Fresh local produce, game from nearby estates, fish and shellfish from the North Sea and Moray Firth all feature on the menu at this fine country house hotel. Roast saddle of hare is cooked with lightly spiced apple and dried fruit, Angus beef comes with a classic Drambuie and Haggis sauce.

Directions: Off A97 Huntly/Ballater Road 35 miles W of Aberdeen

NEWBURGH,
Udny Arms Hotel ✿

Main Street Ellon AB41 6BL
Map 15: NJ92
Tel: 01358 789444
Chef: Marcus Tullett
Owners: Denis & Jennifer Craig
Cost: *Alc* £20, fixed-price L £12. ☺ H/wine £12.95
Times: Last L 2.30pm/last D 9.45pm
Additional: Bar food; Sunday L; Children welcome; 🍴 dishes.
Smoking: No smoking in dining room
Accommodation: 26 en suite
Credit cards: 💳 💳 💳 💳 💳 💳 JCB

Directions: Village centre – A92 Aberdeen/Peterhead, turn right to Newburgh.

Family-run hotel with informal, split-level restaurant. Choose the upper level for views over the golf course to the Ythan Estuary; sit anywhere for carefully prepared dishes based on quality ingredients. Orkney oysters with spicy dip, blackened Shetland salmon with coriander salsa, and chargrilled steaks from locally produced Angus cross beef show the range.

PETERHEAD,
Waterside Inn ✵

Ogilvie's is a spacious, modern, split-level restaurant overlooking a golf course. Menus have recently begun to exhibit genuine flair, and our inspectors have enjoyed crab and prawn bisque, monkfish with saffron and herb beurre blanc and cinnamon-flavoured bread-and-butter pudding. The extensive wine list boasts a good selection of half-bottles.

Additional: Bar food; Sunday L; Children welcome; dishes
Smoking: No smoking in dining room
Accommodation: 109 en suite
Credit cards: ▉ ▉ ▉ ▉ ▉ ▉

Directions: Follow A90 (A952) to roundabout on outskirts of Peterhead; turn L for Fraserburgh

Fraserburgh Road AB42 3BN
Map 15: NK14
Tel: 01779 471121
Fax: 01779 470670
Chef: Robert Horne
Cost: *Alc* £30, fixed-price L £15.50/D £19. H/wine £12.50
Times: Last L 2pm/last D 9.45pm

ANGUS

AUCHTERHOUSE,
Old Mansion House Hotel ✵   NEW

Don't let the grey ghost put you off a meal here! Splendid baronial-style hotel offering unusual but successful items on the menu. Try black pudding with baked beans and mousseline potato, Thai vegetable soup, venison loin with cafe-au-lait sauce, and salmon with vanilla jus. Interesting Swiss wines.

DD3 0QN
Map 11: NO33
Tel: 01382 320366
Fax: 01382 320400
Please telephone for further details

BRIDGEND OF LINRATHEN,
Lochside Lodge ✵✵   NEW

Set in the midst of the Angus glens, this converted farmstead is now home to a superb country restaurant owned and run by husband-and-wife team Stephen and Jackie Robertson. The restaurant itself is situated in the old round house and has superb views through tall windows to the woodland beyond. Stephen uses quality local ingredients to create a short carte of modern Scottish dishes. A recent meal started with a warm flan of sea trout with spinach and Parmesan, served with a sour cream and chive sauce. Main courses such as seared rump steak with pickled walnut and redcurrant sauce, and breast of chicken served with mushroom, pasta and peppercorn cream, competed for our inspector's attention, who opted instead for lambs' livers with sautéed potato and onions topped with crispy bacon. To finish, a wonderful down-to-earth bread-and-butter pudding with a sweet butterscotch sauce.

Directions: From Kirriemuir take B591 Glenisla Rd for 6 miles. Turn L at Lintrathen sign

By Kirriemuir DD8 5JJ
Map 15: NO25
Tel: 01575 560340
Fax: 01575 560202
Chef: Stephen Robertson
Owners: Stephen & Jackie Robertson
Cost: *Alc* L £14/D £23. ☺ H/wine £9.50
Times: Noon-last L 1.45pm/6-last D 9pm. Closed Mon
Additional: No children under 12; dishes
Seats: 36
Smoking: No smoking in dining room
Accommodation: 2 rooms
Credit cards: ▉ ▉ ▉ ▉

CARNOUSTIE,

11 Park Avenue ✤

An unpretentious restaurant tucked away down a side street in the centre of town. The cooking is modern – expect starters along the lines of roast red pepper and goats' cheese salad, and chargrilled tuna with guacamole and lime dressing. The restaurant has a Mediterranean feel, with stencils of orange trees and vines on the walls.

Additional: Bar food L; No children under 10; ● dishes
Smoking: No smoking in dining room
Credit cards: ▆▆▆ ⬜ ▆▆ 🟦 JCB

Directions: From Dundee take A92 N (Arbroath). At 10-12 miles turn R to Carnoustie; at crossroads L, then R at mini-roundabout. Restaurant on L

11 Park Avenue
DD7 7JA
Map 12: NO53
Tel/Fax: 01241 853336
Chef/Owner: Stephen Collinson
Cost: *Alc* L £23, fixed-price L £10 (2 courses). ☺ H/wine £9.25
Times: L by arrangement/last D 10pm. Closed L Sat, all Sun, L Mon (all Mon Sept-March), 1st wk Jan

GLAMIS,

Castleton House Hotel ✤

A distinctive country house hotel complete with a 700 year old moat. A typical spring meal from the imaginative carte could begin with smoked chicken broth and bacon dumplings, followed by pan-fried fillet of pork with roast shallots and basil tagliatelle. For dessert try the chocolate and walnut cheesecake.

Additional: Bar food; Sunday L; Children welcome
Accommodation: 6 en suite
Credit cards: ▆▆ ▆▆ 🔾 ⬜

Directions: 3 miles W of Glamis on A94, between Forfar and Coupar

Forfar DD8 1SJ
Map 15: NO34
Tel: 01307 840340
Fax: 01307 840506
Chef: Raymond Millar
Owners: Anthony & Sheila Lilly
Cost: *Alc:* £17, fixed price L £7.95. ☺ H/wine £9.75
Times: Last L 2pm/last D 9.30pm

INVERKEILOR,

Gordon's Restaurant ✤✤

A new interior seems to have reinvigorated the cooking at this unpretentious little family restaurant serving modern Scottish food. Stained-glass windows, an open fire, beamed ceiling and sandstone walls set the scene for a good dinner that might kick off with a shortcrust pastry case filled with mussels, langoustine and scallops, creamed leeks and smoked bacon, topped with a mild Scottish farmhouse cheddar served with crayfish sauce. To follow, pan-fried supreme of chicken stuffed with haggis, flamed in whisky and served with a Drambuie sauce. Any room left after that can be filled with the likes of lemon and ginger pudding with vanilla sauce, or wicked dark chocolate mousse laced with Cognac and served with strawberry coulis and a Polish pastry biscuit. Or else, there's Scottish farmhouse cheese with fruit, celery and biscuits.

Directions: Just off the A92 from Arbroath to Montrose, at N end of main street.

Main Street By Arbroath
DD11 5RN
Map 15: NO64
Tel: 01241 830364
Chef: Gordon Watson
Owners: Gordon & Maria Watson
Cost: *Alc* £26, fixed-price L £15/D £26. ☺ H/wine £9.80
Times: Noon-last L 2pm/7pm-last D 9pm. Closed L Sat, Mon, 1st 2 wks Jan
Additional: Sunday L; Children welcome; ● dishes
Seats: 30.
Smoking: No pipes & cigars
Accommodation: 2 en suite.
Credit cards: ▆▆ ▆▆ 🔾

ARGYLL & BUTE

ARDBEG,

Ardmory House Hotel ✿

There are views over the bay and Firth of Clyde at this newly redecorated hotel restaurant. There's a good value fixed-price four-course menu and a carte. Seafood is a feature, and local squat lobster and lamb, followed by bread-and-butter pudding, were enjoyed at a test meal.

Additional: Bar food; Sunday L; ✪ dishes
Smoking: No smoking in dining room
Accommodation: 5 en suite
Credit cards: 💳 💳 💳 💳 💳 💳 JCB

Directions: N from Rothesay on A844. 1m turn L up Ardmory road. 300 metres on left

Ardmory Road Isle of Bute
PA20 0PG
Map 10: NS06
Tel: 01700 502346
Fax: 01700 505596
Chef: Edward McGarvey
Owners: D Cameron, B Jeffery
Cost: *Alc* £21.25, fixed-price
D £17.50 (4 courses). ☺ H/wine
£8.90.
Times: Last L 2pm/last D 9pm

ARDUAINE,

Loch Melfort Hotel ✿✿

Oban PA34 4XG
Map 10: NM71
Tel: 01852 200233
Fax: 01852 200214
Chef: Philip Lewis
Owners: Philip & Rosalind Lewis
Cost: Fixed-price D £30 (5 courses).
H/wine £12.50
Times: Noon-2.30pm/7.30-9pm.
Closed 5 Jan-15 Feb
Additional: Bar food;
Children welcome; ✪ dishes
Seats: 70. Private room 20
Smoking: No smoking in dining room
Accommodation: 26 en suite
Credit cards: 💳 💳 💳 💳

Small wonder that seafood is a speciality here: the Loch Melfort's enviable location beside the Arduaine Gardens includes panoramic views over the bay. Passing yacht-owners, discerning locals and hotel guests can appreciate the outstanding scenery through large windows in the light, airy restaurant. A five-course set menu might begin with freshly made soda bread and a lovely mussel soup, where plump bivalves are plopped into creamy, herby stock at the last moment. 'I could have happily eaten this for all of the meal!' enthused one inspector. Salmon and prawn fish cake with good tomato coulis, led on to a main course of tender breast of guinea fowl with Calvados sauce. A well-presented trolley of fresh desserts (including a fine bread-and-butter pud), plus well-cared-for cheeses (with some local specimens) and a thoughtful wine list (good house choices) – add to the appeal.

Directions: From Oban, 20 miles S on the A816; from Lochgilphead, 19 miles N on A816

BUNESSAN, ISLE OF MULL,

Assapol House

PA67 6DW
Map 10: NM32
Tel: 01681 700258
Fax: 01681 700445
Chef: Mrs O Robertson
Owners: Mr TA Robertson,
Mrs O Robertson
Cost: Fixed-price D £18 (4 courses).
☺ H/wine £8.50
Times: D at 7.45pm.
Additional: No children under 10
Smoking: No smoking in dining room
Accommodation: 5 en suite
Credit cards: 💳 💳 💳 💳

Super little hotel that appears to be going from strength to strength. A short dinner menu offers a choice of starters and desserts, with a fixed main. At inspection this translated as salad of smoked beef, venison, and duck, chicken wrapped in bacon with pesto sauce with fresh, simple vegetables, and spicy apple pie. Good Scottish cheeses too.

Directions: Turn off A849 just after Bunessan School and follow sign for 1m on minor road

CLACHAN-SEIL, ISLE OF SEIL,

Willowburn Hotel ❀❀

PA34 4TJ
Map 10: NM71
Tel: 01852 300276
Fax: 01852 300597
Chef: Chris Mitchell
Owners: Chris Mitchell, Jan Wolfe
Cost: Fixed-price D £22 (5 courses).
☺ H/wine £8.75
Times: Last L 2pm/D 8.30pm.
Closed Jan-Feb
Additional: Bar food; Children
welcome; 🍴 dishes
Smoking: No smoking in dining room
Accommodation: 7 en suite
Credit cards: 💳 💳 💳 💳

Directions: 11 miles S of Oban
via A816 and B844 (Easdale) over
Atlantic Bridge

It's all very pleasant and laid back (but quietly efficient) at this small cottage hotel on the water's edge, just south of Oban. Dishes are built around the freshest produce and cooked with passion. Home-baked brown wholemeal bread, plump mussels in wine and garlic sauce, lettuce and pea soup, and lobster (caught that afternoon) with lemon and saffron sauce, and a 'very authentic' cloutie dumpling, show something of the style. An early June dinner took in turbot and prawn en croûte with watercress sauce, spring vegetable soup with herbs, local Dover sole with herb-lobster butter, samphire and lemon, and lemon raspberry fantasy – lemon sorbet sandwiched between two firm wafers of bitter chocolate with fresh raspberries and frosted mint leaves. The wine list is short but house wines are chosen with care.

DERVAIG, ISLE OF MULL,
Druimard Hotel 🏵🏵

Druimard is a beautifully restored country house hotel with stunning views, and the set, five-course dinners are taken in the elegant restaurant. The Scottish island cuisine served here is of a high standard and the creative cooking is based on fine local ingredients – lobsters, crab, monkfish and wild red venison. A sample meal might start with various home-made breads, mille-feuille of local crab served on a bed of oak-smoked salmon, followed by parsnip, ginger and lemon soup or melon sorbet, then pan-fried saddle of hare on a bed of cabbage and smoked bacon with a game sauce. There's a choice of three desserts, but sticky gingerbread pudding served warm with ginger wine and brandy sauce and ice cream is particularly good. Round things off with local and Scottish cheeses, and cafetière coffee with petits fours.

Directions: From the Craignure ferry turn R to Tobermory. Go through Salen, turn L at Aros, signposted Dervaig, hotel on right-hand side before village

PA75 6QW
Map 13: NM45
Tel: 01688 400345/400291
Fax: 01688 400345
Chef: Wendy Hubbard
Owners: Haydn & Wendy Hubbard
Cost: Fixed priced D £23.50 (5 courses). ☺ H/wine £8.95
Times: D only, 6.30-last D 8.30pm. Closed Nov-Mar
Additional: Bar food L (residents only); Children welcome; 🍴 dishes
Seats: 20
Smoking: No smoking in dining room
Accommodation: 6 en suite
Credit cards: �▬ ▬ ▬

DUNOON, Chatters 🏵

Converted small cottage providing an informal atmosphere, good home-baked cakes with morning coffee and afternoon tea, and serious lunch and dinner menus. Our most recent visit yielded warm salad of king scallops and prawns with fresh samphire, well-hung venison with port and green peppercorn sauce, and tangy lemon tart with crème anglaise.

Smoking: No-smoking area
Credit cards: ▬ ▬

Directions: *Telephone for directions*

58 John Street PA23 8BJ
Map 10: NS17
Tel/Fax: 01368 706402
Chef: John Fortune
Owner: Rosmary MacInnes
Cost: Alc £23, fixed-price L £7.95. H/wine £9.95
Times: Last L 2.30pm/last D 9pm. Closed Sun, mid Jan-mid Mar
Additional: Children welcome; 🍴 dishes

DUNOON, Enmore Hotel 🏵

Lovingly restored Georgian summer residence with restaurant offering a four-course modern Scottish table d'hôte menu supplemented by a list of old favourites. Innovative dishes include pheasant wrapped in Savoy cabbage with game charlotte, and venison fillets with spiced fruit sauce. There's fine local cheeses, good coffee and petits fours too.

Smoking: No smoking in dining room
Accommodation: 10 en suite
Credit cards: ▬ ▬ ▬ ▬ ▬

Directions: From Glasgow M8/A8 (Greenock) & ferry, or via Loch Lomond, A815 to Dunoon. Hotel on promenade btw 2 ferry terminals, 1 mile N of Dunoon

Marine Parade Kirn
PA23 8HH
Map 10: NS17
Tel: 01369 702230
Fax: 01369 702148
Chef: David Wilson
Owners: David & Angela Wilson
Cost: Alc £25, fixed-price D £23 (4 courses). ☺ H/wine £12.50
Times: D only, last D 9pm. Closed Mon-Thu
Additional: Bar food D; Children welcome; 🍴 dishes

ERISKA, Isle of Eriska 🏵🏵🏵

About as exclusive as a venue can get, given that it is on a private island, the many regular visitors feel as though they have come home when staying at this unpretentious hotel. The building is an imposing baronial mansion, the grounds akin to

Ledaig by Oban PA37 1SD
Map 10: NM94
Tel: 01631 720371
Fax: 01631 720531
Chef: Robert MacPherson
Owners: The Buchanan-Smith Family

a nature reserve, and the restaurant harvests many of its ingredients from the island, including wild garlic and a variety of mushrooms. The traditional dining room is kitted-out with polished tables, ringed napkins, loads of silverware and a flamboyant trolley from which the daily roast is served. There is also a concise menu featuring just two or three choices per course, which concentrates on contemporary Scottish and French dishes. The cooking is good. Canapés included foie gras on toast, chopped pig's trotter in pastry and smoked salmon roulade. This was followed by braised leg of Gressingham duck served with celeriac and potato mash, then a subtle wild garlic and watercress soup, featuring ingredients picked from the owner's garden. Plump local scallops came seared and served with risotto and crispy seaweed; sea grass asparagus, baby carrots and a bisque-style sauce garnished it admirably. The cheeseboard showed a good selection of Scottish and Irish cheeses plus a creamy Stilton. There was a large chocolate soufflé for dessert, served with an excellent light vanilla sauce, then a savoury of Whitley Goose, which involved no bird just chopped onion and apple with cheese on toast. The wine list offers tremendous value, though we are reluctant to mention it in case they raise the amazing prices!

Cost: Fixed-price D £37.50 (6 courses). H/wine £9.20
Times: D only, 8-last D 9pm. Closed Jan
Additional: Bar food L (residents only); ❹ dishes
Seats: 40. Jacket & tie preferred
Smoking: No smoking in dining room
Accommodation: 17 en suite
Credit cards: ■ ■ ▪ ■ ■ JCB

Directions: On a private island with vehicular access to mainland

KILCHRENAN,
Ardanaiseig Hotel ❀❀❀

The hotel's newsletter helpfully offers a comprehensive guide to traditional Scottish toasts and it ends with the drinker flinging his glass over the left shoulder in a mighty gesture – though they add they would prefer you didn't actually do this while drinking in the Ardanaiseig bar! Actually, this is far too civilised a spot to engage in such rowdy behaviour. The elegant baronial-style house is full of antiques, open fires and inviting corners. Dinner is in the modern Scottish style – loganberries scent the jus with a confiture of Gressingham duck leg, Puy lentils and Agen prunes, and smoked haddock appears as a vichyssoise with a poached egg. Orkney salmon and Oban scallops are interestingly paired in a main course with risotto of calamari, tapenade and essence of saffron. Iced soufflé of Drambuie with marmalade sauce, fresh raspberries and chocolate is a sweet national tribute. A dinner in high summer produced tian of crab, tomato, avocado and apple, then ravioli of lobster in its own bouillon, a well-made granite of mango, excellent roast squab pigeon with braised cabbage, a really well-judged jus and buttery fondant potatoes, and a light prune and Armagnac soufflé with vanilla sauce.

By Taynuilt PA35 1HE
Map 10: NN02
Tel: 01866 833333
Fax: 01866 833222
Chef: Drew Heron
Owner: S Bennie Gray
Cost: Alc £32, fixed price L £16.50/D £29.50 (6 courses). H/wine £14.50
Times: Noon-2pm/7-9pm.
Additional: Bar food L; Sunday L; Children welcome; ❹ dishes
Seats: 36. Jacket & tie preferred
Smoking: No smoking in dining room
Accommodation: 16 en suite
Credit cards: ■ ■ ■ ■ ■

Directions: From A85 take B845 S. At Kilchrenan village, bear left and follow road to hotel

KILCHRENAN,
Taychreggan Hotel ❀❀

Set in a beautiful, peaceful location on the north shore of Loch Awe, this one-time drovers' inn has been here for over three-hundred years. These days it is run as a delightful hotel, perfect for anyone in need of a thoroughly relaxing getaway. The modern Scottish food is good too, and with five or six choices on offer for the main course, choosing the right one may prove tricky. However, whether you opt for steamed fillet of sea bass with saffron noodles or supreme of chicken with goats' cheese and asparagus, you can be sure of a satisfying, enjoyable meal.

Taynuilt PA35 1HQ
Map 10: NN02
Tel: 01866 833211/833366
Fax: 01866 833244
Chef: Martin Wallace
Owner: Annie C Paul
Cost: Fixed-price D £30 (5 courses). H/wine £9.95
Times: 12.30-last L 2pm/7.30-last D 8.45pm

Taychreggan Hotel

Our inspector started an early autumn dinner with a dish of wild pigeon breast with apple and Calvados. Tender noisettes of lamb followed, with a cracked pepper and rosemary crust and a lovely strong Madeira sauce. For puddings try the sloe gin parfait or perhaps a summer pudding of sweetened berries.

Additional: Bar food L; Sunday L; No children under 14
Seats: 45. Private dining room 24
Smoking: No smoking in dining room
Accommodation: 19 en suite
Credit cards: ■ ▨ ⧗ ⓒ ▨ ▨

Directions: One mile before Taynuilt, turn L onto B845 and follow signs to loch side

AA Wine Award-see page 16 Shortlisted for

KILFINAN, **Kilfinan Hotel** ✿✿✿

PA21 2EP
Map 10: NR97
Tel: 01700 821201
Fax: 01700 821205
Chef: Rolf Mueller
Owners: Lynne & Rolf Mueller
Cost: Fixed-price D £28 (4 courses). H/wine £10.50
Times: Noon-last L 2.15pm/7.30-last D 8.45pm. Closed Feb
Additional: Bar food L; No children under 12
Seats: 22. Jacket & tie preferred
Smoking: No smoking in dining room
Accommodation: 11 en suite
Credit cards: ■ ▨ ⧗ ⓒ ▨ JCB

This former coaching inn is set amongst thousands of acres of unspoilt countryside on the east side of Loch Fyne; it is a haven of country pursuits, and relaxation. There's a charming rustic character to the place, with log fires and excellent food adding to the attractions. The kitchen, headed by Rolf Mueller, builds its menus around fresh local produce, much of it on the doorstep, especially game from the adjacent Otter Estate and fish from the loch. The approach is relatively straightforward, with flavour very much the keynote here. One inspection meal highlighted bavarois of trout with horseradish and cranberries, chilled melon and cinnamon soup, cannon of lamb with a herb crust and strong jus, and bavarois of mandarin in a chocolate cup with mango sauce. At another meal, our inspector

particularly noted the clarity of flavours and depth to the
saucing in dishes such as lightly sautéed scallops and
langoustine with tomato brunoise and a mound of freshly
herbed tagliatelle, delicate leek soup, and chocolate tear drop
containing a light bavarois flavoured with Poire William, a little
raspberry purée and a brandy basket of fresh fruit.

Directions: On B8000 between Tighnabruaich and Otter ferry

KILLIECHRONAN, ISLE OF MULL,
Killiechronan House ❀

*Peaceful setting for a Victorian lodge at the head of a 6,000 acre
estate. Cooking is unfussy and true to the region, taking in
interesting soups such as spinach and nettle, as well as monkfish with
cucumber and dill sauce and sea kale, plus a white chocolate mousse
with dark chocolate sauce for dessert.*

Additional: Sunday L (12.30-2.30pm); No children under 10;
❸ dishes
Smoking: No smoking in dining room
Accommodation: 6 en suite
Credit cards: ▇ ▆ ▢

Directions: Leaving ferry turn R to Tobermory (A849), in Salen
(12 miles) turn L to B8035, after 2 miles turn R to Ulva ferry
(B8073). Killiechronan on R

PA72 6JU
Map 10: NM53
Tel: 01680 300403
Fax: 01680 300463
Chef: Patrick Freytag
Owner: Highland Holidays Ltd
Cost: Fixed-price L £14.90/D £24.90
(5 courses). ☺ H/wine £10.
Times: D only, 7-8.30pm.
Closed Nov-Mar

KILMARTIN, **Cairn Restaurant** ❀

*A small, family-run restaurant (a converted shop) that remains as
popular as ever. Marion Thomson's repertoire is based on firm old-
favourites enlivened by many new dishes. Succulent scallops in white
wine and cream sauce, medallions of venison in a tawny port wine
sauce with cranberries, and crunchy lemon cream, are typical.*

Additional: Sunday L; Bar meals; No children under 10 at D;
❸ dishes
Smoking: Air conditioning.
Credit cards: ▆

Directions: On A816 Lochgilphead-Oban road

Lochgilphead PA31 8RQ
Map 10: NR89
Tel: 01546 510254
Chef: Marion Thomson
Owners: Ian & Marion Thomson
Cost: Alc £10. ☺ H/wine £9
Times: Last L 3pm/D 10pm.
Closed Tue, half time Nov-Mar

LUSS, **The Lodge on Loch Lomond** ❀ NEW

*A modern hotel with breathtaking views across Loch Lomond.
Fresh produce is used to good effect in the kitchen, where modern
Scottish dishes such as chargrilled loin of venison with steamed
skirlie dumplings, and aubergine ravioli with smoked cheese and
leek cream, are skilfully produced.*

Smoking: No smoking in dining room
Accommodation: 29 en suite
Credit cards: ▇ ▆ ▢

Directions: From Glasgow take A82 (follow signs for Erskine
Bridge) then N to Luss

By Alexandria,G83 8PA
Map 10: NS39
Tel: 01436 860201
Fax: 01436 860203
Chef: John Hughs
Owners: Niall & Ross Colquhoun
Cost: Alc: £25.50. ☺ H/wine £12
Times: Last L 2.45pm/last D 9.30pm
Additional: Bar food L;
Children welcome; ❸ dishes

OBAN,

Dungallan House Hotel ✤

Gallanach Road PA34 4PD
Map 10: NM82
Tel: 01631 563799
Fax: 01631 566711
Chef: Mrs Janice Stewart
Owners: Mr and Mrs G W &
J M Stewart
Cost: Fixed-price D £25.
H/wine £8.75
Times: Last L 1.45pm/last D 8.30pm
Additional: Bar food; Sunday L;
Children welcome; ✤ dishes
Smoking: No smoking in dining room
Accommodation: 13 (11 en suite)
Credit cards: 〓 〓

*A delightful small hotel overlooking the bay towards the isles of Mull
and Lismore. The daily changing menu features many tried and
tested favourites, as well as daily specials, with an emphasis on fresh
local fish. Main courses could include grilled fillet of lemon sole,
roast rib of beef Balmoral, and beef Wellington with onion gravy.*

Directions: From Argyll Square in Oban follow signs for
Gallanach. Approx 0.5 miles from Square

OBAN,

Manor House Hotel ✤✤

Occupying an elevated position close to the town, this late-
Georgian house (built by the Duke of Argyll and later used as
a dower house) enjoys enviable views across Oban Bay to the
islands beyond. On the food front, the daily changing set-menu
and supporting carte reflect the 'auld alliance', with the best of
Scottish ingredients given the French treatment in dishes such
as an Isle of Mull venison with blackcurrant and Cassis sauce
and puréed parsnips taken at a test dinner. That meal opened
with a pigeon breast with red onion and red cabbage
marmalade, boudin noir and orange sauce and finished with a
rich chocolate marquise with custard sauce (generously
flavoured with Grand Marnier) and fresh fruit garnish.
Canapés in the bar and wrapped chocolates with the coffee
topped and tailed the experience. Cosmopolitan wine list.

Gallanach Road PA34 4LS
Map 10: NM82
Tel: 01631 562087
Fax: 01631 563053
Chef: Neil O'Brien
Owner: Highland Holidays Ltd
Cost: Alc £21.50, fixed-price
D £24.90. ☺ H/wine £12
Times: Noon-last L 2pm/7- last
D 9pm
Additional: Bar food L; Sunday L;
No children under 12; ✤ dishes
Seats: 22
Smoking: No smoking in dining room
Accommodation: 11 en suite
Credit cards: 〓 〓 🗎 〓

Directions: 300 metres past Oban ferry terminal

PORT APPIN,

Airds Hotel ✤✤✤

Elegant, luxurious and unpretentious are words that leap to
mind to describe this former inn on Loch Linnhe. Enter
through the conservatory and resist the temptation to sit and
gaze over the garden and loch (you can do that from the
dining room), enjoy the open fires in the lounges and listen to
the tick of the grandfather clock. Menus are presented in the
afternoon for guests to decide what they want for dinner.
Superb canapés are the first indication that the kitchen is

Appin PA38 4DF
Map 14: NM94
Tel: 01631 730236
Fax: 01631 730535
Chef: Graeme Allen
Owners: The Allen Family
Cost: Fixed-price D £35 (4 courses).
H/wine £18
Times: 8-last D 8.30pm.
Closed 23-27 Dec

committed to producing dishes of the highest order: delicate mushroom tartlet with quail's egg, a salmon fishcake topped with roe. Luxury ingredients like truffles and foie gras may crop up, but the emphasis is very much on local produce. Lovely summery flavours shine out of a starter of pan-fried scallops, as fresh as a daisy, dressed with pesto, while roast breast of quail with wild mushroom risotto and asparagus makes a weightier starter. A soup generally comes next – langoustine with truffle cream, or thick swede and leek – to be followed by a main course of perhaps breast of corn-fed chicken fanned on a chunky mushroom sauce with an eggy mousseline of morels, or fillet of turbot with squat lobsters and a ravioli of crab and coriander. Nicely moist date pudding with caramel sauce may be there for those with room, and prune and Armagnac ice cream for those wanting something lighter. Top-class petits fours – buttery tablet, chocolate truffles and raspberry tartlets among them – are served with coffee in the drawing-room. Quality is what defines the wines, too, with not a dud producer on the lengthy list.

Additional: Light L (12.30-1.30pm); Children welcome
Seats: 36. Jacket & tie preferred
Smoking: No smoking in dining room
Accommodation: 12 en suite
Credit cards: ▆ ▆ ▆ ▆

Directions: Leave the A828 at Appin, hotel is 2.5 miles between Ballachulish and Cannel

SCALASAIG,
Colonsay Hotel ✦

Colonsay is a Hebridean island, with a ferry service every other day. The hotel is the island's focal point for both locals and visitors. The set dinner in the timber-clad dining room might offer mushroom mousse, salmon in white wine sauce with puff pastry, and apple and blackberry crumble.

Smoking: No smoking in dining room
Accommodation: 11 en suite (except singles)
Credit cards: ▆ ▆ ▆ ▆ ▆ ▆ ▆ JCB

Directions: 400 yards west of Colonsay pier

Isle of Colonsay PA61 7YP
Map 10: NR39
Tel: 01951 200316
Fax: 01951 200353
Chef: Christa Byrne
Owners: Kevin & Christa Byrne
Cost: Fixed-price D £23 (4 courses).
☺ H/wine £8
Times: Last L 1.30pm/D at 7.30pm.
Additional: Bar food; Children welcome; ◑ dishes; Jacket & tie preferred

STRACHUR, Creggans Inn ✦

The restaurant at this charming old Highland inn has large picture windows that make the most of the superb views over Loch Fyne. Dinner might start with seafood bisque accompanied by home-baked breads, followed by succulent noisettes of lamb, or chargrilled salmon with lemon butter, and finish with Cointreau bavarois. Excellent wine list.

Additional: Bar food; Sunday L; Children welcome; ◑ dishes
Smoking: No smoking in dining room
Accommodation: 19 en suite
Credit cards: ▆ ▆ ▆ ▆ ▆ ▆ ▆

Directions: From Glasgow via Loch Lomondside, Arrochar, the 'Rest & Be Thankful', the A83, or by Gourock, the car ferry across the Clyde to Dunoon, and the A815

PA27 8BX
Map 10: NN00
Tel: 01369 860279
Fax: 01369 860637
Chef: Kevin Capper
Owner: Sir Charles Maclean
Cost: Alc: £25, fixed-price D £19.50.
☺ H/wine £12
Times: Last L 2.30pm/last D 9pm

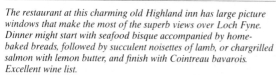

ᴬ Wine Shortlisted for Award-see page 16

AYRSHIRE, EAST

DARVEL, Scoretulloch House

A restaurant with rooms that has the appearance and atmosphere of a cosy hunting lodge, with half-panelling and beams in the dining-room. The kitchen's style is modern without being fussy, letting flavours speak for themselves, and the four-course dinner menus offer a decent selection. An inspector started with salmon rösti fishcakes, went on to creamy carrot and coriander soup, and then chose best end of Ayrshire lamb crusted with Arran mustard and herbs well balanced by a sauce of pink peppercorns and redcurrants, declaring the dish 'succulent and flavoursome'. The finale was rhubarb crumble cream ice – midway between ice cream and parfait – showing 'accurate flavours with a crunch'. Other menus might extend from a salad of scallops and bacon to summer berry Pavlova, with main courses of haunch of Avondale roe-deer braised in Guinness, or West Coast salmon on wilted greens with a cucumber and prawn butter. The wine list shows a preference for France, although five of the seven house wines come from Australia and Chile.

KA17 0LR
Map 11: NS53
Tel: 01560 323331
Fax: 01560 323441
Chef: Tom O'Donnell
Owners: Donald & Anne Smith
Cost: *Alc* £10, fixed-price L £15 (Sun only)/D £25. H/wine £10
Times: Noon-last L 2pm/7-last D 9pm. Closed 25 Dec, 1 Jan
Additional: Bar food L; Sunday L; No children under 12; ✇ dishes
Seats: 50. Private dining room 16
Smoking: No smoking in dining room
Accommodation: 8 en suite
Credit cards: JCB

Directions: Take M74/J 8 for A71. Hotel is clearly signed 1 mile S of A71 (Strathaven-Kilmarnock), just E of Darvel.

FENWICK, Fenwick Hotel ✾ NEW

A friendly hotel that offers refreshingly good cooking along modern Scottish lines. Fresh seafood and game feature regularly on the menu, although starters can range from roasted red peppers and goats' cheese to chargrilled polenta with wild mushroom stew. The bacon chops with honey and mustard glaze are especially recommended.

Additional: Bar food; Children welcome; ✇ dishes
Smoking: No-smoking area
Accommodation: 31 en suite. **Credit cards:**

KA3 6AU
Map 11: NS44
Tel: 01560 600478
Fax: 01560 600334
Chef: Colin Campbell
Owners: Mr & Mrs A Dickson
Cost: Fixed-price D £16.90. ☺ H/wine £9.90
Times: Last L 3pm/last D 9.30pm

Directions: *Telephone for directions*

STEWARTON, Chapeltoun House ✾✾

KA3 3ED
Map 10: NS44
Tel: 01560 482696
Fax: 01560 485100
Chef: Paul Tamburrini
Owners: Mr & Mrs Dobson
Cost: Fixed-price L from £7.95 (2 courses)/D £21.90 (2 courses). ☺ H/wine £11.95.
Times: Noon-last L 2.30pm/7pm-last D 9pm
Additional: Bar food L; Sunday L; No children under 12; ✇ dishes
Seats: 30. Private dining room 12
Smoking: No smoking in dining room
Accommodation: 8 en suite
Credit cards:

The pâtisserie at this fine Edwardian country house is outstanding – a superb lemon and lime tart with orange marmalade was a high point of our visit, but other fine examples of the genre might include warmed apricot and almond flan with vanilla ice cream and apricot coulis. Preceding dishes of galantine of Craufurdland Castle quail with a redcurrant and port conserve and crisp orange salad, and best end of Scotch lamb with glazed root vegetables, mustard seed jus and sautéed kidney, were both well-constructed. Altogether the cooking here has gone into a new dimension with the arrival of a new chef. With dishes such as oven-roasted pepper duck breast with mushroom potatoes, ginger and black-bean glaze and yam crisps, and warm salad of anglerfish topped with herb croûtons and lardons of bacon, in the repertoire, this is a place to watch.

Directions: Take B778 at Stewarton Cross then B769 (Irvine) for 2 miles; hotel is off to R

AYRSHIRE, NORTH

BRODICK,

Auchrannie Hotel ❀❀

Isle of Arran KA27 8BZ
Map 10: NS03
Tel: 01770 302234
Fax: 01770 302812
Chef: Andrew Yuill
Owners: Iain and Linda Johnston
Cost: *Alc* £11.50, fixed-price D £23.50 (4-courses). ☺ H/wine £11.75
Times: 12.30-last L 2.15pm/6.30-last D 9.15pm
Additional: Bar food; Sunday L; Children welcome; ❹ dishes
Seats: 50. Private dining room 25
Smoking: No smoking in dining room
Accommodation: 28 en suite
Credit cards: ▬ ▨ ▢

Developed from an impressive Victorian mansion, the hotel is set amid six acres of wooded and landscaped grounds. The Garden Restaurant has traditional country house decor and a bright conservatory extension. It offers a daily fixed-price menu of two, three or four courses. The emphasis is on Scottish cooking with a contemporary slant, using the best fresh and local produce, notably seafood from the abundant waters of the West Coast. Ravioli of sole and scallops in a chive and grain mustard essence had clearly defined flavours, and cock-a-leekie soup proved an ideal intermediate course. The main dish comprised pan-fried nuggets of new season Arran lamb set around a superbly light bread mousse with broad beans and Madeira sauce. The meal concluded with a Bramley apple tart of filo pastry, served with home-made vanilla ice cream.

Directions: From ferry terminal turn R and follow coast road through Brodick village, then take second L past golf club

BRODICK,
Kilmichael Hotel

Kilmichael is believed to be the oldest house on the island and is beautifully situated in its own extensive grounds in Glen Cloy. The decor is country house in style, with antiques and oriental rugs, and the restaurant is now in a bright new ground-floor extension looking out to the forest. Modern British cooking is offered from a five-course set menu, with an alternative starter, main course and dessert. Between the canapés and coffee with petits fours, one can expect salad of chicken livers with quenelles of duck egg mousse, a soup of yellow pepper and sweetcorn with goats' cheese, tomato and fennel, and new season Arran lamb with red plum sauce. A popular pudding is feuillantine of Scottish fruits and berries with a kirsch sabayon, and to finish there is a selection excellent cheeses.

Directions: Follow Shore Road to golf course, turn L inland at sharp bend. Past church to road end

Glen Cloy Isle of Arran KA27 8BY
Map 10: NS03
Tel: 01770 302219
Fax: 01770 302068
Chef: Antony Butterworth
Owners: Antony Butterworth, Geoffrey Botterill
Cost: Alc £24.50, fixed-price D £29.50 (5 courses). ☺ H/wine £11.95
Times: D only, 7-last D 8.30pm. Closed Xmas
Additional: No children under 12; ◑ dishes
Seats: 24
Smoking: No smoking in dining room
Accommodation: 9 en suite
Credit cards: ■ ▥ JCB

DALRY, **Braidwoods**

Keep your eyes peeled for the sign; the Braidwoods' charming converted millers' cottage is down a path in the middle of a field. The seven-table dining room is tightly run and frequented by a smart clientele. Keith Braidwood knows his stuff; his dexterity shines through in modern Scottish dishes such as pan-fried breast of free-range chicken on braised Puy lentils and tarragon jus; roast loin of red deer with tender squab pigeon and a wild mushroom sauce; and baked fillet of west coast turbot with seared scallops and a smokie and saffron sauce. Starters are along similar lines, and could include warm tart of Parmesan, or oak-smoked chicken and avocado tossed with croûtons and a creamy garlic dressing, and light cream soup of cauliflower and Arran mustard. The interesting wine list has a range to suit most pockets with a number of expensive vintages as well as some reasonable house wines.

Directions: 1 mile from Dalry on the Saltcoats Road

Drumastle Mill Cottage KA24 4LN
Map 10: NS24
Tel: 01294 833544
Fax: 01294 833553
Chef: Keith Braidwood
Owners: Keith & Nicola Braidwood
Cost: Fixed-price L £16/D £26. H/wine £11.95
Times: Noon-1.45pm/7-9pm. Closed D Sun, all Mon, L Tue, 3 wks Jan, 2 wks Sep/Oct
Additional: Sunday L; No children under 12 at D
Seats: 24
Smoking: No smoking in dining room
Credit cards: ■ ▥ ▧ ◖ ▦ ▣

KILWINNING, **Montgreenan Mansion**
House Hotel

Georgian mansion, set in 50 acres of park and woodland, with ornate ceilings and marble fireplaces adorning the gracious public rooms. Dishes sampled include curried pear and parsnip soup, fillet of sole Mornay, and saddle of Ayrshire lamb with tomato concasse and goats' cheese au gratin.

Additional: Bar food L; Sunday L; Children welcome; ◑ dishes
Smoking: No smoking in dining room
Accommodation: 21 en suite
Credit cards: ■ ▥ ◖ ▦ ▣

Directions: 4 miles N of Irvine, & 19 miles S of Glasgow on A736

Montgreenan Estate KA13 7QZ
Map 10: NS34
Tel: 01294 557733
Fax: 01294 850397
Chef: Allan McCall
Owners: The Dobson family
Cost: Alc £25, fixed-price L £13.75/D £25.80 (6 courses). ☺ H/wine £11.20
Times: Last L 2.30pm/last D 9.30pm

AYRSHIRE, SOUTH

AYR, **Brig O'Doon House Hotel** ❀

The Witcherie at the Brig O'Doon, in deepest Robbie Burns' country, is hugely popular with the honest folk of Ayr. Portions are not for the timerous, but are prepared from quality ingredients. Try west coast seafood broth, grilled herring in oatmeal with goosebery jelly, and pannacotta with fresh berries.

Accommodation: 5 en suite
Credit cards: ■ ▆ C ▆

Directions: *Please telephone for directions*

KA7 4PQ
Map 10: NS31
Tel: 01292 442466
Fax: 01292 441999
Chef: Ian Ferguson
Owners: Bill & Cath Costley
Cost: ☺
Times: Last L 2pm/last D 9pm
Additional: Bar food; Children welcome; ◑ dishes
Smoking: No smoking in dining room

AYR, **Fairfield House Hotel** ❀❀

A Victorian mansion house with classic interior design by Lady Henrietta Spencer-Churchill. The hotel boasts two restaurants – the Brasserie offering a lighter, popular style of cooking, open 10am-10pm for morning coffee, light lunches, afternoon tea and full dinners, and the Fleur de Lys Restaurant, only open for evening meals with a style based along modern British lines. In the latter, typical starters include terrine of pheasant with fresh fruits in an Earl Grey syrup, lasagne of chicken livers with oyster mushrooms and shallots, and timbale of smoked salmon filled with a lobster and sweet red pepper bavarois. Main courses range from marinated breast of duck on a bed of roast fennel with Calvados sauce, to roast monkfish tails on a parsnip and potato cake with basil pesto. For dessert try bitter dark chocolate and hazelnut terrine, or perhaps caramelised strawberry tart with a ginger and oatmeal cream.

Directions: Town centre, down Miller Rd to T junction with traffic lights, filter L, immediately R into Fairfield Rd

12 Fairfield Road KA7 2AR
Map 10: NS32
Tel: 01292 267461
Fax: 01292 261456
Chef: Don McGovern
Owners: Mr & Mrs G Martin
Cost: Alc £25, fixed-price L £12. ☺
H/wine £11.95
Times: Noon-last L 2pm/7-last D 9pm
Additional: Sunday L; Children welcome; ◑ dishes
Seats: 24. Private dining room 16
Smoking: No smoking in dining room
Accommodation: 33 en suite
Credit cards: ■ ▆ ⊠ C ▆ ⊡ JCB

AYR, **Fouters Bistro** ❀❀

Loyal customers have been negotiating the narrow stairs down to the bistro-style restaurant for 25 years. This year's anniversary is a tribute to the relaxed atmosphere and uncomplicated, reliably good modern Scottish cooking. The short carte changes about three times a week depending on availability of supplies and the whims of chef/patron Laurie Black. The brasserie menu might feature salad of Ayrshire pigeon and breast of chicken with a lovage cream sauce; the 'Gourmet' menu takes in more stylish dishes such as fillet of local skate wing on a bed of red onion confit with lemon and garlic butter sauce, and breast of locally bred Gressingham duck pan-fried with stir-fried Savoy cabbage and a rich redcurrant and Burgundy wine jus. The midweek chargrill menu includes roast salmon fillet and steaks from certified local herds. Bread-and-butter pudding is always a favourite.

Directions: Town centre, opposite Town Hall, down Cobblestone Lane

2A Academy Street
KA7 1HS
Map 10: NS32
Tel: 01292 261391
Fax: 01292 619323
Chef: Laurie Black
Owner: Fran & Laurie Black
Cost: Alc £11.50, fixed-price D £15/25. ☺ H/wine £12.50
Times: Noon-last L 1.45pm/6.30-last D 9.45pm. Closed Sun, Mon, 25-27 Dec, 1-3 Jan
Additional: Children welcome; ◑ dishes
Seats: 38. Private room 16
Smoking: No-smoking area; No pipes; Air conditioning
Credit cards: ■ ▆ ⊠ C ▆ ⊡ JCB

GIRVAN, Wildings ❀

If you like fish, you'll like Wildings. There are meat dishes such as breast of duck with a peppercorn crust and orange Curaçao sauce, but the emphasis is on fish, mostly locally landed. Tiger prawns with a decent black bean sauce, hake fillet roasted with seared scallops on a potato and apple purée with Dijon mustard cream and Cajun seared salmon on warm potato salad, set the pace.

Additional: Children welcome; ❧ dishes
Seats: 50
Smoking: No smoking in dining room; Air conditioning
Credit cards: None

Directions: Just off A77 at the north end of village

Montgomerie Street KA26 9HE
Map 10: NX19
Tel: 01465 713481
Chef/Owner: Kevin Rae
Cost: Fixed price L £8.95 & £11.95/D £17.90 & £21. ☺ H/wine £10.50
Times: Noon-2pm/6.30-9pm.
Closed D Sun, Mon, Tue, 4 wks Oct, 3 wks Xmas/New Year

TROON,
Highgrove House ❀❀

The two-tier restaurant of this smart country house hotel overlooks the Firth of Clyde. It is a popular place, well patronised by locals for the good cooking. Although the dinner menu is augmented by a brasserie selection, it is the more sophisticated dishes that reflect the kitchen's flare. These are built around Scotland's abundant larder, seen in dishes such as fillet of Cairngorm trout, sautéed in lemon butter, or Moray lamb cutlets with mint and grapefruit sauce. At inspection, west-coast seafood chowder, for example, was memorable for the flavour of the pieces of fish, and herb-crusted best end of lamb with shallots and wild mushroom confit was pronounced perfect. Also enjoyed was a well-constructed chilled chocolate torte with Cointreau sauce, oranges and walnut iced parfait.

Directions: A77 from Ayr (Glasgow), L at Prestwick Airport, first R to Old Irvine. First L to Loans, R at mini roundabout to Highgrove

Loans Road KA10 7HL
Map 10: NS33
Tel: 01292 312511
Fax: 01292 318228
Please telephone for further details

TROON,
Lochgreen House ❀❀❀

Four dining rooms are offered in this regal country house hotel so guests can pick one to suit their mood. As well as the formal restaurant, which looks out over immaculately groomed gardens, you can take meals in the library or one of the two conservatories. Wherever you sit, the food will be delightful, vibrant and good value for money. After the tasty canapés, there are starters such as steamed scallop mousse with blanquette of langoustine, and duck confit with red onion compote and rösti. A similar level of culinary excitement is to be found in main dishes of roast wood pigeon with ravioli of sweetbreads and fresh truffle, or crisply pan-fried fillet of sea bass with scallops and champagne-chive velouté. A stunning choice of dessert is the rhubarb steamed pudding with stem ginger ice cream and warm berry compote. Excellent breads, petits fours and espresso show the restaurant's exemplary attention to detail.

Directions: Off A77 (Prestwick Airport) onto B749, S/E of Troon

Monktonhill Road Southwood KA10 7EN
Map 10: NS33
Tel: 01292 313343
Fax: 01292 318661
Chefs: Andrew Costley & Jason Paton
Owners: Bill & Cath Costley
Cost: *Alc* £17.95, fixed-price L £17.95/D £29.95 (4 courses). H/wine £14.50
Times: Noon-last L 2pm/7-last D 9pm
Additional: Sunday L; ❧ dishes
Seats: 80. Private dining rooms 8-45.
Jacket & tie preferred
Smoking: No smoking in dining room
Accommodation: 15 en suite
Credit cards: ▬ ▬ ▬ ▭ ▬

TROON,

Marine Highland Hotel

The hotel's Fairways Restaurant overlooks the fairway of the Royal Troon Golf Course and over the Firth of Clyde. The selection of British dishes might include an innovative monkfish in saffron batter with lemon mayonnaise, or saddle of local venison pan-fried with braised red cabbage and game sauce.

Additional: Bar food; Sunday L (noon-2.30pm); Children welcome; 🌙 dishes
Smoking: No-smoking area; Air conditioning
Accommodation: 74 en suite
Credit cards: 🔲 🔲 🔲 🔲 🔲 🔲 🔲

Directions: Take A77 from Glasgow (following signs for Prestwick Airport) and turn onto B789 – hotel overlooks 18th fairway of Royal Troon Golf Course

KA10 6HE
Map 10: NS33
Tel: 01292 314444
Fax: 01292 316922
Chef: Richard Sturgeon
Owner: Scottish Highland Hotels
Cost: *Alc* £27, fixed-price D £24.50 (4 courses). ☺ H/wine £11.95
Times: D only, last D 9.30pm

TROON,

Piersland House Hotel

A stylish Edwardian mansion hotel, carefully extended over the years and now a popular venue for both business travellers and holidaymakers. Fine dining is enjoyed in the brasserie, where zappy modern dishes are the order of the day. Typically you can expect the likes of seared sea bass fillet with dressed leaves and salsa, croquette of chicken with chickpeas and pine nuts, and mignons of venison loin with a chestnut and horseradish mash and sloeberry and juniper essence. An early summer inspection meal took in west coast fish chowder, breast of duck and venison with a mixed berry compote and a fine Madeira and redcurrant jus, and finally a neat, delicate dessert of poached pears with home-made honey and walnut ice cream. The hotel, which stands in grounds close to the championship golf course, is linked to the founder of Johnnie Walker whisky, and the owners have developed a subtle whisky theme throughout.

Directions: Opposite Royal Troon Golf Club

Craigend Road KA10 6HD
Map 10: NS33
Tel: 01292 314747
Fax: 01292 315613
Chef: John Rae
Owner: J A Brown
Cost: *Alc* £19.95, fixed-price L £12.95/D £20.95 (4 courses). ☺ H/wine £9.25
Times: Noon-last L 2.30pm/6.45-last D 9.45pm
Additional: Bar food; Sunday L; Children welcome; 🌙 dishes
Seats: 42. Private dining room
Smoking: No smoking in dining room
Accommodation: 28 en suite
Credit cards: 🔲 🔲 🔲 🔲 🔲 🔲 🔲 JCB

TURNBERRY, **Malin Court**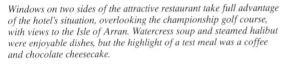

KA26 9PB
Map 10: NS20
Tel: 01655 331457
Fax: 01655 331072
Chef: Andrea Beach
Cost: Fixed-price D £21.95
(4 courses). ☺ H/wine £10.95
Times: Last L 2pm/last D 9pm
Additional: Bar food L; Sunday L;
Children welcome; ✪ dishes
Smoking: Air conditioning
Accommodation: 17 en suite
Credit cards: ▬ ▬ ▣ ▬ ▣

*Windows on two sides of the attractive restaurant take full advantage
of the hotel's situation, overlooking the championship golf course,
with views to the Isle of Arran. Watercress soup and steamed halibut
were enjoyable dishes, but the highlight of a test meal was a coffee
and chocolate cheesecake.*

Directions: On A719 one mile from A77 on N side of village

TURNBERRY, **Turnberry Hotel** ✿✿

KA26 9LT
Map 10: NS20
Tel: 01655 331000
Fax: 01655 331706
Chef: D S Cameron
Owner: Starwood Hotels &
Resorts Inc
Cost: Alc £50; fixed-price D £45
(4 courses). H/wine £19.75
Times: 12.30-2.30pm/7.30-9.30pm
Additional: Bar food L; Sunday L;
Children welcome; ✪ dishes
Seats: 180. Private dining room 16.
Jacket & tie preferred
Accommodation: 132 en suite
Credit cards: ▬ ▬ ▣ ▬ ▣ JCB

Opened in 1906, the Turnberry, in 800 acres of countryside with
spectacular views over the Firth of Clyde to Arran, the Mull of
Kintyre and Ailsa Craig, is famous the world over for its Ailsa
and Arran golf courses. Spacious and comfortable public rooms
provide grand settings for those with less energetic pursuits in
mind, and there are three eating venues to choose from. The
main restaurant has something of the time-warp air of an
ocean-going liner and serves dishes from a classic repertoire
using prime Scottish ingredients: Aberdeen Angus carpaccio
with mustard mayonnaise, or West Coast scallops, their coral
intact, and scampi in creamy lemongrass sauce to start, perhaps,
then Highland venison with celeriac mousse and lavender game
sauce, or veal tournedos and sweetbreads with truffles. Beluga
caviar, foie gras and Chateaubriand inevitably make an
appearance too. Watch the sun set over the Mull as you tuck
into iced passion fruit soufflé, or banana and mango mousse.

Directions: On the main A77. Turn right at Turnberry village,
hotel is half a mile on right opposite golf courses

DUMFRIES & GALLOWAY

GATEHOUSE OF FLEET,
Cally Palace Hotel

DG7 2DL
Map 11: NX55
Tel: 01557 814341
Fax: 01557 814522
Please telephone for further details

Set in 500 acres of forest and parkland, this is one of the few grand hotels where guests can enjoy a round of golf before dinner. The kitchen keeps dishes simple and honest, focusing on true, natural flavours. Well-reported have been ballottine of salmon with a chive crème fraîche, and pot-roasted corn-fed chicken with a rustic fricassée of woodland mushrooms. Save room for desserts that include local delicacies.

KIRKCUDBRIGHT,
Selkirk Arms Hotel

Old High Street DG6 4JG
Map 11: NX65
Tel: 01557 330402
Fax: 01557 331639
Chef: Adam McKissock
Owner: E J Morris
Cost: Fixed-price D £24.95
(4 courses). ☺ H/wine £8.95
Times: Last L 2pm/last D 9.30pm.
Closed D 25 Dec
Additional: Bar food; Sunday L;
Children welcome; ✦ dishes
Smoking: No smoking in dining room

Cosy little Georgian hotel, with a bright, attractive restaurant. Sound cooking – the kitchen follows modern trends and is not afraid to experiment with the likes of smoked chicken and prawn gâteaux with orange crème fraîche and tomato and chilli coulis, and pan-fried saddle of spring Galloway lamb with spring greens, couscous and thyme essence.

Accommodation: 17 en suite
Credit cards: ▬ ▬ ▚ ▙ ▤ C ▥ JCB

Directions: 5 miles S of A75 junction with A711

LOCKERBIE, Dryfesdale Hotel ✿

DG11 2SF
Map 11: NY18
Tel: 01576 202427
Fax: 01576 204187
Chef: Michael Dunbobbin
Cost: £25, fixed-price L £10.95/D
£18.95. ☺ H/wine £10
Times: Last L 2pm/last D 9pm.
Closed 26 Dec
Additional: Bar food; Sunday L;
Children welcome; ✦ dishes

A former Manse, Dryfesdale was built in 1762 and enjoys sweeping views across rolling countryside. Friendly and attentive service are hallmarks of the restaurant, which opens out on to a sun terrace in the summer. Main courses include pan-fried chicken breast with lemongrass, or grilled Dover sole with caper butter.

Smoking: No smoking in dining room
Accommodation: 15 en suite. **Credit cards:** ▬ ▬ ▚ ▙ ▤ C

Directions: Lockerbie M74/J17

MOFFAT, Beechwood Hotel ✿

Harthorpe Place DG10 9RS
Map 11: NT00
Tel: 01683 220210
Fax: 01683 220889
Chef: Carl S Shaw
Owners: Lynda & Jeffrey Rogers
Cost: Fixed-price L £14/D £23.50
(6 courses). ☺ H/wine £9.50
Times: Last L 2pm/last D 8.45pm.
Closed L Mon-Wed, 2 Jan-20 Feb
Additional: Sunday L; Children
welcome; ✦ dishes
Smoking: No smoking in dining room
Accommodation: 7 en suite
Credit cards: ▬ ▬ ▚▚ ▤ JCB

Yes, beech woods provide the backdrop to this attractive Victorian house, set in grounds above the town. The short, well-structured menu changes fortnightly and might start with artichoke hearts and roast peppers on caramelised onions with melted goats' cheese. Zesty, baked Scottish salmon with lime and cream sauce is a highly recommended main course.

Directions: At N end of High Street turn R into Harthorpe Place (hotel signed)

MOFFAT, Well View Hotel

Ballplay Road DG10 9JU
Map 11: NT00
Tel: 01683 220184
Fax: 01683 220088
Chef: Janet Schuckardt
Owners: Janet & John Schuckardt
Cost: Fixed-price D £28 (6 courses).
H/wine £10.50
Times: 12.15-last L 1.15pm/7-last
D 8.30pm. Closed L Sat
Additional: Sunday L;
No children under 6 at D
Seats: 24. Private dining room 6.
Jacket & tie preferred
Smoking: No smoking in dining room
Accommodation: 6 en suite
Credit cards: ▆ ▆ ▆ ▆ ▆

John and Janet Schuckhardt make this Victorian house an essential stop for the travelling foodie. It combines the atmosphere of a family home while producing food cooked in a light contemporary vein with the emphasis on flavour not fussiness. It is necessary to pace oneself through a meal that takes in terrine of chicken, pheasant and Puy lentils with Cumberland sauce, then fillet of salmon with champagne sauce and a tomato, ginger and basil salsa, a sorbet followed by roast breast of duck on a bed of ribbon vegetables with rösti potato and a red wine, orange and honey sauce, a selection of cheeses, then chocolate tart with home-made rum and raisin ice cream and a vanilla sauce, followed by coffee and petits fours in the lounge. A nice touch is a selection of wines on the menu that have been chosen to complement the food.

Directions: From Moffat take A708 (Selkirk); turn left after fire station in Ballplay Road 300 yds to hotel.

NEWTON STEWART,
Creebridge House Hotel **NEW**

Delightful Victorian house close to the town centre, with a country-style restaurant that enjoys views across garden and croquet lawn. The kitchen is quite daring in its approach, and both the carte and daily set menu boast vibrant flavours and interesting ingredients. Expect seared sea bass with a tomato and vegetable compote, and glorious desserts along the lines of iced praline parfait with coffee anglaise.

DG8 6NP
Map 10: NX46
Tel: 01671 402121
Fax: 01671 403258
Chef: Paul Somerville
Owners: Mr & Mrs C Walker,
Mr & Mrs A Butt
Cost: Alc £23.45, fixed-price D £18
(5 courses). ☺ H/wine £9.95
Times: D only, last D 9pm.
Closed Nov-Mar (except Bar)

Additional: Bar food, Sunday L; Children welcome; ◑ dishes
Smoking: No smoking in dining room
Accommodation: 20 en suite
Credit cards: ▆ ▆ ▆ ▆ ▆ ▆ JCB

Directions: *Telephone for directions*

NEWTON STEWART,
Kirroughtree House

Minnigaff DG8 6AN
Map 10: NX46
Tel: 01671 402141
Fax: 01671 402425
Chef: Ian Bennett
Owner: Douglas McMillan
Cost: Alc L £17, fixed-price
L £13.50/D £30 (4 courses).
H/wine £12
Times: Noon-last L 2pm/7-last
D 9pm. Closed 3 Jan-mid Feb
Additional: Bar food L; Sunday L;
No children under 10; ❸ dishes
Seats: 40. Private dining room 20.
Jacket & tie preferred
Smoking: No smoking in dining room
Accommodation: 17 en suite
Credit cards: ▓ ▓ ▓ ▓ ▓

The small, elegant dining-rooms here are named after the people who built this mansion in 1719; this was where Sir Patrick and Lady Heron entertained Robert Burns. The building, in its own forested grounds about a mile north of town, has a traditional country-house atmosphere, with deep sofas and antiques in the lounges and Chippendale-style repro in the dining rooms. A complimentary coffee cup of soup – maybe cold puréed gazpacho – sets the ball rolling, and breads of olive plait and granary rolls don't disappoint either. Boudin blanc with caramelised apples studded with foie gras and truffle on a bed of spinach, or calves' sweetbreads in a tartlet with morel sauce could precede a main course of crisply skinned, moist and pink breast of duck on smooth celeriac purée with two discs of fondant potato, slices of black pudding and a timbale of ratatouille 'a joy to eat,' wrote an inspector. Locally sourced lamb, perhaps with candied aubergine and sauce niçoise, and venison, with cinnamon-scented red cabbage and spiced pear, may make an appearance, as well as steamed fillet of brill with roast scallops and vegetable cannelloni. Scottish farmhouse cheeses are among the selection on offer, with apple tart with vanilla ice cream, or lemon tarte Tatin with lemon sorbet among the pastries. The wine list starts in France then has a quick trot around most of the world before arriving back at Vin de Pays d'Oc house wines.

Directions: From A75 turn left into A712 (New Galloway), hotel entrance 300yds on left

PORTPATRICK,
Fernhill Lodge NEW

DG9 8TD
Map 10: NW95
Tel: 01776 810220
Fax: 01776 810596
Please telephone for further details

Both the restaurant and conservatory dining areas have impressive views over town and sea, and there's sound cooking of fresh produce. Game terrine with Cumberland sauce and pan-fried breast of duck with gin and redcurrant sauce are highly recommended, and the Ecchlfechan tart goes down a treat.

PORTPATRICK,
Knockinaam Lodge

Stranraer DG9 9AD
Map 10: NW95
Tel: 01776 810471
Fax: 01776 810435
Chef: Tony Pierce
Owners: Michael Bricker &
Pauline Ashworth
Cost: Fixed-price D £38 (5 courses).
H/wine £12
Times: Noon-last L 2pm/7.30-last
D 9.30pm
Additional: Bar food L;
No children under 12; ◖ dishes
Seats: 32. Private dining room 6-8
Smoking: No smoking in dining room
Accommodation: 10 en suite
Credit cards: ■ ▥ ▢ ▥ ▣

The Victorian hunting lodge sits in 30 remote acres facing the
Irish Sea, but the cooking stays in touch with contemporary
trends and ideas, based on the extensive use of fresh, local
ingredients. With charming owners, comfortable, flower-filled
surroundings, private beach, friendly staff and Tony Pierce in
the kitchen, a visit here is a restorative pleasure. The nightly-
changing no-choice dinner menu is a delight to read, partly
because of the charming bird and flower illustrations, partly
because of the enticing descriptions. A Saturday night in
February, saw a meal that opened with mosaic of confit chicken
leg and white beans, Madeira wine jelly and truffle vinaigrette,
followed by roast sea scallops, frisée salad and ratatouille-style
dressing, then noisette of Galloway lamb with basil couscous
and a port and juniper reduction. The only choice is between
dessert – warm pear and vanilla tart with bitter chocolate sauce
on this occasion – and a selection of British and French cheeses
served with honey and sultana bread. Great culinary heights
were achieved by a middle course of courgette flower stuffed
with pea and mint mousseline with pancetta and ham hock jus,
which was subtle, attractive and pretty special. Jus and
reductions are a strong point – the port jus accompanying
tender loin of roe deer was excellent, and juniper might flavour
that served with roast squab, pommes fondantes and stuffed
cabbage parcel. The wine list is one to linger over –
predominantly French with some top vintages from the 70s and
80s. There is also an extensive collection of single malts,
including 25 rare private bottlings.

Signature dishes: Ravioli of spinach with a coriander jus,
poached quails' egg and morel sabayon; terrine of native
lobster and calves' sweetbreads with tomato, artichoke and
mango salad; roast lamb cutlet with basil mousse, pommes
Anna, elephant garlic beignets and grated truffle; hot
Christmas pudding soufflé with Granny Smith sorbet

Directions: A77 or A75 follow Portpatrick. 2 miles W of
Lochans watch for Colfin Smokehouse & hotel signs and follow

DUNBARTONSHIRE, EAST

MILNGAVIE,

Thistle Black Bull

A Thistle Hotel sited in a comfortable north-Glasgow suburb. Fresh ingredients are cooked in modern Scottish style at Anton's, the first-floor restaurant. Innovative twists for dinner include lobster bisque laced with green ginger wine, and rack of lamb with a crust of pine kernels and garlic served with port essence.

Smoking: No pipes and cigars
Accommodation: 27 en suite
Credit cards:

Directions: *Telephone for directions*

Main Street G62 6BH
Map 10: NS57
Tel: 0141 9562291
Fax: 0141 9561896
Chef: Karen McPhearson
Owners: Antons
Cost: *Alc* £25, fixed price L £5.95 (2 courses)/D £18.25. ☺ H/wine £10.25
Times: Last L 2pm/last D 9.30pm. Closed 26 Dec, 1 Jan
Additional: Bar food L; Sunday L; Children welcome; ◑ dishes

DUNBARTONSHIRE, WEST

BALLOCH,

Cameron House Hotel ✿✿✿

In its own wooded, landscaped grounds right on the bank of Loch Lomond, Cameron House couldn't have a better outlook: across the loch to the island of Inchmurrin and Ben Lomond rising beyond. The fine mansion has been sympathetically extended and boasts a leisure complex second to none. Three eating venues are on offer, one a bar-diner set by the lochside marina just a five-minute stroll from the hotel, but for fine dining it's got to be the Georgian Room, an elegant restaurant that shares the view of the loch. The kitchen displays a deft touch when it comes to using prime raw materials and turning them into interesting dishes often with an unusual twist. Red pepper and lentil soufflé, or asparagus soup with a nettle dumpling could share starter billing with accurately cooked langoustine, monkfish and halibut in a potato-based beetroot pancake with beetroot cream, a sure hand making sure the beetroot doesn't overpower. Chunky collops of home-smoked venison with a malt whisky sauce may

Loch Lomond G83 8QZ
Map 10: NS38
Tel: 01389 755565
Fax: 01389 759522
Chef: Peter Fleming
Owner: De Vere Hotels Ltd
Cost: *Alc* £45, fixed-price L £18.50/D £38.50 (4 courses). H/wine £14
Times: Noon-last L 1.45pm/7pm-last D 9.45pm. Closed L Sat & Sun
Additional: Bar food L; Sunday L in Smolletts; No children in Georgian Room; ◑ dishes
Seats: 45. Private dining room up to 200. Jacket & tie preferred
Smoking: No smoking in dining room; Air conditioning
Accommodation: 96 en suite
Credit cards:

Directions: M8/A82 to Dumbarton: take road to Luss, hotel signed 1 mile past Balloch on R

be among main courses, with another soufflé, of perhaps apple and walnut, and chocolate fondant among desserts. The differently flavoured breads and petits fours are all in keeping, and the wine list covers all countries of significance as well as classic French vintages.

Signature dishes: Tortellini of langoustine and leeks with frothy sauce américaine; baked squab pigeon with woodland mushrooms and sage potato purée.

CLYDEBANK, **Beardmore Hotel**

The modern, purpose-built hotel is popular with both business travellers visiting the Glasgow area and tourists heading up towards Loch Lomond. The Brasserie Restaurant overlooks the Clyde and is open weekends; otherwise most eating takes place in the brightly coloured Citrus Restaurant. The short, pacy sounding carte reads well with dishes such as soup of Jerusalem artichokes, herb noodles, poached quails' eggs, salad of scallops and lime yogurt dressing, and maize-fed chicken served with leeks and basil, or seared tuna with couscous and ratatouille. As well as desserts such as fig tart, lime syrup and ginger clotted cream, or chocolate mille-feuille, there is a separate, well-chosen cheese menu.

Beardmore Street G81 4SA
Map 11: NS56
Tel: 0141 9516000
Fax: 0141 9516018
Chef: Mark Knowles
Cost: *Alc* £23, fixed-price L £15.50/D £20.50. ☺ H/wine £12.50
Times: Noon-last L 2pm/7-last D 10pm. Closed L Sat
Additional: Bar food; Sunday L buffet only (12.30-2.30pm); Children welcome; ✿ dishes
Smoking: No smoking in dining room; Air conditioning
Accommodation: 168 en suite
Credit cards: 🟥 🟥 🟥 🟥 🟥 🟥

Directions: M8/J19, follow signs for Clydeside Expressway to Glasgow Rd, then Dumbarton Rd (A814), then signs for Clydebank Business Park. Hotel on L within HCI International Medical Centre complex

DUNDEE CITY

DUNDEE, **Stakis Dundee** ✿

Overlooking the waterfront, the purpose-built hotel has been designed to take advantage of the location. Chef's Specialities include seared sea bass with stir-fried fennel with lime, sweet pimento and coriander sauce and fillet of Scotch lamb coated in a herb crust, served with creamed leeks, accompanied by a port wine and redcurrant sauce.

Accommodation: 131 en suite
Credit cards: 🟥 🟥 🟥 🟥 🟥

Directions: Follow signs to Tay Road Bridge. At roundabout outside railway station, take last turning to Olympia Leisure Centre. Hotel is at end of cul-de-sac

Earl Grey Place DD1 4DE
Map 11: NO43
Tel: 01382 229271
Fax: 01382 200072
Chef: Edward Sharkey
Cost: *Alc* £25, fixed price L £9.95/D £18 (4 courses). ☺ H/wine £10.95
Times: Last L 2pm/last D 9.45pm
Additional: Bar food L; Sunday L; Children welcome; ✿ dishes
Smoking: No-smoking area; No cigars or pipes; Air conditioning

EDINBURGH, CITY OF

EDINBURGH, **Atrium** ✿✿✿

Cambridge Street EH1 2ED
Map 11: NT27
Tel: 0131 2288882
Fax: 0131 2288808
Chef: Glyn Stevens
Owners: Andrew & Lisa Radford
Cost: *Alc* L £18/D £30.
H/wine £10.50
Times: Noon-last L 2.30pm/6pm-last
D 10.30pm. Closed Sun,
1 wk Xmas/New Year
Additional: Snack meals L;
Children welcome; ✿ dishes
Seats: 60
Smoking: Air conditioning
Credit cards: 💳 💳 💳 💳 💳

Directions: From Princes Street, turn
into Lothian Road, 2nd L and 1st R,
by the Traverse Theatre.

Hand-blown oil lamps, tables made of jarrah, canvas-covered
chairs, dim lighting, autumnal colours and clean, uncluttered
decor, all in a building that employs 1,200 people in law, fund
management, stockbroking and tax planning. Pop in here after
you've seen your accountant or made a few investments and go
for one of the bargain-priced lunchtime snacks: pork fillet with
haricot beans, roasted garlic and Savoy cabbage, say. Atrium has
been at the cutting edge of the restaurant scene since it opened,
bringing the Mediterranean to Edinburgh and mugging Scottish
dishes when it suits: Cullen skink may make an appearance
alongside roast venison with black pudding and mushroom pasta.
More mainstream to the style is paesano sausage with mash,
lentils, Savoy cabbage and mushroom jus and that's just a starter,
with main courses of chicken breast with Parma ham and roasted
vegetables, or Parmesan-crusted lemon sole with lentils and
black olives. There's no denying the kitchen's skill, ingenuity and
sourcing of impeccable ingredients, with a keen eye for visual
appeal showing up in a starter of cod fillet colourfully presented
with roasted pimento and sugar snaps. Puddings come in the
shape of summer berry tart, a simple and successful dish of a
shortcrust base with vanilla cream, blackberries, raspberries,
blueberries and strawberries, or chocolate mousse with sun-dried
banana, with quality farmhouse cheeses as an alternative. The
wine list is an impressive assembly from around the world. Plenty
are sold by the glass, including a page each of sherries and ports,
pudding wines abound, and there's a handful of appropriately
priced rare vintages.

AA Shortlisted for
Wine Award-see page 16

EDINBURGH, **Balmoral Hotel, Number One** ✿✿

Elegant and imposing, the huge Edwardian building dominates
the east end of Princes Street. The brasserie has been
transformed into a stylish restaurant, Hadrians, offering
contemporary cooking in a 30s setting; however, for a more
formal meal, Number One is the place to choose. Scallops
'smelling and tasting of the Atlantic' arrived topping a leek
timbale and dressed with an asparagus vinaigrette, and duck
foie gras and duck confit, pressed terrine-style, had good rich

1 Princes Street EH2 2EQ
Map 11: NT27
Tel: 0131 5576727
Chef: Jeff Bland
Owners: RF Hotels
Cost: *Alc* £40, fixed-price L £17.95/D
£30.50. ☺ H/wine £15
Times: Noon-last L 2pm/7-last
D 10.30pm. Closed L Sat, L Sun,
2 wks Jan

**Balmoral Hotel,
No 1 The Restaurant**

Additional: Children welcome;
 dishes
Seats: 60. Private dining room up to 30
Smoking: No-smoking area;
Air conditioning
Accommodation: 184 en suite
Credit cards: ▉ ▩ ▩ ▦ ▩ ▣ ▣ JCB

flavours. A warm salad of Bresse pigeon, managed the trick of being both succulent and tender yet rare. In these days of healthy eating, it was cheering to find a rich butter sauce giving depth to a main course of (French) chicken, stuffed and rolled with veal sweetbreads and vegetable mousseline. Reports on desserts have been variable – thumbs up for hot banana soufflé, down for soggy pear tart drowning in eau-de-vie sabayon.

Directions: Hotel at east end of Princes Street; hotel is next to Waverley Station

EDINBURGH, blue bar café ❀   **NEW**

In the heart of Edinburgh's theatre district, the blue bar café is a young, trendy restaurant serving simple European dishes. The interior is minimalist, with hardwood floors, huge windows and blue chairs. A typical light lunch might include thin slices of seared tuna with wasabi dressing, followed by smoked duck and chorizo pasta.

Additional: Children welcome; dishes
Smoking: Air conditioning
Credit cards: ▉ ▩ ▣ ▩ ▣

Directions: From Princes St turn into Lothian Rd, 2nd L, 1st R, on first floor above Traverse Theatre Box Office

Cambridge Street EH1 2ED
Map 11: NT27
Tel: 0131 2211222
Fax: 0131 2288808
Chef: John Rutter
Owners: Andrew & Lisa Radford
Cost: Alc £16. ☺ H/wine £10
Times: Last L 2.30pm/last D 11pm.
Closed 25-26 Dec

EDINBURGH,
Bonars at L'Auberge ❀❀

The Bonars have moved from their country restaurant at Gifford to this long-established city property set on various levels. Douglas Bonar is working at simplifying his style – menu description, for example, are thankfully less gushy than at the previous establishment. We enjoyed a pistachio and pine kernel-studded seafood terrine that was wrapped in spinach and served with a mustard and dill cream, pan-fried venison stuffed with a duxelle of pear, apple and plum and accompanied by caramelised chicken, a Madeira and port wine jus and a timbale of red cabbage. Dessert was a bread-and-plum pudding with a walnut and caramel sauce, an interesting variation on the traditional dish. France is the main player on the wine list, and there is an emphasis on vintage bottles.

Directions: City centre, in old town, off the Royal Mile

56 St Mary's Street EH1 1SX
Map 11: NT27
Tel: 0131 5565888
Fax: 0131 5562588
Please telephone for further details

EDINBURGH,
The Bonham Hotel

Welcome newcomer on the periphery of the city's New Town, fashioned in a modern manner from its Georgian architecture. Adventurous cooking on a catchy menu that features light-hearted food trying hard to be different. Couscous terrine with roasted Med veg, roast duck with strawberry and Puy lentil sauce, lime and chilli potato cake and cabbage and ginger, show something of the tilt.

35 Drumsheugh Gardens EH3 7RU
Map 11: NT27
Tel: 0131 2266080
Please telephone for further details

EDINBURGH, **Caledonian Hotel**

Princes Street EH1 2AB
Map 11: NT27
Tel: 0131 4599988
Fax: 0131 2256632
Chef: Alan Matthews
Cost: *Alc* £23. ☺ H/wine £13.95
Times: 12.30-last L 2pm/6.30-last D 10pm. Closed L Sat
Additional: Sunday L; Children welcome; 🍴 dishes
Seats: 100. Private dining room 220
Smoking: No-smoking area; No pipes & cigars; Air conditioning
Accommodation: 246 en suite
Credit cards: ▬ ▬ ▬ ▬ ▬ ▬

Affectionately known as The Caley, this hotel boasts notable Victorian architecture and fine views of the castle. The splendour of the elegant Pompadour dining room, with its sophisticated service and pianist playing, is perfect for the special occasion. In contrast with the classical setting, the short menu is distinctly contemporary. Ravioli of chicken and truffle with cep sauce is a typical starter. To follow, there may be fillet of monkfish crusted with herbs and served on a mound of mushy peas accompanied by confit of tomatoes and mashed potatoes. Nicely presented vanilla pannacotta comes with oven-dried fruits, pineapple and a star anise sauce. The hotel also has a more informal restaurant called Carriages which, unlike the Pompadour, is open for lunch. The name is a reference to the nearby station, from which guests used to be able to enter the hotel directly. It serves simply cooked traditional favourites such as roast beef and Yorkshire pudding.

Directions: At western end of Princes Street

EDINBURGH,
Carlton Highland Hotel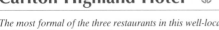

The most formal of the three restaurants in this well-located hotel is Quills. The 'Flavour of Scotland' menu makes an interesting choice – smoked salmon, gâteau of haggis, neeps and tatties, medallions of beef fillet in a forest mushroom jus, and wild berry cranachan.

Additional: Bar food; Children welcome; 🍴 dishes
Smoking: No smoking in dining room; Air conditioning
Accommodation: 204 en suite
Credit cards: ▬ ▬ ▬ ▬ ▬ ▬ JCB

Directions: Turn R onto North Bridge at E/end of Princes St

North Bridge EH1 1SD
Map 11: NT27
Tel: 0131 4723000
Fax: 0131 5562691
Chef: Martin Buttrick
Owner: Scottish Highland Hotels plc
Cost: *Alc* £21, fixed price L £15/D £21 (4 courses). ☺ H/wine £10.95
Times: Last L 2pm/last D 9.30pm. Closed L Sat, all Sun

EDINBURGH, **Channings**

South Learmonth Gardens EH4 1EZ
Map 11: NT27
Tel: 0131 3152225/6
Fax: 0131 3329631
Chef: Richard Glennie
Owner: Peter Taylor
Cost: *Alc* £24.50, fixed-price L £12.50/D £21. ☺ H/wine £10.75
Times: 12.30-last L 2.30pm/7-last D 8pm. Closed L Sat & Sun, 26-28 Dec
Additional: Bar food L; Children welcome; 🍴 dishes
Seats: 65. Private dining room 20
Smoking: No smoking in dining room
Accommodation: 48 en suite
Credit cards: 💳 💳 💳 💳 💳 💳 💳 JCB

Five Edwardian town houses have been converted to create this discreet, rather clubby hotel in a quiet cobbled terrace. An imaginative merging of Scottish and European cooking is on offer in the attractive basement brasserie, using quality Scottish produce. Our test meal, chosen from five options at each course, kicked off with excellent home-made bread and a risotto of smoked red pimento with seared scallop and spring onions. Next came a good combination of caramelised duck with dauphinoise potatoes and Puy lentils, though fairly heavy on the garlic, and a moist chicken pot-au-feu was well liked. Banana tarte Tatin with banana ice cream and fudge sauce was another effective partnership. The wine list is varied, with a good selection of countries and regions.

Directions: From Princes St follow signs to Forth Bridge (A90), cross Dean Bridge and take 4th R into South Learmonth Ave. Follow road to R at bottom of hill

EDINBURGH,
Duck's at Le Marché Noir ❀

2/4 Eyre Place EH3 5EP
Map 11: NT27
Tel: 0131 5581608
Fax: 0131 5560798
Chef: David Connell
Owner: Malcolm Duck
Cost: *Alc* £21, fixed-price D £18.50. ☺ H/wine £9.50
Times: Last L 2.30pm/last D 11pm. Closed L Sat, L Sun, 25-26 Dec
Additional: Children welcome; 🍴 dishes

Cosy atmosphere, smart table appointments and, by its own words, 'a French restaurant offering modern British cooking'. Thus menus take in marbled terrine of pheasant and walnut with a port and cinnamon syrup, collops of venison with stewed plums and port wine jus, and a lemon tart with a sound crème anglaise. Well-compiled wine list.

Smoking: No-smoking area
Credit cards: 💳 💳 💳 💳 💳 💳 💳 JCB

Directions: Follow the 'Mound' across Princes Street, George Street, Queen Street to bottom of Dundas Street

EDINBURGH, **George Inter-Continental** ❀❀

19-21 George Street
EH2 2PB
Map 11: NT27
Tel: 0131 2251251
Fax: 0131 2265644
Chef: Klaus Knust
Owner: Inter-Continental Hotels

With its magnificent classical façade and marble-floored foyer, this grand Victorian building was once the trading hall of an insurance company. Now a well-run hotel, it is popular with business travellers and visitors to the city. It is also home to Le Chambertin, an intimate restaurant with high moulded ceilings,

George Inter-Continental

Cost: *Alc* £18.50, fixed-price L
£15.50 (2 courses)/D £18.50. ☺
H/wine £12.75
Times: 12.30-last L 2.30pm/6.30-last
D 10pm
Additional: Bar food; Sunday L;
Children welcome; ❹ dishes
Seats: 150. Private dining room
Smoking: No-smoking area;
Air conditioning
Accommodation: 195 en suite
Credit cards: ▆ ▆ ▆ ▆ ▆ ▆

Directions: At E end of George St, nr
St Andrew's Square

rich fabrics and long windows overlooking George Street. To
whet your appetite, a typical meal from the extensive *carte*
might include a starter of warm pigeon breast on a lentil and
bacon salad with raspberry vinaigrette, followed by roast
haunch of venison with woodland mushrooms and wild berry
glacé. The highlight of an autumn inspection meal was a well-
executed dish of marinated cutlets of lamb, served 'deliciously
pink' with roast shallots and rosemary jus. Also enjoyed was a
starter of lobster and crayfish ravioli with wasabi cream sauce,
and an excellent lemon tart for dessert. Service is polished,
well paced and attentive.

EDINBURGH, **Iggs** ❀❀

15 Jeffrey Street EH1 1DR
Map 11: NT27
Tel: 0131 5578184
Fax: 0131 4417111
Chef: Coleman Maquire
Owner: Iggy Campos
Cost: *Alc* £27.50, fixed-price L £9.50
(2 courses)/D £25. H/wine £11
Times: Noon-last L 2.30pm/6-last
D 10.30pm. Closed Sun
Additional: Children welcome;
❹ dishes
Seats: 40. Private dining room 20
Smoking: Air conditioning
Credit cards: ▆ ▆ ▆ ▆ ▆ ▆ ▆ JCB

Directions: At the heart of
Edinburgh's Old Town, just off the
Royal Mile

Lovers of Spanish wine will have a field day here, with three of
the wine list's four pages devoted to them. Curiously, the menu
isn't as Iberian as you would expect at a restaurant owned by
Spaniard Iggy Campos. The atmosphere's relaxed and the
menu as cosmopolitan as the clientele. Starters of salt-cod with
garlic, tomato and tarragon, or a salad of snails with bacon
from Spain are as close as you may get to that country. Instead,
there could be braised shank of Parma pork with crackling, or
wild mushroom risotto. Main courses could feature tournedos
of Borders lamb with niçoise salad, confit of tuna with saffron
noodles and sauce vierge, and roast loin of roe-deer, cooked
pink, served with pear and parsnip cream, beetroot relish and
juniper jus. Spain meets France on the cheeseboard, or go for
something like passion fruit crème caramel.

EDINBURGH, **Jacksons** ✤

209 High Street EH1 1PZ
Map 11: NT27
Tel: 0131 225 1793
Fax: 0131 220 0620
Chef: Andrew Smith
Owner: Lyn Mackinnon
Cost: *Alc* £30, fixed-price L £7/D
£22.50. ☺ H/wine £11.95.
Times: Last L 2.30pm/D 10.30pm.
Closed 25-26 Dec
Additional: Sunday L,
Children welcome; ✪ dishes
Smoking: Air conditioning.
Credit cards: ▬ ▦ ◥ 🗌 ▦ JCB

*Set midway between Edinburgh Castle and Holyrood Palace on
the Royal Mile, Jacksons is a great place to sample sound
Scottish cooking in the heart of Scotland's capital. Expect dishes
such as pan-fried collops of wild venison with game sauce and
seasonal berries, and grilled fillet of red snapper, with star-anise
and whisky mustard.*

Directions: On Royal Mile, near St Giles Cathedral

EDINBURGH, **Kelly's Restaurant** ✤✤

46 West Richmond Street EH8
Map 11: NT27
Tel/Fax: 0131 6683847
Chef: Stephen Frost
Owners: Stephen & Anne Frost
Cost: Fixed price D £25. H/wine £10
Times: Noon-2pm/7-9.30pm.
Closed Sun-Tue
Additional: No children under 5;
✪ dishes
Seats: 30
Smoking: No smoking in dining rom
Credit cards: ▬ ▦ ◥ 🗌

Amazing prices coupled with quality cooking make Kelly's, a
small restaurant just off the Pleasance, a definite must for
anyone seeking a great meal out. Oak chairs and fine linen
reflect the quiet formality of the dining room, where Ann Frost
welcomes guests while husband Stephen toils away at the
stove. Modern British dishes mingle with classics on the hand-
written menu, where you will find excellent dishes such as
blackened Cajun chicken supreme with Caesar salad, escalopes
of monkfish with fresh pasta and vegetable noodles, and baked
polenta with peppers and mozzarella. A Saturday lunch started
with smoked salmon fishcakes with creamed leeks and green
beans, followed by risotto of asparagus and peas with carnoli
rice. Typical desserts include ricotta cheesecake with apricot
sauce, and almond meringue cake with whipped cream and red
fruits, although our inspector opted for an excellent poached
pear and chocolate tart.

Directions: *Telephone for directions*

EDINBURGH, **Malmaison Hotel** ✸

1 Tower Place, Leith EH6 7DB
Map 11: NT27
Tel: 0131 5556868
Fax: 0131 5556999
Chef: Lawrence Roberts
Owner: Ken McCulloch
Cost: Alc £24, fixed-price L £9.50
(2 courses)
Times: Last L 2pm/last D 10.45pm
Additional: Bar food; Children
welcome; ◑ dishes
Accommodation: 60 en suite
Credit cards ▨ ▧ ⎿ ▨ ▨

*Bustling Malmaison brings the atmosphere of a French brasserie to
Leith's waterfront, however the food is international with dishes such
as Caesar salad and sticky toffee pudding alongside the coq au vin
and confit. Our inspector rates Malmaison's ham terrine with parsley
and mustard sauce, the chocolate pots and espresso.*

Directions: From the city centre
follow Leith Docklands, through
3 sets of lights and L into Tower Street

EDINBURGH,
Marriott Dalmahoy ✸✸

Kirknewton EH27 8EB
Map 11: NT27
Tel: 0131 3331845
Fax: 0131 3331433
Chef: Wayne Asson
Cost: Alc £25, fixed-price L £15/D
£25. H/wine £12
Times: Noon-last L 2pm/7-last
D 9.45pm. Closed L Sat & Sun
Additional: Bar food;
Children welcome; ◑ dishes
Seats: 100. Private dining rooms.
Jacket & tie preferred
Smoking: No smoking in dining room;
Air conditioning
Accommodation: 151 en suite
Credit cards: ▨ ▧ ▨ ⎿ ▨ ▨

With two golf courses to choose from, as well as a tennis court
and a leisure centre with its own restaurant and bar, guests here
should find themselves with plenty to do. Many of the original
features have been retained in the Adam-designed building,
and the public areas offer a mixture of the formal and informal.
The Pentland Restaurant (the hotel has glorious views of the
Pentland Hills), looking over the 18th hole, is where serious
eating takes place. An inspector enjoyed a meal that was as
interesting as it was enjoyable, with some beautifully presented
innovative combinations: a salad of smoked salmon and
marinated halibut with a mango and balsamic and a sage and
cider dressing, and then moist and tender sea bass in a puddle
of bouillabaisse sauce with fresh, crunchy vegetables on the
side. Kumquat crème brûlée brought things to a happy
conclusion. The wine list is arranged alphabetically by country,
with two pages of house recommendations.

Directions: On A71, 3 miles from Calder roundabout, opposite
Ratho turn off

EDINBURGH,
Martin's Restaurant ❀❀❀

Do not be put off by the location – the dark, narrow back street belies what awaits the diner inside. The decor is pleasing in its simplicity, with lots of fresh flowers and contemporary art work, and the enthusiasm and natural friendliness of the front-of-house proprietors, Gay and Martin Irons, is memorable. Forbes Stott's cooking is unusual, unpredictable and full of big, bold flavours with an emphasis on aromatic spicing: seared tuna with salad leaves, roast peppers and basil pesto, for example. Bouchées filled with sweet pepper, raisins and aubergine set the scene at inspection, as did lovely, close-textured home-baked bread served with a jug of fennel vinaigrette for dunking purposes. The texture of a wild mushroom risotto was spot-on, and another starter of langoustine and saffron broth came packed with flavoursome veggies. More strong flavours – sweet potato, celeriac, tomato and cinnamon – married surprisingly well with grilled supreme of halibut. The good gamey flavour came through in a pan-fried haunch of venison, accompanied by spicy red cabbage with beetroot. Desserts have been somewhat uneven – best of the bunch has been terrific elder flower and thyme sorbet which cut the richness of a crumbly chocolate terrine.

Signature dishes: Scottish game – wild duck such as widgeon, mallard, teal and game birds such as partridge, but not grouse.

70 Rose Street North Lane
EH2 3DX
Map 11: NT27
Tel: 0131 2253106
Chef: Forbes Stott
Owner: Martin Irons
Cost: Alc £34, fixed-price L £14.50 (2 courses). H/wine £10.95
Times: Noon-last L 1.50pm/7-last D 9.45pm. Closed L Sat, all Sun, Mon, 24 Dec-20 Jan, 1 wk May-Jun, 1 wk Sep-Oct
Additional: No children under 8
Seats: 48. Private room 8-12
Smoking: No smoking in dining room
Credit cards: ▬ ▬ ▬ ▬ ▬ ▬ JCB

Directions: North Lane is off Rose Street which runs parallel to and behind Princes Street

EDINBURGH,
Norton House Hotel ❀❀

By day naturally light and airy, at night the Conservatory Restaurant takes on a special atmosphere with subdued lighting and effective canopy drapes. On the food front, the carte and fixed-price menus offer a pretty extensive choice between them. Particularly enjoyed on our most recent visit was a starter of home-smoked lamb (tender and deliciously smoky without being over salted) served on fine aubergine disks with a mint-dressed potato and pine nut salad, and the shortbread hearts served with an elderberry crème brûlée were outstanding. Other offerings included duck breast marinated in five spice and served on a bed of egg noodles with plum sauce and fried ginger, sea bream with coriander and fennel on green tomato chutney and (among several vegetarian options) a celery, thyme and apple strudel with nutmeg cream. The hotel is set in over 50 acres of parkland to the west of the city.

Ingliston EH28 8LX
Map 11: NT27
Tel: 0131 3331275
Fax: 0131 3335305
Chef: John Newton
Owners: Virgin Hotels
Cost: Alc £17, fixed-price D £29.50. ☺ H/wine £12.50
Times: Noon-last L 2.30pm/7-last D 10pm. Closed L Sat
Additional: Bar food; Sunday L; Children welcome; ❹ dishes
Seats: 70. Private dining up to 300
Smoking: No-smoking area; No pipes & cigars
Accommodation: 47 en suite
Credit cards: ▬ ▬ ▬ ▬ ▬ ▬ ▬

Directions: M8/J2, off the A8, 0.5 mile past Edinburgh Airport

EDINBURGH,
Sheraton Grand Hotel ❀❀❀

The Sheraton Grand is a modern building at the heart of the city's West End. A grand staircase leads from the marbled entrance hall to the first-floor bar, a popular venue for drinks or afternoon tea. The Terrace Restaurant, with views of the Usher Hall and the castle beyond, is informal and lively, serving a daily-changing hot and cold buffet, while the Grill Room, small and discreet, combines the finest ingredients Scotland has to

1 Festival Square EH3 9SR
Map 11: NT27
Tel: 0131 2216423
Fax: 0131 2296254
Chef: Nicholas Laurent
Cost: Alc £29.50, fixed-price L £25.50/D £34.50. H/wine £15
Times: Noon-last L 2.30pm/7pm-last D 10.30pm. Closed L Sat, all Sun

Sheraton Grand Hotel

Additional: Bar food; Sunday L;
Children welcome; ❹ dishes
Seats: 45. Private dining room 20
Smoking: No-smoking area;
Air conditioning
Accommodation: 261 en suite
Credit cards: ▆▆ ▆▆ ▆ ▆▆ ▆

Directions: Off Lothian Road

offer with a classical French repertoire. In here, Perthshire wild
mushrooms are incorporated into a gratin with scallops and
smoked foie gras to produce a starter 'superb in flavours and
definitions'. Breast of Gressingham duck is no less impressive,
pink and succulent, its skin crisp, elevated by a so-called
gingerbread sauce and served with vegetables paysanne. In
winter, the same animal could be accompanied by a pâté of
truffles and Madeira sauce. An assortment of banana mini-
desserts may be there for the finale, consisting of crème brûlée,
cheesecake, ice cream and strudel. Incidentals – breads, canapés,
and tablet and truffles with coffee – are highly commended, and
the wine list is largely a global catalogue of vintage wines to suit
discerning palates, with a good range of half-bottles.

Signature dishes: Roast sea bass with tapenade, wild
mushrooms and sauce vierge; squab pigeon en papillote with
braised cabbage and mushroom ravioli.

EDINBURGH, **36** ❀❀

36 Great King Street EH3 6QH
Map 11: NT27
Tel: 0131 5563636
Fax: 0131 5563663
Chef: Malcolm Warham
Owner: Peter Taylor
Cost: *Alc* £25. ☺
Times: Noon-last L 2pm/7-last
D 10pm. Closed L Sat, 25-28 Dec
Additional: Sunday L; ❹ dishes
Seats: 70
Smoking: No smoking in dining room;
Air conditioning
Accommodation: 15 en suite

This splendid Georgian town house, situated in the heart of
Edinburgh's New Town, is home to the stylish modern Scottish
cooking of Malcolm Warham. His innovative style takes the
best of Scottish ingredients and turns them into tempting
dishes with honest flavours. A typical meal might start with a
warm salad of sesame and honey-roast goose breast with crispy
bacon and garlic croûtons, followed by a rosette of salmon
seared with Cajun spices and served on a lemon and vermouth
butter sauce. Other main courses include roast cannon of lamb
with a sweet pepper, sausage and garlic fritter, peppered breast
of Barbary duck with a sweet Cassis and shallot sauce, and filo

pastry strudel of Mediterranean vegetables with a wild mushroom and herb risotto. The extensive wine list features wines from around the world, with a strong representation from the Americas, Australia, South Africa and New Zealand.

Directions: Turn off Princes St into Frederick St for 0.5 mile and turn R into Great King St. Past traffic lights, hotel on L

Credit cards: ▨ ▨ ▨ ▨ ▨ ▨ ▨ JCB

EDINBURGH,

The Vintner's Room ❀❀

800 years ago, Augustinian friars stored wine here for Holyrood Palace. Today, the stone walls and wooden floors are the setting for a popular restaurant and wine bar; one can eat either in the lively bar or the more sedate dining-room, which is illuminated solely by candlelight. The cooking is French provincial, and dishes that have deservedly stood the test of time include sautéed scallops with rhubarb butter sauce, and rare roast Aberdeen Angus served with a sauce marchand de vin, both regularly included on menus by popular demand. A soupe de poissons, with a rich 'bisquey' flavour, featured halibut and sea bass, and tournedos of venison, a huge portion, were tender, pink and wrapped in bacon and served on a zesty galette with heather honey and lemon giving the perfect sweet-and-sour accompaniment. The place is rightly proud of its wine list – carefully compiled, mostly vintage bottles, it includes many halves and good wines by the glass.

Directions: At end of Leith Walk; L into Great Junction Street, R into Henderson Street. Restaurant is in old warehouse on R

The Vaults 87 Giles Street
Leith EH6 6BZ
Map 11: NT27
Tel: 0131 5546767
Fax: 0131 4677130
Chef: A T Cumming
Owners: A T & S C Cumming
Cost: *Alc* £28, fixed-price L £14.50. ☺ H/wine £10
Times: Noon-last L 2pm/7-last D 10.30pm. Closed Sun, 2 wks Xmas
Additional: Children welcome; 🍴 dishes
Seats: 60. Private dining room 36
Smoking: No smoking in dining room
Credit cards: ▨ ▨ ▨ ▨

EDINBURGH, **Winter Glen** ❀

The stylish basement restaurant has exposed stone walls, tartan plates, and twiggy arrangements. Changing fortnightly, the modern Scottish menu may list roast loin of venison, red cabbage compote, glazed apple and rich game gravy, and boneless darne of Scottish salmon with langoustine mousseline and vermouth sauce. Puddings are simple but successful – try the warm chocolate cake.

Smoking: No pipes & cigars. **Credit cards:** ▨ ▨ ▨ ▨ ▨

Directions: Telephone for directions

3A1 Dundas Street EH3 6QG
Map 11: NT27
Tel: 0131 4777060
Fax: 0131 6247087
Chef: Graham Winter
Owners: Blair Glen, Graham Winter
Cost: Fixed-price L £12.95/D £24.95. ☺ H/wine £10.25
Times: Last L 2pm/last D 10pm. Closed Sun, 1st wk Jan
Additional: 🍴 dishes

EDINBURGH,

Witchery by the Castle ❀

Two contrasting rooms in the shadow of Edinburgh Castle: the Secret Garden, with stone walls hung with tapestries and a painted ceiling, and the dark, atmospheric room upstairs, both lit by candles at night. Dishes sampled at our last visit included shellfish soup with rouille, and roast monkfish with smoked bacon confit.

Accommodation: 2 en suite
Credit cards: ▨ ▨ ▨ ▨ ▨ ▨ JCB

Directions: At the entrance to Edinburgh Castle at the very top of the Royal Mile

Castle Hill EH2 1NE
Map 11: NT27
Tel: 0131 2255613
Fax: 0131 2204392
Chef: Douglas Roberts
Owner: James Thomson
Cost: *Alc* £35, fixed price L £14.95/D £23.95. ☺ H/wine £10.95
Times: Last L 4pm/last D 11.30pm. Closed 25-26 Dec
Additional: Sunday L; No children under 5; 🍴 dishes

FALKIRK

GRANGEMOUTH,
Grange Manor Hotel

Glensburgh Road FK3 8XJ
Map 11: NS98
Tel: 01324 474836
Fax: 01324 665861
Chef: Kenny Wilson
Owners: Bill & Jane Wallace
Cost: *Alc* £26.65, fixed-price L £8.95
(2 courses)/D £19.85. ☺
H/wine £9.75
Times: Last L 2pm/last D 9pm.
Closed 26 Dec, 1 Jan
Additional: Bar food; Sunday L;
Children welcome; ◑ dishes
Smoking: No-smoking area
Accommodation: 37 en suite
Credit cards: ▬ ▭ ▅ ⌐ ▦ ◖ ▣

*Every effort is made to make dining at this family-run hotel special,
and the canapés at the bar set the tone. Dishes sampled include
smoked salmon bavarois, and breast of guinea fowl with a peppered
sauce, and a terrine of dark and white chocolate with raspberry
coulis.*

Directions: M9 exit 6 200m on right, M9 exit 5/A905 2 miles

POLMONT, Inchyra Grange **NEW**

*Turn-of-the-century manor house that has seen a huge investment of
capital to provide excellent leisure and corporate facilities. The
restaurant, in particular, is light airy and fresh. Cream of leek and
potato soup, confit of duck with braised red cabbage and an orange
and cardamom gravy, and pineapple Pavlova with mango and
strawberry coulis, show the range.*

Smoking: No smoking in dining room; Air conditioning
Accommodation: 109 en suite
Credit cards: ▬ ▭ ⌐ ▦ ▣

Directions: Telephone for directions

Grange Road FK2 0YB
Map 11: NS97
Tel: 01324 711911
Fax: 01324 716134
Chef: Gordon Dochard
Owners: Macdonald Hotels
Cost: Fixed price L £12.50/D £31
(5 courses). ☺ H/wine £13.50
Times: Last L 2pm/ last D 9.30.
Closed L Sat
Additional: Bar food; Sunday L;
Children welcome; ◑ dishes

FIFE

ANSTRUTHER,
Cellar Restaurant ✿✿✿

Peter Jukes is cooking as soundly as ever. His restaurant, a
former cooperage where barrels were made for the herring
industry, retains an old, rustic feel with open fires, beams and
stone walls. Fish is the driving force here, although meat, such
as fillet of local beef with a green peppercorn sauce and
lyonnaise potatoes, makes an appearance. Jukes has long
adhered to the keep-it-simple principle – new season East

24 East Green KY10 3AA
Map 12: NO50
Tel: 01333 310378
Fax: 01333 321544
Chef/Owner: Peter Jukes
Cost: *Alc* L £15, fixed-price
D £28.50. ☺ H/wine £12.50
Times: 12.30-1.30pm/7-9pm.
Closed Sun, Mon (Nov-Easter)

Neuk crab requires nothing more than toast and lemon mayonnaise, and a signature dish of halibut is simply grilled and served with greens, pine kernels, smoked bacon and a separate pot of hollandaise sauce. What is outstanding about the food here is the unwavering quality of the ingredients used, and the confidence with which they are cooked. Take a spring test meal that opened on a high note with an *amuse-gueule* of lobster and smoked trout quiche, and never missed a beat after that. Fresh hand-picked west-coast scallops of astonishing freshness required nothing more than some well-timed pan-frying and a few roasted green and yellow peppers, whilst seared tuna was served with caramelised onion, wild mushrooms and Madeira jus, and set upon fresh spinach and chopped French beans. Dessert was an unusual combination of trio of chocolate mousses (bitter, white and milk) with an orange liqueur sauce. The wine list has many good young European whites.

Signature dishes: Turbot and scallop with spinach, new season asparagus and Chardonnay sauce; roast cod with pesto and courgette and pepper stew; crayfish and mussel bisque.

Additional: Sunday L
Seats: 32
Smoking: No smoking in dining room
Credit cards: ▨ ▧ ▨ ▨ ▨ ▨

Directions: Behind the Scottish Fisheries Museum

CUPAR, Eden House Hotel

With a grandeur typical of the Victorian period, this large house stands overlooking Haugh Park. Fresh ingredients are treated with respect, and dishes might include home-made chicken liver pâté, poached salmon with a delicate grain mustard sauce, and a 'wicked' sticky toffee pudding.

Smoking: No-smoking area; no pipes & cigars
Accommodation: 11 en suite
Credit cards: ▨ ▧ ▨

Directions: Turn R after railway bridge in Cupar. Hotel is 100 yds to R

2 Pitscottie Road KY15 4HF
Map 11: NO31
Tel: 01334 652510
Fax: 01334 652277
Chef: Alan Lunn
Owners: Mr & Mrs L Vizan
Cost: *Alc* £22, fixed-price L&D £19.
☺ H/wine £9
Times: Last L 2pm/last D 9pm.
Closed L Sun, 25-26 Dec, 1 Jan
Additional: Bar food; Children welcome; ◑ dishes

CUPAR,
Ostlers Close Restaurant ❀❀❀

Bonnygate KY15 4BU
Map 11: NO31
Tel: 01334 655574
Fax: 01334 654036
Chef: James Graham
Owners: James & Amanda Graham
Cost: *Alc* £27. H/wine £9.95
Times: 12.15pm-last L 2pm/7pm-last D 9.30pm. Closed Sun, Mon, 2 wks spring
Additional: No children under 6 at D; ◑ dishes
Seats: 26
Credit cards: ▨ ▧ ▨ ▨ ▨ ▨ JCB

Directions: In small lane off main street (A91) of Cupar.

Located up a narrow close just off the town centre, this small restaurant continues to turn out delightfully simple, unpretentious food of excellent quality. Jimmy Graham runs the kitchen with wife Amanda doubling as front of house hostess and pastry chef. The couple converted the ground-floor kitchen, scullery and stables of the building, which dates back to around 1690, some 15 years ago, to provide an informal setting which they fill with garden flowers and candlelight. The hand-written menus may feature starters such as a roasted red pepper soup with a robust, spiced flavour and light croûtons, or fillet of monkfish with a stir-fry of sea kale and spring onions in a shellfish sauce. Main courses make the most of local ingredients: roast saddle of venison and breasts of wood pigeon with wild mushrooms and game sauce, or ever-popular Scotch beef with shallot and horseradish gravy. The side plate of vegetables offers lots of flavours, such as braised fennel with tomato, cheesy broccoli, dauphinoise potatoes and shredded marinated courgette. Honey, Drambuie and oatmeal ice cream is a local favourite from the dessert menu, while Amanda's pecan and maple tart is a revelation of lightness served with smooth vanilla ice cream. Alternatively, there is a platter of Scottish cheeses. Excellent Italian espresso and good petits fours including meringue Chantilly complete the charming experience of a visit here. The lunchtime menu offers the same fine quality but with a shorter choice of just four starters and main courses. House wines are from Chile and complemented by good-value Australian wines also available by the bottle or glass. Delve further into the eleven-page wine list for a world-wide collection of speciality varieties, half-bottles, champagnes and a delicious selection of dessert wines.

DUNFERMLINE,

Keavil House Hotel ❀

A grand piano is the feature of this conservatory restaurant with pleasant views of the garden. The contemporary food has a Scottish flavour and there is a dedicated Taste of Scotland menu. Wise choices: timbale of crab, monkfish in tomato, garlic and oregano fume, and the delicious rhubarb custard tart with cinnamon anglaise.

Accommodation: 47 en suite
Credit cards: ▬ ▬ 🐦 £ ▬ 🄲 ᴅ

Directions: M90/J3, 7 miles from Forth Road Bridge, take A985, turning R after bridge. From Dunfermline, 2 miles W on A994

Crossford KY12 8QW
Map 11: NT08
Tel: 01383 736258
Fax: 01383 621600
Chef: Volker Steinemann
Owner: Charles Gwyn
Cost: *Alc* £25, fixed-price L £12.50/D £15. ☺ H/wine £9.75
Times: Last L 2pm/last D 10pm
Additional: Bar food; Sunday L; Children welcome; ◑ dishes
Smoking: No smoking in dining room

ELIE,

Bouquet Garni Restaurant ❀❀

51 High Street KY9 1BZ
Map 12: NO40
Tel/Fax: 01333 330374
Chef: Kevin A McElhinney
Owners: Norah & Andrew Keracher
Cost: *Alc* L £14/D £25. ☺ H/wine £12.90
Times: Noon-1.30pm/7-9.30pm. Closed L Mon (Oct-Mar), all Sun, last wk Nov, 2nd-3rd wks Jan
Additional: No children under 12
Seats: 30. Private dining room 12
Smoking: No smoking in dining room
Credit cards: ▬ ▬ 🐦 £

Pretty, countrified restaurant with some nice local paintings, lace cloths and sofas in the bar lounge. The kitchen keeps faith with local and regional produce with the main emphasis on fish, but meat does make an appearance as in the breast of Perthshire pigeon served on a bed of Puy lentils, smoked bacon and wild mushrooms with a Madeira jus that we chose at our June lunch. Fillet of sole followed, stuffed with seafood mousse and served on a bed of spinach which had been sautéed in walnut oil and was accompanied by a pesto cream sauce. Vegetables included good carrots with lime. Chilled nougat glacé with hazelnut, glacé cherries and honey was served with a blackberry and mango coulis.

Directions: 12 miles from St Andrews. Village centre: from A915 (St Andrews) take A917 to Elie

Bouquet Garni Restaurant

GLENROTHES,

Rescobie Hotel ✿

Valley Drive Leslie KY6 3BQ
Map 11: NO20
Tel: 01592 742143
Fax: 01592 620231
Chef: Brian Sinclair
Owners: Tony & Judith Hughes-Lewis
Cost: *Alc* £22, fixed-price D £17.50.
☺ H/wine £10
Times: Last L 2pm/last D 9pm
Additional: Sunday L; Children welcome; ◑ menu
Smoking: No pipes & cigars
Accommodation: 10 en suite
Credit cards: ▆ ▆ ▆ ▆ ▆

Traditional Scottish country house on the outskirts of town. Dishes offered from a choice of menus include Highland game broth, grilled Tay salmon with a herb crust, and grouse (in season) roasted with bacon and served with wild mushrooms and a red wine sauce.

Directions: At west end of Leslie village, turn S off A911

KINCARDINE-ON-FORTH,

Unicorn Inn ✿✿

Sir James Dewar, inventor of the Thermos flask principle, was born here – not perhaps the first person one would associate with a gastronomic shrine. The cooking is Mediterranean influenced, simple and effective. Tapas have been introduced at lunchtime, alongside the good value two-course lunch. These and the evening *carte* are ordered from the blackboard. Crisp garlic bread came with creamy aïoli, and a dish of spaghetti with smoked salmon, fresh mussels, cream and white wine. Sea bass followed, baked whole with white wine and served with garlic, tomato and herbs. Chocolate truffle cake was a surprisingly light dessert, set on a raspberry coulis.

Directions: From S, cross Kincardine Bridge, take 1st L, L again, 1st R

15 Excise Street FK10 4LN
Map 11: NS98
Tel: 01259 730704
Fax: 01259 731567
Chef: Brian Ainslie
Owner: Lesley-Ann Mitch
Cost: *Alc* £25; fixed-price L £7.95 (2 courses)/D £19.50. ☺ H/wine £10.25
Times: Noon-last L 1.45pm/6.30-last D 9.15pm. Closed Sun, Mon
Additional: Children welcome; ◑ dishes
Seats: 60. Private dining room 25
Smoking: No pipes & cigars
Accommodation: 4 rooms
Credit cards: ▆ ▆ ▆ ▆ ▆

LETHAM,

Fernie Castle ✣

KY15 7RU
Map 11: NO30
Tel: 01337 810381
Fax: 01337 810422
Chef: Anthony Carroll
Owner: Marshall Stevens
Cost: *Alc* £20, fixed-price D £19.50.
☺ H/wine £9.95
Times: Last L 2.30pm/last D 9pm
Additional: Bar food; Sunday L;
Children welcome; ✿ dishes
Smoking: No-smoking area
Accommodation: 15 en suite
Credit cards: ▬ ▭ ▚ ▱ ▨ C ▣

*The hotel claims to have a ghost but there is nothing spooky about
the formal restaurant, which offers a contemporary take on the auld
alliance in its blend of Scottish and French food. Try red mullet with
ratatouille salad, honeyed duck with cherry sauce and sweet potato
rösti, lemon tart and home-made truffles.*

Directions: From M90 J6, east onto A91 Tay Bridge/St Andrews
to Melville Lodges Roundabout. L onto A92 signposted Tay
Bridge. Hotel 1.2 miles on R

LUNDIN LINKS,

Old Manor Hotel ✣✣

Leven Road Nr St Andrews
KY8 6AJ
Map 12: NO40
Tel: 01333 320368
Fax: 01333 320911
Chef: Alan Brunt
Owners: The Clark Family
Cost: Fixed-price L £12.50/D £25
(4 courses). ☺ H/wine £10.95
Times: Last L 2pm/last D 9.30pm.
Closed D 25 Dec, 1 Jan
Additional: Bar food; Sunday L;
No children under 3; ✿ dishes

The Lundin Golf Course, Largo Bay, and the Forth Estuary
form a backdrop to a formal restaurant and modern British
cooking. Look out for sautéed chicken livers with walnut
mayonnaise and croûtons, red mullet with stir-fried vegetables,
lobster bisque with cognac, roasted tails of monkfish, mustard,
chive sauce and cucumber noodles, with chocolate torte for
dessert.

Smoking: No smoking in dining room
Accommodation: 24 en suite
Credit cards: ▬ ▭ ▚ ▱ ▨ C JCB

Directions: On A915 Leven-St Andrews road in the village

MARKINCH, **Balbirnie House**

Balbirnie Park KY7 6NE
Map 11: NO20
Tel: 01592 610066
Fax: 01592 610529
Chef: Alan Gibb
Owners: Mr & Mrs Alan Russell
Cost: Alc £15, fixed-price L £13.75/D £29.50 (4 courses). H/wine £12.50
Times: Noon-last L 2.30pm/7-last D 9.30pm
Additional: Bar food L; Sunday L; Children welcome; ◑ dishes
Seats: 45. Private dining rooms 20-45
Smoking: No smoking in dining room
Accommodation: 30 en suite
Credit cards: 🔳 🔳 🔳 🔳 🔳

The welcome at this family-run Georgian mansion is refreshingly natural and unpretentious. Overlooking the formal gardens, the candlelit dining room provides an impressive setting for the modern Scottish cooking of Alan Gibb. European influences are evident in the likes of warm salad of duck with roast celeriac and bitter orange sauce, and pan-fried fillet of salmon with creamy haricots and ham hough. However, traditional Scottish fare also makes an appearance, and first-time visitors to Scotland will find no better introduction to the time-old dish of haggis, neaps and tatties, finished off with a whisky cream sauce. Our inspector visited Balbirnie in April, and couldn't help but comment positively on dishes such as skate and parsley terrine, served with a lemon and sun-dried tomato dressing, and grilled fillet of Dover sole with a tasty tarragon and basil cream sauce. The excellent wine list includes some fine clarets, and there are a few good half-bottles.

Directions: M90/J3, follow signs to Glenrothes & Tay Bridge, turn R onto B9130 to Markinch & Balbirnie Park

PEAT INN, **The Peat Inn**

Cupar KY15 5LH
Map 12: NO40
Tel: 01334 840206
Fax: 01334 840530
Chef: David Wilson
Owners: David & Patricia Wilson
Cost: Alc £34, fixed-price L £18.50 (4 courses)/D £28 (4 courses). H/wine £14

Having celebrated 25 years at the Peat Inn, dedicated owners David and Patricia Wilson have built up an enviable reputation for the excellence of their kitchen, and they probably have the most loyal clientele of any restaurant in Scotland. David Wilson is revered as a teacher and guru by young chefs, and his menus continue to show consistency and accurate handling of mainly Scottish produce. The former old coaching inn stands at the cross-roads in the small village to which it has given its name, just six miles from St Andrews. The restaurant itself is quite cosy, being sectioned so that if there are only a few diners, they don't feel marooned. At dinner, there is a choice of menus: dégustation, set menu of the day and a carte, although they do overlap. Scallops and monkfish on spiced pork and apple was well balanced and accurately cooked, the belly pork, in particular was stunning, lightly spiced and cut in crisp, small chunks. Duck lends itself to multiple uses, here, the leg is braised with green lentils in a salad with venison liver, the breast roasted crisply with spices and roast vegetables and an intense duck reduction, or served as part of the house 'cassoulet' of lamb, pork and duck. Lobster is another favourite, either whole in white wine brandy and cream sauce with fresh pasta, or combined with medallions of monkfish, artichoke hearts and wild mushrooms in a lobster sauce. A white chocolate mousse with caramelised banana slices in an orange syrup was more parfait than mousse. Details are all good – onion quiche canapé, excellent sliced rye or white bread and real decaffeinated coffee stand out.

Signature dishes: Roast scallops with leek potato, smoked bacon and pea purée; whole lobster with asparagus and broad beans, herb broth; roast young grouse; casserole of lamb, pork and duck with flageolet beans

Times: L at 1pm/7-last D 9.30pm. Closed Sun, Mon, 25 Dec, 1 Jan
Additional: Children welcome; ◑ dishes
Seats: 48. Private dining room 12/24
Smoking: No smoking in dining room
Accommodation: 8 en suite
Credit cards: ▰ ▰ ▰ ▰ ▰ ▰

Directions: At junction of B940/B941, 6 miles SW of St Andrews

---

ST ANDREWS,

The Old Course Hotel ❀❀

A Mecca for golfers from around the world, the hotel is located right next to the 17th hole of the famous Old Course. Up on the 4th-floor, the elegant Road Hole Grill offers a fine view over the course and a fixed-price menu that includes innovative modern dishes along with some more familiar favourites. The latter might include Caesar salad, salmon with asparagus and new potatoes, and sirloin of Angus beef with château potatoes and red wine sauce. More adventurous tastes will look to farfalle with chorizo sausage, oven-dried tomatoes and pesto oil, or roasted wood pigeon with parsley risotto, crispy Cajun onion rings and tomato butter, and seared red fish with bok choi, bamboo shoots and a spicy papaya salsa. There's an interesting selection of home-baked breads too. Desserts range from hot chocolate soufflé to iced Pernod and lemon parfait. The comprehensive list of well-chosen wines includes a good selection of half-bottles.

KY16 9SP
Map 12: NO51
Tel: 01334 474371
Fax: 01334 477668
Chef: Mark Barker
Cost: Alc £39, fixed-price L £15.50/D £38.50 (5 courses). H/wine £16.50
Times: 12.30-last L 2pm/7-last D 10pm. Closed Xmas
Additional: Bar food L; Sunday L; Children welcome; ◑ dishes
Seats: 90. Private dining rooms 16-160
Smoking: No-smoking area; No pipes and cigars; Air conditioning
Accommodation: 125 en suite
Credit cards: ▰ ▰ ▰ ▰ ▰

Directions: Situated close to the A91 on the outskirts of the city

---

ST ANDREWS, **Parkland Hotel** ❀

Popular with golfers, this is a castle-style mansion built in the late 19th-century. A typical March meal might include hot smoked salmon with salad leaves, followed by prime Angus ribeye steak topped with a rich Madeira sauce. Finish it all off with a mixed berry summer pudding, or chocolate and hazelnut roulade.

Kinburn Castle
Double Dykes Road KY16 9DS
Map 12: NO51
Tel/Fax: 01334 473620
Chef: Brian J MacLennan
Owners: Brian & Rosemary MacLennan
Cost: Fixed-price L £5.95 (2 courses)/D £18.50. ☺ H/wine £8.50
Times: Last L 2pm/last D 8.30pm. Closed D Sun, all Mon, 25-26 Dec, 1-2 Jan

Additional: Sunday L; Children welcome
Smoking: No smoking in dining room
Accommodation: 15 rooms. **Credit cards:** ▰ ▰ ▰

Directions: West of town centre, opposite Kinburn Park

ST ANDREWS,
Rufflets 🏵🏵

Strathkinness Low Road KY16 9TX
Map 12: NO51
Tel: 01334 472594
Fax: 01334 478703
Chef: Robert Grindle
Owner: Ms Ann Russell
Cost: Fixed-price L £18/D £30.
H/wine £13
Times: 12.30-last L 2pm (Sat & Sun only)/7-last D 9.30pm
Additional: Bar food L; Sunday L; Children welcome; 🍴 dishes
Seats: 80. Private dining room 20
Smoking: No smoking in restaurant
Accommodation: 24 en suite
Credit cards: 💳 💳 💳 💳 💳

Rufflets, in 10 acres of beautiful gardens, is a turreted mansion with white walls built in 1924 by a prominent architect. The Garden Restaurant is contemporary in style, with boldly coloured fabrics, and makes a civilised setting in which to enjoy lunch or dinner. The kitchen uses prime locally sourced ingredients to turn out some interesting dishes. Timbales and terrines – of smoked Shetland salmon, scallops and prawns, and wood pigeon, pheasant and calves' liver – rub shoulders with other starters of lobster bisque, or Brie baked with prosciutto in oatmeal, while grilled collops of Rannoch venison in a port and pickled walnut jus might share main-course billing with pork fillet pan-fried with mushrooms, capers and vermouth, or North Sea monkfish with a salsa of black olives, basil and sweet peppers. A fillet of Aberdeen Angus – tender and flavoursome – has been described as going nicely with its duxelles of mushrooms and haggis, and chocolate parfait shows a good balance of flavour with crème anglaise and coffee cream. Seven wines on the long, international list are sold by the glass.

Directions: On B939 1.5 miles west of St Andrews

ST ANDREWS,
Rusacks Hotel 🏵   NEW

The position overlooking the golf course has always been enviable, but major refurbishment has vastly improved the interior of this imposing Victorian hotel. Modern, brasserie-style cooking takes in pan-seared scallops with sauce vierge and herb tagliatelle, sautéed fillet of monkfish, herb crust and courgette stew, and loin of Perthshire lamb, with mint couscous, caramelised apricots and red wine sauce.

Pilmour Links KY16 9JQ
Map 12: NO51
Tel: 01334 474321
Fax: 01334 477896
Chef: David Kinnes
Owner: Heritage Hotels Ltd
Cost: Fixed-price D £29.95.
H/wine £12.95
Times: Last L 2.15pm/last D 9.45pm

Additional: Sunday L; Children welcome; 🍴 dishes
Smoking: No smoking in dining room
Accommodation: 48 en suite
Credit cards: 💳 💳 💳 💳 💳 💳 JCB

Directions: From M90/J8 take A91 to St Andrews. Hotel on L on entering the town

ST ANDREWS,
St Andrews Golf Hotel

It's a marvellous setting – an oak-panelled, candlelit dining room with spectacular views over St Andrews Bay. Just the place to dream of hole-in-ones as you dine on terrine of smoked game with beetroot and tarragon dressing, followed by seared king scallops with coriander and leek blinis, garlic and herb oil.

Additional: Bar food; Sunday L; Children welcome; dishes; **Smoking:** No smoking in dining room; Air conditioning **Accommodation:** 22 en suite **Credit cards:** ▆ ▆ ▆ ▆ ▆ ▆ JCB

Directions: Enter town on A91, cross both mini-roundabouts, turn L at Golf Place and first R into The Scores. Hotel 200 yards on R

40 The Scores KY16 9AS
Map 12: NO51
Tel: 01334 472611
Fax: 01334 472188
Chef: Colin Mason
Owner: Brian Hughes
Cost: Alc £26.50 fixed price L £15/D £26.50. ☺ H/wine £14
Times: Last L 2pm/last D 9.30pm.
Closed 26-28 Dec

ST MONANS, Ichthus ✿

There's been a change of name at this harbourside restaurant, from The Cabin to Ichthus (Greek for fish). The emphasis is on seafood, though other tastes are catered for. Cullen skink was followed by fillet of halibut with a crust of herbs and sun-dried tomato, served with a mustard beurre blanc.

Additional: Seafood bar menu; dishes **Smoking:** No smoking in dining room **Credit cards:** ▆ ▆ ▆ ▆

Directions: Take A959 from St Andrews to Anstruther, then head west on A917 through Pittenweem. In St Monans go down to harbour then R.

16 West End KY10 2BX
Map 12: NO50
Tel/Fax: 01333 730327
Chef: Craig Millar
Owner: Tim Butler
Cost: Alc £25, fixed-price L £16. ☺ H/wine £9
Times: Last L 2.30pm/last D 9.30pm.
Closed Bh Mon

GLASGOW, CITY OF

GLASGOW, Bouzy Rouge ✿✿ NEW

111 West Regent Street, G2 2RU
Map 11: NS56
Tel: 0141 2218804
Fax: 0141 2216941
Chef: Paul Holmes
Owners: Alan & Audrey Brown
Cost: Alc £21, fixed price L £12.95/D £19.95. ☺ H/wine £11.95
Times: 10am-10pm (D from 5pm).
Closed 1 Jan
Additional: Bar food: Sunday L; Children welcome; dishes
Seats: 68
Smoking: Air conditioning
Credit cards: ▆ ▆ ▆ ▆ ▆ ▆

A striking horseshoe-shaped bar is the focal point of this see-and-be-seen restaurant. The contemporary decor makes use of natural Scottish timbers, hand-crafted iron and stonework and

features colourful mosaics. Equally stylish is the cooking, offered on several menus including a good-value business lunch. A starter of fresh mussel broth proved to be a meal in itself, with lovely plump shellfish in a provencale sauce accompanied by rice timbale. The tender and tasty pan-fried saddle of Rannoch venison was roasted pink and set on a bed of red cabbage marmalade, pommes dauphinoise and port and red wine jus. Side vegetables include turnip in cream sauce, cauliflower hollandaise, new potatoes, carrots and mange-tout. For dessert, a smooth and sharp lemon tart was caramelised and served with vanilla ice cream in a ginger snap tuile and, to finish, a large, frothy cappuccino with wrapped chocolate mint typified the attention to detail. Lip-smackingly good.

Directions: *Telephone for directions*

Bouzy Rouge

GLASGOW,
Buttery Restaurant ❀❀

One of Glasgow's oldest and most popular restaurants, the Buttery is adorned in rich Victorian decor and sited between a housing estate and Kingston Bridge. Old-fashioned standards of service hold sway: waiting staff in white gloves, dishes presented under cloches. There's no fussiness in the cooking, though, with high-quality produce simply prepared in modern global style. Light bar meals, a set luncheon and a four-course dinner are offered. The latter begins with canapés, and ends with petits fours. Starters such as a trio of seafood with herb beurre blanc and a crisp coriander galette indicate highly competent kitchen staff, the scallop, fillet of sea bass and piece of salmon all being correctly cooked. At inspection, medallion of Scottish beef fillet teriyaki exhibited a nice oriental zing and first-class meat for the main course, while a caramelised brioche bread-and-butter pudding was an interesting variation on this popular pud.

Directions: City centre

652 Argyle Street G3 8UF
Map 11: NS56
Tel: 0141 2218188
Fax: 0141 2044639
Chef: William Deans
Owner: Allied Domecq
Cost: *Alc* £27, fixed-price L £16.85.
H/wine £12.50
Times: Noon-last L 2.30pm/7-last
D 10.30pm. Closed L Sat, all Sun,
25-26 Dec, 1-2 Jan
Additional: Bar food L; ❹ dishes
Seats: 50. Private room 10
Smoking: No pipes & cigars;
Air conditioning
Credit cards: 💳 💳 💳 💳 💳 💳 💳

GLASGOW, Devonshire Hotel ❀

Just ten minutes from the city centre, the Devonshire forms part of an imposing tree-lined Victorian terrace. The 'intimate' dining room (i.e. four tables) is open to non-residents. Typical dishes include tagliatelle of exotic mushrooms, pan-fried beast of pheasant with caramelised shallots and red wine jus, and bread-and-butter pudding.

Additional: Bar Food L; Children welcome; dishes
Accommodation: 14 en suite
Credit cards: 💳 💳 💳 💳

Directions: On Great Western Road turn L at lights towards Hyndland, 200 yards turn R and R again

5 Devonshire Gardens
G12 0UX
Map 11: NS56
Tel: 0141 3397878
Fax: 0141 3393980
Chef: Peter Lindsay
Cost: *Alc* £27.50,fixed-price L £20/D
£25. ☺ H/wine £11.50
Times: Last L 2.30pm/D 10pm

GLASGOW, Glasgow Hilton ❀❀

The city-centre landmark is a magnificent polished granite and mirrored glass building, the tallest in Scotland, with superb views from its upper floors. Camerons (named after Cameron

1 William Street G3 8HT
Map 11: NS56
Tel: 0141 2045555
Fax: 0141 2045004
Please telephone for further details

Glasgow Hilton

of Lochiel, chief of Clan Cameron), is one of several restaurants, an intimate, sophisticated place with a menu that has prime Scottish ingredients at its heart. This is sound cooking with our most recent dinner highlighting pot-au-feu of Western Isles shellfish in a Pernod-scented sauce, confit of quail on gnocchi with lentils, mushrooms and smoked bacon, best end of lamb on warm couscous salad and black olive sauce, roast cod on seared vegetables and pesto dressing, and sticky toffee pudding, nut brittle ice cream and caramel sauce. The wine list gives a good global coverage and includes serious vintage clarets and Burgundies. There's also a good range of half-bottles and wines by the glass.

Directions: Charing Cross exit from M8, turn R at 1st traffic lights, R again & follow signs for hotel

GLASGOW,
Glasgow Moat House 🏵

Contemporary high-rise hotel on the banks of the Clyde with a choice of restaurants, the Pointhouse for informal meals and The Mariner for fine dining. Typical dishes include ballotine of chicken with asparagus and pear chutney, and tranche of sea bass with a mousseline of scallops.

Additional: Bar food; Sunday L; Children welcome; 🍴 dishes.
Seats: 50. Private dining rooms
Smoking: No-smoking area; Air conditioning
Accommodation: 283 en suite
Credit cards: 💳 💳 💳 💳 💳 💳 JCB

Directions: Adjacent to Scottish Exhibition & Conference Centre, follow signs

Congress Road G3 8QT
Map 11: NS56
Tel: 0141 3069988
Fax: 0141 2212022
Chef: Thomas Brown
Owner: Queens Moat House
Cost: Alc £22, fixed-price L £15 (2 courses)/D £20.95. ☺ H/wine £12.55
Times: Last L 2.30pm/last D 10.30pm. Closed L Sat, all Sun, 1 wk Jan

GLASGOW,
Killermont Polo Club 🏵

Smart Indian themed on 'Days of the Raj' and polo, and offering consistent cooking and extremely good-value lunches. Familiar dishes take in onion bhaji, vegetable pakora, chicken tikka, lamb dupiaza, and chicken jaipuri. Service is friendly.

2002 Maryhill Road
Maryhill Park G20 0AB
Map 11: NS56
Tel: 0141 946 5412
Please telephone for further details

GLASGOW, **Malmaison Hotel**

278 West George Street
G2 4LL
Map 11: NS56
Tel/Fax: 0141 5721000
Chef: Roy Brett
Owner: Ken McCulloch
Cost: Alc £25. Fixed-price D £23.50.
☺ H/wine £11.95
Times: Last L 2.30pm/last D 11pm
Additional: Children welcome;
🌶 dishes
Accommodation: 72 en suite
Credit cards:

*Stylish city hotel with an informal French-style brasserie noted for its
innovative, up-beat dishes. An early autumn meal took in wild
mushroom risotto served with shavings of Parmesan, fillet of
salmon, crisply seared with cracked pepper and served with polenta,
roasted carrots and parsnips.*

Directions: From George Square take Vincent Street to Pitt
Street – hotel is on corner of this and West George Street

GLASGOW, **Nairns**   NEW

13 Woodside Crescent G3 7UP
Map 11: NS56
Tel: 0141 3530707
Fax: 0141 3311684
Chefs: Nick Nairn & Dan Hall
Owners: Nick & Topher Nairn
Cost: Fixed price L £17/D £23.50. ☺
H/wine £13.50
Times: 12.30-last L 2pm/D 6-last
D 10.30pm. Closed Mon, 25-26 Dec,
1 Jan
Additional: Sunday L;
No children under 10; 🌶 dishes
Seats: 85. Private dining room 30
Accommodation: 4 en suite
Credit cards:

Now that Nick Nairn has moved into a smart city townhouse
(with rooms) from his quaint country place, the glamour of
eating a famous chef's food comes a lot more affordable – the
set price three-course menu is extremely good value. A few
months after opening the kitchen was still settling down, but
showing promise. Terrine of chicken, leek and Parma ham,
came with a not quite spot-on sauce gribiche, but better was a
lasagne of mussels, fennel and saffron. Other dishes sampled
included roasted Barbary duck breast with dauphinoise
potatoes, chicory and lentil gravy, and salmon with fondant
potato, braised little gem and juniper butter sauce. Puddings
included bread-and-butter pudding. 'Farmhouse cheeses in
Good Nick' raised a smile. The gorgeously photographed menu
is a limited edition, on sale for £1.

Directions: *Telephone for directions*

GLASGOW,

One Devonshire Gardens

1 Devonshire Gardens G12 0UX
Map 11: NS56
Tel: 0141 3392001
Fax: 0141 3371663
Chef: Andrew Fairlie
Owner: Ken McCulloch
Cost: Fixed-price L £25/D £40 (4 courses). H/wine £19
Times: Noon-last L 2pm/7.15-last D 10pm. Closed L Sat
Additional: Sunday L; Children welcome; ❸ dishes
Seats: 45. Private dining rooms 10, 16
Smoking: No smoking in dining room
Accommodation: 27 en suite
Credit cards: 🟥 🟦 📶 🟫 🄲 💳 JCB

This unique Victorian town house hotel, set in the leafy West End of Glasgow, includes a stunning restaurant where Andrew Fairlie creates bright, lively modern food noted for attention to detail and sound technique. An evening meal, taken in the luxurious, moody surroundings of the dining room, could start with oak-smoked salmon with herb crème fraîche and salmon caviar, followed by cream of white onion soup glazed with Parmesan. With five choices for main course, you will be hard-pressed to decide between fantastic creations such as grilled fillet of halibut with lemon and roasted garlic risotto, and roast rump of lamb with creamy goats' cheese polenta and thyme jus. Dessert could pose an equally difficult problem: should you go for the iced banana parfait with dark chocolate sauce, or the more zesty passion fruit gratin with mango coulis? Our inspector opted for neither, deciding instead to go for the hot chocolate pudding which arrived, towering, with fondant filling and an excellent vanilla ice. This indulgent finale ended a meal that began some hours earlier with a simple dish of sautéed foie gras with shallot marmalade, sliced pear and a well-balanced anise jus. Three highly enjoyable courses formed the middle section of the meal: crispy langoustine tails with lime, poppyseed and mango sauce; a silky smooth vichyssoise; and perfectly-cooked fillet of halibut on a creamy lemon risotto with strips of pepper, tapenade and fennel. Service is attentive but unobtrusive and sommelier Johnny Walker really is the star. His first-rate wine list focuses on the Old World, but a number of bottles from the New World also make an appearance.

Signature dishes: Home-smoked lobster with lime and herb butter sauce; braised stuffed fillet of rabbit with local wild mushrooms and roasted root vegetables; feuilletté of crayfish and morels with truffle butter

Directions: On Great Western Road turn L at lights towards Hyndland, 200 yards turn R and R again

AA Wine Award—see page 16
Shortlisted for

GLASGOW, # Papingo Restaurant

104 Bath Street G2 2EN
Map 11: NS56
Tel: 0141 3326678
Fax: 0141 3326549
Chef: Derek Marshall
Owner: Alan C Tomkins
Cost: Fixed-price L £8.95 (2 courses)/D £18.95. ☺ H/wine £10.95
Times: Last L 2.30pm/D 10.30pm. Closed L Sun, 26 Dec, 1-2 Jan, D Bhs

'It's refreshing to find a chef who cooks competently, yet at the same time keeps it relatively simple' reports an inspector on this bright, modern-looking basement restaurant with three distinct eating areas within the open-plan layout. We particularly enjoyed a lunch of salmon fishcake with horseradish cream, breast of duck with a honey and ginger sauce that contained apricots and was accompanied by stir-fried vegetables, and a baked lemon tart served with fresh

Papingo Restaurant

Smoking: No-smoking area
Credit cards: JCB

raspberries that contrasted nicely with the lemon. Staff, under the supervision of Kamal Zakaria, are all uniformly dressed in a smart, but informal style, and are very attentive. The lengthy wine list has much of interest.

Directions: 200yds from Glasgow Central Station

GLASGOW, **La Parmigiana** ❀

Angelo and Sandro Giovanazzi's long-established West End trattoria has been serving up sound Italian cooking for more than fifteen years, loyally supported by a growing number of locals. Trusted favourites such as spaghetti carbonara to start and zabaglione for dessert are authentic, while modern dishes such as baked sea bass with lemon butter sauce also vie for attention.

Directions: Close to Kelvinbridge underground station

447 Great Western Road
G12 8HH
Map 11: NS56
Tel: 0141 3340686
Fax: 0141 3323533
Chef: Sandro Giovanazzi
Owners: Angelo & Sandro Giovanazzi
Cost: *Alc* £20, fixed-price L £8.10. H/wine £10.20
Times: Noon-2.30pm/6-11pm. Closed Sun, local holidays
Additional: Children welcome; ❹ dishes
Smoking: No pipes and cigars; Air conditioning
Credit cards: JCB

GLASGOW, **Puppet Theatre** ❀❀ 〔NEW〕

Tucked up a small lane, just off trendy Byres Road, the converted mews is a warren of variously styled dining rooms, nooks and crannies, plus a conservatory full of potted plants. The kitchen is keen, the atmosphere formal, and service attentive without unduly hurrying the diner along. The monthly changing menu is structured around good Scottish ingredients. Terrine of moist and tender rabbit, Savoy cabbage and potato with a mixed herb salad and mustard dressing set the pace well for our inspection meal. Main courses, such as pan-fried cod with twice-baked smoked haddock soufflé, tend

11 Ruthven Lane
Map 11: NS56
Tel: 0141 3398444
Fax: 0141 3397666
Chef: John Quigley
Owners: Ron McCulloch, George Swanson
Cost: Fixed-price L £14.50/D £27.95. H/wine £11.50
Times: Noon-last L 2.30pm/7pm-last D 10.30pm. Closed L Sat, Mon, 25-26 Dec, 1-2 Jan

to the pile 'em high school of presentation. Desserts are a strength – those who want everything can order a plate of ten miniature desserts, such as bread-and-butter pudding, chocolate mousse, and lemon meringue pie, to name but a few. The design of the menu is enchanting enough to merit a special mention.

Directions: Just off Byres Road

Additional: Sunday L;
No children under 12; ✦ dishes
Seats: 65. Private dining room 27
Smoking: Air conditioning
Credit cards: ▆▆ ▆▆ ▆▆ ▆ ▆▆ JCB

GLASGOW, **Rogano** ❀❀

11 Exchange Place G1 3AN
Map 11: NS56
Tel: 0141 2484055
Chef: William Simpson
Owner: Allied Domecq Inns
Cost: Alc £33, fixed-price L £16.50.
H/wine £10
Times: Noon-last L 2.30pm/6.30pm-
last D 10.30pm. Closed 25 Dec,
1-2 Jan
Additional: Bar food; Sunday L;
✦ dishes
Seats: 60. Private dining room 16
Smoking: Air conditioning
Credit cards: ▆▆ ▆▆ ▆▆ ▆ ▆▆ ▆

Any fish lovers in Scotland will be pleased to discover Rogano, which lays claim to being Glasgow's oldest restaurant. Compact, with its original Art Deco design intact, the ground floor offers a bar serving snacks all day alongside the formal main restaurant, while downstairs there is a brasserie-style operation called Café Rogano. In the restaurant, the kitchen offers a no-choice set three-course menu as well as an extensive carte. Good starters include gravad lax with dill and peppercorn cream and a salad of avocado, scallops, bacon and strawberry dressing. If you want a break from seafood, try the roast rack of lamb with herb crust and leek jus, Aberdeen Angus with wild mushrooms and hollandaise, or pheasant with apricot farce. Fishy mains include lobster grilled or Thermidor, roast monkfish with capers and lime, and salmon on a pink peppercorn cream. The desserts will not disappoint and there's a cheese platter including French, English and Scottish varieties.

Directions: City centre between Buchanan Street & Royal Exchange Square

GLASGOW, **Stravaigin** ❀❀❀

Enthusiastically run, this vibrantly coloured subterranean restaurant is situated in the basement of a tenement building with trendy café bar upstairs. Inside the decor is Mediterranean, and bunches of chillies, herbs and garlic hanging from the ceiling go some way towards creating an 'authentic' Med feel. The carte of modern Scottish fare shows cosmopolitan influences in starters such as rosemary-skewered Ullapool monkfish with roast pepper rajas and Kailkenny croquette, crisp Parmesan and roast onion polenta with Tuscan caponata, and asparagus and toasted pine kernel tart in a nest of warm Stilton and wild mushrooms. A spring meal started well with moist rabbit terrine garnished with wild garlic. The

30 Gibson Street G12
Map 11: NS56
Tel: 0141 3342665
Fax: 0141 3344099
Chef/Owner: Colin Clydesdale
Cost: Alc £18, fixed-price L £8.95. ☺
H/wine £10.95
Times: Noon-last L 2.30pm/5-last D
11pm. Closed L Sun, Xmas, New Year
Additional: Bar food; Children
welcome; ✦ dishes
Seats: 80
Smoking: No pipes and cigars;
Air conditioning

main course of fillet of hake was 'really excellent' and arrived on a bed of baby potatoes provençale style with tomatoes, red onion and peppers. The long list of indulgent desserts comes with a handful of suggested pudding wines.

Directions: Next to Glasgow University. 200 yds from Kelvinbridge underground.

Credit cards: ■ ▒ ▚ ⬚ ▩ ▨

GLASGOW,
Ubiquitous Chip ✦

Choose between a verdant, courtyard-like main restaurant and more casual and snacky upstairs balcony at this well-established eaterie near the university. The Scottish menu ranges from pan-fried scallops on potato cake with stewed garlic and Chambery sauce to Perthshire wood pigeon with wild mushroom and game sauce. Good Scottish cheeses and an impressive wine list.

Additional: Sunday L; Children welcome; ✦ dishes
Credit cards: ■ ▒ ▚ ⬚ ▩ ▨

Directions: *Telephone for directions*

12 Ashton Lane G12 8SJ
Map 11: NS56
Tel: 0141 3345007
Fax: 0141 3371302
Chef/Owner: Ronnie Clydesdale
Cost: Bistro *Alc* £12-18, Restaurant fixed price L £23.60/D £31.60. H/wine £10.95
Times: Last L 2.30pm/last D 11pm. Closed 25 Dec, 1 Jan

GLASGOW, **Yes** ✦✦

22 West Nile Street G1 2PW
Map 11: NS56
Tel: 0141 2218044
Fax: 0141 2489159
Chefs: Ferrier Richardson, Iain McMaster
Owner: Ferrier Richardson
Cost: *Alc* £28.50, fixed-price D £11.95 (2 courses). H/wine £11.95
Times: Noon-last L 2.30pm/7-last D 11pm. Closed Sun, Bhs
Additional: Bar food; Children welcome; ✦ dishes
Seats: 100. Private dining room 20
Smoking: No pipes; Air conditioning
Credit cards: ■ ▒ ▚ ⬚ ▩ ▨

Don't say no to a meal at Yes, for you will be agreeing with our inspector that here is food prepared with care and creativity without fuss. The restaurant attracts a genteel, well-heeled clientele looked after by pleasant young staff. The meal begins on the right note with lovely hot bread rolls, made to Yes's recipe by a local baker. A typical starter is the highly enjoyable queen scallop filo tartlet with leek gratin. To follow, perhaps pan-fried wild pheasant with dauphinoise potatoes, wild mushrooms and shallots in Madeira sauce and some tasty haricots wrapped in bacon. Prune and Armagnac soufflé comes authentically moist in the centre and accompanied by a light, smooth caramel ice cream in a chocolate cup. Good strong filtered coffee and home-made petits fours are a fitting end to a delightful meal. The wine list shows the management's care and interest, and the menus are beautifully designed. You will want to return.

Directions: City centre. M8 exit for George Sq. Turn L at 2nd lights into Port Dundas Rd, which joins West Nile St

HIGHLAND

ARDELVE, **Loch Duigh Hotel**

A former drover's inn beside the Road to the Isles, now a welcoming family-run hotel. Bar meals are served in the Duich pub, but an evening meal in the restaurant produces good, honest country cooking. Trout roulade, a lovely rack of lamb coated with herbs and mustard crust, fresh vegetables, and a tipsy laird trifle, are recommended.

Kyle IV40 8DY
Map 14: NG82
Tel: 01599 555213
Fax: 01599 555214
Please telephone for further details

ARDVASAR, **Ardvasar Hotel**

Isle of Skye IV45 8RS
Map 13: NG60
Tel: 01471 844223
Fax: 01471 844495
Chef: Bill Fowler
Owners: Bill and Gretta Fowler
Cost: Alc £10. ☺ H/wine £5.90
Times: Last L 2pm/D 8.45pm
Additional: Bar food; Sunday L;
Children welcome; ✪ dishes
Smoking: No smoking in dining room
Accommodation: 9 en suite
Credit cards: ▆ ▨ ⚏ ⌑

Directions: From Armadale ferry turn L and on through village

A range of Taste of Scotland dishes, prepared from quality island produce, is offered at this welcoming little hotel near the Armadale ferry terminal. Recommended dishes include mussels with white wine and cream, roast breast of Gressingham duck with brandy and apple sauce, and a chocolate and meringue pudding.

ARISAIG, **Arisaig House** ✿✿✿

Beasdale PH39 4NR
Map 13: NM68
Tel: 01687 450622
Fax: 01687 450626
Chef: Duncan Gibson
Owners: Ruth, John & Andrew Smither, Alison Wilkinson
Cost: Fixed-price D £40 (4 courses). H/wine £15
Times: 12.30-2pm/7.30-8.30pm. Closed Nov-Easter
Additional: Bar food L;
No children under 10; ✪ dishes
Seats: 36. Jacket & tie preferred
Smoking: No smoking in dining room
Accommodation: 14 en suite
Credit cards: ▆ ▨ ⌑

Directions: On A830 Fort William to Mallaig road, 3 miles east of Arisaig village

A solid Scottish mansion set amongst oaks and rhododendrons. Its dining room is stately, with well-spaced tables and a set-price menu that reads well. The kitchen, led by Duncan Gibson, concentrates on getting the simple things right, and they certainly succeed, keen to mix classical and modern ideas without being all singing, all dancing trend food. A tarte Tatin of wood pigeon opened one inspection dinner, accompanied by caramelised endive that gave a striking sweet-sour contrast. Soup was a 'divine' velouté of haricot blanc with fresh truffles, and was followed by grilled pavé of salmon with a basil beurre blanc and a tian of aubergines layered with tomatoes that had been 'sneakily stuffed with peppers'. A rich chocolate tart, the pastry rolled to the thickness of a tenner, was superbly baked and melted on the tongue. The marquise centre was deep and smooth, and was served with home-grown raspberries and a simple dollop of clotted cream 'that went straight to my thighs'. Canapés of bacon tarts, smoked salmon tartare en croûte, as well as a big bowl of marinated olives, and good petits fours show consistent standards throughout.

BRORA, Royal Marine Hotel

Designed by a renowned Scots architect, this Georgian house boasts a dining room that looks across the grounds to the sea. The menu offers little creativity but dishes such as asparagus wrapped in smoked salmon and filo, halibut with mustard hollandaise and creme caramel are well made from quality ingredients. A new bistro is also available.

Accommodation: 22 en suite
Credit cards:

Directions: Turn off A9 in village toward beach and golf course

Golf Road KW9 6QS

Map 14: NC90
Tel: 01408 621252
Fax: 01408 621181
Chef: Andrew Hutchinson
Owner: Duncraggie Ltd
Cost: *Alc* £22.50, fixed-price
L £12.95. ☺ H/wine £10
Times: Last L 2pm/last D 8.45pm
Additional: Bar food; Sunday L;
Children welcome; ❹ dishes
Smoking: No smoking in dining room

COLBOST, Three Chimneys Restaurant ✿✿

Dunvegan Isle of Skye
IV55 8ZT
Map 13: NG24
Tel: 01470 511258
Fax: 01470 511358
Chef: Shirley Spear
Owner: Eddie & Shirley Spear
Cost: *Alc* L £18/D £30, fixed price
D £24.50. ☺ H/wine £11.25
Times: 12.30-last L 2.30pm/7-last
D 9pm. Closed Sun, Nov-Mar
Additional: Light lunch;
No children under 8 at D; ❹ dishes
Seats: 30. Private room 15
Smoking: No smoking in dining room
Credit cards: JCB

Directions: From Dungevan take
B884 to Glendale. Restaurant is at
Colbost 4.5 miles from main road
turn off

'The Three Chimneys should be included on every gastronome's food tour of Scotland' enthused one inspector, won over by the charm of this 100-year-old converted crofter's cottage and the sparkling cooking found therein. The restaurant is sited in a tiny village close to the sea, on the shores of Loch Dunvegan. It's a cosy place with a stone-walled interior and open fires, peaceful and remote. Seafood, of course, is what to choose – perhaps lobster and prawn bisque, which needs no brandy or cream to pep it up, just great stock, herbs, and generous chunks of shellfish. Praise, too, for the brochette of scallops, langoustine tails wrapped in bacon, and monkfish served with a lemon butter sauce – exquisitely fresh fish, simply cooked and presented. Hot marmalade pudding with Drambuie custard will provide some ballast to a meal, while the well-chosen wines include several by the glass. Hard to beat.

CONTIN,
Coul House

By Strathpeffer IV14 9EY
Map 14: NH45
Tel: 01997 421487
Fax: 01997 421945
Chefs: Christopher Bentley,
Karl Taylor
Owners: Martyn & Ann Hill
Cost: Alc £25.50, fixed-price
D £27.50 (6 courses). ☺
H/wine £14.94.
Times: Last L 2pm /last D 9pm
Additional: Bar food; Sunday L;
Children welcome; ❹ dishes.
Accommodation: 20 en suite.
Credit cards: 🔳 🔳 🔳 🔳 🔳 🔳 JCB

*On the edge of the village, a family-run, Victorian country house
hotel set in five acres of grounds. The five-course set menu is
supported by a carte offering popular dishes; both feature 'Taste of
Scotland' dishes. Clarets are particularly well represented on a fairly
extensive globetrotting wine list.*

Directions: A9 and A385 to Contin. Half-mile up private drive
on R

DINGWALL,
Kinkell House ✿

*Lovely wee hotel with everything in the best possible taste. Marsha
Fraser's menus are full of modern ideas and fresh produce. Warm
asparagus and three cheese tart, followed by Thai-spiced chicken
baked with lime, coriander, lemongrass and ginger, and apple,
rhubarb, and bramble fudge crumble with vanilla ice cream, shows
the style.*

Easter Kinkell IV7 8HY
Map 14: NH55
Tel: 01349 861270
Fax: 01349 865902
Chef: Marsha Fraser
Owners: Mr & Mrs Steve Fraser
Cost: Alc £20. ☺ H/wine £9
Times: Last L 2pm/D 8.45pm

Additional: Sunday L; Children welcome; ❹ dishes
Smoking: No smoking in dining room
Accommodation: 9 en suite
Credit cards: 🔳 🔳

Directions: On B9169 10 miles N of Inverness, 1 mile from A9
& A835

DULNAIN BRIDGE,
Muckrach Lodge Hotel ✿

*Former Victorian shooting lodge run by enthusiastic owners. The
kitchen shows ambition, and the daily changing five-course menu is
a showcase for Scotland's abundant larder. The wine list reflects the
proprietors interest and offers many wines not normally seen in
hotels.*

PH26 3LY
Map 14: NH92
Tel: 01479 851257
Fax: 01479 851325
Please telephone for further details

Directions: On A938, 0.5 mile from Dulnain Bridge

DUNDONNELL,

Dundonnell Hotel

Seafood features strongly on the menu at this hospitable
Highland holiday hotel, situated by the roadside at the head of
Little Loch Broom. The four course dinners are to be looked
forward too, with fresh ingredients and sound skills very much
to the fore. Dishes might include home-made smoked salmon
terrine with lemon and dill sauce, cream of broccoli soup,
grilled fillets of lemon sole with trout caviar and chive butter,
or roast rib of beef, and profiteroles with chocolate sauce. A
well-reported test meal in late spring produced gâteau of crab,
langoustine and avocado with a gazpacho sauce and shellfish
oil, mussel and saffron soup, pan-fried breast and roast leg of
Guinea fowl with stir-fried cabbage, bacon and thyme gravy,
and a banana and toffee crumble with sauce anglaise.

Directions: On A832 Ullapool/Gairloch road, 14 miles from
Braemore junction

IV23 2QS
Map 14: NH08
Tel: 01854 633204
Fax: 01854 633366
Chefs: Mrs I Bellshaw,
Graham Stewart
Owner: Selbie W Florence
Cost: Fixed price D £24.95
(4 courses). ☺ H/wine £8.75
Times: Last L 2.15pm/last D 8.30pm
Additional: Bar food; Sunday L;
Children welcome; ❀ dishes
Smoking: No smoking in dining room
Accommodation: 28 en suite
Credit cards: 💳 💳 💳 💳 💳

DUNVEGAN,

Atholl House Hotel ❀ ≷≷≷

*Comfortable hotel, warm and welcoming atmosphere, good food.
Well reported have been local mussel and prawn chowder, ribeye
steak with mushroom sauce, fresh vegetables, and strawberries
served with brandy, caramel and pancakes.*

Isle of Skye IV55 8WA
Map 13: NG24
Tel: 01470 521219
Fax: 01470 521481
Please telephone for further details

DUROR, **Stewart Hotel** ❀❀

Welcoming, family-run hotel in an elevated position
surrounded by substantial acreage. The first-floor lounge is
designed to maximise the outstanding loch views. Seafood is a
strength here, although local game – pheasant and venison in
particular – are equally appealing, and the four-course dinner
menu changes daily in order to make the best use of fresh local
ingredients. For those staying the night, breakfast is everything
it should be.

Directions: Midway between Fort William and Oban on A828

Appin PA38 4BW
Map 14: NM95
Tel: 01631 740268
Fax: 01631 740328
Please telephone for further details

FORT WILLIAM,

Crannog Restaurant ❀

*Restaurant on Fort William town pier, right at the water's edge in a
converted fishermen's gear shed. Fresh seafood, simply cooked, is
the philosophy, and the welcome is warm and friendly. Dishes to
enjoy include five whole Loch Linnhe langoustine with garlic butter,
and herb crusted cod with provençale sauce.*

Additional: Children welcome; ❀ dishes
Smoking: No-smoking area; No pipes & cigars
Credit cards:

Directions: On town pier in Fort William; approach from by-pass

PH33 7NG
Map 14: NN17
Tel: 01397 703919
Fax: 01397 705026
Chef: Anne Mackinnon
Cost: Alc £21. ☺ H/wine £9.95
Times: Last L 2.30pm/last D 10pm

FORT WILLIAM,
Inverlochy Castle ❀❀❀

Torlundy PH33 6SN
Map 14: NN17
Tel: 01397 702177
Fax: 01397 702953
Chef: Simon Haigh
Cost: Fixed-price L £29/D £45 (4
courses). H/wine £13
Times: 12.30-last L 1.45pm/7.15-last
D 9.15pm
Additional: Sunday L;
No children under 8; ❀ dishes
Seats: 28 + 16. Private dining room
10-14. Jacket & tie preferred
Smoking: No smoking in dining room
Accommodation: 17 en suite
Credit cards: ▬ ▬ ✈ ▭ ▬ ▶

Exclusive and refined, but also offering a warm welcome,
Inverlochy is one of the best hotels in Scotland, attracting well-
heeled clients who pepper the car park with top-of-the-range
Porsches and Jaguars. The restaurant here is necessarily smart,
with polished tables, candles, a beautifully carved sideboard
and superb views across the mountains to Fort William. The
menu offers four choices per course dominated by Scottish
produce but showing an interesting mix of influences that
avoid the 'eclectic' and 'Pacific Rim' clichés of other venues
aiming to serve modern food. Delicate, carefully prepared
canapés began the meal: a mini croque monsieur, Parmesan
shortbread, guinea fowl confit tartlet and bruschetta with
olives. These were followed by a pithiviers of duck confit and
foie gras accompanied by a strong reduction and caramelised
endive. A lovely cream of carrot and ginger soup arrived
garnished with tiny carrot and ginger dumplings and crème
fraîche. Main course of perfectly sweet, roasted corn-fed
pigeon came with a light, creamy boudin blanc made from
chicken, foie gras and thyme, and fondant sweet potatoes that
were wonderfully smooth. A new pastry chef, has made the
selection of desserts both unusual and unusually good. The
iced rhubarb crumble with Advocaat and ginger ice cream may
have sounded bizarre but proved to be delicious and vibrant.
The pre-dessert of chocolate and ginger mousse with rich
chocolate sauce and the range of fudgy and chocolatey petits
fours showed a similar level of expertise. Inverlochy's
extensive wine list changes regularly and offers a high number
of half-bottles.

Directions: 3 miles N of Fort William on A82, just past the Golf
Club

FORT WILLIAM,
Moorings Hotel ❀

*Modern hotel on the banks of the Caledonian Canal, with views of
Ben Nevis. A four-course dinner is offered in the Jacobean-style
restaurant. Typical dishes are chicken liver and cognac parfait,
baked Mallaig plaice with a medley of citrus fruits, and Moorings
passion cake with Blairgowrie fruit sauce.*

Banavie PH33 7LY
Map 14: NN17
Tel: 01397 772797
Fax: 01397 772441
Chef: Paul Moore
Owner: Lochaber Hotels Ltd
Cost: Fixed-price D £26 (4 courses).
☺ H/wine £9

Moorings Hotel

Times: Last D 9.15pm. Closed Xmas
Additional: Bar food; Sunday L;
Children welcome; dishes
Smoking: No smoking in dining room
Accommodation: 21 en suite
Credit cards: ▆ ▆ ▆ ▆ ▆ JCB

Directions: From A82 take A830 W 1 mile. 1st R over
Caledonian Canal on B8004

GARVE, Inchbae Lodge Hotel ❀

Inchbae IV23 2PH
Map 14: NH36
Tel: 01997 455269
Fax: 01997 455207
Please telephone for further details

Relaxing Highland holiday hotel with no distracting phones or TV in rooms. The best local produce is showcased on the menu, with wood pigeon, Scottish cheeses, and wonderfully fresh vegetables all well reported. Save room for pudding.

Directions: Hotel is on A835, 6 miles on Ullapool side of Garve

GLENFINNAN, The Prince's House ❀

PH37 4LT
Map 14: NM98
Tel: 01397 722246
Fax: 01397 722307
Please telephone for further details

The welcome to travellers is as genuine as ever, and the cooking good. The up-to-date four-course dinner in Flora's Restaurant includes chestnut, porcini and field mushrooms marinated in red wine with Ayrshire ham, and paupiettes of sole filled with dill-marinated salmon.

GRANTOWN-ON-SPEY,
Culdearn House ❀

PH26 3JU
Map 14: NJ02
Tel: 01479 872106
Fax: 01479 873641
Please telephone for further details

Charming Victorian house run by dedicated owners. Good, honest country house cooking of the likes of chicken liver and brandy pâté, breast of pheasant in a light, creamy sauce laced with slices of sweet apple, and served on mashed potato, lovely fresh vegetables, and fresh fruit pavlova bursting with fruit and accompanied by a scoop of ice cream.

HARLOSH, Harlosh House ❀❀❀

Isle of Skye IV55 8ZG
Map 13: NG24
Tel/Fax: 01470 521367
Chef/Owner: Peter Elford
Cost: Fixed-price D £27.50 (4 courses). H/wine £10.20
Times: D only, 7pm-last D 8.30pm. Closed Nov to Easter
Additional: No children under 7
Seats: 16
Smoking: No smoking in dining room
Accommodation: 6 en suite
Credit cards: ▆ ▆ ▆ ▆

Harlosh House couldn't have a more perfect, tranquil setting: it's right on the shore of Loch Bracadale, with views across the water to a backdrop of the Cuillin Hills. As might be expected, the sea provides most of the ingredients that appear at dinner, a four-course meal with no choice until pudding; dedicated meat-eaters take heed. Spiced local crab on toasted brioche, followed by a herb salad or a soup, lovage say, then a main course of fillet of hake baked with Muscadet and shallots is fairly typical. Peter Elford is clearly inspired by the seafood, handling it with a confident and creative touch. The smoked fish chowder tried at inspection had distinct flavours of not just smoked haddock but of bacon and coriander too; diced potatoes retained their shape, and small, sweet steamed mussels floated on the top. This was followed by a lightly dressed salad garnished with tiny capers and croûtons. The main course on this occasion was chargrilled monkfish with an exemplary lemon-flavoured risotto, slightly soupy in texture, as it should be. Thick and eggy crème anglaise is a favoured accompaniment to desserts, turning up with light, well-flavoured ginger pudding and rhubarb compote, and pear and almond pastries. Ice creams and sorbets are made in-house, as are breads. Given the preponderance of fish, it comes as a surprise to see how many red wines there are on the list, but a Cabernet Sauvignon even appears alongside a Sauvignon and a Chardonnay among the house selection.

Directions: 4 miles S of Dunvegan, turn R off A863, signed Harlosh

INVERNESS,

Bunchrew House Hotel

Carefully restored 17th-century mansion set in wooded grounds on the shores of the Beauly Firth. Making the most of the view towards Ben Wyvis across the water, the dining room offers a good fixed-price menu. Dishes may include langoustine and crab bisque, duck with blueberry sauce, and lemon tart with Armagnac sauce.

Accommodation: 11 en suite
Credit cards: ▆ ▆ ▆ ▆ ▆ JCB

Directions: 2.5 miles from Inverness on A862 towards Beauly

Bunchrew IV3 6TA
Map 14: NH64
Tel: 01463 234917
Fax: 01463 710620
Chef: Walter Walker
Owners: Stewart & Lesley Dykes
Cost: Alc L £25. ☺ H/wine £12
Times: Last L 2pm/last D 9pm
Additional: Children welcome;
🍴 dishes
Smoking: No smoking in dining room

INVERNESS, Café 1

A touch of the continent opposite Inverness castle, this chic café features French bistro classics alongside contemporary British combinations, plus a snappy wine list. Good grilled scallops come with crisp veg and black bean jus; liver and bacon is accompanied by onion marmalade and potato-parsnip mash. The cheeseboard offers Brie and a tempting selection of Scottish varieties.

Smoking: No-smoking area; No pipes & cigars
Credit cards: ▆ ▆ ▆ ▆

Directions: Opposite Inverness Castle on Castle Street

75 Castle Street IV2 3EA
Map 14: NH64
Tel: 01463 226200
Fax: 01463 716363
Chef: Barry MacKenzie
Owner: John Ewart
Cost: Alc £12, fixed-price L £6.95
(2 courses)/D £18. ☺ H/wine £8.90
Times: Last L 2.15pm/last D 9.45pm.
Closed L Sun (D Sun Oct-Jun), 25-26
Dec, 1-2 Jan
Additional: Bar food L; Children
welcome; 🍴 dishes

INVERNESS, Culloden House Hotel

It's collar-and-tie dining in the Adam dining room of this fine Georgian mansion. The short Scottish-French menu changes daily and might include hot-smoked haddock tartare with capers, potato and onion in mayonnaise, and lamb cutlets topped with couscous and leek, wrapped in pork caul and served with a rich borderlaise sauce.

Credit cards: ▆ ▆ ▆ ▆ ▆ JCB

Directions: From Inverness take A96 (Airport road), R at sign "Culloden". After 1.2 miles L at dovecote after 2 sets of traffic lights

Culloden IV1 2NZ
Map 14: NH64
Tel: 01463 790461
Fax: 01463 792181
Chef: Michael Simpson
Cost: Alc L £17.50, fixed price D £35
(6 courses). H/wine £12.60
Times: Last L 2.15pm/last D 8.45pm.
Closed 26 Dec
Additional: Sunday L;
No children under 12; 🍴 dishes
Smoking: No smoking in dining room
Accommodation: 28 en suite

INVERNESS, **Dunain Park Hotel**

IV3 6JN
Map 14: NH64
Tel: 01463 230512
Fax: 01463 224532
Chef/Owner: Mrs Ann Nicholl
Cost: *Alc* £25. H/wine £12.50
Times: D only, last D 9pm.
Additional: Children welcome;
👜 dishes
Smoking: No smoking in dining room
Accommodation: 12 en suite
Credit cards: ▆ ▆ ⚒ ▆ ▆ ▉ JCB

Directions: One mile from town
boundary on A82 to Fort William

Shetland salmon and Puy lentil fishcakes is a definitive Scottish-
French combo. Other interesting dishes, served in a Georgian setting,
might include loin of lamb stuffed with figs, with a crêpe filled with
pine nuts, raisins and chicken liver and served with a mint and
cumin sauce, and West-coast scallops with sorrel sauce.

INVERNESS, **La Riviera at the Glenmoriston Hotel** NEW

Popular hotel on the north bank of the River Ness overlooking the
cathedral and Eden Court Theatre. The cooking has strong
Italian/Med overtones, seen in dishes such as scallop mousse ravioli
with lobster sauce and seared scallops, pan-fried fillet of sea bass
lightly dressed in sorrel with a fresh scallop and monkfish in a light
creamy fish sauce, and tiramisu served with a variety of red berries.

Credit cards: ▆ ▆ ⚒ ▆ ▆ ▉

20 Ness Bank IV2 4SF
Map 14: NH64
Tel: 01463 223777
Fax: 01463 712378
Chef: Donald Macloed
Cost: *Alc* £28, fixed price L £10.50/D
£23.95. ☺ H/wine £10.50
Times: Last L 2pm/last D 9.30pm.
Accommodation: 15 en suite

ISLE ORNSAY,
Hotel Eilean Iarmain

Isle of Skye IV43 8QR
Map 13: NG71
Tel: 01471 833332
Fax: 01471 833275
Chefs: Roger Brown, Morag MacInnes
Owners: Sir Iain & Lady Noble
Cost: *Alc* £15, fixed-price L £17.50/D
£30.50 (4 courses). H/wine £14
Times: Last L 1.45pm/last D 8.45pm
Additional: Bar food; Sunday L;
Children welcome; 👜 dishes
Smoking: No smoking in dining room
Accommodation: 12 en suite
Credit cards: ▆ ▆ ⚒ ▆ ▆

Directions: Overlooking harbour –
cross bridge at Kyle of Lochalsh then
take A850 and A851 down to harbour
front

Idyllically situated overlooking the Sound of Sleat, this Gaelic inn
boasts a formal candlelit dining room offering interesting menus that
ably demonstrate the technical skills of the kitchen. Good choices
include ballotine of salmon with scallops, pastry-crusted lamb fillet
with thyme and mushroom 'estouffade' and baked lemon tart.
There's a tempting wine list too.

ISLE ORNSAY, **Kinloch Lodge** ✿✿

Isle of Skye IV43 8QY
Map 13: NG71
Tel: 01471 833214
Fax: 01471 833277
Chefs: Lady Macdonald, Peter Macpherson
Owners: Lord & Lady Macdonald
Cost: Fixed-price D £35 (5 courses). H/wine £5
Times: D only at 8pm.
Closed 23 Dec-1 Feb
Additional: No children under 8
Seats: 30
Smoking: No smoking in dining room
Accommodation: 15 en suite
Credit cards: ■ ▬ ▦

Lord and Lady Macdonald's beautiful home is found at the end of a bumpy forest track which, due to a damaged bridge, replaces the former drive. The building dates from 1540, and the restaurant is adorned with family portraits, along with family silver and glassware. The style is that of dining in a country house, and there is a refreshing simplicity to the cooking. Smoked Achiltibuie chicken with melon and nectarine vinaigrette was an effective starter, and baked fillet of turbot with creamy watercress and shallot cream sauce was just spot-on. Almost our inspector's undoing, was the extremely rich dark chocolate cake with bitter orange and Drambuie sauce.

Directions: 1 mile off main road, 6 miles S of Broadford on A851, 10 miles N of Armadale

KINGUSSIE, **The Cross** ✿✿✿

The Hadleys' converted tweed mill is a delight, and inspectors continue to praise Ruth Hadley's accomplished cooking based on clean fresh flavours and the best ingredients. Tony Hadley runs the dining room where he chats freely to guests and enthuses about wine from the extensive list of over 400 bins – some people collect stamps, Tony collects wine – do listen to his advice, he is willing to share his knowledge. Canapés open the set-price dinner that only offers choice at the main course and dessert stages. The first course could be seafood boudin bursting with flavour and containing scallops, lobster and turbot. Then perhaps, fresh tasting mushroom soup, with a small chunk of wonderful home-smoked salmon to follow. New seasons lamb could be the centrepiece, simple and uncomplicated, accompanied a light, rich jus and fresh vegetables, with a parfait of meringue with a tart blackcurrant coulis getting the balance just right. An April menu could bring West coast prawns with an avocado salad, parsnip soup, spiced crab cakes with a sweetcorn salsa, fillet of beef with grain mustard and red wine sauce, and chocolate mousse cake. Excellent coffee is served in the lounge.

Tweed Mill Brae
Ardbroilach Road PH21 1TC
Map 14: NH70
Tel: 01540 661166
Fax: 01540 661080
Chef: Ruth Hadley
Owners: Tony & Ruth Hadley
Cost: Fixed-price D £35 (5 courses). H/wine from £10
Times: D only, 7pm-9pm.
Closed Tues, 1-26 Dec, 6 Jan-28 Feb
Additional: No children under 12; ✿ dishes
Seats: 28
Smoking: No smoking in dining room

Accommodation: 9 en suite
Credit cards: ■ ▬ ▣ ▦

Directions: Town centre, 300m uphill from lights along Ardroilach Road & turn left onto Tweed Mill Brae

AA Shortlisted for Wine Award-see page 16

KINGUSSIE, Osprey Hotel ❀

Charming hotel in the heart of the Spey Valley. Aileen Burrow's modern cooking mixes English and Scottish ideas to create contemporary dishes such as supreme of guinea fowl with apple and brandy sauce, and fillet of salmon with leek and tarragon sauce. Desserts are a must: try the plum strudel or the whisky and hazelnut parfait.

Accommodation: 8 en suite
Credit cards: ▬ ▬ ▬

Directions: South end of High Street off A9

Ruthven Road PH21 1EN
Map 14: NH70
Tel/Fax: 01540 661510
Chef: Aileen Burrow
Owners: Aileen & Robert Burrow
Cost: Fixed-price D £22 (4 courses).
☺ H/wine £8.
Times: D only, 7.30pm-8.30pm
Additional: No children under 10;
❹ dishes
Smoking: No smoking in dining room

KINGUSSIE,
The Scot House Hotel ❀

Featuring Highland produce whenever possible, the menu at this Victorian former manse has a strong Scottish flavour. Speyside salmon with a sauce of dill and tiger prawns, Culloden pork with mushroom and sherry sauce, and tournedos of Angus beef topped with haggis, onion sauce and Orkney cheddar, demonstrate the style.

Additional: Bar food; Children welcome; ❹ dishes
Smoking: No smoking in dining room
Accommodation: 9 en suite.
Credit cards: ▬ ▬ ▬ ☐ ▶ JCB

Directions: South end of main village street

Newtonmore Road PH21 1HE
Map 14: NH70
Tel: 01540 661351
Fax: 01540 661111
Chef: Andrew Woods
Owners: Morag & Bill Gilbert,
Val & Nigel McConachie
Cost: Alc £24, fixed-price D £18.50
(4 courses). H/wine £9.25. ☺
Times: Last L 2pm/last last D 8.45pm.
Closed 2nd wk Jan-2nd wk Feb

KYLESKU, Kylesku Hotel ❀

The fishing boats land their catch directly outside the door of the old inn, so the pan-fried haddock with lemon butter might be a good bet. Seafood is a speciality but roast loin of local lamb with braised red cabbage, and chicken tikka are also on the menu.

Smoking: No smoking in dining room
Accommodation: 9 en suite
Credit cards: ▬ ▬ ▬ ☐

Directions: 30 miles north of Ullapool

Lairg IV27 4HW
Map 14: NC23
Tel: 01971 502231
Fax: 01971 502313
Chef/Owner: Marcel René Klein
Cost: Alc £17, fixed price L £16/D
£17. ☺ H/wine £7.95
Times: Last L 2.30pm/last D 9.30pm
Additional: Bar food; Sunday L;
Children welcome; ❹ dishes

LOCHINVER,
Inver Lodge Hotel ❀

Dramatic views across Lochinver Bay are just one reason to visit the restaurant at this well-appointed modern hotel. The fresh locally-landed fish is another. Favourites include monkfish with a white wine and cheese sauce, and Lochinver prawns, coated in a beer and rosemary batter and served with herb mayonnaise.

Additional: Bar food L; No children under 7; ❹ dishes
Smoking: No smoking in dining room
Accommodation: 20 en suite
Credit cards: ▬ ▬ ▬ ☐ ▬ ▶ ▣ JCB

Directions: *Telephone for directions*

IV27 4LU
Map 14: NC02
Tel: 01571 844496
Fax: 01571 844395
Chef: John Robertson
Owner: Edmund Vestey
Cost: Alc £23. fixed-price D £27
(7 courses). ☺ H/wine £9.95
Times: Last L 2pm/last D 9pm

LOCHINVER,

Lochinver Larder

Main Street IV27 4JY
Map 14: NC02
Tel: 01571 844356
Fax: 01571 844688
Chefs: Mr & Mrs Stewart,
Mrs W Isbister
Owners: Mr & Mrs I Stewart
Cost: *Alc* £15

Something to suit all tastes. Right on the river bank, plus an unpretentious atmosphere equals a highly popular spot where you usually need to book to get a table. Freshly baked pies, venison Stroganoff, sirloin steaks, and herb-crumbed haddock are all firm favourites.

Additional: Children welcome; ❸ dishes
Smoking: No smoking in dining room
Credit cards: ▬ ▬ ⤳ ▢ JCB

Directions: On A837, second property on R coming from Inverness/Ullapool

MUIR OF ORD,

The Dower House ❀❀

Highfield IV6 7XN
Map 14: NH55
Tel/Fax: 01463 870090
Chef: Robyn Aitchison
Owners: Robyn & Mena Aitchison
Cost: *Alc* £25, fixed-price D £25. ☺
H/wine £13
Times: L by arrangement/7.30-last
D 9pm. Closed Xmas
Additional: No children under 7 at D;
❸ dishes
Seats: 26
Smoking: No smoking in dining room
Accommodation: 5 en suite
Credit cards: ▬ ▬

Just a few miles north of Inverness at the base of the Black Isle, this charming cottage hotel is an ideal location from which to explore the Highlands of Scotland. Lovingly and discreetly run by Robyn and Mena Aitchison, the house nestles in four acres of secluded grounds. The dining room is small and intimate, which makes booking ahead essential. The effort is worthwhile though, and anyone who makes it here will be rewarded with some fine modern British dishes created by Robyn. An early summer meal ran something like this: starter of fine poached egg topped with Parmesan on a bed of fresh rocket and purslane; a 'cracking' piece of John Dory served with a zingy purée of coriander and ratatouille-style vegetables; dessert of warmed strawberries with green peppercorn syrup and mint. The excellent wine list is very reasonably priced.

Directions: From Muir of Ord take A862 (Dingwall) 1 mile, L at double bend

NAIRN,

The Boath House ❀❀   NEW

Auldearn IV12 5TE
Map 14: NH85
Tel: 01667 454896
Fax: 01667 455469
Chef: Charles Lockley
Owners: Don & Wendy Matheson
Cost: ☺ H/wine £12.50
Times: 12.30-last L 2pm/7-last
D 10pm. Closed L Wed, all Mon,
Tue, 2 wks Feb
Additional: Sunday L;
Children welcome; ❸ dishes
Seats: 24. Private dining room 8
Smoking: No smoking in dining room

The classical Georgian mansion is set in 20 acres of lawns, woodlands, lakes and streams. The elegant restaurant overlooks the garden lake and is entirely candlelit at night. Only the best quality ingredients are used to produce the innovative dishes offered from the daily *carte*. This is supported by a balanced and well-chosen wine list. The home-made sun-dried tomato bread made a good first impression, as did a starter of foie gras and chicken liver parfait with its beautifully smooth texture and wonderful flavour. A worthy main course comprised king scallops from Skye, seared and served with fillet of turbot on a truffle risotto with langoustine and brandy sauce.

Accommodation: 7 en suite
Credit cards: ▬ ▬ ⤳ ▢ ▬ ▐ ◈

Directions: *Please telephone for directions*

NAIRN, **Newton Hotel**

Inverness Road IV12 4RX
Map 14: NH85
Tel: 01667 453144
Fax: 01667 454026
Chef: Martyn Woodward
Cost: Fixed price D £23. ☺
H/wine £12.95
Times: Last L 2pm/last D 9pm
Additional: Bar food; Sunday L;
Children welcome; ✪ dishes
Smoking: No smoking in dining room
Accommodation: 43 en suite
Credit cards: 🔲 🔲 🔲 🔲 🔲 🔲

Scottish baronial dining on the grand scale. Expect baked fillet of Angus beef Wellington on Madeira wine jus, steamed fillet of halibut topped with salmon, scallop and turbot mousse scented with lemongrass on a lime and chive sauce, and iced brown-bread parfait in a tuille basket with red berry coulis.

Directions: West of the town centre

ONICH, **Allt-nan-Ros Hotel** ✪ ✪

PH33 6RY
Map 14: NN06
Tel: 01855 821210
Fax: 01855 821462
Chef: Gavin Hughes
Owners: James & Fiona MacLeod
Cost: Fixed-price D £27.50 (5 courses). H/wine £9.75
Times: 12.30pm-last L 1.30pm/7pm-last D 8.30pm
Additional: Bar food L; Sunday L;
Children welcome; ✪ dishes
Seats: 50
Smoking: No smoking in dining room
Accommodation: 21 en suite
Credit cards: 🔲 🔲 🔲 🔲 🔲 🔲 🔲 JCB

Genuine Highland hospitality and good food are all part of the appeal of this comfortable holiday hotel. In the restaurant, picture windows take full advantage of a view across Loch Linnhe to the Morven hills beyond. The fixed-price dinner menu is not extensive but it is well balanced and full of interest, with a modern treatment given to good Scottish ingredients. Following some tasty canapés served in the lounge, our last test meal continued with pan-fried scallops with a basil and pesto dressing around a mound of lettuce topped with crisp vegetable spaghetti – a simple but effective dish. Next came an honestly flavoured leek soup with chicken quenelle garnish, before a main dish of braised turbot on a bed of home-made noodles with a plum-tomato and olive oil coulis. The finale was a beautifully presented raspberry mascarpone mousse. Kilted proprietor James MacLeod presides with the waitresses smartly kitted out in long tartan skirts.

Directions: On the shores of Loch Linnhe, 10 miles S of Fort William on A82

ONICH, Onich Hotel ❀

Hospitable roadside hotel with gardens sweeping down to Loch Linnhe. A busy dining room is the venue for well-constructed set meals such as Glencoe game terrine with onion marmalade; Loch Eil mussel chowder; grilled calves' liver, bacon and onion; and date pudding with caramel ice-cream. Popular, global wine choice.

Smoking: No smoking in dining room
Accommodation: 25 en suite
Credit cards: 💳 💳 💳 💳 💳 💳

Directions: *Telephone for directions*

By Fort William PH33 6RY
Map 14: NN06
Tel: 01855 821214
Fax: 01855 821484
Chef: Alan Clark
Owner: Linleven Hotel Co Ltd
Cost: Fixed price D £21 (4 courses).
☺ H/wine £9.25
Times: Noon-9pm (winter),
10pm (summer). Closed Xmas
Additional: Bar food L; Sunday L;
Children welcome; ♨ dishes

PLOCKTON, Haven Hotel ❀

Set in the village best known as the location for the TV series Hamish Macbeth, this is a charming hotel with an intimate restaurant. Grouse with bacon, and carefully cooked halibut garnished with chanterelles proved enjoyable dishes, followed by a strawberry and Kirsch trifle to complete the meal.

Smoking: No smoking in dining room
Accommodation: 15 rooms
Credit cards: 💳 💳 💳 💳

Directions: On main road to Plockton, on left hand side just before lochside

Innes Street IV52 8TW
Map 14: NG83
Tel: 01599 544223
Fax: 01599 544467
Chef: Ian James
Owners: Annan & Jill Dryburgh
Cost: Alc £ 24, fixed-price D £24 (5-courses). ☺ H/wine £6.95.
Times: Last L 2pm/last D 8.30pm.
Closed 20 Dec-1 Feb
Additional: No children under 7;
♨ dishes

PORTREE, Bosville Hotel ❀

Bosville Terrace
Isle of Skye IV51 9DG
Map 13: NG44
Tel: 01478 612846
Fax: 01478 613434
Chef: Craig Rodger
Owner: Donald W Macleod
Cost: Alc £25, fixed-price L £15.
H/wine £9.95
Times: Open all day, last D 10pm
Additional: Bar food; Sunday L;
Children welcome; ♨ dishes
Smoking: No smoking in dining room;
Air conditioning
Accommodation: 15 en suite
Credit cards: 💳 💳 💳 💳 💳 💳

An attractive, family hotel situated above Portree harbour. Modern Scottish dishes are served in the Chandlery Restaurant, where innovative seafood dishes steal the show. Try smoked salmon tartare as a starter, followed by poached parcel of salmon, filled with a lobster, monkfish and chive mousse. A good selection of wines is available.

Directions: In centre of Portree

PORTREE, Cuillin Hills Hotel ❀

Built in the 1870s as a hunting lodge for Lord Macdonald of the Isles, the hotel enjoys spectacular views over Portree Bay to the Cuillin Hills. Modern cooking produces interesting flavour

Isle of Skye IV51 9LU
Map 13: NG44
Tel: 01478 612003
Fax: 01478 613092
Chef: Jeff Johnston

Cuillin Hills Hotel

Cost: Alc £24. ☺ H/wine £9.95
Times: D only, last D 9pm
Additional: Bar food; Sunday L
(12.30-2pm); Children welcome;
🍴 dishes
Smoking: No smoking in dining room
Accommodation: 25 en suite
Credit cards: 🔳 🔳 🔳 🔳

*combinations in traditional favourites, such as roast best end of lamb
with a Dijon mustard and herb crust.*

Directions: Signed to right 0.25 miles from Portree on A855
north

PORTREE, Rosedale Hotel ❀

Isle of Skye IV51 9DB
Map 13: NG44
Tel: 01478 613131
Fax: 01478 612531
Chef: Tony Parkyn
Owner: Hugh Andrew
Cost: Fixed-price D £26 (5 courses).
☺ H/wine £10.25
Times: D only, last D 8.30pm
Smoking: No smoking in dining room
Accommodation: 23 en suite
Credit cards: 🔳 🔳 🔳 🔳

*Tables are laid with crystal, silver and quality china at this harbour-
facing restaurant. There's a choice of three or five courses from the
daily-changing menu, which might offer the hotel's own gravad lax,
and loin of pork with apricot and pistachio stuffing, roasted fruits
and a port enhanced jus.*

Directions: Centrally located on waterfront in Portree

SHIELDAIG, Tigh an Eilean Hotel ❀

*There is a sense of light and openness in the dining room, helped by
the sea view. The cooking is simple, fresh and good with fresh crab
dijonnaise, grilled lamb cutlets with mint sauce, and poached salmon
hollandaise amongst the choice. Puddings might include home-made
lemon flan plus a selection of local cheeses.*

Strathcarron IV54 8XN
Map 14: NG85
Tel: 01520 755251
Fax: 01520 755321
Chef/Owner: Callum F Stewart
Cost: Fixed-price D £23.50. ☺
H/wine £6
Times: D only, last D 8.25pm.
Closed mid Oct-mid Apr

Additional: Bar food (except Sun); Children welcome
Smoking: No smoking in dining room
Accommodation: 11 en suite
Credit cards: 🔳 🔳 🔳 🔳

Directions: In centre of Shieldaig, at water's edge

SPEAN BRIDGE,

Old Station Restaurant ⊛

A trainspotter's dream – the restaurant occupies a Victorian station on the working West Highland line. Warmed by open fires, you can tuck into garlic mushrooms and prawns in filo, breast of pheasant with blue cheese sauce, and warm bramble and almond tart, whilst watching the London sleeper pass by.

Additional: Children welcome; ◑ dishes
Smoking: No-smoking area
Credit cards: ▬ ▭ ▅◥ ▢ JCB

Directions: Approximately 10 miles N of Fort William, in centre of village (follow signs for BR station)

Station Road PH34 4EP
Map 14: NN28
Tel: 01397 712535
Chef: Richard Bunney
Owners: Richard & Helen Bunney
Cost: Alc £21. ☺ H/wine £10.25
Times: D only, last D 9pm.
Closed Mon, Nov, 24 Dec-28 Mar

STRONTIAN,

Kilcamb Lodge ⊛⊛

With a dream location on the shore of Loch Sunart, this beautifully restored former hunting lodge has been turned into a perfectly peaceful away-from-it-all retreat by the hospitable Blakeways. Scottish produce is very much to the fore on a modern menu that might include pan-fried Moray scallops with tomato and basil in filo pastry, confit of duck leg with mushroom risotto, loin of Argyll venison on a mozzarella, spinach and potato rösti with a game and chocolate sauce, noisettes of Highland lamb and tarragon mousse with polenta pancakes and mushroom one, and seared marinated salmon with squid-ink pasta, pesto sauce and deep-fried spinach. Finish with the likes of bread-and-butter pudding with orange marmalade, a fresh fruit plate, or a selection of Scottish cheeses.

Directions: Over the Corran ferry off A82. Follow A861 to Strontian. First L over bridge in centre of village

Acharacle PH36 4HY
Map 14: NM86
Tel: 01967 402257
Fax: 01967 402041
Chef: Neil Mellis
Owners: Mr & Mrs Peter Blakeway
Cost: Fixed-price D £26.50
(4 courses).
Times: Noon-last L 1.30pm/D at 7.30pm. Closed Dec-Feb
Additional: Bar food L;
No children under 8; ◑ dishes
Seats: 28
Smoking: No smoking in dining room
Accommodation: 11 en suite
Credit cards: ▬ ▭ ▅◥ ▢ ▣ JCB

TAIN, **Mansfield House** ⊛ **NEW**

Solid, stone-built Victorian turreted mansion standing in its own grounds. The kitchen tries hard and delivers the likes of trompette of wild mushroom in a cream sauce, salmon stuffed with prawns in a beurre blanc sauce with dill, and chocolate tart with crème anglaise. The wine list features mostly popular wines and house wines are served by the carafe.

Additional: Bar food; Sunday L; Children welcome; ◑ dishes
Smoking: No smoking in dining room
Accommodation: 18 en suite
Credit cards: ▬ ▭ ▅◥ ▢ ▬ ▣

Directions: *Telephone for directions*

Scotsburn Road, IV19 1PR
Map 14: NH78
Tel: 01862 892052
Fax: 01862 892260
Chef: David Lauritson
Owners: Norman, Norma & David Lauritson
Cost: Fixed price D £25 (4 courses).
☺ H/wine £10
Times: Last L 2pm/last D 9pm

TONGUE, **Ben Loyal Hotel** ⊛

Enthusiastically run holiday and sporting hotel looking out over the Kyle of Tongue and the ruins of Varrich Castle. Look out for soundly cooked pan-fried pheasant with caramelised chestnuts and a

IV27 4XE
Map 14: NC55
Tel: 01847 611216
Fax: 01847 611212
Chef: Mel Cook

Ben Loyal Hotel

Owners: Mel & Pauline Cook
Cost: Fixed-price D £24 (4 courses).
☺ H/wine £10.75
Times: D only, last D 8.30pm.
Closed Dec-Feb
Additional: Bar food; Children
welcome; ❸ dishes
Smoking: No smoking in dining room
Accommodation: 12 en suite
Credit cards: ▆ ▆ ◤ ▆

sweet tarragon jus, or baked fillets of cod with an avocado mousse
and a tomato sauce. Desserts take in lemon meringue pie and melon-
scented crème brûlée.

Directions: The hotel stands in the centre of this village at the
A836/A838 intersection

TORRIDON,

Loch Torridon Hotel ❀❀

Achnasheen IV22 2EY
Map 14: NG95
Tel: 01445 791242
Fax: 01445 791296
Chef: Gerard Boylan
Cost: Fixed-price D £37.50 (5
courses)
Times: Light L (noon-2pm)/D 7.15-last
D 8.30pm
Additional: Bar food;
No children under 12 at D; ❸ dishes
Seats: 40. Private dining room 20.
Jacket & tie preferred
Smoking: No smoking in dining room
Accommodation: 21 en suite
Credit cards: ▆ ▆ ◤ ▆ ▆

The idyllic location overlooking snow-tipped mountains and
beautiful Loch Torridon makes you understand why the first
Earl of Lovelace bagged the spot for a grand Victorian
shooting lodge. Dinner is served in the carefully restored,
wood-panelled dining-room. The set menu, supplemented by
Taste of Scotland dishes, comes with a wide choice of rolls,
including salmon flavoured ones. West coast scampi was served
with good spinach noodles and a nicely acidulated lemon and
shellfish jus, but redundant peppers. Main course venison was
matched with herb and leek mousse, and salmon and West
Coast mussels with scampi and lemon essence, sautéed fennel
and grilled collops of potato. Dessert could be mulled berry
charlotte or peach schnapps cream with peach sauce, plus a
selection of Scottish cheeses with a glass of port.

Directions: From Inverness, follow signs to Ullapool (A835).
At Garve take A832 to Kinlochewe; take A896 to Torridon.
Don't turn off to Torridon village – hotel is one mile on L

ULLAPOOL, **Altnaharrie Inn** 🏵🏵🏵🏵🏵

IV26 2SS
Map 14: NH19
Tel: 01854 633230
Chef: Gunn Eriksen
Owners: Gunn Eriksen, Fred Brown
Cost: Fixed-price D £75 (5 courses).
H/wine £11
Times: D only, at 8pm.
Closed early Nov-Easter
Additional: No children under 8;
🌢 dishes
Seats: 18
Smoking: No smoking in dining room
Accommodation: 8 en suite
Credit cards: ▀ ▀ ◥ ◻ JCB

Directions: Telephone from Ullapool
for directions to ferry

The whole Altnaharrie experience does not disappoint: the trip
over on the little launch, the excited camaraderie between
guests (new and regular) and the superbly tasteful, classy
bedrooms, are all a foretaste of the main event – Gunn
Eriksen's five-course dinner. The dining room is full of
delightful touches: tapestries by Gunn, fresh wild flowers,
beautifully polished tables, views across Loch Broom. The menu
is no choice and this is what an inspector enjoyed one June
evening. *Amuse-bouche* of different caviars served with drinks
in one of the two lounges, then first-class rolls of poppy and
sesame seed, olive, and plain white. The first course was a light
shellfish mousse studded with crab and encased in a light, crisp
filo case and served with three sauces, one a light meat jus, the
other a scallop cream, and the third a sauce made from scallop
corals. Soup was a delicate, frothy langoustine with subtle layers
resulting in a bottomless depth of flavour – sweet, creamy, light,
with some slices of langoustine as an accompaniment. Next
came tender little squab pigeon, served on slices of kohlrabi
roasted in olive oil, a glorious crunch against the succulent meat
of the pigeon. Crisp legs were also served with a slice of foie
gras slipped under the kohlrabi as a surprise. Enoki mushrooms
and wild asparagus were simple vegetable accompaniments, and
the Burgundy base jus was just sticky enough to coat both the
ingredients and the palate without clinging. Then a huge list of
French, Scottish, Irish and English cheeses was reeled off, all
that were served were spot-on, and the light water biscuit and
fruit bread showed more of Gunn's skills. There were three
puddings, always are, and guests can have all three. A light
apricot tart, peach liqueur ice cream, a trio of caramel desserts
including caramel ice cream, a light crème caramel and wafer
slices of caramelised pear, all topped with a whirl of spun sugar,
and an intense, but not sweet, chocolate fondant cake served
with a bitter chocolate ice cream. Good coffee and petits fours
for those who still have room. And breakfast, reported our
inspector, was about the best she'd ever had.

WHITEBRIDGE,
Knockie Lodge Hotel 🏵🏵

IV1 2UP
Map 14: NH41
Tel: 01456 486276
Fax: 01456 486389
Chef: Mark Dexter

Knockie Lodge is a former shooting lodge, built in 1789 for
Lord Lovat, chief of the Clan Fraser. The setting, on the south
side of Loch Ness is dramatic. Today it is an enthusiastically
run hotel, very much in the house-party style, with sound

Knockie Lodge Hotel

Owners: Nicholas Bean,
Louise Dawson
Cost: Fixed-price D £35 (5 courses).
H/wine £11
Times: D only, at 8pm.
Closed 1 Nov-30 Apr
Additional: No children under 10;
dishes
Seats: 32. Jacket & tie preferred
Smoking: No smoking in dining room
Accommodation: 10 en suite
Credit cards: ▉ ▉ ▉ ▉

cooking, generously served, using local materials when
suitable. The set no-choice menu (except dessert) blends the
simple with the more elaborate. Start, for example, with
tomato consommé garnished with tortellini of fresh basil, then
try some fresh Loch Fyne scallops on a bed of buttered leeks,
followed by roast supreme of duck with Puy lentils and a
honey mushroom sauce, some cheese comes next, and then a
choice of fresh local blackberry bavarois with home-made
lemon sorbet, or pear and almond tart with a white chocolate
ice cream.

Directions: On the B862 8 miles north of Fort Augustus

LANARKSHIRE, NORTH

AIRDRIE, **Bouzy Rouge** ✽   NEW

1 Rochsollach Road ML6 9BB
Map 11: NS76
Tel: 01236 763853
Fax: 01236 770340
Chef: Alan Brown
Owners: Alan & Audrey Brown
Cost: Alc £21, fixed-price L £9.95/D
£19.95. ☺
Times: Last L 5pm/last D 10pm.
Closed 1 Jan
Additional: Bar food; Sunday L;
Children welcome; dishes
Smoking: No-smoking area; Air
conditioning
Credit cards: ▉ ▉ ▉ ▉ ▉ ▉ ▉

*Named after a rare French village wine, this busy-road bistro has a
well-compiled wine list, also a rare treat. Colourful walls and lively
music complement the contemporary menus. Local ingredients
include salmon, beef, venison and ostrich combined in interesting
ways: haggis is made into cannelloni, chicken is sprinkled with
oatmeal and served on Orkney clapshot.*

Directions: *Telephone for directions*

CUMBERNAULD,
Westerwood Hotel ❀

1 St Andrew's Drive
Westerwood G68 0EW
Map 11: NS77
Tel: 01236 457171
Fax: 01236 738478
Chef: Kevin Bresun
Owner: Mr A Thresh
Cost: *Alc* £25, fixed-price L £9.95/D £16.50. ☺ H/wine £10.95
Times: Last L 2pm/last D 10pm. Closed L Sat, 24 Dec
Additional: Bar food L; Sunday L; Children welcome; ❹ dishes
Smoking: No-smoking area; Air conditioning
Accommodation: 49 en suite
Credit cards: 🖸 🖸 🖸 🖸 🖸 🖸

A modern hotel and country club with a spacious restaurant serving modern international dishes. Starters include ballotine of chicken filled with light coriander mousse, and warm focaccia with roast tomatoes and pimento. After dessert try one of the speciality coffees, all of which are laced with rum or whisky.

Directions: Take exit from A80 signposted Ward Park. At mini roundabout take 1st L, at 2nd roundabout turn R, leads into St Andrew's Drive

LANARKSHIRE, SOUTH

BIGGAR, **Shieldhill Hotel** ❀❀

The Chancellor family resided for over seven centuries at this fortified mansion, parts of which date from 1199. The imposing building is now a country house hotel set in seven acres of lawns and woodland, but the family's name continues in the Chancellor restaurant, which is resplendent in its baronial furnishings. The short, daily-changing dinner menu begins with the likes of carrot and coriander soup, or chicken, spinach and tomato roulade with herb salad and hazelnut oil. Sliced duck on a three-bean salad, or seared spicy scallops on a basil couscous with pink peppercorn and sweet pepper dressing might follow. Lemon torte with orange crème – nice sharp filling and good pastry – was the star of a recent inspection. Friendly service and a worthwhile wine list also count in the Shieldhill's favour.

Quothquan ML12 6NA
Map 11: NT03
Tel: 01899 220035
Fax: 01899 221092
Chef: Trevor Williams
Owners: Mr & Mrs Lamb
Cost: Fixed-price L £17.50/D £29.50 (4 courses). H/wine £11.50
Times: Noon-last L 2pm/7-last D 9pm
Additional: Bar food; Sunday L; Children welcome; ❹ dishes
Seats: 30. Private room 30
Smoking: No smoking in dining room
Accommodation: 15 en suite
Credit cards: 🖸 🖸 🖸

Directions: Off B7016 (Carnwath), turn L 2 miles from centre of Biggar

LOTHIAN, EAST

DIRLETON, **Open Arms Hotel**

The traditional country hotel stands directly opposite the 13th-century castle that dominates this very picturesque village. An informal modern brasserie has now opened, with the more conservatively decorated restaurant open for dinner only. The fixed-price dinner menu offers a wide choice with starters taking in pan-seared king scallops with crisp stir-fried spring greens with a chilli and red onion butter, or mussel, onion and cider chowder with garlic croûtons, followed by a soup of sorbet. Lemon sole, salmon and sorrel parcels, lightly steamed and served on creamed spinach, or roast rack of spring lamb flavoured with maple syrup, rosemary and smoked garlic with a light jus of the pan juices, are both intriguing sounding main courses. Wonderful desserts range from Pavlova-style meringue filled with strawberries and kiwi fruit, to vanilla crème brûlée caramelised with brown sugar and rum and served with glazed banana and home-made shortcake.

EH39 5EG
Map 12: NT58
Tel: 01620 850241
Fax: 01620 850570
Chef: John Kay
Owner: Tom & Emma Hill
Cost: Fixed-price D £27.50
(4 courses). ☺ H/wine £9.95
Times: Noon-last L 2.30pm/6-last
D 9.30pm
Additional: Bar food; Sunday L;
Children welcome; ◑ dishes
Seats: 50. Private dining room 35
Smoking: No-smoking area;
No pipes and cigars; Air conditioning
Accommodation: 10 en suite
Credit cards: ▨ ▨ ▨ ▨

Directions: From A1 (S) take A198 to North Berwick, then follow signs for Dirleton – 2 miles W. From Edinburgh take A6137 leading to A198.

GULLANE, **Greywalls Hotel**

Created as a hotel 50 years ago, Greywalls is a stunning Edwardian country house set in gardens laid out by Gertrude Jekyll. Within are enticing plump cushions and sumptuous furnishings, log fires and a grand piano, while the dining-room has spectacular views over Muirfield golf course and the distant Firth of Forth. Dinner is a set four courses with a handful of choices at each stage except the second, which is normally a soup, consommé of beetroot, perhaps. Nicely seared tuna on spiced aubergine and sultanas is a combination that kicks the tastebuds into action for the rest of the meal. Tender, pink venison with a purée of Puy lentils sounds like a product of the Auld Alliance, while savouries like Welsh rarebit or anchovy toast figure among puddings, which might include a mille-feuille of white chocolate mousse with mango sorbet. Ingredients are exemplary, beef is Aberdeen Angus, smoked salmon is from Loch Fyne and lamb and farmhouse cheeses are local. The wine list has some top producers and classic vintages as well as an approachable and reasonably priced house selection.

Muirfield EH31 2EG
Map 12: NT48
Tel: 01620 842144
Fax: 01620 842241
Chef: Simon Burns
Owners: Ros & Giles Weaver
Cost: Fixed-price L £17.50/D £35
(5 courses). H/wine £12
Times: 12.30-last L 2pm/7.30-last
D 9.15pm. Closed Nov-Mar
Additional: Bar food L; Sunday L;
Children welcome
Seats: 50. Private room 20.
Jacket & tie preferred
Smoking: No smoking in dining room
Accommodation: 23 en suite
Credit cards: ▨ ▨ ▨ ▨ ▨

Directions: From Edinburgh take A1 to North Berwick slip road, then follow A198 along coast to far end of Gullane – Greywalls is up last road on L

GULLANE, **La Potinière** ✿✿✿

'Still the same as ever. Feels like you're sitting in somebody's front room,' writes an inspector of the Browns' small restaurant. The formula remains: everyone eats at the same time, there's no choice, and lunch is served four times a week, dinner on just Friday and Saturday. Getting in involves reserving a table weeks in advance. 'Keep it simple' may be Hilary Brown's own motto, a precept she adheres to with admirable results. A soup starts

Main Street
EH31 2AA
Map 12: NT48
Tel/Fax: 01620 843214
Chef: Hilary Brown
Owners: David & Hilary Brown
Cost: Fixed-price L £20 (4 courses)/D
£30 (5 courses). H/wine £12.75

things off sweet cream of pepper, say, followed by fish – fillet of sole, lightly steamed, very fresh and soft, comes stuffed with a good contrasting pesto and sauce vierge on a bed of spinach. The main course might be breast of corn-fed chicken fanned on Puy lentils with intensely flavoured morels, 'a lovely combination of flavours and textures, simple, successful', the accompanying pommes dauphinoise seeming almost statutory. The salad that follows the main course brought an inspector to rhapsodies: young leaves, sunflower seeds, peas, sugar snaps and apple, all dressed with walnut oil, 'lovely, stunning'. A slice of cheese comes next, and then the band strikes up again for the superlatives given a simple dessert of pannacotta, just set, very creamy, with a light caramelised sauce and a few nuts. David Brown makes a genial host and is the best source of advice about which wine to go for.

Times: L at 1pm/D at 8pm. Closed L Wed, Fri & Sat, D Sun-Thu, 1 wk Jun, all Oct, Xmas, New Year
Additional: Sunday L; Children welcome.
Seats: 28
Smoking: No smoking in dining room
Credit cards: None

Directions: Village centre

LOTHIAN, WEST

LINLITHGOW, Champany Inn ❀❀

EH49 7LU
Map 11: NS97
Tel: 01506 834532
Fax: 01506 834302
Chef: Clive Davidson
Owners: Clive & Anne Davidson
Cost: *Alc* £50. Fixed-price L £15.75 (2 courses). H/wine £12.50
Times: 12.30-last L 2pm/7-last D 10pm. Closed L Sat, all Sun, 24-26 Dec

An old mill house with loads of character, Champany Inn dates back to the time of Mary, Queen of Scots. Chef Clive Davidson has been creating quality Scottish dishes here for fifteen years now, and his experience shines through in starters such as home-smoked beef with olive oil and fresh oregano, charcoal-grilled salmon with lemon butter, and North Sea prawns with home-made pasta and white wine butter sauce. A recent inspection meal started with a light, smooth chicken liver parfait with tangy onion relish. This was followed by chargrilled pope's-eye steak, cooked to perfection, and for dessert, a sweet crème caramel was served chilled. Other puddings could include hot malted waffles with maple syrup and whipped cream and lemon meringue pie. A vast tome covers in detail the major wine regions of the world. France gets a good shout, while the selection from South Africa offers some of the best bargains.

Additional: Chop & Ale House for: Bar food; Sunday L; Children welcome; ❸ dishes
Seats: 50. Private dining room 32. Jacket & tie preferred
Accommodation: 16 en suite
Credit cards: ▬ ▬ ▬ ▭ ▬ ▣ JCB

AA Wine Shortlisted for *Wine Award-see page* 16

Directions: 2 miles N/E of Linlithgow at junction of A904 & A803

LINLITHGOW,
Livingston's Restaurant

The setting is a converted stable with assorted wooden tables and an intimate candlelit atmosphere. The cooking is modern in style. An unusual but successful starter, consisting of a crepinette of black pudding with a crispy croûton, scrambled egg and sliced oyster mushrooms, opened our inspection meal. The main dish of salmon and cod (both in perfect condition with beautiful colour and texture) came on a bed of buttered tarragon noodles, topped with celeriac crisps with a red and yellow pepper essence. Good vegetables too. Dessert was a crème brûlée made in a coffee cup with a thin crisp caramelised topping and fresh raspberries. Other choices from a sensible length evening menu might include open ravioli of duck and orange, blue cheese tart with onion marmalade, guinea fowl with mustard tagliatelle, and hot chocolate fondant with beetroot sorbet. Look out for the good-value lunch menu.

52 High Street EH49 7AE
Map 11: NS97
Tel: 01506 846565
Chef: David Williams
Owners: Mr & Mrs Ronald Livingston
Cost: Alc £25, fixed price L £11.99.
☺ H/wine £10
Times: Noon-2.30pm/6-9pm.
Closed Sun, Mon, 1st 2wks Jan
Additional: No children under 8 at D;
❸ dishes
Seats: 38
Smoking: No-smoking area;
No pipes & cigars
Credit cards: ▬ ▬ ▭

Directions: Opposite Post Office

UPHALL, **Houston House Hotel**

The three elegant dining rooms in the original part of this historic, much extended hotel and country club, are where the serious eating is done. Haggis in a pastry case makes a witty canapé followed, perhaps, by a delicious smoked salmon mousse wrapped in smoked salmon with beetroot and mango salsa. Main course fillets of lightly seared sea bass all but melted in the mouth, accompanied by a very moreish courgette and aubergine gâteaux and a delicate saffron and balsamic oil. A fine finish to the meal came with an orange and Cointreau soufflé shaped like domino pieces, topped with fresh orange slices and served with coffee and chocolate scented sauce. Menu descriptions are wordy – 'roasted monkfish tails encased in a parsley and scallop mousseline then wrapped in Parma ham and carved on to a mussel, clam and tomato stew' – the cooking does not need such a hard sell.

Broxburn EH52 6JS
Map 11: NT07
Tel: 01506 853831
Fax: 01506 854220
Chef: David Murray
Owner: MacDonald Hotels plc
Cost: Alc £29, fixed-price L £16.50/D £32.50 (4 courses). ☺ H/wine £12.95
Times: Noon-last L 2.30pm/7pm-last D 9.30pm. Closed L Sat
Additional: Bar food L; Sunday L; Children welcome; ❸ dishes
Seats: 70. Private dining room up to 200. Jacket & tie preferred
Smoking: No smoking in dining room
Accommodation: 73 en suite
Credit cards: ▬ ▬ ▭ ▬ ▣

Directions: At junction between A89 and A899

MORAY

ARCHIESTOWN,
Archiestown Hotel

Bistro-style dining in a Victorian hotel at the centre of a 'best-kept' village famous for its flowers. Bistro One has an amazing collection of bric-a-brac associated with whisky, agriculture and wartime, and the atmosphere is tremendous. Bistro Two is more formal, best perhaps for special occasions or business. The cooking style is uncomplicated, with dishes offered from a blackboard menu. Specialities are fish, shellfish, roasts and casseroles served in generous portions. A starter of fresh langoustines and squat lobster with home-made mayonnaise was simple but delicious, and fresh turbot presented in a meunière style all but melted in the mouth.

Directions: Turn off A95 onto B9102 at Craigellachie

Aberlour AB38 7QL
Map 15: NJ24
Tel: 01340 810218
Fax: 01340 810239
Chef: Judith Bulger
Owners: Judith & Michael Bulger
Cost: Alc £25. ☺ H/wine £10
Times: 12.30-1.45pm/6.30-8.15pm.
Closed 1 Oct-9 Feb
Additional: Bar food; Sunday L; Children welcome; ❸ dishes
Seats: 40. Private dining room 20
Smoking: No-smoking area
Accommodation: 9 rooms (6 en suite)
Credit cards: ▬ ▬

CRAIGELLACHIE,
Craigellachie Hotel ❀❀

AB38 9SR
Map 15: NJ24
Tel: 01340 881204
Fax: 01340 881253
Chef: David Tilbury
Cost: *Alc* £25, fixed price D £25.
H/wine £12.50
Times: Noon-last L 2.30pm/6.30-last
D 9.30pm
Additional: Bar food L; Sunday L;
Children welcome; ❹ dishes
Seats: 40. Private dining room 20
Smoking: No smoking in dining room
Accommodation: 26 en suite
Credit cards: ▆ ▆ ▆ ▆ ç ▆ ▆ JCB

Standing proudly at the edge of a Speyside village, this Victorian hotel houses a restaurant spread across three charming dining rooms appropriately decorated in a sporting theme. The adjacent Quaich bar is famed for its impressive range of malt whiskies and the kitchen's contemporary take on Scottish cooking will surely grow in reputation too. Dinner got off to a fine start with an open ravioli of lightly seared scallops laced with fresh spinach, sun-dried tomatoes and sauce vierge for oomph. Fresh seafood also featured in our inspector's main course of pan-fried fish panache – cod, monkfish, salmon, turbot – with a delicate avocado and samphire fricassée, crisp strands of vegetables and lemony couscous. To finish, the deliciously sweet prune and Armagnac soufflé really rose to the occasion, accompanied by liqueur cream. Home-made date and walnut bread accompanies the local cheeseboard. The meal's only downside was some weak coffee. All round, a joy to visit.

Directions: In the village centre

DRYBRIDGE, # The Old Monastry Restaurant ❀❀

Buckie AB56 2JB
Map 15: NJ46
Tel/Fax: 01542 832660
Chef: Douglas Gray
Owners: Douglas & Maureen Gray
Cost: *Alc* £28
Times: Noon-last L 1.30pm/7pm-last
D 9.30pm. Closed Sun, Mon, 2 wks
Nov, 3 wks Jan
Additional: No children under 8;
❹ dishes
Seats: 45.
Smoking: No smoking in dining room
Credit cards: ▆ ▆ ▆ ▆

Credit must go to any restaurant that can maintain such high standards for twelve years. This consistency is rewarded by a large and loyal local following, as well as support from visiting holidaymakers. A terrific value lunch is served in the cosy setting of the Cloisters Bar, the more pricy dinner in the main restaurant. The style is mainstream Scottish/French, the cooking accurate and thoughtful. This translates as wild mushroom risotto, full of honest flavour, signalled by a wonderful aroma from shavings of Parmesan cheese, and lovely fresh North sea scallops, sweet in flavour, lightly cooked to retain moisture and texture, with a delicate 'gravy' of thinly chopped shallots, smoked bacon, thyme, tomatoes, lemon juice and a hint of garlic. A light and airy duo of dark and white chocolate mousses with passion fruit coulis ensured the meal ended on a satisfyingly wicked note.

Directions: Leave A98 at Buckie junction on to Drybridge Road for 2.5 miles; don't turn into Drybridge village

DUFFTOWN, **Taste of Speyside**

Cullen skink, smoked venison with horseradish cream and clootie dumpling with Drambuie cream are amongst the regional specialities on display at this simple little restaurant. The quality of local produce shines through in dishes such as noisettes of lamb roasted on a bed of rosemary. Plenty of malts to sample as well.

Smoking: No-smoking area; No pipes and cigars
Credit cards: ▬ ▬

Directions: Take A941 from Elgin and turn L at Craigellachie; restaurant is on R just before the town square

10 Balvenie Street AB5 4AB
Map 15: NJ34
Tel/Fax: 01340 820860
Chef: Joseph Thompson
Owners: Raymond McLean, Peter Thompson, Joseph Thompson
Cost: Alc L £10/D£17, fixed price D £13. ☺ H/wine £7.90
Times: Last L 5pm/last D 9pm. Closed 5 Nov-28 Feb
Additional: Bar food L; Children welcome; ♨ dishes

ELGIN, **Mansefield House Hotel**

An elegant venue in pink and blue with crisp linens, Mansefield House's dining room nevertheless has a relaxed, friendly atmosphere and strong local following. Seafood is the speciality but meat lovers are well-catered for with chicken liver pâté, Angus steaks with a choice of sauces, and chicken and haggis wrapped in pastry.

Smoking: No smoking in dining room
Accommodation: 21 en suite
Credit cards: ▬ ▬ ▬ ▬ ▬

Directions: From A96 to town centre, R at first roundabout, R at mini roundabout, first L

Mayne Road IV30 1NY
Map 15: NJ26
Tel: 01343 540883
Fax: 01343 552491
Chef: Craig Halliday
Owners: Mr & Mrs T R Murray
Cost: Alc £22, fixed-price L £11. ☺ H/wine £10.95
Times: Last L 2pm/last D 9.30pm
Additional: Bar food L; Sunday L; Children welcome; ♨ dishes

ELGIN, **Mansion House Hotel**

Baronial mansion with an intimate candlelit restaurant. Good Scottish cooking includes Moray Firth mussels with a creamy white wine and garlic sauce, and rack of local lamb roasted with garlic and rosemary. A rich but light chocolate mousse was served in a Paris goblet accompanied by home-made shortbread.

Accommodation: 23 en suite
Credit cards: ▬ ▬ ▬ ▬ ▬ ▬ ▬

Directions: In Elgin turn off the A96 into Haugh Road; hotel is at the end of the road by the river

The Haugh IV30 1AW
Map 15: NJ26
Tel: 01343 548811
Fax: 01343 547916
Chef: Russell Beveridge
Owners: Mr & Mrs J Stirrat
Cost: Alc £24, fixed-price L £12.95/D £25 (4 courses). ☺ H/wine £10
Times: Last L 2pm/last D 9pm
Additional: Bar food; Sunday L; Children welcome
Smoking: No smoking in dining room

FORRES, **Knockomie Hotel** ❀❀

Grantown Road IV36 0SG
Map 14: NJ05
Tel: 01309 673146
Fax: 01309 673290
Chef: Thierry Fournot
Owners: Gavin & Penny Ellis
Cost: Alc £20.85, fixed-price L £10.50/D £28 (4 courses). ☺ H/wine £11.95.
Times: Noon-last L 2.30pm/7pm-last D 9pm. Closed 25-26 Dec
Additional: Bar food (bistro); Sunday L; Children welcome; ♨ dishes
Seats: 30. Private dining room 10-40
Smoking: No smoking in dining room
Accommodation: 15 en suite
Credit cards: ▬ ▬ ▬ ▬ ▬ ▬ JCB

A charming hotel set in four acres of grounds, Knockomie offers genuine hospitality and a choice of eating options, with an informal bistro in addition to the more formal restaurant. The decor of the latter has a Far Eastern theme, although the interesting modern menu has a Scottish flavour. Our latest meal from the carte (there's also a short set menu) began with a double-baked goats' cheese soufflé that was light and moist with a subtle flavour, before tender marinated fillet of pork served with a coriander jus. A trio of chocolate terrines was a successful ending, with a good balance of flavours and textures. Other choices included game soup, and a salmon dish with a scallop mousse set on a bed of lentils with a white wine sauce. There's no house wine but a wide price range on a list that includes some premier cru clarets at well over the £100 mark.

Knockomie Hotel

Directions: On A940 1 mile S of Forres

FORRES, Ramnee Hotel ❁

Victoria Road IV36 0BN
Map 14: NJ05
Tel: 01309 672410
Fax: 01309 673392
Chef: Craig Wilson
Owners: Ardinnes Ltd
Cost: *Alc* £25.50, fixed-price L £13/D £25.50. ☺ H/wine £10
Times: Last L 2pm/last D 9pm

Edwardian country house hotel set in landscaped gardens close to the centre of Forres. Typical dishes include smoked duck breast on continental leaves with a red cherry dressing, and saddle of Morayshire lamb in filo pastry with a mushroom duxelle. A separate vegetarian menu is available.

Additional: Bar food; Sunday L; Children welcome; ❸ dishes
Smoking: No smoking in dining room
Accommodation: 20 en suite
Credit cards: ▆ ▆ ▆ ▆ ▆ ▆ ▆ JCB

Directions: Turn off A96 into eastern side of Forres, hotel is 200 yds on R

ROTHES,
The Rothes Glen Hotel ❁❁

AB38 7AQ
Map 15: NJ24
Tel: 01340 831254
Fax: 01340 831566
Chef: Colin Campbell
Owners: Michael MacKenzie, Frederic Symonds
Cost: Fixed-price D £29.50. H/wine £11.95
Times: 12.15-last L 1.45pm/7.15-last D 9pm
Additional: Sunday L; No children under 7; ❸ dishes
Seats: 30. Private dining room. Jacket & tie preferred
Smoking: No smoking in restaurant
Accommodation: 14 en suite
Credit cards: ▆ ▆ ▆

The proprietors aim to make this Scottish baronial mansion one of the finest country house hotels in the north of Scotland, and they are well on their way to achieving that goal. Service is elegant, friendly and efficient, while a major aspect of the hotel's appeal is the high standard of cooking served up in the attractive dining room. The style is modern Scottish, and the chef ensures that the best local ingredients are used in innovative dishes such as breast of chicken filled with Stilton and broccoli mousse; seared local scallops with gazpacho purée; and Stroganoff of venison with wild rice. The wine list is comprehensive and well-chosen, with a good showing from the New World as well as an impressive range of half-bottles. For guests, trout fishing is available in the small lochan, and if that doesn't appeal, why not try your hand at the ancient art of croquet?

Directions: Six miles S of Elgin on A941

ORKNEY

ST MARGARET'S HOPE,

Creel Restaurant ❀❀

Situated on South Ronaldsay, Orkney's most southern island, is this most pleasant and unpretentious restaurant run with unstinting enthusiasm by Alan and Joyce Craigie. The reason for their success is the simple treatment of the wonderfully fresh seafood, lamb, and beef from the island, married with fresh, locally grown herbs and vegetables. Consistency is the key. Firm favourites are fishcakes (salmon, cod, and halibut rolled in crisp fresh breadcrumbs and served with a tangy home-made mayonnaise) or bresoala, amongst the choice of starters. Specialities include partan bree (crab soup), Aberdeen Angus steak, Orcadian fish stew (salmon, cod, and haddock with a beautifully perfumed tomato and basil sauce), and clootie dumpling parfait.

Directions: 13 miles S of Kirkwall on the A961, crossing the 4 Churchill barriers.

Front Road KW17 2SL
Map 16: ND49
Tel: 01856 831311
Chef: Alan Craigie
Owners: Alan and Joyce Craigie
Cost: Fixed-price D £26.50.
H/wine £8.50
Times: D only, last D 9pm
Additional: Children welcome;
❀ dishes
Smoking: No smoking in dining room
Accommodation: 3 en suite
Credit cards: ▅▅ ▆▆

PERTH & KINROSS

ABERFELDY,

Guinach House Hotel ❀❀

Have a stroll in the three acres of well-tended gardens or the nearby woods, then relax with a drink and canapés before an open fire before going on to dinner in the cosy, quiet dining room of this popular small hotel on the edge of town. Freshly picked herbs from the garden go into a pancake filled with chicken and ham in sherry sauce, and into another starter of prawn tails sautéed in white wine and tomatoes. Crunchy vegetables, full of flavour, also from the garden, accompany main courses of moist and tender monkfish Thermidor, local lamb with mint-flavoured pan juices, or noisettes of pork in sage butter with cider sauce. A pancake may also appear among desserts this time in the shape of a soufflé-type flavoured with vanilla served with cherries; other seasonal

'By the Birks' Urlar Road
PH15 2ET
Map 14: NN84
Tel: 01887 820251
Fax: 01887 829607
Chef/Owner: Albert Mackay
Cost: Fixed-price D £25 (4 courses).
H/wine £9.95
Times: D only, 7-9.30pm.
Closed 4 days Xmas
Additional: Children welcome;
❀ dishes
Seats: 20
Smoking: No smoking in dining room
Accommodation: 7 en suite
Credit cards: ▅▅ ▆▆

Directions: From Aberfeldy: A826 (Crieff) hotel is on R

fruits turn up in a choux pastry basket filled with whipped cream and peaches on a raspberry and peach coulis. Mrs Mackay runs the front of house almost single-handed, while her husband pops out of the kitchen from time to time to see how guests are enjoying themselves. A short, carefully chosen wine list has three house wines and around half-a-dozen halves, including champagne.

ALYTH, **Drumnacree House**

Located at the foot of Glenisla with raspberry fields in the background, this delightful Victorian house is home to the culinary talents of Allan and Eleanor Cull. For ten years the Culls have enjoyed continued success, and no wonder – the short *carte* sampled by our inspector reflected excellent use of quality Scottish ingredients in reliable, modern dishes. On this occasion, dinner started with a lightly textured Arbroath smokie mousse, served warm with a delicate sauce of diced tomato and basil. This was followed by a dish of moist medallions of fresh monkfish with salsa verde and fresh crunchy mange-tout and broccoli. For dessert, temptations such as syrup sponge pudding with crème anglaise and pear tart with caramel sauce were overlooked in favour of a 'wicked' hot ginger pudding with fresh ginger adding the vital 'kick'. The wine list is sensible and realistically priced.

St Ninians Road PH11 8AP
Map 15: NO24
Tel/Fax: 01828 632194
Chefs/Owners: Allan & Eleanor Cull
Cost: *Alc* £21
Times: D only, 7-last D 9pm.
Closed Sun, Mon, Dec-Mar
Additional: Children welcome
Seats: 25. Private dining room 12
Smoking: No smoking in dining room
Accommodation: 6 en suite
Credit cards: ▆▆ ▆▆ ▆▆

Directions: From Blairgowrie take A926 to Alyth and turn L after Clydesdale Bank. Hotel is 300yds on R

AUCHTERARDER,
Auchterarder House

A rather splendid Victorian mansion, peacefully set in mature grounds and overlooking the surrounding countryside. Flair and imagination are evident in the style of food produced by the award-winning kitchen team. Scottish produce is used to great effect in dishes such as roast fillet of Angus beef with brioche crust and Puy lentil jus; baked loin of venison with bacon, garlic and sherry vinegar sauce; and chargrilled sea scallops with crab risotto and herb beurre blanc. Desserts are along the lines of hot blackcurrant soufflé with a lemon and star anise sorbet, and warm banana and hazelnut cheesecake topped with a butterscotch sauce. Guests can enjoy all this in the refined atmosphere of the dining room, an elegant room that retains its original panelling and carved fire place. The carefully selected wine list offers an extensive choice, and is especially strong on clarets and wines from the New World.

PH3 1DZ
Map 11: NN91
Tel: 01764 663646
Fax: 01764 662939
Chef: Kiernan Darnell
Owner: The Wren's Hotel Group
Cost: *Alc* £32.50, fixed-price
L £18.50/D £39.50 (4 courses).
H/wine £14.50
Times: 12.30-3pm/7-9.30pm
Additional: Sunday L; No children under 12; 🍴 dishes
Seats: 40. Private dining room 25.
Jacket & tie preferred
Smoking: No smoking in dining room
Accommodation: 15 en suite
Credit cards: ▆▆ ▆▆ ▆▆ ▆ ▆▆ ▆ ▆ JCB

Directions: 1.5 miles N of Auchterarder on B8062

AUCHTERARDER, Cairn Lodge

The Capercaillie restaurant, part of the elegant small hotel only a few minutes from Gleneagles, serves a well-constructed menu of modern Scottish cooking. Look out for Perthshire pheasant in a game and Madeira jus, and corn-fed chicken with Drambuie sauce stuffed with award-winning Scottish haggis.

Accommodation: 7 en suite
Credit cards:

Directions: From A9 take A824 (Auchterader). Hotel at S end of town, on road to Gleneagles

Orchil Road PH3 1LX
Map 11: NN91
Tel: 01764 662634
Fax: 01764 664866
Chef: Mark Riva
Owners: Mr & Mrs A M Donald
Cost: *Alc* £32, fixed price L £18/D£24. ☺ H/wine £12
Times: Last L 2pm/last D 9.30pm
Additional: Bar food; Sunday L; Children welcome; ♣ dishes
Smoking: No pipes and cigars

AUCHTERARDER,
The Gleneagles Hotel ❀❀❀

Seventy-five years old in 1999, Gleneagles may be a golfer's paradise but also offers an outstanding range of other activities: an equestrian centre, a shooting school, a health spa, even falconry. A club for children, a shopping arcade and a cash dispenser mean you need never leave the hotel. Afternoon tea is served in the drawing-room, drinks in the smart cocktail bar, and the elegant Strathearn Restaurant, where a pianist plays and staff are skilled but friendly, is the place for dinner – for those who can afford it. Using the finest ingredients, the kitchen places a modern, Scottish slant on tradition. Hot foie gras is glazed with raspberry vinegar and accompanied by fried onions and chicory, chargrilled quail and smoked venison by a bean salad, and Parmesan dumplings go into wild mushroom minestrone. Plainly grilled Dover sole, pan-fried calves' liver with smoked bacon and mustard mash, or Lanark Blue soufflé with pine nuts and Cox's apples show that the kitchen is not afraid of producing accurately timed main courses, although an inspector was disappointed by overcooked breast of guinea fowl served on a plate so hot that its sauce had all but evaporated. Baked orange and fig cheesecake with caramel sauce is attractively presented, as is strawberry delice with a tulip crown and spun sugar. The wine list is a weighty affair geared towards fine and expensive vintages.

PH3 1NF
Map 11: NN91
Tel: 01764 662231
Fax: 01764 662134
Chef: Mike Picken
Cost: *Alc* £55, fixed-price L £27/D £41 (4 courses). H/wine £16.50
Times: D only, 7.30-last D 10pm
Additional: Bar food; Sunday L (12.30-2.30pm); Children welcome; ♣ dishes
Seats: 200. Private dining room 12-240
Smoking: No-smoking area; No pipes & cigars
Accommodation: 229 en suite
Credit cards:

Directions: Just off the A9, well signposted

BLAIR ATHOLL,
The Loft Restaurant ❀❀ NEW

The restaurant is located behind the Tilt Hotel in a converted hay loft, reached by a flight of external stairs. Twisted beams, oak floors and stone walls characterise the dining room; there is an after dinner lounge in the tower, and a roof terrace leading from the conservatory bar. The restaurant has been relaunched with a new style of food – modern with a slight French accent. A wonderfully honest lentil and bacon soup began our test meal, followed by a delicious salmon and crab cake, lightly pan-fried and served on a bed of chopped peppers, tomato and diced potato bound in a creamy dressing. To finish, an old favourite, bread-and-butter pudding with vanilla anglaise.

Directions: Off A9, 6 miles north of Pitlochry. In the village turn sharp L at Tilt Hotel.

River Tilt Park PH18 5TE
Map 14: NN86
Tel: 01796 481377
Fax: 01796 481511
Chef: Douglas Wright
Owner: Stuart Richardson
Cost: *Alc* £20, fixed-price L £11.75 (2 courses)/D £26.50 (6 courses). ☺ H/wine £7.50
Times: Noon-2.30pm/7-9.30pm
Additional: Bar food L; Sunday L; Children welcome; ♣ dishes
Seats: 34. Private dining room 12
Smoking: No-smoking area; Air conditioning
Credit cards: JCB

BLAIRGOWRIE,
Altamount Hotel ✤

From the elegant dining room of this lovely Georgian house, diners can watch the family of peacocks meander on the lawn. A choice of menus offers a range of Scottish specialities, including game consommé with poached quail's egg, and Highland venison encased in filo with orange and juniper berry sauce.

Additional: Bar food; Sunday L; Children welcome; ❹ dishes
Smoking: No smoking in dining room
Accommodation: 7 en suite
Credit cards: ▓ ▓ ▓ ▓ ▓ ▓

Coupar Angus Road
PH10 6JN
Map 15: NO14
Tel: 01250 873512
Fax: 01250 876200
Chef: Robert Ramsay
Owners: Robert & Sally Glashan
Cost: *Alc* £25, fixed-price D £20.50.
☺ H/wine £10.50
Times: Last L 2pm/last D 9pm. Closed
1st wk Jan

Directions: On entering town from A93 take 1st R into Golf Course Rd. Continue for 1.5 miles then L at T junction. Hotel 1 mile on L

BLAIRGOWRIE,
Kinloch House Hotel ✤✤✤

PH10 6SG
Map 15: NO14
Tel: 01250 884237
Fax: 01250 884333
Chef: Bill McNicol
Owners: David & Sarah Shentall
Cost: Fixed-price L £15.95/D £29.90
(4 courses). H/wine £12.20
Times: 12.30-2pm/7- 9.15pm.
Closed Xmas
Additional: Bar food L; Sunday L;
No children under 7; ❹ dishes
Seats: 50. Private dining room 20.
Jacket & tie preferred
Smoking: No smoking in dining room
Accommodation: 21 en suite
Credit cards: ▓ ▓ ▓ ▓ ▓ ▓ ▓ JCB

An exceptional list of malt whiskies is one of the star attractions, not that one needs much enticement to come to this fine Scottish country residence with its oak-panelled hall and first-floor galleries. A sign of the times, however, is the quality assurance printed on the back of the carte, which covers the sourcing of ingredients, environmental health standards and guarantees nothing is made with genetically modified materials. Bill McNicol is also willing to show off his kitchen to anyone who asks. There are two fixed price menus – on the Scottish Menu you might find potted hough (shin of beef), Kinloch House smokies cooked with tomato and cheese and cream sauce, or leg of lamb carved from the trolley served with rosemary and redcurrant gravy with caramelised onions. From the main carte, you can choose warm devilled crab mousse set on creamed spinach, coated with hollandaise, or fillet of hare rolled in crushed black peppercorns, marinated in port, set on creamed celeriac and served with a red wine tarragon sauce. Steaks and lobster, cooked in a variety of ways, come as a supplement. Vegetables may be organically home-grown from the walled garden. The dessert menu – lemon mousse with raspberry coulis, shortbread biscuits; chocolate marquise with whisky cream, sliced poached pear and bitter chocolate sauce – also

includes a savoury, perhaps chicken liver wrapped in bacon on a croûton of fried bread, served with plum chutney. The wine list deserves serious study.

Signature dishes: Loin of lamb wrapped in a chicken and tarragon mousse; Kinloch House soufflé pancake; Kyle of Lochalsh scallops in a spicy cream sauce; boned saddle of venison in a mousseline of partridge

Directions: Three miles W of Blairgowrie on A923

COUPAR ANGUS,
Moorfield House ❀❀

Set in landscaped gardens, Moorfield House features wood panelling, open fires, stained-glass windows and a friendly atmosphere. There's an inviting library lounge and a spacious bar where pre-dinner canapés are served – one with prawn, say, or mini-pizzas. Lunches are served in the bar too, with the restaurant providing an elegant setting for four-course dinners with ample choice. Modern Scottish cooking that makes the best use of Scotland's larder could be described as the style. Moist, tender pigeon breast on Savoy cabbage with pine nuts and sorrel may start things off, to be followed by meaty and flavoursome venison sausages with onion gravy. A good combination of flavours shows up in a main course of monkfish topped with sun-dried tomatoes on a bed of vegetable spaghetti set off by a herby beurre blanc, and to finish there may be well-presented hazelnut parfait decorated with strawberry coulis on a bed of the same fruit. Three reasonably priced house wines from France round off a list of around fifty bins.

Myreriggs Road By
Blairgowrie PH13 9HS
Map 11: NO23
Tel: 01828 627303
Fax: 01828 627339
Chefs: Paul Bjormark & Mrs Angela Tannahill
Owners: Jayne & Paul Bjormark
Cost: Fixed-price L £13.50/D £25 (4 courses). ☺ H/wine £9.95
Times: Noon-last L 2pm/6.30-last D 9.30pm. Closed 24-26 Dec
Additional: Bar food; Sunday L; Children welcome; ◑ dishes
Seats: 36. Private dining room 14
Smoking: No pipes & cigars
Accommodation: 12 en suite
Credit cards: ■ ▒ ◖ ▒

Directions: on the A923 halfway between Coupar Angus and Blairgowrie

DUNKELD, Atholl Arms ❀

Bridgehead PH8 0AQ
Map 11: NO04
Tel/Fax: 01350 727219
Chef: Annie Darbishire
Owner: Callum Darbishire
Cost: Alc £16.50. ☺ H/wine £9
Times: Last L 1.45pm/last D 8.45pm
Additional: Bar food; Sunday L; No children under 8 after 6pm; ◑ dishes
Smoking: No smoking in dining room
Accommodation: 14 en suite
Credit cards: ■ ▒ ✈ ◖ ▒ ◖

Take a window seat in this traditional dining room for views over the Tay and good-value cooking. Light leek and potato soup comes with a dash of cream. For mains, there's generously sauced seared salmon on a potato cake. The tasty bread-and-butter pudding and cafetière coffee are a pleasing finish.

Directions: A9 & A923 (Blairgowrie) to Dunkeld, 1st building on R

DUNKELD,
Kinnaird ❀❀❀

Kinnaird Estate PH8 0LB
Map 11: NO04
Tel: 01796 482440
Fax: 01796 482289
Chef: Trevor Brooks
Owner: Mrs C C Ward
Cost: Fixed-price L £26/D £45
(4 courses). H/wine £16
Times: Noon-last L 1.45pm/7.15-last
D 9.30pm. Closed Mon, Tue, Wed in
Jan & Feb
Additional: Sunday L;
No children under 12; ❹ dishes
Seats: 35. Private dining room 20.
Jacket & tie preferred
Smoking: No smoking in dining room
Accommodation: 9 en suite
Credit cards: ▬ ▬ 🄲 ▦

Kinnaird is a magnificent pile of a place, and the extensive grounds really do give meaning to the words 'Scottish baronial'. This is country house living on a grand scale, antiques abound, lounges abound, but this is, however, not a stuffy place and service in particular manages to combine professionalism with a sense of friendliness. Inspectors tend to rave about the river valley view, enjoy the high level of cooking and look forward to returning. Trevor Brooks has taken over in the kitchen and all reports indicate that he is more than maintaining standards. Witness an early summer dinner that opened with lovely canapés of smoked salmon mousse tart and tomato fondant with Parmesan. The first course was a 'wonderfully flavoursome' Skye crab that had been carefully shredded with a delicate salmon terrine – clear and crisp flavours were excellent, and presentation first class. New season's lamb had brilliant flavour 'really unbeatable' and was served with a simple jus with a hint of thyme and a rich galette of aubergine and matching vegetables – 'a super dish'. Dessert was an unusual toasted rice pudding, creamy and light and well-matched by a chilli-roasted fresh pineapple. The serious wine list continues to give a selection of typical wines from each area at the front of the list. Bordeaux is good and half-bottles offer an exemplary choice.

Signature dishes: Breast of duck served with fondant potatoes, fried apples, parsnip purée and a spiced cider sauce; home-cured slices of beef bresaola topped with crispy goats' cheese raviolo; saddle of venison with maple-roast squash, celeriac mash, deep-fried celeriac, red cabbage and a port and pepper sauce.

AA Wine Shortlisted for Award-see page 16

Directions: From A9 north take B898 Dalguise/Kinnaird/ Balnaguard road for approx 4.5 miles. Hotel main gates on R

KILLIECRANKIE,
Killiecrankie Hotel ❀❀

Pitlochry
PH16 5LG
Map 14: NN96
Tel: 01796 473220
Fax: 01796 472451
Chef: Mark Easton
Owners: Colin & Carole Anderson

Many guests return time and again to Colin and Carol Anderson's delightful hotel, close to the historic Pass of Killiecrankie. Enthusiastically run, the Andersons' hands-on approach creates a terrific atmosphere. A short menu at dinner includes traditional Scottish fare as well as a few surprises:

look out for delights such as griddled loin of tuna with olive oil mashed potatoes and herb dressing, and roast loin of lamb stuffed with chicken and olive mousseline. An early summer meal started with a lovely salmon, asparagus and rocket terrine, followed by a lightly-baked fillet of fresh halibut with fresh pasta noodles. The simple dessert list – glazed lemon tart, dark and white chocolate delice, for example – comes with suggestions for accompanying pudding wines, by the glass. The lengthy wine list is carefully chosen, and there is a good selection of malt whiskies to round off the evening.

Directions: From A9 take B8079 for Killiecrankie, hotel on right just past village signpost

Cost: Fixed-price dinner £28 (4 courses). ☺ H/wine £12
Times: D only, 7-last D 8.30pm. Closed 1 wk early Dec, Jan-Feb
Additional: Bar food; No children under 5 at D; ◔ dishes
Seats: 34
Smoking: No smoking in dining room
Accommodation: 10 en suite
Credit cards: ▬ ▬ ▰ ▱

KINCLAVEN,
Ballathie House Hotel ❀❀

Stanley PH1 4QN
Map 11: NO13
Tel: 01250 883268
Fax: 01250 883396
Chef: Kevin MacGillivray
Owner: Ballathie House Hotel Co Ltd
Cost: Alc £15, fixed-price L £16.95/D £32. H/wine £10.50.
Times: 12.30pm-last L 2pm/7pm-last D 9pm

Tall ceilings, muted pastel walls and long swathes of ornate curtaining suggest a rarefied atmosphere, but Ballathie House is unpretentious and a great favourite with the sporting crowd. The turreted building is set in a peaceful and picturesque 1,500 acre estate overlooking the River Tay; from the dining room guests can survey the gardens. Local ingredients feature on the tempting, regularly changing menu. Creamy crab and coriander risotto topped with monkfish, leek and cream soup and dry, home-cured salmon with citrus juices and dill are amongst the delicious starters. Particularly good is the loin of venison wrapped in smoked ham with thyme mousseline, fresh vegetables are served alongside. Make room for the Scottish cheeseboard and well-made desserts such as a lemon tart with citrus sorbet or light treacle tart with butterscotch ice cream. Coffee here is excellent and there's a reasonably priced, very comprehensive wine list.

Additional: Bar food L; Sunday L; Children welcome; ◔ dishes
Seats: 70. Private dining room 30. Jacket and tie preferred
Smoking: No smoking in dining room
Accommodation: 28 en suite
Credit cards: ▬ ▬ ▰ ▱ ▬ ▨ JCB

AA Shortlisted for Wine Award-see page 16

Directions: Off A93 at Beech Hedges, follow signs for Kinclaven, approx 2 miles

KINNESSWOOD,
Lomond Country Inn ⊛

An informal, small village hotel with a broad appeal. Cooking is refreshingly uncomplicated and this, together with good use of quality ingredients, allows natural flavours to shine through. Look out for chicken liver pâté and Cumberland sauce, a wholesome navarin of lamb with red wine gravy, and crème brûlée.

Accommodation: 12 en suite
Credit cards: ▨ ▨ ▧ ▨ ▨ 🄲 🄫 JCB

Directions: On A911, 10 mins from M90/J5 (Glenrothes) or J7 (Milnathort)

KY13 7HN
Map 11: NO10
Tel: 01592 840253
Fax: 01592 840693
Chef: Mark Cooper
Owner: David Adams
Cost: Alc £15, fixed price L/D £10. ☺ H/wine £8.50
Times: Last L 2.30pm/D 9pm
Additional: Bar food; Sunday L; Children welcome; 🄳 dishes
Smoking: No smoking in dining room

KINROSS, Croft Bank ⊛⊛

The Kerr family run this elegant but relaxed restaurant-with-rooms with friendly enthusiasm, and on a cold autumnal day a robust seafood broth, well-stocked and with an intense 'fishy' flavour, was just the job. The seasonal carte, supplemented by a small range of daily specials, is modern Scottish with French influences -smooth chicken parfait with bramble preserve, for example, or casserole of wild rabbit with red wine, garlic and thyme jus, and a paupiette of lemon sole with a light shellfish sauce. The moist, true flavour of breast of wild mallard duck was beautifully brought out by an intense port wine and peppercorn jus. Venison is cooked in a variety of ways – seared roe deer liver with caramelised red onions and game jus, or the haunch roasted with a port game jus. Calorific desserts include meringue layers with bananas and warm chocolate sauce and baked whole fresh pear in filo pastry with fudge sauce.

Directions: Just off M90/J6 towards Kinross

KY13 7TG
Map 11: NO10
Tel/Fax: 01577 863819
Chef: Bill Kerr
Owners: Bill & Diane Kerr
Cost: Alc £20. ☺ H/wine £9.75.
Times: Noon-last L 1.45pm/6.30-last D 9pm. Closed D Sun, Mon, 2 wks Sept
Additional: Bar food L; Sunday L; No children under 6; 🄳 dishes
Seats: 40. Private dining rooms 12, 16, 40
Smoking: No smoking in dining room
Accommodation: 4 en suite
Credit cards: ▨ ▨

PERTH, Huntingtower Hotel ⊛

A fixed-price menu is offered in the panelled restaurant of this country house hotel. A warm salad of seared scallops was a highlight, followed by rack of lamb with a rosemary and mustard crust. And to finish, pineapple and Malibu sabayon with vanilla ice cream in a brandy snap basket.

Directions: 5 mins from Perth, on A85 Crieff/Crianlarich Road. Just off A9

Crieff Road Almondbank PH1 3JT
Map 11: NO12
Tel: 01738 583771
Fax: 01738 583777
Chef: Tim Cribber
Owner: Aristo Hotels
Cost: Fixed-price D £19.95 (4 courses). ☺ H/wine £10
Times: D only, last D 9.30pm
Additional: Bar food; Sunday L (noon-2.30); Children welcome; 🄳 dishes
Smoking: No smoking in dining room
Accommodation: 34 en suite
Credit cards: ▨ ▨ ▧ ▨ ▨ 🄲 🄫 JCB

PERTH, Kinfauns Castle ❀❀

Vast and impressive, Kinfauns Castle dates from 1822 and is set in grounds overlooking the Tay, three miles north-east of Perth. It has recently been restored, and boasts a stately gallery, sweeping staircases and various Eastern artefacts collected by the owners. The Library restaurant features oak-panelled walls, immense windows and a ceiling displaying numerous coats of arms. Its menu, though short, is balanced and appealing; its wine list, though long, complements the food. Freshness and quality of produce are the strengths here. After appetisers and notably good bread, venison arrived carpaccio-style in a peppered coating. Perfectly grilled halibut followed, served with a little stock finished with cream (rather than the advertised velouté). Ratatouille and sauté potatoes completed the dish. Pudding was a warm bilbury and almond tart, while petits fours of very fine chocolates provided a memorable finale.

Directions: Two miles beyond Perth on A90 Dundee road; turn L at sign for Kinfauns Castle

Kinfauns PH2 7JZ
Map 11: NO12
Tel: 01738 620777
Fax: 01738 620778
Chef: Jeremy Wares
Owners: James A & Julia Smith
Cost: Fixed-price L £18.50/D £35
(5 courses). H/wine £13.95
Times: Noon-last L 2pm/7-last
D 9pm. Closed Jan
Additional: Sunday L;
No children under 8; ❀ dishes
Seats: 46. Private dining room 12;
Jacket & tie required
Smoking: No smoking in dining room
Accommodation: 16 en suite
Credit cards: ▨ ▨ ▨ ▨ ▨ JCB

PERTH, Let's Eat ❀❀

Now in its third year, Let's Eat continues to impress: it's 'completely honest' noted an inspector. Housed in what was a theatre and latterly an antique shop, the place is relaxed, friendly and informal with cooking noted for a lot of interest and good flavours. Both lunch and dinner menus – modern British with French overtones – are supported by blackboard specials. Start with a terrine of smoked fish salmon, trout and Arbroath smokie drizzled with lime oil, or black pudding with bacon and a poached egg, and go on to spiced loin of lamb on minted couscous, or turbot with a nicely complementary buttery basil sauce. Rhubarb ice cream comes with steamed ginger pudding with vanilla sauce, and orange ice cream with a dark chocolate 'nemesis'. The short wine list is entirely in keeping with the style.

Directions: On corner of Kinnoull Street and Atholl Street, close to North Inch

77/79 Kinnoull Street PH1 5EZ
Map 11: NO12
Tel: 01738 643377
Fax: 01738 621464
Chef: Tony Heath
Owners: Tony Heath & Shona
Drysdale
Cost: *Alc* L £17.50/D £21.75. ☺
H/wine £9.75
Times: Noon-last L 2pm/6.30-last D
9.45pm. Closed Sun, Mon, 2 wks Jan,
2 wks Jul
Additional: Children welcome;
❀ dishes
Seats: 60
Smoking: No smoking in dining room
Credit cards: ▨ ▨ ▨ ▨ ▨ ▨

PERTH, Murrayshall Hotel ❀❀

Three hundred acres of parkland and spectacular views across the Grampian Highlands are all part of the make-up of this welcoming Scottish country house. This is a golfing hotel to beat all golfing hotels, with an 18-hole course designed by Hamilton Stutt, as well as an indoor golf centre and landscaped driving range with covered bays. The cooking here is certainly up to par, built on a strong traditional base with some classic French twists. Chicken and goose liver parfait with Madeira jelly, for example, or a ragout of wild mushrooms and shallots in a grain mustard jus set in puff pastry. Main courses take in roast loin of lamb with a basil mash and herb butter sauce, or baked breast of duck with pommes Anna and deep-fried parsnips shavings. Desserts are appealing, especially a stack of French meringue layered with seasonal fruit and served with orange coulis.

Directions: From Perth A94 (Coupar Angus) turn R signed Murrayshall before New Scone

New Scone PH2 7PH
Map 11: NO12
Tel: 01738 551171
Fax: 01738 552595
Chef: Craig Davidson
Cost: *Alc* £25. ☺ H/wine £10.50
Times: D only, 7-9.45pm
Additional: Bar food; Sunday L;
No children under 2; ❀ dishes
Seats: 50. Private dining room 30
Smoking: No smoking in dining room
Accommodation: 27 en suite
Credit cards: ▨ ▨ ▨ ▨ ▨ ▨ ▨

PERTH, Number Thirty Three
Seafood Restaurant

Pink and grey decor, banquette seating, and a cocktail-style bar set the scene for meals at Number Thirty three. It's a family affair, fish is their strength, and most items are home-made, including ice cream and the memorable cheese scone served with the olive bread. Stars of the show are mussels with Camembert, and Mary's seafood soup.

33 George Street PH1 5LA
Map 11: NO12
Tel: 01738 633771
Chef: Mary Billinghurst
Owners: Gavin & Mary Billinghurst
Please telephone for further details

Directions: In the city, just off the High Street, near the river

PITLOCHRY,
Knockendarroch House Hotel

The solid Victorian mansion stands in mature grounds above the town, offering fine views over Tummel Valley. Dinner is set with two choices at each course, more for dessert, and offers the likes of cold marinated duck with orange and apple salsa, cream of coriander soup, poached fillet of cod finished with a beer batter sauce and topped with crispy leeks, and rhubarb crumble.

Higher Oakfield PH16 5HT
Map 14: NN95
Tel: 01796 473473
Fax: 01796 474068
Please telephone for further details

Directions: On entering town from Perth 1st R (East Moulin Road) after railway bridge, then 2nd L, last hotel on L

PITLOCHRY,
Pine Trees Hotel

A fine Scottish mansion set above the town amid 14 acres of mature grounds. Carefully prepared Scottish specialities from a daily-changing fixed-price menu are offered in the elegant Garden Restaurant. Expect dishes such as carrot and turnip soup, guinea fowl with redcurrant and thyme sauce, and chocolate mousse.

Additional: Bar food; Sunday L; Children welcome; dishes
Smoking: No smoking in dining room
Accommodation: 19 en suite
Credit cards:

Strathview Terrace
PH16 5QR
Map 14: NN95
Tel: 01796 472121
Fax: 01796 472460
Chef: Javen Walker
Owner: Brian Waller
Cost: Fixed-price L £11.95/D £26
(4 courses). ☺ H/wine £12.
Times: Last L 2pm/D 8.30pm

Directions: Signed at north end of town

SPITTAL OF GLENSHEE,
Dalmunzie House

Fresh food from hill, loch and sea is offered in a traditional Highland dining room, part of a turreted baronial country house. A typical meal may include smoked trout mousse, baked halibut with herb crust and red caviar cream, and sherry trifle. Later, help yourself to coffee and mints in the lounge.

Additional: Bar food L; Sunday L; Children welcome; dishes
Smoking: No smoking in dining room
Accommodation: 16 en suite
Credit cards:

Blairgowrie PH10 7QG
Map15: NO17
Tel: 01250 885224
Fax: 01250 885225
Chef: Ronnie McDonald
Owners: Simon & Alexandra Winton
Cost: *Alc* £25, fixed-price D from
£18. ☺ H/wine £9
Times: Last L 1.50pm/last D 8.30pm.
Closed Dec

Directions: Turn off A93 at Spittal of Glenshee, hotel 200yds on L

ST FILLANS,
The Four Seasons Hotel

The Four Seasons has a prime site on the shores of Loch Earn, and large picture windows make the most of the glorious views. On warm days, visitors can dine on the south-facing terrace. The set three-course dinner offers a good choice, West Coast scallops are usually on the menu, perhaps cooked with lobster and mussels and fresh pasta, or there might be saddle of venison with juniper and apples, or sirloin Angus steak with shallots and Arran mustard. In season, go for the local raspberries with hazelnut meringue, or else try plum and apple pie with cinnamon ice cream or the luscious-sounding triple chocolate marquise with caramel sauce. A more informal lunch, snack and supper menu includes smoked Tay salmon with tossed herb salad, crispy salmon and leek fishcakes with tomato sauce and smoked haddock with bacon and poached egg.

Directions: On A85 overlooking Loch Earn

Loch Earn Crieff PH6 2NF
Map 11: NN62
Tel/Fax: 01764 685333
Chef: Andrew Scott
Owners: The Scott Family
Cost: *Alc* £21.50, fixed-price L £14/D £24. ☺ H/wine £10.
Times: 12.15pm-last L 2pm/6.30pm-last D 9pm. Closed mid Dec-March
Additional: Bar food; Sunday L; Children welcome; ◑ dishes
Seats: 40. Private dining room 6-30
Smoking: No smoking in dining room
Accommodation: 18 en suite
Credit cards: ▬ ▬ ▬ ▬ ▬

RENFREWSHIRE

LANGBANK,
Gleddoch House Hotel

The former home of shipping magnate Sir William Lithgow, commands fine views over the Clyde – the source of his wealth. The sporting amenities attract an upmarket business clientele, as does the modern French style of cuisine. Typical examples are assiette of thinly sliced oak-smoked salmon with brown bread, capers and lemon, feathered with a light mustard dressing, grilled monkfish tails set on a pool of Thermidor sauce. Main courses include pan-fried fillets of spring lamb rolled in a pastry crust with sweet sherry, redcurrant and rosemary pan juices and a potato basket of minted sweetbreads. Chilled white chocolate parfait rolled in toasted sesame seeds served with fresh raspberries, milk chocolate sabayon and dark chocolate scrolls is an example of corporate indulgence.

Directions: From Glasgow take M8 (Greenock) then B789 Houston/ Langbank exit. Follow signs to hotel

PA14 6YE
Map 10: NS37
Tel: 01475 540711
Fax: 01475 540201
Chef: Brian Graham
Cost: *Alc* £30, fixed-price L £19.50/D £33.95 (4 courses). ☺ H/wine £12.50
Times: 12.30-last L 2pm/7.30-last D 9.30pm
Additional: Bar food L; Sunday L; Children welcome; ◑ dishes;
Seats: 70. Private room 28.
Jacket & tie preferred
Accommodation: 38 en suite
Credit cards ▬ ▬ ▬ ▬ ▬

SCOTTISH BORDERS

CHIRNSIDE,

Chirnside Hall

There are magnificent views over the Berwickshire countryside to be had from the dining room of this pleasant country house set at the end of a long, tree-lined drive. The modern cooking is built around the seasons and Scotland's abundant larder. First courses of terrine of venison, pigeon, smoked bacon, cranberry and orange compote, or potato and turnip soup with haggis, could be balanced by main courses with a slight French twist. Baked pork fillet 'en croûte', for example, with a pear and blue cheese stuffing on a white wine jus, or roast monkfish with langoustines and a sauce beurre blanc. The cheeseboard is firmly Scottish, and desserts range from steamed banana and cinnamon pudding to home-made ice cream.

Directions: Turn off A1 onto A6105 (Berwick-upon-Tweed) and pass Foulden village – hotel is on right-hand side before Chirnside village.

TD11 3LD
Map 12: NT85
Tel: 01890 818219
Fax: 01890 818231
Chef: Tom Rowe
Owners: Alan and Karla White
Cost: *Alc* £27, fixed-price L £12.95 (2 courses)/D £22.50. ☺ H/wine £9.95
Times: Noon-last L 2pm/6.30-last D 9pm
Additional: Sunday L; No children under 5; ❹ dishes
Seats: 30. Private dining room 15
Smoking: No smoking in dining room
Accommodation: 10 en suite
Credit cards: 🔲 🔲 🔲 🔲 🔲 🔲 🔲 JCB

KELSO,

Sunlaws House Hotel

Heiton TD5 8JZ
Map 12: NT73
Tel: 01573 450331
Fax: 01573 450611
Chef: Eamon Webster
Owners: Duke & Duchess of Roxburghe
Cost: *Alc* £28.50, fixed-price L £14/D £28.50. H/wine £13.50.
Times: 12.30pm-last L 2pm/7.30pm-last D 9.30pm
Additional: Sunday L; Bar meals L; Children welcome; ❹ dishes
Seats: 44. Private dining room 16-20
Smoking: No smoking in dining room
Accommodation: 22 en suite
Credit cards: 🔲 🔲 🔲 🔲 🔲 🔲

Dinner is served in style at this Jacobean mansion owned by the Duke of Roxburghe, much favoured by shooting parties, fishermen and golfers, all ready to tuck in after a day's sport. The ducal estates provide Tweed salmon and wild game in season, and the extensive wine list has been compiled by His Grace himself. The setting might be classical, but the cooking shows plenty of modern ideas and bold combinations. Chicken liver parfait in brioche with ceps butter could have been mistaken for foie gras in both taste and texture, and more wild mushrooms featured in a main course of sesame seed baked monkfish served with an intense bisque sauce. Other choices might include confit of duck, aubergine jam and garlic cream, or rack of lamb with a herb crust, courgette tapenade and port jus. A dessert of vanilla crème brûlée with fresh figs and honey ice cream was an innovative reworking of an old favourite.

Directions: On A698, 3 miles S of Kelso in Heiton village

MELROSE, **Burts Hotel** ✤✤

The Square TD6 9PN
Map 12: NT53
Tel: 01896 822285
Fax: 01896 822870
Chef: Gary Moore
Owners: The Henderson family
Cost: Fixed-price D £24.75. ☺
H/wine £11.30
Times: Noon-last L 2pm/7-last D 9pm
Additional: Bar food; Sunday L;
Children welcome; ◑ dishes
Seats: 50. Private dining room 22
Smoking: No smoking in dining room
Accommodation: 20 en suite
Credit cards: ▬ ▭ ➹ ▭ ▤ ◕ ▣ JCB

Members of the 'Scotch Beef Club', the hotel's supply comes
only from quality assured farms and steaks are probably best
simply grilled with béarnaise sauce, but the adventurous could
try medallion of beef on a garlic croûte with marinated
beansprouts and chilli jam. Game is another area in which
intriguing ideas are explored, a trio of pigeon, venison and
rabbit mousse, for example, is served with a potato cake on
a ragout of asparagus, cherry tomatoes and courgettes. Meat
dominates the main course, and the single fish choice might
be roast fillet of halibut with spinach and lobster sauce or roast
monkfish tails on a pink grapefruit and orange mâche salad.
A triangular terrine of sole, monkfish and salmon, however,
made an excellent starter with moist, clear flavours. A Selkirk
Bannock pudding, scented with lemon and accompanied
by a shortbread ice cream, would ensure a meal at this plush,
country town hotel finished with a true taste of the Borders.

Directions: Centre of Melrose

PEEBLES, **Cringletie House** ✤

Fresh ideas and a general rejuvenation have brought an extra
sparkle to this long-established hotel. Regional produce features
in a menu that may include courgette and rosemary soup with crème
fraîche, loin of Stobo Estate lamb on Bonchester cheese and white
onion compote, and caramelised apple pastry with home-made ice
cream.

Accommodation: 13 en suite. **Credit cards:** ▬ ▭ ➹ ▭ ▤

Directions: 2.5 miles N of Peebles on A703

EH45 8PL
Map 11: NT24
Tel: 01721 730233
Fax: 01721 730244
Chef: Gregg Russell
Owner: Wrens Hotel Group
Cost: Fixed-price L £14.95/D £29.50
(4 courses). H/wine £9.95
Times: Last L 2pm/last D 9pm.
Additional: Bar food L; Sunday L;
Children welcome; ◑ dishes
Smoking: No smoking in dining room

SWINTON, **Wheatsheaf Hotel** ✤

The small hotel overlooks the village green. Eat either in the
bar/lounge or in the restaurant with its lofty pine ceiling. A spring
menu included breast of wood pigeon and confit of duck, root
vegetables and honeyed Madeira sauce, and supreme of corn-fed
chicken, stir-fried oriental vegetables, egg noodles and hoisin sauce.

Accommodation: 6 rooms, 4 en suite
Credit cards: ▬ ▭ ➹ ▭

Directions: B6461 – half way between Kelso and Berwick-
upon-Tweed; A6112 – half way between Duns and Coldstream.

Main Street TD11 3JJ
Map 12: NT84
Tel: 01890 860257
Fax: 01890 860688
Chefs: Alan Reid, John Keir
Owners: Alan & Julie Reid
Cost: Alc £23. ☺ H/wine £9.45
Times: Last L 2pm/D 9.30pm.
Closed Mon, Xmas, 1 Jan
Additional: Bar food; Sunday L;
Children welcome; ◑ dishes
Smoking: No smoking in dining room

SHETLAND

LERWICK, **Shetland Hotel**

Conveniently located opposite the main ferry terminal, the modern purpose-built hotel houses both a restaurant and bistro. Scottish ingredients are used thoughtfully, taking in local herring fillets marinated in dill and white wine, grouse with oatmeal and orange skirlie, whilst apple and sultana pie with Drambuie ice cream went down a treat.

Accommodation: 65 en suite
Credit cards:

Directions: Opposite P&O ferry terminal, on main route N from town centre

Holmsgarth Road ZE1 0PW
Map 16: HU44
Tel: 01595 695515
Fax: 01595 695828
Chef: Glynn Wright
Owners: Robert Smith, Jim Manson
Cost: *Alc* £23.50. Fixed-price
D £23.50 (4 courses). ☺
H/wine £8.95
Times: Last L 2pm/last D 9.30pm
Additional: Bar food;
Children welcome; ◑ dishes
Smoking: No smoking in dining room

STIRLING

ABERFOYLE, **Braeval**

Nick Nairn is now concentrating on his other restaurant, Nairns in Glasgow (see entry), leaving wife Fiona firmly in control here, with Neil Forbes heading the kitchen. Our inspector called on a cold June day (it was snowing up the road in Aviemore) and the smooth, richly flavoured butternut squash soup deemed an appropriate addition to the menu by the kitchen considering the weather, was just the thing. This was followed by 'a perfectly nice' piece of salmon with crisp skin, perched on top of sweated leeks and lardons of bacon mixed in with sliced new boiled potatoes, all bound in subtle lobster and herb oils. Vanilla parfait with prunes and Earl Grey sauce brought up the rear. Other choices on the short menu could be terrine of marinated salmon with tomato vinaigrette, or carpaccio of organic beef with rocket and Parmesan, with main courses of corn-fed chicken with fondant potato, cabbage and bacon, or grilled turbot with wild mushroom risotto.
Signature dishes: Loin of spring lamb with baked fennel; truffle and wild mushroom risotto; wood pigeon with beetroot and celeriac purée; caramelised puff pastry with summer fruits and cinnamon cappuccino.

Braeval FK8 3UY
Map 11: NN50
Tel: 01877 382711
Fax: 01877 382400
Chef: Neil Forbes
Owner: Fiona Nairn
Cost: Fixed-price L £19.50/D £31.50
(4 courses). H/wine £17.50
Times: 12.30-last L 1.45pm/7.30-last
D 9.15pm. Closed L Wed, D Sun,
all Mon, Tue, 1 wk Feb, Jun & Oct
Additional: Sunday L;
No children under 10
Seats: 36
Smoking: No smoking in dining room
Credit cards:

Directions: On A81 Callander road
1 mile from Aberfoyle

BALQUHIDDER,
Monachyle Mhor

The Lewis family have created a small haven of peace and quiet within this converted farmhouse which forms part of a 2,000 acre estate in the heart of the beautiful, romantic Braes of Balquhidder. The attractive, small dining room in the front extension, overlooks two lochs; the kitchen, close by, shows it understands food and how best to cook it. Sourcing is impeccable: fresh water langoustines with 'a salad of interest'; seared Mallaig scallops with a lemon and dill hollandaise and samphire; roasted noisette of Perthshire lamb with crispy parsnip batons and rosemary jus. Tom Lewis has a natural talent, for example, monkfish in lemon beurre blanc with pasta

Lochearnhead FK19 8PQ
Map 11: NN52
Tel: 01877 384622
Fax: 01877 384305
Chef: Tom lewis
Owners : Jean, Rob & Tom Lewis
Cost: Fixed-price L £18/D £22.50. ☺
H/wine £9.70
Times: Noon-last L 2pm/7pm-last
D 9pm. Closed last 2 wks Jan
Additional: Bar food L; Sunday L;
No children under 12; ◑ dishes
Seats: 32. Private dining room 12.

Monachyle Mhor

Jacket & tie preferred at D
Smoking: No smoking in dining room;
Air conditioning
Accommodation: 10 en suite
Credit cards: ▬ ▬ ▆

Directions: On A84, 11 miles N of
Callander turn R at Kingshouse Hotel.
Monachyle Mhor 6 miles.

was simplicity itself, and a poacher's bag of pigeon and rabbit
with Puy lentils was also simply cooked and presented, yet
bursting with flavour. Home-made puddings might include
bitter chocolate flan with vanilla ice cream.

BRIDGE OF ALLAN, Royal Hotel ✿ NEW

*Within easy reach of the M9, this impressive Victorian hotel features
attractively refurbished bedrooms and a stylish restaurant, where
diners can savour creative dishes prepared from fresh ingredients.
The fixed-price menu may highlight scallops with saffron butter,
haggis-filled chicken with Drambuie sauce, and chocolate marquise
with caramel sauce.*

Additional: Bar food; Sunday L; Children welcome; ♨ dishes
Smoking: No smoking in dining room
Accommodation: 34 en suite
Credit cards: ▬ ▬ ▰ ▆ ▬

Directions: *Telephone for directions*

Henderson Street FK9 4HG
Map 11: NS79
Tel: 01786 832284
Fax: 01786 834377
Chef: Mike Singer
Owner: Monument Leisure Ltd
Cost: Alc £23.50, fixed-price
L £12.50/D £22.50 (4 courses). ☺
H/wine £11
Times: Last L 2.30pm/last D 9.30pm

CALLANDER, Roman Camp Hotel ✿✿

FK17 8BG
Map 11: NN60
Tel: 01877 330003
Fax: 01877 331533
Chef: Ian McNaught
Owners: Eric & Marion Brown
Cost: Alc £45, fixed price L £18/D
£34 (4 courses). H/wine £14.50
Times: Noon-last L 2pm/7-last D 9pm

Seventeen acres of parkland and gardens that extend down
to the banks of the River Teith is an idyllic setting for this
charming country house hotel, where only the odd passing
peacock interrupts the tranquil atmosphere. The updated
restaurant offers a menu based on prime Scottish ingredients,
and fruit and vegetables from the hotel's own walled garden.

This translated at inspection as a chicken and truffle sausage liberally laced with pistachio nuts and served with a delicious foie gras sabayon, a lovely fresh fillet of turbot, lightly pan-fried and accompanied by crisp deep-fried spaghetti vegetables on a bed of leeks and cep noodles and a delicate mustard butter sauce. Dessert was 'positively wicked' – a bitter chocolate and Amaretto soup with almond 'croûtons' with a wonderfully smooth white chocolate ice cream. Good strong coffee and hand-made dark and white chocolates made a great finish. The wine list is extensive and well-chosen with some fine vintages from around the world.

Directions: Turn L into driveway at east end of Callander main street

Additional: Sunday L;
No children under 4; ● dishes
Seats: 65. Private dining room 40.
Jacket & tie preferred
Smoking: No smoking in dining room;
Air conditioning
Accommodation: 14 en suite
Credit cards: ▆▆ ▆▆ ▆▆ ▆ ▆▆ ▆

DUNBLANE,
Cromlix House Hotel ❀❀

Kinbuck By Dunblane
FK15 9JT
Map 11: NN70
Tel: 01786 822125
Fax: 01786 825450
Please telephone for further details

The Edwardian country house at the heart of a substantial estate is a pleasure from the outside and enjoyed for its range of public rooms – an elegant morning room with deep sofas and easy chairs, twin dining rooms with gleaming silver and crisp white linen, the upstairs library, and a conservatory where breakfast is usually served. Dinner is a limited choice, five-course affair, and makes the most of Scotland's larder, even down to haggis balls as canapés, and farmhouse Scottish cheeses. A spring dinner produced pan-fried calves' liver with Savoy cabbage and a Puy lentil jus that was bursting with flavour, then an effective dish of roast loin of lamb with a herb crust and wild mushrooms, shallots and a Madeira jus followed, with mille-feuille of roast banana and hazelnut over a butterscotch sauce a brilliant finish. Good, strong cafetière came with petits fours. The wine list is extensive and demonstrates a knowledgeable selection.

Directions: From A9 take B8033 (Kinbuck), through village, 2nd L after small bridge

KILLEARN, **Black Bull** ❀❀

Killearn nestles below the Campsie Fells, and the first-floor lounge at this 19th-century inn has views of the Endrick Valley. A new chef has introduced a *carte* in the spacious Conservatory restaurant, which overlooks the attractive gardens (alfresco dining a possibility in summer). Herb and ricotta risotto with Parmesan butter made a promising start to an inspector's meal, going on to no less enjoyable pigeon breast stuffed with pigeon mousseline served with a brochette

The Square G63 9NG
Map 11: NS58
Tel: 01360 550215
Fax: 01360 550143
Chef: Eric Avenier
Owner: James Wilson
Cost: *Alc* £18, fixed-price D £28. ☺
H/wine £9
Times: Open all day, noon-last
D 9.30pm

of potatoes and purée vegetables, all elements producing a well-rounded dish enhanced by an intense stock-based sauce. A trio of differently textured, rich chocolate mousses – bitter, milk and white – made an appealing end to the meal. Other main courses may be Perthshire lamb wrapped in ham with Savoy cabbage, breast of Grampian chicken with egg noodles, and fillet of Tay salmon under a scallop mousseline and baked in puff pastry. The wine list offers three house wines as well as a list of fine French wines, with a realistically priced global selection. The brasserie here offers all-day eating.

Directions: Take A81 N from Glasgow towards Aberfoyle. Turn off on A875 to Killearn, just past distillery.

Additional: Bar food; Sunday L; Children welcome; ❸ dishes
Seats: 40
Smoking: No-smoking area; No pipes & cigars
Accommodation: 11 en suite
Credit cards: 🔳 🔳 🔳 🔳 🔳

PORT OF MENTEITH, Lake Hotel ❀❀

Stirling FK8 3RA
Map 11: NN50
Tel: 01877 385258
Fax: 01877 385671
Chef: Michael Clayton
Owner: Highland Holidays Ltd
Cost: Fixed-price L £13.75/D £24.90.
☺ H/wine £10.50
Times: Noon-last L 2pm/7-last D 8.30pm
Additional: Sunday L; No children at D; ❸ dishes
Seats: 34. Jacket & tie preferred
Smoking: No smoking in dining room; Air conditioning
Accommodation: 16 en suite
Credit cards: 🔳 🔳 🔳 🔳

This is a relaxed, civilised holiday hotel which stands beside the shore of Lake Monteith overlooking the Isle of Inchmaholme. Indeed, the conservatory restaurant enjoys stunning views over the lake. The kitchen cooks a set-price menu with several choices for each course. Chicken liver parfait with sun-dried tomato dressing could precede tomato soup of sorbet, for example. Fillet of beef served on potato, bacon and garlic with a horseradish sabayon and red wine sauce, or grilled fillet of monkfish with tomato risotto, pepper fondue and saffron sauce are typical main course choices. Hot chocolate fondant with Grand Marnier sauce is worth saving room for. Coffee comes with petits fours.

Directions: On the A873 in Port of Monteith

STIRLING, River House ❀ ⟪NEW⟫

Multi-function restaurant and conference/seminar venue, located in a new business park in the shadow of Stirling Castle. A good-value lunch comprised chicken galantine with grape relish, baked fillet of cod with oatmeal crust, and apple crisp with vanilla sauce. Special menu and crèche for children.

Additional: Bar food L; Sunday L; Children welcome; ❸ dishes
Smoking: No pipes & cigars
Credit cards: 🔳 🔳 🔳 🔳

Directions: 3 mins from J10 of M9. Follow signs for Stirling ring road and Castle Business Park

Castle Business Park
Craigforth SK9 4TW
Map 11: NS79
Tel: 01786 465577
Fax: 01786 462255
Chef: Nick Parkes
Owners: Simon Littlejohn, Alex Knight
Cost: *Alc* £18.95, fixed-price L £5.95 (2courses). ☺ H/wine £7.95
Times: Last L 2.30pm/last D 9.30pm. Closed 25, 26 Dec, 1 Jan

STIRLING,

Stirling Highland

The hotel was once a school, so calling the restaurant Scholars was rather obvious. However, its 'good grub' with candles, flowers, good silver, crisp linen, high backed chairs, and great staff – friendly and fun – adding to the comforts. Menus read well, and a lot of effort is being made to produce some satisfying food; certainly, at inspection, dinner was a treat with our two Rosette award applying to this meal only. Asparagus soup was full of flavour, smooth, light, and based on good stock. Cod set on a potato purée with champagne sauce, was accompanied by 'super' dauphinoise with nutmeg, sweet carrots, crisp mange-tout, and great cauliflower hollandaise. Pudding was a splendid apple and pecan tart Tatin with a cinnamon anglaise.

Directions: In the road leading to Stirling Castle – follow Castle signs

Spittal Street FK8 1DU
Map 11: NS79
Tel: 01786 475444
Fax: 01786 472929
Chef: Paul Cook
Owners: Scottish Highland Hotels plc
Cost: *Alc* £30, fixed-price D £19.95.
☺ H/wine £10.95
Times: Last L 1.45pm/last D 9.30pm.
Closed L Sat
Additional: Sunday L;
Children welcome; ✇ dishes
Seats: 75. Private room 40
Smoking: No smoking in dining room
Accommodation: 78 en suite
Credit cards: 🖪 🖪 🖪 🖪 🖪 🖪 JCB

STRATHBLANE,

Country Club Hotel   NEW

Decorated in classical style, the Ardinning Room at the Country Club Hotel provides innovative food. We sampled a goats' cheese soufflé on creamed spinach and forest mushrooms, and roast marinated breast of duckling on braised red cabbage with apple and green ginger.

Additional: Bar food; Sunday L; Children welcome; ✇ dishes
Smoking: No smoking in dining room
Accommodation: 10 en suite
Credit cards: 🖪 🖪 🖪 🖪 🖪 🖪

Directions: From Glasgow take A81 (Milngavie/Aberfoyle). Hotel on R before entering village of Strathblane

Milngavie Road G63 9AH
Map 11: NS56
Tel: 01360 770491
Fax: 01360 770345
Chef: Adi Schmidt
Owner: John Kay
Cost: Fixed-price D £24.95. ☺
H/wine £10.95
Times: Last L 2.30pm/last D 9.30pm

STRATHYRE,

Creagan House

The Gunns have converted this former farmhouse, built in the 17th century, into a charming, cosy hotel. It's surrounded by mountains, rivers and forest, with free access to quiet walks with wonderful views. Dinner is taken at large wooden tables in the impressive dining room with its grand open fireplace. Gordon Gunn's style is bold and innovative. At inspection, a starter of hashed duck – like a burger in appearance – impressed with its flavour; it came with a sauce of pomegranate and thyme and squash oatcakes. This was followed by mushroom and parsnip soup, then a main course of 'first-class' codling with perfectly cooked scallops wrapped in bacon, set on garlicky mashed potato. Dark chocolate cake, with three distinct flavours and textures is 'a killer', it's so rich and full-flavoured. The long, annotated wine list has a good range of halves and a house selection of eight bottles.

Directions: Lies 0.25 miles N of village off A84

Callander FK18 8ND
Map 11: NN51
Tel: 01877 384638
Fax: 01877 384319
Chef: Gordon A Gunn
Owners: Gordon & Cherry Gunn
Cost: Fixed-price D £22.50. ☺
H/wine £9
Times: D only, 7.30-last D 8.30pm.
Closed 1 wk Oct, Feb
Additional: No children under 10
Seats: 15. Private room 6
Smoking: No smoking in dining room
Accommodation: 5 en suite
Credit cards: 🖪 🖪 🖪

WALES
ANGLESEY, ISLE OF

BEAUMARIS,
Ye Old Bulls Head Inn

Castle Street LL58 8AP
Map 6: SH67
Tel: 01248 810329
Fax: 01248 811294
Chef: Keith Rothwell
Owners: Keith Rothwell,
David Robertson
Cost: Alc £25, fixed-price D £21. ☺
H/wine £13.50
Times: D only, 7.30-last D 9.30pm.
Closed 25-26 Dec, 1 Jan
Additional: Bar food L (not Sun);
Sunday L (noon-2.30pm);
No children under 7; 🍴 dishes
Seats: 50
Smoking: No smoking in dining room
Accommodation: 15 en suite
Credit cards: ▆▆ ▆▆ 🐲 ☐ ▆▆ ▆ JCB

No visit to Beaumaris is complete without a visit to the massive moated castle; the Old Gaol, with its treadmill, is worth seeing too. Ye Old Bulls Head is not without history either: built in 1472, it became a coaching inn in the 17th century, and it shows its age well, with beams and timbers, open fireplaces, and an impressive display of antique weaponry in the ground-floor bar, where lunch is served from Monday to Saturday. Dinner is served in the upstairs dining room, where there's a choice of a fixed set-price menu – perhaps pan-fried skate wing with capers, roast leg of Welsh lamb, and a choice of puddings – or a *carte*. The kitchen uses a broad palette, with starters of moules marinière, smoked breast and confit of duck with orange and fig chutney, and Arbroath smokies. Main courses might range from pan-fried fillet of beef with melted onions, a quail's egg and pink peppercorns, through a hotpot of Llanrwst goats' cheese with creamy leaks and tomatoes, to poached fillet of halibut with black pasta, scallops and clams. Some quality producers show up on the well-constructed wine list, with an unusual South African red among the house wines. A brasserie is planned for early 1999.

Directions: Town centre, main street

TREARDDUR BAY,
Trearddur Bay Hotel

A modern hotel catering for both business and leisure visitors. The all-day bar serves a wide range of snacks and light meals, and the more formal hotel restaurant promises sound cooking of fresh seasonal produce.

Holyhead LL65 2UN
Map 6: SH27
Tel: 01407 860301
Fax: 01407 861181
Please telephone for further details

Directions: Take A5 from Bangor to Valley crossroads, continue onto B4545 then turn L after 3 miles

BRIDGEND

BRIDGEND, Coed-y-Mwstwr

The arched timbers and oak panelled walls give something of a church-like appearance to the Eliot Restaurant. Those in the window pews can look out over the gardens whilst friendly local staff deliver a range of modish dishes that make much of Welsh produce. Examples of the latter have included sausage of Wye salmon with air-dried ham and seared bass from Carmarthen Bay with a compote of spring onions.

Smoking: No pipes & cigars
Accommodation: 23 en suite
Credit cards: ▬ ▬ ▬ ▄ ▬ ▬ ▬

Directions: M4 exit 35, A473 (Bridgend) into Coychurch, R at petrol station and up hill for 1 mile

Coychurch CF35 6AF
Map 3: SS97
Tel: 01656 860621
Fax: 01656 863122
Chef: Tony Duce
Owner: Virgin Hotels
Cost: *Alc* £25, fixed-price L £10.50 (2 courses)/D £17.95 (2 courses). ☺ H/wine £10.75
Times: Last L 2pm/last D 10pm
Additional: Bar food; Sunday L; Children welcome; ♨ dishes

BRIDGEND, The Great House ✿

Dinner is candlelit in the well-appointed dining room of this lovingly restored Grade II listed building. Between them, the carte and fixed-price evening menus offer a good choice of dishes in which the flavours of good quality ingredients are well to the fore.

Smoking: No smoking in dining room. Air conditioning
Accommodation: 16 en suite
Credit cards: ▬ ▬ ▬ ▄ ▬ ▬ ▬ JCB

Directions: M4/J35, A473 then A48 signed Porthcawl and Laleston

Laleston CF32 0HP
Map 3: SS97
Tel: 01656 657644
Fax: 01656 668892
Chefs: Neil Hughes, Stuart Beven
Owners: Norma & Stephen Bond
Cost: *Alc* £25, fixed-price L £10.95/D £19.95. ☺ H/wine £9.75.
Times: Last L 2pm/D 9.30pm. Closed L Sat, D Sun, 25-26 Dec
Additional: Bar food, Sunday L, Children welcome, ♨ dishes

CARDIFF

CARDIFF, Cardiff Bay Hotel ✿✿

What was once a Victorian fruit and vegetable warehouse on Cardiff's waterfront is now a modern hotel that looks from the outside similar to a liner coming into dock; recent expansion and refurbishment has resulted in additional conference facilities and extra lounge areas. A nautical theme runs throughout – hence the restaurant's name, Halyard's. In here, the kitchen's lightness of touch keeps flavours buoyant, and ingredients are properly handled and intelligently combined. Caesar salad is a unique version involving goats' cheese along with the other ingredients, while fluffily textured cod fishcakes come with gently spiced banana chutney. Chargrilled pork escalopes with potato and apple mash may be among main courses, and iced coffee and praline mousse with coffee-laced cream sauce one of the desserts. You can burn off unwanted calories in the health and fitness club afterwards.

Directions: From A48M follow 'Docks & Cardiff E'. L at r/bout, R fork onto flyover. At 3rd r/bout take 2nd exit (Ocean Way – Atlantic Wharf). L at r/bout (Penarth). Over next r/bout, under flyover, L at 1st lights; hotel on R

Schooner Way
Atlantic Wharf CF1 5RT
Map 3: ST17
Tel: 01222 475000/465888
Fax: 01222 481491
Chef: Peter Farrow
Cost: *Alc* £25, fixed-price L £9.95/D £17.50. ☺ H/wine £9.95
Times: Noon-last L 2pm/7pm-last D 10pm. Closed L Sat, L Bhs
Additional: Bar food; Sunday L; Children welcome; ♨ dishes
Seats: 100. Private dining room 6-200
Smoking: No-smoking area; No pipes & cigars; Air conditioning
Accommodation: 157 en suite
Credit cards: ▬ ▬ ▬ ▄ ▬ ▬

CARDIFF, Le Cassoulet

Decorated in red and black – the colours of the Toulouse rugby team – Le Cassoulet is an authentic French bistro with plenty of continental character. Not surprisingly the menu is entrenched in the Viader's home region: dishes are proudly trumpeted in French but are accompanied by generous English annotation. There is an emphasis on the classics of French cooking, and it is the more traditional elements of the menu that have the most striking impact. Try, for example, cassoulet toulousain – a masterly and affectionate version of the brilliant, self-contained dish made with white haricot beans, neck of pork, confit of duck and Toulouse sausage. Other dishes to look out for include roasted venison topped with apples and cinnamon, and pan-fried chicken breast with spring onion mashed potatoes. The wine list is a patriotic celebration of the French regions, and includes a number of authentic bottles at reasonable prices.

5 Romilly Crescent Canton CF1 9NP
Map 3: ST17
Tel/Fax: 01222 221905
Chef: Gilbert Viader
Owner: Mr & Mrs G Viader
Cost: Alc £28.50, fixed-price L £14.95. ☺ H/wine £10.95
Times: Noon-last L 2pm/7-last D 10pm. Closed Sun, Mon, 2 wks Xmas, Aug
Additional: Children welcome; ◑ dishes
Seats: 40
Smoking: No pipes & cigars
Credit cards: 🔲 🔲 🔲 🔲 🔲 🔲 🔲 JCB

Directions: From M4 follow B4267 Canton, Restaurant is next to Post Office

CARDIFF, Chikako's Japanese Restaurant ✿

The commodious, smartly furnished basement restaurant brings an authentic touch of the Far East to west Wales. Dishes include chicken teriyaki and beef tataki; teppanyaki and sukiyaki are cooked at table. Yosenabe is a selection of seafood and vegetables cooked in boiling fish stock.

Smoking: No-smoking area; Air conditioning
Credit cards: 🔲 🔲 🔲 🔲 🔲 JCB

Directions: Opp Marriott Hotel, in 'The Hayes' café quarter

10-11 Mill Lane CF1 1FL
Map 3: ST17
Tel/Fax: 01222 665279
Chef/Owner: Mrs Chikako Cameron
Cost: Fixed price D £18 (2 courses). ☺ H/wine £8.60
Times: L by prior arrangement/last D 11pm
Additional: Children welcome; ◑ dishes

CARDIFF, Copthorne Cardiff-Caerdydd ✿

Popular modern hotel with bright open-plan public areas. The busy Raglans Restaurant overlooks the lake in the grounds and offers both a set menu and a carte. More informal meals are served in Beauchamps Brasserie.

Directions: M4/33 take A4232 (Cardiff West); after 3 miles turn onto A48

Copthorne Way, Culverhouse Cross CF5 6XJ
Map 3: ST17
Tel: 01222 599100
Fax: 01222 599080
Please telephone for further details

CARDIFF, Gilby's Restaurant ❀

Old Port Road
Culverhouse Cross CF5 6DN
Map 3: ST17
Tel: 01222 670800
Fax: 01222 594437
Chef: Gareth Silcock
Owner: Anthony Armelin
Cost: *Alc* £22.50, fixed-price L £6.95
(2 courses)/D £9.95 (6-7pm only). ☺
H/wine £9.95
Times: Last L 2.30pm/last D 10.30pm.
Closed D Sun, all Mon, 25, 26 Dec,
1 Jan
Additional: Sunday L;
No children under 7; ❹ dishes
Smoking: No-smoking area;
No pipes & cigars
Credit cards:

*Situated on the western edge of the city and craftily converted from
two 18th-century barns, there is nonetheless a metropolitan feel to
this welcome addition to the capital's cuisine. Much of this is down
to a modish menu which offers plenty of well-chosen fish, together
with punchy brasserie dishes such as pan-fried calves' liver and
braised shank of lamb.*

Directions: From M4 J33 follow signs for Airport/Cardiff West.
Take A4050 Barry/Airport road and R at 1st mini roundabout.

CARDIFF, **Manor Parc Hotel** ❀

*Smart country house set in mature grounds and gardens. Classical
Italian and French dishes are served in the elegant dining room,
which features a domed lantern ceiling. Main courses range from
stuffed breast of chicken with leeks and bacon, to pan-fried escalope
of fresh salmon with oyster mushrooms, champagne sauce and
chives.*

Additional: Sunday L; Children welcome; ❹ dishes
Smoking: No cigars and pipes; Air conditioning
Accommodation: 12 en suite
Credit cards:

Directions: N of Cardiff on A469

Thornhill Road CF4 5UA
Map 3: ST17
Tel: 01222 693723
Fax: 01222 614624
Chef: Giovanni Morabito
Owners: Efisio Cinus & Salvatore
Salimeni
Cost: *Alc* £26. H/wine £9.75
Times: Last L 1.45pm/last D 9.45pm.
Closed D Sun

CARDIFF,

Metropolis Restaurant ❀

*Converted from an old clothing factory, Metropolis has a striking
modern/Art Deco interior and up-to-date menu emphasising fresh
flavours in simple combinations. Chicken and rocket roulade with
lemongrass dressing, smoked haddock mousse with scrambled eggs,
monkfish with choucroute and juniper berry butter sauce, and
guinea fowl with lime and redcurrant demonstrate the style.*

Additional: Bar food L; Sunday L; Children welcome; ❹ dishes
Smoking: No-smoking area; Air conditioning
Credit cards:

60 Charles Street CF1 4EG
Map 3: ST17
Tel: 01222 344300
Fax: 01222 666602
Chef: James Roedemer
Owner: David Williams
Cost: *Alc* £21, fixed-price L £5.95
(2 courses). ☺ H/wine £8.95
Times: Closed D Sun, D Mon

Directions: In city centre, off Queen Street

CARDIFF, New House Hotel

Thornhill CF4 5UA
Map 3: ST17
Tel: 01222 520280
Fax: 01222 520324
Chef: Ian Black
Owner: Julian Hitchcock
Cost: *Alc* £30, fixed-price L £14.95/D
£18.50. ☺ H/wine £9.95
Times: Last L 1.45pm/last D 9.45pm
Additional: Bar food; Sunday L;
🌢 dishes
Seats: 40. Private dining room 150.
Jacket & tie preferred
Smoking: No smoking in dining room
Accommodation: 33 en suite
Credit cards: 💳 💳 💳 💳 💳 💳 💳

In actual fact the New House is a converted and extended
Georgian residence, perched midway up the hillside that
separates Cardiff from the South Wales valleys; the nearest
new houses are at least a mile away. From the dining room one
can survey both the Capital and, on a clear day, the north
Devon coast whilst sampling the efforts of a kitchen that copes
well with an ambitious, long menu. Much of the strength is in
the consistency of the cooking, with pastry being a strong
point, seafood tartlet with crunchy langoustine, for example,
and well-executed classic techniques such as beef fillet with
béarnaise. The studied approach is particularly apparent in
desserts along the lines of velvety three-chocolate mousse, and
extends to good petits fours.

Directions: Take the A469 to the north of city. Entrance on L
shortly after crossing the M4 flyover

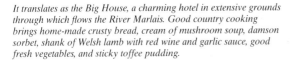

CARMARTHENSHIRE

BRECHFA,
Tŷ Mawr Country Hotel

*It translates as the Big House, a charming hotel in extensive grounds
through which flows the River Marlais. Good country cooking
brings home-made crusty bread, cream of mushroom soup, damson
sorbet, shank of Welsh lamb with red wine and garlic sauce, good
fresh vegetables, and sticky toffee pudding.*

Additional: Bar food L; Sunday L; Children welcome
Smoking: No smoking in dining room
Accommodation: 5 en suite
Credit cards: 💳 💳 💳 💳 💳 💳 JCB

Directions: In village centre 6.5 miles from A40/B4310 junction
at Nantgaredig

SA32 7RA
Map 2: SN53
Tel: 01267 202332/202330
Fax: 01267 202437
Chef: Veronica Weston
Owners: Roger & Veronica Weston
Cost: Fixed-price D £23 (5 courses).
☺ H/wine £9.25
Times: Noon-1.30pm/7.30-9pm

CARMARTHEN,

Old Cornmill Restaurant

A family-run restaurant in a converted mill, offering honest Anglo/French cooking that would satisfy any hungry guest. Main courses could include pan-fried steak of wild boar with orange sauce, and roast saddle of lamb stuffed with sausage meat and apricots. Summer lunches can be taken in the gardens, overlooking the river.

Additional: Sunday L; Children welcome; ❹ dishes
Smoking: No pipes & cigars
Credit cards: ▄▄ ▄▄ ▄

Directions: 0.5 mile from Cynwyl Elfed on A484, 7 miles NW of Carmarthen

Cynwyl Elfed SA33 6UJ
Map 2: SN42
Tel: 01267 281610
Chef: Jack de Wreede
Owners: Sue & Jack de Wreede
Cost: Alc £19. ☺ H/wine £7.90
Times: D only, last D 9pm.
Closed D Sun, all Mon & Tue, Feb

CARMARTHEN,

The Four Seasons

NEW

A spacious farmhouse restaurant with a rural cottage feel to its white stone walls, exposed wooden rafters, and sturdy pine furniture. Dishes from the up-to-date menu include rack of saltmarsh lamb with aubergine caponata, tender pork fillet with a piquant Beaune mustard, and fillet of Welsh black beef au poivre.

Additional: No children under 5 in dining room; ❹ dishes
Accommodation: 5 en suite
Credit cards: ▄▄ ▄▄ ▄ ▢ ▣ JCB

Directions: From A40 turn onto B4310 at Nantgaredig; L up hill, 0.25 mile on R

Nantgaredig SA32 7NY
Map 2: SN42
Tel: 01267 290238
Fax: 01267 290808
Chefs/Owners: Mayam Wright, Charlotte Pasetti
Cost: Fixed-price D £20 (4 courses).
☺ H/wine £9.50
Times: D only, 7pm-9.30pm.
Closed Sun, Mon, Xmas

LAUGHARNE, Cors Restaurant

The interior of this former vicarage is strikingly original and bold, exhibiting a confidence in vivid colour combinations that few would dare to experiment with but which are a brilliant success. The brooding, claret-walled restaurant, candlelit and made large by the use of an enormous wall filling gilt-framed mirror, has a dense and temple-like ambience. By contrast, adjacent lounges and separate bar are wood floored, with abundant greenery and look out through french doors onto the garden beyond. An Ital/Med bias in the cooking matches the decor: primary colours, bold, bright flavours, simple concepts, and the best of local ingredients. The short wine list has lots of character from modish New World and new wave producers.

Newbridge Road
Map 2: SN31
Tel: 01994 427219
Chef/Owner: Nick Priestland
Please telephone for further details

LLANDEILO,

Cawdor Arms Hotel

Enthusiastic new owners have brought a new lease of life to this impressive Georgian coaching inn. Traditional Welsh dishes with modern, global touches characterise the daily-changing *carte*. Typically, guests will be asked to choose between high quality dishes such as roast breast of guinea fowl with tarragon pancake and parsnip purée, charred breast of

Rhosmaen Street SA19 6EN
Map 3: SN62
Tel: 01558 823500
Fax: 01558 822399
Chef: Rod Peterson
Owners: Mr & Mrs John Silver
Cost: Fixed-price L £13.50/D £20. ☺
H/wine £9.90

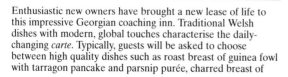

local duckling with honey compote, and marinated salmon in soy and balsamic vinegar with oyster sauce. Starters include risotto of asparagus, ginger and poached egg, and sweet and sour parfait of duck liver and apricot with mustard brioche and plum syrup. A mid-winter meal started with home-made tomato and basil soup, served piping hot and full of flavour. Grilled fillet of Welsh beef proved to be a substantial main course, served on a bed of cabbage with a smoked bacon and herb crumble topping. Dessert was a triumph – steamed pudding of peanut butter and jam with sauce anglaise.

Directions: Large Georgian building in town centre

Times: Noon-last L 2pm/7.30-last D 9pm
Additional: Bar food L; Sunday L; Children welcome; ✦ dishes
Seats: 90. Private dining room 45
Smoking: No smoking in dining room
Accommodation: 17 en suite
Credit cards: 🃏 🃏 🃏 🃏 🃏

NEWCASTLE EMLYN,
Emlyn Arms Hotel ❀❀

Welsh pride shines through in the cooking at this rural 18th-century coaching inn. Fresh local produce is used wherever possible, and dishes such as roast rib of Welsh black beef and seared supreme of Teifi salmon are commonplace. However, chef Mark Freeman (from Le Cassoulet, Cardiff) has an eye on modern trends, and amongst the traditional Welsh fare are a number of modern dishes, such as shiitake, oyster mushroom and truffle oil risotto with saffron and herb nage, crispy leg of duck with warm apple chutney and peppered rocket leaves, and quail breasts and beetroot wrapped in bacon and served with broad beans and balsamic vinegar sauce. Desserts range from dark chocolate and banana mousse to bara brith-and-butter pudding with mango ice cream. The three-course set-menu has five choices at each course and changes every two to three days; in addition the 'Concept Menu' suggests specific wines to accompany each dish.

Directions: Turn off A484 at Newcastle Emlyn; turn R into town centre – hotel at bottom of main street on L just before river

Bridge Street SA38 9DU
Map 2: SN34
Tel: 01239 710317
Fax: 01239 710792
Chef: Mark Freeman
Owner: John Retallick
Cost: Fixed-price L £10.50/D £20. ☺ H/wine £8.95
Times: Noon-3pm/7-10.30pm.
Closed 26 Dec
Additional: Bar food; Sunday L; Children welcome; ✦ dishes
Seats: 40
Smoking: No smoking in dining room
Accommodation: 35 en suite
Credit cards: 🃏 🃏 🃏 🃏

CEREDIGION

ABERPORTH,
Penbontbren Farm Hotel ❀

The restaurant is housed in a former cowshed with stone walls and pine ceilings. A comprehensive carte might include Rhydlewis Terrine, a mixture of locally smoked salmon, mackerel and trout served with fennel mayonnaise, and seared medallions of pork with apricot and brandy sauce. There's also a vegetarian selection.

Additional: Bar food L; Children welcome; ✦ dishes
Smoking: No smoking in dining room; Air conditioning
Accommodation: 10 en suite
Credit cards: 🃏 🃏 🃏 🃏 🃏 🃏 🃏 JCB

Directions: E from Cardigan on A487 to Tanygroes. 1 mile after Tanygroes take 2nd R signposted Penbontbren

Glynarthen Cardigan SA44 6PE
Map 2: SN25
Tel: 01239 810248
Fax: 01239 811129
Chef: Nan Humphreys
Owners: G B & M M (Nan) Humphreys
Cost: *Alc* £16
Times: D only, last D 8.15pm.
Closed Xmas

ABERYSTWYTH,
Belle Vue Royal Hotel

A family-run hotel, over 170 years old, situated on the promenade.
Fresh local produce combines with sound cooking skills to produce
dishes such as timbale of garlic sautéed prawns with laverbread and
bacon, and rack of Ystwyth lamb with a herb and French mustard
crust and tarragon sauce.

Directions: Overlooking Cardigan Bay

Marine Terrace
SY23 2BA
Map 6: SN58
Tel: 01970 617558
Fax: 01970 612190
Chef: Mark Hughes
Owners: Alan & Marilyn Davies,
David & Thelma Jones
Cost: H/wine £9 ☺
Times: Last L 1.45pm/D 9.15pm.
Closed 26 Dec
Additional: Bar food L; Sunday L;
Children welcome; ④ dishes
Smoking: No-smoking area;
No pipes & cigars; Air-conditioning
Accommodation: 37 rooms
(34 en suite)
Credit cards: 💳 💳 💳 💳 💳 💳 💳

ABERYSTWYTH, **Conrah Hotel** ✿✿

Spectacular mountain views and quality cooking ensure that
visitors leave with many fine memories. Set in 20 acres of
mature grounds, this country house hotel also provides a
number of leisure and conference facilities. The restaurant
offers an excellent range of modern and classical dishes, and
there are plenty of Welsh specialities to choose from. The
kitchen rightly favours good regional produce, and this is
used to great effect in dishes such as cannon of Welsh
lamb coated in sesame, poppy and mustard seeds and served on a
bed of butter beans, or chargrilled fillet of Welsh black beef
with shallots, oranges and Cointreau sauce, and smoked
breast of local pheasant accompanied by caramelised apples,
wild mushrooms and Calvados sauce. Enjoy home-made
canapés in the lounge, before moving to the elegant candlelit
restaurant.

Ffosrhydygaled Chancery
SY23 4DF
Map 6: SN58
Tel: 01970 617941
Fax: 01970 624546
Chef: Stephen M West
Owners: Mr FJ & Mrs P Heading
Cost: Fixed-price L £16/D £26.
H/wine £11
Times: Noon-last L 2pm/7pm-last
D 9pm. Closed Xmas wk
Additional: Bar food L; Sunday L;
No children under 5; ④ dishes
Seats: 50.
Smoking: No smoking in dining room
Accommodation: 19 en suite
Credit cards: 💳 💳 💳 💳 💳 💳 💳 JCB

Directions: On A487, 3 miles S of Aberystwyth

ABERYSTWYTH, **Groves Hotel**

*A friendly family-run hotel close to the shops and the seafront.
A traditional Welsh dish of laverbread on a base of fried bread
with diced bacon and cockles, was followed by lamb cutlets with
a sauce of orange and laver. The pudding, a rich treacle tart,
is recommended.*

Additional: Bar food; Children welcome; 𝄐 dishes
Smoking: No smoking in dining room
Accommodation: 9 en suite
Credit cards: 💳 💳 💳 💳 💳 💳 💳

Directions: Town centre, take road opposite station & 2nd R

44-46 North Parade SY23 2NF
Map 6: SN58
Tel: 01970 617623
Fax: 01970 627068
Chef/Owner: Steve Albert
Cost: Fixed-price D £16. ☺
H/wine £7.50.
Times: Last L 2pm/last D 8.30pm.
Closed Sun, Xmas

EGLWYSFACH,
Ynshir Hall ❀❀❀

Machynlleth SY20 8TA
Map 6: SN69
Tel: 01654 781209
Fax: 01654 781366
Chef: Chris Colmer
Owners: Rob & Joan Reen
Cost: Fixed-price D £31 (4 courses).
H/wine £15
Times: 12.30-last L 1.30pm/7-last
D 8.30pm. Closed 5-21 Jan
Additional: Bar food L; Sunday L;
No children under 9; 𝄐 dishes
Seats: 30. Private dining room 16
Smoking: No smoking in dining room
Accommodation: 8 en suite
Credit cards: 💳 💳 💳 💳 💳 💳 💳 JCB

Reports on this splendid mansion set against a backdrop of
majestic scenery focus on the merits of the kitchen. The menu
may have its fair share of country house stalwarts, but Chris
Colmer's cooking displays a more modern edge and takes
note of the seasons. A typical dinner, taken in April, shows
the style: veal bolognaise and lobster ravioli with Reggiano
Parmesan, mizuno salad and a jus of vine tomatoes, oak-
smoked ham boudin with mushy peas and a tarragon beurre
blanc, then saddle of Welsh venison, red wine risotto, carrot
and smoked sausage sauerkraut, partnered by a saddle of
rabbit with butterbean purée scented with lime leaves and a
vanilla jus, and wild strawberry tart with lemongrass ice
cream with sauce Suzette, and chilled apple and ginger confit,
apple and cinnamon rice pudding, vanilla bean ice cream and
apple crisps. Then there's the great selection of breads –
walnut, olive, white – canapés of onion bhaji, monkfish and
slender lamb kebabs, and good petits fours, showing that the
kitchen remains on the ball where even small details are
concerned.
   Signature dishes: Lemon chicken with a nage of baby leeks
and herb gnocchi; velouté of pumpkin scented with tarragon,
topped with roasted pumpkin seeds; oak-smoked ham boudin
with mushy peas and onion gravy; wild strawberry tart with
lemongrass ice cream and sauce Suzette.

Directions: On the A487, 6 miles from Machynlleth & 11 miles
from Aberystwyth

LAMPETER, **Falcondale Mansion**

A mid-Victorian mansion located at the head of a forested valley overlooking the town. The restaurant makes the best of the view and offers dishes ranging from leek and potato soup, and roast leg of Welsh lamb, to ham and walnut parfait, and duckling oriental.

Additional: Bar food; Sunday L; Children welcome; ❹ dishes
Smoking: No smoking in dining room
Accommodation: 20 en suite
Credit cards: ▆▆ ▆▆ ▆▆ ▆ ▆▆ ▆

Directions: From High Street turn right up South Drive

SA48 7RX
Map 2: SN54
Tel: 01570 422910
Fax: 01570 423559
Chef: Michael Green
Owners: Mr & Mrs Stephen Smith
Cost: *Alc* £20, fixed-price D £18.50.
☺ H/wine £8.75
Times: D only, last D 9.30pm.
Closed 2nd & 3rd wk Jan

CONWY

ABERGELE, **Kinmel Arms**

St George LL22 9BP
Map 6: SH97
Tel/Fax: 01745 832207
Chef/Owner: Gary Edwards
Cost: *Alc* £19.50, fixed-price
D £12.95. ☺ H/wine £8.50
Times: Noon-2pm/7-9pm.
Closed D Mon
Additional: Bar food; Sunday L;
Children welcome; ❹ dishes
Seats: 38. Private dining room 24
Smoking: No smoking in dining room
Credit cards: ▆▆ ▆▆ ▆▆ ▆ JCB

The Kinmel Arms is a former coaching house on the edge of the historic Kinmel Estate, and is said to date from the 17th century. This is a pleasant, personally run, informal place with a cottage-style bar (good bar menu) and smart restaurant. The latter menu is short – some five choices at each course – but with daily specials that were mostly fish on our visit. Confit of duck leg with Puy lentils and a port wine glaze, or potted salmon and prawns with rocket salad, could precede chargrilled ribeye steak with a tomato and smoky bacon salsa and roast potato wedge, or breast of chicken with white wine, tarragon and new potatoes. Save room for the chocolate crème brûlée.

Directions: Take A55 towards Conwy; L turn signed 'St George'; L at top of hill and inn on L

BETWS-Y-COED,
Tan-y-Foel Hotel

The name translates as 'the house under the hillside', and Tan-y-Foel sits high in a tranquil valley with superb views from the part 16th-century manor house. Dinner is taken in the smartly appointed, intimate restaurant that extends into a

Capel Garmon LL26 0RE
Map 6: SH75
Tel: 01690 710507
Fax: 01690 710681
Chef: Janet Pitman
Owners: Peter & Janet Pitman

Tan-y-Foel Hotel

Cost: Fixed-price D £25. H/wine £11
Times: D only, 7 for 7.45pm.
Closed Xmas (check times Dec/Jan)
Additional: No children under 7
Seats: 16
Smoking: No smoking establishment
Accommodation: 7 en suite
Credit cards: ▆ ▆ ▆ ▆ ▆ ▆ ▆ JCB

conservatory. Although the menu is highly restricted, the cooking is of a superb standard and careful checks at the time of booking ensure that guests' culinary requirements are well catered for. Chef-owner Janet Pitman prefers classic techniques and combinations, basically French but using as much Welsh produce as possible, and her highly focused style results in precise, well-judged meals. Our inspector's visit included melt-in-the-mouth salmon, moist and perfectly cooked, napped by a light and creamy hollandaise and served on a bed of zingy wild rocket for contrast and bite. Main course fillet of Welsh lamb proved to be an unusual combination of textures and flavours, with tender pink meat sitting on top of crisp, minted rösti and super mushy pea purée, accompanied by floods of mustard sauce. Truly intense nut flavours characterised the crisp, chewy hazelnut meringue served with fresh whipped cream and sharp, plump raspberries. A generous plate of washed rind St David's cheese with biscuits and apple was strictly a fourth course, then there were sweetmeats and good coffee to finish a delightful evening. Clientele in the restaurant is mainly residential, though outside trade is encouraged and building (booking is essential). But it is worth staying for the night because breakfast is splendid.

Directions: A5 onto A470; 2 miles N towards Llanrwst, then turning for Capel Garmon. Hotel on L before village

COLWYN BAY,
Café Niçoise ❀❀

The old Victorian shop has a warm, dusky pink interior and is candlelit at night. The approach to cooking here is robust, sometimes bold, fired with keenness and enthusiasm, and dishes such as tournedos of Welsh black beef with glazed vegetable and a Madeira jus, or roast monkfish with parsley noodles and a tomato fondue, show an awareness of modern trends. Starters might be velouté of celery with a chive cream, or venison sausage with a seed mustard sauce, while desserts of toasted almond ice cream with roasted nectarines or Cape brandy pudding and Chantilly cream earn full marks.

Smoking: No-smoking area
Credit cards: ▆ ▆ ▆ ▆ ▆

Directions: From A55 take Old Colwyn exit, L at slip road, R at mini-roundabout, R towards Bay; restaurant is on L

124 Abergele Road
LL29 7PS
Map 6: SH87
Tel: 01492 531555
Chef: Carl Swift
Owners: Carl & Lynne Swift
Cost: Alc £23.50, fixed-price L/D
£13.95. ☺ H/wine £8.95
Times: Noon-2pm/7-10pm.
Closed all Sun, L Mon & Tue,
1 wk Jan, 1 wk Jun
Additional: No children under 7 at D;
❹ dishes
Seats: 32

CONWY, The Old Rectory ❀❀❀

Llanrwst Road Llansanffraid Glan
Conwy LL28 5LF
Map 6: SH77
Tel: 01492 580611
Fax: 01492 584555
Chef: Wendy Vaughan
Owners: Michael & Wendy Vaughan
Cost: Fixed-price D £25.
H/wine £13.90
Times: D only at 8pm.
Closed 10 Dec-1 Feb
Additional: No children under 5
Seats: 16
Smoking: No smoking in dining room
Accommodation: 6 en suite
Credit cards: ▆ ▆ ▆ ▆ ▆

You can't help but be impressed by the views of Conwy Castle, the estuary and Snowdonia from the Old Rectory's mature grounds. That the building dates from Georgian times is clear from the proportions of the elegant lounge and dining-room, with their antiques and paintings. Michael Vaughan makes an excellent host, creating a rare combination of what has been described as 'informal formality', while Wendy Vaughan's presence in the kitchen is no less appreciated. She discusses guests' preferences with them, sources her materials locally, and constructs appealing yet reassuring menus that come to fruition on the plate. Fish is often favoured for a starter, medallions of monkfish in a mustard and tarragon sauce, for example, or simply roasted red bream with a compote of tomatoes and onions, sliced black potatoes and a tomato and laverbread sauce. Anything involving Welsh mountain lamb or Black beef can be regarded as a signature dish, while saddle of Brecon venison is roasted with smoked bacon and oyster mushrooms and served with chocolate sauce. Pastrywork is clearly a strength, as evinced by a 'light and crisp' tart of summer berries topped with airy frangipane crumble, with intense raspberry ice cream of velvety texture, or one of chocolate mousse, its filling deeply flavoured and light. The wine list is distinguished by its collection of clarets of noble vintages from equally noble producers, but there's plenty of interest elsewhere on the list, with a broad range of half-bottles, and prices are competitive.

Directions: On A470, 0.5 mile S of junction with A55

LLANDUDNO,
Bodysgallen Hall Hotel ❀❀❀

Conwy Castle and Snowdonia form a peerless backdrop at this 17th-century mansion, and where better to enjoy the setting than the walled rose garden, the rockery with its cascade, or the box-hedged herb garden? The interior has the character to match the magnificent surroundings, and first impressions from the large oak-panelled, mullioned-windowed entrance hall are not knocked by the other rooms. Antique furniture and old paintings in the dining-room back up the feeling of age and solid comfort, although Mike Penny's menus are as up-to-date as they come. He takes his ingredients seriously, using fruit and vegetables from the gardens, organising weekly deliveries from

LL30 1RS
Map 6: SH78
Tel: 01492 584466
Fax: 01492 582519
Chef: Mike Penny
Owner: Historic House Hotels
Cost: Fixed-price L £17/D £29.50.
H/wine £11.75
Times: 12.30pm-last L
1.45pm/7.30pm-last D 9.30pm
Additional: Bar food L; Sunday L;
No children under 8;
❹ dishes

Bodysgallen Hall Hotel

Seats: 55. Private dining room 40.
Jacket & tie preferred
Smoking: No smoking in dining room;
Air conditioning
Accommodation: 35 en suite
Credit cards: ▆ ▆ ▅ ▆ ▆

France, and calling on local produce: Anglesey crab, Welsh lamb and Black beef, Cheshire ham. An inspector was impressed by the combinations of flavours and textures in a starter of crab and chive fishcakes, served with pan-fried langoustines on rocket with a little gingery jus. No less effective was a main course of succulent breast of guinea fowl, its leg minced and turned into a sausage, with bacon-flavoured sauce, a tasty polenta cake enriched with garlic and Parmesan, and caramelised onions. The kitchen shows a fondness for fruit at dessert stage, with raspberry soufflé and honey ice cream, and light blackberry mousse with poached pear, or there might be cup-shaped iced coffee parfait sitting on a 'saucer' of bitter chocolate. Most wine-producing regions of the world are represented on the wine list, where there's a decent number of house recommendations and affordable prices.

Directions: From A55 take A470 (Llandudno). Hotel 1 mile on R

LLANDUDNO,
Empire Hotel ⊛

Popular hotel in restored Victorian building near promenade, run by the same family for 50 years. Distinctive flavours typify the daily-changing menu, from starters such as Texas-style blackened beef with lime aïoli, to a main course trio of sautéed sea bass, monkfish fillets and king scallops. Long wine list.

Directions: In Llandudno, follow promenade along entire length, turn sharp L into Church Walks. Hotel 150yds on R

Church Walks LL30 2HE
Map 6: SH78
Tel: 01492 860555
Fax: 01492 860791
Chefs: Michael Waddy, Nick Davies
Owners: Len & Elizabeth Maddocks
Cost: Fixed-price L £14.50 (4 courses)/D £24.50 (5 courses). ☺
H/wine £14.50
Times: Last L 2pm/last D 9.30pm.
Closed L Mon-Fri, Xmas
Additional: Bar food; Sunday L;
Children welcome;
🍴 dishes
Smoking: No-smoking area;
No pipes & cigars; Air conditioning
Accommodation: 58 en suite
Credit cards: ▆ ▆ ▅ ▆ ▆ ▆ ▆ JCB

LLANDUDNO, **Imperial Hotel**

Large sea-front hotel where the spacious, wood-panelled restaurant offers a monthly-changing menu that makes good use of local foodstuffs. In January, terrine of Welsh forest game with thyme and pears, could be followed by pheasant with ham and lettuce roulade and Burgundy sauce. Extensive wine list. Friendly, informed service.

Smoking: No smoking in dining room
Accommodation: 100 en suite
Credit cards:

Directions: On The Promenade

The Promenade LL30 1AP
Map 6: SH78
Tel: 01492 877466
Fax: 01492 878043
Chef: Andy Goode
Owners: Greenclose Hotels Ltd
Cost: *Alc* £12, fixed-price D £20. ☺ H/wine £10
Times: Last L 2pm/D 9.30pm
Additional: Bar food L; Sunday L; Children welcome; ◔ dishes

LLANDUDNO,
Number One's Bistro

An informal bistro where Stephen Rawicki's cooking has been pleasing diners for more than ten years. Between them, the monthly-changing set menu and carte provide a good choice. French onion soup with Welsh rarebit croûton, mustard-coated rack of lamb, spicy Thai-style curry. A blackboard lists the best of the day's seafood.

Additional: Children welcome; ◔ dishes
Credit cards: ▬ ▭ ▚ ▭ ▬ **C** JCB

Directions: Old Road is three streets from the Promenade, running between Church Walks and Llewelyn Avenue

1 Old Road LL30 2HA
Map 6: SH78
Tel/Fax: 01492 875424
Chef: Stephen Rawicki
Owners: Stephen & Jacquie Rawicki
Cost: *Alc* £22.50, fixed-price D £15.95. ☺ H/wine £9.50
Times: Last L 1.45pm/last D 9.30pm. Closed Sun, L Mon, occasional 3 day breaks

LLANDUDNO, **St Tudno Hotel** ❀❀❀

Promenade LL30 2LP
Map 6: SH78
Tel: 01492 874411
Fax: 01492 860407
Chef: David Harding
Owners: Martin & Janette Bland
Cost: Fixed-price L £16.95/D £29.50 (5 courses). ☺
Times: 12.30-last L 1.45pm/7-last D 9.30pm
Additional: Bar food L; Sunday L; No children under 5 at D; ◔ dishes
Seats: 60
Smoking: No smoking in dining room; Air conditioning
Accommodation: 20 en suite

A splendid Victorian seaside hotel full of 19th-century charm – Alice Liddell (of Wonderland fame) once stayed here as a girl. At the centre of the hotel is the Garden Room restaurant, decorated in 'Chinese Chippendale' style, with hand-painted trellis, chinoiserie panels, lime-green cane-backed chairs and sunny daffodil cloths. Modern British dishes with Welsh local ingredients are prepared by head chef David Harding, and choices from the short 'gourmet' *carte* could include Trelough duckling with an onion sauce and roasted shallots, grilled fillet of turbot with a spicy crab cake and lobster sauce, and aubergine pattie with asparagus tart, wild mushrooms and a chive butter sauce. The dessert list provides even more choice: look out for banana fritters with white chocolate sauce;

raspberry and Drambuie fool with shortbread biscuit; and strawberry and pistachio nut tart with a cappuccino sabayon. A meal in February produced a good, robust tortellini of prawn and lobster with crayfish sauce, and a delicious hot-pot of Conwy mussels in a simple leek velouté, as starters. The main course of marinated saddle of venison had good flavour and was served with an excellent red wine and juniper sauce. The wine list is carefully planned and makes interesting reading, and includes wines from traditional areas of France, such as Bordeaux and Burgundy, as well as introducing a number of classic wines from Australia, New Zealand and America.

Signature dishes: Saddle of Welsh spring lamb with aubergine pattie, ratatouille sauce and thyme jus; fricassée of scallops and turbot with champagne; fillet steak of Welsh black beef with truffles; tartlet of ox kidneys in a grain mustard sauce

Credit cards: ▆▆ ▆▆ ▆▆ ▆ ▆▆ ▆ ▆ JCB

Directions: Town centre, on Promenade opposite the pier entrance

---

TREFRIW, Chandlers

Corn chandler's, general store, post office – this venerable building set in one of the Conwy Valley's oldest villages underwent several metamorphoses before becoming a brasserie. It is crewed by the Rattenbury family: Adam behind the stove, his wife Penny at the helm out front. Slender wooden tables on a floor of local slate grace the restaurant, bright pictures decorate white walls. Tucked in a corner are two sofas, where aperitifs are served. Adam Rattenbury's cooking concentrates on primary ingredients, allowing flavours to be expressed. Such lightness of touch is exemplified by delicate fritters of fried aubergine, made piquant by a roasted red pepper sauce. Sea trout, sourced locally, is chargrilled with precision and accompanied by a restrained beurre blanc. The restaurant's own ice creams often feature in desserts, making an excellent companion to the likes of Normandy apple tart. The wine list is assembled, from local sources, by Penny Rattenbury.

Directions: On the main B5106, on left if coming from Conwy. Parking at rear

LL27 0JH
Map 6: SH76
Tel: 01492 640991
Chefs/Owners: Adam & Penny Rattenbury
Cost: *Alc* £23, fixed-price L £8.50. ☺
H/wine £9.50
Times: Noon-last L 2pm/7-last D 9.30pm. Closed Sun, Mon, D Tue, Wed & Thur, L Fri & Sat, all L Oct-May (best phone to check)
Additional: Children welcome; ⋈ dishes
Seats: 24
Smoking: No smoking in dining room
Credit cards: ▆▆ ▆▆ ▆▆ ▆ ▆▆

TREFRIW, Princes Arms Hotel ✿

A family-run hotel with excellent views across the River Conway from its recently refurbished Victorian-style restaurant. Tomato and basil soup, melon with tropical fruits, noisette of lamb with shallot and port sauce, and pan-fried sea bass with shellfish sauce typify the daily-changing fixed-price menu. There's also a more extensive brasserie menu.

LL27 0JP
Map 6: SH76
Tel: 01492 640592
Fax: 01492 640559
Chef: Mark Smith
Owners: Ann & Lindsay Gordon
Cost: *Alc* £25, fixed-price L £11.50/D £15.50. ☺ H/wine £8.45.
Times: Last L 2pm/ D 9.30pm
Additional: Bar food; Sunday L; Children welcome; ⋈ dishes
Smoking: No smoking in dining room; Air conditioning
Accommodation: 18 en suite
Credit cards: ▆▆ ▆▆ ▆▆ ▆ ▆▆ ▆ JCB

Directions: At far end of village on L

DENBIGHSHIRE

LLANDEGLA, **Bodidris Hall**

The centuries-old manor house is the business: set in ornamental gardens and mature woodland with original oak timbers and inglenook fireplaces, and a unique duellists staircase complete with uneven steps, fine antiques and period pieces. Our inspector was impressed that such a place 'out in the sticks with no local population', should be busy with non residents who had come from far afield for dinner. Terrine of pressed chicken livers and lamb, served with a pear poached with rosemary and a rich redcurrant and ginger sauce, delivered all the promised flavours. Delicately flavoured red mullet fillets were pan-fried and accompanied by fondant potatoes and a soft asparagus mousse and fresh vegetables. Dessert was a plate of baked cherry halves with a raspberry coulis and honey and walnut ice cream. Several complimentary dishes came between courses: seafood mousse, Granny Smith sorbet, and a rich chocolate parfait as a pre dessert. The wine list of some 75 bins takes a global view.

Wrexham LL11 3AL
Map 7: SJ25
Tel: 01978 790434
Fax: 01978 790335
Please telephone for further details

Directions: Llandegla is on A525 (Wrexham-Ruthin). In village (from Wrexham direction) turn R onto A5104. Hotel is signed 1 mile on L

LLANDRILLO,
Tyddyn Llan Hotel

Corwen LL21 0ST
Map 6: SJ03
Tel: 01490 440264
Fax: 01490 440414
Chef: Jason Hornbuckle
Owners: Peter & Bridget Kindred
Cost: Fixed-price L £15/D £27 (4 courses). H/wine £12.50
Times: 12.30-last L 2pm/7-last D 9pm. Closed L Mon, 2 wks Jan
Additional: Bar food L; Sunday L; Children welcome; ✤ dishes
Seats: 50. Private dining room 40
Smoking: No smoking in dining room
Accommodation: 10 en suite
Credit cards:

An idyllic country retreat with rather quirky decoration thanks to the owner's previous life as a set designer for television programmes, including Fawlty Towers. There is nothing faulty about the cooking however, as Jason Hornbuckle offers an imaginative selection of dishes created from quality local produce. A good choice of home-made breads served with fine butter begin the meal. Lobster ravioli proved to be an excellent choice of starter, the pasta perfectly thin and encasing a tender, full-flavoured morsel of lobster. Alongside there was another piece of lobster and a large, meaty marinated scallop. The plate was attractively dressed with lobster oil and a black olive and tomato concasse. Local Welsh lamb was presented four ways in the unusual main course, but all were perfectly cooked: a generous, carefully trimmed pink cutlet, meltingly tender liver, carefully prepared kidney and a croquette of braised, pressed and rolled lamb's breast. The intense sauce was a reduction of the lamb breast's cooking juices combined with black olives. These were served with crushed new potatoes flavoured with garlic and olive oil and a purée of broccoli. Icky Sticky soufflé is a speciality, a golden, well-risen caramel soufflé accompanied by a generous slab of delicious banana parfait and a drizzle of buttery fudge sauce, the flavours complementing each other perfectly. Strong coffee and home-made petits fours end the meal on a high note, making it easy to see why this elegant, relaxing restaurant attracts a good local following in addition to enthusiastic hotel guests. If staying, enjoy the wonderful breakfast.

Directions: Take B4401 from Corwen to Llandrillo. Restaurant on R leaving village

LLANGOLLEN, **Bryn Howel Hotel**

Splendid views across the Vale of Llangollen are to be had from this late-Victorian house. The cooking is imaginative, and makes good use of local produce in dishes such as avocado mousse layered with celeriac, delice of salmon topped with fillet of plaice and a fennel purée in filo pastry, and bara brith gâteau with caramel mousse and cherry coulis.

Smoking: No smoking in dining room
Accommodation: 36 en suite
Credit cards: ▨ ▨ ▨ ▨ ▨ ▨ JCB

LL20 7UW
Map 7: SJ24
Tel: 01978 860331
Fax: 01978 860119
Chef: Dai Davies
Owners: John E Lloyd, Anne M Lloyd
Cost: *Alc* £25. ☺ H/wine £13.40
Times: Last L 1.45pm/last D 8.45pm
Additional: Bar food L; Sunday L; Children welcome; ❹ dishes

Directions: Two miles east of Llangollen on A539

RUTHIN, **Ye Olde Anchor** ❀❀

Rhos Street LL15 1DX
Map 6: SJ15
Tel: 01824 702813
Fax: 01824 703050
Chef/Owner: Rod England
Cost: *Alc* £20, fixed price L & D £20.
☺ H/wine £8.50
Times: Noon-last L 1.30pm/7-last D 9.30pm
Additional: Bar food L; Sunday L; Children welcome; ❹ dishes
Seats: 40. Private room 40. Jacket and tie preferred
Smoking: No smoking in dining room
Accommodation: 17 en suite
Credit cards: ▨ ▨ ▨ ▨ ▨ ▨ JCB

There's likely to be a happy mixture of locals and visitors in both restaurant and bar of this hotel in the charming market town of Ruthin. Although updated and enlarged, it still retains much of the character of a bygone age. Fish, bought fresh from market, features on the restaurant's specials menu, backed up by a list of things like steaks and chicken. Dinner could start with devilled crab topped with cheese and go on to fillet of hake in a sauce of bacon, parsley and garlic. Alternatives on the daily menu might include sweet pepper soup or a plate of interesting antipasti among the starters, followed by sweet-and-sour pork, chicken breast stuffed with prawns in avocado sauce, or Cajun-style fillet of beef. House wines from France head the list of just over 20 bottles.

Directions: Situated in Ruthin at the junction of A525 & A494

FLINTSHIRE

EWLOE,

St David's Park ❀

St David's Park CH5 3YB
Map 7: SJ36
Tel: 01244 520800
Fax: 01244 520930
Chef: Graham Wilson
Cost: *Alc* £35, fixed-price L £12.95 (2 courses)/D £18.50. ☺ H/wine £10.95
Times: Last L 2pm/last D 10pm
Additional: Bar food; Sunday L; Children welcome; ❁ dishes
Smoking: No smoking in dining room; Air conditioning
Accommodation: 145 en suite
Credit cards: ▬ ▭ ◪ ▩ JCB

Modern hotel with a full range of conference and function facilities. Expect a gâteau of monkfish and sea bass with lobster and balsamic dressing, supreme of guinea fowl with a smoked provençale sausage, deep-fried leeks and shallot jus, and nutmeg and raspberry bavarois, raspberry ice cream and nutmeg anglaise, and some fine Welsh farmhouse cheeses.

Directions: A494 Queensferry to Mold for 4 miles, then B5127 towards Buckley.

NORTHOP,

Soughton Hall Hotel ❀❀

Set in 150 acres of parkland and approached along a long avenue of limes, this former Bishop's Palace, built in 1714, is exquisitely furnished with antiques, French tapestries and Persian carpets; marble fireplaces and drapes over the high windows complete the picture. The converted stables provide informal eating and drinking, while the State Dining Room, as its name suggests, is all polished wood, candelabra, high ceilings and crystal. What comes on the plate is as modern as the setting is grand. A starter of pigeon breast is served with grilled polenta, Parma ham and red onion confit, while home-cured river trout sees the addition of deep-fried mussels and lime and ginger sauce. Well-flavoured chargrilled wild boar is plated with its own sausage, gingered parsnip purée and port jus, and roasted salmon with saffron potato, spring onion purée and watercress sauce. Puddings can range from a classic pear tarte Tatin to a banana and coconut tart with rum and raisin ice cream and Malibu sauce, the latter a good marriage, noted an inspector. A Welsh white is one of six house wines.

CH7 6AB
Map 7: SJ26
Tel: 01352 840811
Fax: 01352 840382
Chef: James Elwood
Owners: John & Rosemary Rodenhurst
Cost: Fixed-price L £24.50/D £34.50
Times: 12.30-2pm/7.30-10pm. Closed Sun
Additional: No children under 12; ❁ dishes
Seats: 45. Private dining room 20
Smoking: No smoking in dining room
Accommodation: 14 en suite
Credit cards: ▬ ▭ ◪ ▩

Directions: Turn off A55 expressway at Northrop, and follow the A5119 towards Mold. After 0.5 mile, the hotel is signposted on L.

GWYNEDD

ABERDYFI,
Penhelig Arms ✤

LL35 0LT
Map 6: SN69
Tel: 01654 767215
Fax: 01654 767690
Chef: Janie Howkins
Owners: Robert & Sally Hughes
Cost: Fixed-price D £19. ☺
H/wine £9.50
Times: Last L 2pm/last D 9pm.
Closed 25-26 Dec
Additional: Bar food; Sunday L;
Children welcome; ❸ dishes
Smoking: No smoking in dining room
Accommodation: 10 en suite
Credit cards: ▬ ▭ ⚑ ⬚ ▐

*A delightful village inn opposite the old harbour with views over the
estuary to the mountains beyond. The owners are committed to
providing quality food at reasonable prices, and this is reflected in
the menu. Check out seared fillet of salmon with spring onion and
basil, or chargrilled leg of lamb with roast peppers.*

Directions: From Machynlleth take A439 coastal route (9 miles)

ABERDYFI,
Plas Penhelig ✤

*Edwardian country house set in 14 acres of gardens and grounds.
Lunch can be taken on the sunny terrace overlooking the Dyfi
Estuary. Typical dishes include avocado and Cardigan Bay crab
salad, roast rack of Welsh lamb with a herb crust and peppercorn
sauce, and hazelnut and raspberry tart.*

Additional: Bar food L; Sunday L; No children under 8;
❸ dishes
Smoking: No smoking in dining room
Accommodation: 11 en suite
Credit cards: ▬ ▭ ⚑ ⬚ ▐ ▨

LL35 0NA
Map 6: SN69
Tel: 01654 767676
Fax: 01654 767783
Chef: Nicole Ledet
Owner: David Richardson
Cost: Fixed-price L £13.50/D £19.50.
☺ H/wine £10.95
Times: Last L 1.45pm/last D 8.45pm.
Closed Dec-Feb

Directions: From Machynlleth take A493 coastal route (9 miles)

ABERSOCH, **Neigwl Hotel** ✤

*Enjoy panoramic views over Cardigan Bay to Snowdonia from the
dining room at this delightful, family-run hotel, located in the centre
of Abersoch. Fresh local produce forms the basis of the four-course
menus. Expect scallops in garlic butter, rack of lamb with juniper
and redcurrant sauce, and raspberry and lemon sauce sponge.*

Accommodation: 9 en suite.
Credit cards: ▬ ▭ ⚑ ⬚ ▐ ▨ JCB

Directions: 400 yards through village centre on the L

Lon Sarn Bach
Pwllheli LL53 7DY
Map 6: SH32
Tel/Fax: 01758 712363
Chef: Nigel Higginbottom
Owners: The Heptonstall Family
Cost: Fixed-price D £20 (4 courses).
☺ H/wine £9
Times: D only, last D 9pm
Additional: Children welcome;
❸ dishes

ABERSOCH, Porth Tocyn Hotel

Bwlch Tocyn Pwllheli
LL53 7BU
Map 6: SH32
Tel: 01758 713303
Fax: 01758 713538
Chefs: David Carney,
Louise Fletcher-Brewer
Owners: The Fletcher-Brewer Family
Cost: Fixed-price D £29 (5 courses).
H/wine £10.95
Seats: 50. Jacket and tie preferred
Smoking: No smoking in dining room
Accommodation: 17 en suite
Credit cards: ▦ ▦ ▯

Directions: 2.5 miles beyond village of Abersoch, through hamlets of Sarn Bach and Bwlch Tocyn. Follow signs marked 'Gwesty/Hotel' and 'Remote Hotel' from Sarn Bach onwards.

It is 50 years since the Fletcher-Brewer family took a row of lead miners' cottages superbly positioned over Cardigan Bay and fashioned it into this country hotel. Nick Fletcher-Brewer is the latest of the clan to carry the torch, dispensing bonhomie among guests and announcing dinner with a rap on a gong. The broadly traditional dinner menu takes in some flourishes. Thus, sea trout comes with a coulis of lime, lemon, chilli and coriander and deep-fried prawns, and poached plaice on chargrilled brioche with smoked prawn sauce. Pan-fried loin of lamb on sweet potato purée with a split-pea jus, or roast fillet of Scottish beef in a red wine sauce with a garlic and shallot confit broadens the range of main courses, while starters pick up ideas from here, there and everywhere: tuna sashimi with pickled ginger and soy sauce, venison sausage on bubble-and-squeak, or gravad lax with potato salad and dill pesto. Return to home base with spotted Dick or banana fritters with butterscotch sauce. A wide-ranging wine list, with a house selection of six bottles, complements the whole experience.

ABERSOCH,
The White House Hotel

Pwllheli
LL53 7AG
Map 6: SH32
Tel: 01758 713427
Fax: 01758 713512
Chef: Dafydd E Jones
Owners: David & Jayne Smith
Cost: *Alc* £21.50, fixed-price
D £19.50. ☺ H/wine £12
Times: D only, last D 8.30pm.
Closed 2 wks Feb
Additional: Sunday L (noon-1.30pm);
Children welcome; ◑ dishes
Smoking: No smoking in dining room
Accommodation: 11 en suite
Credit cards: ▦ ▦ ▧ ▯ ▣

Panoramic views over Cardigan Bay can be enjoyed from this family-run hotel's attractive restaurant. Fresh produce is also a highlight, with dishes such as local crab tartlet glazed with Old Shire cheese, followed by loin of Welsh lamb with a tagliatelle of leeks, featuring on the extensive menu.

Directions: Hotel on A499
Pwllheli/Abersoch Road, on R (from Pwllheli)

BALA, **Palé Hall** ❀❀

Palé Estate Llandderfel LL23 7PS
Map 6: SH93
Tel: 01678 530285
Fax: 01678 530220
Chef: Wendy Phillips
Owner: Saul Nahed
Cost: Fixed-price D £23.95.
H/wine £9.95
Times: Noon-2pm/7-8.30pm
Additional: Bar food L; Sunday L;
❀ dishes
Smoking: No smoking in dining room
Seats: Private dining room 18.
Jacket & tie preferred
Accommodation: 17 en suite
Credit cards: ▬ ▬ ▬ ☐ JCB

Peacocks strut about the well-maintained grounds of this imposing Victorian mansion. Inside, the vaulted ceiling and the galleried oak staircase can't fail to impress in the entrance hall; off this are the library bar, two elegant and comfortable lounges and the recently refurbished dining room. The menu offers decent choices, and it's good to see traditional Glamorgan sausages among the starters, served here on a spicy tomato relish. Others may be warm smoked salmon topped with a poached egg in chervil sauce, or roast pigeon breast on champ. Local lamb and beef – the former in a mint crust in a mint and caper sauce with, appropriately, a leek timbale, the latter with sautéed wild mushrooms and a confit of garlic – are possible main courses, with fillet of turbot on wilted spinach with saffron sauce among fish options. Fruity-type puddings may appear in summer – raspberry jelly, apricot crème brûlée and a fruit terrine in mango sauce, say. Interesting canapés, home-made bread and a varied and reasonably priced wine list all contribute to the experience of dining here.

Directions: Just off B4401, 4 miles from Llandrillo

BANGOR,
Menai Court Hotel ❀❀

There's a fine view across the Menai Straits to Anglesey to be enjoyed from this small, friendly hotel located in a residential part of town. The elegant restaurant attracts local business folk, tourists and residents alike. On offer are menus priced by the course, as well as a *carte* providing a choice between such standards as avocado and prawns with Marie Rose sauce, beef Stroganoff, and steaks alongside more adventurous dishes such as shark Venetian style (an Italian fish casserole), and Jamaican chicken (marinated escalopes chargrilled and served with herbed potatoes and soured cream). Desserts might include chocolate marquise, meringue Alaska and bara brith bread-and-butter pudding. The wine list includes a good selection of half-bottles.

Craig y Don Road
LL57 2BG
Map 6: SH57
Tel/Fax: 01248 354200
Chef: John Connor
Owners: Elwyn & Judy Hughes
Cost: *Alc* £23, fixed-price L £11.95/D
£21.95. ☺ H/wine £9.20
Times: 12.30-last L 1.45pm/7-last
D 9pm. Closed L Sat, allSun,
Additional: No children under 6;
❀ dishes
Seats: 45
Smoking: No smoking in dining room
Accommodation: 13 en suite
Credit cards: ▬ ▬ JCB

Directions: Turn L out of railway station, R at top of hill by Bank into College Road, 1st L into Craig y Don Road

BARMOUTH,

Ty'r Graig Castle Hotel

Unusual Gothic-style hotel with impressive stained-glass windows and wood-panelled walls. Some sea views from the restaurant. A small, fixed menu offers Mexican paella, oven-roasted lamb cutlets with fresh vegetables, and warm orange and almond cake with raspberry coulis. Good, balanced wine list.

Llanaber Road LL42 1YN
Map 6: SH61
Tel: 01341 280470
Fax: 01341 281260
Please telephone for further details

Directions: On coast road 0.75 miles towards Harlech

BARMOUTH, Wavecrest Hotel

Victorian house on the seafront, now a charming hotel run personally by the Jarmans for nearly twenty years. Inspectors continue to praise Shelagh Jarman's set-dinner menus. They are built around fresh produce and the style is sound country cooking. The wine list takes a global view and offers decent, modestly priced wines, as well as over fifty malt whiskies.

8 Marine Parade LL42 1NA
Map 6: SH61
Tel/Fax: 01341 280330
Chef: Shelagh Jarman
Owners: Eric & Shelagh Jarman
Cost: *Alc* £16, fixed-price D £15. ☺
Times: D only, last D 9pm.
Closed Nov-Mar

Additional: Children welcome; 🍴 dishes
Smoking: No smoking in dining room
Accommodation: 10 en suite.
Credit cards: 🟦 🟫

Directions: On seafront, at the centre of the promenade

BONTDDU,

Bontddu Hall Hotel

Dolgellau LL40 2UF
Map 6: SH61
Tel: 01341 430661
Fax: 01341 430284
Chef: Didier Bienaime
Owners: Michael & Margaretta Ball
Cost: *Alc* D (Brasserie) £16, fixed-price L (Brasserie) £12/D £23.50. ☺
H/wine £11.25
Times: Noon-last L 2pm/7-last D 9.30pm. Closed Nov-March
Additional: Bar food; Sunday L; No children under 3; 🍴 dishes
Seats: 60. Private room 30.
Jacket and tie preferred
Smoking: No smoking in dining room
Accommodation: 20 en suite
Credit cards: 🟦 🟫 🟥 💷 🟩 🟦 🟦 JCB

The elegant restaurant gives superb views of the Mawddach Estuary and mountains at this impressive 19th-century Gothic pile. The 14 acres of grounds, landscaped when the house was built, are a paradise for plant-lovers and twitchers, as well as those who want to soak in the vista over the estuary. The lunchtime Brasserie Menu is from the school of pork dijonnaise, tagliatelle carbonara and herby breadcrumbed cod fillet, while the Anglo-Cymric-French leanings of the kitchen come into their own at dinner. Good home-made breads – tomato, perhaps, or cheese – could be presented with a first course of Welsh cawl, or there might be moules marinière. Local salmon stuffed with creamed leeks and baked en croûte is a main course that neatly straddles two cultures; other choices could include tender Welsh mountain lamb with garlic and rosemary jus, and herb mash, and Anglesey cod with tomato provençale sauce. Desserts can run from bread-and-butter pudding to classic lemon tart with Chantilly cream and orange syrup. Staff are friendly and skilled, and the serviceable wine list is biased towards France.

Directions: From A470 1 mile N Dolgellau take A496 to Barmouth, then 4 miles to Bontddu. Hotel on R as you enter village

CAERNARFON, **Seiont Manor Hotel**

Cleverly created from the farmstead of a Georgian manor, and set in 150 magnificent acres, the hotel boasts a three-room restaurant including a conservatory. Imaginative ideas and sound cooking translate into the likes of black pudding en croûte with caramelised apple, and collops of monkfish with saffron-scented dill mash.

Additional: Bar food; Sunday L; Children welcome; ❹ dishes
Smoking: No-smoking area; No pipes & cigars
Accommodation: 28 en suite
Credit cards: 💳 💳 💳 💳 💳 💳 💳 JCB

Llanrug LL55 2AQ
Map 6: SH46
Tel: 01286 673366
Fax: 01286 672840
Chef: Martyn Williams
Owner: Virgin Hotels Ltd
Cost: *Alc* £26, fixed-price L £10.50 (2 courses)/D £23.50. ☺ H/wine £10.50
Times: Last L 2pm/D 10pm. Closed L Sat

Directions: From Bangor follow signs for Caernarfon. Leave Caernarfon on A4086. The hotel is 3 miles on L

CAERNARFON, **Ty'n Rhos** ❀❀

Seion Caernarfon LL55 3AE
Map 6: SH56
Tel: 01248 670489
Fax: 01248 670079
Chef: Cary Davies
Owners: Nigel & Lynda Kettle
Cost: *Alc* £25, fixed-price D £19.50 (4 courses). ☺ H/wine £9.50
Times: D only, 7pm-9pm. Closed D Sun, L Mon-Tue, 1 wk Aug, 1 wk Xmas, 1 wk Jan
Additional: Conservatory L (Noon-2.30pm); Sunday L; No children under 6; ❹ dishes
Seats: 35. Private dining room 20
Smoking: No smoking in dining room; Air conditioning in 1 dining room
Accommodation: 14 en suite
Credit cards: 💳 💳 💳 💳 💳 JCB

Although there are traditional elements to the cooking at this farmhouse-style hotel, set in glorious, open countryside, local Welsh produce is given a makeover in many of the tempting dishes. Anglesey scallops are served in a spaghetti of vegetables with sweet red chilli and spring onion salsa, and home-made game sausage comes with black pudding and potatoes 'draped' with a Guinness sauce. Escalope of pork with apricot and hazelnut seasoning on a cushion of creamed risotto with coarse grain mustard sauce proved a typically good combination. Many vegetables and salad leaves are home-grown, and bread is also home-baked. Tartlet of rhubarb crumble with caramel ice cream and nutmeg sauce made a memorable dish out of basic ingredients. All the staff are efficient and friendly – they try hard to please, and succeed well.

Directions: In hamlet of Seion between B4366 & B4547

DOLGELLAU,
Dolserau Hall ❀

A Victorian conservatory, with wonderful valley views, is the setting for the Winter Garden restaurant at this country house hotel. Dishes like swordfish steak and tiramisu sometimes find a place on an otherwise traditionally British menu of Orkney herring salad, roast chicken with all the trimmings and spotted Dick.

Additional: No children under 6; ❹ dishes
Smoking: No smoking in dining rom
Accommodation: 15 en suite
Credit cards: ▰ ▰ ▰ ▱

Directions: Situated 1.5 miles from Dolgellau on lane between A470 to Dinas Mawddwy and A494 to Bala

LL40 2AG
Map 6: SH71
Tel: 01341 422522
Fax: 01341 422400
Chef: Huw Roberts
Owners: Marion & Peter Kaye
Cost: Fixed-price D £19.95 (4 courses). ☺ H/wine £7.95
Times: D only, last D 8.30pm. Closed Nov-Feb except Xmas

DOLGELLAU,
Penmaenuchaf Hall ❀❀

The house, which has an enviable, elevated position overlooking the Mawddach estuary, has been lovingly furnished, and there's a genuinely warm Welsh welcome on the elegant mat. A rather menacing historical portrait hangs above the fireplace in the formal, panelled dining room, but the smiling a smiling waitress dispels all Sunday-best gloom. The kitchen takes pride in using good local produce – marinated fillets of Mawddach Estuary grey mullet, for example, may be shallow-fried with a sweet chilli dressing, and Pembrokeshire quail marinated in honey and soy, and served with snow peas, grapes and Cassis sauce. Pot-roast pork fillet with grain mustard sauce was full of rustic flavour, and an amicable truce was declared between the orange and tarragon that defined a sauce served with superbly fresh, beautifully cooked salmon. A sticky toffee pudding was a lighter variant on the usual offerings. An interesting and varied choice of Welsh cheeses are kept in optimum condition.

Directions: From A470, take A493 (Tywyn/Fairbourne), entrance 1.5 miles on L by sign for Penmaenpool

Penmaenpool LL40 1YB
Map 6: SH71
Tel: 01341 422129
Fax: 01341 422787
Chefs: Hugh Cocker, David Banks
Owners: Mark Watson, Lorraine Fielding
Cost: Alc £30, fixed-price L £14.95/D £25 (4 courses). H/wine £10.95
Times: Noon-last L 2pm/7-last D 9.30pm. Closed 2nd wk Jan
Additional: Bar food L; Sunday L; No children under 6; ❹ dishes
Seats: 36. Private dining room 16. Jacket & tie preferred
Smoking: No smoking in dining room
Accommodation: 14 en suite
Credit cards:  JCB

DOLGELLAU,

Plas Dolmelynllyn Hall

Peacefully situated in three acres of terraced gardens, this fine house dates from the 16th century and enjoys superb valley and mountain views. Imaginatively cooked dishes, making good use of fresh local produce, may include cauliflower and tarragon soup, seared tuna on garlic noodles with ratatouille dressing, and raspberry crumble cake.

Additional: Bar food L; No children under 8; ☺ dishes
Smoking: No smoking in dining room
Accommodation: 10 en suite
Credit cards: ▬ ▀ ▒

Directions: Village centre on the A470, 4 miles N of Dolgellau

Ganllwyd LL40 2HP
Map 6: SH71
Tel: 01341 440273
Fax: 01341 440640
Chef: Joanna Reddicliffe
Owners: Jonathan Barkwith & Joanna Reddicliffe
Cost: Fixed-price D £24.50 (4 courses). ☺ H/wine £9.75
Times: Last L 2pm/last D 9pm.
Closed Dec, Jan, Feb

HARLECH, Castle Cottage

Really a cottage with castle connections: quaint exposed beams, lowish ceilings, an unusual pig theme with paintings, jars and everything you can imagine that's capable of having a pig on it. There's a superb atmosphere here, Glyn Roberts lives for his kitchen and offers a weekly-changing menu built around seasonal availability. Feuilleté of duck livers with a port and grape sauce had excellent texture and flavour, rack of local Welsh lamb was juicy with plenty of flesh, had a light herby crust and came with a 'tasty' rösti of baby leeks and a red wine and rosemary jus. Date and walnut sponge with a butterscotch sauce was light and satisfyingly rich. For those who lack a sweet tooth, there is always a savoury on offer, perhaps grilled mussels and bacon on toast. The 70 plus wines on the wine list come from all over the world and are reasonably priced.

Directions: Just off High Street (B4573) 100yds from Harlech Castle

Pen Llech LL46 2YL
Map 6: SH53
Tel/Fax: 01766 780479
Chef: Glyn Roberts
Owners: Mr & Mrs G H Roberts
Cost: Fixed-price D £21.50. ☺ H/wine £10
Times: D only, 7-last D 9pm.
Closed 3 wks Feb
Additional: Sunday L (12.30-2pm); Children welcome; ☺ dishes
Seats: 45
Smoking: No smoking in dining room
Accommodation: 6 (4 en suite)
Credit cards: ▬ ▀ ▚ ▒ ▬ ▐

LLANBERIS, Y Bistro

There are several cosy bar areas with comfortable seating, and the restaurant is also in two parts, candlelit and atmospheric with Welsh folk music in the background. The menu, in Welsh with English translations, might offer wild mushroom risotto, and sirloin steak of Welsh black beef.

Additional: Children welcome; ☺ dishes
Smoking: No-smoking area
Credit cards: ▬ ▀ ▚ ▒ ▬ ▐ JCB

Directions: In the centre of the village at the foot of Mount Snowdon by Lake Padarn

43-45 Stryd Fawr (High Street) LL55 4EU
Map 6: SH56
Tel/Fax: 01286 871278
Chef: Nerys Roberts
Owners: Danny & Nerys Roberts
Cost: Fixed-price D £28.50. ☺ H/wine £9
Times: D only, last D 9.45pm.
Closed Bh Sun

PORTMEIRION,

The Hotel Portmeirion

Sir Clough William Ellis's stunning Italianate village was the setting for the cult TV series *The Prisoner*. Summer day-trippers may shatter the illusion of mystery that hangs over the place, but the hotel nestling under the wooded sloped below the

Penrhyndeudraeth LL48 6ET
Map 6: SH53
Tel: 01766 770000
Fax: 01766 771331
Chef: Colin Pritchard
Owner: Portmeirion Ltd

The Hotel Portmeirion

Cost: Fixed-price L £13.50/D £30.
H/wine £10.50
Times: 12.30pm-last L 2pm/D 7pm-last 9.30pm. Closed L Mon
Additional: Bar food D; Sunday L; Children welcome; ᪲ dishes
Seats: 100. Private dining room 12 & 30
Smoking: No smoking in dining room
Accommodation: 39 en suite

village and looking out over the sandy estuary towards Snowdonia, is a haven of tranquillity. The curvilinear dining room facing on to the estuary, can give the impression of being afloat; this must be one of the finest settings in Wales. Colin Pritchard cooks well, describing his style as 'modern Welsh cuisine' – menus are in Welsh (with English subtitles), and local produce, especially fish, is a feature.

Credit cards: ▬ ▦ ➹ ⬚ ▦ ⬛ ▣ JCB

Directions: Off A487 at Minffordd

PWLLHELI, **Plas Bodegroes** ❀❀❀

Nefyn Road LL53 5TH
Map 6: SH33
Tel: 01758 612363
Fax: 01758 701247
Chef: Shaun Mitchell
Owners: Christopher & Gunna Chown
Cost: Alc £32, fixed-price D £29.50. H/wine £12
Times: D only, 7-9.30pm .
Closed Mon, Dec-Feb
Additional: Sunday L (Noon-2pm); Children welcome; ᪲ dishes
Seats: 35. Private dining room 16
Smoking: No smoking in dining room
Accommodation: 11 en suite
Credit cards: ▬ ▦ ➹ ⬚ JCB

Directions: On A497, 2 miles NW of Pwllheli

Georgian manor meets Scandinavian chic in the dining room of this utterly charming restaurant-with-rooms. Wooden floor, contemporary art and clever lighting make for an urbane, intimate atmosphere, light years removed from the seaside jollities of nearby Pwllheli. Shaun Mitchell has a good store cupboard of ingredients on which to call – the area is renowned for seafood, whilst Welsh lamb and beef are on the doorstep. The hotel garden supplements local supplies of herbs and vegetables. Inspirations go beyond the boundaries of the Principality, however; for example, there might be sushi salmon, marinated salmon and brill cured in beetroot as an *amuse-bouche*. Filo parcel of crab and lobster with coconut leeks and chilli salsa made an interesting starter. An excellent, sweet-tasting piece of lamb, came with the rack coated with a parsley crust and served with garlicky butter beans. A terrific main course of chargrilled calves' liver with slow-cooked osso buco, celeriac purée and sage and onion gravy was a truly stellar dish. Poaching makes a welcome appearance with fish dishes, as in poached halibut fillet with chive mashed potatoes and rarebit sauce, and flavourings such as baked fillet of local sea bass with fennel and tarragon sauce, are kept classically simple. Greater clarity of flavour would have improved a sherry and Rioja jelly with caramelised oranges and mascarpone, otherwise a great idea. A nice local twist on a standard is bara brith-and-butter pudding with apricot and whisky sauce and apricot ice cream.

Signature dishes: Roast rack of salt marsh lamb with garlic butter beans, parsley crust and rich port sauce; filo parcel of crab and lobster with coconut leeks and chilli salsa; poached fillet of halibut with chive mashed potatoes and rarebit sauce; fillet of Welsh black beef seasoned with mustard, duck liver and horseradish parfait, red wine sauce.

TAL-Y-BONT, **Lodge Hotel**

The Lodge Hotel is set in a peaceful part of the Conwy valley. Visitors study the daily-changing menu while a log fire burns in the bar. Much produce comes from the hotel's own gardens. Try roast sirloin of beef with Yorkshire pudding, beef stroganoff, or Welsh lamb with a honey and orange glaze.

Smoking: No smoking in dining room
Accommodation: 10 en suite
Credit cards: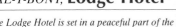

Directions: From Conwy Castle take B5106 to village of Tal-y-Bont. The Lodge is on R, 100yds into village

Conwy LL32 8YX
Map 6: SH67
Tel: 01492 660766
Fax: 01492 660534
Chef: Simon Baldon
Owners: Simon & Barbara Baldon
Cost: Alc £17.95, fixed-price L £6.25/D £14.95. ☺ H/wine £9.50
Times: Last L 1.45pm/last D 9pm. Closed L Mon
Additional: Sunday L; Children welcome; ❸ dishes

TAL-Y-LLYN, **Minffordd Hotel** ❀

Delightful 17th-century drovers' inn situated in spectacular countryside beneath Cader Idris. Exposed timbers and stone walls abound in the elegantly furnished lounge and restaurant. Chef/proprietor Mark Warner uses quality local produce in creating dishes such as cheese and chive soufflé, venison with damson wine sauce, and banana bara brith toffee pudding.

Accommodation: 6 en suite.
Credit cards:

Directions: Take A470 from Dolgellauf, and turn R onto A487 – hotel is at the junction of that road with the B4405

Tywyn LL36 9AJ
Map 6: SH71
Tel: 01654 761665
Fax: 01654 761517
Chef: Mark Warner
Owners: Mary McQuillan, Mark Warner
Cost: Fixed-price D £19.50 (4 courses). ☺ H/wine £8.65
Times: D only, 7.30-9.30pm.
Closed Ded-Mar
Additional: No children under 5
Smoking: No smoking in dining room

TALSARNAU,
Hotel Maes y Neuadd ❀❀❀

The hall in the field nestles on a wooded hillside in its own well-tended grounds (source of the kitchen's herbs, vegetables and fruit) with views across Snowdonia and the Lleyn Peninsula. The beamed bar was part of the original 14th-century house, and later additions, the dining-room, for instance, were added in Georgian times. Canapés of cockles with lemon mayonnaise and salami with olives and chutney precede Peter Jackson's lively, well-balanced dinner menus. Start with crab and a julienne of vegetables parcelled up in filo, or duck liver on a salad with a light garlic dressing. Soup normally follows – curried pumpkin, or smooth asparagus – and then a fish course of maybe fresh and moist red snapper, zingy with a dressing of olive oil and poppy seeds. New season's lamb is a favoured main course, the leg roasted rare and tender and appearing with plump grains of barley and a reduction of its cooking juices. 'Diweddglo mawreddog' (the grand finale) announces the dessert stage. Farmhouse cheeses – Pencarreg, smoked Caerphilly, Stilton, with impressive herb bread and oatcakes – are followed by up to three puddings: clafoutis-like prune and Armagnac tart with berried custard, pineapple with rum syrup and almonds, and then ice creams and sorbets. The wine line-up is a great line-up from France, and quality shows up in the rest of the world. The house selection includes a bottle from the Vale of Glamorgan.

Signature dishes: Pan-fried sea bass with herbs and olive oil; roast partridge, brown lentils and chanterelles; bara brith, cinnamon custard.

Harlech LL47 6YA
Map 6: SH63
Tel: 01766 780200
Fax: 01766 780211
Chef: Peter Jackson
Owners: June & Michael Slatter, Olive & Malcolm Horsfall
Cost: Fixed-price L £13.25/D £32 (5 courses). H/wine £9.75
Times: 12.15-last L 1.45pm/7-last D 9pm
Additional: Bar food L; Sunday L; No children under 7 at D; ❸ dishes
Seats: 40. Private dining room 12
Smoking: No smoking in dining room
Accommodation: 16 en suite
Credit cards: JCB

Directions: Off B4573 between Talsarnau & Harlech (sign on corner of unclassified road)

MONMOUTHSHIRE

ABERGAVENNY,

Llansantffraed Court Hotel

Llanvihangel Gobion
NP7 9BA
Map 3: SO21
Tel: 01873 840678
Fax: 01873 840674
Chef: Didier Bienaimé
Owners: Mike & Heather Morgan
Cost: *Alc* £30, fixed-price L £14.50/D
£19.50. ☺ H/wine £9.95
Times: Noon-last L 2pm/7.30-last
D 9.30pm
Additional: Bar food L; Sunday L;
Children welcome; ❹ dishes
Seats: 50. Private dining room 28
Smoking: No smoking in dining room
Accommodation: 21 en suite
Credit cards: 💳 💳 💳 💳 💳 💳 💳 JCB

The restaurant in this imposing red brick country house hotel is definitely one to watch. The menu is French-influenced but not too heavy, as shown in the delightful *amuse-gueule* of local salmon marinated in shallot and lime juice – a shrewd, sharp appetite whetter. A coarse pressed terrine of excellent duck confit with rich foie gras came parcelled in crisp ribbons of leek and accompanied by home-made shallot chutney and warm brioche, making a most satisfying starter. The main course was beautifully judged: braised saddle of rabbit with an intense game flavour stuffed with prunes and spinach, served with baby onions and carrots. Caramelised rice pudding flavoured with white chocolate and poached summer fruits was supremely light and topped with a crisp leaf of sugar. To finish, good petits fours and coffee. Despite the food's French influence, the enterprising wine list ventures further afield.

Directions: From Abergavenny take B4598 signposted Usk towards Raglan. Stay on this road for 3.5 miles. White gates on L are hotel entrance.

ABERGAVENNY,

Llanwenarth Arms

Brecon Road NP8 1EP
Map 3: SO21
Tel: 01873 810550
Fax: 01873 811880
Chef: D'Arcy McGregor
Cost: *Alc* £19. ☺ H/wine £7.95
Times: Last L 1.45pm/last D 9.45pm

Spectacular views of the Usk valley can be enjoyed while dining in the bright conservatory restaurant. Expect simple English dishes such as pan-fried breast of chicken carbonara with fresh Parmesan, or seared fresh salmon with tarragon butter sauce. For dessert try a home-made waffle with hot maple syrup.

Additional: Bar food; Sunday L; Children welcome; ❹ dishes
Smoking: Air conditioning
Accommodation: 18 en suite
Credit cards: 💳 💳 💳 💳 💳 💳 💳

Directions: On A40 midway between Abergavenny and Crickhowell

CHEPSTOW, **Beaufort Hotel**

Now a popular hotel, this 16th-century coaching inn has a traditional-style dining room, light and airy with three Georgian windows. Imaginative and carefully prepared dishes include smoked salmon salad, and chargrilled pork cutlet topped with Welsh goats' cheese and served on a roast garlic and tomato sauce.

Smoking: No-smoking area; No pipes & cigars
Accommodation: 19 en suite
Credit cards: ▆ ▆ ▆ ▆ ▆ ▆ ▆

Directions: Turn L from A48 immediately before St Mary's Church then L again; car park is at top of Nelson Street

Beaufort Square NP6 5EP
Map 3: ST59
Tel: 01291 622497
Fax: 01291 627389
Chef: Justin Sterry
Owner: Michael Collins
Cost: Alc £22, fixed-price L & D £12.95. ☺ H/wine £7.25
Times: Last L 2pm/last D 9.30pm
Additional: Bar food; Sunday L; Children welcome; ❃ dishes

LLANDEWI SKIRRID,
Walnut Tree Inn ❀❀❀

When Franco and Ann Taruschio opened their country inn in the mid-1960's the Italian influence on Welsh cuisine extended little further than the high street cafés still to be found in many South Wales towns. Since then the culinary ripples from the Walnut Tree have been felt far beyond the Principality, and 30 odd years later the lanes to Llandewi Skirrid remain a favoured route of culinary pilgrims from far and wide. In essence, the building is a simple country pub, and all the better for it. The complete absence of pretension is a breath of fresh air, and whilst in strictly physical terms, lunch in the bar may not offer much in the way of comfort, the relaxed atmosphere is ample compensation. Happily, the honesty finds its way to the plate and this is cooking that comes from the heart as much as the head. Fine produce (much of it local) is affectionately prepared and always given the room to speak for itself. Hence many dishes are strikingly simple: carpaccio of salmon with balsamic dressing and capers; a pungent pairing of goats' cheese crostini and wafers of truffle, or marinated fillets of mackerel with new potatoes. Fish often benefits most from the spare approach whether its sea bass with pancetta or a fat fillet of roasted cod with caponata and pine nuts. Plenty of sturdy puds to be had too, with tiramisu and Sicilian cheesecake finding favour at recent inspection meals. The wine list naturally favours the Italians with abundant variety to complement the hand-written, daily changing menu.

Abergavenny NP7 8AW
Map 3: SO31
Tel: 01873 852797
Chef: Franco Taruschio
Owners: Ann & Franco Taruschio
Times: L from noon/7pm-last D 10.15pm. Closed Sun, Mon, 1 wk Xmas, 2 wks Feb
Additional: Children welcome; ❃ dishes
Seats: 46 (60 Bistro)
Credit cards: None

Directions: Three miles N/E of Abergavenny on the B4521

LLANGYBI, **Cwrt Bleddyn Hotel**

As we went to press Nicholls restaurant was about to be transformed into "Jesters" a brasserie style operation with, as the name suggest, a brighter less formal ambience. An early menu suggests a punchy, no-nonsense approach with offerings such as a warm salad of hickory-smoked chicken dressed with capsicums and veal schnitzel with Parmesan mash.

Smoking: No smoking in dining room
Accommodation: 33 en suite
Credit cards: ▆ ▆ ▆ ▆ ▆ ▆

Directions: Near Llangybi village on A449 between Caerleon and Usk

Usk NP5 1PG
Map 3: ST39
Tel: 01633 450521
Fax: 01633 450220
Chef: Nigel Godwin
Cost: Alc £30, fixed-price L £16.95/D £24.50. ☺ H/wine £11.50
Times: 12.30-last L 2pm/7-last D 10pm
Additional: Bar food; Sunday L; Children welcome; ❃ dishes
Seats: 68. Private dining room up to 200

TINTERN, **Parva Farmhouse Hotel** ✿

Fishing items in the restaurant, with its inglenook fireplace, are appropriate for the Wye Valley setting of this former farmhouse. Expect a good range of interesting dishes: sturdily flavoured mushrooms gratinated with bacon and Malmsey, Welsh venison baked with gin and junipers, or poached monkfish, rounded off with perhaps fruit Pavlova.

Accommodation: 9 en suite. **Credit cards:** ▬ ▬ ▭ ▬ JCB

Directions: North end of Tintern on A466 alongside the Wye, 0.75 mile from the Abbey

Chepstow NP6 6SQ
Map 3: SO50
Tel: 01291 689411
Fax: 01291 689557
Chef: Dereck Stubbs
Owners: Dereck & Vickie Stubbs
Cost: Fixed-price D £18.50 (4 courses). ☺
Times: D only, last D 8.30pm
Additional: Children welcome; 🦐 dishes
Smoking: No smoking in dining room

TINTERN, **Royal George Hotel** ✿

A former 17th-century coaching inn close to Tintern Abbey where the menu offers pleasing contemporary touches. Go wild with boar and ostrich, or choose classics like delicate asparagus and dill soup, steak au poivre and dauphinoise potatoes. The citrus bavarois has a refreshing flavour. Follow with the fine coffee and petits fours.

Chepstow NP6 6SF
Map 3: SO50
Tel: 01291 689205
Fax: 01291 689448
Chef: Cliff Randall
Owners: Tony & Maureen Pearce
Cost: Fixed-price L £12.25/D £21 (both 4 courses). ☺ H/wine £8.25
Times: Last L 2pm/last D 9.30pm
Additional: Bar food; Sunday L; Children welcome; 🦐 dishes
Smoking: No smoking in dining room; Air conditioning
Accommodation: 16 en suite
Credit cards: ▬ ▬ ▬ ▭ ▬ ◼ ▬ JCB

Directions: On A466 between Chepstow & Monmouth, 10 minutes' drive from M4 exit 22

USK, **Three Salmons Hotel** ✿

Town centre coaching inn offering a warm, friendly atmosphere and modish cooking in the more formal restaurant. Toasted brioche with chicken livers and a rich thyme jus, seared fillet of salmon, tangy horseradish mash and sharp watercress vinaigrette, and a chocolate and pistachio soufflé, formed a good winter dinner.

Smoking: No-smoking area; No pipes & cigars
Accommodation: 24 en suite. **Credit cards:** ▬ ▬ ▬ ▭ ▬ ▭

Directions: M4/J24, A449 N, first L A472 to Usk. Hotel in centre of village

Bridge Street NP5 1BQ
Map 3: SO30
Tel: 01291 672133
Fax: 01291 673979
Chef: Nick Williams
Owners: Town & Country Hotels Ltd
Cost: Alc £25, fixed-price L £15/D £20. H/wine £9.50.
Times: Last L 2.30pm/last D 9.30pm. Closed D Sun
Additional: Bar food; Sunday L; Children welcome; 🦐 dishes

WHITEBROOK,

Crown at Whitebrook ✿✿✿

The densely wooded Whitebrook Valley makes a gloriously secluded setting for this splendid hotel. Sandra Bates cooks in a totally unpretentious manner, flavours are clear and everything is on the plate for a reason. Take a February dinner that began with canapés – brochette of tender steak and

Monmouth
NP5 4TX
Map 3: SO50
Tel: 01600 860254
Fax: 01600 860607
Chef: Sandra Bates
Owners: Roger & Sandra Bates

peppers, quite spicy, and a cooling diced cucumber and smoked salmon on a crisp croûton with dill – and went on to spot-on cod fishcakes with orange and basil dressing. Braised ox tongue was the main course, pressed and cooked on the premises, it was firm and delicate, almost melting in the mouth, and served with a quite intense, almost fruity sauce of reduced braising liquor with some diced vegetables and capers included. Celeriac purée topped with roasted shallots was a great accompaniment. For pudding, baked apple charlotte – chunks of just cooked apple in a crisp pastry, with nicely spiced clove ice cream and delicious thin dried apple slices. Good glazed poppy seed and wholemeal rolls, and home-made chocolates come with coffee. Roger Bates compiles the wine list and he knows his stock well; he is happy to make sensible suggestions and offers unusual combinations where he thinks customers might appreciate it.

Cost: *Alc*: £16.50, fixed-price L £15.95/D £27.95. H/wine 9.95
Times: Noon-last L 1.30pm/7-last D 9pm. Closed L Mon, D Sun, 2 wks Jan, 2 wks Aug
Additional: Bar food L; Sunday L; ❹ dishes
Seats: 28. Private dining room 12
Smoking: No smoking in dining room
Accommodation: 10 en suite
Credit cards: ▆ ▆ ▆ ▆ ▆ ▆ ▆ JCB

Directions: Turn W off A66 immediately S of Bigsweir Bridge (5 miles from Monmouth), 2 miles up this unclassified road

NEATH PORT TALBOT

PORT TALBOT,
Aberavon Beach Hotel

In an area not over-endowed with good places to eat, this large seafront hotel has created something of an oasis. A lengthy menu is nevertheless based on fresh raw materials assembled with imagination and presented with flourish. Welsh produce is used whenever possible with dishes such as Brecon venison with a game jus showing off the local bounty to good effect. Plenty of fish too.

Accommodation: 52 en suite
Credit cards: ▆ ▆ ▆ ▆ ▆ ▆

Directions: On seafront

SA12 6QP
Map 3: SS78
Tel: 01639 884949
Fax: 01639 897885
Chef: Wayne Williams
Owner: Conference Hotels Ltd
Cost: *Alc* £20, fixed-price L £12/D £15. ☺ H/wine £8
Times: Last L 2pm/last D 10pm
Additional: Bar food L; Sunday L; Children welcome; ❹ dishes
Smoking: No smoking in dining room

NEWPORT

NEWPORT, Celtic Manor Hotel

The scale of expansion has been simply staggering this last year – the beautifully restored 19th-century manor house is now the centrepiece of a huge hotel and leisure complex, including three championship standard golf courses. Hedleys Restaurant is the focus for big spenders, with a *carte* that doesn't stint on luxury ingredients: assiette of marinated salmon with caviar and quails' egg; roast pigeon with mushy peas, rösti potato, pan-fried foie gras and jus; steamed supreme of prime turbot on a bed of baby spinach with trompettes de la mort and chive cream sauce. Money bags of confit of duck are served alongside breast of Herefordshire duck glazed with honey and soya, bok choi and lemongrass scented jus. High-roller desserts include pear bavarois filled with cherry sauce served on a nougat disc with pear sorbet and fanned pears.

Directions: On A48 just off M4/J24 towards Newport

Coldra Woods NP6 2YA
Map 3: ST38
Tel: 01633 413000
Fax: 01633 412910
Chef: Trefor Jones
Owners: Celtic Manor Hotel, Mr Terry Matthews
Cost: *Alc* £30, fixed-price L £14 (2 courses)/D £23 (4 courses). ☺ H/wine £12.50.
Times: Noon-last L 2pm/7pm-last D 10.30pm. Closed L Sat, Sun, Mon, Bhs
Additional: Children welcome; ❹ dishes
Seats: 58. Private dining room 20
Smoking: No-smoking area; No pipes & cigars
Accommodation: 73 en suite
Credit cards: ▆ ▆ ▆ ▆ ▆ ▆ JCB

NEWPORT, Junction 28 ❀

Former railway station, now a bright, informal restaurant serving straight-forward dishes, with an emphasis on fish. Our inspector enjoyed a May meal of bacon and mange-tout with balsamic vinaigrette, followed by best end of lamb with garlic cream. Also look out for fillet of John Dory with fried celeriac.

Additional: Sunday L (noon-4pm); Children welcome; ✪ dishes
Smoking: No-smoking area; No pipes & cigars; Air conditioning
Credit cards: ▬ ▩ ▚ ▢ 🅒 JCB

Directions: M4 (junction 28), follow signs Risca, then L in 0.5m signed Caerphilly. Turn R at mini-roundabout, then 1st left beyond St Basil's church.

Station Approach Bassaleg
NP1 9LD
Map 3: ST38
Tel: 01633 891891
Chef: Jon West
Owners: Jon West, Richard Wallace
Cost: Alc £20, fixed-price D £11.95.
☺ H/wine £8.95
Times: Last L 2pm/last D 9.30pm.
Closed D Sun

PEMBROKESHIRE

FISHGUARD, Tregynon Country Farmhouse Hotel ❀❀

A remote, peaceful haven, this converted 16th-century farmhouse lies in the picturesque Gwaun Valley and its restaurant continues to offer highly enjoyable food. The owners have a predilection for the natural and honest, exemplified by their discerning use of vegetables and the hotel's smoke-house, which provides the traditionally oak-smoked bacon and gammon used in the restaurant. Apart from the Welsh cheeseboard, the menu changes daily. Starters may include a soup such as carrot and lentil, a hot pasta dish and a ploughman's plate. A selection of interesting vegetable dishes accompany the mains, of which there is always a vegetarian choice such as mushroom Stroganoff. Meat lovers will enjoy lamb cutlets with plum and rosemary sauce or local beef with bacon, walnuts and lime baked in red wine sauce. Desserts are home-made and include nectarines filled with fruit mince, tempting ice creams and sticky toffee pudding.

Directions: At intersection of B4313/B4329 take the former towards Fishguard. Take 1st R and 1st R again and follow signs

Gwaun Valley SA65 9TU
Map 2: SM93
Tel: 01239 820531
Fax: 01239 820808
Chefs: Peter & Jane Heard, Sian Davies
Owners: Peter & Jane Heard
Cost: Alc £25.45, fixed-price D £19.95. ☺ H/wine £10.95
Times: D only, 7.30-last D 8.30pm
Additional: No children under 8; ✪ dishes
Seats: 14. Private dining room 8
Smoking: No smoking in dining room
Accommodation: 6 en suite
Credit cards: ▬ ▩ ▚ ▢ 🅒 JCB

PEMBROKE, Court Hotel ❀

Lamphey SA71 5NT
Map 2: SM90
Tel: 01646 672273
Fax: 01646 672480
Chef: Simon Backhouse
Owners: AW & TF Lain
Cost: Alc £21.50. ☺ H/wine £9.75
Times: Last L 1.45pm/last D 9.30pm
Additional: Bar food; Sunday L; No children under 2; ✪ dishes
Smoking: No smoking in dining room.
Accommodation: 37 en suite
Credit cards: ▬ ▩ ▚ ▢ ▦ 🅒 ▣ JCB

Directions: Hotel signed in Lamphey

Fine Georgian house set in several acres of mature grounds and landscaped gardens. Eat in either the restaurant or less formal conservatory from a menu that ranges from soup of the day and curried beef, to mackerel mousse and Oriental-style cod.

Court Hotel

ST DAVID'S, Morgan's Brasserie

St David's is Britain's smallest city and, appropriately, there is a touch of metropolitan modishness about this smart brasserie with its simple white walls, bright artwork and brisk, chatty clientele. The kitchen, though, has its roots in the locality, and is rightly proud of the quality of the fish caught nearby. The cooking shows due respect – the just-netted flavours and sumptuous white flakes of a fat fillet of grilled sea bass needed no more than its simple dressing of garlic butter and snipped herbs. Other dishes are in a more earthy, French country style, such as confit of guinea fowl, tender and full of flavour. Desserts are similarly focussed and to the point – tarte au citron impressed, and a lime syllabub inspired our inspector to flights of poetic fancy, 'light almost to the point of non-existence, drifting in like a sea mist, but sharp as a piercing shaft of sunlight'.

20 Nun Street SA62 6NT
Map 2: SM72
Tel/Fax: 01437 720508
Chef: Ceri Morgan
Owners: Ceri & Elaine Morgan
Cost: Alc £20. ☺ H/wine £9.
Times: D only, 6pm-9pm.
Closed Sun, Jan
Additional: Children welcome; ✪ dishes
Seats: 34
Smoking: No smoking in dining room
Credit cards: ▬ ▬ ▬

Directions: 60yds off Cross Square

ST DAVID'S, St Non's Hotel

Close to the cathedral and Bishop's Palace, St Non's offers traditional dishes in a relaxed setting. Among the choices for dinner there could be fillet of pork medallions with a brandy and peppercorn sauce, and steak and kidney pudding with a rich red wine sauce. For dessert try blackberry and apple crumble with custard.

Accommodation: 22 en suite
Credit cards: ▬ ▬ ▬ ▢

Directions: Close to Cathedral and St Non's Retreat

Catherine Street SA62 6RJ
Map 2: SM72
Tel: 01437 720239
Fax: 01437 721839
Chef: Shane Morrissey
Owner: Peter Trier
Cost: Fixed-price D £18. ☺ H/wine £8.90
Times: Last L 2pm/last D 9pm.
Closed Nov, Dec
Additional: Bar food; Children welcome; ✪ dishes
Smoking: No smoking in dining room

ST DAVID'S, St David's, Warpool Court Hotel

Boasting outstanding views over unspoilt countryside, Warpool Court Hotel was built in 1860 to house the cathedral choir and this place is certainly one to sing about. The spacious dining room overlooks the gardens towards the sea and offers a menu concentrating on fresh ingredients used in an innovative fashion that remains true to the flavours of the produce. Everything is home-made, including the smoked salmon. The canapés include an excellent mini-Glamorgan sausage served piping hot. An impressively light chicken and thyme sausage starter came with a centre of goose liver and a coriander, shallot and balsamic dressing. Our inspector followed it with perfectly poached monkfish tail with delicate salmon mousse stuffing laid on crunchy spinach leaves. Lemon flan with citrus fruit syrup had a vivid flavour and smart shortcrust. There was a good variety of petits fours, delicately composed. Service is friendly and attentive but not overbearing.

Directions: From Cross Square, left by Midland Bank into Goat St, at fork follow hotel signs.

SA62 6BN
Map 2: SM72
Tel: 01437 720300
Fax: 01437 720676
Chef: John Daniels
Owner: Peter Trier
Cost: Fixed-price L £19/D £32.50 (4 courses). H/wine £9.90
Times: Noon-last L 2pm/7-last D 9.15pm. Closed Jan
Additional: Bar food; Sunday L; Children welcome; ✪ dishes
Seats: 50. Private dining room 22
Smoking: No smoking in dining room
Accommodation: 25 en suite
Credit cards: ▬ ▬ ▬ ▢ ▬ ▢

TENBY **Atlantic Hotel** ✿

Seafront hotel with a formal dining room offering skilled service and carefully prepared food. Plenty of local seafood in season. Expect hearty garlic mushrooms in puff pastry with wine, fresh herbs and cream, monkfish wrapped in spinach with Thermidor sauce, and bitter chocolate mousse.

Smoking: No-smoking area; No pipes & cigars
Accommodation: 42 en suite
Credit cards: ▬ ▬ 📉 💷 ▬ 💳

Directions: Town centre, halfway along The Esplanade on R

The Esplanade SA70 7DU
Map 2: SN10
Tel: 01834 842881
Fax: 01834 842881 ext 256
Chef: Julian Rees
Owners: William & Doris James
Cost: *Alc* £22, fixed-price L £7.95/D £19. ☺ H/wine £8.25
Times: Last L 2pm/last D 9.30pm. Closed 18 Dec-22 Jan
Additional: Bar food; Sunday L; No children under 6; ❹ dishes

TENBY, **Penally Abbey** ✿

Set in five acres of garden and woodland, this friendly country house hotel enjoys splendid views of the sea and Caldey Island. In the elegant dining room the attraction is a well-balanced menu that makes good use of local produce including Tenby bass, Brecon venison and Welsh lamb.

Smoking: No smoking in dining room
Accommodation: 12 en suite
Credit cards: ▬ ▬ 📉 💷 ▬ 💳 JCB

Directions: From Tenby take A4139 to Penally

Penally SA70 7PY
Map 2: SN10
Tel: 01834 843033
Fax: 01834 844714
Chefs: Mrs E Warren, Miss J Deely
Owners: Mr & Mrs S T Warren
Cost: *Alc* £25, fixed-price D £26 (4 courses). H/wine £11.50
Times: D only, last D 9.30pm
Additional: Bar food L; No children under 7; ❹ dishes
Seats: 44

WOLF'S CASTLE,
Wolfscastle Country Hotel ✿

A sturdy, stone-built hotel with a warm and intimate atmosphere. The kitchen uses sound, fresh ingredients with a local slant wherever possible. Starters include roast fillet of brill wrapped in Parma ham, home-made cream of asparagus soup, and fresh pear and watercress salad with blue cheese and roasted hazelnuts.

Additional: Sunday L; Bar meals; Children welcome; ❹ dishes
Smoking: No smoking in dining room
Accommodation: 20 en suite
Credit cards: ▬ ▬ 📉 💷 ▬ 💳 JCB

Directions: On A40, in centre of village

SA62 5LZ
Map 2: SM92
Tel: 01437 741225/741688
Fax: 01437 741383
Chef: Steve Brown
Owners: Andrew & Pauline Stirling
Cost: *Alc* £21
Times: Last L 1.45pm/last D 9pm. Closed 24-26 Dec

POWYS

BRECON,
Castle of Brecon Hotel ✿

True to its name this friendly hotel is adjacent to the castle. Get a window seat if you can and look out over the river and town whilst enjoying some adventurous and modish cooking that can include warm chorizo salad with a poached egg, or in-house gravad lax. Plenty of fish and game; Welsh beef, for example, has been successfully paired with a leek dauphinoise.

Castle Square LD3 9DB
Map 3: SO02
Tel: 01874 624611
Fax: 01874 623737
Please telephone for further details

BUILTH WELLS,

Caer Beris Manor Hotel

*Country house set in 30 acres of grounds. The menu frequently dips
into the plentiful Welsh bounty with such pleasing results as sweet
cannon of Welsh lamb with Madeira sauce. That dish was topped
and tailed by Pencerrig goats' cheese with bitter leaves and a sherry
vinaigrette, and crème caramel with rum-soaked raisins. Unstuffy
service delivered with professionalism. The wine list shows real
enthusiasm.*

LD2 3NP
Map 3: SO05
Tel: 01982 552601
Fax: 01982 552586
Please telephone for further details

Directions: Off A483 on W side of town

CRICKHOWELL, **Bear Hotel**

NP8 1BW
Map 3: SO21
Tel: 01873 810408
Fax: 01873 811696
Chef: Denver Dodwell
Owners: Mrs J L Hindmarsh,
 Stephen Hindmarsh
Cost: *Alc* £25. ☺ H/wine £8.50
Times: Noon-last L 2pm/7-last
D 10pm. Closed D Sun
Additional: Bar food; Sunday L;
No children under 5; ♨ dishes
Seats: 100. Private dining room 30
Accommodation: 35 en suite
Credit cards: ▆ ▆ ▆ ▆ ▆ ▆ JCB

A 15th-century coaching inn that is still very much at the heart
of life in the community, having been run in friendly fashion by
the Hindmarshes for over 20 years. Of the twin dining rooms
one boasts old beams, stone walls and rug-strewn flagstones,
while the other is more intimate with fresh flowers and lace
tablecloths. Whichever you choose, the same good food is on
offer from a menu that endeavours to make use of local
ingredients wherever possible: tartlets of locally smoked
haddock with Puy lentils and a mustard cream sauce; loin of
Welsh lamb with provençale vegetables in a filo pastry case
and rosemary jus; smoked loin of local venison, bacon and
shallot rösti with parsnip purée and a Cassis jus. More exotic
options might include Japanese nori rolls, or a vegetarian dish
based on North African couscous. There's a good selection of
wines by the glass on a price-friendly list.

Directions: Town centre off the A40

CRICKHOWELL,

Gliffaes Hotel

The panelled dining-room of this family-owned 18th-century
country house looks out over the River Usk, where there is
trout fishing to be enjoyed. The cooking is well-judged and can
deliver punchy textures and flavours without too much fuss on
the plate. An intelligently handled starter of warm, spicy
chorizo salad with butter beans and crunchy, bitter leaves was
a model of its kind, whilst rump of lamb with rösti cake and

NP8 1RH
Map 3: SO21
Tel: 01874 730371
Fax: 01874 730463
Chef: Mark Coulton
Owner: Nick & Peta Brabner
Cost: Fixed-price D £22.50. ☺
H/wine £11.75.
Times: 7.30pm-last D 9.15pm

glazed shallots was simple and accurate, sweet and tender. A trio of rich chocolate desserts simply demanded to be finished. Other dishes might include seared cod with fennel butter sauce or braised beef with lemon and chilli, served with stir-fried oriental vegetables. Home-cured salmon with fresh herbs and spices is matched with a mango salsa. The wine list has some well-chosen items at fair prices, plus some good clarets from the better vintages.

Directions: 1 mile off A40, 2.5 miles W of Crickhowell

Gliffaes Hotel

Additional: Bar Food L; Sunday L (12.30-2.30pm); Children welcome; dishes
Seats: 80. Private dining room 40. Jacket and tie preferred for D
Smoking: No smoking in dining room
Accommodation: 22 en suite
Credit cards: ▆ ▆ ▆ ▆ ▆ ▆

CRICKHOWELL,
Manor Hotel ⊛   NEW

The hotel is stunningly located on the hillside of the Usk Valley way above the town, and the restaurant has panoramic views. Robust dishes served in hearty portions include Italian fish soup with hunks of ciabatta, sautéed calves' liver with roasted shallots, and caramelised apple and cinnamon Tatin.

Additional: Bar food; Sunday L; Children welcome; dishes
Smoking: No smoking in dining room
Accommodation: 18 en suite
Credit cards: ▆ ▆ ▆ ▆ ▆ ▆ ▆ JCB

Directions: 0.5 mile W of Crickhowell on A40 Brecon rd

Brecon Road NP8 1SE
Map 3: SO21
Tel: 01873 810212
Fax: 01873 811938
Chefs: Peter Ranstead, Shaun Ellis
Owners: G Bridgeman, S Gerrard
Cost: *Alc* £25, fixed price L £11.95/D £17.95. ☺ H/wine £9.95
Times: Last L 2.15pm/last D 9.30pm

CRICKHOWELL,
Nantyffin Cider Mill Inn ⊛   NEW

Bustling 15th-century inn run by the same enterprising team as the nearby Manor Hotel (see entry). The menu, which makes much of local fish and game, is the same whether taken on the wooden tables of the bar or in the slightly more formal dining room. Well-conceived and to the point dishes, have included a generous wild mushroom salad with artichokes and chunky hake with couscous followed by a sprightly lemon tart.

Additional: Bar food; Sunday L; Children welcome; 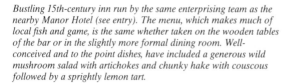 dishes
Smoking: No smoking in dining room
Credit cards: ▆ ▆ ▆ ▆ ▆ ▆ JCB

Directions: 1 mile west of Crickhowell on A40 at J with A479

Brecon Road NP5 1SG
Map 3: SO21
Tel/Fax: 01873 810775
Chefs: Sean Gerrard, Simon Kearly
Owners: Sean Gerrard, Glyn Bridgeman
Cost: *Alc* £18.50, fixed-price L (Sun) £12.95/D (pre-7.45pm) £11.95. ☺ H/wine £9.95
Times: Last L 2.25pm/last D 9.30pm. Closed Mon, 1 wk Nov, 2 wks Jan

HAY-ON-WYE,
Kilverts Hotel

A Victorian stone house, now a lively town centre hotel bustling with character and charm. An evening meal in Colin's Restaurant could start with deep-fried mushrooms stuffed with Stilton and Cheddar, followed by braised hock of lamb in a rich root vegetable and redcurrant sauce.

Additional: Bar food; Children welcome; ◑ dishes
Accommodation: 11 en suite
Credit cards: ▦ ▦ ▰ ▱ ▦ ▣

Directions: Centrally placed in Hay

The Bull Ring HR3 5AG
Map 3: SO24
Tel: 01497 821042
Fax: 01497 821580
Chefs: Colin Thomson & Miss J Glen
Owner: Colin Thomson
Cost: Alc £18, fixed price D £15. ☺
H/wine £8.50
Times: Last L 2pm/last D 9.30pm.
Closed 25 Dec

HAY-ON-WYE,
Old Black Lion Hotel ✿✿

26 Lion Street HR3 5AD
Map 3: SO24
Tel: 01497 820841
Chefs: Peter Bridges, R Sime
Owners: John & Joan Collins
Cost: Alc £22. ☺ H/wine £8.25
Times: Noon-last L 2.30pm/7-last
D 9.30pm
Additional: Bar food; Sunday L;
No children under 5; ◑ dishes
Seats: 24
Smoking: No smoking in dining room
Accommodation: 10 en suite
Credit cards: ▦ ▰ ▦

Authentic country inn, dark and atmospheric, with heaps of painting and eclectic ephemera. Eat in the bar (stripped old pine tables, hum of conversation, bustling lively feel) or in the restaurant that is almost tea-roomish with its appealing clutter of ornaments and pictures. In the latter, the *carte* is supplemented by daily specials that are also available in the bar. It's a varied menu of robust dishes and lively, informal presentation that suits the style of the place. An earthy, straightforward deep-fried black pudding with field mushrooms and bacon gives something of the tilt, as does a hearty Italian fish stew of great hunks of cod, mackerel, and tuna with shell-on langoustine in basil and garlic infused aromatic tomato casserole. Puddings take in the likes of raspberry parfait. The wine list is an enterprising selection with many wines from lesser known regions such as China and Mexico.

Directions: Town centre, 100 yards from junction of Brecon Road & Oxford Road

HAY-ON-WYE,
The Swan-at-Hay Hotel ❀

Church Street HR3 5DQ
Map 3: SO24
Tel: 01497 821188
Fax: 01497 821424
Chef: Nathan Millikin
Owners: Colin & Rosemary Vaughan
Cost: Alc £17.50. ☺ H/wine £9.95
Times: Last L 2pm/last D 9.30pm
Additional: Bar food; Sunday L;
Children welcome; ❹ dishes
Smoking: No pipes & cigars
Accommodation: 19 en suite
Credit cards: 💳💳💳💳💳 💳 JCB

Directions: From Hereford enter
town, follow Brecon sign, hotel on R

Family-run former coaching inn where the Cygnet Restaurant offers garden views and a real fire in winter. The menu might include ostrich steak and oriental vegetable stir-fry alongside gammon with pineapple, rack of Welsh lamb with herb crust, and duck with peaches and Grand Marnier sauce.

KNIGHTON,
Milebrook House Hotel ❀

Milebrook LD7 1LT
Map 7: SO27
Tel: 01547 528632
Fax: 01547 520509
Chef: Beryl Marsden
Owners: Mr & Mrs RT Marsden
Cost: Fixed-price L £11.95/D £18.95.
☺ H/wine £9.80
Times: Last L 1.45pm/last D 8.15pm.
Closed L Mon
Additional: Bar food; Sunday L;
No children under 8; ❹ dishes
Smoking: No smoking in dining room
Accommodation: 10 en suite
Credit cards: 💳💳💳💳💳 💳 JCB

Directions: 2 miles E of Knighton on
A4113 (Ludlow)

Warm hospitality and an obvious love of food and wine are welcoming features at this charming small hotel set in the Teme valley. Quality ingredients and honest flavours successfully combine to create lamb noisettes wrapped in bacon with rosemary and redcurrants, venison casserole and iced almond mousse, all listed on the short evening menu.

LLANFYLLIN, **Seeds** ❀

Seeds is full of interest, offering visitors books to read, games on the tables and artefacts collected on the Seagers' travels. The evening menu offers the likes of grilled sardines with garlic butter, panaché of fish with white wine and cheese sauce, and rack of Welsh lamb with Dijon and herb crust. Homely puds.

Smoking: No smoking in dining room
Credit cards: 💳💳💳

Directions: Village centre, on A490 13 miles from Welshpool

5 Penybryn Cottage
High Street SY22 5AP
Map 7: SJ11
Tel: 01691 648604
Chef: Mark Seager
Owners: Mark & Felicity Seager
Cost: Alc £13.55 L only, fixed-price
D £18.95. ☺ H/wine £10
Times: Last L 2.15pm/last D 9pm.
Closed L Mon, 2 wks Jan
Additional: Sunday L;
Children welcome; ❹ dishes

LLANGAMMARCH WELLS,
Lake Country House ✤✤

LD4 4BS
Map 3: SN94
Tel: 01591 620202
Fax: 01591 620457
Chef: Jeremy Medley
Owners: Mr & Mrs J P Mifsud
Cost: *Alc* £15.50, fixed-price L
£17.50/D £30 (both 5 courses)
H/wine £9.75
Times: Noon-last L 1.45pm/7-last
D 9pm
Additional: Bar food L; Sunday L;
No children under 7; ✤ dishes

Directions: A483 from Garth, turn L
for Llangammarch Wells & follow
signs to hotel

That food is taken seriously at this impressive hotel perched on
a hillside in its own acres among verdant countryside is borne
out by the fact that breads and cakes for afternoon tea are
baked in-house; breakfast gets the thumbs-up too. Dinner, of
four courses with a handful of options at each course except
the first, starts off with a soup – broccoli and almond, say, or
root vegetables in winter. A second-course risotto with scallops
has been impressive, and other fish choices may run to pan-
roasted hake, with quail pie among the meat. A main course of
tenderloin of pork has been served with modish black pudding
mash, and the kitchen shows its confidence in presenting pot-
roast brill with foie gras and truffle, or cod with Parma ham
and artichokes. Pudding might be old-school banana fritters
with chocolate sauce, explosively intense chocolate marquise
with custard, or, something of a signature dish, Grand Marnier
soufflé. The magnificent wine list runs to 30-plus pages, and
you may be spoiled for choice among just the house
recommendations. Owner Mr Mifsud, though, is an impeccable
source of advice.

LLANWDDYN, Lake Vyrnwy Hotel ✤✤

Lake Vyrnwy SY10 0LY
Map 6: SJ01
Tel: 01691 870692
Fax: 01691 870259
Chef: Andrew Wood
Cost: Fixed-price L £15.95/D £25.50.
H/wine £9.95

Built in the 1880s at the same time as the eponymous lake was
created to provide fresh water for Liverpool, the hotel has an
unrivalled position overlooking the water. In the dining room
the window tables have the best views but wherever you sit the

menu offers the best of Welsh produce (much from the estate, lake and their own garden). Well-constructed and enjoyable dishes include soufflé of Welsh farmhouse Cheddar with white wine sauce and Parmesan shavings, or Vyrnwy rainbow trout on a potato galette with crayfish tails and a tomato and basil sauce, and chargrilled fillet of Welsh Black beef with sweetbreads, celeriac purée and port wine sauce. Desserts range from the traditional summer pudding and crème brûlée with fresh raspberries, to a terrine of dark Swiss chocolate with an orange and Grand Marnier sauce. The well-composed wine list includes half-a-dozen house wines that are all available by the glass.

Directions: Follow Tourist signs on A495/B4393, 200 yards past dam at Lake Vyrnwy

Times: 12.30pm-last L 1.45pm/7.30pm-last D 9.15pm
Additional: Bar food; Sunday L; Children welcome; 🍴 dishes
Seats: 80. Private dining room 110. Jacket & tie preferred
Smoking: No smoking in dining room
Accommodation: 35 en suite
Credit cards: ■ ▩ ⦿ ▩ C ⦿

LLANWRTYD WELLS,

Carlton House ❀❀❀

It is a touch ironic that the self-proclaimed 'smallest town in Britain' has become home to a personality as large as that of Mary Ann Gilchrist. Not that this has held her back. One gets the feeling that if she decided to relocate to a cave on some remote Welsh hillside, the path to her kitchen would soon be well worn. In truth, Carlton House is far from isolated. But the title of the Gilchrists' self-published book of recipes *Three Quarters of an Hour From Anywhere*, betrays an exasperation that whilst a plethora of well-populated towns are within easy reach, most pilgrims are from much further afield. No matter. The seven bedrooms frequently fill the much improved dining room, where Alan Gilchrist is an eloquent advocate of both his wife's cooking and his own carefully compiled list of wines. 'Back to basics' might have been a disaster as a political philosophy, but at Carlton House it is a winning culinary ethos. As usual, less is more, and the sparer, more direct style of the cooking these days has without doubt taken a further step forward. Take a simple starter of fried pigeon breast, a potato galette and a beetroot confit. Perfectly executed and finely balanced, the result of a successful dish (and a happy inspector). Imagination is there but on a leash of well-judged length. Thus a fillet of very fine sea bass comes with a squid ink risotto and a shellfish sauce of well defined, friendly flavours, and striking presentation. Dessert-wise, the options are lengthening, and those that shy away from 'a serious attack by chocolate', would be well advised to consider a caramelised tapioca pudding, a successful example of the crunchy without, creamy within approach. Ciabatta, petits fours, and canapés are all solo efforts from Mary Ann, and at breakfast some of the best scrambled eggs on the planet. Good enough to make you want to stay the night, even if you are within three quarters of an hour's drive.
Signature dishes: Aromatic roast cannon of Welsh spring lamb; seared fillet of Towy sewin; roast partridge with juniper-scented cabbage; pan-fried fillet of Welsh Black beef with wild mushrooms.

Directions: In the town centre

Dolycoed Road LD5 4RA
Map 3: SN84
Tel: 01591 610248
Fax: 01591 610242
Chef: Mary Ann Gilchrist
Owners: Dr A J & Mrs M A Gilchrist
Cost: *Alc* £30, fixed-price L £12.50/D £19.95. ☺ H/wine £9.95
Times: 12.30-last L 1.45pm/7-last D 8.30pm. Closed Sun, L Mon, Xmas
Additional: No children under 8; 🍴 dishes
Seats: 14
Smoking: No smoking in dining room
Accommodation: 7 rooms (5 en suite)
Credit cards: ■ ▩ ⦿ ⦿ JCB

LLYSWEN, **Griffin Inn** ❀

Whether bar or restaurant, the menu is the same – happily based on local produce with the emphasis on the game for which this splendid country inn is noted. The kitchen's approach to cooking concentrates on bringing out the flavour of quality ingredients, and this was exemplified for us by a moist fillet of salmon served on a bed on crunchy samphire.

Additional: Bar food; Sunday L; Children welcome; 🍴 dishes
Smoking: No smoking in dining room
Accommodation: 7 en suite
Credit cards: 🁢 🁢 🁢 🁢 🁢 🁢 🁢 JCB

Brecon LD3 0UR
Map 3: SO13
Tel: 01874 754241
Fax: 01874 754592
Chefs: Andrew Addis-Fuller, Richard Stockton
Owners: Richard & Di Stockton & family
Cost: *Alc* £20, fixed-price L £15/D £20 (4 courses). ☺ H/wine £8.25
Times: Last L 2pm/D 9pm.
Closed D Sun, Dec 25-26

Directions: On A470 in village

LLYSWEN, **Llangoed Hall** ❀❀❀

Brecon LD3 0YP
Map 3: SO13
Tel: 01874 754525
Fax: 01874 754545
Chef: Ben Davies
Owner: Sir Bernard Ashley
Cost: *Alc* £38, fixed-price L £15 (2 courses)/D £35 (4 courses)
Times: 12.15pm-last L 2pm/7.15pm-last D 9.30pm
Additional: Sunday L; No children under 8; 🍴 dishes
Seats: 50. Private dining room 50. Jacket & tie preferred
Smoking: No smoking in dining room
Accommodation: 23 en suite
Credit cards: 🁢 🁢 🁢 🁢 🁢 🁢 🁢 JCB

Laura Ashley fabrics and furnishings fill the imposing, largely Edwardian country house, re-modelled by Clough Williams-Ellis (of Portmeirion fame), and transformed by Sir Bernard Ashley into a splendid hotel that tempers grandeur with comfort. Chef Ben Davies matches the opulent surroundings with some accomplished cooking constructed from top-notch ingredients. Welsh produce naturally looms large – Welsh Black beef fillet may be served on a foie gras potato cake as well as a tortellini of wild mushrooms and sage with a red wine sauce, and assiette of Welsh lamb comprises cutlet, leg, kidney and 'wanton' of shoulder, intriguingly served with lemongrass sauce. Classical and modern influences are deftly mixed. A terrine of confit guinea fowl incorporates foie gras and red wine shallots in a deep-scented combination, lightened by a crunchy green bean and truffle salad. Fish is sympathetically handled, with a lightness of touch that is evidence of a commendable wish to protect the principal flavours. Moist and flaky John Dory fillets, with a timbale of saffron couscous, marinated tomatoes and light butter sauce, caressed rather than assaulted the palate. Equally delicate is salmon and shrimp mousse wrapped in Savoy cabbage with braised baby leeks, fresh linguine and Vermouth sauce. Desserts show an element of fun, for example, a quintuplet of perfect baby toffee apples guarding a chocolate wrapped caramel mousse with a vanilla cream. Service is an attentive mix of the courteous and the unstuffy. This is one country house hotel that gets it just right. The wine list is impeccably sourced throughout and offers plenty of thoughtful lesser bottles to go with the pages of grandeur.

AA Wine Award *Shortlisted for -see page 16*

Signature dishes: Assiette of Welsh lamb; salad of queen scallops, Carmarthen ham and red wine dressing; breast of pigeon with foie gras mousse and truffle sauce; pot-roasted pheasant and wild mushroom ravioli and Madeira sauce

Directions: On A470, 2 miles from Llyswen heading towards Builth Wells

NANT-DDU,
Nant Ddu Lodge Hotel ✿

Once a shooting lodge, this riverside Georgian house is now a hotel with a bustling bistro. Fresh ingredients and punchy cooking are hallmarks of the extensive blackboard menu. Breast of pheasant was served with casserole of the leg. This followed robust artichoke-heart risotto and preceded creamy lime cheesecake. No-nonsense heartiness.

Accommodation: 22 en suite
Credit cards: ▆▆ ▆▆ ▆▆ ◻ ▆▆ ◻

Directions: 6 miles N of Merthyr Tydfil, and 12 miles S of Brecon on A470

Cwm Taf Nr Merthyr Tydfil
CF48 2HY
Map 3: SO12
Tel: 01685 379111
Fax: 01685 377088
Chef: John McAveney
Owners: The Ronson Family
Cost: *Alc* £18. ☺ H/wine £7.95
Times: D only, last D 9.30pm.
Closed D Sun, D 25 & 26 Dec
Additional: Bar food; Sunday L;
Children welcome; ◑ dishes
Smoking: No smoking in dining room

NEW RADNOR, Red Lion Inn ✿

It's quite isolated, but folk come from miles around to enjoy the good food and excellent atmosphere at this old drovers' inn. A blackboard menu reflects both the seasons and the market with dishes ranging from Welsh cheese ploughman's, to terrine of Brecon venison with plum chutney, and Wye salmon with butter sauce.

Accommodation: 3 en suite
Credit cards: ▆▆ ▆▆ ▆▆ ◻ JCB

Directions: Directly road-side on N side of A44, 7 miles E of Crossgates and 3 miles W of New Radnor

Llanfihangel-nant-Melan LD8 2TN
Map 3: SO26
Tel/Fax: 01544 350220
Chef: Gareth Johns
Owners: Keith, Liz & Gareth Johns
Cost: *Alc* £16. ☺ H/wine £6.95
Times: Last L 2pm/last D 9pm.
Closed Tue, L Wed, L Thu, 1 wk Nov
Additional: Bar food; Sunday L;
Children welcome; ◑ dishes
Smoking: No smoking in dining room

PWLLGLOYW,
Seland Newydd ✿✿   NEW

The kitchen at this traditional 17th-century inn deserves credit for hard work and the nous not to overstretch itself in terms of concept and execution. Uncomplicated dishes, such as salmon, egg and herb terrine, and pan-fried breast of chicken with sun-dried tomato stuffing on a polenta mash with roasted pepper sauce, allow flavours to speak for themselves. Home-cured gravad lax of salmon bound in Greek yogurt and dill with a sauce vierge, and roast rack of lamb with creamed potato, Welsh faggot and soubise sauce, make intelligent use of local produce. On our visit, desserts showed exceptional skill – pear crème brûlée was delicately crisp and creamy, and a superb-looking coffee cheesecake, mirror-like with a deep black glaze on top, drew gasps from the crowds! Even more impressive, taste and texture matched the visual standard. And how can anyone resist a selection of desserts called 'The Full Monty'? Nice one.

Directions: 4 miles north of Brecon on B4520

Brecon LD3 9PY
Map 3: SO03
Tel: 01874 690282
Chef: Maynard Harvey
Owners: Mr Maynard Harvey &
Mrs Freya Harvey
Cost: *Alc* £21, fixed price D £24.95
(4 courses). ☺ H/wine £8.75
Times: Noon-last L 2pm/6.30-last
D 9pm
Additional: Bar food; Sunday L;
Children welcome; ◑ dishes
Seats: 35. Private room 12
Credit cards: ▆▆ ▆▆ ▆▆ ◻ ◻ JCB

THREE COCKS, **Three Cocks** ❀❀

The 15th-century former coaching inn is the business: antiques, rugs, winter fires, lovely summer garden. Cooking here is accurate and appealing. Fish is a strength, whether mussel soup, a warm salad of king scallops, or fillet of brill baked with grain mustard on a coulis of tomato perfumed with thyme. Elsewhere on the short menu there's much to interest. Loin of wild boar is served with a poivrade sauce, pear and seasonal fruits, or there could be a classic pan-fried veal 'Grand Mere', perhaps breast of duck with honey and Grand Marnier.

Accommodation: 7 rooms
Credit cards: ▆ ▆

Directions: On A438 in the village of Three Cocks, 4 miles from Hay-on-Wye, 11 miles from Brecon.

Brecon LD3 0SL
Map 3: SO13
Tel: 01497 847215
Fax: 01497 847339
Chef: Michael Winstone
Owners: Michael & Marie-Jeanne Winstone
Cost: *Alc* £33, fixed-price D £27 (5 courses). H/wine £8.75
Times: Lunch by arrangement/D 7-9pm. Closed D Tue, Dec & Jan
Additional: Children welcome
Seats: 30
Smoking: No pipes & cigars

WELSHPOOL,
Edderton Hall Hotel ❀❀

It was a cold evening when our inspector called, driving up the long, potholed drive that leads to this Georgian house perched on the edge of the valley across from Powis Castle, and getting the full blast of the wind and horizontally driven rain. The log fire was particularly welcome and the candles on the tables were there in case of power cuts rather than for effect. This was June. However, such is Evelyn Hawksley's passion for cooking that it is well worth braving the elements for a meal here. Ingredients are local, as in a first course of Welshpool ham from a nearby butcher, served with chicory, both roasted and a timbale, a potato rösti, and a red onion and thyme cream sauce. Rump of lamb followed, it had wonderful flavour, and was served on a mound of wilted spinach, fine beans, ribbon carrots, mixed herbs and lavender, and quite a concentrated jus of home-grown redcurrants. Two accompanying dishes of potatoes were enough to feed the village – minted new, and a gratin. A fully flavoured citrus tart with a tangy lime syrup rounded things off nicely. Home-made breads and canapés are all moreish.

Directions: From Welshpool follow A490 towards Churchside and turn right at sign post

Forden SY21 8RZ
Map 7: SJ20
Tel: 01938 580339
Fax: 01938 580452
Chef: Evelyn Hawksley
Owners: Warren & Evelyn Hawksley
Please telephone for further details

WELSHPOOL,
Golfa Hall Hotel ❀

Set within the main, historic part of the hall, the beamed restaurant offers atmosphere and comfort. The set dinner menu may list oven-baked fillet of free-range chicken on a fricassée of wild mushrooms, roast rack of Welsh lamb and creamed leeks, or pan-fried wild boar steak with a port and Pommery mustard sauce.

Additional: Bar food; Sunday L; Children welcome; ❹ dishes
Smoking: No pipes & cigars
Accommodation: 15 en suite
Credit cards: ▆ ▆ ▆ ▆ ▆ ▆ ▆ JCB

Directions: On A458 (Dolgellau), 1.5 miles W of Welshpool on R

Llanfair Road SY21 9AF
Map 7: SJ20
Tel: 01938 553399
Fax: 01938 554777
Chef: Angus James Cameron
Owners: Mr & Mrs David Bowen
Cost: *Alc* £24.50, fixed-price L £12.50/D £17.95. ☺ H/wine £9.95
Times: Last L 2pm/last D 9pm

RHONDDA CYNON TAFF

MISKIN,

Miskin Manor Hotel ®®

An impressive manor house, no more than a stone's throw from the M4, yet tucked away in its own grounds. The stone façade gives way to a wood-panelled interior where an army of smartly attired staff dispense courteous service. Menus are unstuffy, with bright ideas drawn from both modern British and Mediterranean influences, and with the emphasis on flavour – the best dishes are often the simplest. Note a carpaccio of veal, a sparkling success, with a perfectly judged soy and red wine vinaigrette. Main courses major on stout offerings such as braised lambs' liver with onion gravy and bubble-and-squeak, a dish that delivered hefty, uncompromising flavours, but produced with some dexterity and an eye for striking presentation. Desserts have more of a classical approach, with a baked lemon tart eye-popping with citrus flavour.

Directions: 8 miles W of Cardiff. M4/J34, follow hotel signs

Pendoylan Road Groes Faen
Pontyclun CF72 8ND
Map 3: ST08
Tel: 01443 224204
Fax: 01443 237606
Chef: Ian Presgrave
Owners: Mr & Mrs C & L Rosenberg
Cost: Alc £26, fixed-price L £15.95/D £22.95. ☺ H/wine £10.50.
Times: Noon-last L 2pm/7pm-last D 9.45pm.
Additional: Bar food; Sunday L; Children welcome; ❸ dishes
Seats: 60. Private dining room 24
Smoking: No smoking in dining room; Air conditioning
Accommodation: 43 en suite
Credit cards: None

PONTYPRIDD,

Llechwen Hall Hotel ®

Llanfabon CF37 4HP
Map 3: ST08
Tel: 01443 742050
Fax: 01443 742189
Chef: Louis Huber
Owners: Mr & Mrs Huber
Cost: Alc £26.95, fixed-price L £10.95/D £18.95. ☺ H/wine £7.99
Times: Last L 2.30pm/last D 9.30pm
Additional: Bar food; Sunday L; Children welcome; ❸ dishes
Smoking: No pipes & cigars
Accommodation: 20 en suite
Credit cards:

Overlooking four valleys from its mountain-top perch, this 17th-century Welsh longhouse is now run as an impressive country house hotel. A typical meal in the Victorian dining room might start with smoked fillet of trout, followed by sirloin of Welsh Black beef, topped with mushrooms and glazed with garlic cheese.

Directions: 1 mile off the A4054 (Cilfynydd) NE of Pontypridd

SWANSEA

LANGLAND,
Langland Court ❀

Langland Court Road
SA3 4TD
Map 2: SS68
Tel: 01792 361545
Fax: 01792 362302
Chef: Michael Knight
Owner: Colin R Birt
Cost: Alc £25, fixed-price L £11.25/D
£14.95. ☺ H/wine £8.50
Times: Last L 2pm/last D 9.30pm
Additional: Bar food; Sunday L;
Children welcome; ❹ dishes
Smoking: No smoking in dining room
Accommodation: 21 en suite
Credit cards: ▨ ▨ ▨ ▨ ▨ ▨ JCB

*Enjoy award-winning garden views from the oak-panelled dining
room of this family-run, mock-Tudor hotel. Seafood tartlet with
hollandaise sauce, smoked duck with orange salad, chicken with
lemon and asparagus, and sirloin steak with brandy and peppercorn
sauce typify a menu that is priced according to the number of
courses taken.*

Directions: Take the A4067 Swansea-Mumbles road then the
B4593 (Caswell); turn L at St Peter's Church (hotel signed)

MUMBLES,
Hillcrest House Hotel ❀

*A great deal of imagination has gone into the transformation of this
modern property. The hotel's bar/bistro have an African feel,
conjured up by muslin, leopard skin and plants. Quality Welsh
ingredients are the mainstay of the seasonal menus, some given an
oriental twist.*

Additional: Bar food; Children welcome; ❹ dishes
Smoking: No smoking in dining room
Accommodation: 7 en suite
Credit cards: ▨ ▨ ▨ ▨

Directions: From Swansea take coast road to Mumbles.
Go through village, 4th turning on L by church. On L at next
crossroads.

1 Higher Lane SA3 4NS
Map 2: SS68
Tel: 01792 363700
Fax: 01792 363768
Chef/Owner: Yvonne Scott
Cost: Fixed-price D £17. ☺
H/wine £9.50
Times: Last L 2.45pm/last D 8.45pm.
Closed L Mon, L Tue, all Sun, Xmas,
New Year

REYNOLDSTON,
Fairyhill ❀❀❀

With a name like Fairyhill one expects a little magic, and whilst
we cannot vouch for the presence of spirits or elves, this is a
special little hotel. Now firmly established as a fine country
house with an emphasis on food, Fairyhill has become a
favoured destination for the gastronomes of South Wales and

SA3 1BS
Map 2: SS48
Tel: 01792 390139
Fax: 01792 391358
Chefs: Paul Davies, Adrian Coulthard
Owners: Paul Davies, Andrew
Hetherington, Jane & Peter Camm

beyond. Recent months have seen Paul Davies take a step back from the stove to take on a more supervisory role, and although there have been some understandable hiccups along the way, a June inspection meal found the team well into their stride. Always a great advocate of Welsh produce, the crispy fried cockles offered in the bar are an instant reminder of the treasure to be found on the nearby coastline. It is also an early indication that fish is central to the menu with, for instance, firm fillets of poached brill living up to their own superlative in a dish that included a wispy tempura of fennel. Dishes are intelligently composed of just two or three key ingredients and combinations such as duck liver and foie gras parfait with Muscat jelly are sensibly inclined to the classic. Some weighty main course items might include lemon-roasted poussin with a tarragon and bread sauce, or griddled calves' liver with garlic mash and crispy bacon, on a menu that appears to draw inspiration from a variety of sources. The welcome inclusion of a savoury – what else but a variation on Welsh rarebit – adds interest to a dessert menu that also includes a delicately handled apple and tarragon tartlet. Wine is an enthusiasm here, and the list, which offers plenty of depth, has plenty of character too.

Signature dishes: Scrambled eggs with cockles and roasted peppers; local sea bass with wilted garden greens, butter sauce; marsh-fed lamb on a leek purée spiked with chives; fillet of beef, steak and kidney pudding and sauce.

Directions: Just outside Reynoldston, off the A4118 from Swansea

Cost: Fixed-price L £14.50/D £29.50. H/wine £12.50
Times: 12.30-last L 1.45pm/7.30-last D 9pm. Closed Bhs
Additional: Sunday L; No children under 8; ❺ dishes
Seats: 40. Private dining room 40
Smoking: No smoking in dining room
Accommodation: 8 en suite
Credit cards: ▨ ▨ ▨ ▨ ▨ ▨ JCB

AA Wine Award-see page 16
Shortlisted for

SWANSEA, **Beaumont Hotel** ❀❀

72 Walter Road SA1 4QA
Map 3: SS69
Tel: 01792 643956
Fax: 01792 643044
Chefs: Jon Choolsen, Dermot Slade
Owners: J W Jones, J K Colenso
Cost: Fixed-price D £24.50. ☺ H/wine £10.50
Times: D only, 7.30-last D 9.30pm. Closed Xmas
Additional: Bar food L; Children welcome; ❺ dishes
Seats: 40
Smoking: No pipes & cigars; Air conditioning
Accommodation: 16 en suite
Credit cards: ▨ ▨ ▨ ▨ ▨ ▨ ▨

There's an intimate, almost country-house feel about this elegant hotel close to Swansea's hub. The attractive and cheerful conservatory restaurant is the venue for some accomplished cooking, with the kitchen showing up-to-the-minute awareness of current trends. Venison and wild rabbit terrine is served with a grape, walnut and cranberry dressing, and king prawns come on haggis and neeps with a garlic sauce. A main course of goose breast is accompanied by green lentils, bacon, port and wild mushrooms, and collops of monkfish with grilled vegetables and a dressing of coriander and tomato. The kitchen is not without a sense of humour either: witness a starter of poached eggs (free range) with crisply latticed potato, the 'bacon' replaced with zippy chorizo, or another of a nest of melon served with two sorbets, one of whisky and ginger, the other of gin and tonic. An impressive cage of spun

sugar may accompany a dessert like cappuccino mousse. Three house wines from South Africa, France and Germany kick off a list of around 60 bottles, all arranged by style of grape, with a generous selection of half-bottles.

Directions: N/W of town centre on A4118, opposite St James' Church in an area called Uplands

SWANSEA, **Number One Wind Street** ❀❀

Just off the main shopping centre, this restaurant has long been one of the best places to eat in Swansea. While Peter Gillen administers front-of-house with theatrical flair, it is chef-patron Kate Taylor who brings the modern Anglo-French menu to life. At our last meal a fresh lobster ravioli with basil butter sauce (in-house pasta with steaming chunks of lobster and lots of fresh basil) was followed by roast grouse (delicious pink slices of nicely hung bird with the traditional accompaniments) before a well-executed tarte Tatin. Other dishes that caught the eye included potted goose in white wine aspic with Agen prunes in Armagnac, braised maize-fed chicken in Riesling with ceps, and quenelles of sea bass with crispy laverbread and prawn sauce. There's good value to be found in a well-chosen, mainly French wine list.

1 Wind Street SA1 1DE
Map 3: SS69
Tel: 01792 456996
Chef: Kate Taylor
Owners: Kate Taylor, Peter Gillen
Cost: Alc £13.50, fixed-price L £13.50/D £21. ☺ H/wine £9.50
Times: Noon-2.30pm/7-9.30pm. Closed Sun, Mon, Bhs
Additional: Children welcome; ❸ dishes
Seats: 50. Private room 20
Credit cards:

Directions: *Telephone for directions*

SWANSEA, **Windsor Lodge Hotel** ❀

Mount Pleasant SA1 6EG
Map 3: SS69
Tel: 01792 642158/652744
Fax: 01792 648996
Chefs: Ron Rumble, Tina Stewart
Owners: Ron & Pam Rumble
Cost: Fixed-price D £22.32. ☺ H/wine £8.95
Times: L by prior arrangement/last D 9.30pm. Closed Sun, 25-26 Dec
Additional: Bar food; Children welcome; ❸ dishes
Smoking: No smoking in dining room
Accommodation: 19 en suite
Credit cards: JCB

In a quiet residential area, just off the town centre, the Lodge has been personally run by the Rumbles for nearly 30 years. An interesting and varied menu might include provençale tart, Thai chicken and coriander soup, rack of lamb with a bacon, shallot and herb stuffing, and duck breast with apricot, white wine and ginger sauce.

Directions: Town centre, L at station, R immediately after 2nd set of lights

VALE OF GLAMORGAN

BARRY, Egerton Grey Hotel 🏵🏵

Porthkerry CF62 3BZ
Map 3: ST16
Tel: 01446 711666
Fax: 01446 711690
Chef: Craig Brookes
Owners: Anthony & Magda Pitkin
Cost: Fixed-price D £24. ☺
H/wine £10.50.
Times: 12.15-last L 1.45pm/7-last
D 9.30pm
Additional: Sunday L;
Children welcome; 🍴 dishes
Seats: 40. Private dining room 14
Smoking: No smoking in dining room
Accommodation: 10 en suite
Credit cards: ▬ ▬ 🟦 💳 ▬ 🅲 💳 JCB

A genteel and restrained county house hotel, where aperitifs and canapés are taken in the drawing room amongst the signed photos of esteemed guests. The cooking is, however, more direct and focused than the elaborate menu descriptions would suggest, and the style is both studied and pragmatic. The defining features of our last meal were accuracy in technique and intelligence in composition. Hence a red pepper bavarois was light and fluffy, but strikingly lit by fresh and sweet capsicum flavour that belied the delicate texture. A buttery supreme of guinea fowl was fine, but usurped by a terrific roulade of the leg with a whipped chestnut mousse that was sweet and nutty. Iced tiramisu parfait on Kahlua sauce with a sabayon of Amaretto orange and griottine cherries was, despite the description, a major success being a kind of inverted Black Forest gâteau. The wine list has some impressive older bins and is generally fairly priced.

Directions: M4/J33, follow signs for Airport then Porthkerry, & L at hotel sign by thatched cottage

WREXHAM

MARCHWIEL, Cross Lanes Hotel

Cross Lanes Bangor Road Marchwiel
LL13 0TF
Map 7: SJ35
Tel: 01978 780555
Fax: 01978 780568
Chefs: Ian Chapman, Nick Crump
Owner: Michael Kagan
Cost: Fixed-price L £7.95 (2 courses)
Times: Last L 2pm/last D 9.30pm.
Closed D 25-26 Dec
Additional: Bar food; Sunday L;
Children welcome; dishes
Smoking: No-smoking area;
No pipes & cigars
Accommodation: 16 en suite
Credit cards: ▩ ▩ ▣ ▩ ▣ ▣

*Built as a private house in 1890, the hotel stands in six acres of
grounds. The brasserie restaurant has slate and oak floors, a drinks
patio for summer use and log fires in winter. Impressively presented
dishes include smoked salmon tortellini, and pan-fried chicken on a
bed of wild rice.*

Directions: 3 miles SE of Wrexham on A525

ROSSETT, Llyndir Hall Hotel ❀

*Peaceful parkland surrounds this 19th-century Gothic-style house, a
popular conference venue with indoor swimming pool and
extensive gym equipment. The conservatory restaurant is the setting
for some modern, ambitious cooking that is built around fresh
produce.*

Additional: Bar Food; Sunday L; Children welcome; dishes
Smoking: No smoking in dining room
Accommodation: 38 en suite
Credit cards: ▩ ▩ ▩ ▣ ▩ ▣ JCB

LL12 0AY
Map 7: SJ35
Tel: 01244 571648
Fax: 01244 571258
Chef: Jeremy Stone
Owner: Celebrated Group plc
Cost: Alc £25, fixed-price L £14.25/
D £18.95 (4 courses). ☺
H/wine £10.95
Times: Last L 2pm/D 9.30pm.
Closed L Sat

Directions: S from Chester on A483 to Wrexham, follow signs
for Pulford/Rossett B5445. Llyndir Hall signed on the R

ROSSETT, Rossett Hall Hotel ❀

*Mature gardens, lovely countryside and a renovated 18th-century
house are the draw. So too is decent wine and a menu that takes in
mille-feuille of avocado guacamole with celeriac wafers and dill
pesto, plus well-executed main courses such as Welsh Black beef
fillet on herb risotto with tomato butter sauce.*

Additional: Bar food; Sunday L; Children welcome; ❹ dishes
Smoking: No smoking in dining room
Accommodation: 30 en suite
Credit cards: ▩ ▩ ▩ ▣ ▩ ▣ ▣ JCB

Chester Road LL12 0DE
Map 7: SJ35
Tel: 01244 571000
Fax: 01244 571505
Chef: John Holt
Cost: Alc £20, fixed-price L £11.25.
☺ H/wine £9.95
Times: Open all day, last D 10pm

Directions: M56, take M53 to Wrexham – becomes A55. Take
A483 Chester/Wrexham exit to Rossett (B5445). Hotel in centre
of village

NORTHERN IRELAND
ANTRIM

BALLYMENA, Galgorm Manor

The 19th-century mansion is in a spectacular setting beside the River Maine. Within, wall murals, chandeliers, candles and fresh flowers characterise the elegant restaurant. Alastair Fullerton (ex head chef, Roscoff, see entry) now drives the kitchen, and although it was early days when our inspector called for lunch, things are looking up. Alastair does have a good touch, and there is a lot more finesse and balance to the cooking now. The lunch menu is short and kept deliberately simple, but the quality does come through. Fruit soda bread was a great start, followed by a seafood tagliatelle with delicious home-made pasta and a creamy saffron and basil sauce. Lightly roasted rack of tender lamb followed – 'restored my faith in lamb' – accompanied by a tapenade jus and good vegetables. To finish, dark and white chocolate mousse with orange syrup. The wine list has been improved; it's a comprehensive list from around the world with some vintages worthy of note and a good range of half-bottles.

BT42 1EA
Map 1: D5
Tel: 01266 881001
Fax: 01266 880080
Chef: Alastair Fullerton
Owners: Nicholas & Paul Hill
Cost: Alc £28, fixed-price L £15/D £28. H/wine £11.50
Times: Last L 2.30pm/last D 9.30pm
Additional: Bar food L; Sunday L; Children welcome; ✪ dishes
Smoking: No-smoking area; Air conditioning
Accommodation: 23 en suite
Credit cards: ▬ ▭ ▭ ▭

Directions: One mile outside Ballymena, on the A42 between Galgorm and Cullybackey

PORTRUSH, Ramore

Downstairs is a popular wine bar, upstairs an informal dining room, with an open kitchen and lovely views over the harbour. Waitresses, with white shirts, black trousers and long aprons, match the black and white colour scheme, as did our inspector's first course of lightly seared, moist scallops on a bed of pasta coloured black by squid ink and contrasted by a drizzle of creamy white fish sauce. The main course, chosen from the list of blackboard specials, kept up the high standard – a tender fillet of turbot on a bed of sliced tomato and red onion, topped by a coriander and chilli mayonnaise. Other main courses might include roast confit of 'Peking Duck', with spiced onion galette and Thai sauce, and fillet steak with wild garlic mushrooms, button onions, pommes sauté and a pepper cream. For dessert, pear brûlée with honey ice cream and caramel sauce arrived in style on a vivid blue glass plate.

The Harbour BT56 8DF
Map 1: C6
Tel: 01265 824313
Fax: 01265 823194
Chef: George McAlpin
Owners: George & Jane McAlpin
Cost: Alc £25. ☺ H/wine £8.95
Times: D only, 6.30pm-10.30pm. Closed Sun, Mon
Additional: Children welcome
Seats: 70
Smoking: Air conditioning
Credit cards: ▬ ▭ ▭ ▭

Directions: On the harbour

BELFAST

BELFAST, Barnett Restaurant

Set in a lovely old house in extensive parkland, the restaurant serves European-style cooking with an Ulster accent. Note medallions of breast of pigeon dressed with parsley pesto and walnut oil, and noisettes of lamb with port wine jus – plus two kinds of potatoes. Bread-and-butter pudding is not to be missed.

Malone House
Malone Road BT9 5PB
Map 1: D5
Tel: 01232 681246
Fax: 01232 682197
Chef: Martin Wilson
Owner: John E McQuillan
Cost: Alc £24, fixed price L £12.95. ☺ H/wine £8.95
Times: Last L 3pm/last D 9.30pm. Closed Sun, Easter Mon, 12 Jul, 25 Dec

Additional: Children welcome; ✪ dishes
Smoking: No smoking in dining room; Air conditioning
Credit cards: ▬ ▭ ▭ ▭ ▭

Directions: At junction of Malone Road and Shaw's Bridge.

BELFAST,
Culloden ✿

Bangor Road Holywood
BT18 0EX
Map 1: D5
Tel: 01232 425223
Fax: 01232 426777
Chef: Paul McKnight
Owner: Hastings Hotels
Cost: *Alc* £25, fixed-price L £18.50 (2 courses)/D £24.50. ☺ H/wine £10.25
Times: Last L 2.30pm/last D 9.45pm. Closed L Sat, 24-25 Dec
Additional: Sunday L; No children under 3; ♨ dishes
Smoking: No-smoking area
Accommodation: 79 en suite
Credit cards: ▰ ▰ ▰ ▰ ▰ ▰

Once a bishop's palace, Culloden is now a well-appointed hotel set in twelve acres of gardens. Overlooking Belfast Lough, the elegant restaurant serves modern dishes which make the most of local produce. Try baked sea bass with roast tomatoes and mango salsa, or grilled sirloin steak with blue cheese and a whiskey cream sauce.

Directions: From M3 take A3 then A2 (Bangor); hotel is on L just through Holywood

---

BELFAST, **Deanes** ✿✿✿

There is sexy food to accompany the bordello-style decoration of this large, street-level brasserie with fine dining room above. Downstairs, three-foot-high gilded cherubs hang from the ceiling, and there is blood-red crushed velvety upholstery and blinds. Upstairs, the more restrained yet spacious lemon and burgundy coloured restaurant with high-backed chairs and proper linens just gets better and better. Colour-coded mandarin-jacketed waiters offer attentive, formal service and you can see the chef surveying customers and putting the finishing touches to dishes in his open kitchen. Deane's style is understated and classical yet takes some inspiration from the Pacific Rim. A starter of squab terrine with foie gras and herb jelly featured soft-as-butter slices of bird, seared liver and a dark jelly mosaic flavoured with pigeon jus and set with slivers of liver and pigeon drizzled with white truffle oil. It was lovely, the only down side being that the foie gras was too runny for perfection. Chicken and mushroom pie sounds too simple to be a real stunner but here was fine buttery shortcrust pastry filled with slices of juicy chicken, pan-fried mushrooms, spinach and béchamel sauce. It was topped with a single flat leaf of crispy spinach and an excellent caramelised galette and surrounded by a strong, glossy Madeira reduction. Dessert too was excellent, a rhubarb crumble with the tender, slightly acidic fruit topped with a ball of cinnamon ice cream and a sail-shaped tuile. Good espresso and petits fours finished a very fine meal indeed – make sure you go.

38-40 Howard Street
BT1 6PD
Map 1: D5
Tel: 01232 560000
Fax: 01232 560001
Chef: Raymond McArdle
Owners: Michael Deane, Brian & Lynda Smyth
Times: Noon-3pm/5.30-10.30pm. Closed Sun, Xmas, July
Seats: 120
Smoking: No-smoking area; Air conditioning
Credit cards: ▰ ▰ ▰ ▰ ▰

Directions: *Telephone for directions*

BELFAST, Roscoff ❀❀

The discreet, frosted glass frontage may give little clue, but this ground-breaking Northern Irish restaurant is an absolute hive of activity. Along with the cosmopolitan sweep of the clientele (prices remain cheerfully accessible) there is the buzz of a burgeoning empire that takes in cafés, a bakery, brasserie, as well as the hectic media career of the Rankins themselves. Interior design, by contrast, is decidedly cool, with chrome, black leather and polished wood forming a chic backdrop to cooking that continues to be invigorated by intercontinental touches. Working on the premise that the Irish can get along with anybody, it should be no surprise to find the local eels cosying up to salsa verde, or to find the sweetest of Strangford prawns in a particularly happy partnership with risotto cakes and chilli tomato compote. Other combinations may be more familiar Glenarm Salmon with hollandaise and asparagus, for example, but bright flavours persist throughout the menu, not least in an ebullient plate of mango desserts.

Directions: At top of Belfast's 'Golden Mile', Shaftesbury Square area

7 Lesley House
Shaftesbury Square BT2 7DB
Map 1: D5
Tel: 01232 331532
Fax: 01232 312093
Chef: Paul Rankin
Owners: Paul & Jeanne Rankin
Cost: Fixed-price L £17.50/D £29.95. H/wine £12.95
Times: 12.15-last L 2.30pm/6.30-last D 10.30pm. Closed L Sat, all Sun, 25-26 Dec, Easter Mon, 12 Jul
Additional: Children welcome; ⓓ dishes
Seats: 65
Smoking: No-smoking area; Air conditioning
Credit cards:

HOLYWOOD,
Rayanne Country House ❀❀

60 Desmesne Road
BT18 9EX
Map 1: D5
Tel: 01232 425859
Fax: 01232 423364
Chef: Raymond McClelland
Owners: Raymond & Anne McClelland
Cost: *Alc* £27.50. ☺ H/wine £11.50
Times: D only, 7-9pm. Closed Sun, 25 Dec-2 Jan
Additional: Children welcome; ⓓ dishes
Seats: 30. Private dining room 10
Smoking: No smoking in dining room
Accommodation: 6 en suite
Credit cards:

An elegant Victorian house set well back from the road in an elevated position overlooking its own lawns. International dishes are served in the peaceful surroundings of the dining room, which enjoys views over the garden to Belfast Lough. Raymond McClelland creates a range of varied fresh dishes such as lasagne of salmon and plaice with spinach and cheese sauce, baked fillet of pork with prunes and almonds in an Armagnac cream sauce, and roast breast of duckling with a compote of plums and ginger laced with port. Typical starters include Stilton and apple flan with spiced apple, walnut and raisin chutney, a seafood risotto on a fresh red pepper and herb sauce, and skewered fillets of monkfish with beansprout salad and sweet-sour sauce. The owners work hard to give guests a warm welcome and ensure they are well looked after during their visit.

Directions: From A2 take Belfast Road into Holywood; immediate R into Jacksons Road leading to Desmesne Road

DOWN

BANGOR, Chablis ❀❀

NEW

Formerly chef at the nearby Clandeboye Lodge (see entry below), Jean-Pierre Carré is striking out on his own at this restaurant-with-rooms in a terrace overlooking the marina and Belfast Lough. Decor features stencilled vines on lemon-coloured walls and lots of Chablis bric-a-brac. Although the cooking is very French, Jean-Pierre makes use of local produce in dishes such as rabbit terrine with shallot chutney, supreme of pigeon on a Jerusalem artichoke mash, crab mousse-filled sole with a ginger and lemongrass sauce, and medallions of veal flambéed with Cognac on a truffle sauce. Finish with a dessert like lemon and hazelnut mousse with passion fruit coulis or the French cheese platter. An exclusively French wine list includes some serious bottles at serious prices but most of the list is much more reasonable with plenty of choice under £20.

9 & 11 Gray's Hill, BT20 3BB
Map 1: D5
Tel: 01247 467747
Fax: 01247 469098
Chef: Jean-Pierre Carré
Owners: Alison Nesbitt, Jean-Pierre Carré
Cost: Alc £22, fixed price L £21.50/D £19.95. ☺ H/wine £9.95
Times: 12.30-last L 2.30pm/7-last D 10pm. Closed L Sat, Sun, L Mon
Additional: ✪ dishes
Seats: 60. Private room 16
Smoking: No-smoking area; No pipes and cigars
Accommodation: 4 en suite
Credit cards: 🖼 🖼 🖼 🖼 🖼

Directions: *Please telephone for directions*

BANGOR,
Clandeboye Lodge Hotel ❀

Genuine hospitality and attentive service are the hallmarks of Clandeboye Lodge, situated just off the main road to Belfast. The restaurant is dominated by an impressive arched window with European dishes and local produce typifying the menu. A meal may include good confit of duck on salad leaves, then white chocolate and vanilla mousse.

10 Estate Road Clandeboye BT19 1UR
Map 1: D5
Tel: 01247 852500
Fax: 01247 852772
Chef: Marcus Lemon
Cost: Fixed-price D £18.50. ☺ H/wine £9.50
Times: D only, last D 9.30pm

Additional: Bar food; Sunday L (noon-2.30pm); Children welcome; ✪ dishes.
Smoking: No-smoking area
Accommodation: 43 en suite
Credit cards: 🖼 🖼 🖼 🖼 🖼 🖼

Directions: Leave A2 at Newtownards sign, 1st junction left, 300 yds.

BANGOR, Royal Hotel ❀

Substantial Victorian hotel overlooking the Marina, with serious eating in Quays restaurant. Fillet of salmon with prawns and grain mustard sauce was full of flavour, and scallops with spinach and creamy brandy sauce were sweet and tender. Try the tiramisu with home-made ice cream for dessert.

Seafront BT20 5ED
Map 1: D5
Tel: 01247 271866
Fax: 01247 467810
Please telephone for further details

BANGOR, Shanks ❀❀❀

Uniquely situated at the side a golf club-house, Shanks is the most stylish 19th hole in the UK and certainly one of the best restaurants in Northern Ireland. The light, airy space (designed by Sir Terence Conran and unsurprisingly award-winning) features a collection of bright Hockney Californian prints, red leather banquettes, walnut-backed chairs and a kitchen that is

The Blackwood Crawfordsburn Road BT19 1GB
Map 1: D5
Tel: 01247 853313
Fax: 01247 852493
Chef: Robbie Millar
Owners: Robbie & Shirley Millar

visible to customers behind a clear-glass screen. Alongside the great atmosphere is some very special food. Shank's breads are stunning, particularly the onion focaccia, and sliced mustard bread. Starters include local lobster tails in a velvety smooth, richly flavoured shellfish sauce with lightly truffle-flavoured gnocchi and long strands of courgette. Deliciously juicy and tender lamb skordalia is a loose interpretation of the classic Greek dish with creamed potato, parsley jus, egg, garlic, olive oil and a panaché of spring vegetables. Or you may prefer the estate venison with local ceps, grilled polenta and red wine. Chocolate is the chef's particular passion, so for dessert our inspector ordered the chocolate tart, which featured an incredibly thin, light case, and was served with apricots, crème anglaise and rich vanilla ice cream. Prune and Armagnac crème brûlée is another dish of which he is particularly proud. The husband-and-wife team running Shanks offer some superb-value lunches – well worth the 15 minute trip out from the city.

Cost: Fixed-price L £16.95/D £28.50. H/wine £10.50
Times: 12.30-last L 2.15pm/7-last D 10pm. Closed L Sat, all Sun & Mon, 1 wk Xmas
Additional: Children welcome; 🍴 dishes
Seats: 60. Private dining room 26/28
Smoking: No-smoking area; No pipes & cigars; Air conditioning
Credit cards: 🔲 🔲 🔲 🔲 🔲

Directions: From A2 (Belfast-Bangor), turn R onto Ballysallagh Road 1 mile before Bangor, 1st L after 0.5 miles (Crawfordburn Road) to Blackwood Golf Centre. Shanks is in the grounds.

PORTAFERRY,

Portaferry Hotel ❀❀

10 The Strand BT22 1PE
Map 1: D5
Tel: 012477 28231
Fax: 012477 28999
Chef: Gerry Manley
Owners: John & Marie Herlihy
Cost: Fixed-price D £19.50. ☺ H/wine £10.50
Times: 12.30-last L 2.30pm/7-last D 9pm. Closed 24-25 Dec
Additional: Bar food L; Sunday L; Children welcome; 🍴 dishes
Seats: 80
Smoking: No-smoking area; No pipes and cigars
Accommodation: 14 en suite
Credit cards: 🔲 🔲 🔲 🔲 🔲 JCB

Its core a terrace of houses dating from the mid-18th century, this hotel is right on Strangford Lough. The comfortable, smart public rooms make the most of the views over the waters and the ferry plying her way across the mouth of the lough. A broad range of items is on the three-course dinner menu. Impressive home-made wheaten bread sets the tone. Salmon and scallop terrine was an enjoyable and successful start to an inspector's meal; it was accompanied by creamy tarragon and spring onion dressing. Lightly grilled escalope of salmon came next, with deep-fried beetroot on smoked fish risotto with champagne butter sauce, all components working well together. Crème brûlée capped it all. Mussel soup, or Portavogie prawns Thermidor could also crop up among starters, and roast rack of lamb on mint and mushroom mousse with tarragon jus, or roast monkfish with tomato and chive sauce among mains. The wine list has a Connoisseur's Choice to keep the buffs happy.

Directions: Opposite Strangford Lough ferry terminal

LONDONDERRY

LIMAVADY, **The Lime Tree** ❀

Small, informal restaurant on tree-lined Catherine Street. Generous portions of modern Irish fare, with many dishes featuring modish Med influences. Typical main courses include breast of chicken with roasted pepper sauce, and venison casserole with parsley suet dumplings and game sauce. Fresh fish is a speciality.

Additional: Sunday L; Children welcome; ♨ dishes
Credit cards: ▨ ▧ ▧ ▢ ▨

Directions: Entering Limavady from the Derry side, the restaurant is on the right side on a small slip road

60 Catherine Street BT49 9DB
Map 1: C5
Tel: 015047 64300
Chef: Stanley Matthews
Owners: Stanley & Maria Matthews
Cost: *Alc* £20. ☺ H/wine £7.95.
Times: Last L 2pm/last D 9.30pm.
Closed Mon, Tue some mths of the year

LONDONDERRY,
Beech Hill Hotel ❀   NEW

Dating from 1729, Beech Hill is an impressive mansion house set in 32 acres of parkland. The elegant restaurant provides an appropriate setting for the innovative cooking based on sound ingredients. At inspection, mille-feuille of lemon sole with herb salsa, seared salmon 'orso' with creamy basil sauce, and passion fruit mousse were heavily endorsed.

Additional: Bar food; Sunday L; Children welcome; ♨ dishes
Smoking: No smoking in dining room
Accommodation: 17 en suite
Credit cards: ▨ ▧ ▢ ▨

Directions: Along A6 Londonderry to Belfast road, turn off at Faughan Bridge travelling 1 mile further to Ardmore Chapel. Hotel entrance is opposite.

32 Ardmore Road BT47 3QP
Map 1: C5
Tel: 01504 349279
Fax: 01504 345366
Chef: James Nicholas
Cost: *Alc* £24.80, fixed price L £15.95 (4 courses)/D £23.95 (8 courses). ☺ H/wine £10
Times: Last L 2.30pm/last D 9.30pm.
Closed 24-25 Dec

LONDONDERRY, **Everglades Hotel** ❀

A stylish hotel with a bright, airy restaurant with Sherwood green striped walls and dark apricot panels. The menu is a feast of modern Irish dishes peppered with continental influences. A typical meal could begin with oak-smoked salmon with lemon and caper horseradish cream, followed by tournedos of cod and mange-tout.

Additional: Bar food; Sunday L; Children welcome; ♨ dishes
Smoking: No-smoking area
Accommodation: 64 en suite
Credit cards: ▨ ▧ ▢ ▨ ▨

Directions: 1 mile from city centre on main Dublin road

Prehen Road BT47 2PA
Map 1: C5
Tel: 01504 346722
Fax: 01504 349200
Chef: John Crowe
Owner: Hastings Hotels
Cost: Fixed-price D £19.95 (5 courses). ☺ H/wine £10.50
Times: Noon-last D 9.45pm.
Closed D Sun

MAGHERA,
Ardtara Country House ❀❀

A charming Victorian manor house with a friendly and relaxed atmosphere, Ardtara is set in nine acres of grounds on the outskirts of the village of Upperlands. Daylight streams into

8 Gorteade Road Upperlands
BT46 5SA
Map 1: C5
Tel: 01648 44490
Fax: 01648 45080

the dining room – originally the snooker room – through a large skylight, illuminating the original wood panelling and hand-painted wallpaper. Here guests enjoy the traditional Irish country house cooking of chef Patrick McLarnon, who produces quality dishes along the lines of cutlet of wild boar with caramelised apples; Dublin bay prawns tossed in caper butter sauce; and pan-fried fillet of beef with forest mushroom sauce. Desserts are equally mouth-watering: try rich chocolate mousse with pistachio tuile and mandarin sauce, or the house speciality, toasted oatmeal and Bushmills brûlée. What the wine list lacks in variety – only two house wines are offered from a 30-plus selection – it more than compensates for with reasonable prices.

Directions: From Belfast follow M2 to A6. After Castledawson, take A29 to Maghera/Coleraine. Follow B75 (Kilrea) until Upperlands.

Chef: Patrick McLarnon
Owner: Maebeth Fenton
Cost: *Alc* £25, fixed-price L £12.50/D £20. ☺ H/wine £9.50
Times: 12.30-last L 2.30pm/7-last D 9.30pm. Closed L Sat, D Sun, 25-26 Dec
Additional: Sunday L; No children under 10; ♨ dishes
Seats: 40. Private dining room 12
Smoking: No smoking in dining room
Accommodation: 8 en suite
Credit cards: ■ ■ ■

MAGHERAFELT, **Trompets** ❀❀

A chic venue for serious food – chef/owner Noel McMeel knows his stuff and produces a sophisticated *carte* of Anglo-American dishes with Pacific Rim touches. Typical starters include barbecued rabbit salad with roast garlic and ginger, warmed potato, red onion and bacon salad, and curried crab cakes with a fresh mango relish. An early summer meal started with a selection of tasty breads – banana, rye, wheat and soda – served with chilli tomato oil and sesame dip. Grilled red snapper followed, accompanied by rice noodles, deep-flavoured whole roasted plum tomatoes and drizzled with chilli-oiled pesto. The meal continued with rack of lamb wrapped in fine lattice strips of potato and garnished with a ratatouille on chive mash. Desserts range from praline Pavlova with fresh strawberries and framboise zabaglione, to 'Trompets eclectic white chocolate soup' served with a lime and walnut tuile.

Directions: On axis of A29 and M2/A6

25 Church Street BT45 6AP
Map 1: C5
Tel: 01648 32257
Fax: 01648 34441
Chef/Owner: Noel McMeel
Cost: Fixed-price D £22.95. ☺ H/wine £9.95
Times: Noon-last L 2.30pm/6-last D 10pm. Closed D Sun, all Mon, 1 wk Jan, 2 wks Jul
Additional: Sunday L; Children welcome; ♨ dishes
Seats: 50. Private dining room 25
Smoking: No-smoking area; Air conditioning
Credit cards: ■ ■ ■ ■ ■

REPUBLIC OF IRELAND

The Republic of Ireland hotels and restaurants listed below have built their reputations on the quality of their food; all have earned our coveted Rosette award. The information has been supplied by AA Hotel Services, Blackrock, Dublin.

Please note that the area codes for numbers in the Republic of Ireland apply only within the Republic. If dialling from outside you should check the telephone directory. Area codes for numbers in Britain and N. Ireland cannot be used directly from the Republic.

COUNTY CARLOW

Dolmen Hotel ❀

Kilkenny Road, Carlow 0503 42002

COUNTY CAVAN

Slieve Russell Hotel ❀

Ballyconnell 049 26444

COUNTY CLARE

Gregans Castle ❀❀

Ballyvaughan 065 77005

Temple Gate Hotel ❀

The Square, Ennis 065 23300

Sheedy's Spa View Hotel & Orchid Restaurant ❀❀

Lisdoonvarna 065 74026

Dromoland Castle Hotel ❀❀

Newmarket-on-Fergus 061 368144

COUNTY CORK

Bay View Hotel ❀❀

Ballycotton 021 646746

Sea View Hotel ❀❀

Ballylickey 027 50073

Baltimore Harbour Resort Hotel ❀

Baltimore 028 20361

Casey's of Baltimore ❀

Baltimore 028 20197

Arbutus Lodge Hotel ❀❀

Middle Glanmire Road, Montenotte, Cork 021 501237

Bendicks Restaurant ❀

Blackrock Castle, Cork 021 357414

Hayfield Manor ❀

Perrott Avenue, College Road, Cork 021 315600

Courtmacsherry ❀

Courtmacsherry 023 46198

Garryvoe Hotel ❀

Garryvoe 021 646718

Innishannon House Hotel ❀❀

Inishannon 021 775121

Trident Hotel ❀

Worlds End, Kinsale 021 772301

Castle Hotel ✻

Main Street, Macroom 026 41074

Longueville House Hotel ✻✻✻

Mallow 022 47156

Midleton Park ✻✻

Midleton 021 631767

Aherne's Seafood Restaurant ✻✻

163 North Main Street, Youghal 024 92424

Devonshire Arms Hotel ✻

Pearse Square, Youghal 024 92827

Kee's Hotel ✻✻

Stranorlar, Ballybofey 074 31018

COUNTY DONEGAL

Harvey's Point Country Hotel ✻✻✻

Lough Eske, Donegal 073 22208

Arnold's Hotel ✻

Dunfanaghy 074 36208

Fort Royal Hotel ✻✻

Fort Royal, Rathmullan 074 58100

Sand House Hotel ✻✻

Rossnowlagh 072 51777

COUNTY DUBLIN

Berkeley Court Hotel ✻

Lansdowne Road, Dublin 4 01 6601711

Buswells Hotel ✻

23-27 Molesworth Street, Dublin 2 01 6146500

The Clarence ✻✻✻

6-8 Wellington Quay, Dublin 2 01 6709000

Clarion Stephen's Hall All-Suite Hotel ✻✻

The Earlsfort Centre, Lower Leeson Street, Dublin 2 01 6381111

The Commons ✻

85-86 Stephen Green, Dublin 01 4752608

Conrad International Dublin ✻✻

Earlsfort Terrace, Dublin 2 01 6765555

Hibernian Hotel ✻✻✻

Eastmoreland Place Ballsbridge, Dublin 4 01 6687666

Jurys Hotel Dublin ✻

Pembroke Road Ballsbridge, Dublin 4 01 6605000

Kapriol Restaurant ✻

45 Lower Camden Street, Dublin 2 01 4751235

Longfield's Hotel ✻✻

Fitzwilliam Street, Dublin 2 01 6761367

Marine Hotel ✻✻

Sutton Cross, Dublin 13 01 8390000

The Merrion Hotel ❀❀❀

Upper Merrion Street, Dublin 01 6030600

One Pico Restaurant ❀❀

No 1 Upper Camden Street, Dublin 2 01 4780307

Roly's Bistro ❀❀

7 Ballsbridge Terrace, Dublin 4 01 6680623

The Shelbourne ❀❀

St Stephen's Green, Dublin 2 01 6766471

La Stampa ❀❀

35 Dawson Street, Dublin 01 6778611

Thornton's Restaurant ❀❀❀

1 Portobello Road, Dublin 8 01 4549067

Finnstown Country House Hotel ❀

Newcastle Road, Lucan 01 6280644

Portmarnock Hotel ❀❀

Strand Road, Portmarnock 01 8460611

The Red Bank Restaurant ❀

7 Church Street, Skerries 01 8491005

COUNTY GALWAY

Hayden's Hotel ❀

Ballinasloe 0905 42347

Ballynahinch Castle ❀

Ballynahinch 095 31006

Cashel House Hotel ❀❀

Cashel 095 31001

Zetland Country House Hotel ❀❀

Cashel Bay, Cashel, Connemara 095 31111

Abbeyglen Castle Hotel ❀

Sky Road, Clifden 095 21201

Ardagh Hotel ❀❀

Ballyconneely Road, Clifden 095 21384

Rock Glen Country House Hotel ❀❀

Clifden 095 21035

Glenlo Abbey Hotel ❀❀

Bushypark, Galway 091 526666

Galway Bay Hotel ❀❀

Oranmore 091 790500

Lough Inagh Lodge Hotel ❀❀

Inagh Valley, Recess 095 34706

Eldons Hotel ❀

Roundstone, Connemara 095 35933

COUNTY KERRY

The White Sands Hotel ❀

Ballheige 066 33102

Park Hotel Kenmare ❀❀❀

Kenmare 064 41200

Sheen Falls Lodge ❀❀

Kenmare 064 41600

Aghadoe Heights Hotel ❀❀❀

Killarney 064 31766

Arbutus Hotel ❀

College Street, Killarney 064 31037

Cahernane Hotel ❀❀

Muckross Road, Killarney 064 31895

Killarney Park Hotel ❀❀

Kenmare Place, Killarney 064 35555

Muckross Park Hotel ❀

Muckross Village, Killarney 064 31938

Great Southern Hotel ❀

Parknasilla 064 45122

Butler Arms Hotel ❀

Waterville 066 74144

Leixlip House Hotel ❀❀

Captains Hill, Leixlip 01 6242268

Moyglare Manor ❀❀

Moyglare, Maynooth 01 6286351

Keadeen Hotel ❀❀

Newbridge 045 431666

Barberstown Castle ❀❀

Straffan 01 6288157

The Kildare Hotel ❀❀❀

Straffan 01 6017200

Mount Juliet Hotel ❀❀

Thomastown 056 73000

COUNTY LIMERICK

Adare Manor ❀

Adare 061 396566

Dunraven Arms Hotel ❀❀❀

Adare 061 396633

Castle Oaks House Hotel ❀

Castleconnell 061 377666

Castletroy Park Hotel ❀❀

Dublin Road, Limerick 061 335566

Jurys Hotel ❀❀

Ennis Road, Limerick 061 327777

Limerick Ryan Hotel ❀

Ennis Road, Limerick 061 453922

COUNTY MAYO

Belmont Hotel ❀

Knock 094 88122

Knockranny House Hotel ❀

Knockranny, Westport 098 28600

The Olde Railway Hotel ❀

The Mall, Westport 098 25166

COUNTY MONAGHAN

Nuremore Hotel ❀❀

Carrickmacross 042 61438

COUNTY ROSCOMMON

Hodson Bay Hotel ❀❀

Hodson Bay, Athlone 0902 92444

COUNTY SLIGO

Markree Castle ❀❀

Collooney 071 67800

Silver Swan Hotel ❀

Sligo 071 43231

COUNTY TIPPERARY

Cahir House Hotel ❀

The Square, Cahir 052 42727

Minella Hotel ❀

Clonmel 052 22388

Nenagh Abbey Court Hotel ❀

Dublin Road, Nenagh 067 41111

Grant's Hotel ❀❀

Castle Street, Roscrea 0505 23300

COUNTY WESTMEATH

Prince Of Wales Hotel ❀

Athlone 0902 72626

COUNTY WEXFORD

Dunbrody Country House ❀❀

Arthurstown 051 389600

Courtown Hotel ❀

Courtown Harbour 055 25210

Marlfield House Hotel ❀❀

Gorey 055 21124

Brandon House Hotel ❀

Wexford Road, New Ross 051 421703

Kelly's Resort Hotel ❀❀

Rosslare 053 32114

Ferrycarrig Hotel ❀❀

Ferrycarrig, Wexford 053 20999

Talbot Hotel ❀

Trinity Street, Wexford 053 22566

Wexford Lodge Hotel ❀

Wexford 053 23611

White's Hotel ✿

George Street, Wexford 053 22311

Whitford House Hotel ✿

New Line Road, Wexford 053 43444

COUNTY WICKLOW

Enniscree Lodge Hotel ✿

Glencree Valley, Enniskerry 01 2863542

Hunter's Hotel ✿

Rathnew 0404 40106

Tinakilly Country House ✿✿

Rathnew 0404 69274

Woodenbridge Hotel ✿

Wooden Bridge 0402 35146

STOP PRESS

REPUBLIC OF IRELAND
TELEPHONE NUMBER CHANGES

Some telephone codes will change during the currency of this guide. From August 1998, both old and new telephone numbers can be dialled. From December 1998, calls to the old numbers will be connected to a recorded announcement which will advise the caller of the new number, which the caller will then have to redial. From August 1999, only the new number can be dialled.

National Dialling Code (NDC)	Numbering Area	Leading Digits of Current Numbers	New Prefix
41	Drogheda	2, 3, 4, 7, 8	98
41	Ardee	5, 6	68
42	Dundalk	2, 3, 5, 7, 8	93
42	Carrickmoss	6, 90, 91, 92, 94, 98	96
42	Castleblayney	4, 95	97
49	Cavan	3, 6, 7	43
49	Cootehill	5	55
49	Oldcastle	4	85
49	Belturbet	2	95
65	Ennis	2, 3, 4, 6	68
65	Ennistymon	7, 8	70
65	Kilrush	5	90
66	Tralee	2, 3, 4, 8	71
66	Dingle	5	91
66	Cahirciveen	7	94
66	Killorglin	6, 9	97

NUMBER CHANGES IN THE CORK AREA

In the Cork area there will be a two-phase process. Local numbers beginning with 40, 43 or 33 will be prefixed with a 2 or a 7 (see Phase 1 below). In phase two, these new 2 or 7 numbers will be prefixed with a 4 (see Phase 2 below), as will the other first digits.

National Dialling Code (NDC)	Numbering Area	Leading Digits of Current Numbers	New Prefix
PHASE 1			
21	Cork	40	2
21	Coachford	43, 33	7
PHASE 2			
21	Cork	2, 3, 5, 8, 9	4
21	Midleton	6	4
21	Kinsale	7	4

IN CASE OF DIFFICULTIES, PLEASE CONSULT DIRECTORY ENQUIRIES

child-Free zone

We asked all the restaurants which appear in the Guide this year whether they feel that they 'genuinely go out of their way to welcome families with children of all ages'. If the answer was yes, and they placed no age restriction on children, we highlighted their entry with a teddy bear symbol. Many establishments welcome children but did not wish to be highlighted - however, 'Children welcome' does appear in the narrow column of their entries. Other places do not accept children under a particular age - and these are listed below. Some do not accept babies, others no children

under 12 or 14 - the age limit is given after the name of the establishment. The list is useful for many reasons - you may have children yourself and want a child-free break, or just prefer a meal without the distraction of young children at other tables. Again, some establishments, especially hotels, are very children friendly places, but prefer not to have children in their restaurant at dinner - therefore we have not given them a symbol.

If you are planning on taking your family to a restaurant, it is always best to check whether there are any age restrictions.

London
Al Bustan, SW1 - 4
Les Associes, N8 - 6
Boyd's Atrium Restaurant, W1 - 7
Cadogan Hotel, SW1 - 10
Chavot, SW3 - 7
Chez Bruce, SW17 - no young
  children at D
Chez Moi, W11 - no babies
Chez Nico, W1 - 7
Chinon, W14, no small children
Dans Restaurant, SW3 - no infants
The Dorchester, The Oriental, W1 - 5
The Fish Restaurant at 190, SW7 - 6
Goring Hotel, SW1 - 5
Granita, N1 - no young children
The Hothouse, E1 - 8
Indian Connoisseurs, W2 - 10
Interlude, W1 - 12
Leith's Restaurant, W11 - 7
Mims, EN4 - 7
Moshi Moshi Sushi, EC2 -5
Nico Central, W1 - 10
Park Lane Hotel, W1 - 10
Quality Chop House, EC1 -no babies
Salloos, SW1 - 6
Savoy Grill, WC2 - 14
Simply Nico, SW1 -12
Sotheby's, The Cafe, W1 - not suitable
  for children
The Sugar Club - 14
Suntory, SW1 - 6
Tatsuso, EC1 - 12
Thistle Cannizaro House, SW19 - 8
Tui Restaurant, SW7 - 5
Turners, SW3 - 11
Vasco & Piero's Pavillion, W1 - 5
Villa, SW1 - 12
Wiltons, SW1 - 12

Bedfordshire
Flitwick Manor Hotel, Flitwick - 6

Berkshire
Monkey Island Hotel, Bray - 5
Waterside Inn, Bray -12
Royal Oak Hotel, Yattendon - no
  babies

Bristol
Harveys, Bristol - 8

Buckinghamshire
West Lodge Hotel, Aston Clinton - 12
Hartwell House, Aylesbury -8
Stoke Park, Stoke Poges - 8

Cheshire
Churche's Mansion,
  Nantwich - 10 at D
Nunsmere Hall, Sandiway - 10

Cornwall & Isles of Scilly
Hell Bay Hotel, Bryher (Scilly) - 5
Star Castle, St Mary's (Scilly) - 5
The Thyme & Plaice, Callington - 8
Danescombe Valley, Calstock - 12
Treglos Hotel, Constantine Bay - 7
Nansloe Manor Hotel, Helston - 10
Budock Vean, Mawnan Smith - 7
Food for Thought, Fowey -12
Tregildry Hotel, Gillan - 8
Cormorant Hotel, Golant - 7
The Horn of Plenty, Gulworthy - 13
Pencubitt Hotel , Liskeard - 12
Well House Hotel, Liskeard - 8 at D
Headland Hotel, Newquay - no
  toddlers at D in main restaurant
Hotel Bristol, Newquay - 4

The Seafood Restaurant, Padstow - 6
Tarbert Hotel, Penzance - 10
Wards Brasserie, Penzance - 8
The Kitchen, Polperro - 12
Cornish Cottage Hotel, Polzeath - 12
Port Gaverne Hotel, Port Isaac - 7
The Castle Rock Hotel, Port Isaac - 5
Critchards Seafood Restaurant,
  Porthleven - 6 in main restaurant
Hundred House Hotel, Ruan High
  Lanes - 8
Garrack Hotel, St Ives - 4
Mermaid Seafood Restaurant,
  St Ives - 7
Pig 'n' fish, St Ives - 2
Old Rectory House Hotel,
  St Keyne - 12
Wenn Manor, St Wenn - 12
Allhays Country House,
  Talland Bay - 10
Trebrea Lodge, Tintagel - 12

Cumbria
Lovelady Sheild, Alston - 7
Fisherback Hotel,
  Ambleside - 5 in restaurant
Borrans Park Hotel, Ambleside - 7
Nanny Brow Hotel, Ambleside - 12 in
  restaurant
Rothay Manor, Ambleside - 6 at D
Wateredge Hotel, Ambleside - 7
Overwater Hall Hotel,
  Bassenthwaite - 3
Borrowdale Gates Hotel,
  Borrowdale - 6
Farlam Hall, Brampton - 5
Crosby Lodge, Carlisle - 5
Uplands Hotel, Cartmel - 8
Gold Rill Hotel - Grasmere - 5

Grasmere Hotel, Grasmere - 10
Michael's Nook, Grasmere - 7
White Moss, Grasmere - 8
Sharrow Bay, Howtown - 13
Dale Head Hall, Keswick - 10
Grange Hotel, Keswick - 7
Swinside Lodge, Keswick - 10
Thwaite Howe Hotel, Keswick - 12
Underscar Manor, Keswick - 12
A Bit on the Side, Penrith - 7
Bay Horse Hotel, Ulverston - 12
Old Church Hotel, Watermillock - 10
Rampsbeck Hotel, Watermillock - 5
Fayrer Garden House, Windermere - 5
Gilpin Lodge, Windermere - 7
Holbeck Ghyl, Windermere - 8
Jerichos, Windermere - 12
Lindeth Fell, Windermere - 7
Linthwaite House, Windermere - 7
Miller Howe, Windermere - 8
Quarry Garth Hotel, Windermere - 8

Derbyshire
Riverside House Hotel, Ashford-in-the-
    Water - 10
Fischer's Baslow Hall, Baslow - 12
    after 7pm
Risley Hall, Risley - 10

Devon
Bark House, Bampton - 5
Bridge House Hotel, Beaminster - 12
Old Steam Bakery, Beer - 11
Edgemoor Hotel, Bovey Tracy - 8
Maypool Park Hotel, Brixham - 12
22 Mill Street, Chagford - 8
Easton Court, Chagford - 12
Gidleigh Park, Chagford - 5
Highbullen Hotel, Chittlehamholt - 8
The Exchange, Dartmouth - 2
Lower Pitt Restaurant,
    East Buckland - 10
Buckerell Lodge Hotel, Exeter - 10
Rock Inn, Haytor - 6 months
Buckland-tout-Saints,
    Kingsbridge - 6 at D
Pitt House Restaurant,
    Kingkerswell - 8
Percy's at Coombeshead,
    Launceston - 12
Lewtrenchard Manor, Lewdown - 8
Thatched Cottage, Lifton - 12
Rising Sun Hotel, Lynmouth - 7
River House Restaurant,
    Lympstone - 6
Chough's Nest Hotel, Lynton - 5

Lynton Cottage Hotel, Lynton - 14
Old Rectory Hotel, Martinhoe -14
Penhaven Country House,
    Parkham - 10
Chez Nous, Plymouth - 8
The Jack in the Green,
    Rockbeare - 10
Soar Mill Cove Hotel,
    Salcombe - 5 at D
Tides Reach Hotel, Salcombe - 8
Brownlands Hotel, Sidmouth - 8
Glazebrook House, South Brent -
    no small babies
Marsh Hall Hotel, South Molton - 12
Corbyn Head Hotel, Torquay - 5
The Table Restaurant, Torquay - 11
Princes Hall Hotel, Two Bridges - 8
Pophams, Winkleigh - 14
Watersmeet Hotel, Woolacombe - 8
Belfry Hotel, Yarcombe - 12

Dorset
Summer Lodge, Evershot - 7 at D
Stock Hill, Gillingham - 7
The Lord Bute Restaurant,
    Highcliffe - 9
Le Petit Canard, Maiden Newton - 9
Wayfarers Restaurant, Shaftesbury - 7
Priory Hotel, Wareham - 8

Durham, Co
Morritt Arms Hotel, Barnard
    Castle - 11
Headlam Hall, Darlington - 7
Krimo's Restaurant, Hartlepool - 8
Mansion House Hotel, Poole - 5
Redworth Hall Hotel, Redworth - 8
Rose & Crown, Romaldkirk - 6
Eden Arms Swallow Hotel,
    Rushyford - no babies

Gloucesterhire
Crown Inn, Blockley - 2
Dial Hopuse Hotel, Bourton-on-the
    Water - 9
Buckland Manor, Buckland - 12
The Greenway, Cheltenham - 7
Restaurant on the Park,
    Cheltenham - 10
Polo Canteen, Cirencester - 6 months
Tudor Farmhouse, Clearwell - 6
New Inn, Coln-St-Andrews - 10 in
    restaurant
Restaurant on the Green, Frampton on
    Severn - 10
Lower Slaughter Manor, Lower
    Slaughter - 12

Fischers Restaurant, Stroud - 6
Thornbury Castle, Thornbury - 12
Lords of the Manor,
    Upper Slaughter - 7

Greater Manchester
Moss Nook Restaurant,
    Manchester - 12

Hampshire
Hunters, Alresford - 4
Esseborne Manor, Andover - 7
Careys Manor, Brockenhurst - 7
Thatched Cottage Hotel,
    Brockenhurst - 12
Fox & Hounds, Crawley - 7
Hour Glass, Fordingbridge -
    5 at L/10 at D
Gordleton Mill, Lymington - 6
South Lawn Hotel, Milford On Sea - 7
Rocher's Restaurant,
    Milford on Sea - 7
Chewton Glen Hotel, New
    Milton - no babies
De Vere Grand Harbour,
    Southampton - 10 in restaurant

Herefordshire
Ancient Camp Inn, Hereford - 12 at D
The Marsh Country Hotel,
    Leominster - 12
Pengethley Manor, Ross-on-Wye - 10
The Steppes Hotel, Ullingswick - 12

Hertfordshire
The Manor St Michael's Village,
    St Albans - 5
Marriot Hanbury Manor, Ware -
    8 in restaurant

Kent
Ebury Hotel, Canterbury - 3
The Bow Window Inn,
    Littlebourne - 2
King William IV, Littlebourne - 10
The Spa Hotel Royal Tunbridge
    Wells - 1

Lancashire
Foxfields Country Hotel,
    Blackburn - 1
Didier's, Thornton - 6

Lincolnshire
Stapleford Park, Melton
    Mowbray - 12

Black Horse Inn, Bourne - 14
Kingsway Hotel, Cleethorpes - 5
Harry's Place, Grantham - 5

Merseyside
Beadles, Birkenhead - 7
Beachers Brook, Liverpool - 8

Norfolk
Grey Gables Hotel, Cawston - 5
Congham Hall, Grimston - 12
Brasted's, Norwich - 5
By Appointment, Norwich - 12
Cumberland Hotel, Norwich - 12
Romford House, Swaffham - 8
The Old Rectory, Thorpe
   St Andrew - 1
Elderton Lodge Hotel,
   Thorpe Market - 6
Wymondham Consort Hotel,
   Wymondham - 8

Northumberland
Longhirst Hall, Morpeth - 8

Oxfordshire
Sir Charles Napier, Chinnor - 7 at D
Morel's, Chipping Norton - Sunday
   only
Dexters Restaurant, Deddington - 3
Fallowfields Hotel, Kingston
   Bagpuize - 10
Kings Head Inn, Woodstock - 10

Shropshire
Redfern Hotel, Cleobury Mortimer - 5
Albright Hussey Hote, Shrewsbury - 3

Somerset
Clos du Roy, Bath - 8
Combe Grove Manor, Bath - 7
The Moody Goose, Bath - 7
Ston Easton, Ston Easton - 7
Truffles Restaurant, Bruton - 5
Ashwick House Hotel, Dulverton - 8
Exmoor House Hotel, Dunster -12
Periton Park Hotel, Minehead - 12
The Oaks Hotel, Porlock - 8
Simonsbath House Hotel,
   Simonsbath - 10
Shrubbery Hotel, Shepton Mallet - 9
Farthings Hotel, Taunton - 14
The Mount Somerset Hotel,
   Taunton - 12
Bindon House Hotel, Wellington - 14
Curdon Mill, Williton - 8

Saverys at Karslake House,
   Winsford - 15
Royal Oak Inn, Withypool - 2
Langley Marsh Hotel,
   Wiveliscombe - 7

Staffordshire
The Moat House, Acton Trussel - 1

Suffolk
Scott's Brasserie, Ipswich - 14
Theobalds Restaurant, Ixworth - 8 at D
White Hart Inn, Nayland - 10 after 8pm
Satis House Hotel, Yoxford - 7

Surrey
Le Petit Pierrot, Claygate - 8
Bishop's Table Hotel, Farnham - 14
Swan Hotel, Southwold - 5 in
   restaurant
Gemini, Tadworth - children at L only

E Sussex
Moonraker's Restaurant, Alfriston - 8
PowderMills Hotel, Battle - 10
One Paston Place, Brighton - 5 at D
The Downland Hotel, Eastbourne - 10
Hungry Monk, Polegate - 4
Hooke Hall/La Scaletta, Uckfield - 8
Horstead Place, Uckfield - 5
Crossways Hotel, Wilmington - 12

W Sussex
Amberley Castle, Amberley - 10
Burpham Hotel, Arundel - 10
George & Dragon, Arundel - 6
Cliffords Cottage Restaurant,
   Bracklesham - 5
Baliffscourt Hotel, Climping - 8
Gravetye Manor, East Grinstead - 7
Findon Manor Hotel, Findon - 12
Random Hall Hotel, Horsham - 8
South Lodge Hotel, Lower Beeding - 9
Southdowns Hotel, Midhurst - 12
Roundabout Hotel, West
   Chiltington - 3

Tyne & Wear
Forsters Restaurant, Boldon - 8
Fishermans Lodge Restaurant,
   Newcastle-upon-Tyne - 9 at D

Warwickshire
Chapel House Hotel, Atherstone - 10
Lansdowne Hotel, Royal
   Leamington Spa - 5

Mallory Court, Royal
   Leamington Spa - 9
The Shakespeare,
   Stratford-upon-Avon - 5

West Midlands
New Hall, Sutton Coldfield - 8
Jonathans, Hotel, Birmingham - 11

Wight, Isle of
Seaview Hotel, Seaview - 7 at D
George Hotel, Yarmouth - 8

Wiltshire
Lucknam Park, Colerne - 12 in
   restaurant
The Grosvenor Arms, Hindon - 5
London House Restaurant, Pewsey - 7

Worcestershire
The Lygon Arms, Broadway - 8
The Mill at Harvington, Evesham - 10
Brown's Restaurant, Worcester - 8

E Yorkshire
The Manor House, Beverley - 12

N Yorkshire
Appleton Hall, Appleton-le-Moor - 12
Amerdale House Hotel, Arncliffe - 8
King's Arms Hotel, Askrigg - 10
Feversham Arms, Helmsley - 6
Foresters Arms, Leyburn - 12 in
   restaurant
Millers house Hotel, Middleham - 10
Black Bull, Moulton - 7
Mallyan Spout Hotel, Whitby - 6
Middlethorpe Hall, York - 8

S Yorkshire
Rafters Restaurant, Sheffield - 5

CHANNEL ISLANDS
Alderney
Inchalla Hotel, St Anne - 2

Guernsey
Hotel Bon Port, St Martin - 12
La Frégate Hotel, St Peter Port - 10
Le Nautique Restaurant,
   St Peter Port - 5

Jersey
Hotel L'Horizon, St Brelade - 12

SCOTLAND
Aberdeenshire
Balgonie Hotel, Ballater, - 5
Lochside Lodge, Bridgend of
 Lintrathen - 12
The Old Manse of Marnoch, Bridge of
 Marnoch - 12

Angus
11 Park Avenue, Carnoustie -10

Argyll & Bute
Taychreggan Hotel, Kilchrenan - 14
Kilfinan Hotel, Kilfinan - 12
Assapol House Hotel, Bunessan - 10
Killiechronan House, Killiechronan -
 10
Cairn Restaurant, Kilmartin -10 at D
Manor House Hotel, Oban - 12

E Ayrshire
Scoretulloch House, Darvel - 12
Chapeltoun House, Stewarton - 12

N Ayrshire
Kilmichael Hotel, Brodick -12
Braidwoods, Dalry - 12 at D

Dumfries & Galloway
Well View Hotel, Moffat - 6 at D
Knockinaam Lodge Hotel,
 Porpatrick - 12

W Dunbartonshire
Cameron House Hotel, Balloch, - 14
 (in Georgian Room)

Edinburgh, City of
Kelly's Restaurant - 5
Martins Restaurant - 8
The Witchery by the Castle - 5

Fife
Ostlers Close, Cupar - 6 at D
Bouquet Garni,Elie - 12
Old Manor Hotel, Lundin Links - 3

Glasgow, City of
Nairns - 10
Papingo - 14
Puppet Theatre - 12

Highland
Arisaig House, Arisaig -10
Three Chimneys, Colbost - 8 at D
Knockie Lodge Hotel, Whitebridge -10

Harlosh House, Harlosh, Skye - 7
Culloden House, Inverness - 12
Kinloch Lodge, Isle Ornsay, Skye - 8
Osprey Hotel, Kingussie - 10
Inver Lodge, Lochinver - 7
The Dower House, Muir of Ord - 7 in
 dining room
Haven Hotel, Plockton - 7
Kilcamb Lodge, Strontian - 8
Loch Torridon, Torridon - 12
Altnaharrie Inn, Ullapool - 8
Inverlochy Castle Hotel,
 Fort William - 8

W Lothian
Livingston's Restaurant,
 Linlithgow - 8 at D

Moray
The Old Monastry Restaurant,
 Drybridge - 8
Rothes Glen Hotel,Rothes - 7

Perth & Kinross
Auchterader House, Auchterader - 10
Kinloch House Hotel, Blairgowrie - 7
Atholl Arms Hotel, Dunkeld - 8 at D
Kinnaird, Dunkeld - 12
Killiecrankie Hotel, Killiecrankie - 5 in
 dining room
Croft Bank, Kinross - 6
Kinfauns Castle, Perth - 8
Murrayshall Country House, Perth - 2

Scottish Borders
Chirnside Hall, Chirnside - 5

Stirling
Braeval, Aberfoyle - 10
Monachyle Mhor, Balquhidder - 12
Roman Camp, Callander - 4
Lake Hotel, Port of Monteith - no
 children at dinner
Creagan House, Strathyre - 10

WALES
Anglesey, Isle of
Ye Olde Bulls Head Hotel,
 Beaumaris - 7

Cardiff
Gilby's Restaurant, Cardiff - 7
Carmarthenshire
The Four Seasons Restaurant,
 Carmarthen - 5

Ceredigion
Conrah Hotel, Aberystwyth - 5

Conwy
Tan-y-Foel, Betws-Y-Coed - 7
Café Niçoise, Colwyn Bay - 7 at D
Bodysgallen Hall Hotel, Llandudno,
 Conwy - 8
The Old Rectory, Conwy - 5
St Tudno Hotel, Llandudno - 5 at D

Flintshire
Soughton Hall, Northop - 12

Gwynedd
Plas Penhelig, Aberdyfi - 8
Menai Court Hotel, Bangor - 6
Bontddu Hall, Dolgellau - 3
Dolmelynllyn Hall, Dolgellau - 8
Dolserau Hall, Dolgellau - 6
Penmaenuchaf Hall, Dolgellau - 6
Ty'n Rhos, Llanddeiniolen - 6
Hotel Maes y Neuadd,
 Talsarnau - 7 at D
Minffordd Hotel, Tal-y-Llyn - 5

Pembrokeshire
Tregynon Country Farmhouse Hotel,
 Fishguard - 8
Court Hotel, Pembroke - 2
Penally Abbey Country House,
 Penally - 7
Atlantic Hotel, Tenby - 6

Powys
Bear Hotel, Crickhowell - 5
Gliffaes Hotel, Crickhowell - no babies
Ynyshir Hall, Eglwysfach - 9
Old Black Lion Hotel, Hay-on-Wye - 5
Milebrook House Hotel, Knighton - 8
Lake Country House Hotel,
 Llananmarch Wells - 7
Carlton House Hotel, Llanwrtyd
 Wells - 8
Llangoed Hall, Llyswen - 8

Swansea
Fairyhill, Reynoldston - 8

NORTHERN IRELAND
Belfast
Culloden Hotel, Holywood - 3

Londonderry
Ardtara Country Hotel - Upperlands -
 10

Central London

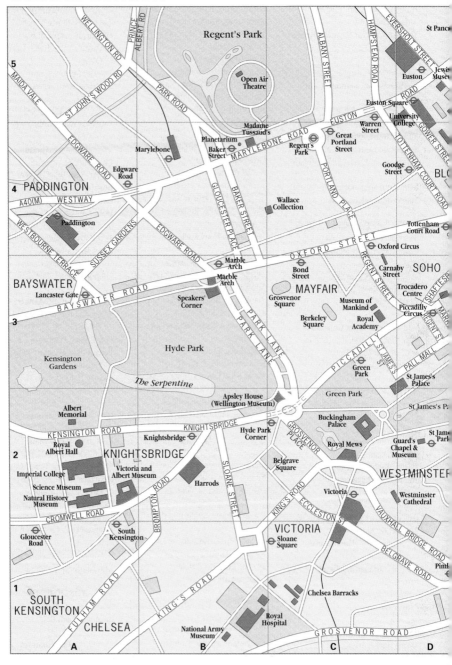

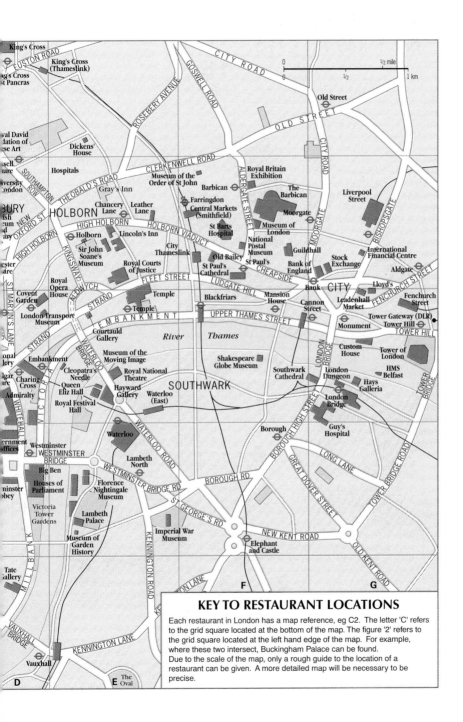

KEY TO RESTAURANT LOCATIONS

Each restaurant in London has a map reference, eg C2. The letter 'C' refers to the grid square located at the bottom of the map. The figure '2' refers to the grid square located at the left hand edge of the map. For example, where these two intersect, Buckingham Palace can be found.
Due to the scale of the map, only a rough guide to the location of a restaurant can be given. A more detailed map will be necessary to be precise.

For Greater London plan please see page 843

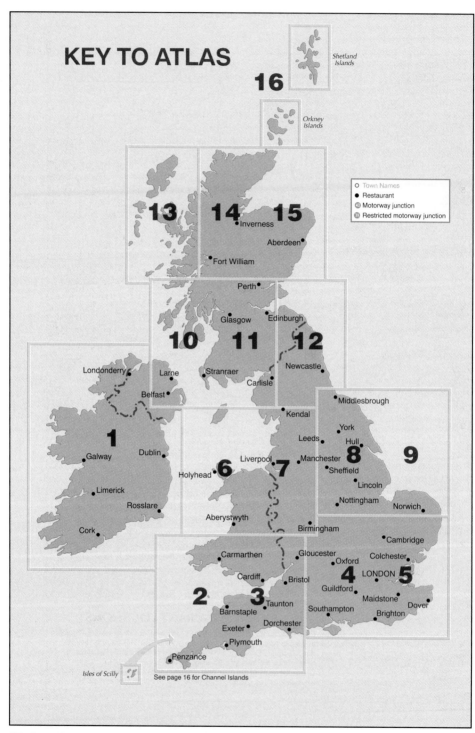

KEY TO ATLAS

16

Shetland Islands

Orkney Islands

○ Town Names
● Restaurant
⑩ Motorway junction
⑪ Restricted motorway junction

13   14   15
Inverness
Aberdeen
Fort William

Perth

Glasgow   Edinburgh
10   11   12

Londonderry   Larne   Stranraer   Newcastle
Belfast   Carlisle   Middlesbrough
1   Kendal   York
Galway   Dublin   Leeds   Hull
    Liverpool   Manchester   8   9
Holyhead   6   7   Sheffield
Limerick   Lincoln
Rosslare   Nottingham   Norwich
Aberystwyth   Birmingham
Cork   Cambridge
Carmarthen   Gloucester   Colchester
Cardiff   Oxford
2   3   Bristol   4   LONDON   5
Taunton   Guildford   Maidstone
Barnstaple   Southampton   Dover
Exeter   Dorchester   Brighton
Plymouth
Penzance

Isles of Scilly   See page 16 for Channel Islands

© The Automobile Association 1998

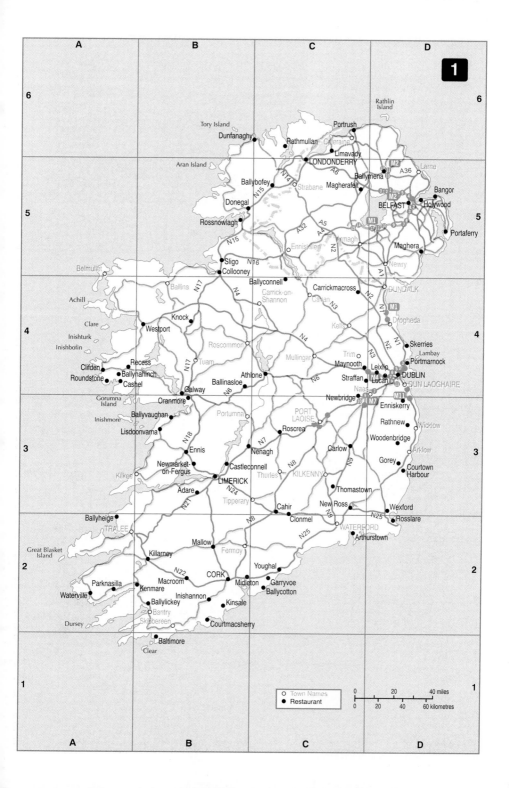

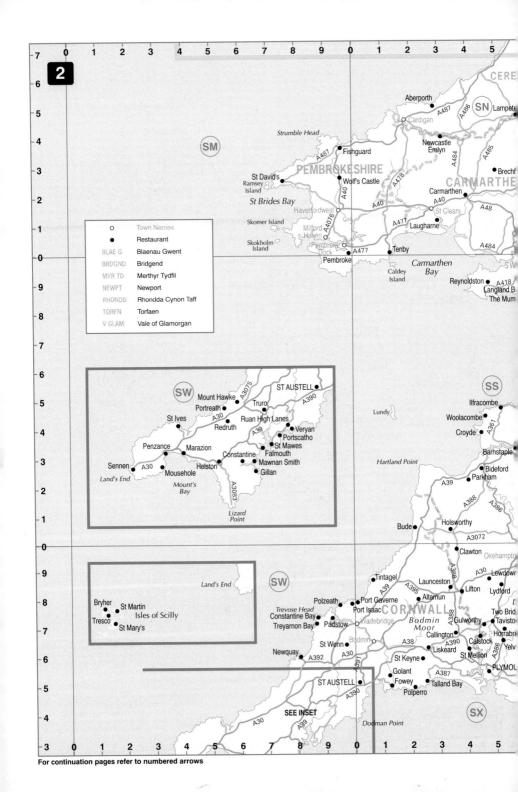

2

For continuation pages refer to numbered arrows

Legend:

○	Town Names
●	Restaurant
BLAE G	Blaenau Gwent
BRDGND	Bridgend
MYR TD	Merthyr Tydfil
NEWPT	Newport
RHONDD	Rhondda Cynon Taff
TORFN	Torfaen
V GLAM	Vale of Glamorgan

CERE

Aberporth
SN Lampete
Cardigan
A487
A486

Newcastle
Emlyn
A484
A485

SM

Strumble Head

Fishguard

PEMBROKESHIRE
A487

St David's
Ramsey
Island
Wolf's Castle
A478
A40

Brechf
CARMARTHE
Carmarthen
A40
A40
A48

St Brides Bay
Haverfordwest
A4076
St Clears

Skomer Island
A477 Laugharne
SW

Milford
Haven
Skokholm
Island
Pembroke
Dock
A477 Tenby

Pembroke
Caldey
Island
Carmarthen
Bay
Reynoldston
A418
Langland B
The Mum

SW
Mount Hawke
A3075
ST AUSTELL
SS
Ilfracombe

Portreath
Truro
A390
Woolacombe
A361

St Ives
A30
Ruan High Lanes
Lundy
Croyde
A39

Redruth
Veryan
A39
Portscatho
St Mawes

Penzance
Marazion
Falmouth
Barnstaple

Sennen
A30
Constantine
Mawnan Smith
Hartland Point
Bideford
Parkham

Land's End
Helston
Gillan
A39
A388
A386

Mousehole
Mount's
Bay
A3083

Lizard
Point
Bude
Holsworthy
A3072

Clawton
Okehampto

SW
Land's End
Tintagel
Launceston
A30
Lewdowr
Lydford

Bryher
St Martin
Polzeath
Port Gaverne
A39
A395
Altarnun
Lifton
Two Brid

Tresco
Isles of Scilly
Trevose Head
Constantine Bay
Port Isaac
CORNWALL
Gulworthy
Tavisto

St Mary's
Treyarnon Bay
Padstow
Wadebridge
Bodmin
Moor
Callington
Horrabri
Yelv

Newquay
A392
St Wenn
Bodmin
A30
A38
Liskeard
A390
Calstock
St Mellion
PLYMOU

ST AUSTELL
A390
St Keyne
Golant
Fowey
A387
St Mellion
A386

SEE INSET
Polperro
Talland Bay
SX

A30
A39
Dodman Point

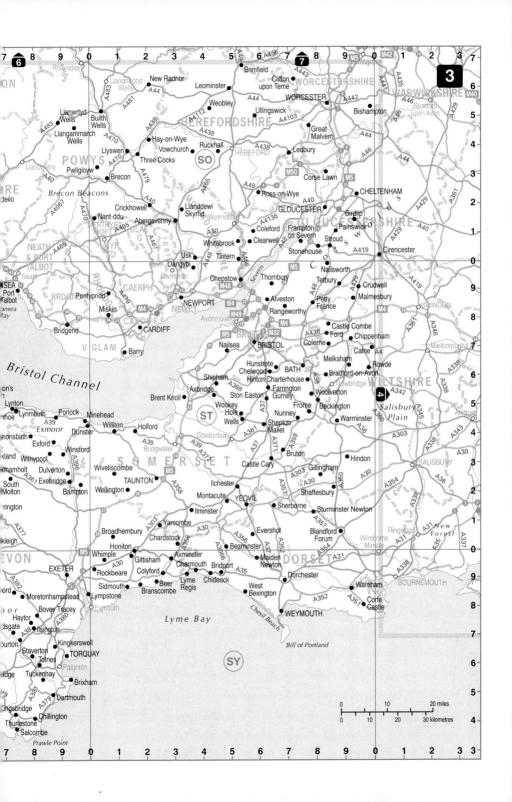

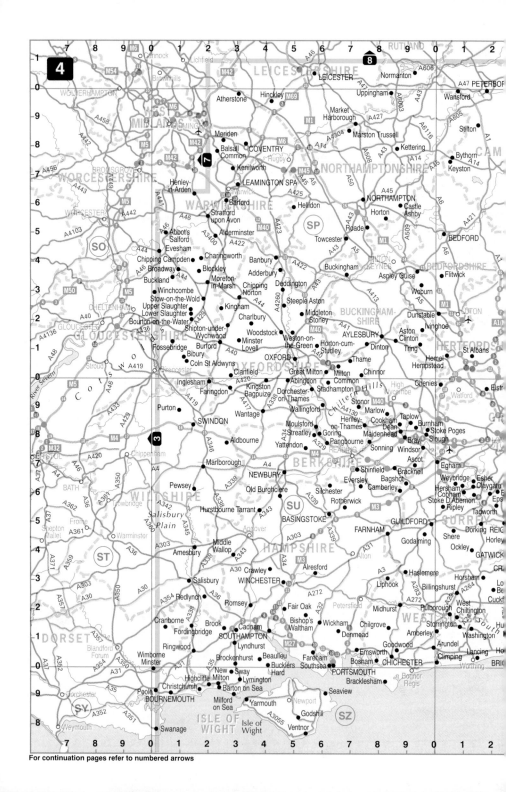

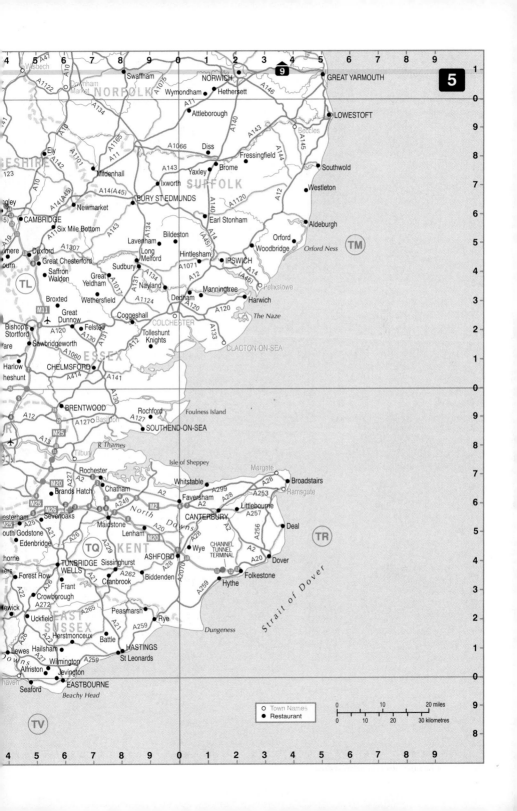

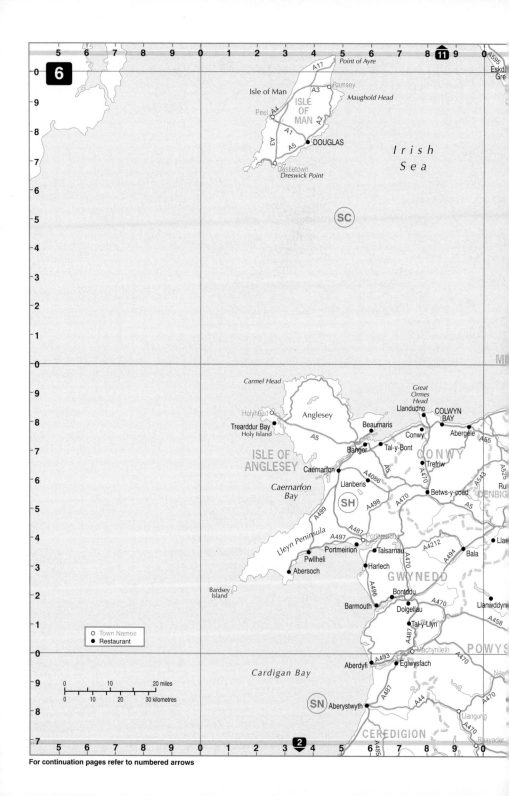

Point of Ayre
A17
Isle of Man
A3 Ramsey
Maughold Head
Peel A4
ISLE OF MAN
A2
A1
A3
A5
DOUGLAS
Castletown
Dreswick Point

Irish Sea

SC

Carmel Head

Holyhead
Anglesey
Great Ormes Head
Llandudno
COLWYN BAY
Trearddur Bay
Holy Island
Beaumaris
Conwy
Abergele
A55
A5
Bangor
Tal-y-Bont
CONWY
ISLE OF ANGLESEY
Caernarfon
Trefriw
A52
A543
Ru
Caernarfon Bay
A4086
A5
A470
SH
Llanberis
Betws-y-coed
DENBIG
A498
A5
A499
A487
A470
Lleyn Peninsula
A497
Porthmadog
A4212
A494
Lla
Portmeirion
Talsarnau
Bala
Pwllheli
Harlech
A470
A470
GWYNEDD
Abersoch
Bardsey Island
Bontddu
A496
Barmouth
Dolgellau
A470
Llanwddyn
A470
A458
Tal-y-Llyn
A487
Machynlleth
POWYS
A493
A470
Cardigan Bay
Aberdyfi
Eglwysfach
A487
A44
A470
SN
Aberystwyth
A44
Llangurig
A485
CEREDIGION
A470
Rhayader
New

○ Town Names
● Restaurant

0   10   20 miles
0   10   20   30 kilometres

A595
Eskda
Gre

MI

For continuation pages refer to numbered arrows

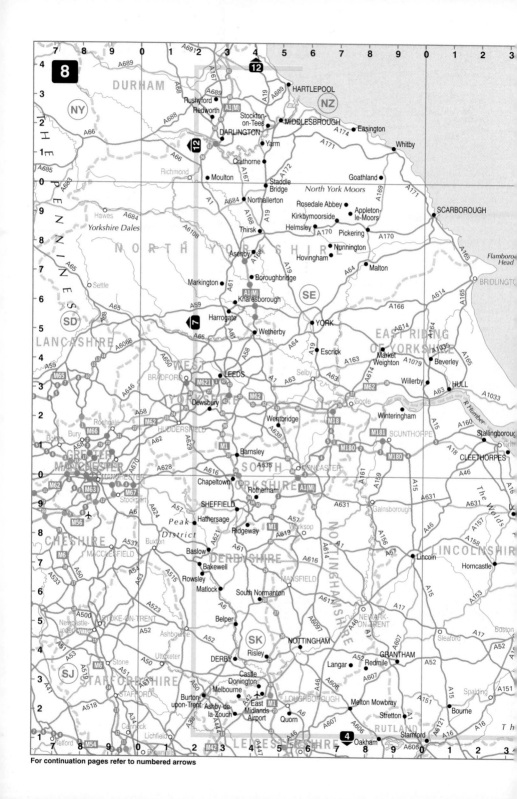

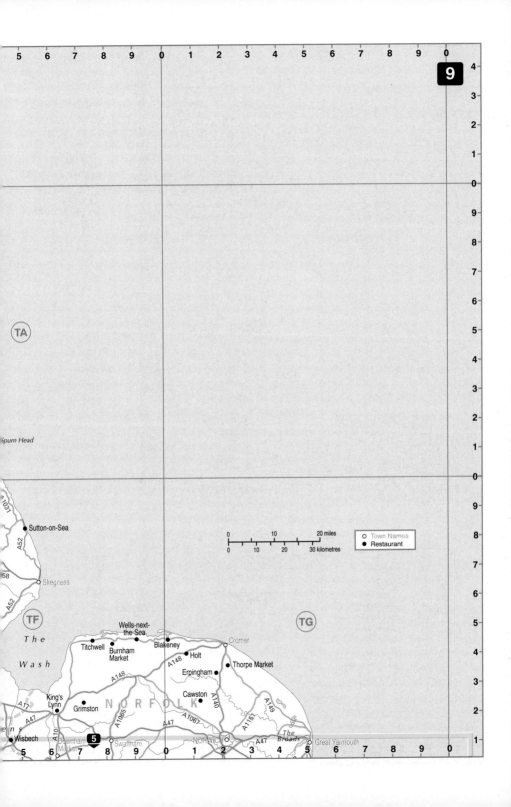

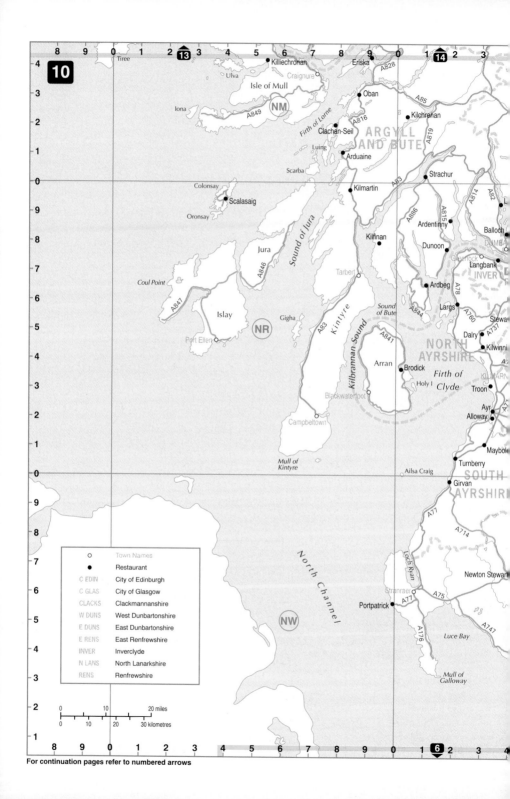

For continuation pages refer to numbered arrows

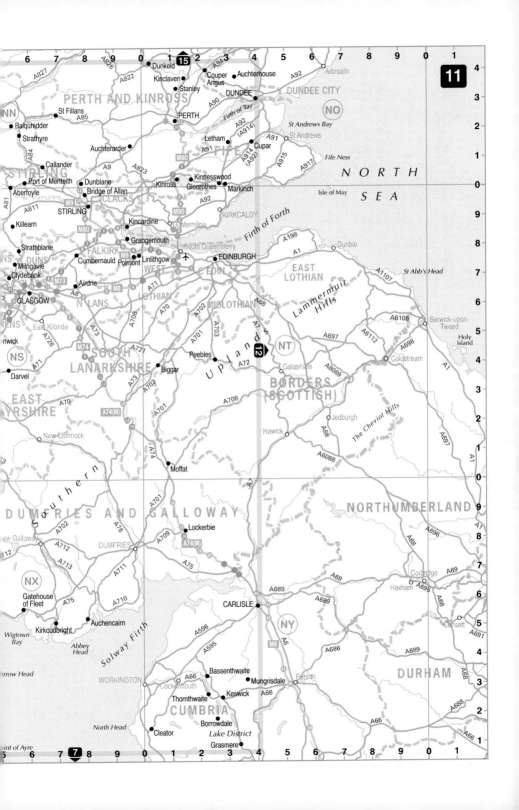

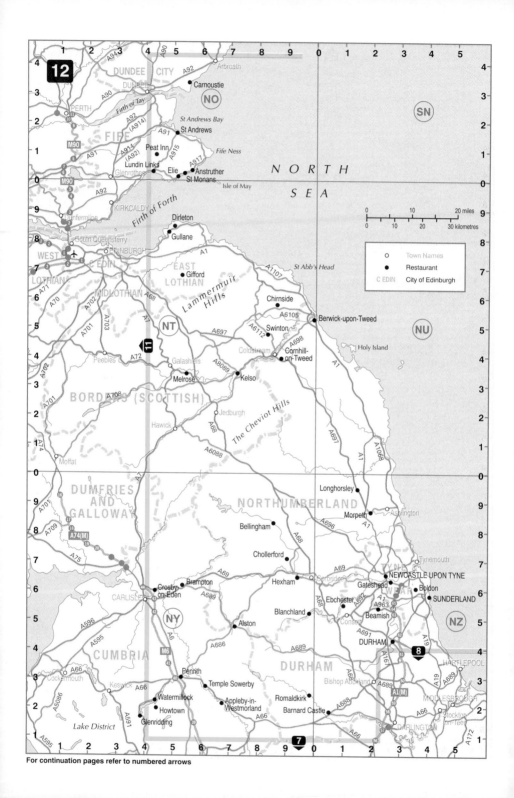

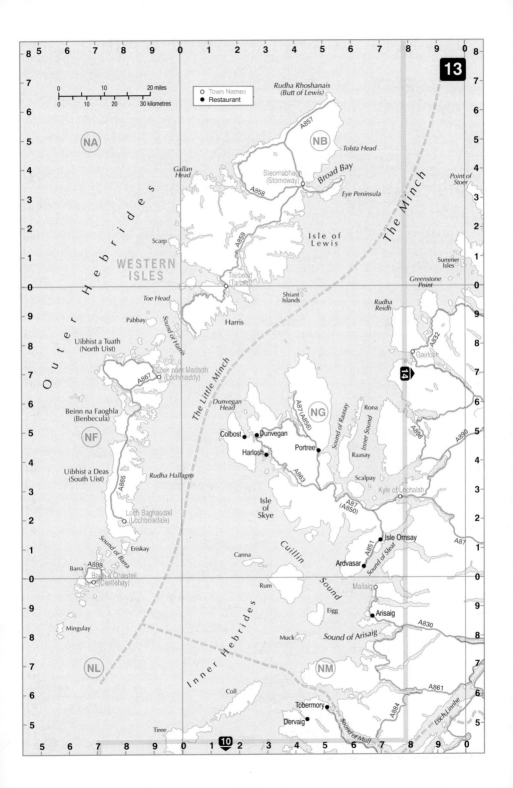

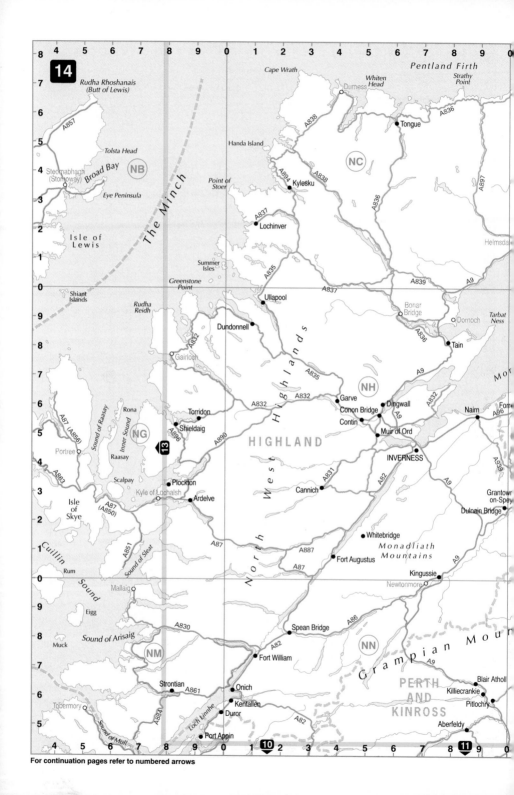

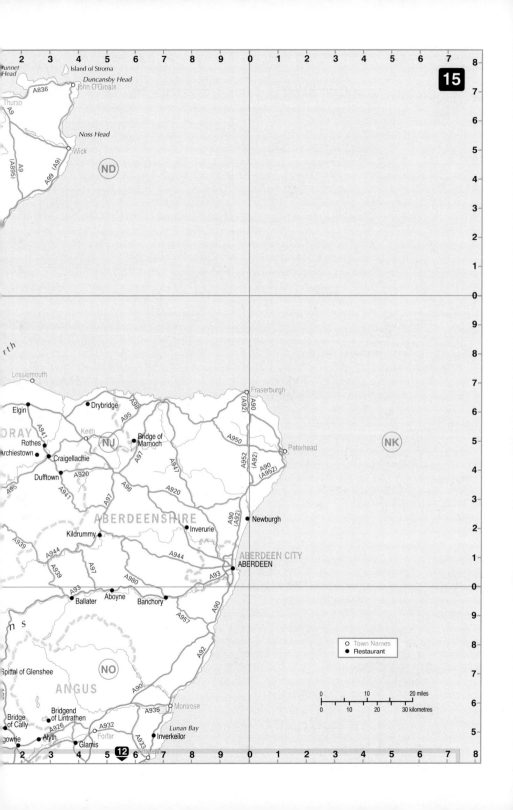

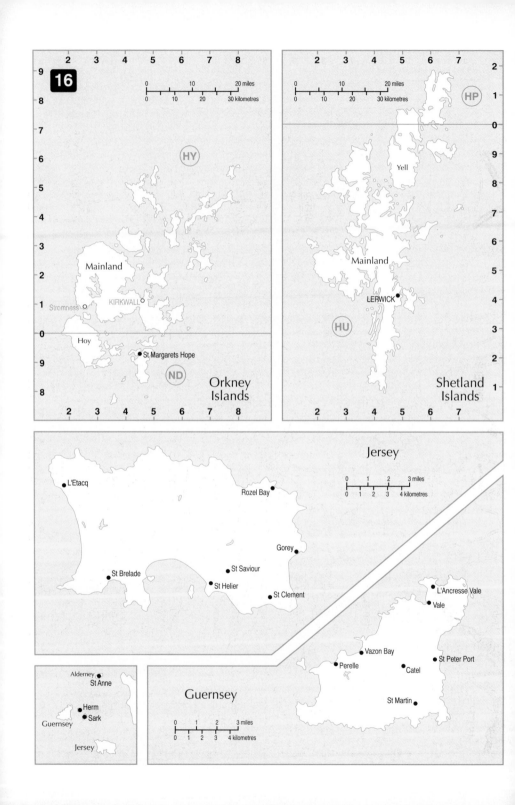

16

0 10 20 miles
0 10 20 30 kilometres

HY

Mainland

Stromness KIRKWALL

Hoy

St Margarets Hope

ND

Orkney
Islands

0 10 20 miles
0 10 20 30 kilometres

HP

Yell

Mainland

LERWICK

HU

Shetland
Islands

Jersey

L'Etacq

Rozel Bay

0 1 2 3 miles
0 1 2 3 4 kilometres

Gorey

St Saviour

St Brelade

St Helier

St Clement

L'Ancresse Vale

Vale

Vazon Bay

St Peter Port

Perelle

Catel

Alderney
St Anne

Herm

Guernsey Sark

Jersey

Guernsey

St Martin

0 1 2 3 miles
0 1 2 3 4 kilometres

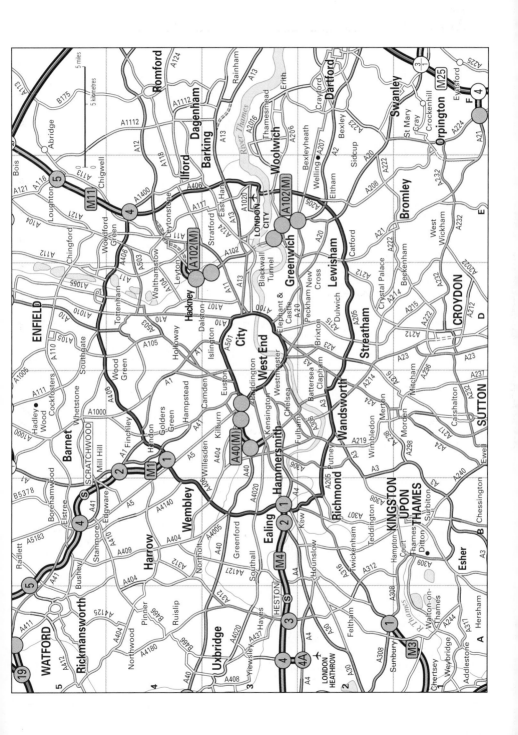

London Postcode Index

Index